T0226948

30TH EUROPEAN SYMPOSIUM ON COMPUTER AIDED PROCESS ENGINEERING

PART C

30TH EUROPEAN SYMPOSIUM ON COMPUTER AIDED PROCESS ENGINEERING

PART C

Edited by

Sauro Pierucci
AIDIC Servizi s.r.l.,
Milano, Italy,
sauro.pierucci@polimi.it

Flavio Manenti
SuPER Team, Sustainable Process Engineering Research
Dipartimento di Chimica, Materiali e Ingegneria Chimica,
Politecnico di Milano, Milano, Italy,
flavio.manenti@polimi.it

Giulia Luisa Bozzano
SuPER Team, Sustainable Process Engineering Research
Dipartimento di Chimica, Materiali e Ingegneria Chimica,
Politecnico di Milano, Milano, Italy,
giulia.bozzano@polimi.it

Davide Manca
PSE-Lab - Process Systems Engineering Laboratory,
Dipartimento di Chimica, Materiali e Ingegneria Chimica,
Politecnico di Milano, Italy,
davide.manca@polimi.it

ELSEVIER

Amsterdam – Boston – Heidelberg – London – New York – Oxford
Paris – San Diego – San Francisco – Singapore – Sydney – Tokyo

Elsevier
Radarweg 29, PO Box 211, 1000 AE Amsterdam, Netherlands
The Boulevard, Langford Lane, Kidlington, Oxford OX5 1GB, UK
50 Hampshire Street, 5th Floor, Cambridge, MA 02139, USA

Copyright © 2020 Elsevier B.V. All rights reserved.

No part of this publication may be reproduced or transmitted in any form or by any means, electronic
or mechanical, including photocopying, recording, or any information storage and retrieval system,
without permission in writing from the publisher. Details on how to seek permission, further
information about the Publisher's permissions policies and our arrangements with organizations such
as the Copyright Clearance Center and the Copyright Licensing Agency, can be found at our website:
www.elsevier.com/permissions.

This book and the individual contributions contained in it are protected under copyright by the
Publisher (other than as may be noted herein).

Notices
Knowledge and best practice in this field are constantly changing. As new research and experience
broaden our understanding, changes in research methods, professional practices, or medical treatment
may become necessary.

Practitioners and researchers must always rely on their own experience and knowledge in evaluating
and using any information, methods, compounds, or experiments described herein. In using such
information or methods they should be mindful of their own safety and the safety of others, including
parties for whom they have a professional responsibility.

To the fullest extent of the law, neither the Publisher nor the authors, contributors, or editors, assume
any liability for any injury and/or damage to persons or property as a matter of products liability,
negligence or otherwise, or from any use or operation of any methods, products, instructions, or ideas
contained in the material herein.

British Library Cataloguing in Publication Data
A catalogue record for this book is available from the British Library

Library of Congress Cataloging-in-Publication Data
A catalog record for this book is available from the Library of Congress

ISBN (Part C): 978-0-12-823513-3
ISBN (Set) :   978-0-12-823377-1
ISSN: 1570-7946

For information on all Elsevier publications visit our
website at https://www.elsevier.com/

Working together
to grow libraries in
developing countries

www.elsevier.com • www.bookaid.org

Publisher: Susan Dennis
Acquisition Editor: Kostas Marinakis
Editorial Project Manager: Lena Sparks
Production Project Manager: Paul Prasad Chandramohan
Designer: Greg Harris

Typeset by SPi Global, India

Contents

BIORESOURCES, BIOPROCESSES AND BIOMEDICAL SYSTEMS

EDUCATION IN CAPE AND KNOWLEDGE TRANSFER

Sauro Pierucci, Flavio Manenti, Giulia Bozzano, Davide Manca (Eds.)
Proceedings of the 30th European Symposium on Computer Aided Process Engineering
(ESCAPE30), May 24-27, 2020, Milano, Italy. © 2020 Elsevier B.V. All rights reserved.
http://dx.doi.org/10.1016/B978-0-12-823377-1.50229-9

Assessment of Innovative Carbon Capture Technologies Applied for Flexible Energy Vectors Poly-generation

Calin-Cristian Cormos[*], Ana-Maria Cormos, Ionela Dumbrava

Babes-Bolyai University, Faculty of Chemistry and Chemical Engineering, Arany Janos 11, Cluj-Napoca, RO-400028, Romania
cormos@chem.ubbcluj.ro

Abstract

Reducing CO_2 emissions from energy-intensive industrial applications is of paramount importance today. Various carbon capture, utilisation and storage (CCUS) technologies can be applied to reduce the carbon footprint of industrial processes. This paper is presenting, through various illustrative gasification-based examples, some innovative carbon capture technologies used for decarbonised flexible energy vectors poly-generation (e.g. power, hydrogen, methanol etc.). The reactive gas-liquid and gas-solid methods are evaluated as CO_2 capture methods with emphasize on innovative energy-efficient chemical looping systems. The overall carbon capture rate of the plant is set to min. 90 %. The proposed conceptual designs were simulated using process flow modelling, the generated mass & energy balances as well as the various thermal integration tools (e.g. pinch method) were used to quantify and optimize the key technical and environmental plant performance indicators. The assessments show that flexible carbon capture technologies have significant advantages in reducing the environmental impact of energy-intensive industrial applications as well as the CO_2 capture energy penalty, increasing the overall energy efficiency, improving plant cycling capabilities (flexible energy vectors poly-generation) with clear benefits in the modern energy systems where time-irregular renewable sources have an increase share.

Keywords: Flexible energy vectors poly-generation, Carbon Capture, Utilisation and Storage (CCUS) technologies, Reactive gas-liquid and gas-solid systems.

1. Introduction

Climate change and energy are one of the most important topics in the modern society. Greenhouse gas emissions (mainly CO_2) resulted from human activity are the main contributor to the global warming. To efficiently combat climate change, the fossil CO_2 emissions needs to be drastically reduced e.g. at European Union level the power generation is foreseen to be fossil CO_2 neutral by 2050 (European Commission, 2018). To achieve the global target of reducing CO_2 emissions a wide range of technical measures are to be used e.g. boosting renewable energy sources, increase energy conversion and end-use efficiencies, large scale deployment of CCUS technologies etc. (International Energy Agency, 2015).This paper is evaluating potential technical and environmental benefits of reactive gas-liquid (physical and chemical absorption) and gas-solid (chemical looping) systems used in conjunction with gasification technology for decarbonised flexible energy vectors poly-generation. The evaluations are focused on the conceptual design and the technical & environmental assessment of CCUS technologies with potential applications in heat & power generation as well as chemicals (e.g. hydrogen, methanol, substitute natural gas etc.). Gasification was chosen as energy conversion technology for its multi-fuel multi-product capability (Cormos et al., 2015). The ability of energy conversion system to adjust its energy carriers over time would be a great asset for future energy systems where time-irregular renewable sources are predicted to have an increase share (Szima et al., 2019). The key innovative element of this paper towards the current state of the art in the field is the assessment of technical and environmental performance indicators of flexible energy vectors poly-generation based on gasification process with carbon capture.

2. Gasification-based flexible energy vectors poly-generation with CCUS

The conceptual design of gasification plant operated in a flexible energy vectors poly-generation scenario with CO_2 capture is presented in Figure 1. This plant concept can timely adjust the generated energy carriers considering the current situation in the energy system (e.g. power grid). A period with high production of renewable electricity implies that the plant will produce mostly chemicals (to be used either as energy carriers or as chemicals) since a period with low renewable electricity implies that the plant will generate mostly power. In both situations, most of the plant will operated base load with benefic technical and economic consequences (Mikulčić et al., 2019).

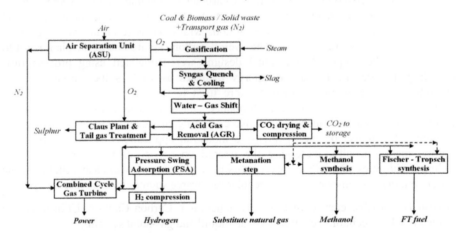

Figure 1. Layout of gasification-based flexible energy vectors poly-generation

Pre-combustion syngas decarbonisation can be done either by reactive gas-liquid absorption or reactive gas-solid system based on chemical looping cycle. For gas-liquid absorption, alkanolamines are mostly used, for instance Methyl-Di-Ethanol-Amine (MDEA) for which the chemical reaction is the following:

$$MDEA + CO_2 + H_2O \leftrightarrow MDEAH^+ + HCO_3^- \tag{1}$$

For reactive gas-solid system, the Calcium Looping (CaL) cycle was used in a pre-combustion capture scenario as Sorbent Enhanced Water Gas Shift (SEWGS) being based on the carbonation - calcination cycle (Mantripragada and Rubin, 2017):

$$CO + H_2O + CaO \leftrightarrow CaCO_3 + H_2 \tag{2}$$

$$CaCO_3 \leftrightarrow CaO + CO_2 \tag{3}$$

3. Plant concepts, model assumptions and process integration aspects

Shell gasifier was chosen as gasification reactor to take advantage of dry feed design and gas quench configuration (which both increase the overall energy efficiency). The gasification plant without carbon capture was also considered as benchmark concept (Case 1). As pre-combustion carbon capture options the reactive gas-liquid (Case 2) and gas-solid (Case 3) systems presented above were evaluated. After syngas decarbonisation, the hydrogen-rich gas can be used for generation of total (e.g. power, hydrogen) or partial decarbonised (methanol, SNG, FT fuel) energy carriers. As illustrative example, flexible hydrogen and power co-generation is presented in details. As evaluated fuels, coal alone or in mixture with renewable biomass (sawdust) were considered. Table 1 is presenting the main design assumptions of evaluated cases.

Table 1. Design assumptions of evaluated gasification-based poly-generation systems

Process unit	Design assumptions
Fuels	Coal: 25.35 MJ/kg calorific value (as received)
	Biomass: 16.05 MJ/kg calorific value (after drying)
Air Separation Unit (ASU)	Composition (% vol.): 95 % O_2, 3 % N_2, 2 % Ar
	ASU power consumption: 200 kWh/t oxygen
Gasification island	Shell gasification reactor operated at 40 bar
	Gas quench design to 800 °C final temperature
Water gas shift conversion	Sour catalyst (cobalt-molybdenum catalyst)
(Case 1)	High & low temperature shift: 400 – 500 °C / 250 – 350 °C
	CO conversion efficiency: >98 %
Syngas desulphurization unit	Gas-liquid absorption cycle coupled with Claus plant
	Sulphur removal efficiency: >98 %
Gas-liquid CO_2 capture unit	50 wt.% MDEA aqueous solution
(Case 1)	Absorption/desorption columns: 20/10 stages
Gas-solid CO_2 capture unit	Calcium-based sorbent: natural limestone
(Case 2)	Carbonation reactor temperature: 500 – 650 °C
	Calcination reactor temperature: 850 – 950 °C
CO_2conditioning unit	TEG gas-liquid absorption dehydration unit
(drying and compression)	Final delivery purity and pressure: >95 % (vol.) / 120 bar
	Multi-stage inter-cooling compressor with 85 % efficiency
Hydrogen purification unit	Pressure Swing Adsorption (PSA) system
	Final hydrogen purity and pressure: 99.95 % vol. / 60 bar
Power block	Combined cycle based on one M701G2 gas turbine
	Steam cycle pressure: HP 120 bar / MP 34 bar / LP 3 bar
	Final steam expansion pressure: 45 mbar

The evaluated gasification-based poly-generation systems were simulated using ChemCAD and Thermoflex software packages. The assessed designs were subject of detailed energy integration analysis using pinch method for maximisation of overall energy efficiency. As illustrative example for Case 2 (pre-combustion CO_2 capture based on reactive gas-liquid design), Figure 2 present the hot and cold composite curves for the gasification island and syngas conditioning train (left) and the combined cycle gas turbine - CCGT (right). In addition of heat (steam) integration across the plant, other heat and power integration analysis were performed e.g. air integration between gas turbine compressor and air separation unit, ancillary energy consumptions for the carbon capture unit (both assessed options). The mass and energy balances of all evaluated gasification-based systems were then used for quantification of main technical and environmental performance indicators presented in next section of the paper.

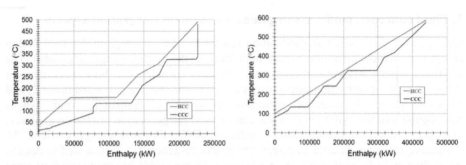

Figure 2. Composite curves for the syngas treatment line (left) and the combined cycle (right)

4. Results and discussions

The following Integrated Gasification Combined Cycle (IGCC) conceptual designs with and without carbon capture capability were evaluated:

> Case 1 – Coal-based IGCC without carbon capture (benchmark case);
> Case 2.a – Coal-based IGCC with CO_2 capture by MDEA process;
> Case 2.b – Coal and biomass-based IGCC with CO_2 capture by MDEA process;
> Case 3.a – Coal-based IGCC with CO_2 capture by CaL process;
> Case 3.b – Coal and biomass-based IGCC with CO_2 capture by CaL process.

The above mentioned designs were evaluated firstly in power generation only conditions (corresponding to base load conditions). Table 2 presents the most important technical and environmental performance indicators.

Table 2. Main technical and environmental indicators of evaluated cases (power only)

Key parameter	UM	Case 1	Case 2.a	Case 2.b	Case 3.a	Case 3.b
Fuel flowrate	t/h	147.80	165.70	180.45	226.71	246.89
Calorific value	MJ/kg			25.35 / 16.05		
Fuel thermal input	MW$_{th}$	1,040.88	1,166.98	1,177.68	1,596.60	1,611.24
Gas turbine output	MW$_e$	334.00	334.00	334.00	334.00	334.00
Steam turbine output	MW$_e$	224.00	200.50	199.25	410.55	408.75
Gross power output	MW$_e$	558.50	535.75	533.85	745.95	743.75
Power consumption	MW$_e$	74.10	109.85	113.01	154.82	155.12
Net power output	MW$_e$	484.40	425.90	420.84	591.13	588.63
Gross efficiency	%	53.36	45.91	45.74	46.72	46.16
Net efficiency	%	46.53	36.49	35.73	37.02	36.53
Carbon capture rate	%	0.00	91.20	92.25	95.80	95.75
CO_2 emissions	kg/MWh	741.75	85.65	74.12	33.25	35.10

As can be noticed from Table 2, there is an energy penalty for CO_2 capture in the range of 9.5 - 10.8 net energy efficiency percentage points. The coal-based gasification concepts are slightly more efficient than the combined coal & biomass gasification concepts by about 0.5 to 0.75 net energy efficiency points. Also, calcium looping option is more energy efficient than reactive gas-liquid absorption. The major benefit of CCS concepts is the substantial reduction of the specific CO_2 emissions. The carbon capture rates and CO_2 emission values presented in Table 2 were calculated considering that the whole carbon as fossil, when consider that for biomass the carbon is renewable, the CO_2 emissions are lower by about 15 - 18 %.

After evaluating the plant concepts in a fixed operation scenario (power only base load conditions), the flexible hydrogen and power co-generation option was assessed. The flexible evaluation was done considering that the gas turbine is turned down gradually to displace a hydrogen stream to be purified and send to external customers (corresponding to the situation when power requirements from the grid are decreasing). The plant flexibility in this concept was restricted to 75 – 100 % from the nominal gas turbine power output (334 MW net). Table 3 presents the variation of key performance indicators vs. hydrogen output for Case 2.a considered as illustrative example.

Table 3. Main technical and environmental indicators of hydrogen and power co-generation

Key parameter	UM	Power only	Hydrogen and power co-generation	
Fuel flowrate	t/h		165.70	
Calorific value	MJ/kg		25.35	
Fuel thermal input	MW$_{th}$		1,166.98	
Gas turbine power output	MW$_e$	334.00	293.00	252.00
Steam turbine power output	MW$_e$	200.50	180.10	159.85
Gross power output	MW$_e$	535.75	474.35	413.52
Hydrogen thermal output	MW$_{th}$	0.00	100.00	200.00
Ancillary power consumption	MW$_e$	109.85	110.25	110.80
Net power output	MW$_e$	425.90	364.10	302.72
Net power efficiency	%	36.49	31.20	25.94
Hydrogen thermal efficiency	%	0.00	8.57	17.13
Cumulative energy efficiency	%	36.49	39.77	43.08
Carbon capture rate	%	91.20	91.20	91.20
Specific CO$_2$ emissions	kg/MWh	85.65	78.00	72.01

As can be noticed from Table 3, the overall plant performance indicators (e.g. cumulative energy efficiency, specific CO$_2$ emissions) are improving with the hydrogen output. The cumulative energy efficiency is increasing by about 3.3 net percentage points for each 100 MW$_{th}$ hydrogen output. The specific CO$_2$ emissions are also decreasing with hydrogen output because more energy is produced by the plant. Another positive aspect is that the ancillary energy consumption of the plant is not changing much with hydrogen output. The flexible hydrogen and power co-generation evaluated here is just partial by changing the gas turbine load in a range that not affect its performances. If a fully flexible scenario is desirable, a separate steam turbine is needed to cover the ancillary energy consumption (see Starr et al., 2007).

The next evaluated operational scenario for gasification plants was based on co-generation of power and various partial decarbonised energy vectors (e.g. methanol, synthetic natural gas, Fischer-Tropsch fuel). For these concepts, the gasification island is producing the syngas which is then partially decarbonised by capturing a part of carbon dioxide stream, the rest being used for synthetic fuel production. As for the case of hydrogen and power co-generation, these concepts can be used very efficiently to make the overall power plant more flexible to the variations imposed by the electricity grid. The main performance indicators for these concepts (considering coal and biomass processing - Case 2.b) are presented in Table 4. As can be noticed, the co-generation of various partially decarbonised energy carriers is beneficial for increasing the overall energy efficiency although these concepts do not have very high carbon capture rates as for power and hydrogen and power co-generation (40 - 60 vs. 90 %).

Table 4. Co-generation of power and various energy carriers based on gasification with CCS

Key parameter	UM	Methanol	SNG	FT fuel
Fuel flowrate	t/h	36.60	200.00	200.00
Fuel thermal input	MW_{th}	282.60	1,235.50	1,235.50
Steam turbine power output	MW_e	36.90	163.25	192.00
Methanol thermal output	MW_{th}	141.50	-	-
SNG thermal output	MW_{th}	-	800.00	-
FT fuel thermal output	MW_{th}	-	-	700.00
Ancillary power consumption	MW_e	21.85	115.35	74.85
Net electrical efficiency	%	15.05	3.87	9.48
MeOH / SNG / FT efficiency	%	50.00	64.75	56.65
Cumulative energy efficiency	%	65.05	68.62	66.13
Carbon capture rate	%	48.20	60.75	47.50
Specific CO_2 emissions	kg/MWh	25.75	7.05	40.05

Several important conclusions can be drawn from this evaluation: (i) combination of chemical routes with heat & power production will give an increased overall plant energy efficiency; (ii) once-through poly-generation plants will provide synthetic fuels at much lower cost than recycle plants designed to maximize the fuel output and (iii) poly-generation plants can provide decarbonised power at lower costs of greenhouse gas emissions avoided than stand alone fossil fuel power plants.

5. Conclusions

Flexible production of power and other energy carriers (hydrogen, synthetic fuels) was evaluated based on coal and coal & biomass gasification systems. As carbon capture options, two reactive gas-liquid (MDEA) and gas-solid (CaL) systems were evaluated, the calcium looping option having superior energy efficiency (by about 0.5 - 0.75 net electricity points) and carbon capture rate (95-96 vs. 91-92 %). The flexible power and hydrogen co-generation has also significant advantages in term of higher cumulative energy efficiency, lower specific CO_2 emissions, plant cycling etc.

References

A.M. Cormos, C. Dinca, C.C. Cormos, 2015, Multi-fuel multi-product operation of IGCC power plants with carbon capture and storage (CCS), Applied Thermal Engineering, 74, 20-27

European Commission, 2018, A European strategic long-term vision for a prosperous, modern, competitive andclimate neutral economy, COM(2018) 773 final, Brussels, Belgium

International Energy Agency, 2015, Energy Technology Perspectives 2015 - Mobilising Innovation to Accelerate Climate Action, Paris, France

H.C. Mantripragada, E.S. Rubin, 2017, Chemical looping for pre-combustion and post-combustion CO_2 capture, Energy Procedia, 114, 6403-6410

H. Mikulčić, I.R. Skov, D.F. Dominković, S.R. Wan Alwi, Z.A. Manan, R. Tan, N. Duić, S.N. Mohamad, X. Wang, 2019, Flexible Carbon Capture and Utilization technologies in future energy systems and the utilization pathways of captured CO_2, Renewable and Sustainable Energy Reviews, 114, 109338

F. Starr, E. Tzimas, S. Peteves, 2007, Critical factors in the design, operation and economics of coal gasification plants: The case of the flexible co-production of hydrogen and electricity, International Journal of Hydrogen Energy, 32, 1477-1485

S. Szima, S.M. Nazir, S. Cloete, S. Amini, S. Fogarasi, A.M. Cormos, C.C. Cormos, 2019, Gas switching reforming for flexible power and hydrogen production to balance variable renewables, Renewable and Sustainable Energy Reviews, 110, 207-219

Sauro Pierucci, Flavio Manenti, Giulia Bozzano, Davide Manca (Eds.)
Proceedings of the 30th European Symposium on Computer Aided Process Engineering
(ESCAPE30), May 24-27, 2020, Milano, Italy. © 2020 Elsevier B.V. All rights reserved.
http://dx.doi.org/10.1016/B978-0-12-823377-1.50230-5

Holistic Approach for the Optimization of Industrial Hybrid Energy Hubs with MILP

Verena Halmschlager [a] and René Hofmann [a,b]

[a]*Technische Universität Wien, Institute for Energy Systems and Thermodynamics, Getreidemarkt 9/E302, 1060 Vienna, Austria*
[b]*AIT Austrian Institute of Technology GmbH, Center for Energy, Sustainable Thermal Energy Systems, Giefinggasse2, 1210 Vienna, Austria*
rene.hofmann@tuwien.ac.at

Abstract

This work presents a holistic approach for the optimization of Energy Hubs with mixed integer linear programming for industrial applications. As a use case, a chipboard production plant is used, which produces different products depending on current orders. The use case includes units for power and steam generation, energy conversion, energy and material storages as well as continuous and batch production machines. Additionally, power is sold to the grid and energy in form of heat covers the demand of two district heating suppliers. To model and optimize such extensive industrial systems efficiently, a generic and modular modelling approach is proposed. The entire process is modelled based on five generic modules, which can be configured for specific tasks. To evaluate the viability of the proposed approach, three different scenarios within the industrial use case (without storage, with thermal energy storage, with material storage) were optimized. The results show, that this approach is well suited for scheduling and the assessment of process design improvements of existing industrial plants, due to its easily adaptable modular structure and the ability to use simple data-driven models.

Keywords: Industrial Energy Hub (IEH), Optimization, Mixed Integer Linear Programming (MILP), Scheduling, Demand Side Response (DSR)

1. Introduction

The increased application of renewable energies, combined with the complex energy market and new flexible technologies, challenges today's industry. This increases the need for holistic energy efficiency solutions. In industry, optimal production scheduling - discussed in (Merkert et al., 2015) - and Demand Side Response (DSR) - discussed in (Lindberg et al., 2014) - are promising solutions. However, in many processes, other energy carriers like steam, oil or gases need to be considered as well as the product and electric power. (Hybrid) Energy Hubs (EH) are an option for integrated management of these Multi Energy Systems, where different energy carriers can be converted, coupled and stored. Only few publications deal with the optimization of EHs, most of them focusing on the residential or commercial buildings sector (Sadeghi et al., 2019).

The idea of the EH was first expressed in (Favre-Perrod, 2005) and further researched in several papers. (Mohammadi et al., 2017) and (Sadeghi et al., 2019) provide a good overview of recent publications within this topic. Terms such as "Multi-Energy System", "Multi-Carrier Energy Systems" and "Natural Gas Multi Energy Services" usually describe systems that are all based on the concept of the EH.

In this work, a concept for the modelling and optimization of an Industrial Energy Hub is proposed. The optimization of the Industrial Energy Hub is intended to be used for optimal production and energy scheduling as well as the analysis of different scenarios within an industrial process. The work is structured as follows: Section 2 describes the general concept of the Industrial Energy Hub. Section 3 deals with the holistic and modular modelling and optimization approach. In Section 4, the industrial use case - a chipboard production plant - is modelled and optimized and results are shown. The conclusion is presented in Section 5.

2. Industrial Energy Hub Concept

In contrast to the commonly used EH concept presented in (Geidl et al., 2007; Mohammadi et al., 2017; Sadeghi et al., 2019), we propose the Industrial Energy Hub (IEH) that also takes into account the production in an industrial plant. Thus, in addition to different energy carriers like electrical and thermal power, also the product acts as a carrier in the IEH. Figure 1 illustrates the concept of the IEH. This approach emphasizes the importance of energy in production processes and enables the integration of different energy carriers and networks into the modelling and optimization of an industrial production plant.

In analogy to a classification of general EH systems in (Mohammadi et al., 2017), the parts of the IEH can be divided into four units: *conversion, storage, input* and *output*. In contrast to the general EH system, the product is taken into account in each of these units in the IEH system. In *conversion* units, the characteristics and quality of a carrier can be changed (adapting converters) or a carrier can be transformed into other forms (changing converters). Both types of converters can be either operated continuously or in (semi-)batch mode. In the IEH, typical *conversion* units for energy are generators, thermal power plants or heat exchangers. *Conversion* units for the product are all machines or devices that are part of the production chain. *Storage* units in the IEH can be energy storages, but also material storages. *Input* and *output* units in the IEH are process requirements or limits that need to be considered. Typical *inputs* are energy from the grid, fuel for production machines and energy converters, as well as primary product materials. Typical *outputs* of the IEH are heat for district heating (DH) supply, power for the electricity grid, gas that is fed into the gas network as well as the product of the plant. Thus, the IEH concept and its classification to the four units *conversion, storage, input* and *output* enables a generic description of a variety of different industrial processes and can be used as a basis for the optimization of IEH systems.

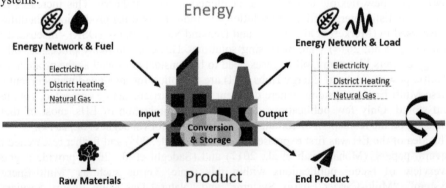

Figure 1: Illustration of the IEH concept

3. Modelling and Optimization Approach

The optimization of the IEH aims to determine the optimal energy and product flow in order to achieve minimal costs over a time horizon, whilst taking into account production specifications and external requirements. The approach is intended to be used for scheduling of existing industrial processes, but also for the assessment of different process design scenarios, e.g. to evaluate the implementation of additional machines/devices or storages. However, in existing industrial processes, the creation of detailed models is often not possible because only little data is available. Thus, simple and easily adaptable models are chosen for this applied approach. For this reason, the approach is based on an adaptable modular structure and uses a mixed integer linear programming (MILP) formulation with only linear, mostly data-based correlation. This way, modelling and optimization of an existing process and different design scenarios can be done in a time-saving manner with available process data.

3.1. MILP Formulation

The optimization problem is formulated as a MILP problem with linear constraints and a linear objective function. The optimization is set up in Matlab® with an object oriented approach. Process variables that can be varied and therefore optimized are called decision variables. These decision variables can be restricted by constraints. Binary decision variables (0 or 1) are used to indicate, if a device is switched on (1) or off (0). The objective function includes real costs, as well as penalties or rewards on decision variables to shift the optimization towards a desired goal. By using a MILP problem formulation, the optimization can be solved with state-of-the-art solvers (e.g. GUROBI) and results in a global optimum.

3.2. Holistic Modular Approach

To create an optimization model of the IEH with the MILP formulation, the industrial process is split into part models, called units. Based on the previous classification of the IEH system, all parts of the IEH can be divided in four units: *conversion, storage, input* and *output*. In addition to the former described first four units, also a *connection* unit is used in the optimization approach. For each of the five units, a generic module exists that acts as a basis model for all its parts/devices. Each generic module has an adaptable structure and offers the option to implement different preconfigured constraints and objectives. These are used to tailor a generic module to a specific device. The main advantage of this holistic approach is, that all part models can be easily adapted, omitted or added anywhere in the overall process model. In the following paragraphs, the structure, constraints and objectives of each module and its carriers (e.g. heat, product) are described in detail.

Conversion modules are used to model units that can adapt or transform a carrier in the IEH. Thus, converters are all machines/devices that consume or generate energy or a product. All converters are based on a generic input/output module and configured in detail by linear constraints. In the case that linear correlations are not capable to describe the behavior of the converter adequately, non-linear behavior can be approximated by piecewise linear relations and a differentiation in two or more operation modes. Constraints for converters can be divided into adaption/conversion constraints, carrier constraints and technical constraints. Constraints for adaption/conversion are used to describe the internal behavior of the converter, e.g. the amount of input that is required to generate a certain output. Carrier constraints are used to restrict the carriers when entering or exiting a converter. They include minimal and maximal constraints, as well as ramp up and ramp down constraints and represent limitations of the converter itself or the connection between different converters (e.g. pipes, conveyors). To model a converters technical limitations, start up and shut down times as well as minimal and maximal up and down times of a converter can be implemented. In addition to the constraints, the costs (start up or shut down costs, operation costs, material costs) of the converter can be added in the objective function.

Storage (energy or material) modules can have the same constraints as *conversion* modules. Additionally, constraints to model the integrative and dynamic charging and discharging behavior as well as thermal losses are added in the *storage* module.

The *input and output* module includes minimal and maximal constraints, as well as ramp up and ramp down constraints. If the input or output restriction varies over time, time sequence or integrative constraints can be used. Time sequence constraints can model demands or forecasts that need to be met by a certain carrier of a converter or storage. Integrative constraints are used to implement a production schedule over the time horizon. Both sequence and integrative constraints can be implemented directly as constraints, or added to objective function with a penalty or reward term.

The *connection* module connects the input and output streams of every module (converter, storage, in/outputs) with a mass or energy balance constraint.

The modelling of an IEH with the modular approach can be summarized as follows: Any carrier can be adapted and transformed in converters as well as stored in storages. Different converters and storages are connected with each other by connecting the according input and output streams of their carries with connections. External process inputs and outputs can be connected to converters or storages. They can represent time-dependent demands or a production sequence.

4. Use Case - Chipboard Production

To demonstrate the capability of the IEH approach, a simplified industrial chipboard production plant is considered as a use case, which is presented in Figure 2. The optimization model of the chipboard production is based on the IEH approach and uses industrial process data. A fictive district heating (DH) demand and a fixed price for electrical power are used. The optimization minimizes the overall process costs over a time horizon of 50 hours. For a design analysis of the process, three scenarios A, B and C are optimized.

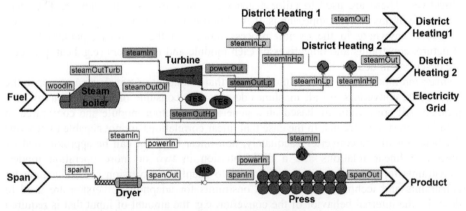

Figure 2: Use case - Flowchart of the simplified chipboard production

4.1. Analyzed Scenarios

In all scenarios, thermal and electrical energy that is required for the production is generated by a steam boiler and a steam turbine. As the amount of energy produced exceeds the demand of the production process, heat is fed into two DH networks with changing demands over time and electric power is sold to the grid. A production schedule defines the generation of two different products in two time intervals (product 1: 9-16 h, product 2: 23-38 h). Satisfying the production limits has highest priority in the process. The described external requirements are equal in all scenarios. The three scenarios only differ in the availability of storages. In the standard scenario A, no storages are available. In scenario B, two thermal energy storages (TES - steam accumulators for high and low pressure steam) with an efficiency of 99% are implemented. In scenario C, a material storage (MS) for dried span is added to scenario A. The location of the storages can be seen in the flowchart in Figure 2.

4.2. Optimization Results

Figures 3, 4 and 5 show the cumulative thermal energy (TE) that is used for the production process and fed into the DH network over a time horizon of 50 hours for the optimized scenarios A, B and C. Additionally, the charging and discharging behavior of the storages is depicted for scenarios B and C. In scenario A, the DH demand cannot be met over the entire time horizon (~93 % energy coverage), because not enough TE can be generated in times of high DH demand (after ~10 and 35 h) and production. In scenario B with the TES, more TE is produced in times of little production and used in times of high TE demand. In scenario C with the material storage, the generation of TE is shifted in time and used to process and store the chipboards in times of low DH demand. Hence, both storages can improve the processes efficiency by increasing its flexibility and enable the full coverage of DH demand.

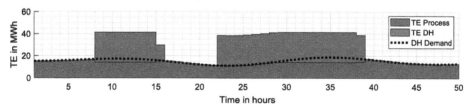

Figure 3: Optimization results of scenario A (no storage)

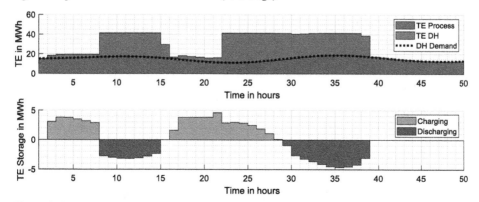

Figure 4: Optimization results of scenario B (thermal energy storage)

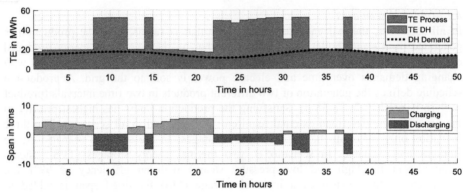

Figure 5: Optimization results of scenarios C (material storage)

5. Conclusion

The concept of the IEH and a holistic modelling and optimization approach were proposed. In the IEH, energy as well as the production of an industrial plant is considered. This enables the integration of different energy carriers and networks into the modelling and optimization of industrial plants. With the proposed approach, an industrial process can be modelled and optimized with five generic modules (converter, storage, input, output, connection). The generic and modular structure enables a fast implementation, combined with a high model adaptability. The results of the optimization can be used for scheduling, as well as for process design improvements. The viability of the approach was demonstrated with a use case. It confirms, that this holistic approach offers a straightforward and fast method to model and optimize industrial plants with process data. Future work will analyze the application of the proposed approach to extensive use cases and more comprehensive scenarios.

Acknowledgment

This work was funded by the cooperation doctoral school Smart Industrial Concept (SIC!). We particularly like to thank our industrial partner FunderMax, who enabled the analysis of the chipboard production and provided the required data. The authors want to express their great acknowledgment.

References

Favre-Perrod P 2005. A vision of future energy networks. Proceedings of the inaugural IEEE PES conference and exposition in Africa. Piscataway, NJ: IEEE Service Center; 13–17.

Geidl M, Koeppel G, Favre-Perrod P, Klöckl B, Andersson G, Fröhlich K 2007. The energy hub-A powerful concept for future energy systems. Third Annual Carnegie Mellon Conference on the Electricity Industry: 13–4.

Lindberg C-F, Zahedian K, Solgi M, Lindkvist R 2014. Potential and Limitations for Industrial Demand Side Management. Energy Procedia; 61: 415–8.

Merkert L, Harjunkoski I, Isaksson A, Säynevirta S, Saarela A, Sand G 2015. Scheduling and energy – Industrial challenges and opportunities. Computers & Chemical Engineering; 72: 183–98.

Mohammadi M, Noorollahi Y, Mohammadi-ivatloo B, Yousefi H 2017. Energy hub. Renewable and Sustainable Energy Reviews; 80: 1512–27.

Sadeghi H, Rashidinejad M, Moeini-Aghtaie M, Abdollahi A 2019. The energy hub. Applied Thermal Engineering; 161: 114071.

Sauro Pierucci, Flavio Manenti, Giulia Bozzano, Davide Manca (Eds.)
Proceedings of the 30th European Symposium on Computer Aided Process Engineering
(ESCAPE30), May 24-27, 2020, Milano, Italy. © 2020 Elsevier B.V. All rights reserved.
http://dx.doi.org/10.1016/B978-0-12-823377-1.50231-7

Agile Operation of Renewable Methanol Synthesis under Fluctuating Power Inputs

Christopher Varela,[a,*] Mahmoud Mostafa,[a] Elvis Ahmetovic,[b] Edwin Zondervan[a]

[a]*Laboratory of Process Systems Engineering, Faculty of Production Engineering, University of Bremen, Leobener Str. 6, 28359 Bremen, Germany*

[b]*Faculty of Technology, University of Tuzla, Univerzitetska 8, 75000 Tuzla, Bosnia and Herzegovina*

varela@uni-bremen.de

Abstract

The fluctuating production of renewable energy constraints the operation of Power-to-X processes such that steady-state conditions are unattainable without energy storage. It seems eminent to establish operation strategies considering significant disturbances along the process and to determine those scenarios where the operation becomes unfeasible. In this work, an industrial methanol Lurgi-type reactor, embedded in a Power-to-Jet process (Figure 1), is evaluated under fluctuating feed conditions. The simulated scenarios consist of step functions up to 20 % (w/w) increments in the feed flowrate as consequence of the fluctuating power input on the electrolysis stage. A one-dimensional dynamic model for a multi-tubular fixed bed reactor is implemented, considering both the gas and catalyst phase. The mathematical model is solved numerically using orthogonal collocation at the spatial domain and backward differences at the time domain. The system shows rapid response to disturbances, reaching steady state conditions in 1.5 minutes. Furthermore, it is evidenced that the feasible region to increase the production of methanol is narrowed down by rises of carbon dioxide feed flowrate up to 5 % (w/w).

Keywords: Power-to-X, methanol synthesis, renewable energy, process dynamics.

1. Introduction

By the conversion of electric power into chemicals, denoted as Power-to-X, renewables can substitute petrol-based feedstock in energy intensive industries with high greenhouse gas emissions. Methanol, with a global demand of 40 million tons per year (Olah et al., 2009), is one of the most relevant products for Power-to-X technologies as energy carrier and building block for a wide range of products, namely plastics, paints or synthetic fuels. By the Mobil process, methanol is converted into gasoline and a range of distillates (Tabak et al., 1986) with a distribution highly dependent on the zeolite catalyst shape (Schmidt et al., 2018). Hence aviation fuel, whose annual growth rate is 4.5 %, can be produced through the synthetic methanol pathway (Schmidt et al., 2016) as alternative to its conventional fossil-based production. The proposed route for the Power-to-Jet process is presented in Figure 1, where renewable power (photovoltaic, wind) and water are used to produce hydrogen on the electrolysis stage. Carbon dioxide is captured from concentrated sources and converted into methanol by hydrogenation. On the final stage, methanol is transformed into aviation fuel, gasoline and other distillate fractions by the MTGD (methanol to gasoline and distillates) process.

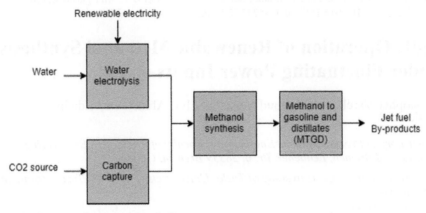

Figure 1 – Power-to-Jet process block diagram.

Such a process has the capability to directly convert excess renewable energy into commodities, although with high investment and operation costs mainly on the electrolysis stage (Schmidt et al., 2018). The fluctuating power input in the Power-to-Jet technologies introduces new challenges to the process design and operation.

Some effort has recently been put into finding optimal process conditions for the synthesis of renewable methanol; aiming to combine hydrogen produced through electrolysis with carbon dioxide captured from either air or concentrated sources such as flue gas streams (Schmidt et al., 2018; Van-Dal et al., 2013; Leonzio et al., 2019). A kinetic model that accounts for catalyst activity under different carbon dioxide to hydrogen ratios (Seidel et al., 2018) gives precise information on the reaction dynamics. Figure 2 describes the renewable methanol synthesis from the Power-to-Jet process (Figure 1), in which the fluctuations of renewable power cause a variation of hydrogen feed flowrate.

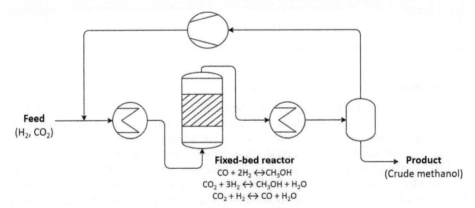

Figure 2 – (Crude) Methanol synthesis process from renewable energy.

2. Model development

2.1. Fixed-bed reactor model

The reactor model consists of a one-dimensional component and energy differential balance for the fluid and solid (catalyst) phase, considering convection, mass and heat transfer at the interphase, and reaction at the catalyst surface. To account for the porous catalyst ($Cu/ZnO/Al_2O_3$), the effectiveness factor is calculated by a diffusion-reaction balance within the catalyst cylindrical pellet (Lommerts et al., 2000).

$$\varepsilon \frac{\partial c_g^i}{\partial t} = -v \frac{\partial c_g^i}{\partial z} + a_v k_g^i \left(c_s^i - c_g^i \right) \tag{1}$$

$$(1-\varepsilon) \frac{\partial c_s^i}{\partial t} = a_v k_g^i \left(c_g^i - c_s^i \right) + \rho_b \sum_{j=1}^{N} v_j^i \eta_j R_j \tag{2}$$

$$\varepsilon \frac{\partial \left(\rho_g Cp_g T_g \right)}{\partial t} = -v \frac{\partial T_g}{\partial z} + a_v h_f \left(T_s - T_g \right) + \frac{4U_w}{d_i} \left(T_w - T_g \right) \tag{3}$$

$$\rho_b \frac{\partial \left(Cp_s T_s \right)}{\partial t} = a_v h_f \left(T_g - T_s \right) + \rho_b \sum_{j=1}^{N} \eta_j \left(-\Delta_R H_j \right) R_j \tag{4}$$

$$\frac{1}{x} \frac{d}{dx} \left(D_i^{eff} x \frac{dc_x^i}{dx} \right) = \rho_b \sum_{j=1}^{N} v_j^i R_j \tag{5}$$

Empirical correlations for mass and heat transfer, and commercial catalyst characteristics are conveniently provided by Rezaie et al. (2005).

2.2. Reaction kinetics

The kinetics are the most relevant part of the model since the aim of this work is to evaluate the reactor under varying feed compositions. To study the dynamic behavior, the detailed kinetic model proposed by Seidel et al. (2018) is used. It follows the general Langmuir-Hinshelwood kinetics:

$$R_j = \left[\text{kinetic factor} \right] \frac{\left[\text{driving force} \right]}{\left[\text{adsorption term} \right]} \tag{6}$$

The adsorption term includes the variable "ϕ" that accounts for the morphological changes in the catalyst surface for disturbances in the feed composition. Its transient behavior is described as follows:

$$\frac{d\phi}{dt} = k_1^+ \left(y_{H_2} (1-\phi) - \frac{1}{K_1} y_{H_2O} \phi \right) + k_2^+ \left(y_{CO} (1-\phi) - \frac{1}{K_2} y_{CO_2} \phi \right) \tag{7}$$

2.3. Numerical solution

The partial differential equations from the original model (Equations 1 to 4) are converted into ordinary differential equations using orthogonal collocation with 9 collocation points at the axial domain of the reactor. The collocation points correspond to the zeros of Jacobi polynomials (Rice et al, 1995). The solution of the ODE system is obtained using backward differences while the balance within the catalyst pellet (Equation 5) is solved with a three-points orthogonal collocation and Powell's method. Python is used as simulation environment.

3. Transient behaviour analysis

The open loop response to the hydrogen step changes of 5 %, 10 %, 15 % and 20 % (w/w) feed flowrate denotes a moderate variation in the production of methanol and no effect in the temperature at the fluid phase. The response for a hydrogen feed step change of 20 % in 20 seconds is shown in Figure 3.

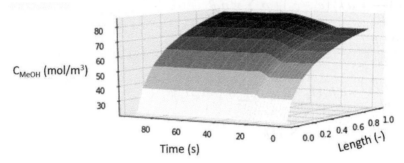

Figure 3 – Concentration profile of methanol for hydrogen feed step change of 20 % at t = 20 s.

To overcome the thermodynamic limitations of the chemical system, large recycle streams are required for the methanol synthesis. This excess of components being present in the reactor reduces the disturbance effects. However, during the simulation time of 90 seconds (Figure 3), the production of methanol increases by 11.26 %. Assuming a low-price electricity due to excess generation from renewables, the profit is expected to increase. In that case, the complete process has to be simulated, including the electrolysis stage. The concentration profile of methanol and hydrogen at the outlet of the reactor are shown in Figure 4.

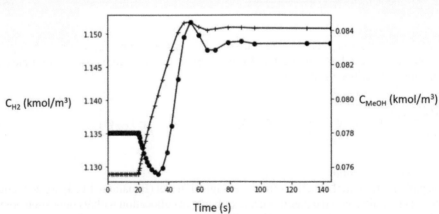

Figure 4 – Concentration profiles at reactor outlet for hydrogen feed step change of 20 % at t = 20 s for methanol (+) and hydrogen (•).

After 15 seconds of the applied disturbance (from t = 20 s to t = 35 s) methanol is diluted at the gas phase, still taking 55 seconds (from t = 35 s to t = 90 s) to balance the complex reaction system and transfer phenomena at the two phases. The relative fast dynamics and the proportional increase on the methanol production offers the opportunity to convert excess renewable energy into hydrogen and, consequently, into methanol.

4. Reactor operation strategy

For the operation of the Power-to-Jet process (Figure 1), more aspects have to be investigated along with the fluctuating hydrogen feed such as temperature and carbon dioxide to hydrogen ratio at the reactor feed stream. In this work, scenarios for carbon dioxide feed step change of 5 %, 10 %, 15 %, 20 % and 50 % (w/w) are chosen. A combination with the former scenarios for hydrogen feed step change (5 %, 10 %, 15 %, 20 %) results in twenty additional simulated scenarios. The results are shown in Figure 5, where the greyscale represents the conversion of carbon atoms into methanol along the reactor, the horizontal axis is the increment of carbon dioxide and the vertical axis the increment of hydrogen at the feed stream.

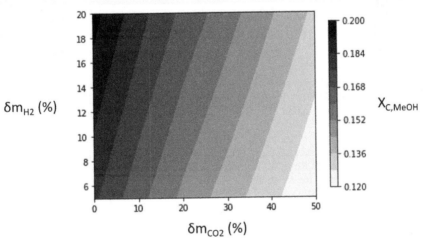

Figure 5 – Reactor performance in terms of conversion of carbon into methanol for different increments of hydrogen and carbon dioxide at the reactor feed.

It is proved that after a 10 % increase of the carbon dioxide intake, the reactor exhibits suboptimal operation conditions despite of any additional increment of hydrogen feed flowrate. Furthermore, it is shown that the operation window should be limited at 5 % extra carbon dioxide for the highest disturbance of hydrogen flow rate. This way, the performance of the reactor is not compromised in terms of conversion of carbon atoms into methanol, while the production of methanol is increased due to the fluctuations at the generation of renewable energy.

5. Conclusions and future work

The heterogeneous model for the catalytic reactor with tailor-made kinetics for dynamic simulation can be used to describe the transient behaviour of the methanol synthesis reactor under varying renewable energy inputs. The reactor reaches steady-state in roughly 90 seconds which is a relatively fast response for the significant disturbance at the feed of 20 % (w/w) hydrogen. An operation strategy considering the ratio of carbon dioxide to hydrogen was investigated. By simulating several scenarios, a suitable operating region for up to 5 % of carbon dioxide and up to 20 % hydrogen feed flowrate is identified. The renewable methanol synthesis is feasible in terms of short reaction times and smooth profiles with open loop response.

The effects of the disturbances on the temperature of the fluid and solid phase were negligible. Besides the reason stated at Section 3 related to dilution of the components, a one-dimensional model is less adequate in computing accurately the energy balance due to significant radial heat transport. Therefore, the model presented in this work can be extended to a two-dimensional model to account for the radial heat transfer on the reactor. In future work, different stages of the Power-to-Jet process (Figure 1) have to be simulated together in order to evaluate the opportunities for a dynamic renewable energy-driven operation. Regarding renewable methanol synthesis, the operation with different types of fixed-bed reactor are to be investigated, including scenarios for the long-run operation.

Acknowledgments

Funding of this research by the German Federal Ministry of Economic Affairs and Energy within the KEROSyN100 project (funding code 03EIV051A) is gratefully acknowledged.

References

G. Olah, A. Goeppert, G.K. Surya (2009), Beyond Oil and Gas: The Methanol Economy, 118

P. Schmidt, W. Weindorf (2016), Power-to-Liquids Potentials and Perspectives for the Future Supply of Renewable Aviation Fuel, German Environmental Agency Background no. Septemeber 2016, 10

S.A. Tabak, A.A. Avidan, F.J. Krambeck (1986), Production of synthetic gasoline and diesel fuel from nonpetroleum resources, American Chemical Society Volume 31:2, 293-299

P. Schmidt, V. Batteiger, A. Roth, W. Weindorf, T. Raksha (2018), Power-to-Liquids as Renewable Fuel Option for Aviation: A Review, Chem. Ing. Tech. 2018, 90 No. 1-2, 127-140

E. Van-Dal, C. Bouallou (2013), Design and simulation of a methanol production plant from CO2 hydrogenation, Journal of Cleaner Production 57 (2013), 38-45

G. Leonzio, E. Zondervan, P. Foscolo (2019), Methanol production by CO2 hydrogenation: Analysis and simulation of reaction performance, International Journal of Hydrogen Energy 44 (2019), 7915-7933

C. Seidel, A. Jörke, B. Vollbrecht, A. Seidel-Morgenstern, A. Kienle (2018), Kinetic modeling of methanol synthesis from renewable resources, Chemical Engineering Science 175 (2018), 130-138

N. Rezaie, A. Jahanmiri, B. Moghtaderi, M.R. Rahimpour (2005), A comparison of homogeneous and heterogeneous dynamic models for industrial methanol reactors in the presence of catalyst deactivation, Chemical Engineering and Processing 44 (2005), 911-921

B.J. Lommerts, G.H. Graaf, A.A.C.M. Beenackers (2000), Mathematical modeling of internal mass transport limitations in methanol synthesis, Chemical Engineeering Science 55 (2000), 5589-5598

R.G. Rice, D.D Do (1994), Applied Mathematics and Modeling for Chemical Engineers, John Wiley & Sons Inc., Chapter 8

Sauro Pierucci, Flavio Manenti, Giulia Bozzano, Davide Manca (Eds.)
Proceedings of the 30th European Symposium on Computer Aided Process Engineering
(ESCAPE30), May 24-27, 2020, Milano, Italy. © 2020 Elsevier B.V. All rights reserved.
http://dx.doi.org/10.1016/B978-0-12-823377-1.50232-9

Power-to-Syngas Processes by Reactor-Separator Superstructure Optimization

Andrea Maggi[a], Marcus Wenzel[b], Kai Sundmacher[a,b,*]

[a]*Max Planck Institute for Dynamics of Complex Technical Systems, Department Process Systems Engineering, Sandtorstr. 1, 39106 Magdeburg, Germany*
[b]*Otto-von-Guericke University Magdeburg, Process Systems Engineering, Universitätplatz 2, 39106 Magdeburg, Germany*
sundmacher@mpi-magdeburg.mpg.de

Abstract

The effects of global warming and the depletion of fossil resources call for technological solutions. Syngas, a mixture of carbon dioxide and hydrogen, can bridge chemicals and fuels production with renewable feedstocks and energy sources. In this contribution, a reactor-separator network for syngas production is proposed by superstructure optimization based on thermodynamics. Interactions among the network elements are quantitatively explored for different H_2/CO ratios and electricity production scenarios: zero-carbon and power plant operations.

Keywords: Syngas, Separation, Process Network

1. Introduction and Motivation

The transition from fossil (coal, oil, gas) to renewable feedstocks and energy carriers (solar, wind, water, biomass) has become a matter of importance in industry. Prompt actions are required to face arising challenges, such as the intermittency and geographical displacement of resources, resulting in storage and transportation issues. Schack et al. (2018) identified cost-optimal conversion pathways from renewables to valuable target products. Syngas, a mixture of hydrogen and carbon monoxide, is an ideal candidate due to its versatility as a reactant for different, well-known, downstream conversion systems, characterized by high production volumes. Table 1 exemplifies the composition requirements for such applications. Therefore, syngas represents a strategic hub between state-of-the-art processes and sustainable power and carbon sources. In this contribution, possible synergies among methane steam reforming (SR), reverse water-gas shift (RWGS) and water electrolysis (EL) are explored based on thermodynamics. All together, they allow for flexibility in terms of raw materials. SR can either be fed by CH_4 from biogas or, if not available, by natural gas. Similarly, RWGS can be fed by H_2 from water electrolysis and CO_2 from external sources (e.g. air capture, capture from flue gases etc.) or by excess H_2 from SR. Alternative separation techniques are proposed within an optimization framework.

Table 1: Downstream applications and typically required compositions, adapted from Wenzel et al. (2017)

Process	H_2/CO
Phosgene Monsanto	0.0
Hydroformylation	0.0-0.02
Direct Reduction of Iron Ore	1.0-1.2
FischerTropsch	1.3-1.5
Alcohol Synthesis	1.6-2.3
	2.0-2.3

2. Methods

2.1. Conversion steps

RWGS and SR are endothermic conversion steps ($\Delta H^{\circ}_{R,RWGS}$ = 41 kJ/mol, $\Delta H^{\circ}_{R,SR}$ = 206 kJ/mol at 298 K). For the electrochemical conversion of H_2O into H_2, an electrical power input of 385 kJ/mol$_{H2}$ for 60% stack efficiency is accounted for in a low-pressure electrolyzer as in Bensmann et al. (2013). CH_4 is provided by the anaerobic digestion of biomass (AD), resulting in a mixture of CH_4 and CO_2 (biogas). As stated in Section 1, syngas is used as feed stream for different downstream applications, each requiring a well-defined ratio of $r=H_2/CO$. Therefore, syngas conditioning is required and achieved by flowrate adjustment at the reactors and at the electrolyzer. High syngas ratios can be attained by conversion of CO into CO_2 within an oxy-combustion step (COMB), where O_2 is provided as a by-product of the electrolyzer. In principle, a WGS reactor can be combined with SR, which is the typical solution for H_2 production plants, also reported in LeValley et al. (2014). For pure H_2 production, such a configuration leads to consistent energy savings but larger CO_2 emissions with respect to its alternative, water electrolysis. Nonetheless, for syngas ratios lower than three, an additional capital investment on a WGS reactor is not justified.

2.2. Feasible separation methods

Separation sequences of gas-phase mixtures might be negatively affected by the presence of H_2O, which can condense along the process pathways, thus leading to clogging. Therefore, most of the moisture should be removed at the reactor outlets by temperature-driven condensation (CD). Feasible separation methods for specific feed mixtures are identified from the literature. For the sake of brevity, a generic ternary mixture will be denoted as (A,B,C), while the task of separating A out of (A,B,C) is denoted as A/(B,C). Hydrogen, CH_4 and O_2 can leave the plant after compression or cryogenic condensation.

2.2.1. RWGS separation sequences

After condensation, the outlet stream from RWGS comprises of CO, unreacted CO_2 and H_2, and traces of H_2O (ca. 0.3%$_{vol}$). Metz et al. (2005) reported high permeability of water in poly-dimethylsiloxane. Lower permeabilities for the other components of the mixture were reported by Merkel et al. (2001). Therefore, a membrane separator (MS) can be implemented for gas dehydration followed by a tree of alternatives for the final product separation and conditioning: 1. CO/(CO_2,H_2) (Gao et al., 2016) followed by CO_2/(H_2) on activated carbons or by recycle of the reactants (CO_2,H_2), both steps via vacuum pressure swing adsorption (VPSA); 2. H_2/(CO_2,CO) and CO/(CO_2) via VPSA; 3. CO_2/(H_2,CO) by amine absorption (AA) and H_2/(CO) (VPSA) and/or bypass to the product.

2.2.2. SR separation sequence

As for the RWGS separation train, SR requires water condensation followed by a membrane dehydration step. Afterwards, CH_4/(CO,H_2) is performed by cryogenic condensation (CR), possibly followed by recycle of CH_4. Lastly, VPSA (possibly by-passed) allows for syngas conditioning. Biogas provides methane to SR: after anaerobic digestion, it is separated into CH_4 and CO by VPSA.

2.3. Modeling strategies

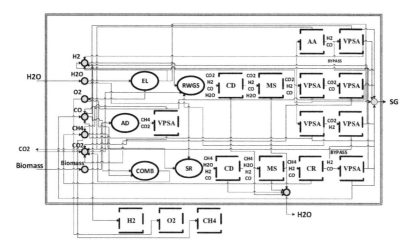

Figure 1 Fully connected superstructure.

Reactors and separators are assembled into a superstructure (see Figure 1). Nodes for the chemical components receive and deliver process streams. The outlets of the reactors are at their equilibrium compositions. Besides, the assumption of sharp-split separators allows to calculate each process stream flowrate as a function of the mole fractions after condensation at the reactor outlet,

$$\dot{n}_A = \dot{n}_{(A,B,C)} \frac{x_A}{x_A + x_B + x_C} = \dot{n}_{(A,B,C)} \xi_{A/(B,C)} , \qquad (1)$$

where component A is separated from a feed stream (A,B,C), whereas $\dot{n}$ and x are the mole flowrates and mole fractions, respectively, of the stream leaving from the condensation steps. The split factor for the separation task A/(B,C) is denoted by $\xi_{A/(B,C)}$. Temperature and pressure levels are fixed. Moreover, a stoichiometric feed is assigned to the reactors. As a result, ξ is fixed and Equation 1 is linear with respect to the mole flowrates. Given that no compression is considered before water is condensed, the selected pressure level at the reactors also defines the amount of water fed to the membrane separators. The partial pressure of water in the membrane separator must be less than its vapor pressure to avoid condensation. For RWGS and SR, the thermal energy requirements are calculated from the reaction enthalpy at T_{RWGS} and T_{SR}, respectively. Normalized temperature and pressure (i.e. normal conditions) are assigned to the substance nodes. Therefore, a recycle stream will reach the normal conditions before being heated and compressed to the actual conditions at the reactors. Separation methods such as VPSA and AA comprise sequences of operation and regeneration steps, each being associated with pre-defined (T,p) values. Changes in T and p between consecutive tasks are performed via adiabatic compression and heating from external utilities. Expansion and cooling are not energetically considered. An exception is made for cryogenic condensation and storage, whose power demand is calculated from the definition of coefficient of performance (COP) which is 60% of its ideal value. The ideal COP corresponds to the ratio between T_L and (T_H-T_L), where T_H and T_L are the condensation and evaporation temperature of the refrigerant fluid, respectively. Furthermore, vacuum is normalized by adiabatic expansion.

2.4. Optimization problem

Three different optimization problems are defined:

$$\min \quad \dot{W} + \dot{Q} \tag{I}$$

$$\min \quad \frac{1}{LHV_{CH4}} \dot{Q} \tag{II}$$

$$\min \quad \frac{1}{LHV_{CH4}} \frac{1}{\eta_{PP}} \dot{W} + \frac{1}{LHV_{CH4}} \dot{Q} \tag{III}$$

Problem (I) represents the minimization of the total power requirement, where no distinction is made between electrical ($\dot{W}$) and thermal power ($\dot{Q}$). As stated earlier, neither thermal nor electrical power recovery is considered: gas expansion and cooling are not accounted for by the objectives. Problem (II) represents the CO_2 generated with a reference fuel (methane) as thermal power source, where LHV stands for lower heating value: the electricity is provided via zero-emissions sources, i.e. solar and wind. The minimization of CO_2 emissions is given by (III), where electricity is provided by a reference power-plant of assigned efficiency η_{PP}=34%, fueled by methane (see Descamps et al. (2008)). Linear programs are implemented and solved by the dual-simplex algorithm. In the post-processing of results from objectives (II) and (III), the CO_2 flowrate required as a chemical reactant at RWGS is subtracted from the CO_2 generated by combustion and process-streams emissions: the direct inclusion of this term in the objectives would lead to unboundedness, i.e. infinite flowrate at RWGS.

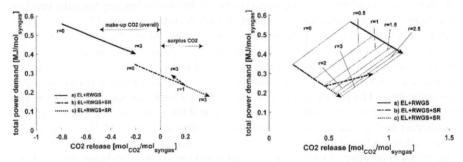

(B) Renewable electricity: objectives (I) and (II)   (B) Electricity from power plant: objectives (I) and (III); a) and b) suboptimal.

Figure 2: Identification of the optimal process patterns.

3. Results and discussion

Figure 2A illustrates the results from a combination of objectives (I) and (II) into a single multi-objective optimization problem, which accounts for totally renewable electrical power. The syngas ratio r spans between zero and three. Three process configurations a), b), and c) are determined and their relevant flowrates are shown in Figure 3A, 3B, and 3C, respectively. Configuration a) implements EL + RWGS, followed by water condensation, membrane dehydration and VPSA separation of CO which recycles (CO_2,H_2); b) and c) allow for SR and the associated separation scheme: they coincide for $r \in [0,1)$ and diverge with respect to energy consumption and carbon dioxide generation for $r \in [1,3]$. The combination of objectives (I) and (III) results in optimal configuration c), whereas a) and b) are suboptimal (see Figure 2B).

Configuration a) requires the largest amount of power due to the high electrical duty for EL. If electricity is provided via renewables, the CO_2 generated within the plant is not sufficient to fulfill the feed requirements at RWGS: an external carbon source must be allowed for, i.e. direct air capture or CO_2 from industrial flue gases. Configuration a) represents the least attractive solution if electricity is provided by power plants, both energy-wise and in terms of CO_2 generation. The inversely proportional trends between total power duty and r can be explained by Figure 3A: the outlet flowrate from EL is constant regardless of the value of r, which implies a constant power demand at this unit. On the other hand, the energy duty at RWGS decreases for increasing r. Part of the

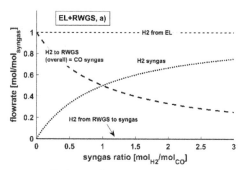

(C) Relevant flowrates, EL+RWGS, a)

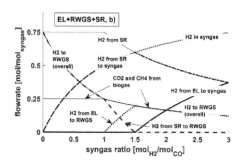

(B) Relevant flowrates, EL+RWGS+SR, b

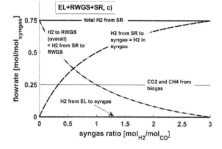

(A) Relevant flowrates, EL+RWGS+SR, c)

Figure 3: Flow-patterns.

H_2 generated by EL leaves as syngas, whereas the remaining amount is converted into CO by RWGS. Consequently, to preserve a fixed syngas flowrate, the productivity of RWGS must decrease, and so does its energy demand. Since RWGS is a sink for carbon dioxide, the system behavior with respect to the CO_2 generation in Figures 2A and 2B is also explained: the less CO is produced, the less CO_2 is consumed by RWGS. SR can substitute EL as a producer of H_2 for RWGS. Process configurations allowing for SR are only suboptimal: it is less energy-intensive and more sustainable to generate part of the CO by RWGS. For $r \in [0,1)$ in b) and $r \in [0,3]$ in c), SR provides all the H_2 required at RWGS and syngas. In this case, the outlet flowrate from SR does not change for different values of r. For $r \geq 1$ in b) (see Figure 3B), the electrolyzer starts to feed H_2 to RWGS, gradually substituting SR, whereas for $r \geq 1.5$ it totally replaces it. Furthermore, the biogas generated from AD is entirely converted within the battery limits according to the overall stoichiometry $CH_4 + CO_2 = 2H_2 + 2CO$. Therefore, RWGS is always operated.

4. Conclusions

In this contribution, a reactor-separator superstructure for the syngas production is proposed. Optimization results identify possible synergies between EL, SR and RWGS. Unreacted H_2 and CO_2 are recycled by VPSA after RWGS, whereas CO and H_2 leave as syngas. EL is highly energy demanding and only sustainable if renewable electricity is available. Thus, if electricity is provided via conventional power plants, EL is not a favourable option. Therefore, the implementation of EL and RWGS would be unable to ensure a sustainable production for scenarios where renewable electricity is not sufficiently available. In such cases, process systems comprising EL, RWGS and SR allow for lower CO_2 generation levels and energy demand because SR can substitute or complement EL as H_2 source for RWGS.

References

B. Bensmann, R. Hanke-Rauschenbach, I. P. Arias, K. Sundmacher, 2013. Energetic evaluation of high pressure pem electrolyzer systems for intermediate storage of renewable energies. Electrochimica Acta 110, 570–580.

C. Descamps, C. Bouallou, M. Kanniche, 2008. Efficiency of an integrated gasification combined cycle (igcc) powerplant including co2 removal. Energy 33 (6), 874–881.

F. Gao, Y. Wang, S. Wang, 2016. Selective adsorption of co on cucl/y adsorbent prepared using cucl2 as precursor: Equilibrium and thermodynamics. Chemical Engineering Journal 290, 418–427.

T. L. LeValley, A. R. Richard, M. Fan, 2014. The progress in water gas shift and steam reforming hydrogen production technologies–a review. International Journal of Hydrogen Energy 39 (30), 16983–17000.

T. Merkel, R. Gupta, B. Turk, B. D. Freeman, 2001. Mixed-gas permeation of syngas components in poly (dimethyl-siloxane) and poly (1-trimethylsilyl-1-propyne) at elevated temperatures. Journal of Membrane Science 191 (1-2),85–94.S.

J. Metz, W. Van de Ven, J. Potreck, M. Mulder, M. Wessling, 2005. Transport of water vapor and inert gas mixtures through highly selective and highly permeable polymer membranes. Journal of Membrane Science 251 (1-2), 29–41.

M. Wenzel, L. Rihko-Struckmann, K. Sundmacher, 2017. Thermodynamic analysis and optimization of rwgs processes for solar syngas production from co2. AIChE Journal 63 (1), 15–22.

Sauro Pierucci, Flavio Manenti, Giulia Bozzano, Davide Manca (Eds.)
Proceedings of the 30th European Symposium on Computer Aided Process Engineering
(ESCAPE30), May 24-27, 2020, Milano, Italy. © 2020 Elsevier B.V. All rights reserved.
http://dx.doi.org/10.1016/B978-0-12-823377-1.50233-0

Search Space Analysis in Work and Heat Exchange Networks Synthesis using MINLP Models

Lucas F. Santos,[a*] Caliane B. B. Costa,[a] José A. Caballero,[b] Mauro A. S. S. Ravagnani[a,b]

[a]*Chemical Engineering Graduate Program, State University of Maringá, 5790 Colombo Av., Maringá – 87020900, Brazil*
[b]*Department of Chemical Engineering, University of Alicante, Ap. Correos 99, Alicante – 03080, Spain*
lfs.francisco.95@gmail.com

Abstract

Superstructure-based optimization models have been used as important approaches in solving process systems engineering problems. Despite its promising results, mixed-integer nonlinear programming (MINLP) optimization models are usually complex, once they involve integer and continuous variables, and nonlinear, non-convex functions. For work and heat exchange networks (WHEN) synthesis, even in problems of few process streams, the derived MINLP models have large combinatorial and continuous search spaces. In the present paper, the search spaces of two equivalents MINLP models for WHEN synthesis are analyzed to test their influence on optimization performance. The models are derived from the same superstructure, but one of those uses strategies to reduce the number of decision variables that provides a considerable diminution of combinatorial problem. The same bi-level meta-heuristic optimization approach in which Simulated Annealing deals with the combinatorial level and Particle Swarm Optimization with the continuous one is used to solve both MINLP problems. The mean values of total annualized cost and elapsed time from several optimization runs of both models are compared. The results show that the decision-variable-reduced model is more efficient and consistent than the standard-decision-variable one. It can be concluded that combinatorial search space reduction is important for optimization performance of highly complex decision-making problems such as WHEN synthesis and should be addressed in WHEN modeling because the problem's complexity increases exponentially with the number of the model binary variables.

Keywords: Work and heat exchange networks. MINLP. Search space. Optimization performance. Combinatorial analysis.

1. Introduction

Energy has fundamental importance in chemical processes as it fuels the transformation of matter into desired products. However, consuming energy sources implies costs and environmental footprint. One way to use this resource with less waste is by means of energy integration. The synthesis of optimal work and heat exchange networks (WHEN) performing work and heat integration is deeply important to guarantee economic competitiveness and viability of chemical processes that demand high energy consumption for compression, heating, and cooling tasks. WHEN synthesis is a rather complicated decision-making task because it comprises choosing existence, sequence, and sizes of heat exchangers, heaters, cooler, compressors, turbines, single-shaft-turbine-compressors (SSTC), and valves and considering thermal identity change due to pressure manipulation, phase transition, and thermodynamic cycles. Since decisions must be taken to reduce a value of interest, such as total annualized cost (TAC), it is intuitive and useful to use mathematical optimization. In this context, superstructures help systematizing possible WHEN configurations from which mixed-integer nonlinear programming (MINLP) models can be derived. The resulting MINLP models are usually large scale, non-convex problems; therefore, difficult to solve to global optimality.

In recent years, many researchers have employed superstructure-based optimization for WHEN synthesis. Wechsung et al. (2011) published the first paper on this subject. Those authors proposed a heat exchanger network (HEN) superstructure that allowed streams to compress and expand in pre-defined routes based on heuristics for appropriate placement of compressors and turbines from Gundersen et al. (2009). Razib et al. (2012) proposed a multi-stage work exchange network (WEN) superstructure that considered heating and cooling streams using utilities. They introduced in their superstructure the possibility of direct work integration via single-shaft-turbine-compressors (SSTC). Onishi et al. (2014a; 2014b) extended previous superstructures by implementing the well-known stage-wise HEN superstructure from Yee and Grossmann (1990) to improve heat integration. Onishi et al. (2018) proposed a superstructure and disjunctive-MINLP model that did not pre-classify streams with respect to its temperature and pressure, so that heating, cooling, compression, and expansion had no fixed routes. This improvement made WHEN superstructures more generic to deal with non-trivialities such as thermal identity change, and thermodynamic cycles, at the price of making the mathematical problem more complicated. Pavão et al. (2019) presented interesting WHEN results using a new superstructure and MINLP model and a bi-level meta-heuristic optimization approach. In their framework, simplified routes of temperature and pressure manipulations were fixed, but complicated heat integration configurations were allowed based on a new HEN superstructure (Pavão et al., 2018).

In the above-mentioned works, the complexity of the MINLP problems was reduced by means of simplifications in the superstructures and models. These considerations simplify the problem, but reduce its generality and exclude possible promising WHEN configurations. Based on that, Santos et al. (2020) reported interesting and non-trivial WHENs using a new superstructure and MINLP model that included strategies to reduce the number of decision variables by means of changes of variables and third-level optimization. Mathematical simplifications based on additional calculations and extra information that did not necessarily reduce the model generality were introduced.

Given this background of different MINLP models for WHEN synthesis, the current literature lacks on mathematical characterization of these models via, for instance, search space, combinatorial, and convex analyzes. Therefore, the purpose of the present paper is to analyze the search space of two MINLP models for WHEN synthesis and its influence on the optimization performance. Both models are equivalent and derived from the same superstructure. One of them, however, is in a more intuitive formulation, whereas the other presents strategies for reducing the number of decision variables.

2. WHEN models

The superstructure and MINLP models analyzed in the present paper were proposed by Santos et al. (2020). Authors presented a multi-stage WHEN superstructure divided into four sections: classification, heat integration, temperature adjustment, and work exchange network, as illustrated in Figure 1.

Decision-variable-reduced model

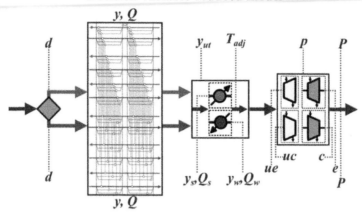

Standard-decision-variable model

Figure 1. Stages of WHEN superstructure with decision variables of both models.

Using changes of variables and third level optimization to reduce the optimization search space, their MINLP model (Eq. (1)) aims to minimize total annualized cost (*TAC*) and has the following decision variables: d, y, y_{ut}, p, Q, T_{adj}, and P. These variables stand for thermal classification, existence of heat exchanger, activation of temperature adjustment section, activation of pressure manipulation section, heat load of heat exchanger, adjusted temperature, and manipulated pressure, respectively. Notice that d, y, y_{ut}, and p are binary variables, and Q, T_{adj}, and P are continuous ones. The reader is referred to Santos et al. (2020) for more information regarding the model and superstructure.

$$\min \quad TAC\left(d, y, y_{ut}, p, Q, T_{adj}, P\right)$$

Thermodynamic and operating constraints

s.t.
$$\left\{ \begin{array}{ll} d \in \{0,1\}^{n_1}, & n_1 = S \cdot Ns \\ y \in \{0,1\}^{n_2}, \quad Q \in \mathbb{R}^{n_2}, & n_2 = S^2 \cdot Ns^2 \cdot K \\ y_{ut} \in \{0,1\}^{n_3}, \quad T_{adj} \in \mathbb{R}^{n_3}, & n_3 = S \cdot (Ns - 1) \\ p \in \{0,1\}^{n_4}, \quad P \in \mathbb{R}^{n_4}, & n_4 = S \cdot (Ns - 2) \end{array} \right. \tag{1}$$

Note that S is the number of process streams, Ns the number of WHEN stages in the superstructure, and K the number of heat integration stages. Now, by simply removing the strategies of reducing the number of decision variables, the resulting and equivalent MINLP (Eq. (2)) has the following decision variables: d, y, Q, and P and y_s, y_w, e, c, ue, uc, Q_s, and Q_w. The latter set of variables contains those that represent the existence of heater (y_s), cooler (y_w), turbine coupled to work integration shaft (e), compressor coupled to the shaft (c), electric turbine (ue), electric compressor (uc), heater heat load (Q_s), and cooler heat load (Q_w). Notice that d, y, y_s, y_w, e, c, ue, and uc are binary variables, and Q, P, Q_s, and Q_w are continuous ones.

$$\min \quad TAC(d, y, y_s, y_w, e, c, ue, uc, Q, Q_s, Q_w, P)$$

Thermodynamic and operating constraints

s.t.
$$\left\{ \begin{array}{ll} d \in \{0,1\}^{n_1}, & n_1 = S \cdot Ns \\ y \in \{0,1\}^{n_2}, & n_2 = S^2 \cdot Ns^2 \cdot K \\ y_s, y_w \in \{0,1\}^{n_3}, \quad Q_s, Q_w \in \mathbb{R}^{n_3}, & n_3 = S \cdot (Ns - 1) \\ e, c, ue, uc \in \{0,1\}^{n_4}, \quad P \in \mathbb{R}^{n_4}, & n_4 = S \cdot (Ns - 2) \end{array} \right. \tag{2}$$

2.1. Search space analysis

A degrees of freedom (DoF) analysis of these models shows that (1) has $2 \cdot S^2 \cdot N_s^2 \cdot K + S \cdot (5 \cdot N_s - 6)$ DoF and (2) has $2 \cdot S^2 \cdot N_s^2 \cdot K + S \cdot (10 \cdot N_s - 14)$ DoF. Although each DoF must be fulfilled with a decision variable, increasing the problem dimension, it is not enough to measure the MINLP search space by the number of decision variables. One reason for that is because continuous space is determined by the binary configuration that activates and deactivates continuous variables. Therefore, not all continuous variables are considered, but only the ones activated by binary configuration. Another reason is that the number of binary combinations is more relevant to determine the combinatorial search space than the number of binary variables. Given that, let us consider that the search space can be divided into continuous and combinatorial (binary).

The continuous search space of both standard-decision-variable model (SDVM) (2) and decision-variable-reduced model (DVRM) (1) are equivalent. Even though the number of continuous decision variables is $S \cdot (N_s - 1)$ higher in the SDVM, the number of active continuous variables at equivalent topologies is always the same. For example, Q_s and Q_w cannot coexist; therefore, they are analogous to the single variable T_{adj}.

The combinatorial search spaces change considerably from SDVM to DVRM. The resulting combinations of temperature adjustment in SDVM are $3^{S \, (N_s - 1)}$, which come from three possible binary results of y_s, $y_w = \{[0,0], [1,0], [0,1]\}$ for each stream $s = 1, ..., S$, and stage $n = 1, ..., N_s - 1$. On the other hand, for DVRM the combinations in this section are $2^{S \, (N_s - 1)}$ from two possible results of $y_{ut} = \{0, 1\}$ for the same s and n. In the work exchange section, the difference is even stronger. In the SDVM there are $5^{S \, (N_s - 2)}$ combinations from e, c, ue, $uc = \{[0,0,0,0], [1,0,0,0], [0,1,0,0], [0,0,1,0], [0,0,0,1]\}$ for each stream $s = 1, ..., S$, and stage $n = 1, ..., N_s - 2$. The same section in DVRM presents only $2^{S \, (N_s - 2)}$ combinations from $p = \{0, 1\}$ for the same s and n. The heat integration section is the same for both models. Thus, SDVM has $3^{S \cdot (N_s - 1)} \cdot 5^{S \cdot (N_s - 2)} / 2^{S \cdot (2N_s - 3)}$ times more binary combinations than DVRM. For a simple example of $S = 4$ and $N_s = 4$, SDVM binary combinations are 197,977 times higher than those of DVRM, and it clearly escalates exponentially with S and N_s.

3. Case study

Both models were implemented in C++ language in a computer with a 3.20 GHz Intel® Core™ i5-4460 processor and 8.00 GB of RAM. The models were used to solve a two-stream work and heat integration case study, whose data are presented in Table 1. This case study is inspired by Onishi et al. (2014a), and was used by Pavão et al. (2019). However, in order to complicate the problem, the pressure differences and heat capacity flow rate were increased by a factor of 10.

Table 1. Process streams and utilities data

Stream	T_{in} [K]	T_{out} [K]	CP [kW.K^{-1}]	h [kW.m^{-2}.K^{-1}]	P_{in} [MPa]	P_{out} [MPa]
$s1$	650	370	30	0.1	0.1	5
$s2$	410	650	20	0.1	5	0.1
HU	680	680	–	1.0	–	–
CU	300	300	–	1.0	–	–

The superstructure parameters for this case study are $S = 2$, $N_s = 4$, $K = 2$. Thus, the resulting optimization problems (1) and (2) has 284 (146 binary) and 308 (164 binary) decision variables, respectively. The problem is solved using a bi-level meta-heuristic optimization approach with Simulated Annealing (SA) in the combinatorial problem and Particle Swarm Optimization (PSO) in the NLP, as proposed by Santos et al. (2020). This solution approach was selected instead of deterministic global solvers because, as reported in the literature (Onishi et al., 2018), they are too time-consuming when applied to MINLP problems from WHEN synthesis. However, the same search space analysis using deterministic methods for global optimization will be the subject of future work. Considering the non-deterministic behavior of meta-heuristic techniques, each optimization was run 50 times and the resulting TAC and elapsed time (τ) were saved for further analysis. The reader is referred to case study 1 of Santos et al. (2020) for more information about the problem as well as solver parameters. The mean value and standard deviation of TAC and τ obtained for both SDVM and DVRM are presented in Table 2.

Table 2. Optimization results of SDVM and DVRM.

	SDVM			DVRM		
	TAC ($.y^{-1})	τ (min)	Failure (%)	TAC ($.y^{-1})	τ (min)	Failure (%)
Mean	9.304.802	10	2	8.637.935	9	0
Standard deviation	339.964	0.4	-	225.777	0.9	-

As presented in Table 2, DVRM performed better and more consistently, *i.e.* lower TAC mean value and standard deviation and less failure (infeasible solution). One reason for that is the combinatorial analysis of these models. Let the search space of binary variables be all possible configurations of binary variables as explained in 2.1. Then, the binary search space of SDVM is 445 times greater than DVRM, considering the superstructure parameters used (S, Ns, and K). Knowing that the number of topologies evaluated in SDVM was 2480 and DVRM was 930, which are far from all combinations possible, it can be inferred that the reduction of 445 times guarantees the solver to investigate proportionally more of the whole binary search space. The difference between the numbers of topologies evaluated in each model is because of the DVRM third-level optimization. In order to approximate elapsed time for a fair comparison, more SA trials were available for SDVM.

These results show the importance of not only evaluating the degrees of freedom of a problem for decision variables choice, but also paying attention to the number of binary combinations of a MINLP model. Knowing that the latter grows exponentially, it increases the problem complexity a lot and quickly.

4. Conclusions

Two MINLP models for WHEN synthesis are compared regarding their search spaces. These models are equivalent and derived from the same superstructure, but strategies for reducing the number of decision variables are applied in one of them (Santos et al., 2020). One finding of search space comparison is that the ratio of binary combinations between SDVM and DVRM increases exponentially ($3^{S \cdot (Ns-1)} \cdot 5^{S \cdot (Ns-2)} / 2^{S \cdot (2Ns-3)}$) with respect to the number of streams (S) and stages (Ns) of the work and heat integration superstructure. It means that the higher is S and Ns, the more significant is the combinatorial search space diminution due to the strategies. The optimization results showed that the DVRM outperformed the SDVM in both performance (lower mean TAC), and consistency (lower TAC standard deviation and failures). Regarding elapsed time, DVRM was slower than SDVM because of its time-consuming third-level optimization. Therefore, it can be concluded that, in WHEN synthesis MINLP models, combinatorial search space reduction is extremely important for optimization performance as it simplifies the complexity of decision-making problem.

Acknowledgements

The authors acknowledge the National Council for Scientific and Technological Development – Brazil, processes 440047/2019-6, 311807/2018-6, 428650/2018-0 148184/2019-7, 305055/2017-8, and Coordination for the Improvement of Higher Education Personnel – Brazil for the financial support.

References

T. Gundersen, D. O. Berstad, and A. Aspelund, 2009, Extending Pinch Analysis and Process Integration into Pressure and Fluid Phase Considerations, Chemical Engineering Transactions, 18, 33–38.

V. C. Onishi, M. A. S. S. Ravagnani, and J. A. Caballero, 2014a, Simultaneous Synthesis of Heat Exchanger Networks with Pressure Recovery: Optimal Integration between Heat and Work, AIChE Journal, 60, 3, 893–908.

V. C. Onishi, N. Quirante, M. A. S. S. Ravagnani, and J. A. Caballero, 2018, Optimal Synthesis of Work and Heat Exchangers Networks Considering Unclassified Process Streams at Sub and Above-Ambient Conditions, Applied Energy, 224, 8, 567–81.

V. C. Onishi, M. A. S. S. Ravagnani, and J. A. Caballero, 2014b, Simultaneous Synthesis of Work Exchange Networks with Heat Integration, Chemical Engineering Science, 112, 6, 87–107.

L. V. Pavão, C. B. B. Costa, and M. A. S. S. Ravagnani, 2019, A New Framework for Work and Heat Exchange Network Synthesis and Optimization, Energy Conversion and Management, 183, 3, 617–632.

L. V. Pavão, C. B. B. Costa, and M. A. S. S. Ravagnani, 2018, An Enhanced Stage-Wise Superstructure for Heat Exchanger Networks Synthesis with New Options for Heaters and Coolers Placement, Industrial & Engineering Chemistry Research, 57, 7, 2560–73.

M. S. Razib, M. M. F. Hasan, and I. A. Karimi, 2012, Preliminary Synthesis of Work Exchange Networks, Computers & Chemical Engineering, 37, 2, 262–277.

L. F. Santos, C. B. B. Costa, J. A. Caballero, M. A. S. Ravagnani, 2020, Synthesis and optimization of work and heat exchange networks using an MINLP model with a reduced number of decision variables, Applied Energy, 262, 114441.

A. Wechsung, A. Aspelund, T. Gundersen, and P. I. Barton, 2011, Synthesis of Heat Exchanger Networks at Subambient Conditions with Compression and Expansion of Process Streams, AIChE Journal, 57, 8, 2090–2108.

T. F. Yee, and I. E. Grossmann, 1990, Simultaneous Optimization Models for Heat Integration-II. Heat Exchanger Network Synthesis, Computers & Chemical Engineering, 14, 10, 1165–1184.

Sauro Pierucci, Flavio Manenti, Giulia Bozzano, Davide Manca (Eds.)
Proceedings of the 30th European Symposium on Computer Aided Process Engineering
(ESCAPE30), May 24-27, 2020, Milano, Italy. © 2020 Elsevier B.V. All rights reserved.
http://dx.doi.org/10.1016/B978-0-12-823377-1.50234-2

Modelling and Simulation of the Conversion of Chicken Fat to Produce Renewable Aviation Fuel through the Hydrotreating Process

Ana Laura Moreno Gómez[a], Claudia Gutiérrez-Antonio[a*], Fernando Israel Gómez-Castro[b], Salvador Hernández[b]

[a] Facultad de Química, Universidad Autónoma de Querétaro, Av. Cerro de las Campanas s/n, Col. Las Campanas,76010, Querétaro, Mexico

[b] Departamento de Ingeniería Química, División de Ciencias Naturales y Exactas, Campus Guanajuato, Universidad de Guanajuato, Noria Alta S/N. Col. Noria Alta, 38010, Guanajuato, Guanajuato, México
claudia.gutierrez@uaq.mx

Abstract

In the transport sector, aviation has the higher growth; thus, more fuel will be required for its operation in the forthcoming years. In order to guarantee the sustainable development of the aviation sector, the use of renewable fuels has been proposed. The renewable aviation fuel can be produced from different types of biomass through several conversion processes. One of these processes is the hydrotreating, where triglyceride feedstock is converted to renewable aviation fuel, light gases, naphtha and green diesel, which are later separated by distillation; in hydroprocessing, the cost of raw material contributes around 80% to the final cost of the biojet fuel. Due to this, the use of waste oils and fats represents an interesting alternative to produce biojet fuel with competitive prices. In addition, this kind of raw material is available all the year, and its generation is in constant increasing due to the population growth. Therefore, in this work the modelling and simulation of the hydrotreating process to produce biojet fuel, considering chicken fat as raw material, is presented. The study is performed using the software Aspen Plus. Two conventional hydrotreating processes are defined and evaluated in terms of total annual costs, CO_2 emissions and price of biojet fuel. It has been found that the hydrotreating process that includes the direct conventional sequence has the lowest energy consumption. Also, a significantly decrease in the price of biojet fuel is observed when chicken fat is used as raw material, in comparison with oils from *Jatropha curcas*, castor bean and micro-algae. The use of chicken fat represents a promissory raw material to produce biojet fuel, considering its low-cost and constant availability along the year.

Keywords: Biojet fuel, hydrotreating process, chicken fat, renewable aviation fuel.

1. Introduction

Nowadays the aviation sector faces two important challenges: the decrease of oil reserves and the global warming. The forecasts indicate that the growth of aviation sector will be of 4.8 % for each year until 2036 (Chacin, 2010); thus, more fuel will be required for its operation in the forthcoming years, with the consequent increase in CO_2 emissions. Moreover, considering that the fuel represents around 30% of the total operation costs of airlines, the fluctuations in the price of aviation fuel affect considerably the profitability. On the other hand, the global warming is associated with the excessive use of fossil fuels;

in this context, the growth of aviation sector will contribute to the global warming problem. Thus, in order to guarantee the sustainable development of the aviation sector, the International Air Transport Association (IATA) promotes the development of renewable biofuels, also known as biojet fuel or biokerosene. Biojet fuel can be produced from several types of biomass through different conversion processes; one of them is the hydroprocessing of triglyceride feedstock. In this process, triglyceride are converted through hydrodeoxygenation to generate long chain lineal hydrocarbons, which later are cracked and isomerized to generate hydrocarbons in the boiling point range of biojet fuel; these reactions are carried out at high pressure and temperature, and they also required hydrogen as another reactant (Shalaby et al., 2015). In addition, other hydrocarbons are produced such as light gases, naphtha, and green diesel, which are separated by distillation. Several raw materials have been explored to produce renewable aviation fuel, including oils from second and third generation. From these studies, it can be concluded that the processing of these raw materials is technically feasible to produce renewable aviation fuel, but their cost is the major contributor to the biofuel price (at least 80%. Gutiérrez-Antonio et al., 2018). Thus, the use of waste triglyceride feedstock is a promissory alternative to produce biojet fuel with a competitive selling price, in comparison to its fossil counterpart. Therefore, this work presents the modelling and simulation of the hydroprocessing of chicken fat to produce renewable aviation fuel. This kind of raw material offers the opportunity to reduce the production cost of biojet fuel and, consequently, its selling price.

2. Methodology

The selected raw material is chicken fat, which consists on free fatty acids (6%) and triglycerides (94%) (Kaewmeesri et al., 2014). The composition of the raw material is shown in Table 1.

Table 1. Composition for the raw material (Hanafi et al., 2016)

Component	Composition (%mass)
Palmitic Acid	1.48
Estearic Acid	0.35
Oleic Acid	2.68
Linoleic Acid	2.18
Tripalmitin	20.62
Triestearin	4.91
Triolein	37.32
Linolein	30.44

The oil derived from chicken fat is converted to biojet fuel through the hydrotreating process, which includes three main sections: conditioning zone, reactive zone, and distillation zone, as shown in Figure 1. In the conditioning zone, the temperature and pressure of the reactants (hydrogen and oil) is increased, through heat exchangers, a pump and a compressor, to reach the adequate conditions (480 °C and 6 MPa) to be fed in the reactive zone. The reactive zone is integrated by two reactors: hydrodeoxygenation/hydrocracking and hydroisomerization. In the first reactor, the conversion of the oil derived from chicken fat is modelled according to the data reported by Hanafi et al. (2016), where hydrodeoxygenation and hydrocracking reactions are carried out; moreover, H_2 is fed in a proportion of 450 v/v H_2/oil, and 100 kg/h of oil are

Modelling and simulation of the conversion of chicken fat to produce renewable aviation fuel through the hydrotreating process

1401

fed to the reactive zone. The hydrotreating reactor was modelled using the RYield module of Aspen Plus.

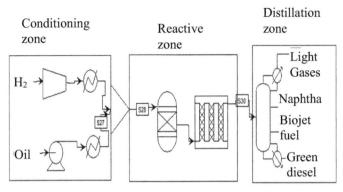

Figure 1. Main zones of the hydrotreating process.

The effluent of the first reactor is fed to the hydroisomerization reactor, which was modelled with the RPlug module based on the kinetic model reported by Calemma et al. (2000); it is considered an activation energy of 3,500 cal/mol, and the reactions proposed by Romero-Izquierdo (2015), which are shown in Table 2. The hydroisomerization reactor operates at 480 °C and 8 MPa; from the second reactor, a mixture of four products was obtained in the effluent: light gases, naphtha, biojet fuel, and green diesel.

Table 2. Reactions used to model the hydroisomerization reactor (Romero-Izquierdo, 2015)

$C_5H_{12} \rightarrow isoC_5 H_{12}$
$C_6H_{14} \rightarrow isoC_6 H_{14}$
$C_7 H_{16} \rightarrow isoC_7 H_{16}$
$C_8H_{18} \rightarrow isoC_8H_{18}$
$C_9H_{20} \rightarrow isoC_9H_{20}$
$C_{10}H_{22} \rightarrow isoC_{10} H_{22}$
$C_{11} H_{24} \rightarrow isoC_{11}H_{24}$
$C_{12} H_{26} \rightarrow isoC_{12} H_{26}$
$C_{16}H_{36} \rightarrow isoC_{16} H_{36}$

The effluent of the hydroisomerization reactor was conditioned to reduce its pressure and temperature using a turbine, which allows to generate electricity. After that, the hydrocarbon stream is fed to the distillation zone. Several alternatives for the separation of the mixture are possible, since there are four products; however, only two sequences allow the separation in the first column of the light gases, which is necessary to avoid the excessive use of refrigerants. Therefore, only two sequences are analysed in this work: the direct and the direct-indirect schemes. In both schemes, a partial condenser was used in the first distillation column, while the second and third distillation columns employ total condensers. The use of each one of these distillation schemes defines two scenarios, where the conditioning and reactive zones are the same; the difference lies in the use of the direct sequence in scenario 1, while the direct-indirect sequence is considered in scenario 2. The simulation was performed in Aspen Plus V10. The employed thermodynamics methods were Peng-Robinson for the conditioning and reactive zones, and BK10 for the distillation zone.

The price of the raw material was obtained from a market study taking as suppliers the local merchants of the poultry line. In order to calculate the biojet fuel price, the methodology proposed for Romero-Izquierdo (2015) has been used. The methodology of Guthrie (Turton et al., 2004) is used to calculate the cost of the equipment. Finally, to obtain the CO_2 emissions the methodology proposed by Romero-Izquierdo (2015) is used.

3. Results

This section shows the results of both scenarios in terms of total annual costs, biojet fuel price and CO_2 emissions. Table 3 shows the yield and mass flow of the products generated in the hydrotreating reactor. As it can be observed, the obtained yield of hydrocarbons in the jet fuel range is the highest, compared with the yield of the other three products.

Table 3. Yield and mass flow of hydrotreating reactor

Products	Total flow (kg/h)	Yield
Light gases	12.8	0.1227
Naphtha	20.33	0.1948
Biokerosene	31.52	0.3020
Green diesel	25.84	0.2477

In the hydroisomerization reactor it was possible obtain 44% of isomers in the effluent; therefore, a total biokerosene flow of 40 kg/h. The total electricity consumed in the process was 25.31 kW; if the energy produced with the turbine is used, the electricity consumption can be reduced by 88.4%. The energy requirements in both distillation sequences are shown in Table 4.

Table 4. Reboiler energy consumptions of both distillation sequences.

Equipment	Energy requirement (kW)	Distillation sequence
Reboiler of distillation column 1	5.25	
Reboiler of distillation column 2	8.23	Direct
Reboiler of distillation column 3	8.30	
Total	21.78	
Reboiler of distillation column 1	5.25	
Reboiler of distillation column 2	14.57	Direct-Indirect
Reboiler of distillation column 3	6.07	
Total	25.89	

The summary of economic and environmental parameters for both scenarios is presented in Table 5. The price of raw material represents only 6.83% of the total processing cost, which makes it very attractive since a significant price reduction is observed; this reduction is up to 97% in comparison with microalgae oil and *Jatropha Curcas* oil (Gutiérrez-Antonio et al., 2018; Gutiérrez-Antonio et al., 2016). In the Scenario 2, CO_2

emissions are higher than in scenario 1, due mainly to the high energy requirement in the second reboiler of the distillation scheme.

Table 5. Summary of economic and environmental parameters for scenarios 1 and 2.

Scenario	Cost of equipment (USD/ year)	Processing Cost (USD/year)	CO_2 emissions (Ton/year)	Cost of raw material (USD/year)	Biojet fuel price (USD/L)
1	$1,963,384.12	$1,864,701.78	66,199.1397	$127,500.00	$0.543
2	$2,215,893.95	$1,867,003.31	79,339.4034		$0.557

4. Conclusions

The modelling and simulation of the hydroprocessing of chicken fat has been presented. Results shown that a considerable decrease in the biojet fuel price is obtained, as result of the low price of the raw material. The high energy requirements in the process opens enhancement opportunities, as the implementation of strategies as energy integration or process intensification to reduce those requirements.

Acknowledgements

Financial support provided by CONACyT, grant 279753, for the development of this project is gratefully acknowledged.
Also, A.L. Moreno Gómez was supported by a scholarship from CONACYT for the realization of her postgraduate studies.

References

R. Turton, R.C. Bailie, W.B. Whiting, J.A. Shaeiwitz, D. Bhattachayya, 2012, Analysis, synthesis, and design of chemical processes, 4th edition, Prentice Hall, New Jersey, 850-872.

E. Chacin, 2010, La OACI y los combustibles alternativos sustentables de aviación, Taller de Financiamiento, Legislación, Logística y Distribución, Plan de Vuelo, 21 (Spanish).

V. Calemma, S.Paratello, C. Perego, 2000, Hydroisomerization and hydrocracking of long chain n-alkanes on Pt/amorphous SiO2-Al2O3 catalyst, Applied Catalyst A, 190, 207-218.

S.A. Hanafi, M.S.Elmelawy, N.H.Shalaby, H.A.El-Syed, G.Eshad, M.S.Mostafa, 2016, Hydrocracking of waste chicken fat as a cost effective feedstock for renewable fuel production: A kinetic study, Egyptian Journal of Petroleum, 25, 531-537.

International Energy Agency (IEA), 2017, Key World Energy Statistics, 1,7 -97.

C. Gutiérrez-Antonio, F.I. Gómez-Castro, G.A. de Lira-Flores, S.Hernandez, 2017, A review on the production process of renewable jet fuel, Renewable and Sustainable Energy Reviews, 79, 709-729.

C. Gutiérrez-Antonio, A.G. Romero-Izquierdo, F. I. Gómez-Castro, S. Hernández, 2016, Energy Integration of a Hydrotreatment Process for Sustainable Biojet Fuel Production, Industrial and Engineering Chemistry Research, 55, 8165–8175.

C. Gutiérrez-Antonio, A.G. Romero-Izquierdo, F. I. Gómez-Castro, S. Hernández, 2018, Modeling, simulation and intensification of hydroprocessing of micro-algae oil to produce renewable aviation fuel, Clean Technologies and Enviromental Policy, 20, 1589-1598

C. Gutiérrez-Antonio, F.I. Gómez-Castro, S. Hernández, 2018, Sustainable production of renewable aviation fuel through intensification strategies, Chemical Engineering Transactions, 69, 1-6.

A.G. Romero-Izquierdo, 2015, Integración energética de un proceso para la producción de combsutible renovable para aviación, Thesis, Universidad de Guanajuato (Spanish).

R. Kaewmeesri, A.Srifa, V. Itthibenchapong, K. Faungnawakij, 2014, Deoxygenation of Waste Chicken Fats to Green Diesel over Ni/Al$_2$O$_3$: Effect of Water and Free Fatty Acid Content, energy and fuels, 29, 833-840.

N.Shalaby, S.H. Harap, M.S. Elmelawy, 2015, Hydrocracking of waste cooking oil as renewable fuel on NiW/SiO2-Al2O3, Journal of Advanced Catalyst Science and Technology, 2, 27-37.

Sauro Pierucci, Flavio Manenti, Giulia Bozzano, Davide Manca (Eds.)
Proceedings of the 30th European Symposium on Computer Aided Process Engineering
(ESCAPE30), May 24-27, 2020, Milano, Italy. © 2020 Elsevier B.V. All rights reserved.
http://dx.doi.org/10.1016/B978-0-12-823377-1.50235-4

Mixed-Integer Dynamic Scheduling Optimization for Demand Side Management

Florian Joseph Baader[a], Maximilian Mork[a], André Xhonneux[a], Dirk Müller[a,b], André Bardow[a,c], Manuel Dahmen[a,*]

[a]*Institute of Energy and Climate Research - Energy Systems Engineering (IEK-10), Forschungszentrum Jülich GmbH, 52425 Jülich, Germany*
[b]*E.ON Energy Research Center, Institute for Energy Efficient Buildings and Indoor Climate, RWTH Aachen University, 52074 Aachen, Germany*
[c]*Institute of Technical Thermodynamics, RWTH Aachen University, 52056 Aachen, Germany*
m.dahmen@fz-juelich.de

Abstract

With fluctuating electricity prices, demand side management (DSM) promises to reduce energy costs. DSM of processes and energy supply systems requires scheduling optimization to consider transient behavior and binary on/off-decisions resulting in challenging mixed-integer dynamic programs. In this work, we present an efficient scheduling optimization approach that captures scheduling-relevant dynamics in a linear scale-bridging model and relies on collocation for time discretization. The resulting mixed-integer linear program (MILP) can be solved with state-of-the-art solvers. We apply the approach to a case study on building DSM. A detailed simulation model represents an office building, which allows load shifting through dynamic concrete core activation and is heated by a heat pump with minimum part-load. The DSM scheduling optimization approach reduces energy cost significantly compared to a rule-based scheduler without DSM if electricity price volatility is high. At the same time, the optimization is sufficiently fast to perform online scheduling.
Keywords: Mixed-Integer Dynamic Optimization, Demand Side Management, Mixed-Integer Linear Programming

1. Introduction

Many policies to reduce greenhouse gas emissions aim for increasing renewable electricity supply. The intermittency of renewable electricity sources increases volatility in prices. This volatility gives flexible power-intensive processes and building energy systems the opportunity to reduce costs via demand side management (DSM) (Zhang and Grossmann, 2016). Conceptually, DSM of building energy systems is similar to DSM of chemical processes: Energy supply is needed to maintain a controlled variable (the temperature) within a quality band (the occupant comfort range). The energy consumption can be shifted in time using the thermal inertia of building construction elements.

A promising DSM method is scheduling optimization that can account for transient process behavior, and on/off- decisions in the energy supply system; however, such scheduling optimization requires solving computationally challenging mixed-integer dynamic optimization problems. Scheduling or real-time optimization are decision layers that typically consider time-scales from hours to weeks and optimize set-points for the underlying control (Daoutidis et al., 2018). Online scheduling optimization in receding horizon allows to react to changing prices and model plant mismatch, however, necessitates optimization runtimes to be in the order of minutes. Therefore, efficient problem formulations are needed. A particularly promising approach is to use scale-bridging models introduced by Baldea and co-workers (Du et al., 2015) that – in contrast to first-principle models – only account for the slow closed-loop process dynamics.

For DSM, we propose to extend the scale-bridging model concept by Du et al. (2015) to the domain of energy systems with its many discrete on/off-decisions. To this end, we change the formulation from continuous to discrete time. Thereby, we can integrate the scale-bridging dynamics in mixed-integer linear programming (MILP). We use this MILP-based approach for DSM of building energy systems. In section 2, we explain our approach for DSM scheduling optimization with a scale-bridging model. In section 3, we apply the approach to a case study on building DSM through concrete core activation to demonstrate its capabilities. Section 4 concludes the paper.

2. DSM Scheduling Optimization with Scale-Bridging Model

Operational optimization of energy systems is often approached with MILP formulations (Voll et al., 2013). For DSM, we need to represent the process dynamics. To still retain a MILP formulation, we propose to use a linear scale-bridging model of the scheduling-relevant closed-loop process dynamics (Du et al., 2015). The linear closed-loop response is enforced by an underlying control that also ensures stability. In contrast to Du et al. (2015), we formulate the scheduling optimization problem in discrete instead of continuous time, because (i) discrete time often performs better for varying energy prices (Castro et al., 2009), and (ii) linear differential algebraic equations (DAEs) discretized with collocation in discrete time lead to linear constraints (Biegler, 2010). The resulting scale-bridging model consists of linear mixed-integer DAEs:

$$\frac{d\boldsymbol{x}}{dt} = \boldsymbol{f}_{SBM}(\boldsymbol{x}, \boldsymbol{y}, \boldsymbol{z}, \boldsymbol{w}_{SP}, t) \tag{1 a}$$

$$0 = \boldsymbol{g}_{SBm}(\boldsymbol{x}, \boldsymbol{y}, \boldsymbol{z}, \boldsymbol{w}_{SP}, t) \tag{1 b}$$

with differential states $\boldsymbol{x}$, algebraic variables $\mathbf{y}$, discrete variables $\mathbf{z}$, set-points $\boldsymbol{w}_{SP}$, time t, and linear functions $\boldsymbol{f}_{SBM}, \boldsymbol{g}_{SBM}$. In the following, we describe the three main steps of our approach.

2.1. Adapt Control System to Achieve Linear Closed-Loop Response

Whereas Du et al. (2015) use input-output feedback linearization control to enforce a linear closed-loop response, we propose to place a linear set-point filter before the control. The advantage is that we can also use classical non-model-based tracking controls like PID control. The set-point filter converts a piecewise constant set-point trajectory to the desired linear closed-loop response, which can then be tracked by the underlying control. A set-point filter of order r can be modelled as a cascade of first-order filters for which the filtered set-point $w_{SP,fl,1}$ evolves depending on the current set-point w_{SP} and the filter constant $\tau_{SP,1}$:

$$\frac{dw_{sp,fl,1}}{dt} = \frac{1}{\tau_{SP}}(w_{SP} - w_{SP,fl,1}) \tag{2}$$

The resulting control loop including the set-point filter is visualized in Fig. 1. The control manipulates inputs u such that the controlled variable y_{cv}, e.g., product quality in a reactor or temperature in a building, follows the filtered set-point $w_{SP,fl,r}$. The set-points w_{SP} are determined in scheduling optimization, where we assume $y_{cv} = w_{SP,fl,r}$, i.e., the desired linear closed-loop response is tracked sufficiently accurate. To ensure $y_{cv} = w_{SP,fl,r}$ with good accuracy, the set-point filter must be sufficiently slow such that system and control can follow. Note that a too slow set-point filter would deteriorate process performance. The filter constants are therefore tuning factors.

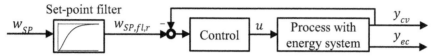

Figure 1: Control loop and set-point filter. y_{ec} denotes the resulting energy costs.

2.2. Set Up of the Scale-Bridging Model

The scale-bridging model represents the slow dynamics of the control loop in Fig. 1. Therefore, the scale-bridging model receives the set-point w_{SP} as input and has the controlled variable y_{cv} and the energy costs y_{ec} as outputs. Because $y_{cv} = w_{SP,fl,r}$ on the scheduling timescale, the set-point filter equations essentially model the dynamics of the controlled variable y_{cv}. The energy costs y_{ec} depend on the process energy demand and the efficiencies of the energy system components. For nonlinear part-load efficiencies, we use piecewise-linear approximations (Voll et al., 2013). To compute the energy demand of the process, we use a linear data-driven or gray-box model. We refer to Tsay and Baldea (2019) who review data-driven models for process systems, and Li and Wen (2014) who review gray-box models for building energy systems.

2.3. Set Up of the Scheduling Optimization Problem

Based on the scale-bridging model, we create the scheduling optimization problem by adding an objective function, performing time discretization, and adding problem constraints. The objective function minimizes the integral over the energy costs y_{ec}. For time discretization, we use three time grids: Grid 1 is given by the market and contains piece-wise constant electricity prices with a fixed time step. Grid 2 is used to discretize the discrete variables z as piece-wise constant. Grid 3 is used to discretize the continuous variables x, y via collocation polynomials. Grids 2 and 3 are discretized finer, i.e., the number of time steps for grid 2 and 3 is a multiple of the number of time steps for grid 1. As constraints, we consider upper and lower variable bounds, problem-specific constraints, and on/off-constraints to account for the minimum part-load of energy system components. The resulting scheduling optimization problem is a MILP and can be solved with state-of-the-art solvers.

3. Case Study: Building Energy System

Flexible building energy systems can perform DSM because the thermal inertia of building construction elements allows to shift load in time. For the purpose of optimization and control, building energy systems can often be modeled sufficiently well by linear DAE models called gray-box or resistor-capacitor models (Li and Wen, 2014). For buildings operated in a market with an on-/off-peak pricing structure, Touretzky and Baldea (2016) propose to use an integrated scheduling and control architecture that avoids binary decision variables through a slot-based continuous-time reformulation. In contrast, here we consider a pricing structure with hourly changing electricity prices and thus need to consider binary decisions in every time step. To test our scheduling optimization approach, we simulate an office room with concrete core activation in detail. The virtual office has a temperature control that receives the optimized set-point trajectory from scheduling optimization. We assume that the air temperature T_{air} has to be in a comfort range from minimum temperature $T_{min} = 20$ °C to maximum temperature $T_{max} = 22$ °C from 08:00 to 20:00 o'clock. During the night (20:00 to 08:00 o'clock), the room temperature is allowed to drop to $T_{min} = 16$ °C. For comparison, we also assess the performance of a rule-based scheduler that sets the set-point temperature equal to $T_{min} = 20$ °C during the day and equal to $T_{min} = 16$ °C during the night.

3.1. Virtual Office

To construct the detailed simulation model of a corner office room (Fig. 2) and PI temperature controllers for air and concrete core, we use the AixLib Modelica modeling library (Müller et al., 2016). The AixLib provides models of building components and parametrized controllers. The zero-dimensional corner office is surrounded by two outside walls, two inside walls, a ceiling, and a concrete core. Outside walls exchange heat with the environment. We only consider half of the wall volume for inside walls and assume zero heat transfer in the middle of these walls. This assumption is reasonable if the temperature in the neighboring rooms is controlled similarly. An air-source heat pump with minimum part-load of 12.5 % (Bischi et al., 2014) heats a fluid system which transports the heat to a radiator and the concrete core. As the concrete core has a considerable thermal inertia, it offers a high DSM potential. In total, the detailed model has 122 differential states. Time-varying model inputs are: ambient temperature, room occupancy, and electricity price. We distinguish three electricity price scenarios. Scenario 1 uses historical German EPEX-spot day-ahead prices from 25th and 26th February 2019. For scenario 2, we increase the deviation between the prices and the arithmetic mean of the historical time series by a factor of two. For scenario 3, we apply a factor of three to the deviation in the historical data.

3.2. Building DSM

To apply the DSM scheduling optimization approach, we follow the three steps presented in section 2. First, we adapt the underlying control by placing second-order set-point filters before the PI-controllers. We choose second-order filters such that the transitions forwarded to the tracking control start and end smoothly. Second, for the scale-bridging model, we use the set-point filter equations (Equation (2)) as a model for the room and concrete core temperatures. The efficiency of the energy system is given by the coefficient of performance (COP) of the heat pump. Since we consider an air-source heat pump and assume that the ambient temperature is known, the COP is a predefined time-varying parameter. To compute the energy demand of the building, we derive linear differential equations for the temperatures of air, walls, radiator, ceiling, and concrete core by assuming constant heat transfer coefficients fitted to simulation data. Such a model is commonly called resistor-capacitor model (Li and Wen, 2014). The resulting scale-bridging model has only 16 differential states: the temperatures, the filtered set-points, and the integrated electricity cost of the heat pump.

For setting up the scheduling optimization problem, we introduce an objective function that minimizes the integrated electricity costs. The considered time horizon lasts 33 hours starting at 0:00 o'clock on day one and ending at 09:00 o'clock on day two. Thereby, we end in the occupancy period where the temperature has to be within the comfort range. Electricity prices vary hourly and we use four discretization elements per hour for the discrete and continuous variables. For the continuous variables, we use fourth-order collocation polynomials within the discretization elements. We add on/off-constraints describing the heat pump minimum part-load. Furthermore, we add constraints to account for the fact that we can only heat the air and the concrete core but we cannot cool them. In the following, we describe this effect for the air temperature T_{air}. If heating is required

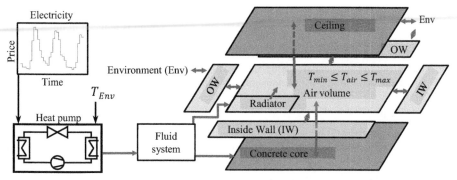

Figure 2: System considered in case study: Corner-office with concrete core and radiator heated by a heat pump; heat flows are denoted by thick red arrows (↔); OW: Outside wall

($T_{air} \leq T_{air,SP,fl,2}$), the temperature-control is *active* and regulates the heat flow to the radiator Q_{rad} such that the air temperature increases to the filtered set-point $T_{air,SP,fl,2}$. In contrast, if heating is not required ($T_{air} > T_{air,SP,fl,2}$), the temperature-control is *inactive* ($Q_{rad} = 0$). We implement these two operating regimes with a binary variable and big-M constraints. The same logic applies to the temperature-control of the concrete core. The scheduling optimization problem is solved with IBM CPLEX 12.8.0 on an Intel Core i5-8250U processor. We limit the optimization runtime to 5 minutes, which is well below the interval length of the decision variables (15 minutes).

3.3. Results

The results show that the DSM potential strongly depends on the electricity price volatility. In scenario 1 (historical prices), DSM scheduling optimization does not reduce cost compared to the rule-based scheduler. With the stronger price fluctuations, DSM scheduling optimization reduces electricity costs by 6.8 % (scenario 2) and by 20.8 % (scenario 3). Fig. 3 shows exemplarily the results for scenario 2. Our approach for DSM scheduling optimization is able to shift energy consumption to times of lower prices in

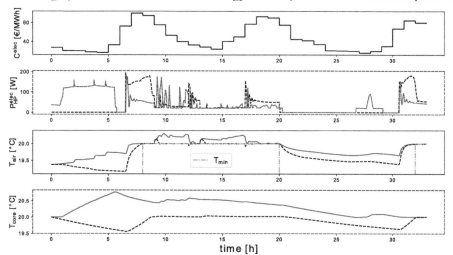

Figure 3: Results for building energy system in scenario 2 (top to bottom): electricity price C^{elec}, electric power of heat pump P_{HP}^{elec}, room temperature T_{air}, and core temperature T_{core}. Rule-based scheduler (black dashed line) and DSM scheduling optimization (blue solid line).

the morning (1:00 – 5:00 o'clock, day 1; 2:00 – 5:00 o'clock, day 2) mainly by increasing the concrete core temperature. Consequently, the electricity consumption is reduced in times of high prices (6:00 – 9:00 and 17:00 – 20:00 o'clock, day 1; 6:00 – 7:00 o'clock, day 2). Like the rule-based scheduler, the DSM scheduling optimization ensures that the air temperature is always above the minimum comfort temperature. After the maximum runtime of 5 minutes, the optimization returns a near-optimal solution with a remaining optimality gap of 3.3 %.

4. Conclusion

Scheduling optimization for demand side management (DSM) of dynamic processes is computationally challenging, as it needs to account for process dynamics and a large number of binary on/off-decisions in the energy supply system. To tackle such problems, we propose a linear scale-bridging model of the closed-loop process dynamics in discrete time combined with a linear model of the energy supply system. Thereby, we obtain a mixed-integer linear program (MILP) that can be solved efficiently with state-of-the-art solvers. Applied to a virtual office with concrete core activation, our DSM approach improves the economic performance of the building energy system compared to a rule-based scheduler, if energy price fluctuations are sufficiently large. The optimization is fast enough to allow for online scheduling.

Acknowledgements

The present contribution is supported by the Helmholtz Association under the Joint Initiative 'Energy Systems Integration'.

References

L. T. Biegler, 2010, Nonlinear programming, SIAM, Philadelphia

A. Bischi, L. Taccari, E. Martelli, E. Amaldi, G. Manzolini, P. Silvam, S. Campanari, E. Macchi, 2014, A detailed MILP optimization model for combined cooling, heat and power system operation planning, Energy, 74, 12-26

P. M. Castro, I. Harjunkoski, I. E. Grossmann, 2009, New continuous-time scheduling formulation for continuous plants under variable electricity cost, Industrial & Engineering Chemistry Research, 48, 6701-6714

P. Daoutidis, J. H. Lee, I. Harjunkoski, S. Skogestad, M. Baldea, C. Georgakis, 2018, Integrating operations and control: A perspective and roadmap for future research, Computers & Chemical Engineering, 115, 179-184

J. Du, J. Park, I. Harjunkoski, M. Baldea, 2015, A time scale-bridging approach for integrating production scheduling and process control, Computers & Chemical Engineering, 79, 59-69

X. Li, J. Wen, Review of building energy modeling for control and operation, Renewable and Sustainable Energy Reviews, 37, 517-537

D. Müller, M. Lauster, A. Constantin, M. Fuchs, P. Remmen, 2016, AixLib - An open-source Modelica library within the IEA-EBC Annex 60 Framework, Proceedings of the CESBP and BauSIM 2016, Ed. J. Grunewald, Dresden, 3-9

C. R. Touretzky, M. Baldea, A hierarchical scheduling and control strategy for thermal energy storage systems, Energy and Buildings, 110, 94-107

C. Tsay, M. Baldea, 2019, 110th Anniversary: Using data to bridge the time and length scales of process systems, Industrial & Engineering Chemistry Research, 58, 16696-16708

P. Voll, C. Klaffke, M. Hennen, A. Bardow, 2013, Automated superstructure-based synthesis and optimization of distributed energy supply systems, Energy, 50, 374–388

Q. Zhang, I. E. Grossmann, 2016, Planning and scheduling for industrial demand side management: Advances and challenges, Alternative Energy Sources and Technologies, Ed. M. Mariano, Cham: Springer International Publishing, 383-414

Sauro Pierucci, Flavio Manenti, Giulia Bozzano, Davide Manca (Eds.)
Proceedings of the 30th European Symposium on Computer Aided Process Engineering
(ESCAPE30), May 24-27, 2020, Milano, Italy. © 2020 Elsevier B.V. All rights reserved.
http://dx.doi.org/10.1016/B978-0-12-823377-1.50236-6

Design of a Sustainable Power-to-methanol Process: a Superstructure Approach Integrated with Heat Exchanger Network Optimization

Philipp Kenkel,[a*] Timo Wassermann,[a] Edwin Zondervan[b]

[a]*University of Bremen, Advanced Energy Systems Institute , Enrique-Schmidt-Straße 7, 28359 Bremen, Germany*
[b]*Univeristy of Bremen, Advanced Energy Systems Institute, Leobener Straße 6, 28359 Bremen, Germany*
kenkel@uni-bremen.de

Abstract

This work presents a bi-criteria superstructure optimization of a PtM (power-to-methanol) design regarding techno-economic and environmental key figures. The general modeling approach based on mass- and energy balances is applied to a case study depicting a potential plant located in the region of northern Germany Schleswig-Holstein. The selected case study demonstrates minimal net production costs of 1,346 €/t of methanol and minimal net production emissions of -2.29 t_{CO2}/t of methanol. Hence, PtM concepts are not cost competitive as compared to conventional methanol. However, utilizing renewable electricity, PtM can contribute to CO_2 abatement in the process sector.

Keywords: Superstructure optimization, power-to-methanol, CO_2 utilization

1. Introduction

To counter climate change, Germany has set out a strategy to considerably reduce its greenhouse gas emissions by 2050. A transition in the mobility-sector, as well as the process industry poses major challenges due to their inert behavior and strong dependency on fossil fuels. As long as there are no other near zero-emission alternatives for these sectors, innovative concepts for renewable production of synthetic liquid fuels and other hydrocarbons are a viable option for defossilization. One promising option is the production of methanol from renewable hydrogen and carbon dioxide via the power-to-methanol (PtM) process. Methanol is an important platform chemical as well as a potential liquid fuel and intermediate for kerosene or gasoline synthesis.

The PtM process requires 5 process steps which are 1) hydrogen production via electrolysis, 2) carbon dioxide preparation using carbon capture technologies, 4) the methanol synthesis step itself as well as 4) upgrading and 5) waste stream management [1], [2]. Each of these steps can be designed using various technological alternatives for example carbon can be captured from the ambient air or from power plant flue gases. In addition, some process steps are exothermic and others are highly endothermic. Therefore, a major challenge is the design of a cost-optimal PtM process from the given myriad of possibilities including the options to reach a suitable degree of heat recovery. It is noted however that even such PtM concepts are not emission free due to energy demand in terms of electricity and process heat as well as emissions related to required solvents and other chemicals. Ergo, the process should not only be optimized in terms of methanol costs but also in terms of life cycle CO_2 emissions, this leads to a bi-criterion optimization problem.

2. Methodology

The work at hand presents a practical way for the assessment and optimization of a PtM process design comparing different technology alternatives for techno-economic as well as environmental key figures, utilizing the concept of superstructure optimization. A superstructure is a representation of all possible combinations of technologies from raw materials up to the final products. This formulation enables the investigation of energy- and mass integration potentials, leading to a multi-energy system which could also be interpreted as an energy hub specialized on the production of liquid fuels [3], [4]. The superstructure representation is converted into a mathematical program, which can be solved using well-known software packages and optimization solvers.

2.1. Mathematical approach

The mathematical program utilizes general mass- and energy balances inspired by Galanopoulos et al. [5]. Mass balances are defined using a three-step methodology of mixing, reaction and separation by means of fixed split factor parameters (cf. Figure 1).

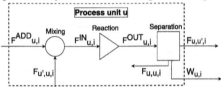

Figure 1: Representation of mass balance methodology for process unit u. The inlet flow $F^{IN}_{u,i}$ is calculated as the sum of entering streams from other units $F_{u',u,i}$ and added chemicals $F^{ADD}_{u,i}$. The outlet flow is calculated using stoichiometric or yield reactions. Unit connecting flows ($F_{u,u',i}$) are calculated from the outlet flow using predefined split parameters, while waste streams $W_{u,i}$ are determined by balance.

The energy balance for utility Ut is based on specific energy demands (τ^{Ut}_u) as well as specific flows (M^{Ut}_u) as shown exemplary for electricity in Eq. 1-3. Non-linearities resulting from the use of integer decision variables (Y_u) are linearized by means of Big-M constraints using upper bound parameters (α_u).

$$E^{EL}_u \leq \alpha_u \cdot Y_u \tag{1}$$

$$E^{EL}_u \leq M^{EL}_u \cdot \tau^{EL}_u + \alpha_u \cdot (1 - Y_u) \tag{2}$$

$$E^{EL}_u \geq M^{EL}_u \cdot \tau^{EL}_u - \alpha_u \cdot (1 + Y_u) \tag{3}$$

The generated mass- and energy balances are used for calculation of the equipment, utility, raw material and fixed operating costs [5]. This leads to a mixed-integer linear programming (MILP) problem, which can be solved using open source modeling software as well as open source optimization algorithms.

2.2. Objective functions

The superstructure optimization is performed independently for two different objective functions. The first one is the total annual costs (TAC) of a fixed amount of methanol (200,00 t/y). The TAC are calculated by the sum of the annualized capital costs (CAPEX) and the annualized operational costs (OPEX), using the approach of Peters et al. The OPEX arise from the usage of utilities such as electricity, raw materials like water as well as fixed costs like maintenance expenses [6]. Profits from sold by-products like oxygen (PROFITS) are subtracted from the costs (cf. Eq. (4)).

Design of a sustainable power-to-methanol process: a superstructure approach integrated with heat exchanger network optimization

1413

$$TAC = CAPEX + OPEX - PROFITS \tag{4}$$

The second objective represents an environmental quantity. The total annual CO_2 emissions (TAE) are calculated by means of mass- and energy balances. The CO_2 emissions (W_{u,CO_2}) in all process units u are added to the emissions which can be assigned to the used utilities (Ut). This is done by multiplying emission factors (ζ) with the actual amount of consumed goods E_{Ut}^{tot}. Using the approach of avoided burden, CO_2 that enters the system from carbon capture ($F_{CO_2}^{IN,CC}$) as well as reference emissions for oxygen production ($F_{O_2}^{PROD}$) are subtracted (cf. Eq. (5)) [7].

$$TAE = \sum_u W_{u,CO_2} + \sum_{Ut} \zeta_{Ut} \cdot E_{Ut}^{tot} - \zeta_{O_2} \cdot F_{O_2}^{PROD} - F_{CO_2}^{IN,CC} \tag{5}$$

3. Case study

The generic formulation offers the possibility to investigate different technologies and process designs based on the implemented data. In this work a power-to-methanol process design is examined for a specific location in northern Germany, Schleswig-Holstein. This special location leads to unique carbon sources such as the flue gases of a local oil refinery as well as CO_2 from a nearby cement factory. In addition, the choice of location defines the studied sources of electricity.

3.1. Investigated technologies

The case study at hand investigates the production of methanol from electricity and captured CO_2. Electricity is used to produce hydrogen and oxygen (which can be sold as by-product). Five different water electrolysis technologies are considered, namely ambient / high pressure proton-exchange membrane electrolysis (LP / HP-PEMEL), ambient / high pressure alkaline electrolysis (LP / HP-AEL) and high temperature solid oxide electrolysis (SOEL). CO_2 can be either captured from ambient air using low temperature direct air capture (LT-DAC), or it can be obtained from point sources such as the refinery power plant flue gas using monoethanolamine in absorption-based carbon capture (MEA-CC) as well as from a nearby cement factory using oxyfuel combustion with subsequent CO_2 purification technology (CEMENT-OXY). The raw materials H_2 and CO_2 are pressurized to 70 bar and converted to methanol via direct hydrogenation at 250 °C (MeOH SYN). Arising off gas, containing unreacted raw materials as well as carbon monoxide (CO) and methanol (MeOH), is separated using a series of flash separators combined with compressors and intercoolers (cumulated in FLASH) and either burned to produce heat in form of steam (FURNACE) or electricity using a combined power circle (GAS TUR). The crude methanol is purified in a last step using a distillation column (DC 1). Figure 2 displays the superstructure representation of the given case study.

3.1.1. Main assumptions

Two specific cases are considered in this study. The main difference is the source of the applied electricity. In both cases, all prior mentioned technologies are investigated. However, CASE 1 uses electricity from the German energy grid, while CASE 2 investigates the use of a direct power supply by offshore wind energy which could be especially interesting for the location of northern Germany, where a lot of wind energy is produced resulting in high amounts of surplus energy.

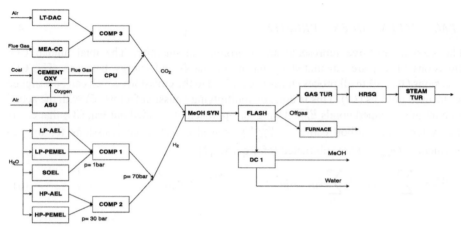

Figure 2: Case study superstructure representation with technologies: LT-DAC: Low temperature direct air capture, MEA-CC: Amine based carbon capture from refinery power plant flue gases, CEM OXY: Cement factory oxyfuel process, ASU: Air separation unit, CPU: CO_2 purification unit, COMP 1-3: Compression for hydrogen and CO_2, LP / HP-AEL: Ambient pressure / High pressure alkaline electrolysis, LP / HP-PEMEL: Ambient pressure / High pressure proton exchange membrane electrolysis, SOEL: Solid oxide electrolysis, MeOH SYN: Methanol synthesis reactor, FLASH: Flash unit, DC 1: Distillation column, GAS TUR: Gas turbine, HSRG: Heat recovery and steam generation unit, STEAM TUR: Steam turbine, FURNACE: Furnace for heat generation.

The assumptions of CASE 1 and 2 lead to different full load hours (FLH) of the plant as well as different emission factors for the provided electricity [8]. Other parameters such as utility costs, yearly methanol production or oxygen selling price are constant. A list of the most important assumptions for both cases is given in Table 1.

Table 1: Main assumptions for the different cases: CASE 1: Electricity purchase from the German electricity grid, CASE 2: Electricity purchase from direct supply of offshore wind energy [8]–[10]

Parameter	CASE 1	CASE 2
Full load hours per year (h/y)	8,260	4,500
CO_2-eq. of electricity (t/MWh)	0.628	0.015
Electricity price (€/MWh)	87.7	
External heat price (€/MWh)	55	
Cooling water costs (€/MWh)	0.22	
Yearly methanol production (t/y)	200,000	
Oxygen selling price (€/t)	26.3	
Interest rate (%)	5	
CO_2-eq. of heat (t/MWh)	0.294	
CO_2-eq. of reference O_2 production (t/t)	0.695	
CO_2-eq. of reference MeOH production (t/t)	0.525	
Cost of reference MeOH Production (€/t)	333	

4. Results and discussion

4.1. *Mathematical programming results*

Each case of the presented study is an optimization problem with 11,763 constraints, 10,876 variables of which 2,082 are binary and 8,794 are continuous. These MILP problems are implemented in python PYOMO version 5.6.6 and solved within 32 seconds on a MacBook Pro with a 2 GHz Intel Core i5 processor using the open source GNU linear Programming Kit (GLPK) independently for both objective functions. This leads to four optimization calculations and four main results.

*Design of a sustainable power-to-methanol process:a superstructure approach
integrated with heat exchanger network optimization*

1415

4.2. Optimization results

The results of the optimization for CASE 1 and 2 for either the techno-economic objective function (a) or the environmental objective function (b) are shown in Table 2.

A techno-economic optimized design with electricity from the German grid (CASE 1a) with 8,260 FLH per year uses an ambient pressure alkaline electrolyser with subsequent compression for hydrogen supply. CO_2 is captured at the cement factory using oxyfuel combustion, while arising off gas is combusted in order to produce electricity in a combined power cycle. Relating the TAC and TAE of this design to the overall production of 200,000 t/y of methanol yields net production costs (NPC) of 1,346 €/t and net production emissions (NPE) of 4.67 t_{CO2}/t.

When optimized for minimal CO_2-emissions (CASE 1b), the alkaline electrolyser is replaced by a solid oxide electrolyser, resulting in higher NPC of 1,642 €/t but lower NPE of 1.19 t_{CO2}/t. Both cases are neither cost competitive nor environmentally beneficial as compared to the reference methanol produced from natural gas. This is due to high specific emission factors of the electricity from the German electricity grid as well as high electricity prices and installation costs for electrolyser technologies. Due to higher emissions compared to the reference process a calculation of CO_2 abatement costs is not reasonable for CASE 1a and 1b.

Table 2: Main results from optimization: CASE 1a/b: Electricity from the German electricity grid optimized for TAC/TAE, CASE 2a/b: Electricity from direct offshore wind energy supply optimized for TAC/TAE

Parameter	Case 1a	Case 1b	Case 2a	Case 2b
Total annualized costs (TAC) in M€/y	269.3	314.8	309.4	328.5
Total annualized emissions (TAE) in Mt_{CO2}/y	0.934	0.383	-0.389	-0.459
Net production costs (NPC) in €/t	1,346	1,642	1,547	1,574
Net production emissions (NPE) in t_{CO2}/t	4.67	1.19	-1.95	-2.29
CO_2 abatement costs (CAC) in €/t_{CO2}	-	-	490	440

Switching the electricity supply from grid electricity to direct power supply from an offshore wind farm shows a different picture. A cost optimal design (CASE 2a) utilizes CO_2 directly captured at the refinery, H_2 produced from ambient pressure alkaline electrolysis as well as off gas combustion for electricity production purposes. This design leads to NPC of 1,547 €/t of methanol with NPE of -1.95 t_{CO2}/t. If optimized for minimal emissions (CASE 2b), CO_2 is captured again from the cement factory while the remaining design is constant. This leads to a marginally higher NPC of 1,574 €/t but a lower NPE of -2.29 t_{CO2}/t. Using reference costs and emissions for conventional methanol the CO_2 abatement costs (CAC) are 490 €/t_{CO2} and 440 €/t_{CO2} for case 2a and 2b, respectively. It is apparent that a PtM process shows possibilities to reduce the greenhouse gas emissions only if renewable electricity is applied. However, in the case of northern Germany the overall renewable PtM process is not cost competitive related to conventional methanol production.

4.3. Sensitivity Analysis:

Due to the large influence of the energy supply to the costs and environmental impact a sensitivity analysis was performed varying the costs of external heat and external electricity. Figure 2 shows the dependency of the NPC from the external heat costs. The effect on the NPC is quite weak; resulting in a cost decrease of only around 5 % even if heat is free of charge. However, the effect of the electricity costs is much higher (cf. Figure 4). NPC drop to around 550 €/t if wind energy is free of charge. This indicates, that with cost reductions in offshore wind energy production as well as electrolysis combined with rising CO_2 taxes a renewable PtM concept could be cost efficient.

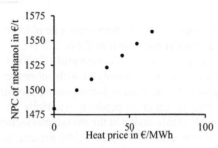

Figure 3: Sensitivity analysis for varying heat prices for electricity price of 87.7 €/MWh and 4500 FLH

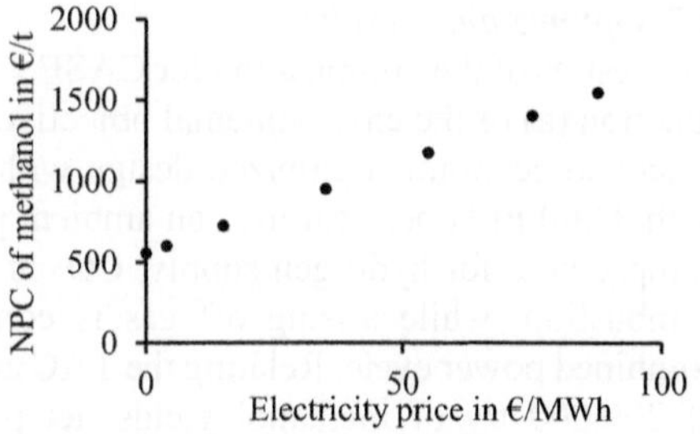

Figure 4: Sensitivity analysis for varying electricity prices for heat price of 55 €/MWh and 4500 FLH

5. Conclusion

A superstructure model was developed and tested on a PtM process located in northern Germany, Schleswig-Holstein using either electricity from the German electricity grid or from direct supply of offshore wind energy. The optimization indicates, that only PtM concepts utilizing renewable electricity are environmental beneficial compared to conventional methanol resulting in net production emissions of -1.95 t_{CO2}/t (conv. 0.525 t_{CO2}/t). This however comes at a price of higher net production costs of 1,547 €/t of methanol compared to conventional 333 €/t of methanol. The performed sensitivity analysis demonstrates a large influence of the electricity price on the net production costs with minimal costs of around 550 €/t if electricity is free of charge. This suggests a potential business model for the utilization of surplus energy if CO_2-certificates become more expensive.

Funding

Funding of this research by the German Federal Ministry of Economic Affairs and Energy within the KEROSyN100 project (funding code 03EIV051A) is gratefully acknowledged.

References

[1]   D. Bongartz *et al.*, "Comparison of light-duty transportation fuels produced from renewable hydrogen and green carbon dioxide," *Appl. Energy*, vol. 231, no. May, pp. 757–767, 2018.

[2]   M. Martín and I. E. Grossmann, *Enhanced production of methanol from switchgrass : CO 2 to methanol*, vol. 38. Elsevier Masson SAS, 2016.

[3]   M. Mohammadi, Y. Noorollahi, and B. Mohammadi-ivatloo, "Energy hub : From a model to a concept – A review," vol. 80, no. July, pp. 1512–1527, 2017.

[4]   A. Quaglia, C. L. Gargalo, S. Chairakwongsa, G. Sin, and R. Gani, "Systematic network synthesis and design : Problem formulation , superstructure generation , data management and solution," *Comput. Chem. Eng.*, vol. 72, pp. 68–86, 2015.

[5]   C. Galanopoulos, P. Kenkel, and E. Zondervan, "Superstructure optimization of an integrated algae biorefinery," vol. 130, 2019.

[6]   M. S. Peters, K. D. Timmerhaus, and R. E. West, *Plant Design and Economics for Chemical Engineers*, Fifth Edit. New York: McGraw-Hill, 2003.

[7]   N. Von Der Assen, J. Jung, and A. Bardow, "Life-cycle assessment of carbon dioxide capture and utilization: Avoiding the pitfalls," *Energy Environ. Sci.*, 2013.

[8]   C. Kost, T. Schlegl, and F. Ise, "Stromgestehungskosten Erneuerbare Energien," 2018.

[9]   F. G. Albrecht, D. H. König, N. Baucks, and R. Dietrich, "A standardized methodology for the techno-economic evaluation of alternative fuels – A case study," *Fuel*, vol. 194, pp. 511–526, 2017.

[10]   G. Wernet, C. Bauer, B. Steubing, J. Reinhard, E. Moreno-ruiz, and B. Weidema, "The ecoinvent database version 3 (part I): overview and methodology," *Int. J. Life Cycle Assess.*, vol. 3, pp. 1218–1230, 2016.

Sauro Pierucci, Flavio Manenti, Giulia Bozzano, Davide Manca (Eds.)
Proceedings of the 30th European Symposium on Computer Aided Process Engineering
(ESCAPE30), May 24-27, 2020, Milano, Italy. © 2020 Elsevier B.V. All rights reserved.
http://dx.doi.org/10.1016/B978-0-12-823377-1.50237-8

Optimization of Retrofit and Cleaning Schedules for Heat Exchanger Networks Subject to Fouling

Federico Lozano Santamaria, Edward Honein, Sandro Macchietto

Department of Chemical Engineering, Imperial College London South Kensington

Campus, London SW7 2AZ, UK

Abstract

Retrofit of heat exchanger networks (HEN) is commonly done to increase their efficiency or respond to changing operational needs. It involves modifying the structure of the network and/or the design of individual units. Decisions are usually based on simplified, steady state models, ignoring performance decay due to fouling, the system dynamics, and possible mitigation actions during operation. However detailed dynamic simulations show all these aspects are important. Here, a mathematical formulation and solution are presented for the optimal retrofit of HEN under fouling that consider realistic exchanger models, fouling dynamics, and cleaning scheduling at the same time. A case study for a refinery preheat train demonstrates that simultaneous optimization of retrofit and cleaning schedules significantly reduces operating cost and capital investment.
Keywords: heat exchanger networks, energy recovery, fouling, optimal retrofit, optimal cleaning scheduling.

1. Introduction

Heat exchanger networks (HEN) are extensively used to recover energy. Because of operational or production changes, or inadequate performance, they are often retrofitted to increase energy recovery or to reach a different operating target. Retrofit options include: i) changing the configuration of the network (i.e. connectivity among existing units), ii) introducing new units in key locations of the network, or iii) modifying the heat transfer area or flow pattern of existing units (e.g. by changing the number of tubes, introducing heat transfer enhancement technology). These are capital investment decisions in a large complex system with many feasible alternatives. Extensive research using Pinch analysis and mathematical optimization has been done to address the retrofit and the related HEN synthesis problems (Bagajewicz et. al 2013; Sreepathi et. al 2014). Most approaches assume that the HEN operates at steady state and use simple exchanger models. However, in many cases (e.g. refining and food applications) fouling, a dynamic process, significantly affects performance, reducing heat transfer and increasing operational cost over time. Using detailed dynamic models in simulation, it has been shown (Coletti et. al 2011) that ignoring fouling when deciding on retrofit alternatives for the network structure may well lead to wrong choices or benefits substantially smaller than expected. In other studies the problem of area retrofit or including inserts has been addressed considering fouling (Wang and Smith 2013; Pan et. al 2013), but they ignore any fouling mitigation action, their cost, and how they affect the retrofit alternatives.

The optimal operational strategies to mitigate fouling (e.g. periodic cleanings, flow distribution control) are directly related to the HEN configuration after retrofitting. Conversely, the best retrofit alternative depends on the future fouling mitigation actions. Although these two problems are intimately connected, they have typically been assumed to be independent and considered separately. The optimal retrofit problem has been studied using pinch analysis or mathematical programming, mainly considering steady sate conditions (Bagajewicz et. al 2013). Georgiadis et al.,1998 addressed the optimal design of HEN subject to fouling using detailed dynamic models, but not their retrofit. For an existing HEN, the simultaneous operations optimization of cleaning schedules and flow control with detailed dynamic exchanger models was considered (Lozano Santamaria and Macchietto 2018). In principle, optimal operation and retrofit can be considered together in a MINLP formulation. However, size, combinatorial nature, and strong interactions and trade-offs between operational and retrofit decisions, make finding a suitable formulation and solution rather challenging.

This work presents an integrated formulation and efficient solution of the optimal retrofit and cleaning scheduling problems, with application to HEN used in refining applications. Section 2 presents the models and formulation, Section 3 introduces a realistic case study, Section 4 discusses results and benefits, and Section 5 summarizes the main conclusions.

2. Heat exchanger and network models for retrofit

The main application considered here is the retrofit of the preheat train of a refinery. The problem formulation is an extension of previous work (Lozano Santamaria and Macchietto 2018) dealing with the optimal cleaning scheduling and flow control problems for an *existing* HEN. The complete formulation is not presented because of space limitation, however the new elements regarding optimal retrofit are described. In that case, all exchangers and the network structure are fully defined. The network is represented as a directed multigraph where the nodes are the exchangers, mixers, splitters, sources and sinks. The exchangers, of shell and tube type, are modelled using an axially lumped P-NTU representation, but a radial temperature distribution is included to capture the effect of the various thermal resistances, including the (time-varying) deposit layer. The radial distribution also determines the changes in pressure drop due to deposition. The time representation is key to consider the process dynamics, while reducing the number of binary time dependent decisions. A continuous time representation with variable length periods is employed. The reader is referred to (Lozano Santamaria and Macchietto 2018; Lozano Santamaria and Macchietto 2019) for details of formulation, and numerical solution aspects, respectively.

The above formulation is used as a basis for defining the optimal retrofit and fouling mitigation problem. The additional retrofit decisions considered are: i) the addition of new heat exchangers of specified geometry (and related connecting streams) in specified network locations (binary variables $y_{h,i} \in \{0,1\} \forall i \in HEX_R$), and ii) the percent increase or decrease of heat transfer area (here limited to +/-50%) in selected existing units, for example by increasing the number of tubes (continuous variables $x_{a,i} \in [0.5,1.5] \forall i \in HEX_R$). HEX_R is the set of heat exchangers considered as retrofit alternatives to include/remove or modify, and is a subset of all the exchangers in the network (set HEX). All exchangers (including the retrofit options) are thus included in the HEN. The retrofit decisions regarding the existence of exchangers are modelled using the variables $y_{p,i} \in \{0,1\} \forall i \in HEX, p \in Periods$ associated with the cleanings in the cleaning scheduling formulation, where index p is related to the periods used in the time discretization. That is, when an exchanger does not exist, it is modelled as being in cleaning mode at all times. To include retrofit decisions in the cleaning scheduling problem, Eq. 1 - Eq. 6 are added as constraints to the original problem formulation. Eq. 1 defines the retrofitted heat transfer area, which is used in the heat duty constraints, and in the calculation of the mass flux in the exchanger tube-side. Eq. 2 - Eq. 6 link the cleaning constraints of the original formulation with the retrofit decisions. Eq. 2 states that if a unit does not exist, it is always being cleaned. Eq. 3 is a constraint to avoid consecutive ineffective cleanings modified according to the retrofit state of the unit. Eq. 4 and Eq. 5 are the lower and upper bounds for z_p, a binary variable representing whether one or more exchangers are being cleaned in a period $p \in Periods$. This binary variable is used to define the cleaning time and the bounds in the length of the periods when there are no cleanings It was modified relative to the original formulation to enable a retrofit alternative to be modelled as a cleaning. Finally, Eq. 6 is the modification of the maximum number of cleanings per unit allowed over the time horizon.

$$A_i = \pi d_i L N_T(x_{a,i}), \qquad \forall i \in HEX_R \qquad \text{Eq. 1}$$

$$1 - y_{h,i} \le y_{p,i}, \qquad \forall p \in Periods, i \in HEX_R \qquad \text{Eq. 2}$$

$$y_{p+1,i} \le 1 - y_{p,i} + 1 - y_{h,i}, \qquad \forall p \in Periods\backslash\{N_P\}, i \in HEX_R \qquad \text{Eq. 3}$$

$$y_{p,i} - (1 - y_{h,i}) \le z_p, \qquad \forall p \in Periods, i \in HEX \qquad \text{Eq. 4}$$

$$z_p \le \sum_{i \in HEX} \left(y_{p,i} - (1 - y_{h,i}) \right), \qquad \forall p \in Periods \qquad \text{Eq. 5}$$

$$\sum_{p \in Periods} y_{p,i} \le N_{cl}^{max} y_{h,i} + N_P(1 - y_{h,i}), \qquad \forall i \in HEX \qquad \text{Eq. 6}$$

This set of new constraints is included in the original optimal cleaning scheduling and flow distribution problem so that retrofit decisions are simultaneously considered. For the retrofit alternatives regarding including or removing units of the network, the HEN graph represents a superstructure with more alternatives and combinations than those feasible. Some of the exchangers will never be in service at the final optimal solution of the problem. As in the original cleaning scheduling formulation, units out of service or being cleaned, and the non-existing ones are ignored using bypasses around them on both the tube and shell sides. The bypass flows are decision variables constrained by the binary variables defining the cleanings and the unit retrofit.

The objective function (Eq. 7) is modified from Coletti and Macchietto (2011) to include in the total cost both operating costs (for energy (P_E), cleaning (P_{cl}), and carbon emitted (P_{co})) and the capital cost of the retrofit alternatives. The cleaning cost is subject to the existence of the exchanger. The capital cost of the exchangers (P_{HEX}) is assumed to be fixed for new retrofit units (their area is known) and proportional to the increase in area for those units subject to a heat transfer area retrofit.

$$\min J = \int_0^{t_f} [P_E Q_f + P_{co} m_{co} Q_f] dt + \sum_{i \in HEX} \sum_{p \in Period} P_{cl}(y_{p,i} - 1 + y_{h,i})$$
$$+ \sum_{i \in HEX_R} P_{HEX} y_{h,i} + \sum_{i \in HEX} P_{HEX} (x_{a,i} - 1) \qquad \text{Eq.7}$$

The problem thus defined for the simultaneous HEN retrofit, cleaning scheduling, and flow control is a large scale MINLP, which is combinatorial in nature due to the many possible cleaning sequences and network structures. For a given HEN, the cleaning scheduling problem was solved efficiently and quickly using a reformulation via complementarity constraints (Santamaria and Macchietto 2019). After relaxing the binary variables and imposing complementarity, it is solved sequentially using a regularized ϵ approach that converges to the solution of the original problem. The same solution strategy is used here for the combined retrofit and cleaning scheduling problem because it inherits the same structure from the previous formulation. As the modified constraints are linear, and the number of new retrofit variables is much smaller than the cleaning variables, the algorithm is directly applicable without compromising its performance.

3. Case study

The case study, adapted from Coletti et al., (2011), considers the hot end of a preheat train in a small real refinery. Figure 1 shows the superstructure of the preheat train network including the retrofit alternatives. The original network (base case, C1) includes exchangers HEX1 to HEX7, the desalter and the furnace. Three new network structures are explored by possibly including a new exchanger in one of three different locations (exchangers with diagonal grey pattern). These are the same structures considered by simulation in Coletti et. al., (2011). HEX1, HEX2 and HEX3 do not exhibit fouling due to their low operating temperature, the desalter has a temperature drop of 4.5°C, and all other exchangers follow a deposition dynamics characterized by the Ebert-Panchal model. Note that this is a dynamic model where fouling depends on operating conditions, and all decisions involved consider the effect of time on the network performance.

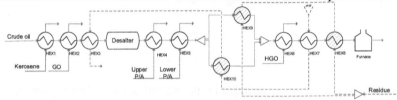

Figure 1. Network superstructure for the optimal retrofit case study

The main retrofit options considered are the inclusion of one of the exchangers HEX8, HEX9, or HEX10 (all with the same specifications) in the positions noted in Figure. 1, and a +/-50% change of the heat transfer area in all units. If the heat transfer area is decreased, there no additional capital cost. The two retrofit decisions are considered both separately and simultaneously in two scenarios. In all cases the decay in the heat transfer due to fouling, and the possible mitigation actions (cleanings) are accounted for. A time horizon of 600 days is considered, and the total capital cost of the retrofit alternatives is included in the objective function. The time horizon is discretized using 20 periods of variable length, and each period has 1 finite element and 3 Radau collocation points. It is expected that including an additional exchanger will increase the overall heat recovery, but there is a complex trade-off on the overall benefit because of fouling in the new unit, impact on fouling of other units, cost of cleanings, and extra capital cost.

The following retrofit scenarios are considered: i) retrofit of units, with and without scheduling of cleanings over the given horizon, and ii) retrofit of units and their heat transfer area, with and without scheduling of cleanings over the given horizon. These scenarios cover all combinations of decisions. The goal is to demonstrate the importance of considering retrofit and fouling mitigation decisions simultaneously, and that the dynamic formulation presented here can cope efficiently with it.

4. Results and analysis

Figure 2 and Figure 3 show the furnace duty profiles– the additional energy provided by the furnace – for the optimal retrofit, without and with cleanings, respectively. In both cases, the optimal network configuration is the one that includes HEX10. The figures also compare the optimal retrofit alternatives against the base case HEN configuration (C1). In all scenarios the energy consumed in the furnace is reduced significantly over all the operation, which represents significant economic savings. Including the retrofit options to increase the heat transfer area of the exchangers leads to an even better performance of the network, reducing energy consumption further. The total operating cost for the base case, $ 5.04 MM, is reduced to $ 4.54 MM when HEX10 is introduced, and to $ 4.14 MM when area retrofit options are also included. The capital cost of these two alternatives are $ 0.17 MM and $ 0.43 MM, respectively, which for the time horizon considered still represent a more profitable operation than the base case.

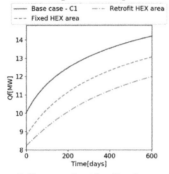

Figure 2. Furnace duty for Case1a - optimal retrofit options without cleanings

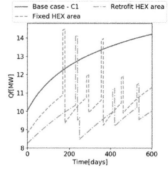

Figure 3. Furnace duty for Case1b - optimal retrofit options with cleanings

Introducing cleanings to mitigate fouling simultaneously with the network retrofit does not change the optimal structure of the network, but provides larger economic savings. With cleanings, selected units can recover their efficiency, hence reduce the overall energy requirements of the furnace. It is observed in Figure 3 that during cleanings the furnace duty increases significantly (as one or more units are out of service), but then it decreases for a long period thereafter. When cleanings are optimized together with retrofit alternatives, the operating cost is reduced to $ 4.26 MM for the optimal unit allocation, and to $ 3.92 MM when area retrofit is also included. These costs include the cost of the cleanings and in both cases the capital cost is much lower than the operating cost ($ 0.17 MM and $ 0.42 MM, respectively).

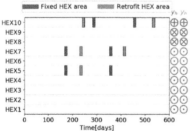

Figure 4. Optimal cleaning schedule for simultaneous cleaning and retrofit.

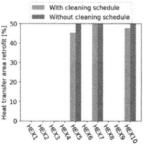

Figure 5. Optimal retrofit of heat transfer area

In this case study, optimizing cleanings together with the retrofits does not change the optimal structure of the network, but affects the optimal area retrofit decisions. Also, the optimal area retrofit affects the cleaning schedule of the units. Clearly, these two problems are strongly related and should not be decoupled to achieve the best possible operation and configuration of the heat exchanger network. Figure 4 shows the optimal cleaning schedule when both schedule and retrofit are optimized, with and without area retrofit. In both cases, only exchanges 5, 7, and 10 (new unit) are cleaned over the 600 days of operation. These exchangers have a larger duty and higher fouling rate than the others, because of the high temperature of the residue stream. When the heat transfer area of the units is modified, the total number of cleanings is reduced from 6 to 5, and most of the cleanings are moved to later times, indicating that they can operate for longer between cleanings. Finally, the interaction between cleaning schedule and area retrofit is observed in Figure 5 that shows the optimal percent increase of the heat transfer area of all exchangers. The area of old exchangers 5, 7, and new exchanger 10 (the same units involved in the cleanings) is modified. The area of these units is increased by the maximum allowed 50% in the case without cleanings, but a lower increase is observed when cleanings are also optimized, i.e. smaller, and cheaper, modifications are required.

5. Conclusions

The optimization formulation presented allows to optimally retrofit heat exchanger networks, taking into account detailed models, fouling dynamics, cleaning of the units, the complex interactions caused at network level by both fouling, cleanings, and retrofit alternatives. The formulation, an extension of the optimal cleaning scheduling problem, considers network retrofit alternatives and area retrofit of individual units simultaneously with fouling mitigation strategies. The extension requires only few additional integer variables and constraints, and is therefore solved efficiently with the methods developed earlier for optimizing HEN operation and fouling mitigation. A realistic case study shows the ability of the formulation to handle problems of industrially relevant size, and that it can efficiently integrate retrofit and fouling mitigation decisions. It was demonstrated that such integrated solution allows to reduce the total cost of HEN operation. Future work will investigate the applicability of the formulation to larger networks with more retrofit alternatives and parallel branches, and a further extension to include optimal flow distribution in the formulation.

References

Bagajewicz, M., G. Valtinson, and D. Q. Nguyen Thanh. 2013. "Retrofit of Crude Units Preheating Trains: Mathematical Programming versus Pinch Technology." *Industrial & Engineering Chemistry Research* 52 (42): 14913–26.

Coletti, F, and Macchietto, S. 2011. "Refinery Pre-Heat Train Network Simulation Undergoing Fouling: Assessment of Energy Efficiency and Carbon Emissions." *Heat Transfer Engineering* 32 (3–4): 228–36.

Coletti, F., Macchietto, S, and G. T. Polley. 2011. "Effects of Fouling on Performance of Retrofitted Heat Exchanger Networks: A Thermo-Hydraulic Based Analysis." *Computers & Chemical Engineering* 35 (5): 907–17.

Georgiadis, M. C, G. E Rotstein, and Macchietto, S. 1998. "Optimal Design and Operation of Heat Exchangers under Milk Fouling." *AIChE Journal* 44 (9): 2099–2111.

Lozano Santamaria, F., and Macchietto, S. 2018. "Integration of Optimal Cleaning Scheduling and Control of Heat Exchanger Networks Undergoing Fouling: Model and Formulation." *Industrial & Engineering Chemistry Research* 57 (38): 12842–60.

Lozano Santamaria, F., and Macchietto, S. 2019. "Integration of Optimal Cleaning Scheduling and Control of Heat Exchanger Networks under Fouling: MPCC Solution." *Computers & Chemical Engineering* 126 (July): 128–46.

Pan, M., I. Bulatov, and R. Smith. 2013. "Exploiting Tube Inserts to Intensify Heat Transfer for the Retrofit of Heat Exchanger Networks Considering Fouling Mitigation." *Industrial & Engineering Chemistry Research* 52 (8): 2925–43.

Sreepathi, B. K., and G P Rangaiah. 2014. "Review of Heat Exchanger Network Retrofitting Methodologies and Their Applications." *Industrial & Engineering Chemistry Research* 53 (28): 11205–20.

Wang, Y., and R. Smith. 2013. "Retrofit of a Heat-Exchanger Network by Considering Heat-Transfer Enhancement and Fouling." *Industrial & Engineering Chemistry Research* 52 (25): 8527–37.

Sauro Pierucci, Flavio Manenti, Giulia Bozzano, Davide Manca (Eds.)
Proceedings of the 30th European Symposium on Computer Aided Process Engineering
(ESCAPE30), May 24-27, 2020, Milano, Italy. © 2020 Elsevier B.V. All rights reserved.
http://dx.doi.org/10.1016/B978-0-12-823377-1.50238-X

Optimal Design of Integrated Urban Energy System Under Uncertainty and Sustainability Requirements

Zhihao Chen,[a,b] Styliani Avraamidou,[b] Pei Liu,[a*] Efstratios N. Pistikopoulos[b,c]

[a]State Key Lab of Power Systems, Department of Energy and Power Engineering, Tsinghua University, Beijing, 100084, China
[b]Texas A&M Energy Institute, Texas A&M University, College Station, TX 77843, USA
[c]Artie McFerrin Department of Chemical Engineering, Texas A&M University, College Station, TX 77843, USA
liu_pei@tsinghua.edu.cn

Abstract

Urban energy consumption and consequent environmental impacts such as the massive amount of energy-related greenhouse gas emission and water consumption are posing significant pressure on sustainable development. Energy systems of the future should satisfy the ever-increasing energy demand and reduce negative externalities. This paper proposes an integrated urban energy system modelling and optimisation approach. Based on the main features of urban energy systems, the model is established as a mixed-integer linear program. Multi-objective optimisation is used to reveal the trade-offs among economic and environmental concerns, and stochastic programming is adopted to treat the uncertainties rooted in energy supply. A new urban area is used as a case study to illustrate the functions of the model and to provide insights for energy system design.

Keywords: Integrated urban energy system, energy system design, carbon emission mitigation, energy-water nexus, stochastic programming.

1. Introduction

Energy underpins modern society. Large scale energy use in urban areas leads to several environmental problems. Cities are responsible for the majority of global energy-related greenhouse gas emissions, and water consumption of urban energy supply exacerbate water stress. These issues are expected to become more severe since the urbanisation trend is expected to continue. Therefore, the optimal design of urban energy systems is needed for the realisation of affordable and sustainable energy supply.

Recently, we have witnessed an increased research interest in energy system design. The energy hub (EH) concept has been widely used in multi-generation systems (Mohammadi et al., 2017). Superstructure-based modelling has become a general approach in process system design; combined with the EH concept, it provides a systematic way to consider all possible energy flow pathways, technology options, network configurations, and operation modes (Demirhan et al., 2019). Many planning models are either at the macroscopic scale (Guo et al., 2017) or microscopic scale (Zhou et al., 2013), but rarely at an urban scale. Growing attention has been paid to the externalities of energy supply, such as greenhouse gas emissions (Liu et al., 2010) and energy-water nexus (Allen et al., 2019). Also, many researchers have considered the stochastic nature of energy systems (Mavromatidis et al., 2018). However, very few models at the urban scale cover all the aspects above and incorporate the main features of urban systems in a holistic framework.

This work aims to build an integrated urban energy system modelling framework that is suitable for optimal system design. The core model is introduced in Section 2. Section 3 illustrates the main functions of the model through a case study, in which the uncertainty and sustainability requirements are considered. Conclusions are drawn in the final part.

2. Methodology

2.1. Superstructure representation

Urban energy systems should have commonalities of general energy systems and particularities of urban systems. In the past, different energy systems were designed separately and operated individually. However, urban energy systems are multi-energy systems that encompass a variety of energy sources, needs, and conversion paths. While centralised generation still dominates the energy supply, distributed generation is playing a more critical role. Energy systems of the future should utilise the strengths of both types of production. Planning decisions, usually made on an annual or longer basis, should be able to meet the energy demand in each time slot under real operating constraints, such as capacity range and ramping rate limit.

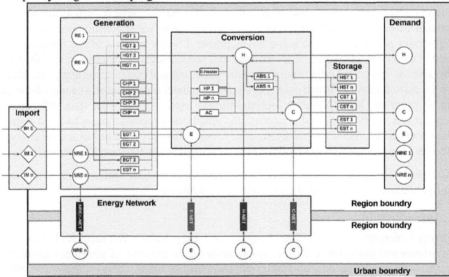

Figure 1. Structure of integrated urban energy systems

Figure 1 illustrates the superstructure representation of the integrated urban energy systems. We use the adjective 'integrated' to highlight the interaction of multiple energy forms, the synthesis of centralised and distributed generation, and the coordination of design and operation phases. The two white blocks represent two different regions inside the city, each of which can be considered as an energy hub. Energy can be imported from outside the city, collected on-site, or transmitted and distributed between regions through energy networks. Inside each energy hub, there are energy generation, conversion, and storage sectors. Different varieties of primary energy (both renewable and non-renewable) are transformed into secondary energy (e.g. electricity, heat, and cooling) in the generation sector. In the conversion sector, secondary energy can be converted from one form into other forms. Storage facilities help to store the excess energy at a time for later use. These three sectors, as well as energy import and energy networks, work together to meet the final energy demand in each region.

2.2. Mathematical formulation

The superstructure representation is expressed as an optimisation model comprised of algebraic equations. The equations include objective functions, design constraints, and operating constraints.

2.2.1. Objective functions

As a multiple criteria decision-making problem, it has several objective functions. The total cost of the system consists of capital expenditure, operating and maintenance cost, and fuel cost. And the total carbon dioxide emissions are derived from fossil fuel consumption and emission index. The ε-Constraint method is adopted for multi-objective optimisation. The total cost remains as the objective function, while the emission function is converted to a constraint. The optimal solution at each discretised emission point can be obtained by solving a single-objective problem.

2.2.2. Design constraints

Infrastructure selection, sizing and location are the core issues in energy planning. The installed capacities of different technologies in each region are determined by Eq. (1). The notations of the model are defined in Table 1 and Table 2.

$$ic_{t,r} = iu_{t,r} \cdot SCAP_t \tag{1}$$

2.2.3. Operating constraints

Energy balance is a fundamental principle. The balance of each form of energy is specified by Eq. (2) for primary energy and Eq. (3) for secondary energy.

$$x^{imp}_{s,h,r,pe} + \sum_{r'} \sum_n \left(x^{tri}_{s,h,r,r',pe} \cdot \eta_n - x^{tri}_{s,h,r',r,pe} \right) + x^{onsite}_{s,h,r,pe} - \\ \sum_{gnt} x^{in}_{gnt,s,h,r,pe} = FED_{s,h,r,pe} \tag{2}$$

$$x^{imp}_{s,h,r,se} + \sum_{r'} \sum_n (x^{tri}_{s,h,r,r',se} \cdot \eta_n - x^{tri}_{s,h,r',r,se}) + \sum_{gnt} x^{out}_{gnt,s,h,r,se} + \\ \sum_{cvt}(x^{out}_{cvt,s,h,r,se} - x^{in}_{cvt,s,h,r,se}) + \sum_{stt}(x^{out}_{stt,s,h,r,se} - x^{in}_{stt,s,h,r,se}) = FED_{s,h,r,se} \tag{3}$$

For energy generation and conversion components, the relation between input and output is expressed by Eq. (4). For energy storage devices, energy balance between adjacent time periods is given by Eq. (5).

$$\sum_e x^{in}_{t,s,h,r,e} \cdot \eta_{t,e'} = x^{out}_{t,s,h,r,e'} \tag{4}$$

$$str_{stt,s,h+1,r,e} = str_{stt,s,h,r,e} \cdot \eta_{stt} - \frac{x^{out}_{stt,s,h+1,r,e} \cdot \Delta h}{\eta^{out}_{stt}} + x^{in}_{stt,s,h+1,r,se} \cdot \Delta h \cdot \eta^{in}_{stt} \tag{5}$$

Technology can only be operated within a specific load range, as shown in Eq. (6) and (7). The output of renewable generation is restricted by resource availability, given by Eq. (8). Ramp-up and ramp-down rates are constrained by Eq. (9) and (10).

$$\sum_e x^{out}_{t,s,h,r,e} \leq op^{operate}_{t,s,h,r} \cdot SCAP_t \tag{6}$$

$$\sum_e x^{out}_{t,s,h,r,e} \geq (op^{operate}_{t,s,h,r} - op^{startup}_{t,s,h,r}) \cdot SCAP_t \cdot \underline{LOL_t} \tag{7}$$

$$\sum_e x^{out}_{rgt,s,h,r,e} \leq op^{operate}_{rgt,s,h,r} \cdot SCAP_{rgt} \cdot \overline{RA_{rgt,s,h}} \tag{8}$$

$$\sum_e (x^{out}_{t,s,h+1,r,e} - x^{out}_{t,s,h,r,e}) \leq (op^{operate}_{t,s,h,r} + op^{startup}_{t,s,h+1,r}) \cdot \overline{RU_t} \cdot SCAP_t \tag{9}$$

$$\sum_e (x^{out}_{t,s,h,r,e} - x^{out}_{t,s,h+1,r,e}) \leq (op^{operate}_{t,s,h,r} \cdot \overline{RD_t} + op^{shutdown}_{t,s,h+1,r}) \cdot SCAP_t \tag{10}$$

Each technology may have several units, and the status of each unit can be operating, starting up, shutting down, or closed. The number of units in use cannot exceed existing units at that period.

Energy can only be imported at specific locations under certain capacity limits. Cross-region energy flows can not exceed the capacity of the network in use. Land use constraints are also contained. The full detailed model formulation is not given in this work because of space limitations.

3. Illustrative example and results

3.1. Case specification

The model introduced in the previous section is applied to a new urban area in China. This new area consists of six regions. We consider three seasons (i.e. winter, mid-season, and summer), one typical day for each season, and 24 hours for each day, for a total of 72 time intervals. The hourly energy demands of the new area are exogenously specified. Here we consider 17 types of generation technologies (e.g. NGCC w/o CCS, Nuclear, PV, wind turbine, gas turbine CHP, NGCC CHP, coal boiler, and gas boiler), four conversion technologies (i.e. absorption chiller, air-source heat pump, ground-source heat pump, and AC), three storage technologies (i.e. battery, thermal storage, and ice storage), and four energy networks (i.e. gas pipe, heat pipe, cooling pipe, and power grid). Technical and economic parameters such as efficiency, lifetime, capital expenditure, fixed and variable operating cost, are mainly collected from IEA-ETSAP and 2019 Annual Technology Baseline (NREL 2019). Solar and wind resource data are found from Pfenninger and Staffell (2016). CO_2 emission index is adopted from 2018 Energy Data (Wang, 2018). Water consumption data are gathered from Gerdes and Nichols (2009) and UCS (2013).

3.2. Trade-offs among economic and environmental criteria

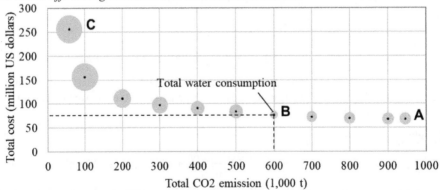

Figure 2. The Pareto Front of total cost and CO_2 emission

Figure 2 illustrates the results of multi-objective optimisation, taking cost and CO_2 emission as two conflicting interests. Each point corresponds to a Pareto optimal solution, while the area of each bubble represents the amount of water consumption. Along with the decline of CO_2 emission boundary, the total cost rises at an ever-increasing speed. The change in water consumption, however, is not monotonous. From cost minimum point A to point B, the water consumption decreases, because the system adopts more CHP and PV technologies that are less water consuming. To further reduce CO_2 emission, NGCC plants start to apply CCS technology and are finally replaced by nuclear plants, both of which are water hunger. In other words, less CO_2 emission does not necessarily mean less water consumption. The energy-water nexus shouldn't be overlooked, especially in areas that suffer from water shortage.

3.3. The deterministic and stochastic design plan of the new area energy system

Decision-makers can choose any point from the Pareto Front according to their design requirements or specific interests. Once their decision is made, the developed optimisation model can supply them with a holistic plan for the system design. Compared with point A, CO_2 emissions and water consumption at point B decreased by 36.5% and 52.6% respectively, and the total cost increased by only 13.7%. Figure 3(a) illustrates the energy network design solution of point B.

Previous discussions are based on the deterministic model. However, renewable generation technologies such as PV and wind turbine introduce uncertainty into the system. To simply address this problem, we assume that PV might operate at a lower output with a probability of 0.2 or at a higher output with a probability of 0.8 on each typical day. Similar settings are applied to wind turbines. Thus, we get $2^3 \times 2^3 = 64$ scenarios. In Figure 3(b), white rectangles represent the deterministic solution of energy technology design in region 1, and dark grey rectangles refer to extra technology capacity required to meet the energy demand and the CO_2 emission limit in all the scenarios. In response to the uncertainty, region 1 should adopt Li-Battery and build more gas turbine CHP and air-source heat pump (ASHP).

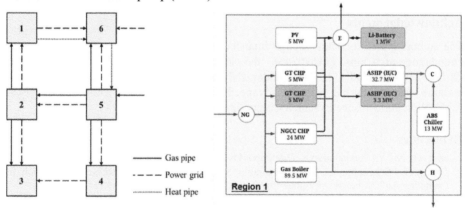

(a) Energy flow across regions   (b) Energy technology deployment in region 1

Figure 3. The energy system design solution of point B

4. Conclusions

In this paper, we developed an optimisation approach for integrated urban energy system design under uncertainty and sustainability requirements. This approach has been applied to a new area in China. The results reveal that more stringent carbon emission limit requires a higher investment, while the relationship between carbon emission and water use is complicated. Decision-makers can choose the proper design point based on their specific interests and constraints. Once renewable technologies such as PV and wind turbine are to be deployed, the impact of uncertainty should be considered to avoid the suboptimal design.

Table 1. Definition of variables

Continuous Variables		Integer Variables	
x	Energy flow	ic	Installed capacity
str	Energy stored in storage facilities	iu	Installed units
		op	Units in use

Table 2. Definition of sets, superscripts, and parameters

Sets and superscripts		Parameters	
s	Season	η	Efficiency
h	Hour	FED	Final energy demand
r	Region	$SCAP$	Single unit capacity
e	Energy	Δh	Length of a time-slot
pe	Primary energy	$\underline{LOL}$	Lower operating level limit
se	Secondary energy	$\overline{RA}$	Renewable availability limit
t	Technology	$\overline{RU}$	Ramping up limit
gnt	Generation technology	$\overline{RD}$	Rampin down limit
cvt	Conversion technology		
stt	Storage technology		
imp	Energy imported from outside		
tri	Energy transmitted across regions		
$onsite$	Renewables collected onsite		
in/out	Technology inlet/outlet		

Acknowledgements

The authors gratefully acknowledge financial supports from National Natural Science Foundation of China (71690245), the Program of China Scholarship Council (201806210214), and U.S. NSF under INFEWS project 1739977. Portions of this research were conducted with the advanced computing resources provided by Texas A&M High Performance Research Computing.

References

Allen R. C., Nie Y., Avraamidou S., Pistikopoulos E. N., 2019. Infrastructure Planning and Operational Scheduling for Power Generating Systems: An Energy-Water Nexus Approach. In Computer Aided Chemical Engineering (Vol. 47, pp. 233-238). Elsevier.

Demirhan C. D., Tso W. W., Ogumerem G. S., Pistikopoulos E. N., 2019. Energy systems engineering-a guided tour. BMC Chemical Engineering, 1(1), 11.

Gerdes K., Nichols C., 2009. Water requirement for existing and emerging thermoelectric plant technologies. Office of Systems, Analysis & Planning, National Energy Technology Laboratory, DOE/NETL-402/080108, p13.

Guo Z., Cheng R., Xu Z., Liu P., Wang Z., Li Z., Jones I., Sun Y., 2017. A multi-region load dispatch model for the long-term optimum planning of China's electricity sector. Applied Energy 185, 556–572.

Liu P., Pistikopoulos E. N., Li Z., 2010. An energy systems engineering approach to the optimal design of energy systems in commercial buildings. Energy Policy, 38(8), 4224-4231.

Mavromatidis G., Orehounig K., Carmeliet J., 2018. Design of distributed energy systems under uncertainty: A two-stage stochastic programming approach. Applied Energy, 222, pp.932-950.

Mohammadi M., Noorollahi Y., Mohammadi-Ivatloo B., Yousefi H., 2017. Energy hub: from a model to a concept–a review. Renewable and Sustainable Energy Reviews, 80, 1512-1527.

NREL (National Renewable Energy Laboratory). 2019. 2019 Annual Technology Baseline. Golden, CO: National Renewable Energy Laboratory.

Pfenninger S., Staffell I., 2016. Long-term patterns of European PV output using 30 years of validated hourly reanalysis and satellite data. Energy, 114, 1251-1265.

UCS (Union of Concerned Scientists), 2013. How it Works: Water for Nuclear.

Wang Q., 2018. 2018 Energy Data. Beijing: Innovative Green Development Program.

Zhou Z., Liu P., Li Z., Ni W., 2013. An engineering approach to the optimal design of distributed energy systems in China. Applied Thermal Engineering, 53(2), pp.387-396.

Sauro Pierucci, Flavio Manenti, Giulia Bozzano, Davide Manca (Eds.)
Proceedings of the 30th European Symposium on Computer Aided Process Engineering
(ESCAPE30), May 24-27, 2020, Milano, Italy. © 2020 Elsevier B.V. All rights reserved.
http://dx.doi.org/10.1016/B978-0-12-823377-1.50239-1

Optimal Integration of a Stratified Thermal Energy Storage into a Multi-Component Industrial Energy System

Karl Schenzel [a], René Hofmann [a,b*]

[a]*Technische Universität Wien, Institute for Energy Systems and Thermodynamics, Getreidemarkt 9/BA, 1060 Vienna, Austria*
[b]*AIT Austrian Institute of Technology GmbH, Center for Energy, Sustainable Thermal Energy Systems, Giefinggasse 2, 1210 Vienna, Austria*
rene.hofmann@tuwien.ac.at

Abstract

One way of balancing the increasing shares of fluctuating renewables in the energy mix are flexible consumers. For utilizing system flexibility and load shifting, thermal energy storages are of vital importance. Concerning optimal operation, the use of optimization becomes inevitable, as decisions for optimal storage management are based on future energy prices and demand predictions. Due to the nonlinear character, the formulation of stratified thermal energy storage models in optimization problems are crucial, especially when temperature distributions inside the storage are of interest.

Inspired by a specific industrial use case this work aims to analyze the flexibility of the corresponding energy system through proper storage management based on load predictions and profiles of energy prices using mathematical optimization. Considering the selection of a suitable modelling approach, stratification and convection inside the centrally located sensible water storage were of special interest, thus a detailed nonlinear approach was chosen. Based on the comparison of three scenarios the outcomes of this work demonstrate the usefulness and strength of applied mathematical optimization for both economic operation and prediction of system states and conditions for multi-connected sensible thermal energy storages.

Keywords: Flexible Consumer, Demand Response, Thermal Energy Storage, Stratification, Operation Optimization

1. Introduction

Sensible water storages can be found in almost any industrial process, nevertheless they are used in most cases more as hydraulic switch rather than acting as a storage in the proper sense. By making use of their storage potential through a proper and predictive storage management, consumers can be timely more flexible in their energy demand and can thus benefit from cheaper off-peak energy prices. Considering the entire industrial sector, this shows huge unused potential that can be utilized to increase demand side flexibility.

The industrial plant of the considered use case consists of several different components surrounding a centrally located and multi-layer-connected hot water storage tank. As it represents the most complex and decisive component in terms of system flexibility, the storage is of main focus. Concerning optimal operation the use of optimization models becomes inevitable as decisions for optimal storage management are based on future energy prices and demand predictions. In Schütz et al. (2015) and Baeten et al. (2015) different optimization formulations for stratified thermal storage were compared.

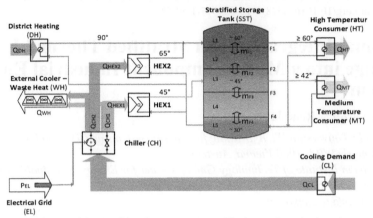

Figure 1: Flow-Scheme of the considered energy system: Having a closer look at the storage it is discretized into five equally sized layers: Three layers in which it has inputs and outputs and one intermediate layer each. In the following the layers are identified with the letter L, the faces, which letter F.

However, in the considered energy systems, the storage had only one inlet and one outlet what results in a uniform flow distribution. In order to be able to model the different inflows and outflows at different vertical positions, the nonlinear model approach was extended in this work in order to be able to consider uneven flow distributions within the stratified water storage.

2. Use Case

At present, instead of using predictive control tools, single components as well as storage management are operated by human plant managers only based on their experience. Consequently also the overall system of this industrial plant is operated inefficiently. In general a too large amount of waste heat cannot be used and has to be released to the environment by the external coolers. Also the control of the district heating supply does not work properly what often results in too high temperatures inside the storage tank. This is followed by negative impacts on both, the production quality and energy costs.

As the storage is of main interest in this work a simplified subsystem of the real complex industrial plant was derived. The corresponding energy system is shown in Figure 1 and consists of two heat consumers on different temperature levels (HT and MT), a Chiller (CH) for cooling services (CL), a district heating supply (DH) and an external cooler for waste heat release. All of them are connected to the stratified storage tank (SST) at three different temperature levels. This work aims to be an introductory contribution as basis of developing an operation planning and predictive control tool for the whole industrial site with its complex interconnected system.

3. Method and Approach

With special focus on the storage, the aim was to use a detailed nonlinear approach - mainly for the following reasons: On the one hand the precise temperature distributions are of central interest as they are of importance for the quality of the production process. Also, the current control system is only based on temperature measurements.

On the other hand, since there are currently no flow measurements available, this model can also be used to calculate mass flow rates. Furthermore the model considers the convection and heat conduction inside the storage as well as the heat losses to the ambient what makes the model more complex. Regarding the surrounding components, the goal was to model them as simply as possible, but to provide the connections to the storage in sufficient detailed. If not stated explicit in the text, all considered variables are defined positive and unbounded. Due to a lack of existing measurements, the model validation could not be done using real component data. As a workaround another stratified storage tank, similar in size and geometry, was taken for parameter estimation and validation.

3.1. Storage Model

A stratified thermal storage physically consists of various temperature layers having different temperatures with the highest on the top and the lowest on the bottom. A suitable way of modelling stratification is to vertically divide the storage in N volumes, with each having a constant mass and a uniform temperature that can vary over time. Each volume can have several input and output flows which impact the convection flow rates to and from the neighboring layers. Depending on the combination of the different inlet and outlet flows, from one layer simultaneously flows into the upper and lower neighboring layers can occur. Because both, layer temperatures which represent the states of the transient model, as well as flow rates are considered variables of the optimization problem this is a nonlinear model. Heat conduction between layers and heat losses to the ambient are modeled using a constant heat conduction coefficient. The layer energy balances are the governing equations regarding transient system behavior. Considering all features described above, this state constraint equation can be - for an exemplary layer - read as followed in Eq.(1).

$$\frac{Mc_w(T_{(L)}^{t+1} - T_{(L)}^t)}{\Delta t} = \dot{m}_{(F+)}c_w(T_{(L+1)}^{t*} - T_{(L)}^{t*}) + \dot{m}_{(F-)}c_w(T_{(L-1)}^{t*} - T_{(L)}^{t*})$$

$$+ \sum_{i,in}(\dot{m}_{i,in}\,c_w(T_{i,in} - T_{(L)}^{t*})) + k_{amb}\,A_{amb}(T_{amb} - T_{(L)}^{t*}) \qquad (1)$$

$$+ k_F\,A_F(T_{(L+1)}^{t*} - T_{(L)}^{t*}) + k_F\,A_F(T_{(L-1)}^{t*} - T_{(L)}^{t*})$$

The upper indices refer to the time at which the respective value is taken. The marker* stands for the central interpolated timepoint: $T_{(L)}^{t*} = 0.5(T_{(L)}^{t+1} - T_{(L)}^t)$

Table 1: Abbreviations used in Eq. (1)

Abbreviation	Definition	Abbreviation	Definition
M	*Mass content*	k	*Heat conduction*
$\dot{m}$	*massflow rate*		*coefficient*
c_w	*heat capacity water*	A	*Surface*
T	*Temperature*	*amb*	*Ambient*

3.2. Cooling and Heat Recovery System

The chiller that provides cooling services performs similar to a heatpump. After the enthalpy increase due to the compression the refrigerant releases heat at a higher temperature (Q_{CH2}) in a desuperheater and at a lower temperature in a condenser (Q_{CH1}). By varying the electrical power input the compressor unit offers some flexibility in operation. Increasing the electric power input leads to higher superheating of the refrigerant and so the proportion of heat released at high temperature level (Q_{CH2}) is increased. Thus the ratio of heat released at the higher temperature to the total heat released by the chiller can vary between 0.2 and 0.25. Eq.(4) states this constraint. When superheating is at its maximum the total COP is 2.5, with minimal superheating the total COP is 3.2. In between, there is linear interpolation. The waste heat from the chiller can either be released to the environment level (Q_{WH}) or supplied to the stratified tank via the two heat exchangers HEX1 and HEX2, which have a maximum capacity of 500kW and 100kW respectively.

$$Q_{CL} + P_{EL} = Q_{CH2} + Q_{CH1} \quad (2) \quad COP = \frac{Q_{CH1} + Q_{CH2}}{P_{EL}} \quad (3) \quad 0.2 \le \frac{Q_{CH2}}{Q_{CH1} + Q_{CH2}} \le 0.25 \quad (4)$$

3.3. Consumers, Electricity- and District Heating Suppliers

These components represent the boundaries of the system. The corresponding load and price profiles which are the same for the first and second 24hours of the observation period are specified in Figure 2.

According to observations of the real operation a constant outflow temperature of 90°C is assumed for the district heating supply. As indicated in Figure 1 the inflow temperature of the HT- and MT-Consumer correspond to its sources, Layer 1 and Layer 3. At minimum 60°C and 42°C are required by the HT-and MT- Consumers. Although too high inflow temperatures can cause quality losses in the attached processes no upper boundaries are considered in the consumers. However, in scenario 3 this is taken into account by a soft constraint. As measurement data show almost constant temperature drops between the different distribution and collection networks in the consumption side, constant temperature drops ΔT_{HT} and ΔT_{MT} are assumed for the consumers.

3.4. Optimization and Objective Function

The system was modelled and implemented in MATLAB using the toolbox YALMIP. The described nonlinear program was solved using the IPOPT algorithm. The optimization was executed for an observation period of 48 hours with a discrete time-step of 5 minutes. At this point it should be noted that the observation period refers to a finite horizon rather than a periodic time cycle.

To analyze the systems flexibility three different scenarios are compared, with each having the same load and price profiles as boundary conditions (shown in Figure 2) but different optimization objectives. In scenario A only the minimization of total operation costs is taken into account (c_{WH}=0, c_{TL1}=0).In scenario B Waste Heat release is minimized (c_{WH}=1000, c_{TL1}=0). In scenario C the temperature of the highest layer is tried to be kept as low as possible (c_{WH}=0, c_{TL1}=1000). The optimization problem is stated with the objective function given in Eq.(5) where pr_{El} pr_{DH} stand for the prices for electricity and district heating.

$$Min \quad z = Q_{DH} \; pr_{DH} + P_{EL} \; pr_{EL} + c_{WH} \; \| Q_{WH} \| + c_{TL1} \; \| T_{(L1)} - T_{HT\,min} \| \qquad (5)$$

4. Results and Discussion

The results shown in Table 2 give a comparison of the overall performance of the three scenarios. Immediately it can be seen that scenario A, where cost minimization is the only objective, has the lowest energy costs. This means that the additional objectives in the other scenarios can only be met by accepting higher energy costs.

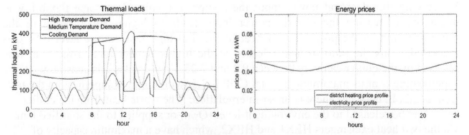

Figure 2: Loads and prices – valid for the first and second 24h-period

Table 2: Comparison of the three scenarios

Scenario/ Objective	A-Minimization of operation costs	B-Minimization of Waste Heat	C-Minimization of Temperature in Layer 1
Operation Costs in €	572.5	596.8	647.8
Waste Heat in kWh	6854.1	6649.3	8545.5
District Heat in kWh	3556.0	4072.7	5250.3
Electricity in kWh	5142.9	5142.2	5142.2

The waste heat reduction of 3% in scenario B can be achieved by a cost increase of 4.2%. When looking at the temperature behaviors shown in Figure 3, layer 1 and layer 3 are of particular interest as these are also the inflow temperatures of the consumers which have to be at least 60°C and 42°C, respectively. In the cost-effective scenario A the consumption peaks in the morning and midday lead to higher temperatures than actually required. As the behavior in scenario B shows only minor difference to scenario A, a further comparison here is neglected. The optimization strategy in scenario C aims at improving the operation of the HT-consumer and reduces the influence of the consumption peaks for the highest layer. However, in the other layers constantly higher temperatures are observed over the whole observation period, what is also reflected in a significant increase in energy consumption (19.5%), operating costs (+15%) and waste heat release to the environment(+24%).

It should be noticed that the beginning and end of the first and second 24h period show different behavior although the boundaries are the same. This is due to the finite horizon optimization, where only the initial and final constraints are considered. Instead a periodic horizon would include the consideration of the entire previous and subsequent periods and result in identical profiles.

Considering the interconnections of the storage and taking into account the layer mass balances, it becomes clear that the vertical flows of the two lower and the two upper faces must be equal. Especially the flow rate in the upper section is of interest, as it gives indication how the different suppliers are co-operating.

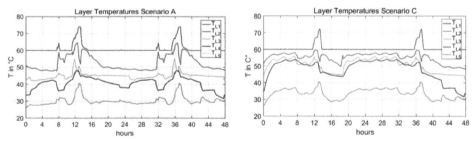

Figure 3: Layer temperatures for scenario A (left) and scenario C (right)

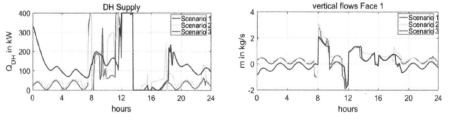

Figure 4: District heating supply (left) and upper section vertical flows (right), for first 24h-period

For example Figure 4 shows that in scenario C district heating is used most frequently, especially during off-peak periods. This causes an increased inlet flow entering the highest layer, what results in the upper vertical flow to be directed downwards (shown as negative values in figure 4). By looking at Figure 3, it can also be analyzed well how the temperatures of neighboring layers affect each other through the appearing vertical flows.

5. Conclusion

According to proven static analytical methods and energy-economic aspects, optimal storage management means storing energy from off-peak periods as well as waste heat in order to save energy and costs. Away from this, the presented results show that optimal operation of the considered hot water storage tank does not entirely follow these rules. Reduction of waste heat release has not been identified as a cost-effective objective and a more stringent temperature control is associated with considerable increase in costs and waste heat. Regarding the analysis of the systems flexibility, it can be derived from the scenarios that the identical energy demand can be met by very different ways of operating the suppliers. Under the given circumstances a potential of about 20% of the energy consumption can be utilized and offered for demand side flexibility by this process.

Especially when intricately integrated into diversified systems, the optimal management of stratified storages is a complex problem and requires advanced methods of predictive control as well as suitable and problem specific modelling approaches. The example demonstrates the usefulness and strength of mathematical optimization for operational planning in addition to common analytical methods such as pinch and exergy analysis.

In Outlook to further work the considered energy system will be extended to represent the whole industrial site. Of particular focus is the introduction of a CHP-plant and a high-temperature heat pump as well as the derivation and analysis of alternative linearized models in order to execute operational optimization with subject to design aspects.

References

Baeten, B., Rogiers, F., Patteeuw, D., Helsen, L. (2015). Comparison of optimal control formulations for stratified sensible thermal energy storage in space heating applications In: The 13th International Conference on Energy Storage.

Schütz, T., Streblow, R., Müller, D. (2015). A comparison of thermal energy storage models for building energy system optimization. In: Energy and Buildings 93, S. 23–31.

Sauro Pierucci, Flavio Manenti, Giulia Bozzano, Davide Manca (Eds.)
Proceedings of the 30th European Symposium on Computer Aided Process Engineering
(ESCAPE30), May 24-27, 2020, Milano, Italy. © 2020 Elsevier B.V. All rights reserved.
http://dx.doi.org/10.1016/B978-0-12-823377-1.50240-8

Portfolio Optimisation of Integrated Renewable Energy Cogeneration Systems

Houd Al-Obaidli,[a] Ahmed AlNouss,[a] Yusuf Bicer,[a] Tareq Al-Ansari[a,b*]

[a]*Divison of Sustainable Development, College of Science and Engineering, Hamad Bin Khalifa University, Qatar Foundation, Doha, Qatar.*

[b]*Division of Engineering Management and Decision Sciences, College of Science and Engineering, Hamad Bin Khalifa University, Doha, Qatar.*
talansari@hbku.edu.qa

Abstract

The global energy sector is predominated by fossil fuels for the production of electricity and freshwater. This is more pronounced in the Gulf Cooperation Council (GCC) region experiencing fast economic growth driven by major oil and gas infrastructure. Conventional cogeneration systems typically encounter higher operational efficiencies and relatively lower costs compared to renewables-based systems. Their use of fossil fuels as a primary energy source generates high levels of CO_2 emissions resulting in a substandard environmental performance per capita. Renewable energy sources can be integrated into the energy portfolio mix to improve overall resilience and diversification, whilst improving on overall sustainability as environmental emissions are restrained. In this study, an integration of solar and biomass renewable energy into existing energy infrastructure is proposed and analysed using Aspen Plus. The focus is to compare different water and power cogeneration configurations and identify the optimal configuration using MATLAB's optimisation toolbox. A techno-economic assessment is performed to review the effects of renewable energy integration on the overall performance of the grid. The optimal configuration indicate overall levelised costs and emissions approximated at \$0.79 and 184.78 gCO_2e per unit output, respectively, compared to \$2.61 and 350.01 gCO_2e per unit output for the base case. The results demonstrate improvements in the environmental and economic performance. The integration of renewable energy into a portfolio mix offer significant economic and environmental advantages and can be considered a promising and viable option for the provision of water and electricity in the GCC region.

Keywords: Solar, Biomass, Cogeneration, Techno-economic, Portfolio optimisation.

1. Introduction

The Gulf Cooperation Council (GCC) region, like many developing regions in the world, is facing an ever-growing demand for vital services such as electricity and water. This demand is fuelled by rapid economic growth coinciding with population expansion within the local and expatriate communities to meet the monumental development needs of the region. The GCC, which is located in the Arabian desert, is home to some of the largest fossil-fuel reservoirs. However, many areas are vulnerable to severe climate conditions exerting further pressure on essential amenities such as freshwater and energy for space cooling throughout the year. As a result of the vast reserves, fossil fuels dominate the energy sector where utilisation is protected from fuel price volatility through heavy government subsidies. Over-reliance on carbon technologies for power and water production over the last few decades result in fossil fuel-based economies result in large CO_2 emissions per capita metrics for this region (World Bank, 2019). As such, there is an opportunity to explore the integration of renewable energy sources into the energy portfolio mix to reduce these emissions. The GCC nations along with many countries in the global community have supported climate action plans and are signatories to the Kyoto protocol and Paris COP agreement. Initial investment projects in renewable energy began recently in the region (IRENA, 2019), where Abu Dhabi has completed the Shams-1 100 MW CSP project and a 1,177 MW solar PV farm is under construction. A large-scale solar PV facility is underway in Dubai with a capacity exceeding 2,000 MW. The state of Qatar is also embarking on solar energy through its first solar PV project with a planned capacity of 700 MW. Moreover, many other small-to-medium-scale renewable energy projects are either planned or under construction in Saudi Arabia, Kuwait, Oman and Bahrain. However, the adoption of renewable energy induces particular challenges; government subsidies for fossil-fuels and household utility services such as water and electricity; inefficient use of resources especially water, considering the desert climate conditions and the increasingly depleting physical freshwater resources; and lack of a clear and firm government targets/commitments to curb down carbon emissions.

Previous studies evaluated techno-economic metrics of integrated portfolio configurations with regional context. Seawater desalting methods applied to fourteen combined power and desalting plant (CPDP) configurations in Kuwait were analysed by Darwish *et al.* (2009). A techno-economic study was conducted using energy and fuel cost together with GHG emissions. Thermal driven desalination technologies were identified as the most inefficient while the combination of combined-cycle gas turbine (CCGT) and seawater reverse-osmosis (SWRO) proved to be the most economic configurations. Kaya *et al.* (2019) proposed a renewable based energy desalination technology for the emirate of Abu Dhabi to reduce emissions and improve sustainability. A reverse-osmosis plant driven by solar PV was modelled and analysed using levelised cost of water (LCW) methodology. Their results indicate levelised costs of 0.28 $/m^3 for the best case and 0.35 $/m^3 for the most conservative case. The intermittent nature of the solar resource and its implication on total costs outside of a portfolio mix was however neglected. Abdul-Wahab *et al.* (2019) used HOMER to identify the most economic PV system for the Sultanate of Oman. It was estimated that the application of PV technology instead of natural gas or diesel power generation will reduce carbon emissions by 9.7 and 13.1 million kg/year, respectively. The cost of energy was also estimated to witness a reduction to 0.085 $/kWh. Al-Obaidli *et al.* (2019) reviewed several CPDP configurations within the GCC region. A rigorous genetic algorithm optimisation technique was used and an optimal configuration was proposed based on most favourable economic and environmental results. The study made a case supporting renewable energy infusion into existing infrastructure to promote sustainability and resilience. AlNouss *et al.* (2019) compared a blend of biomass feedstock application to produce: methanol, urea, liquid fuels and power. The techno-economic-environmental approach demonstrated that methanol production was the most economic while the urea process resembled the lowest environmental emissions. The study didn't identify biomass integrated gasification combined-cycle (BIGCC) particularly favourable in terms of economic and environmental performance especially in the case of standalone operation outside of an energy portfolio mix. Based on the review above, a limited number of integrated technology options were analysed. The aim of this paper is to evaluate multiple electricity and water cogeneration schemes through a techno-economic evaluation and to identify the optimal portfolio mix which can promote a more sustainable coupled energy and water sector. Four configurations are considered: base reference case; renewable energy integration using 3 renewable energy options; a renewable energy exclusive configuration; and an optimal portfolio mix based on the outcome of the optimisation method.

2. Methodology

Integration of efficient and clean renewable energy sources with fossil-based systems in a portfolio mix is a common approach for achieving sustainability targets. Many integrated configurations are possible to provide the necessary demand targets in a sustainable manner. Due to primary energy resource availability, and environmental and operational considerations, the following five production technologies were selected for this study: CCGT; BIGCC; concentrated solar power (CSP); multi-stage flash (MSF); and SWRO. An integrated model was developed using the listed technologies. The process flow diagram of the model describing the different components of the system and the main inputs and outputs is shown in Figure 1.

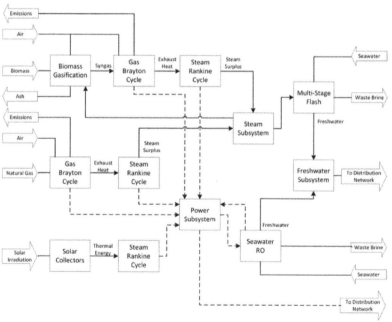

Figure 1. Process flow diagram of the integrated cogeneration system.

The CCGT is the predominant power generation technology in the GCC and in Qatar due to the vast natural gas reserves. It consists of a gas Brayton cycle combined with a steam Rankine cycle to increase the power yield and improve overall energy efficiency. The BIGCC is a renewable energy source based on biomass gasification process which can be used to generate power whilst reducing organic waste. As with the CCGT, it utilises a combined cycle in which syngas, rather than natural gas, is combusted in a gas Brayton cycle and the exhaust heat is used to drive a steam Rankine cycle. The CSP, also, has a great potential for power production due to solar resource availability throughout the year. A parabolic trough collector (PTC) system is used in which the parabolic mirrors concentrate direct irradiation from the Sun into a focal line which coincides with a pipe carrying heat transfer fluid (HTF) which absorbs thermal energy and transports it to the rest of the system. A direct steam Rankine cycle at the end is used to generate power.

MSF is used widely for water desalination in a cogeneration configuration due to availability of surplus steam from the power block. Seawater in the MSF passes through multiple stages of flash drums in which the temperature rises causing seawater to boil. The resultant water vapour is then condensed and collected as freshwater. The process also produces high-salinity seawater brine which is typically diverted to waste disposal. The SWRO is a popular and promising desalination technology due to its improved water recovery ratio and utilisation of high-pressure waste brine to recover energy. Feed seawater passes through a high-pressure pump to a set of special membranes that separate freshwater from salty brines through reverse-osmosis process. The design specifications for the five systems are listed in Table 1. The model is designed under the assumption of stable and ideal economic and operational conditions.

Table 1. Design specifications for production technologies.

Quantity	Value	Quantity	Value
CCGT			
Mass flow (natural gas)	0.5 kg/s	Air-fuel ratio	26.9
High heating value	51.74 MJ/kg	Pressure Ratio (gas)	20
Pressure Ratio (steam)	72.5	Efficiency (isentropic)	90 %
Efficiency (overall)	65 %		
BIGCC			
Mass flow (syngas)	1.1 kg/s	Air-fuel ratio	15
Low heating value	23.72 MJ/kg	Pressure Ratio (gas)	20
Pressure Ratio (steam)	72.5	Efficiency (isentropic)	90 %
Efficiency (overall)	60 %		
CSP			
Absorbed solar irradiation	594 W/m^2	Aperture area	91 m^2
Mass flow (HTF)	10 kg/s	Pressure Ratio (steam)	100
Efficiency (isentropic)	90 %	Efficiency (overall)	18 %
MSF & SWRO			
Mass flow (seawater)	83.3 kg/s	Recovery Ratio (MSF)	12
Salinity (seawater)	30,000 ppm	Recovery Ratio (SWRO)	20
Pressure Ratio (pump)	20	Efficiency (isentropic)	90 %

Key operational design assumptions were made to suit the regional climate conditions such as reference temperature and pressure and solar irradiation. A techno-economic multi-objective-genetic-algorithm (MOGA) method was used to identify the optimal portfolio configuration where two optimisation objectives were envisaged: levelised costs (equivalent to discounted lifecycle costs over lifecycle throughput) and global warming potential (GWP) for each of the five technologies:

$$Minimise \sum_i c_i x_i \qquad (1)$$

$$Minimise \sum_i e x_i \qquad (2)$$

Where, c and e are levelised cost and GWP emission factors per technology, respectively. The optimisation problem was subject to the following constraints:

$$X_{CCGT} + X_{BIGCC} + X_{CSP} = \tag{3}$$

$$X_{MSF} + X_{SWRO} = 1 \tag{4}$$

$$0 \leq x_i \leq 1 \tag{5}$$

3. Results and Discussion

Five generation technologies were selected based on suitability for operations within the region and were modelled in Aspen Plus which is a commonly used process modelling software in academia and industry. The models contained both technical and economic data relevant to each of the technologies. As part of the techno-economic analysis, four power and water cogeneration system configurations were selected for comparison and are presented in Table 2.

Table 2. Power and water cogeneration configurations.

Configuration	Power	Water
0 – Base	1.0 CCGT (100%)	1.0 MSF
1 – All renewables	0.5 BIGCC + 0.5 CSP	1.0 SWRO
2 – All technologies	0.33 CCGT + 0.33 BIGCC + 0.33 CSP	0.5 MSF + 0.5 SWRO
3 – Optimal mix	x CCGT + y BIGCC + z CSP	p MSF + q SWRO

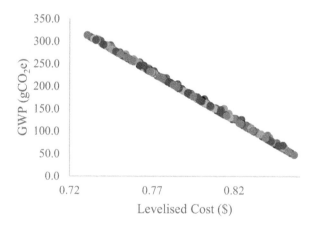

Figure 2. Optimisation function Pareto curves (20 iterations).

Application of the model resulted in levelised costs and GWP factors for each technology and integrated system configuration. A multi-objective genetic algorithm (MOGA) optimisation function in MATLAB was used to compute the optimal cogeneration configuration. In order to improve the reliability of the results, 20 iterations were made and the pareto curve results of the optimisation are presented in Figure 2. Due to the choice of generation technologies and configurations, the apparent linear behaviour of the pareto set indicate that a global optimal configuration is not feasible as normally observed in pareto solutions. However, several configurations that were relatively optimal in comparison to the two extreme points were possible and an optimal configuration was selected from the middle of the pareto set. The optimal configuration predominately consisted of CCGT and CSP for power and SWRO for water. A comparison of total levelised costs and GWP for each scenario is presented in Figure 3. From the results, it is evident that the base configuration is the most suboptimal with the highest cost and the worst environmental performance whereas configuration 2 performed moderately. Configurations 1 and 3 offered the best combination of low-cost and environmental performance, where configuration 3 had a slight advantage in terms of carbon emissions since BIGCC, which emits more CO_2 compared to CCGT, was excluded from the mix by the optimisation algorithm.

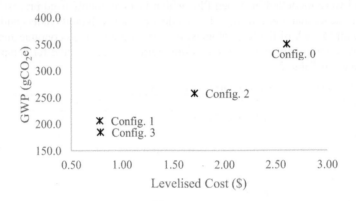

Figure 3. Levelised costs and GWP results for all scenarios.

4. Conclusions

A techno-economic assessment was conducted to evaluate levelised costs and CO_2 emissions from four different electricity and water cogeneration configurations. The configurations represented current installations and future renewable portfolio mixes for the GCC region. An optimisation based on MOGA was applied to identify the optimal cogeneration portfolio configuration. The results show 70 % and 47 % improvement in economic and environmental performance, respectively, for the optimal configuration compared to the base configuration. The integration of renewable energy into the cogeneration portfolio mix proves to deliver substantial benefits to the sector improving overall sustainability.

References

S. Abdul-Wahab, Y. Charabi, A. M. Al-Mahruqi, I. Osman, S. Osman, 2019, Selection of the best solar photovoltaic (PV) for Oman, Sol. Energy, 188, 1156–1168.

A. AlNouss, G. McKay, T. Al-Ansari, 2019, A techno-economic-environmental study evaluating the potential of oxygen-steam biomass gasification for the generation of value-added products, Energy Convers., 196, 664–676.

H. Al-Obaidli, S. Namany, R. Govindan, T. Al-Ansari, 2019, System-Level Optimisation of Combined Power and Desalting Plants, Comput. Aided Chem. Eng., 46, 1699–1704.

M. A. Darwish, N. M. Al-Najem, N. Lior, 2009, Towards Sustainable Desalting in the Gulf Area, Desalination, 235, 58–87.

IRENA, 2019, Renewable Energy Market Analysis: GCC 2019.

A. Kaya, M. E. Tok, M. Koc, 2019, A Levelised Cost Analysis for Solar-Energy-Powered Sea Water Desalination in The Emirate of Abu Dhabi, Sustainability.

World Bank, 2019, CO2 Emissions (metric tons per capita), https://data.worldbank.org.

Sauro Pierucci, Flavio Manenti, Giulia Bozzano, Davide Manca (Eds.)
Proceedings of the 30th European Symposium on Computer Aided Process Engineering
(ESCAPE30), May 24-27, 2020, Milano, Italy. © 2020 Elsevier B.V. All rights reserved.
http://dx.doi.org/10.1016/B978-0-12-823377-1.50241-X

Techno-Economic Assessment of Conceptual Design for Methanol Production Using Coal and Natural Gas Based Parallel Process Configuration

Usama Ahmed[*a], Umer Zahid[a], Nabeel Ahmad[b]

[a]Chemical Engineering Department, King Fahd University of Petroleum and Minerals, Dhahran, Saudi Arabia
[b]Department of Chemical Engineering, COMSATS University Islamabad, Lahore Campus, Pakistan
usama.ahmed@kfupm.edu.sa

Abstract

Methanol production has gained a lot of attention due to its wide application in both the process and product industries. This study aims to investigate the coal/methane based process for simultaneous methanol and power generation. Two process models were developed in Aspen Plus and techno-economically compared. Case 1 is taken as a base case model that represents the coal to methanol (CTM) technology. Case 2 represents the sequential integration between the coal gasification and methane reforming technologies to enhance both the synthesis gas and methanol production capacity. It has been seen from results that case 2 design has a potential to boost up the methanol production compared to the case 1 design. In terms of process performance, the overall process efficiencies for the case 1 and case 2 is calculated as 63.2% and 70.0%, respectively. Moreover, the carbon conversion efficiency for case 2 design is nearly 6% higher than the case 1 design. In terms of methanol production cost, case 1 and case 2 offered 0.25€/kg and 0.23€/kg, respectively. While evaluating other process performance and environmental quality control indicators, it has been analysed from results that case 2 offers higher process feasibility compared to the case 1 design.

Keywords: Gasification, Reforming, Methanol Synthesis, Synthesis Gas.

1. Introduction

During the last many decades, fossil fuels remained the main source of energy and power generation that not only increased the greenhouse gas emissions to unsafe levels but also caused global warming. The damaged caused by fossil fuels to environment especially by the coal based systems can be minimized using an alternative energy conversion technologies. The conventional routes of producing the methanol from fossil fuel includes two stages. In the first stage, the synthesis gas is generated from fuel which is then cleaned prior to its conversion into methanol. Natural gas to methanol (NGTM) technology has been extensive utilized around the world to meet the methanol production and supply demand. The synthesis gas can be efficiently converted to methanol if the HCR (hydrogen to carbon) ratio in the synthesis gas is between 2-2.05. Usually, steam methane reforming (SMR) technology is used to generate synthesis gas from natural gas which offers higher HCR in the synthesis gas. On the other hand, coal to methanol (CTM) converts the coal into synthesis gas by the gasification technologies. The synthesis gas generated from the coal has a lower value HCR and contains more CO_2 and CO. The synthesis gas from the coal gasification process is usually integrated with the water gas shift (WGS) reactors to convert the CO in the synthesis gas to H_2 on reaction with the H_2O. Yi et al. (2015) reported that CTM technologies produces 2.6 ton of CO_2 for each ton of methanol (MeOH) production, whereas, SMR technologies offers higher HCR ratio in the synthesis gas and shows very less CO_2 emissions. Comparing the current prices and reserves of natural gas and coal, the opportunities to develop the dual fuel conversion technologies have gained a lot of attention. The SMR and coal derived synthesis gas can be mixed to regulate the higher HCR ratio at the inlet of methanol synthesis reactor. Recently, Blumberg et al. (2019) integrated the different methane reforming technologies for enhancing the H_2 production, which offers higher exergetic efficiency for methanol synthesis. Ahmed et al. (2017, 2019) also showed an improvement in the power and H_2 production by integrating the gasification and reforming technologies in the series design configuration. Similarly, Kler et al. (2018) proposed a model for simultaneous production of methanol and electricity from coal. Chen et al. (2019) developed a model using multiple feed-stocks for MeOH synthesis while reducing the CO_2 emissions. In this study, coal and natural gas feed-stocks are used for the MeOH synthesis and electricity production by using the parallel design integrations between the gasification and reforming technologies. The key idea of this research is to utilize the heat energy from the gasification unit into the reforming unit to sustain the high enthalpy SMR reactions. This integration not only reduces the overall process energy requirements but also enhances the syngas production with the higher HCR ratio. The focus of this research article is to perform the techno-economic analysis of the proposed design and its comparison with the conventional processes.

2. Process Simulation and Methodology

The process models were developed in Aspen Plus v10 where Peng Robinson with Boston Mathias equation of state is selected as an effective thermodynamic package. Coal is usually considered as an unconventional component and its composition is defined in terms of key components through Proximate, ultimate and sulfanal analysis. RGibbs reactor model is selected for the modelling of gasification, water gas shift, reforming and methanol synthesis reactor which generates the reaction products on the principle of Gibbs free energy minimization. Table 1 highlights some of the design assumptions for the design of major unit processes.

Table 1: Design Assumptions for Model Development

Unit/Component/System	Modelling Unit	Parameter
Gasification Reactor	RGibbs (Reactor)	Coal flow rate= 62.01kg/s Temp/Press: 1350-1370°C/56 bar
Reformer	RGibbs (Reactor)	NG flow rate: 5.5 kg/sec $H_2O:CH_4 = 3:1$ Temp/Press: 900°C/ 32 bar
Air Separation Unit (ASU)	HeatX, Compr	Oxygen Purity 95% (vol)
Methnanol Reactor	RGibbs (Reactor)	Cu based catalyst Pressure/Temp: 55bar/200°C

2.1. Case 1- Conventional Coal to Methanol (CTM) Process

Case 1 is considered as a conventional CTM where coal water slurry is fed to the coal gasification unit at 56bar, which is partially oxidized to generate synthesis gas at the temperature of 1370°C. The synthesis gas is then cooled in the radiant and convective heat exchangers followed by H_2S removal. The sulphur free synthesis gas is then passed over the Cu based catalyst in the methanol reactor at the standard temperature and pressure of 200°C and 55 bar. Figure 1 represents the conventional methanol production process from coal. Finally, series of flash drums and distillation columns are sequentially used in the downstream process chain to enhance the purity of methanol in the product stream to 99%.

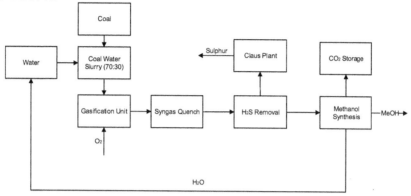

Figure 1: Coal to Methanol (CTM) Process

2.2. Case 2- Coal and Natural Gas based Process for Methanol Production (CNPM)

Case 2 is considered as a conceptual design where coal and natural gas feed-stocks are used for methanol synthesis as represented in Figure 2. The coal gasifier derived synthesis gas usually contains high amounts of sulphur which must be removed in the H_2S removal section prior to its mixing with the reformed natural gas. The temperature and pressure of the syngas at the inlet of the methanol reactor is also maintained at 200°C and 55 bar, respectively, as done in the case 1 design. This parallel design configuration of integrating the gasification unit with the reforming unit not only reduces the process energy requirements but also helps in increasing the overall methanol production.

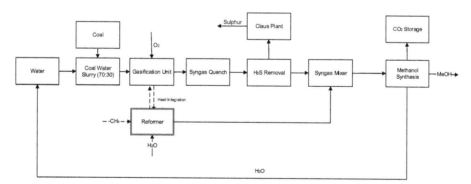

Figure 2: Coal and Natural Gas based Methanol Production Process

3. Results and Discussion

Case 1 was modelled as the conventional CTM process where cold gas efficiency (CGE) of the syngas is based on the gasifier operational conditions, type of feed and the heat integration network. The case 1 design is then retrofitted with the SMR technology to generate the case 2 design to utilize the key technical benefits of both the gasification and reforming technologies. This retrofitting of SMR unit in the parallel design configuration not only allowed to utilize the high enthalpy heat from the gasifier derived synthesis gas but also helps in increasing the HCR ratio at the inlet of the methanol reactor. In both the cases, 62.19kg/s of the bituminous coal has been used as a feedstock for the gasification unit. Unlike case 1, the case 2 design consumes an additional natural gas at the rate of 5.5kg/s in the reforming unit. The coal to natural gas ratio of 5.5:1 is maintained in the case 2 design to utilize maximum heat from the gasification unit for the reforming of natural gas without any additional heat supply. The results showed that there is a signification increase in syngas production capacity in the case 2 design compared to the case 1. The HCR (hydrogen to carbon ratio) obtained in the case 2 design is also higher than case 1 design. Figure 3 shows the synthesis gas composition at the inlet of methanol reactor for case 1 and case 2 designs.

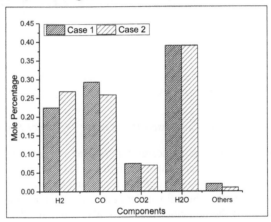

Figure 3: Synthesis gas composition at the inlet of Methanol Reactor

To ensure the unbiased analysis, the process performance indictor for calculating the overall process efficiency has been used as given in the equation 1. The overall energy efficiency is a function of heat input rates in the form of thermal energy and the heating value of the produced methanol along with the power generation potential for each case.

$$\text{Energy Efficiency} = \frac{\text{Produced electricity} + \text{Heat of Produced MeOH}}{\text{Feed stock heating value} + \text{Energy Consumed}} \, [\%] \tag{1}$$

The results showed that the process efficiency calculated for case 1 and case 2 is 63% and 70%, respectively. The heat generated from both the cases has been utilized for electricity generation using steam turbine cycle. The results showed that the electricity generation potential from the case 1 and case 2 is calculated as 11.26MW$_e$ and 16.70MW$_e$, respectively. Methanol production capacity and energy requirement from a specific fuel is also an important criterion to analyze the process technical and economic feasibility. The difference in the process configuration and the heat exchanger network highly effects the overall production capacity. The simulation results showed that the methanol production capacity from case 1 and case 2 is calculated as 171 MT/hr and 212 MT/hr, respectively, where the case 2 design shows 24% higher methanol production capacity compared to case 1. Figure 4 also represents the comparison between two cases in terms of process efficiency (%), methanol production energy (kg/kW$_e$) and methanol production

Techno-Economic Assessment of Conceptual Design for Methanol Production
Using Coal and Natural Gas Based Parallel Process Configuration.

1445

capacity (ton/hr). The results showed that the the specific methanol production for case 1 and case 2 is calculated as 0.7 kg/watt and 0.8 kg/watt, respectively.

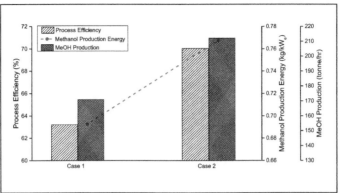

Figure 4: Comparison of Methanol Production Rates and Energy for Case 1 and Case 2

The estimation of capital (CAPEX) and operational (OPEX) expenditures are important factors to analyze the sustainability of any chemical process. The fixed CAPEX includes the cost of equipment, cost of land, installation costs etc. The OPEX involve the cost of feedstocks, catalysts and the utilities. The CAPEX for both the cases is calculated using the power law of capacity as shown in the equation 2, where, x represents the capacity factor which is taken as 0.6 in this research.

$$\text{Cost}_{\text{New}} = \text{Cost}_{\text{Old}} \times \left(\frac{\text{Capacity}_{\text{New}}}{\text{Capacity}_{\text{Old}}}\right)^{X} \times \frac{\text{CEPCI}_{\text{New}}}{\text{CEPCI}_{\text{Old}}} \tag{2}$$

The results showed that the CAPEX required for case 1 and case 2 is 2594.89M€ and 2895.06M€, respectively. Similarly, the OPEX calculated on the yearly basis for case 1 and case 2 is calculated as 190M€ and 225M€, respectively. Despite the higher value of the overall OEPX and CAPEX for case 2 design, the per unit cost for methanol production is lower than the case 1 due to its higher methanol production capacity. In terms of specific cost for methanol production, case 1 and case 2 offers nearly 275.2 €/ton and 258.4 €/ton, respectively. In terms of cash flow analysis throughout the lifetime of the project, the minimum payback time of the project and the expected profit has been also calculated.

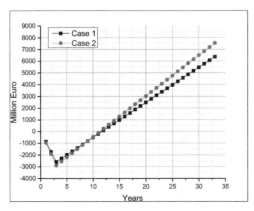

Figure 5: Cumulative cash flow for Case 1 and Case 2

Figure 5 represents the cumulative cash flow analysis for both case 1 and case 2 design where the life time of the project is assumed to be 33 years. It has been analyzed from the results that the payback time for both the case 1 and case 2 is calculated as 11 years, where the case 2 design showed a higher profit potential of 2600-2700M€ as compared to the case 1 design throughout the life time of the project.

4. Conclusion

This paper represents the techno-economic analysis of two processes for methanol production. Case 1 is taken as a conventional coal to methanol (CTM) processes, whereas, case 2 represent the conceptual design of integrating of the reforming unit with the gasification unit to utilize the maximum heat to sustain the reforming reactions. It has been analyzed from the results that the case 2 design offers higher process performance and economics compared to the case 1 design in terms of methanol production. Case 2 design not only represents higher methanol production rates but also showed a reduction in the per unit production energy requirements. Moreover, case 2 design offers higher rate of return on the investments, which makes its design more sustainable compared to the conventional process.

Acknowledgement

The authors would like to acknowledge the support provided by the King Fahd University of Petroleum & Minerals (KFUPM) for funding this work through project No. SR181006.

References

Ahmed U, Zahid U, Lee Y. Process simulation and integration of IGCC systems for H_2/syngas/electricity generation with control on CO_2 emissions. International Journal of Hydrogen Energy. 2019;44(14):7137-48.

Ahmed U, Kim C, Zahid U, Lee C-J, Han C. Integration of IGCC and methane reforming process for power generation with CO_2 capture. Chemical Engineering and Processing: Process Intensification. 2017;111:14-24.

Blumberg T, Morosuk T, Tsatsaronis G. CO_2-utilization in the synthesis of methanol: Potential analysis and exergetic assessment. Energy. 2019.

Chen J, Yang S, Qian Y. A novel path for carbon-rich resource utilization with lower emission and higher efficiency: An integrated process of coal gasification and coking to methanol production. Energy. 2019;177:304-18.

Kler AM, Tyurina EA, Mednikov AS. A plant for methanol and electricity production: Technical-economic analysis. Energy. 2018;165:890-9.

Yi Q, Li W, Feng J, Xie K. Carbon cycle in advanced coal chemical engineering. Chemical Society Reviews. 2015;44(15):5409-45.

Sauro Pierucci, Flavio Manenti, Giulia Bozzano, Davide Manca (Eds.)
Proceedings of the 30th European Symposium on Computer Aided Process Engineering
(ESCAPE30), May 24-27, 2020, Milano, Italy. © 2020 Elsevier B.V. All rights reserved.
http://dx.doi.org/10.1016/B978-0-12-823377-1.50242-1

Sustainable Exergoeconomic Optimization of Petroleum Production Systems

Meziane Akchiche[a,b], Jean-Louis Beauquin[a], Sabine Sochard[b], Sylvain Serra[b], Jean-Michel Reneaume[b], Pascal Stouffs[b]

[a]*Production & Well Performance Department, TOTAL SA, France*
[b]*Universite de Pau et des Pays de l'Adour, E2S UPPA, LaTEP, 64000, Pau, France*
meziane.akchiche@univ-pau.fr

Abstract

This paper presents a new methodology to improve the conception of petroleum production systems by incorporating environmental perspectives, in addition to energy and economic aspects, over their entire life-cycle. We first proposed generic oil production system configurations that include the most common technologies. In this work, two objective functions are suggested to evaluate the performance of an oil production system, which can be operated by different equipment during its whole life-cycle: i) Cumulative Net Exergy (CNE), ii) Cumulative Net Profit (CNP). In this dynamic optimization problem, considering that optimization variables may be continuous, binary, or discrete, that most of the production systems have a non-linear response and that the imposed constraints make the problems non-convex, we are usually dealing with Mixed Integer Non-Convex Non-Linear Optimization Problems (MINLP). The stated problem is then solved using a multiphase flow simulator, coupled with a thermodynamics calculator for the exergy analysis. The Genetic Algorithm included within the chosen software is then used to solve the multiperiod MINLP problem. The optimization results show that for a non-eruptive oil well, the most energy-efficient artificial lift and boosting methods are not always the most cost-effective. It therefore appears that it is necessary to combine exergy and economics (exergoeconomics) for the optimization purposes at the level of petroleum production system components for designing sustainable systems.

Keywords: Oil & Gas production system, Exergy, MINLP, Superstructure, Optimization

1. Introduction

In accordance with the International Energy Agency (IEA, 2018), fossil fuels will remain relevant to the energy system for decades. In 2018, global oil supply exceeded 100 million barrels per day for the first time, and world natural gas demand increased by 4.9 percent compared to 2017 (IEA, 2018). The growing need for hydrocarbons is driving petroleum exploitation to cross new borders: technical borders, economic borders, and also environmental borders. Oil and gas companies are increasingly going after deep and/or complex petroleum reservoirs to meet hydrocarbon demand. Developing these fields requires the construction of more elaborate production systems and the implementation of fluid and power processing, transportation, and delivery systems. Also, power generation is a high source of greenhouse gas (GHG) emissions. Therefore, the main challenge for oil and gas companies is to select the most economically viable and, at the same time, the least GHG emitting development scheme.

Fig.1 illustrates a typical oil production profile that we can split into three distinct periods. First, the start-up period corresponds to the extent of time during which producing wells are sequentially brought into production. Then, the plateau period begins when the full installed capacity is used, and a constant production rate is maintained by using a choke valve. This production restriction is imposed by technical and economic criteria, while the real production potential may be

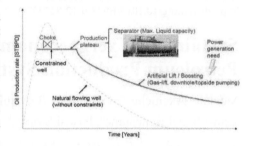

Fig.1 : Oil production profile

more significant. Finally, the decline period refers to the time when producing wells, and more generally, the overall field production falls at a rate of 1% to 10% per year.

Fig 2 shows some of the most common configurations of oil production systems. As long as the natural energy of a reservoir (P_{Res}, T_{Res}) is sufficient to achieve the production plateau, fluids flow naturally from the reservoir to surface facilities (Fig.2a) and may be restrained by a choke valve (THC). When this natural energy is not or no longer sufficient to maintain production due, for example, to reservoir depletion over time, it becomes necessary to provide an external energy boost by using artificial lift and boosting equipment. Fig.2b depicts an oil production system equipped with gas-lift. The pressurized gas injection lightens the gradient in the tubing resulting in a lower Bottom Hole Pressure (P_{BH}) that increases the liquid production rate (G. Takacs, 2005). Fig.2c and Fig.2d show two different downhole pumping technologies. The first one is an Electrical Submersible Pump (ESP) that is made of centrifugal pump stages (G.Takacs, 2009), while the second one called Electrical Submersible Progressing Cavity Pump (ESPCP) is a positive displacement pump (H. Cholet et al., 2012). These two pumping technologies can be equipped with a separator or not, depending on the nature of the produced effluents. In addition to the downhole artificial lift technologies, it is also possible to use surface artificial lift methods, such as, for example, Progressive cavity pumping (PCP) systems.

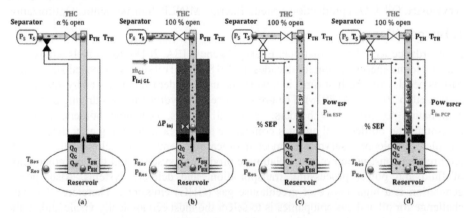

Figure 2. Oil Production system models

2. Methodology

2.1. Objective functions

We want to evaluate the influence of selecting two different objective functions on the whole life-cycle of an oil production system. The first objective function is a Cumulative Net Profit (CNP) to be maximized, while the second one is a Cumulative Net Exergy (CNE) to be also maximized. The objective functions are defined as follows:

$$F_1 = CNP\,[MM\$] = CHS - CBE \tag{1}$$
$$F_2 = CNE[GWh] = Ex_{oil+gas}^{ch} - Ex_{inv}^{ch} \tag{2}$$

Where CHS [MM\$] is the Cumulative Hydrocarbon Sales, CBE [MM\$] is the Cumulative Boosting Expenses (CAPEX + OPEX), $Ex_{oil+gas}^{ch}$ [GWh] is the cumulative chemical exergy of produced hydrocarbons, Ex_{inv}^{ch} [GWh] is the cumulative exergy invested (as an example, the artificial power generation). The CBE term includes the costs of switching from one technology to another between two periods. The different changes in reservoir conditions and fluid properties over time require more flexible petroleum production systems. Fig.3 shows the evolution of the petroleum production system during different time steps.

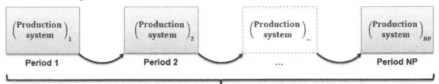

Figure 3. Optimization of the objective functions over all periods

Fig.4 shows the superstructure of alternative configurations of the oil production system that includes all the artificial lift and boosting methods mentioned in Fig.2. At each period, topological variables will be used to select a production system among all the possible topologies offered by the superstructure. For example, a possible configuration is to have an ESP pump equipped with a downhole separator at the subsurface level and no boosting method at the surface level (ESP + D-SEP + Natural F).

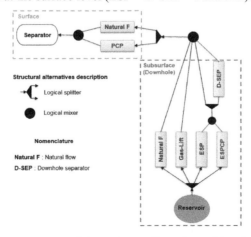

Figure 4. The superstructure of alternative configurations of the oil production system

2.2. Resolution strategy

Usually, we model each part of the petroleum production system within the dedicated tools to catch the complexity of the physical-chemical phenomena involved at each step of the production chain. These specialized tools that model the different parts of the field can, therefore, be connected and exchange data dynamically to implement a full field model. This combined architecture is called Integrated Production Modeling (IPM). In this study, the Petex IPM suite of tools (MBAL®, PROSPER®, GAP®, RESOLVE®) was used to model and optimize the entire production system (Petex, 2019). The nodal analysis of petroleum production systems is the method used within the IPM suite to evaluate the flow performance of the oil production system for a given configuration and design parameters as well as a set of steady-state operating parameters. The production system is split into several discrete nodes that separate the system components. Flow correlations and thermal models are then used to calculate pressure, flow rates, and temperature at each node. A Black oil method and an enthalpy balance temperature model were used to describe the fluid flow through the entire oil production system.

RESOLVE® is the platform that brings together external applications, such as, for example EXCEL, in addition to including multiple optimization modules. Exergy calculations were carried out with Simulis thermodynamics® that is available as a Microsoft Excel® add-in (ProSim, 2019). The same Excel model was used for economic calculations. We have then formulated the MINLP problem using the optimization module (GIRO) at the RESOLVE® level, allowing to have GAP®, MBAL®, and EXCEL as underlying applications. GIRO is based on Genetic Algorithm (GA) principles and does not allow using continuous variables, nor does it handle constraints. To solve the formulated problem with the GIRO algorithm, we have discretized (in the sense of encoding) the continuous variables and developed a workflow to meet the constraints. The methodology described in Fig.5 was used to solve the formulated MINLP problem.

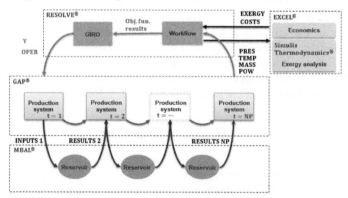

Figure5. Workflow for formulation and solution of dynamic MINLP problem

At each GIRO iteration, topological and operating variables are provided. For each period, the knowledge of the chosen technology (linked to topological variables **Y**) and the operating variables (**OPER** in Fig.5 and variables in blue in Fig.2), together with (P_{Res}, T_{Res}) and P_S (in red in Fig.2) enable GAP® to calculate, in quasi-static state, the produced flow rates (oil, gas, and water), temperatures, and pressures for all the nodes (in black in Fig.2). P_S is the fixed pressure of the surface facilities' first separator. At the end of the period, these results are provided to MBAL®, which calculates the new reservoir conditions. At the end of this calculation sequence, all the temperatures, pressures, and mass flow rates at each node for each period are sent back to RESOLVE® level. The workflow checks the constraints (maximum production, open choke valve if an artificial lift method is used, etc.): if a constraint is not met, the objective function of this iteration is not considered. Then, the excel model calculates economics and exergy functions, and the results are sent to the workflow, which estimates the objective function.

3. Results & discussion

The studied case is based on a realistic reservoir model. The separator pressure (P_s) was fixed to 30 bars for all cases, and the maximum production constraint (Qmax) set at 5000 STBPD. Table 1 shows the results of the optimized objective functions. The whole period is 12 years, simulated with quasi-static approximation with periods of 6 months.

Table 1: optimization results

Objective function	Cumulative Net profits (CNP) MM$	Cumulative Net Exergy (CNE) Gwh	Cumulative production MMSTB[1]	CO2 emissions kt	Topologic variables Y
Max. Cumulative Net Profit (CNP)*	613*	19594	12.4	9.8	Natural F + GL
Max. Cumulative Net Exergy (CNE)**	610	19947**	12.6	6.7	Natural F + ESP

[1] MMSTB: Millions Standard (1bar, 60°F) Barrels

In both cases of maximizing the CNP or the CNE, the oil production system is first producing naturally (Natural Flow) while respecting the maximum production constraint. After some time, water progressively gains access to the producing well at the expense of hydrocarbons and increases the weight of the fluid column (density). Therefore, the total liquid flow decreases, and an artificial lift or boosting system is needed to maintain production and prevent the well shutdown.

When the CNP was maximized, the optimizer has selected the gas-lift system as it ensures to maintain the liquid production rate as high as possible while being less expensive than an ESP that produces the same flow rate. On the other side, when it is a matter of improving energy efficiency by maximizing the CNE, an ESP is selected. It is not only due to increased cumulative chemical exergy of produced hydrocarbons, but also because Gas-lift systems are high energy consumers. However, it can be pointed out that a decrease of 0.5% in CNP leads to an increase of 1.8% in CNE but, above all, a reduction of about 32% in CO_2 emissions. From the two objective functions point of view, the optimum solution may be a compromise.

4. Conclusion & perspectives

Due to their high pressure (P_{Res}), petroleum reservoirs give the essential part of the energy required to extract and transport hydrocarbons to surface facilities. Once this pressure is not sufficient to overcome the sum of pressure losses occurring along the flow path to the separator, artificial lifting and boosting methods are used to provide the additional mechanical exergy. The cost (OPEX+ CAPEX), as well as the GHG emissions of these methods, are directly linked to the mechanical exergy to be delivered to the fluid vein and the overall performance of the artificial lifting and boosting systems.

In the present work, we succeeded in solving a dynamic optimization problem to select suitable technologies over the life cycle of an oil production system. To our knowledge, it is the first study of this kind. It has been done in the IPM suite of tools used by many petroleum companies. The objective functions were economic and exergy functions. The exergy analysis by itself does not make it possible to choose the most suitable production system as it does not include the economic aspect. The most important criterion to select a suitable development scheme is the economic viability of the development.

On the other hand, the cheapest technologies are not always the most energy-efficient (ex. Gas-lift). It may be interesting to formulate a multiobjective optimization problem taking into consideration both economics and energy efficiency (via exergy analysis). Moreover, it appears essential to add, within the superstructure, technologies that reduce exergy losses and, above all, that recover some of the lost exergies to reduce the power needed by the production facilities, and therefore, reduce GHG emissions.

Nomenclature

Variables		Vectors*	
$\dot{m}$	mass rate	**COSTS**	Cost results
P	pressure	**EXERGY**	Exergy results
Pow	Power	**PRES**	Node pressures
T	Temperature	**TEMP**	Node temperatures
THC	Tubing Head Choke	**MASS**	Node mass flow rates
ΔP	Pressure drop	**POW**	Equipment powers
%SEP	Separation percentage	**Y**	Topological variables
Subscript		**OPER**	Operating variables
GL	Gas-Lift	**INPUTS**	Input variables
inj	injection	**RESULTS**	Results
Res	Reservoir		
s	separator	* these vectors include, for each iteration, all the variables of	
TH	Tubing Head	interest over all the periods	

References

G. Takacs, 2005, Gas Lift Manual, PennWell Books

G. Takacs, 2009, Electrical Submersible Pumps Manual Design, Operations, and Maintenance, Gulf Professional Publishing

H. Cholet et al., 2012, Progressing Cavity Pumps, Technip

IEA, 2018, Global Energy & CO2 Status Report

IEA, 2018, Energy Technology Perspectives

Petex. (2019, Novembre). Integrated Production Modelling Software for Oil and Gas Fields. Récupéré sur Petroleum Experts Oil, Gas, Structural Geology Software: http://www.petex.com/products/ipm-suite/

ProSim. (2019, November). Simulis Thermodynamics - Mixture properties and fluid phase equilibria calculations. Récupéré sur PROSIM: chemical process simulation software and services: http://www.prosim.net/fr/logiciels-simulis-thermodynamics-calculs-proprietes-melanges-dequilibres-entre-phases--3.php

Sauro Pierucci, Flavio Manenti, Giulia Bozzano, Davide Manca (Eds.)
Proceedings of the 30th European Symposium on Computer Aided Process Engineering
(ESCAPE30), May 24-27, 2020, Milano, Italy. © 2020 Elsevier B.V. All rights reserved.
http://dx.doi.org/10.1016/B978-0-12-823377-1.50243-3

Power-to-Methanol at Refineries as a Precursor to Green Jet Fuel Production: a Simulation and Assessment Study

Timo Wassermann [a,*], Christian Schnuelle [a], Philipp Kenkel [a], Edwin Zondervan [b]

[a] *University of Bremen, Advanced Energy Systems Institute, Enrique-Schmidt-Straße 7, 28359 Bremen, Germany*
[b] *University of Bremen, Advanced Energy Systems Institute, Leobener Straße 6, 28359 Bremen, Germany*
timo.wassermann@uni-bremen.de

Abstract

The growing interest in power-to-methanol (PtM) in policy, industry and academia illustrates the need for studies assessing the concept's potential in the context of energy transition. Although there are already studies, which evaluate PtM in a generic way, application-specific analyzes for refineries considering the option of further jet fuel synthesis are lacking. This study provides a unique assessment of the techno-economic feasibility and the environmental impacts of PtM plants at refineries as a precursor to green jet fuel production. The utilization of the flue gas of a single refinery, the Heide refinery, is sufficient for the production of 415,095 t_{MeOH}/y. As methanol production via PtM avoids 2.50 kg_{CO2eq}/kg compared to conventional methanol, it is favorable in terms of greenhouse gas emissions. However, net production costs are 2.9-4.6 times higher than the market price. Subsequent jet fuel synthesis allows a production of at least 83 kt_{Jet}/y on basis of the refinery's flue gas.

Keywords: CO_2 utilization, power-to-methanol, jet fuel, refinery

1. Introduction

Ongoing climate change is one of the most urgent socio-ecological problems as well as one of the most demanding socio-techno-economic challenges confronting humanity. To face this problem, Germany declared to reduce greenhouse gas (GHG) emissions by 80-95 % until 2050 compared to 1990 levels (BMU, 2016). In this context, substitution of conventional chemicals and fuels by synthetic electricity-based products seems to be a viable alternative, as it allows an extensive reduction of GHG emissions. A prominent option is the production of synthetic methanol. Such methanol is identical in chemical structure and composition to its conventional counterpart and can be utilized as chemical feedstock, as fuel or for synthesis of drop-in fuels (Bertau et al., 2014). Conventional crude oil refineries could serve as breeding hub for the realization of commercial PtM plants. They are experienced in the processing of hydrocarbons and their flue gas streams have significant carbon capture potential. In addition, refinery operators in Germany are facing increasingly restrictive emission regulations that require a realignment towards renewable products, e.g. electricity-based methanol and derived drop-in jet fuel.

2. Case study

The state of Schleswig-Holstein, Germany, with its significant on- and offshore wind energy potential is particularly suited as model region for power-to-liquid plants (Flachsbarth and Kasten, 2017). Within this work, the Heide refinery is studied as specific site for a PtM plant. The flue gases emitted by its in-house combined heat and power (CHP) plant, catalytic reformer and steam cracker are considered as CO_2 point source and limiting factor for the PtM plant's production capacity. These facilities are responsible for about 70 % of the refinery's CO_2 emissions. The main properties of the merged flue gas stream are listed in Table 1, neglecting trace components like NO_X and SO_X.

Table 1: Mass flow and composition of the merged flue gas stream based on Finnern (2019)

Facilities	$\dot{m}_{Flue\ gas}$ [t/h]	w_{CO2} [wt%]	w_{H2O} [wt%]	w_{O2} [wt%]	w_{N2} [wt%]
CHP plant, catalytic reformer and steam cracker	570.1	13.9	8.8	4.1	73.2

3. Methodology

Rigorous techno-economic analysis (TEA) and life-cycle assessment (LCA) are conducted based on process modeling and simulation using Aspen Plus V11. The technologies considered are primarily selected according to their maturity level: Alkaline electrolysis (TRL 9), CO_2 extraction via absorption with monoethanolamine (TRL 9) and methanol synthesis via direct CO_2 hydrogenation (TRL 8).

3.1. Process concept: alkaline electrolysis
Alkaline electrolysis (AEL) is represented by literature data. An efficiency of 4.8 kWh/Nm^3_{H2} is assumed at the electrolyzer-system level, i.e. including periphery (Buttler and Spliethoff, 2018). Hydrogen is provided to the methanol unit with a purity of 99.9 vol%, at a pressure of 30 bar and at 25 °C.

3.2. Process concept and modeling: carbon capture
The modeled carbon capture concept via MEA scrubbing builds on the work disseminated by Nguyen and Zondervan (2018). Flow-sheet modifications have been implemented, which include a relocation of the flue gas blower as well as the integration of two recycle/inter-cooling streams within the absorber column (Figure 1). These modifications are primarily based on findings at the Niederaussem pilot plant (Schmidt, 2014).

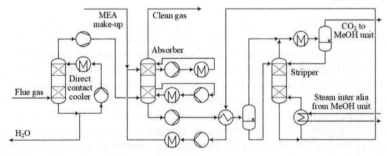

Figure 1: PFD carbon capture unit

A rigorous rate-based model of the carbon capture process is developed using FLEXIPAC 250Y as structured packing. The unsymmetrical electrolyte NRTL property method (ENRTL-RK) is applied as thermodynamic model, while the electrolyte solution chemistry of the MEA-CO_2-H_2O system is modeled considering equilibrium and kinetic reactions. The respective equilibrium constants are calculated from Gibbs-free energy and power law equation is applied for calculation of the reaction rates (Li et al., 2016). The model is calibrated for 90 % capture efficiency and the characteristics of the captured CO_2 stream (T=40 °C, p=1.75 bar, w_{CO2}=95.7 wt%) are used for methanol synthesis modeling.

3.3. Process concept and modeling: methanol synthesis

Methanol synthesis is considered via the direct CO_2 hydrogenation process concept proposed by Bongartz et al. (2019) (Figure 2). AA-grade methanol is produced at a reaction pressure of 70 bar, a reaction temperature of 250° C, a molar H_2:CO_2 ratio of 3.0 and application of commercial $Cu/ZnO/Al_2O_3$ catalyst. An isothermal fixed bed reactor is modeled as a plug flow reactor using kinetics of Van-Dal and Bouallou (2013). NRTL is considered as thermodynamic model for units operating below 10 bar, while the Redlich-Kwong-Soave equation of state with modified Huron-Vidal mixing rules is applied for units operating above 10 bar. It is noted, that one percent of the recycle stream is purged to prevent accumulation of inert gases. The combustion of the purge stream together with heat from the exothermic methanol synthesis is used for steam generation, with the steam being integrated in the carbon capture unit's stripper.

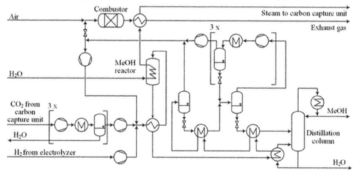

Figure 2: PFD methanol synthesis unit adopted from Bongartz et al. (2019)

3.4. Techno-economic analysis

The TEA is carried out according to a standard methodology proposed by Peters et al. (2003). It yields the net production costs (NPC), defined as the ratio of the total annualized costs of production (TAC) by the annual product output. Table 2 lists the main assumptions for the TEA. The CAPEX are based on the component's specific acquisition costs (C_i). For the carbon capture and the methanol unit Aspen Economic Analyzer is applied for generation of C_i, while a value of 500 €/kW_{el} is assumed for the AEL (IEA, 2019). A ratio factor is applied to take account of further capital requirements, i.e. to calculate the total capital investment. For the electrolysis unit, a decreased ratio factor is sufficient as it is not a thermo-chemical (TC) but an electro-chemical process (EC), being delivered as skid-mounted unit.

Table 2: Basic assumptions of the TEA

Parameter	Value	Unit	Parameter	Value	Unit
Year of comparison	2018	-	Catalyst	95.24	€/kg
Plant lifetime	25	y	MEA	1,450.00	€/t
Plant availability	8,260	h/y	Deionized water	1.00	€/t
Interest rate	5	%	Cooling water	0.00125	€/t
Ratio factor	EC: 1.81, TC: 5.93	-	Waste water	0.40	€/t
Electricity	87.00	€/MWh	Oxygen	26.30	€/t
Medium pressure steam	55.00	€/MWh	CO_2 certificate	24.00	€/t

3.5. Life-cycle assessment

LCA is conducted by application of openLCA V1.8 software for modeling and calculating, while ecoinvent V3.3 database is used in background processes. A comparison of the global warming potential of conventionally produced methanol from natural gas with methanol based on renewable electricity is intended. The system boundaries are defined according to the cradle-to-gate approach, the production of 1 kg methanol is considered as functional unit and CML 2001 is taken as impact assessment method.

The life cycle inventory data builds on the generated mass- and energy balance and takes account of plant construction. The CO_2 provision processes, i.e. the refinery facilities, are not taken into account, as the uncaptured CO_2 is classified as waste. Thus, the environmental impacts of the conventional refinery process are not affected.

4. Results and discussion

4.1. Power-to-methanol

Utilization of the refinery's flue gas output results in a synthetic methanol production capacity of 415,095 t_{MeOH}/y. This corresponds to 0.1 tons of synthetic methanol per ton of crude oil processed and equals 22 % of German methanol production. The energy requirements of the PtM process as well as its mass in- and outputs are shown in Table 3. The steam generated in the methanol unit covers 27.0 % of the heat demand of the stripper of the carbon capture unit and thus improves the efficiency of the overall process. The energy conversion efficiency of the process is 46.4 % based on the lower heating value of methanol. In terms of energy input, the electrical power demand is most significant. It corresponds to a rated power supply of 531 MW_{el} for electrolysis and 545 MW_{el} for the overall process, being in the order of magnitude of a typical German offshore wind farm's nominal load.

Table 3: Energy, utilities and outputs of the integrated PtM process

Stream	Energy MJ/kg$_{MeOH}$	Stream	Mass kg/kg$_{MeOH}$	Stream	Mass kg/kg$_{MeOH}$
Electricity	39.07	Deionized water	1.98	Waste water	-0.57
Medium pressure steam	3.77	Cooling water	136.19	Oxygen	-1.57
		Flue gas	11.34	Exhaust	-0.50
		MEA	2.13E-03		

The net production costs are 1,146 €/t_{MeOH}. This corresponds to a ratio of 2.9-4.6 to the price of conventional methanol in the European market, considering its price level in the last 8 years (Methanex, 2019). Based on the bare acquisition costs of 265.5 M€ for the electrolyzer, 14.7 M€ for the CO_2 capture unit and 26.1 M€ for the methanol unit, the plant's total capital investment is 723.3 M€, including 15 % working capital. A breakdown of the TAC is shown in Figure 4. 88 % of the TAC can be attributed to the electrolyzer unit. These costs are in turn primarily attributable to electricity purchase, while electricity accounts for 82 % of the TAC at the overall process level.

Sensitivity of the NPC on the electricity price is shown in Figure 5, while its sensitivity on full load hours (FLH) is displayed in Figure 6. At electricity purchase costs of about 2 ct/kWh, while keeping the other assumptions constant, electricity-based methanol actually becomes competitive. However, since OPEX are dominant, reduction of the FLH has rather small effect on the NPC. When adjusting the TEA assumptions for direct power purchase from an offshore wind farm (FLH: 4,500 h/y), the product output decreases to 226,141 t_{MeOH}/y, while the net production costs reach 1,324 €/t_{MeOH}.

A comparison of the global warming potential (GWP_{100}) of offshore wind energy based PtM methanol from refinery flue gas with methanol from natural gas is shown in Figure 3. At -1.97 kg_{CO2eq}/kg, the net emissions of the PtM route are much lower than those of the conv. alternative with 0.53 kg_{CO2eq}/kg. Thus, production via PtM avoids 2.50 kg_{CO2eq}/kg, although GHG emissions are still present, in particular for steam provision. The negative value for PtM results from the avoided burden approach, where captured CO_2 as well as reference emissions for oxygen production are considered as credit.

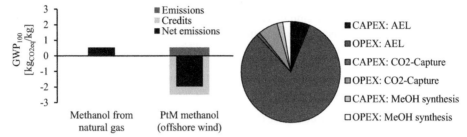

Figure 3: GWP conventional methanol vs. PtM methanol	Figure 4: Total annualized costs of production breakdown

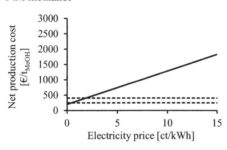 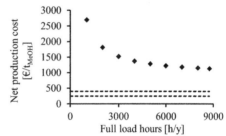

Figure 5: NPC sensitivity on electricity price; dashed lines: conv. methanol price range	Figure 6: NPC sensitivity on full load hours; dashed lines: conv. methanol price range

4.2. Outlook methanol-to-jet (MtJ)

The general capability of methanol-based jet fuel synthesis was demonstrated in the early 1980's by Mobil's MtO/MOGD technology and by Lurgi's MtSynfuels technology in the early 2000's (Tabak et al., 1986; Liebner and Wagner, 2004). These processes are built on the following sequence: olefin synthesis, olefin oligomerization, hydrogenation and fractionation. However, in contrast to alcohol-to-jet via ethanol and isobutanol, the route via methanol has not yet been approved by the relevant specification for aviation turbine fuel containing synthesized hydrocarbons, namely ASTM D7566.

According to Liebner and Wagner (2004) 0.200 kg_{Jet}/kg_{MeOH} can be yielded with 0.163 kg_{Diesel}/kg_{MeOH}, 0.046 $kg_{Gasoline}$/kg_{MeOH} and 0.039 kg_{LPG}/kg_{MeOH} as by-products. Assuming this product distribution, 83 kt_{Jet}/y can be produced via synthetic methanol on basis of the flue gas of the Heide refinery. This corresponds to a max. blending ratio of 18.7 % taking into account the refinery's jet production of 360 kt_{Jet}/y in 2018 (Finnern, 2019). A substitution of the German jet fuel production of 5,110 kt_{Jet}/y would require 25,602 kt_{MeOH}/y as intermediate and 278 TWh electricity for synthetic methanol production, which even surpasses Germanys renewable energy generation of 225 TWh in 2018 (Statistisches Bundesamt, 2019; UBA, 2019). The prior given numbers are highly reliant on the jet fuel selectivity and the MtJ synthesis is expected to have improvement potential with respect to this parameter.

5. Conclusion

Utilization of the flue gas of a single refinery, namely Heide refinery, is sufficient to cover 22 % of German methanol production. Production of such electricity-based methanol allows the avoidance of 2.50 kg_{CO2eq}/kg compared to its conventional production, provided that renewable electricity is applied. From an economic point of view, however, it should be noted that the net production costs of 1,146 €/t_{MeOH} are 2.9-4.6 times the methanol market price. The implementation of PtM at refineries therefore requires far-reaching regulatory measures for emission avoidance or incentive mechanisms. For the subsequent MtJ synthesis it is found that at least 83 kt_{Jet}/y can be produced from Heide refinery's flue gas. Although this concept is promising, substitution of the entire German jet fuel production via power-to-jet is not realistic on a national level, but must be accompanied by imports.

Funding - Funding of this research by the German Federal Ministry of Economic Affairs and

Energy within the KEROSyN100 project (funding code 03EIV051A) is gratefully acknowledged.

Acknowledgement - This paper is dedicated to Prof. Dr. Stefan Gößling-Reisemann, who inspired us, shared his knowledge with us and unfortunately cannot be with us today.

References

M. Bertau, H. Offermanns, L. Plass, F. Schmidt, H.-J. Wernicke, 2014. Methanol: The Basic Chemical and Energy Feedstock of the Future. Springer, Berlin, Heidelberg.

BMU, 2016. Klimaschutzplan 2050 - Klimaschutzpolitische Grundsätze und Ziele der Bundesregierung. Berlin.

D. Bongartz, J. Burre, A. Mitsos, 2019. Production of Oxymethylene Dimethyl Ethers from Hydrogen and Carbon Dioxide - Part I: Modeling and Analysis for OME 1. Industrial & Engineering Chemistry Research, 58, 4881–4889.

A. Buttler, H. Spliethoff, 2018. Current status of water electrolysis for energy storage , grid balancing and sector coupling via power-to-gas and power-to-liquids: A review. Renewable and Sustainable Energy Reviews. 82, 2440–2454.

S. Finnern, 2019. Personal data provision. Raffinerie Heide.

F. Flachsbarth, P. Kasten, 2017. Aktuelle Potenziale der Produktion von PtX-Kraftstoffen auf Basis von zusätzlich integrierten Erneuerbaren Energien. Öko-Institut Working Paper, 3.

IEA, 2019, The Future of Hydrogen. Paris.

K. Li, A. Cousins, H. Yu, P. Feron, M. Tade, W. Luo, J. Chen, 2016. Systematic study of aqueous monoethanolamine-based CO2 capture process: model development and process improvement. Energy Science & Engineering, 4, 23–39.

W. Liebner, M. Wagner, 2004. MtSynfuels, die effiziente und wirtschaftliche Alternative zu Fischer-Tropsch-Treibstoffen. Erdoel Erdgas Kohle, 120, 10, 323–326.

Methanex, 2019. Durchschnittlicher Preis für Methanol auf dem europäischen Markt in den Jahren von 2012 bis 2019. Statista.

T. B. H. Nguyen, E. Zondervan, 2018. Ionic Liquid as a Selective Capture Method of CO2 from Different Sources: Comparison with MEA. ACS Sustainable Chemistry & Engineering, 6, 4845–4853.

M. S. Peters, K. D. Timmerhaus, R. E. West, 2003. Plant Design and Economics for Chemical Engineers. McGraw-Hill, New York.

S. Schmidt, 2014. Optimierung und experimentelle Untersuchung der CO2-Abtrennung mit Monoethanolamin für braunkohlegefeuerte Kraftwerke. Technische Universität München.

Statistisches Bundesamt, 2019. Statistisches Jahrbuch 2019. Wiesbaden.

S. A. Tabak, A. A. Avidan, F. J. Krambeck, 1986. Production of synthetic gasoline and diesel fuel from non-petroleum resources. Am. Chem. Soc., Div. Gas Fuel Chem., 31, 293–299.

UBA, 2019. Zeitreihen zur Entwicklung der erneuerbaren Energien in Deutschland. Dessau-Roßlau.

É. S. Van-Dal, C. Bouallou, 2013. Design and simulation of a methanol production plant from CO2 hydrogenation. Journal of Cleaner Production, 57, 38–45.

Sauro Pierucci, Flavio Manenti, Giulia Bozzano, Davide Manca (Eds.)
Proceedings of the 30th European Symposium on Computer Aided Process Engineering
(ESCAPE30), May 24-27, 2020, Milano, Italy. © 2020 Elsevier B.V. All rights reserved.
http://dx.doi.org/10.1016/B978-0-12-823377-1.50244-5

Optimizing the Capacity of Thermal Energy Storage in Industrial Clusters

Mandar Thombre,[a] Sandeep Prakash,[a] Brage Rugstad Knudsen,[b] Johannes Jäschke[a*]

[a] *Norwegian University of Science and Technology, Trondheim 7491, Norway*
[b] *SINTEF Energy Research, Trondheim 7491, Norway*
johannes.jaschke@ntnu.no

Abstract

A key factor for energy-efficient industrial clusters is the recovery of waste heat. To this end, thermal energy storage (TES) is an appealing technology that facilitates dynamic heat integration between supplier and consumer plants. A long-term strategy for energy savings must involve adequate consideration for the optimal design of the TES. From an industrial perspective, finding the capacity of the TES unit is often based on heuristic rules which may lead to suboptimal design. This approach does not account for the short-term variability in operation of the TES system. Scenario-based stochastic programming approaches, where the operational uncertainty is described in form of discrete scenarios, can be used to find the best design for the TES system. We present two problem formulations for finding the optimal capacity of the TES unit. The first is a single-level formulation where the design and operating constraints are combined for all scenarios, with the objective of minimizing the combined cost of design and operation. The second is a bilevel formulation where the design decisions are taken on the upper level to minimize overall system cost, whereas the lower level problems (one per scenario) represent the optimal operation for the chosen design variables, each minimizing the operating cost for their respective scenarios. We compare the results of the two approaches with an illustrative case study of an industrial cluster with one supplier plant and one consumer plant exchanging heat via a TES unit.
Keywords: thermal energy storage, bilevel programming, industrial cluster

1. Introduction

Storage and reuse of industrial waste heat is vital for improving energy efficiency of many energy-intensive processes. When multiple industrial plants operate in close proximity of each other, waste heat can be recovered from one plant and supplied to another plant in need of it. Thermal energy storage (TES) can mitigate the issue of asynchronous heat supply and demand by storing energy during off-peak periods and discharging it during peak demands, leading to savings in operating costs. The capital investment costs for installing a TES system are proportional to the capacity of the TES, and may become significantly high. In order to find a trade-off between high capital costs (large capacity) and high operating costs (small capacity), it is worth investigating methods for optimally sizing the TES. A well designed TES system has to contend with operational uncertainty, for example the daily/weekly fluctuations in heat supply and demand. By incorporating this uncertainty information in the design phase itself, it is possible to size a TES system that is robust against this uncertainty. Solving a single deterministic optimization problem that spans across the entire operation horizon of the TES (typically multiple years), and accounts for all the heat profile fluctuations therein, is computationally intractable. To overcome this, stochastic programming approaches can be used to optimize the design decisions over a set of representative scenarios.

Our aim is to find a measure for the optimal sizing of the TES equipment - the volume of a TES unit and the areas of the HEX delivering/extracting heat from the TES unit - by rigorously accounting for the uncertain heat supply and demand in operation phase. For the TES system, the decisions can be divided into two stages - design and operation. In the extensive form of stochastic programming (Birge and Louveaux, 2011), the design variables are "here-and-now", whereas the "wait-and-see" operation variables are assigned to each scenario. This results in a single-level optimization problem, where the objective function represents the overall system cost. The design constraints and the operating constraints for each scenario are all imposed together in this formulation.

Another stochastic approach is the bilevel formulation, based on a Stackelberg leader-follower hypothesis. The upper level problem (leader) identifies the optimal design decisions that minimize the overall cost over a set of scenarios. On the other hand, the lower level problems (followers), representing different scenarios, aim to minimize their corresponding operating cost (see Xu et al. (2017), for example). Bilevel problems are typically nonconvex and NP-hard. However, for cases where the lower level problems are convex and follow some constraint qualifications, the lower level problems can be replaced with their Karush-Kuhn-Tucker (KKT) optimality conditions (Dempe and Franke (2019)). The KKT reformulation turns the bilevel problem into a single-level mathematical program with complementarity constraints (MPEC). The complementarity constraints can be further linearized using disjunctive programming (Fortuny-Amat and McCarl, 1981), rendering the problem a mixed-integer program.

In this paper, we develop a linear model for the TES system and present the two formulations for optimizing the TES design. The results are compared with the help of a case study that is motivated from an industrial district heating network in northern Norway. We compare the results of the two approaches in terms of design parameters for the TES - its volume, the HEX area and the associated capital investment.

2. Methodology

Topology of a TES system with one supplier and one consumer is shown in Figure 1. We employ a simplified linear model in terms of heat duties (MW) to represent the TES system. The heat supplier needs to reject $Q_{supply}(t)$ amount of duty, whereas the consumer has a heat demand $Q_{demand}(t)$ to be met. If the TES cannot meet the total demand of the consumer, the excess energy $Q_{peak}(t)$ is imported from an external peak heating source. Similarly, if all of supplied heat cannot be extracted from the supplier, the excess energy $Q_{dump}(t)$ is rejected into a cooling water system. The resulting heat flows in and out of the tank are denoted by $Q_{tes}^{in}(t)$ and $Q_{tes}^{out}(t)$. The energy in the TES unit is denoted by $E_{tes}(t)$ (MWh). Heat losses from the TES unit to the surroundings are denoted by $Q_{loss}(t)$, which proportional to its energy content. The peak heating and heat dumping duties, along with the energy in the TES unit represent the operating variables in the system. $x_{opr} := \{Q_{peak}(t), Q_{dump}(t), E_{tes}(t)\}$ The associated costs (NOK/MWh) of importing and dumping heat are $C_{peak}(t)$ and $C_{dump}(t)$ respectively. Considering an operating period from t_0 to t_f, the total operating cost can be shown as

$$C_{opr} := \int_{t_0}^{t_f} \left(C_{peak}(t)Q_{peak}(t) + C_{dump}(t)Q_{dump}(t) \right) dt \qquad (1)$$

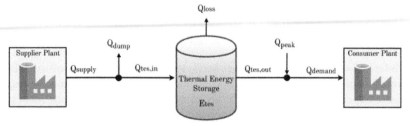

Figure 1: Industrial cluster with one supplier and one consumer exchanging heat through TES.

In context of the system design, the required total energy capacity of the TES unit (MWh) is denoted by CAP_{tes}, whereas the required maximum power rating for heat exchange with the TES unit (MW) is POW_{tes}. For taking design decisions, the former gives the basis for choosing the total volume of the tank. Similarly, the maximum power rating, often serving as the heat exchanger (HEX) design point is related to the HEX area required to deliver and withdraw heat from the TES unit. Thus, CAP_{tes} and POW_{tes} represent the design variables in the system. $x_{des} := \{CAP_{tes}, POW_{tes}\}$. The prices associated with these variables are C_{cap}(NOK/MWh) and C_{pow}(NOK/MW) respectively. The total design cost is: $C_{des} := C_{cap}CAP_{tes} + C_{pow}POW_{tes}$.

Our aim is to identify optimal design parameters for TES system under some information about the operational uncertainty. Uncertainty is modeled in terms of N scenarios, each representing a discrete combination of the heat supply and demand profiles $Q_{supply}(t)$ and $Q_{demand}(t)$ across the operating period. We consider two different formulations of the design optimization problem, a single-level formulation and a bilevel formulation.

2.1. Single-Level formulation

Considering N scenarios of operation, the single-level problem is formulated as (2).

$$\min_{x_{des}, x_{opr}} \quad C_{des} + \sum_{n=1}^{N} \omega_n C_{opr,n} \tag{2a}$$

$$s.t. \quad CAP_{tes} \geq 0 \tag{2b}$$

$$POW_{tes} \geq 0 \tag{2c}$$

$$\dot{E}_{tes,n}(t) = Q^{in}_{tes,n}(t) - Q^{out}_{tes,n}(t) - Q_{loss,n}(t) \qquad n = 1,...,N \tag{2d}$$

$$0 \leq Q_{peak,n}(t) \leq Q_{peak,max} \qquad n = 1,...,N \tag{2e}$$

$$0 \leq Q_{dump,n}(t) \leq Q_{dump,max} \qquad n = 1,...,N \tag{2f}$$

$$0 \leq Q^{in}_{tes,n}(t) \leq POW_{tes} \qquad n = 1,...,N \tag{2g}$$

$$0 \leq Q^{out}_{tes,n}(t) \leq POW_{tes} \qquad n = 1,...,N \tag{2h}$$

$$0 \leq E_{tes,n}(t) \leq CAP_{tes} \qquad n = 1,...,N \tag{2i}$$

Here, the subscript n represents the nth scenario of operation. In the objective (2a), ω_n is the probability associated with the nth scenario. Equation (2d) is the energy balance equation for the TES, where $\dot{E}_{tes,n}(t)$ is the derivative of the energy in the TES unit. The heat flows in and out of the TES unit are upper bounded by the POW_{tes}, and energy in TES unit is upper bounded by its capacity CAP_{tes}. For implementation, we discretize all the continuous variables in (2) using constant time steps. The integral in the objective (2a) is thus replaced by summation over all the discretized time steps.

Moreover, we employ a forward Euler scheme to discretize the energy balance equation (2d). This transforms (2) into an LP, solvable by MILP solvers like Gurobi and CPEX.

2.2. Bilevel formulation

In the bilevel formulation (3), the lower level operating variables are constrained to be the optimal solutions of the lower level problems (3d), corresponding to their respective scenarios of operation. The upper level objective function is the overall cost (same as (2)), whereas the objective function of each lower level problem is the operating cost for the corresponding scenario.

$$\min_{x_{des}, x_{opr}} \quad C_{des} + \sum_{n=1}^{N} \omega_n \, C_{opr,n} \tag{3a}$$

$$s.t. \quad CAP_{tes} \geq 0 \tag{3b}$$

$$POW_{tes} \geq 0 \tag{3c}$$

$$x_{opr,n} \in \arg\min_{x_{opr,n}} \quad C_{opr,n} \qquad\qquad n = 1,...,N \tag{3d}$$

$$s.t. \quad \dot{E}_{tes,n}(t) = Q_{tes,n}^{in}(t) - Q_{tes,n}^{out}(t) - Q_{loss,n}(t)$$

$$0 \leq Q_{peak,n}(t) \leq Q_{peak,max}$$

$$0 \leq Q_{dump,n}(t) \leq Q_{dump,max}$$

$$0 \leq Q_{tes,n}^{in}(t) \leq POW_{tes}$$

$$0 \leq Q_{tes,n}^{out}(t) \leq POW_{tes}$$

$$0 \leq E_{tes,n}(t) \leq CAP_{tes}$$

The notation used for various variables is the same as in (2). Note that the lower level constraints involve the upper level variables. We also use the same discretization scheme as (2) to convert (3) into a linear bilevel program. This linear bilevel program is still nonconvex is nature owing to the constraints (3d). However, since the lower level problems (3d) are LPs after discretization, the bilevel problem (3) can be reformulated as an MILP as explained in Section 1, and can thus be solved by solvers like Gurobi and CPLEX. The formulation (3) has tighter feasible set than (2). Problem (3) is thus expected to result in more conservative solutions than (2). However, the bilevel formulation is more representative of the design problem since in practice the problem has a hierarchical nature with the operator's decisions following those of the designer's, with both trying to optimize their respective objectives.

3. Case study – design basis

An industrial TES system with one supplier and one consumer of heat is studied. To formulate the design problem, 5 years of operation is assumed for the TES unit. The overall objective function (Equations (2a) and (3a)) in the formulation then consists the design cost and the operating cost for 5 years of operation. On the operation level, we consider only hourly variation in the heat duties and, to maintain computational tractability, an operating horizon of one week (168 hours). On the design level, we approximate the total 5-year operating cost by extrapolating the weekly operating cost from the operation level over 5 years of operation. The scenarios for weekly operation are taken from the 2017 winter data for heat supply/demand provided by Mo Fjernvarme, a district heating company in northern Norway. Further, all scenarios are considered equally likely in the formulations (2) and (3). The prices for peak heating,

C_{peak} are taken to be the corresponding hourly 2017 electricity prices in northern Norway. The prices for heat dumping, C_{dump}, are assumed to be 1/10th of the peak heating prices. The maximum peak heating and heat dumping rates $Q_{peak,max}$ and $Q_{dump,max}$ are set to be 50 MW each. The design basis for calculating the TES volume and HEX area is as follows. The maximum energy storage capacity CAP_{tes} is related to the TES volume and depends on the total enthalpy change of the TES fluid in the tank between the fully charged and fully discharged state, $CAP_{tes} = \rho C_p V_{tes} \Delta T$. Assuming water as the storage medium and an operating window of $20°C$ for the storage tank, the following relation is obtained:

$$V_{tes} \, (\text{m}^3) = 43.06 \, CAP_{tes} \, (\text{MWh}) \tag{4}$$

The maximum power rating POW_{tes} corresponds to the maximum duty transferred across the HEX to and from the TES unit, given by $Q = UA(\Delta T)_{LMTD} = mC_p \Delta T$. Charging to a nearly fully charged TES or discharging from a nearly discharged TES unit would give the maximum area requirement of the HEX. We assume that the TES unit is large enough to have a nearly flat profile across the HEX and use a $10°C$ approach temperature in the HEX. Using the fluid properties of water, we estimate the lowest $(\Delta T)_{LMTD}$ to be $19.5°C$, and get the relation between POW_{tes} and an upper bound for the area required for the HEX as:

$$A_{hex} \, (\text{m}^2) = 60.24 \, POW_{tes} \, (\text{MW}) \tag{5}$$

Finally, we use a linearized approximation of the total purchased equipment cost as provided by Sinnott and Towler (2009), to estimate our design costs C_{cap} and C_{pow}. Following the factorial method to convert the purchase costs to total design costs, we get the following approximate relations:

$$C_{cap} \, (\text{mil. NOK 2017}) = 0.7 + 0.11 \, CAP_{tes} \, (\text{MWh}) \tag{6}$$

$$C_{pow} \, (\text{mil. NOK 2017}) = 0.095 + 0.3 \, POW_{tes} \, (\text{MW}) \tag{7}$$

4. Results and discussions

We compare the results between the two formulations while considering 5, 10 and 20 weekly scenarios, chosen from the 2017 winter data. Also, when considering real data, care has to be taken to avoid any outliers that may skew the results of the design optimization. Figure 2 shows that the single-level formulation results in higher TES capacities, whereas the bilevel formulation emphasizes higher HEX areas for efficient heat transfer. This implies that, at higher TES capacities, optimal lower level solutions result in a higher design cost for the bilevel formulation. The bilevel formulation prioritizes minimizing the design objective at the expense of operation objective. Although this results in a higher operation cost for the bilevel formulation (Figure 3), it ensures that the chosen design parameters lead to optimal operation on the lower level. Also interesting to note is that the design costs from the bilevel formulation remain unchanged when scenarios are increased from 10 to 20. The single-level formulation leads to lower overall costs, but optimal operation is not guaranteed explicitly for any of the chosen scenarios. Including more scenarios seems to reduce the design cost in single-level formulation. Availability of more data would allow us to check if this cost converges to a particular value.

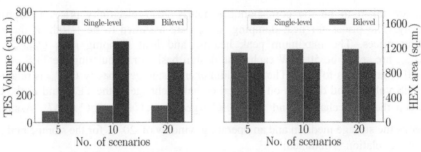

Figure 2 : TES volume and HEX area for the two formulations

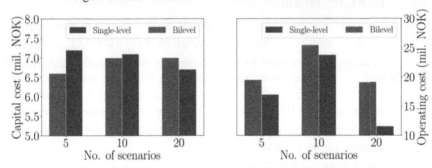

Figure 3 : Design and operating cost for the two formulations

5. Conclusion

In this paper, we compared two stochastic formulations for design optimization of TES systems. The results show that the bilevel formulation prioritizes minimizing the design cost, leading to higher operating costs. On the other hand, the single-level formulation minimizes the overall cost, but does not explicitly account for optimal operation.

Acknowledgements

This publication has been funded by HighEFF - Centre for an Energy Efficient and Competitive Industry for the Future, an 8-year Research Centre under the FME-scheme (Centre for Environment-friendly Energy Research, 257632). The authors gratefully acknowledge the financial support from the Research Council of Norway and user partners of HighEFF. The authors thank Mo Fjernvarme AS in particular for providing industrial data on heat supply and demand.

References

J. R. Birge, F. Louveaux, 2011. Introduction to Stochastic Programming, 2nd Edition. Springer Publishing Company, Incorporated.

S. Dempe, S. Franke, 2019. Solution of bilevel optimization problems using the KKT approach. Optimization 68 (8), 1471–1489

J. Fortuny-Amat, B. McCarl, 1981. A representation and economic interpretation of a two-level programming problem. Journal of the Operational Research Society 32 (9), 783–792

R. Sinnott, G. Towler, 2009. Chemical Engineering Design. Butterworth-Heinemann/IChemE series. ButterworthHeinemann.

B. Xu, Y. Wang, Y. Dvorkin, R. Fernández-Blanco, C. A. Silva-Monroy, J. Watson, D. S. Kirschen, 2017. Scalable planning for energy storage in energy and reserve markets. IEEE Transactions on Power Systems 32 (6), 4515–4527.

Sauro Pierucci, Flavio Manenti, Giulia Bozzano, Davide Manca (Eds.)
Proceedings of the 30th European Symposium on Computer Aided Process Engineering
(ESCAPE30), May 24-27, 2020, Milano, Italy. © 2020 Elsevier B.V. All rights reserved.
http://dx.doi.org/10.1016/B978-0-12-823377-1.50245-7

Heat Decarbonisation Pathways in the UK: Modelling and Policy Insights

Vassilis M. Charitopoulos[a,b], Chi Kong Chyong[a], David Reiner[a*]

[a]*Judge Business School, Energy Policy Research Group, University of Cambridge, Trumpington Street, Cambridge CB2 1AG, United Kingdom*

[b]*Department of Chemical Engineering, Centre for Process Systems Engineering, University College London, Torrington Place, London WC1E 7JE, United Kingdom.*

dmr40@cam.ac.uk

Abstract

Although most progress on decarbonisation in the UK has been made in the power sector, heat accounted for 44% of total energy consumption and approximately 37% of GHG emissions in 2017. Given the efficiency and cost-competitiveness of the incumbent gas-based system, decarbonising the heat sector signals a transition that requires judicious planning and defensible policy intervention. We present a novel spatially explicit MILP model for integrated optimisation of heat and power to assess the implications of heat electrification. For the first time, real-world regional hourly heat demand data are employed and the optimal share of regional heat electrification is explored by taking into account operational and investment decisions. Finally, we propose the concept of heat carbon budgets to assist policy interventions and systematically assess the transition to a low-carbon heat system.

Keywords: heat decarbonisation, spatially explicit modelling, energy systems, unit commitment, heat electrification.

1. Introduction

1.1. Background and motivation

By 2017, the UK managed to reduce its greenhouse gas (GHG) emissions by 43% compared to 1990 levels, with 75% of those reductions coming from the power sector, the decarbonisation of the heat and transportation sectors remains a big challenge (CCC, 2018). The need for addressing all sectors of a carbon-neutral economy has been reinforced when the UK government adopted a net-zero target in June 2019. Heat was the biggest energy consumer in the UK, accounting for 44% of total energy consumption in 2017, producing 37% of UK's GHG emissions (BEIS, 2018). Peak heat demand in the UK can reach 300 GW, approximately five times greater than the current electricity system's peak demand (Ofgem, 2016; Eyre & Baruah, 2015). Owing to the existing gas infrastructure system in the UK, balancing between the demand and supply sides can be achieved without excessive capacity investments (Dodds, 2014). However, for the electricity system this is not the case since instantaneous balancing is required to avoid power outages.

1.2. Literature review

Sansom & Strbac (2012) examined the impact of electrifying heat for different settings. Later on, Quiggin & Buswell (2016) presented a model for estimating the impact of heat electrification in the UK from a demand-supply viewpoint. Heinen et al. (2017) examined the impact of exploiting thermal building inertia and the effect of weather events on heat demand in Ireland. Qadrdan et al. (2019) presented a linear programming model with electricity dispatch consideration to study the impact of heat electrification on the UK gas and electricity system. A common shortcoming of the aforementioned works is that the spatial dimension is restricted to single-node representations. A spatially-explicit, multi-period MILP model was developed by Jalil-Vega & Hawkes (2018) to investigate the heat supply and network infrastructure trade-offs in the City of Bristol. Recently, Zhang et al. (2018) presented a whole-system study on the decarbonisation of heat in the UK so to optimally decide on the end-use heat generation system design involving heat-pumps, district heat networks (DHN) and hybrid deployment of heat pumps with gas boilers (HP-B). The authors concluded that the HP-B pathway presents economic and operational benefits over the other alternatives, due to the lower capital cost of decommissioning existing domestic gas-boilers and the avoidance of reinforcing the electricity network because of heat peak demand.

Thus, to date, most studies examine heat decarbonisation by considering aggregate representations of the spatial and temporal scales of problem on a national level. Moreover, region-specific hourly heat demand data, detailed transmission capacities and interconnection have not been considered so far. It is the goal of this article to address these issues and present a novel model to investigate the impact of heat electrification in future integrated power and gas systems. The remainder of the article is organized as follows: in Section 2 the key modelling contributions of the present work are outlined while details about heat demand data and energy data processing are given in Section 3. In section 4, we employ the proposed model to investigate the impact of heat electrification in a future scenario for the UK while conclusions are drawn in section 5.

2. Integrated heat and power systems optimisation model

2.1. Spatially explicit modelling & power system

In the present work, the UK was divided in 13 regions based on the established local distribution zones of the gas network as shown in Fig. 1 while electricity network transmission capacities where derived by National Grid's Ten Year Statement (National Grid, 2018a). The electricity demand in each region (g) as shown in eq. (1), comprises of two parts: (i) non-heat demand ($DemElec_{g,c,h}$) and (ii) heat-related demand ($P^{heat}_{g,r,c,h}$) which results from the optimised electrification share of the regional heat demand and is an endogenous model decision.

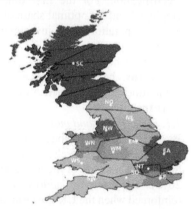

Figure 1. Spatially explicit modelling of the UK by local distribution zone (LDZ)

$$Dem_{g,c,h} = DemElec_{g,c,h} + \sum_r P^{heat}_{g,r,c,h} \qquad \forall g,c,h \qquad (1)$$

The electricity balance in each region is given by eq. (2) and can be envisaged in Fig. 2. In each region we consider power generation within the region ($P_{g,j,c,h}$), grid level storage charging ($CH_{g,j,c,h}$) and discharging ($DC_{g,j,c,h}$), bidirectional power transmission with other regions ($TR_{g,g',c,h}$), renewables curtailment for the case of excessive generation ($L^{curtail}_{g,c,h}$), load shedding for unmet power demand ($L^{shed}_{g,c,h}$) and bidirectional interconnection with third countries ($PIM_{g,i,c,h}$).

$$\sum_{j\in je} P_{g,j,c,h} (1 - PL_j) + \sum_{g'\in N_{g,g'}} TR_{g',g,c,h}(1 - \alpha \cdot LDD_{g'g}) +$$
$$\sum_{j\in jes} DC_{g,j,c,h} + \sum_{i\in IG_{i,g}} PIM_{g,i,c,h}(1 - \gamma_{i,g}) = Dem_{g,c,h} + \qquad (2)$$
$$\sum_{g'\in N_{g',g}} TR_{g,g',c,h} + \sum_{j\in jes} CH_{g,j,c,h} + L^{curtail}_{g,c,h} - L^{shed}_{g,c,h} \qquad \forall g,r,c,h$$

Notice that for thermal generators we consider a parasitic load factor (PL_j) to account for the net power production as well as a linear loss factor (α) proportional to the transmission distance when power is transmitted across regions and the related losses in interconnection through the factor $\gamma_{i,g}$. Further to these constraints, we formulate the security and ramp-rate constrained unit commitment problem for thermal generators by explicitly accounting for: (i) start-ups/shut-

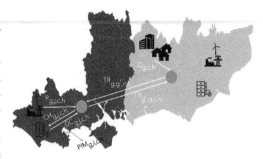

Figure 2. Visual representation of different electricity flows within and across two regions

downs, (ii) minimum uptime/downtime, (iii) ramp-rate constraints (up/down), (iv) upward & downward short term operating reserve provision and (v) minimum/maximum generation limits building on our previous work (Chyong et al., 2019).

2.2. Heat supply chain modelling

With regards to the heat supply chain, eq. (3) represents the spatiotemporal energy balance where the heat demand at each region (g) representative day (c) and hour (h) ($HDem_{g,r,c,h}$) is equal to the heat supplied ($Q^{heat}_{g,r,j,c,h}$) by the different heating technologies ($j \in J_h$) minus the thermal energy discharged at each time period ($Q^{dheat}_{g,r,c,h}$) plus the thermal energy stored ($Q^{sheat}_{g,r,c,h}$). Notice that in each region (g) we differentiate between areas (r) that are connected to the gas grid.

$$HDem_{g,r,c,h} = \sum_{j \in J_h} Q^{heat}_{g,r,j,c,h} - Q^{dheat}_{g,r,c,h} + Q^{sheat}_{g,r,c,h} \qquad \forall g,r,c,h \qquad (3)$$

Eqs. (4)-(5) describe the resulting demand in electricity ($P^{heat}_{g,r,c,h}$) and fuel ($V^{heat}_{g,r,f,c,h}$) that result by the heat demand respectively by taking into account the efficiency of each heating technology ($\eta_{g,r,j,c,h}$).

$$P^{heat}_{g,r,c,h} = \sum_{j \in J_{he}} \frac{Q^{heat}_{g,r,j,c,h}}{\eta_{g,r,j,c,h}} \qquad \forall g,r,c,h \qquad (4)$$

$$V^{heat}_{g,r,f,c,h} = \sum_{j \in J_h \wedge JF_{f,j}} \frac{Q^{heat}_{g,r,j,c,h}}{\eta_{g,r,j,c,h}} \qquad \forall g,r \in R_{grid}, f,c,h \qquad (5)$$

For an air-source heat pump (ASHP), efficiency is not constant but rather temperature-dependent and we assume that eq. (6) holds following the work of Zhang et al. (2018).

$$\eta_{g,r,'ASHP',c,h} = 0.07 T_{g,r,c,h} + 2.07 \; (-5°C \leq T_{g,r,c,h} \leq 25°C) \; \forall g,r,c,h \qquad (6)$$

To model the thermal energy storage technologies we employ eqs. (7)-(13) which represent the energy content balance, storage duration limits and charging/discharging limits respectively. In the present work we consider as thermal energy storage technology hot water tanks with self-discharge rate (β) 1%/h and ratio of capacity to the power rating (TES) of 4h.

$$S^{heat}_{g,r,c,h} = S^{heat}_{g,r,c,h-1}(1 - \beta) - Q^{dheat}_{g,r,c,h} + Q^{sheat}_{g,r,c,h} \qquad \forall g,r,c,h \qquad (7)$$

$$S^{heat}_{g,r,c,h} \leq S^{cap}_{g,r} TES \qquad \forall g,r,c,h \qquad (8)$$

$$Q^{dheat}_{g,r,c,h} \leq S^{cap}_{g,r}, \; Q^{sheat}_{g,r,c,h} \leq S^{cap}_{g,r} \qquad \forall g,r,c,h \qquad (9)\text{-}(10)$$

$$S^{heat}_{g,r,c,h} = 0 \qquad \forall g,r,c,h = \{0,23\} \qquad (11)$$

Finally, investment-related decisions on the capacity of the heat-end technology capacities are calculated based on eq (12)-(13).

$$Q^{heat}_{g,r,c,h} \leq Heat^{cap}_{g,r} \quad and \quad Q^{sheat}_{g,r,c,h} \leq S^{cap}_{g,r} \qquad \forall g,r,c,h \qquad (12)\text{-}(13)$$

2.3. Overall model formulation

In summary, the model is formulated as a mixed integer linear program (MILP) with a total system cost minimisation objective and the overall formulation is given below in brief.

$$\min \text{TotalCost} = \text{OPEX} + \text{CAPEX} + \text{CIMP} + \text{CEM} + \text{CSHED}$$

$$\text{Subject to:} \begin{cases} \text{Security \& Ramp-rate constrained unit commitment} \\ \text{Transmission \& Interconnection bounds} \\ \text{Grid-level storage constraints} \\ \text{Heat supply chain constraints} \\ CO_2 \text{ emissions constraints} \end{cases}$$

The total system cost comprises of the operating cost for power and heat generation and storage (OPEX), the capital cost for the final portfolio of heating technologies (CAPEX), the cost of interconnection (CIMP), the cost related to environmental penalties for emissions (CEM) and the cost of shedding demand or operating reserve (CSHED).

3. Data preparation and processing

3.1. Regional heat demand data

In order to capture seasonality and volatility of heat demand, several years (2014-18) of historical regional hourly gas consumption data were collected from the UK gas distribution companies. The data accounted for industrial, domestic and commercial loads which were further disaggregated so as to segment heat-related demands. A key

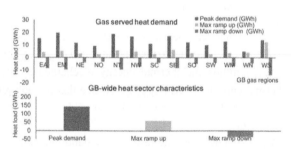

Figure 3. Regional heat demand operational characteristics

novelty and benefit of this approach is that (i) we do not rely on synthetic data, (ii) the after-diversity demand factors do not need to be calculated to provide realistic loads (Sansom & Strbac, 2012) and (iii) the derived heat demands represent the actual energy load that will be considered for electrification within each region. In Fig. 3, an overview of region-specific heat load characteristics are provided.

3.2. Regional power sector data

The incumbent power generation fleet is mapped in the different regions under study together with the related transmission capacity of interconnections with third countries. The base year of our study is 2015 where UK generation capacity consists of 10% nuclear, 23% unabated coal, 37% unabated gas, 3% biomass and 27% renewables (DUKES, 2018).

3.3. Chronologically-ordered spatiotemporal data clustering

Data clustering techniques have been widely used in optimisation models for energy systems because of their ability to reduce the related computational burden while at the same time provide a good approximation to the full-dimensional problem (Heuberger et al., 2017). We employ K-means clustering to select ten representative days of the year but, in contrast to previous works, we modify the clustering algorithm so as to impose the chronological order of the resulting days since this is important in preserving the heat demand seasonality. On top of the aforementioned 10 days we also include two additional days, accounting for peak electricity and peak gas demand days.

4. Case study: Heat electrification options for a 2030 UK system

In this section, we employ the capacity mix of National Grid's "Two degrees" future energy scenario for 2030 (National Grid, 2018b) to demonstrate the model's capabilities. First, we investigate the simultaneous decarbonisation of the heat and power sector under a single "carbon-budget" with a reduction goal of 15% for heat-related emissions compared to their 2015 levels (BEIS, 2018) in addition to the existing carbon budget for the incumbent power sector. The optimal generation schedule is shown in Fig. 4 and the impact of electrifying heat becomes obvious on the second representative day which in the original time-series was the peak (gas) heat demand day. There is a great increase in the marginal price of electricity during "Day 2" due to operating reserve shedding so as to meet the resulting additional heat-related demand. For this case, the regional change in gas-fuelled properties from 2015 to 2030 can be seen in Fig. 5.

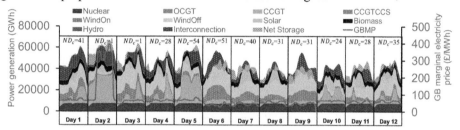

Figure 4. Optimal generation schedule and the resulting GB-wide marginal price of electricity in 2030 under a single carbon budget and 15% reduction in heat emissions. (ND_c: frequency of day)

Finally, motivated by the fact that for the case of single carbon budget the heat-related emissions reduction goal was never achieved but rather a deeper decarbonisation of the electricity sector was preferred as optimal, we investigate and propose for the first time the stipulation of heat-specific carbon budgets so as to guide and surveil the decarbonisation more efficiently. The impact of stipulating a single carbon budget different carbon budgets and the role of intraday heat storage can be seen in Fig. 6 where sector-specific carbon budgets and intraday heat storage enable a deeper level of decarbonisation to be achieved at more reasonable costs.

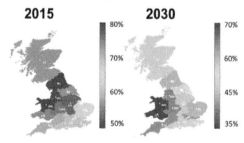

Figure 5. Regional percentages of gas-fueled properties in 2015 vs optimal 2030 scenario for 15% reduction in heat emissions.

5. Conclusions

Our novel spatially-explicit MILP model allows us to investigate the impact of different levels of heat electrification in the UK. The model accounts for investment decisions for the heat supply chain while a security & ramp-rate constrained unit commitment formulation allows for evaluation of the adequacy and operability of the power system. For the first time, real-world heat demand data are employed to analyse heat decarbonisation and we propose a novel clustering framework to preserve seasonality, account for bidirectional interconnection and propose the notion of "heat carbon budgets".

Going forward, we plan to investigate the role of hydrogen in heat of heat as well as incorporating generation capacity expansion planning decisions in heat decarbonisation.

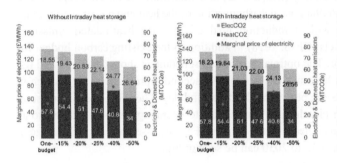

Figure 6. Impact of heat storage and the stipulation of "heat carbon budgets" on the cost of decarbonisation. The yellow and blue columns represent power and heat-related CO2 emissions respectively, while the red diamonds indicate the resulting average GB marginal price of electricity.

Acknowledgements: Financial support for this project from the Engineering and Physical Sciences Research Council (EPSRC Grant EP/P026214/1) is gratefully acknowledged. We also gratefully acknowledge the hourly historical data supplied to us by the gas distribution networks: Cadent Gas, Northern Gas Networks, Wales & West Utilities and SGN.

References
CCC, 2018, Reducing UK emissions 2018 progress report to parliament, London: Committee on Climate Change.
BEIS, 2018, Clean growth: Transforming heating- overview of current evidence, London: Department for Business, Energy & Industrial Strategy.
Ofgem, 2016, The decarbonisation of heat, Ofgem's Future Insights Series, 1-16.
Eyre, N., & Baruah, P., 2015, Uncertainties in future energy demand in UK residential heating. Energy Policy, 87, 641-653.
Dodds, P. E., 2014, Integrating housing stock and energy system models as a strategy to improve heat decarbonisation assessments. Appl. Energy, 132, 358-369.
Sansom, R., & Strbac, G., 2012, The impact of future heat demand pathways on the economics of low carbon heating systems. In *BIEE-9th Academic conference*, 2-10.
Quiggin, D., & Buswell, R. (2016). The implications of heat electrification on national electrical supply-demand balance under published 2050 energy scenarios. *Energy*, *98*, 253-270.
Heinen, S., Turner, W., Cradden, L., McDermott, F., & O'Malley, M. (2017). Electrification of residential space heating considering coincidental weather events and building thermal inertia: A system-wide planning analysis. *Energy*, *127*, 136-154.
Qadrdan, M., Fazeli, R., Jenkins, N., Strbac, G., & Sansom, R. (2019). Gas and electricity supply implications of decarbonising heat sector in GB. *Energy*, *169*, 50-60.
Jalil-Vega, F., & Hawkes, A.D. (2018). Spatially resolved model for studying decarbonisation pathways for heat supply and infrastructure trade-offs. *Appl. Energy*, *210*, 1051-1072.
Zhang, X., Strbac, G., Teng, F., & Djapic, P. (2018). Economic assessment of alternative heat decarbonisation strategies through coordinated operation with electricity system–UK case study. *Appl. Energy*, 222, 79-91.
Chyong, C., Newbery, D., & McCarty, T., 2019, A Unit Commitment and Economic Dispatch Model of the GB Electricity Market – Formulation and Application to Hydro Pumped Storage, Energy Policy Research Group Working Paper 1924. Cambridge: University of Cambridge.
Heuberger, C.F., Rubin, E.S., Staffell, I., Shah, N., & Mac Dowell, N., 2017, Power Generation Expansion Considering Endogenous Technology Cost Learning, *Comput. Aid. Chem. Eng*, 40, 2401-2406
National Grid, 2018a, Electricity Ten Year Statement.
National Grid, 2018b, Future Energy Scenarios.

Sauro Pierucci, Flavio Manenti, Giulia Bozzano, Davide Manca (Eds.)
Proceedings of the 30th European Symposium on Computer Aided Process Engineering
(ESCAPE30), May 24-27, 2020, Milano, Italy. © 2020 Elsevier B.V. All rights reserved.
http://dx.doi.org/10.1016/B978-0-12-823377-1.50246-9

Energy System Design for the Production of Synthetic Carbon-neutral Fuels from Air-captured CO$_2$

Lukas Weimann[a], Alexa Grimm[a], Janet Nienhuis[a], Paolo Gabrielli[b],
Gert Jan Kramer[a], Matteo Gazzani[a*]

[a]*Copernicus Institute of Sustainable Development, Utrecht University, 3584 CS Utrecht, The Netherland*
[b]*Institute of Process Engineering, ETH Zurich, 8092 Zurich, Switzerland*
m.gazzani@uu.nl

Abstract

In this work, we investigate the design and operation of an energy system for the production of a carbon-rich CO$_2$-neutral fuel, i.e. where hydrogen reacts with CO$_2$ from air to give synthetic methane. As the systems consists of multiple energy conversion and storage technologies, we make use of the energy hub approach coupled with MILP optimization to identify optimal plant designs and operation. We investigate the effect of flexible vs. steady operation of the fuel synthesis and direct air capture, as well as the effects of different geographical locations. We find that if the system is optimized for cost, electricity is mainly supplied by the grid, and therefore the electricity prices and grid emission factors determine the economic and environmental performance. Moreover, the location plays a minor role in the cost of the minimum emissions point, as the direct air capture cost largely control the total plant costs. Along this line, the optimal design was found to rely on steady operation of the synthesis and direct air capture ensemble, as this allows for the lowest associated capital expenditure.

Keywords: multi energy system, MILP, direct air capture, net-zero, negative emissions technologies

1. Introduction

One of the biggest technical challenges society is facing in its endeavor to meet the goals set by the Paris Agreement is the decarbonization of (i) high temperature endothermic processes in heavy industry and (ii) transportation, especially aviation. While renewable energy sources can rather easily substitute fossil fuels for electricity generation and household energy demands, (part of) the sectors mentioned above will keep requiring energy-dense carbon-based fuels. Therefore, in a system compliant with net-zero CO$_2$ emission, as the one depicted by the IPCC 1.5 °C report (IPCC, 2018) for approximately 2050, a CO$_2$-neutral production of carbon-rich fuel will be needed. One such possibility – others being indeed the use of fuels derived from biomass or CCS – is producing synthetic fuels via using CO$_2$ recovered from air (direct air capture, or DAC) and H$_2$, provided that the energy required to drive the whole process has no CO$_2$ footprint. While the advocates of the synthetic fuel route typically identify this process as viable when cheap and abundant green electricity will be available, the design and operation of the fuel production process and the associated energy system remain largely an open question. Therefore, with this contribution we aim at understanding (i) how the production of a synthetic fuel is optimally designed and operated, (ii) what are the associated CO_2 emissions and production costs, and (iii) how electricity import and onsite generation are controlled for various designs along a cost-emission pareto front. To this end, we have modified an existing MILP framework so as to take into account the performance and energy input/output of a synthetic fuel production unit coupled with a direct air capture plant. Due to the inherent aleatory nature of renewable power generation (i.e. PV and wind turbines), and to the large variations in the annual electricity cost profile, we explore the effect of pursuing a static vs. a flexible operation of the ensemble DAC+fuel synthesis. Moreover, we investigate the effect of the geographical plant location by considering different sites with different weather profiles and electricity costs: (i) the Netherlands, (ii) Spain, (iii) California (US), and (iv) United Arabic Emirates.

2. Background and Methodology

In the following, we focus on the novelties of this contribution, namely the application of the modelling framework developed by (Gabrielli et al., 2018b, 2018a) to a system lacking detailed analysis so far (section 2.1) and the required extension of the framework to realize this (section 2.2).

2.1. System description

The investigated system is sized considering that the direct air capture unit delivers 1 Mt/y of high purity CO_2. This was chosen as an exemplary large scale production plant. The CO_2 is utilized for fuel production (FP), here represented with a methanation step (Sabatier reaction). For simplicity, the FP unit is modeled via mass and energy balances (see section 2.2.1), fulfilling a constant synthetic natural gas (SNG) demand of 22.1 MW or 194 GWh annually. The required amount of hydrogen is produced via a polymer electrolyte membrane (PEM) electrolyzer. It is important to note that DAC and FP are simulated as coupled units, i.e. sizing and operation is proportionate.

Electricity is provided through photovoltaic panels, wind turbines, or the grid, while heat is provided by solar thermal panels or hydrogen boilers. Hence, the only source of CO_2 derives from the carbon footprint of the electricity grid, which is here considered as location-dependent. In addition to these conversion technologies, batteries for electricity storage and pressurized tanks for hydrogen storage are considered. Moreover, the installation of a PEM fuel cell in combination with the PEM electrolyzer and the hydrogen storage can work as a power-to-gas-to-power system. Finally, the sole purpose of the SNG storage is to allow for flexible production, i.e. vary the output of the DAC-FP unit,

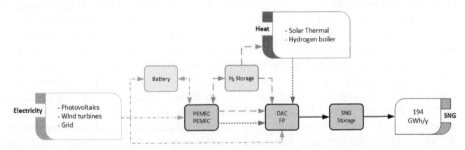

Figure 1: Schematic representation of the system investigated in this study

despite having a constant SNG demand profile. Figure 1 shows a graphic representation of the described system and its possible configuration.

The system optimization was carried out via mixed integer linear programming (MILP) as framed in the energy hub approach (Geidl et al., 2007) and as implemented by Gabrielli et al. (Gabrielli et al., 2018b, 2018a). The framework allows for optimizing the design – via technology selection and sizing – and the operation of multi-energy systems (MES), while also retaining adequate description of the technology performance. The considered time span is the full year 2018 at hourly resolution. The various locations are accounted for through their wind speed, solar irradiation, and electricity price profiles.

2.2. Modeling of direct air capture and SNG production

2.2.1. Performance parameters

In order to simulate the combined DAC-FP unit, it was assumed that the CO_2 capture process follows the CO_2 demand of the methanation process. For the electricity and heat input for the DAC the values reported in (Sutter et al., 2019) are used. The inputs for the methanation process are obtained from Müller et al. (Müller et al., 2011), who conducted thermodynamic simulations based on an existing methanation plant. The performance parameters are summarized in Table 1.

2.2.2. Cost parameters

Because of the large uncertainties associated with estimating the costs of new technologies (e.g. fuel synthesis and DAC), the cost results presented in this paper should be regarded mainly as preliminary estimates and as a way to distinguish between the different operating points. Currently, there exist two main technological pathways for DAC, which rely either on the use of an aqueous solutions or on the use of solid sorbents as means to capture CO_2. For the former chemical sorbents like potassium hydroxide are used which strongly bind the CO_2. This process benefits from the experience gained in post-combustion CO_2 capture but requires high quality fuels for regeneration. On the other hand, solid sorbent processes shows more favorable thermodynamics during the regeneration step, and requires low quality heat. For this reason, they are a good fit with renewable-based technologies, and are therefore assumed as DAC process here.

Table 1: Performance parameters for direct air capture (DAC), fuel production via methanation (FP) and the coupled DAC-FP unit

	DAC	FP	DAC-FP
Heat [kWh/kWh$_{SNG}$]	0.366	-0.167	0.199
Electricity [kWh/kWh$_{SNG}$]	0.052	0.023	0.076
Hydrogen [kWh/kWh$_{SNG}$]	-	1.198	1.198
CO_2 [kg/kWh$_{SNG}$]	-	0.209	0.209
Efficiency			0.679

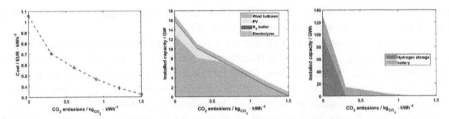

Figure 2: Graphic summary of the system design in the Netherlands, used as base case in this work. (left) pareto front, (middle) sizes of installed conversion technologies along the pareto front, (right) sizes of installed storage technologies along the pareto front

To estimate the CAPEX and O&M of an adsorbtion-based direct air capture system, the commonly used value of 600 EUR/t_{CO2} (Socolow et al., 2011) is applied to the Climeworks pilot plant of 1000 t_{CO2}/y, i.e. total unit cost of 12'000 EUR/(t_{CO2}/y) assuming 20 years lifetime. The values reported in (Alhajaj et al., 2016) for heat, electricity, and labor cost and an additional 10 % of CAPEX for maintenance and other financial factors, together with the performance parameters described in the previous section, allow to extract the CAPEX from the known total cost, giving 5294 EUR/(t_{CO2}/y) or 9699 EUR/kW$_{SNG}$. For the methanation, a value of 130 EUR/kW$_{SNG}$ was assumed (Götz et al., 2016) resulting in total CAPEX of 9829 EUR/kW$_{SNG}$ for the DAC-FP unit.

3. Results

Henceforth, we define the Netherlands with static production, i.e. without SNG storage (compare with Figure 1), as base case. Figure 2 shows the pareto front and the technology sizing for all optimal designs of this base case, i.e. ranging from minimum cost to minimum emissions. The total system costs range from 0.33 to 1.06 EUR/kWh$_{SNG}$. While all electricity is imported for the cheapest design (high-emission side of the pareto front), wind turbines are the main source of electricity upon emission reduction. Given Dutch weather conditions, photovoltaics are only used when very low emissions are aimed for. Looking at the storage technologies, it can be observed that hydrogen storage clearly dominates for low emissions and even hits the arbitrarily set cap of 100 GWh for the emission-free scenario. The correlation between installed wind power capacity and hydrogen storage is in accordance with the scientific consensus that the seasonal character of renewable power generation favors seasonal storage solutions like power-to-hydrogen (Gabrielli et al., 2020). Along those lines, hydrogen storage also dominates for UAE, where the system relies entirely on photovoltaics and electricity from the grid. However, with a maximum installed capacity of 36 GWh it does not hit the cap. This indicates that the costs, 21 EUR/kWh for hydrogen storage compared to 150 EUR/kWh for batteries, are another significant driver for the dominance of hydrogen storage over batteries given that supporting facilities like electrolyzers have to be installed anyway in this setting. Flexible operation of the DAC-FP unit facilitated by SNG storage was not observed. This can be explained by the high investment cost of DAC-FP, resulting in a situation where the gain through flexible operation does not justify the increase in costs due to required oversizing of the DAC-FP unit.

3.1. Effect of location

Differences in solar irradiation and wind speed profiles but also in electricity prices and electricity grid emission factors are the drivers for local differentiation of the results.

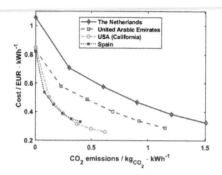

Figure 3: Pareto fronts for the 4 locations considered in this work

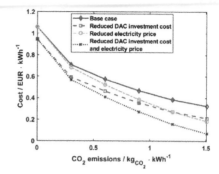

Figure 4: Pareto fronts for the Dutch system design using different cost assumptions. The reduced DAC investment cost is 1453 EUR/kW$_{SNG}$ and the electricity price is reduced by a factor 100

From Figure 3 it can be observed that the emissions for the cheap designs vary significantly, driven by the difference in emission factors. Nevertheless, as the electricity import from the grid gradually reduces upon emission reduction, and given the high contribution of the DAC's costs to the total system costs, the minimum emission specific cost is similar for all considered locations despite differences in the energy system design. In the Netherlands, the total system costs are higher along the full pareto front, mainly due to higher oversizing of wind turbines and photovoltaics to compensate for more volatile wind and irradiation profiles.

3.2. Effect of DAC investment cost and electricity price

To investigate the effect of the highly uncertain costs of DAC and electricity, the base case was simulated with lowered costs. For the DAC, costs of 1453 EUR/kW$_{SNG}$ (Keith et al., 2018) were used, resulting in a cost reduction for the coupled DAC-FP unit of 85 %. The electricity price was lowered by a factor 100.

As can be seen in Figure 4, decreasing both DAC investment cost and electricity price decreases the system cost to a range of 0.07 (high-emission) to 0.95 (low-emission) EUR/kWh$_{SNG}$. Comparing this with the household retail price for conventional national gas of roughly 0.06 EUR/kWh (EU-28 average 2019) shows that the investigated system can be economically competitive if cheap clean electricity is available and carbon tax is factored in.

As expected, decreasing the DAC cost facilitated flexible operation. Nevertheless, with technology oversizing of just 2.9 % the effect was minor.

4. Conclusion

In this work, we investigated the economic and environmental performance of SNG production from air-captured CO₂ and hydrogen, and its related energy supply system for four different locations. With the current electricity price and DAC cost, and if the system is optimized for cost, electricity is mainly supplied by the grid. Hence, electricity prices and emission factors determine the economic and environmental performance, ranging from 0.26 to 0.33 EUR/kWh$_{SNG}$ and 0.4 to 1.5 kgCO2/kWh$_{SNG}$ for the four locations. From those figures, it can be concluded that the location affects the environmental performance and the exact energy system design, but the influence on the final economic performance is limited. Decreasing the cost of DAC by 85 % leads to a cost reduction for an emission free design of about 11 % (0.95 compared to 1.07 EUR/kWh$_{SNG}$). Further reduction of investment cost for DAC is necessary to make this system economically feasible, though unlikely to happen in the short/medium term. Moreover, it was found that cheap clean electricity will be key to bring the costs down, especially as the contribution of the DAC investment cost decreases. Finally, a flexible DAC system, which is capable of operating following the electricity and demand as best for the objective function, was found to have limited effects on the costs. Indeed, more severe reduction on the investment cost would be necessary to justify the required oversizing.

References

Alhajaj, A., mac Dowell, N., Shah, N., 2016. A techno-economic analysis of post-combustion CO2 capture and compression applied to a combined cycle gas turbine: Part II. Identifying the cost-optimal control and design variables. International Journal of Greenhouse Gas Control 52, 331–343.

Gabrielli, P., Gazzani, M., Martelli, E., Mazzotti, M., 2018a. Optimal design of multi-energy systems with seasonal storage. Applied Energy 219, 408–424.

Gabrielli, P., Gazzani, M., Mazzotti, M., 2018b. Electrochemical conversion technologies for optimal design of decentralized multi-energy systems: Modeling framework and technology assessment. Applied Energy 221, 557–575.

Gabrielli, P., Poluzzi, A., Kramer, G.J., Spiers, C., Mazzotti, M., Gazzani, M., 2020. Seasonal energy storage for zero-emissions multi-energy systems via underground hydrogen storage. Renewable and Sustainable Energy Reviews 121, 109629.

Geidl, M., Koeppel, G., Favre-Perrod, P., Klöckl, B., Andersson, G., Fröhlich, K., 2007. Energy hubs for the future. IEEE Power and Energy Magazine 5, 24–30.

Götz, M., Lefebvre, J., Mörs, F., McDaniel Koch, A., Graf, F., Bajohr, S., Reimert, R., Kolb, T., 2016. Renewable Power-to-Gas: A technological and economic review. Renewable Energy 85, 1371–1390.

Keith, D.W., Holmes, G., st. Angelo, D., Heidel, K., 2018. A Process for Capturing CO2 from the Atmosphere. Joule 2, 1573–1594.

IPCC, 2018. Global Warming of 1.5 °C. An IPCC Special Report on the impacts of global warming of 1.5°C above pre-industrial levels and related global greenhouse gas emission pathways, in the context of strengthening the global response to the threat of climate chan.

Müller, B., Müller, K., Teichmann, D., Arlt, W., 2011. Energiespeicherung mittels Methan und energietragenden Stoffen ein thermodynamischer Vergleich. Chemie-Ingenieur-Technik 83, 2002–2013.

Socolow, R., Desmond, M., Aines, R., Blackstock, J., Bolland, O., Kaarsberg, T., Lewis, N., Mazzotti, M., Pfeffer, A., Sawyer, K., Siirola, J., Smit, B., Wilcox, J., 2011. Direct Air Capture of CO2 with Chemicals: A Technology Assessment for the APS Panel on Public Affairs, APS physics.

Sutter, D., van der Spek, M., Mazzotti, M., 2019. 110th Anniversary: Evaluation of CO2-Based and CO2-Free Synthetic Fuel Systems Using a Net-Zero-CO2-Emission Framework. Industrial and Engineering Chemistry Research 58, 19958–19972.

Sauro Pierucci, Flavio Manenti, Giulia Bozzano, Davide Manca (Eds.)
Proceedings of the 30th European Symposium on Computer Aided Process Engineering
(ESCAPE30), May 24-27, 2020, Milano, Italy. © 2020 Elsevier B.V. All rights reserved.
http://dx.doi.org/10.1016/B978-0-12-823377-1.50247-0

Computational Tools used in Hybrid Renewable Energy Systems Optimization-An overview

H. O. Guelleh, I. M. Mujtaba[*], R. Patel

School of Engineering, Faculty of Engineering and Informatics.,
University of Bradford. Bradford, West Yorkshire BD7 1DP, UK
I.M.Mujtaba@bradford.ac.uk

Abstract

In nowadays, renewable energy has become a key area of interest for solving many problems such as climate changes, security of energy supply, and poverty reduction. To face these challenges and issues, the penetration and the implementation of renewable energy technologies have been done through Hybrid energy systems (HES). The aim of this work is to highlight an overview of software tools used in HES to get an optimum design of HES to get a better reliability and efficiency of electricity generated and to save the cost of installation. Within this context, the most software tools used widely in terms of techno-economic design of HES are so far HOMER, iHOGA, and RETScreen. This paper will help policy makers, academic researchers and energy planners to take a better decision for the paradigm shift of renewable energy.

1. Introduction

Concerns about climate change with GHG emissions, energy security supply and depletion of fossil fuel resources have certainly contributed the urgent search for alternative renewable energies.   However, one of the United Nations Sustainable Development Goals (SDGs), Goal#7, which defines global goals for sustainable, affordable, and clean energy, and Kyoto protocol, a part of United Nations Framework Convention on Climate Change (United Nation, 2018), are not the only factors pushing developing countries in the direction of renewable and clean energy. But, developing countries see this opportunity to compensate their insufficient electricity-production capacity, in order to reduce fossil fuel dependence, and imported electricity from neighbouring countries for their energy security supply by developing their potential indigenous renewable resources. Moreover, these renewable resources are mostly intermittent such as solar, wind, and wave energy resources. But if they are combined of two or more renewable energy unit and fossil fuel unit (Diesel generators), they form Hybrid Energy System (HES). These HES could be stand alone or grid-connected HES such as wind-hydro-PV, Solar-Wind-Diesel generator, Solar-Wind-Battery, Solar-Wind-Biomass, or solar-wind grid connected. In electricity sector, HES improves the reliability, efficiency and the production of electricity generated (Abhishek, et al, 2018). To avoid high installation cost, having adequate sizing, simulation and optimization software tools are very essential for the efficient utilization of hybrid energy systems.

This paper presents an overview of software tools used in hybrid energy systems optimization. The extensive approaches of optimization in hybrid energy system are beyond the scope of this paper. The structure of this paper will be as follows. Section 2 describes literature review. In section 3, software tools for hybrid energy systems are presented. In section 4, the results and a brief discussion are presented, and section 5 will conclude the work proposed in this paper.

2. Literature overview

2.1 Overview of hybrid energy systems optimization techniques
Combining different renewable energy units in HES can be costly and technically difficult to be feasible. Therefore, an optimal planning of HES design is deemed necessary in order to minimise the cost of the installation. The first process of optimizing of the hybrid energy system is creating an appropriate model which, in turn, will determine the objective function of a problem mathematically. After modelling, the next step is to choose the appropriate software tool in order to make the simulation and find the optimal solution (Tezer et al. 2017).

In the literature, to solve the optimization problem for HES, various optimization techniques have been used in hybrid Energy systems (Connolly et al. 2010). Some various optimizations methods or techniques are listed in table 1.

Table 1. Various optimization techniques used in hybrid energy system design

• Neural Networks	• Linear programming methodology
• Parametric and numerical approaches	• Iterative and probabilistic approaches
• Quasi-Newton methodology	• Evolutionary algorithm
• Response surface methodology	• Dynamic programming
• Simplex algorithm	• Design space based approach
• Stochastic approach	• "Energy hub" concept
• Matrix approach	

Negi and Matthew (2014) highlighted also that several optimization techniques available for sizing optimization of HES in order to minimize the cost while maintaining the reliability. These techniques are probabilistic approach, graphical construction method, iterative technique, artificial intelligence method, etc.

2.2. Software tools for hybrid Energy Systems

The online market is sometimes a daunting place to find suitable software energy tools for the integration of renewable energy into energy systems or hybrid renewable energy systems (HRES). Many tools have been developed and applied to energy sector that is itself divided into electricity sector, heat sector and transport sector. Right in the beginning of a project, the researcher or the energy planner needs to define the job that the software tool is going to perform, the kind of software tool they require to perform the job and how the software tool is going to perform that job. The following example in table 2 is given to understand better.

Table 2. Example of choice for software energy tool selection

Energy capability categorization	External process of software tool selection	Technical process of software tool requirements to complete the job needed.
Example: -Pre-feasibility study -Short-term energy planning -Future energy planning	Example: -Energy software tool must be freely available without charge for downloading -It must support technical and economic analysis -Complete software package -Short software training –1 to 3 days	Example: -Energy model -Simulation and optimization - Technical and economic analysis -Greenhouse gas analysis -Financial summary -Sensitivity and risk analysis

Suresh and Meenakumari (2018) have discussed briefly 17 energy software tools for. Out of these 17 energy software tools, HOMER, iHOGA, and IGRYHSO simulate and optimise as hybrid energy systems software tools.

Connolly et al. (2010) had done an extensive research and reviewed 37 computer energy tools out of 67 outlining briefly their application. The goal of their study was to provide the individual description of these 37 computer energy tools so that the reader or the decision-maker can choose the right energy tool suitable to accomplish the primary goal of their project. In this regard, Connolly et al. (2010) highlighted that HOMER can perform techno-economic optimization for hybrid energy systems. In another study, Bernal-Agustin and Dufo-Lopez (2009) revised some of the simulation and optimization software tools of hybrid systems. HOMER, HYBRID2, HOGA, TRNSYS, HYGROGEMS, INSEL, ARES, RAPSIM, SOMES, SOLSIM. Out of these hybrid systems software tools, HOMER, HOGA, and HYDROGEMS can only perform economical optimization. However, HYDRGOGEMS has got some limitations. It is not a whole program but series of libraries. It can only perform optimization if it goes with TRNSYS.

3. Software tools for Hybrid Energy Systems

The following figure1 represents an example of HES's schematic configuration.

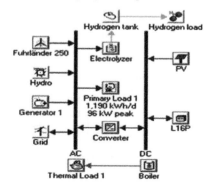

Figure 1. Hybrid Renewable Energy System configuration

From literature review and academic experience, the following table 3 gives an overview of software tools for simulation and optimization of hybrid energy systems

Table 3. Up to date Software tools for simulation and optimization of Hybrid Energy Systems

Software tools	Simulation	Economic Optimization	Availability on the market	Free of charge or commercial
HOMER	YES	YES	YES	FREE
RETScreen	YES	YES	YES	FREE
EMPS	YES	NO	YES	PRICED
EnergyPRO	YES	NO	YES	PRICED
TRNSYS	YES	NO	YES	PRICED
HYBRIDS2	YES	NO	YES	DEMO version with password free
INSEL	YES	NO	NO	-
SOLSTOR	YES	YES	NO	-
HySim	YES	NO	NO	-
HybSim	YES	NO	NO	-
HySys	YES	NO	NO	-
IPSYS	YES	NO	NO	-
RAPSIM	YES	NO	NO	-
SOLSIM	YES	NO	NO	-
iHOGA	YES	YES	YES	EDU version free.
iGRYHSO	YES	YES	Spanish version	PRICED

4. Results and Discussions

4.1. Results: software tools for HRES optimization

The following table 4 summarizes software tools which have the capability to do optimization for hybrid energy systems techno-economic design. As it can be noticed from table 3, most software tools supporting hybrid energy system have the capability of performing simulation. However, three of them support only their optimization in order to reduce the cost of their installation and to get the best optimum design for their technicality.

Table 4. Software tools supporting Hybrid Energy Systems optimization

TOOLS	Free of charge or commercial?	Duration of training
HOMER	Download Free of charge from https://www.homerenergy.com	1 day
iHOGA	EDU version is free from https://ihoga.unizar.es/en/descarga/	1 day
RETScreen	free-of-charge from https://www.nrcan.gc.ca/energy/retscreen/7465	1 day

The following points give a brief explanation of HOMER, iHOGA, and RETScreen capable of supporting HES optimization.

- ## *HOMER*

Hybrid Optimization Model for Electric Renewable (HOMER) is developed by National Renewable Energy Laboratory (NREL) in USA. It is available on the market. Many researchers have used it for the prefeasibility, sizing HES technologies, and techno-economic analysis of their projects. The newest version HOMER Pro and HOMER Grid can be downloaded with a 21 free trial days and a variety of licences. However, older versions such as HOMER 2.68 beta can be freely downloaded through permission by contacting Homer Energy.

- ## *iHOGA*

Improved Hybrid Optimization by Genetic Algorithm is a hybrid system optimization tool developed by University of Zaragoza, Spain. It has replaced the older version HOGA. iHOGA is available in English. It has got two versions namely PRO+ and EDU. EDU version is freely downloadable. However, it can only simulate a maximum daily load of 10kWh.

- ## *RET Screen*

Renewable Energy Technologies Screen (RETScreen) is developed by Ministry of Natural Resources in Canada. It helps to determine the techno-economic viability of hybrid energy systems (HES) or integrated renewable energy systems (IRES). Mostly it is used to perform the feasibility study of simulation of cogeneration projects but it can also perform optimization of hybrid energy systems. However, RETScreen Expert is available free of charge in viewer mode as an advanced premium version. To get the ability options to save, print or export files, RETScreen Expert in professional mode is necessary and it needs to be purchased.

4.2. Discussions

Many researchers have given an extensive literature review on software tools. Essential constraints that were included such as the availability these tools on the market or whether they are free-of-charge or commercial and the duration of the training in order to use the model tool. This information is important for the academic researchers if their educational institutions do not provide these tools to save some time. This is due to the fact that some software tools can be very expensive and it can take also up to several months of training to use the software. For example, according to Connolly et al. (2010) EPMPS costs NOK 500, 000 (€54,930) and takes one month of training to use it. Moreover, some energy tools for HES are no longer used or maintained such as SOLSTOR, HySim, and SOMES. Besides, some of them are not available for external users or they are not for sale such as AELIUS, H2RES. Hybrid 2 software is free to be downloaded. However, it does not work on windows platforms later than Windows XP such as Windows 10. And iHOGA can simulate only a maximum 10kWh of daily load.

5. Conclusion

Hybrid Energy Systems have the following advantage:

- To save fossil fuel
- To have a higher reliability and a better efficiency in electricity generation
- To save the cost of HES technologies when optimum design is used.

In this study, an overview of HES simulation and optimization is given. It has been concluded that only few software tools have the capability so far of giving an optimum design for the implementation of hybrid renewable energy systems. These tools are HOMER (widely used), iHOGA, and RETScreen. The following figure 2 shows the screens of these three software tools.

References

K.S.N.Abhishek ,M.K.V.Kiran Kumar, R.S.Mansoor Ali, 2018.Analysis of Software Tools for Renewable Energy Systems. International Conference on Computation of Power, Energy, Information and Communication (ICCPEIC), IEEE:pp. 179-185, ISBN: 1538624478

José L., Bernal-Agustín, and Rodolfo Dufo-López, 2009. Simulation and optimization of stand-alone hybrid renewable energy systems. Renewable and Sustainable Energy Reviews, 13(8):pp. 2111-2118

D. Connolly, H. Lund , B.V. Mathiesen , M. Leahy, 2010. A review of computer tools for analysing the integration of renewable energy into various energy systems. Applied Energy, 87 (4) , pp. 1059-1082.

Samir M. Dawoud, Xiangning Lin, Merfat I. Okba, 2018. Hybrid renewable micro-grid optimization techniques: A review. Renewable and Sustainable Energy Reviews. Volume 82:p. 2039-2052

S., Negi, and L., Matthew, 2014. Hybrid renewable energy system: a review. International Journal of Electronic and Electrical Engineering, 2014. Volume 7, Issue 5: P. 535-542.

M., Suresh, and R., Meenakumari, 2018. Software Tools for Analyzing the Integration of Various Renewable Energy Systems, . Issue 2456-8449:p. 135-140

T. Tezer, Tuba, R. Yaman, and G.Yaman, 2017. Evaluation of approaches used for optimization of stand-alone hybrid renewable energy systems. Renewable and Sustainable Energy Reviews, Volume 73: P.840-853.

United Nations, The Sustainable Development Goals 2018. New York, United Nations, P.40.
https://unstats.un.org/sdgs/files/report/2018/TheSustainableDevelopmentGoalsReport20 18-EN.pdf [Access Date: 15 September 2019]

Sauro Pierucci, Flavio Manenti, Giulia Bozzano, Davide Manca (Eds.)
Proceedings of the 30th European Symposium on Computer Aided Process Engineering
(ESCAPE30), May 24-27, 2020, Milano, Italy. © 2020 Elsevier B.V. All rights reserved.
http://dx.doi.org/10.1016/B978-0-12-823377-1.50248-2

Sour Gas Sweetening Technologies for Distributed Resources – A Process Simulation Study

Shuang Xu[a], Yushi Deng[a], Kylie Webb[b], Harrison Wright[b], Paul S. Dimick[b],
Selen Cremaschi[a] , Mario R. Eden[a]

[a]*Department of Chemical Engineering, Auburn University, Auburn, AL 36849, USA*
[b]*Intramicron, Inc., Auburn, AL 36832, USA*
edenmar@auburn.edu

Abstract

With increasing natural gas consumption, a wider range of gas fields/resources is being explored, however utilization of distributed natural gas resources remains a challenge. The primary reasons are that the cost of processing/treatment and transport, which can be higher than the natural gas selling price. Furthermore, distributed/stranded gas resources are typically limited in volume/capacity, which may them uneconomic to recover. Therefore, the identification of low cost small scale gas treatment processes is a key enabling step in utilization of distributed natural gas resources. Desulfurization is a critical natural gas treatment process, as it removes H_2S, which is a catalyst poison and also avoids the formation of SO_2. In order to identify a suitable small scale desulfurization process, we evaluate three technologies, triazine absorption, LOCAT, and SourCat, and analyze their techno-economic performance at different conditions.

Keywords: Natural gas desulfurization, small scale operation, process simulation

1. Introduction

Desulfurization is a very important step in utilization of natural gas resources, not only in terms of preventing the formation of SO_2 after combustion, but also to avoid catalyst poisoning in subsequent processing steps. It is estimated that 30% of the global natural gas reserves are distributed, i.e. located away from the processing infrastructure and/or market demand (Baldea et al., 2017). In Alaska, for example, there are large amounts of natural gas stranded in oil fields, and the gas is not being utilized due to both the cost of recovery and required pipeline construction. Current practice for transporting distributed gas resources to market is either by pipeline or as liquefied natural gas (LNG). Wood et al. (2008) have shown that the most economic transportation mode is actually through gas to liquid (GTL) processing, when the production rate is small and the gas well is far away from the intended market. As a result, identification of low cost small scale desulfurization processes can stimulate utilization of stranded natural gas through scalable GTL processes. In this paper, we briefly review current desulfurization processes and present a simulation-based economic study for three small scale processes along with the preferred operational scale for each.

2. Background

In general, desulfurization processes can be classified by three primary types, i.e. absorption, chemical oxidation, and adsorption. Absorption processes use a solvent to absorb (either chemically or physically) the sulfur component(s) and then the solvent is regenerated in a stripping column. The concentrated gas leaving the stripping column is typically sent to a chemical oxidation process. Current industrial practice involves the use of various solvents including amines, caustic, triazine, and methanol. It should be noted that while the triazine based process does not regenerate the solvent, but it exhibits very good performance at small scale. As mentioned above, the concentrated sulfur stream is fed to a chemical oxidation step to produce elemental sulfur or sulfuric acid. Typical processes include solid bed oxidation (Claus, SourCat), liquid redox (LOCAT/Sulferox), and wet sulfuric acid (WSA), some of which are widely applied at commercial/large scale. SourCat and LOCAT/Sulferox have shown potential for small scale operation (Catalyst Commercialization, 2017; Echt et al., 2017). Therefore, triazine absorption, LOCAT, and SourCat were selected for this study.

3. Process Simulation

The sour gas feedstream is at 95°C and 115 psi and the sulfur concentration should be reduced to less than 4 ppm (Faramawy et al., 2016) before it can be sent to downstream processing. Furthermore, to illustrate the process performance at different scales the feed flow rate is varied from 100,000 standard cubic feet per day (MSCFD) to 100,000,000 standard cubic feet per day (MMSCFD), and the H_2S content ranges from 500 to 2000 ppm. All three desulfurization processes are simulated using Aspen Plus and the Aspen Process Economic Analyzer is used to calculate equipment sizes etc.

3.1. Triazine-based Absorption

Three reactions take place in the absorption column (Eqs. 1-3) with the primary reaction given in Eq. (1). The product of the reaction in Eq. (2) forms a solid inside the vessel, which may cause plugging problems. To avoid the formation of solids, the triazine feed is kept at 20% excess. The process flowsheet is given in Figure 1. The feed gas is first mixed with water to mimic the actual saturated sour gas conditions. Next, the saturated gas is cooled to the reaction temperature. After that, the sour gas along with a 52 wt% triazine solution is fed to an absorber, where the sulfur components are captured at temperatures ranging from 10 to 70°C. The sweet gas stream leaving the absorber contains less than 4 ppm sulfur, and the liquid stream consists of spent triazine, which will be sent to disposal. As such, the process costs are primarily related to the solvent usage and thus the triazine price will greatly influence the operating costs.

$$C_9H_{21}N_3O_3 + 3H_2S \rightarrow C_3H_6O_3 + 3C_2H_7NO \tag{1}$$
$$C_9H_{21}N_3O_3 + H_2S \rightarrow C_7H_{16}N_2O_2S + C_2H_7NO \tag{2}$$
$$C_7H_{16}N_2O_2S + H_2S \rightarrow C_5H_{11}NOS_2 + C_2H_7NO \tag{3}$$

3.2. Liquid Redox (LOCAT)

The LOCAT process (shown in Figure 2) uses a liquid catalyst (chelate iron) to convert the sulfur component(s) to elemental sulfur and then the catalyst is regenerated using oxygen. The reactions are show in Eqs. (4-5). Because of the ferric ions in the system, the pH of the solution should be strictly maintained between 8 and 9. Typically, sodium is added to the system to help with pH control. The inlet iron concentration is 250 ppm and the Fe^{3+}: H_2S molar ratio is kept at 4:1. Different to the triazine process above, the saturated sour gas is cooled to remove the water to avoid diluting the liquid catalyst. Next, the dry sour gas along with the liquid catalyst solution is fed to an absorber to generate elemental sulfur at temperatures ranging from 27 to 55°C and pressures from 1 to 34 atm. The gaseous stream leaving the absorber contains the sweetened gas, while the liquid phase contains sulfur and ferrous ions is fed to the regeneration column, where the ferric ions are regenerated by reaction with oxygen. Finally, the solid sulfur is captured using a filter, and the liquid catalyst along with makeup catalyst material is recycled to the absorber. Depending on the type of filter used, the sulfur cake mass fraction varies from 30% to 90%. To balance the accumulation of water and catalyst recovery, the sulfur cake mass fraction is specified at 48%.

$$2Fe^{3+} + HS^- \rightarrow 2Fe^{2+} + S + H^+ \tag{4}$$
$$2Fe^{2+} + \tfrac{1}{2}O_2 + H_2O \rightarrow 2Fe^{3+} + 2OH^- \tag{5}$$

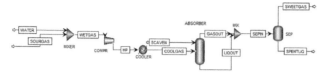

Figure 1. Triazine absorption process flow diagram.

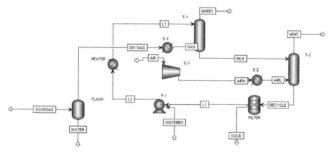

Figure 2. Liquid redox (LOCAT) process flow diagram.

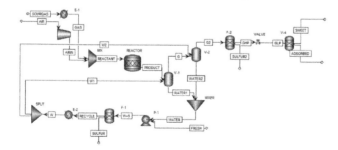

Figure 3. Process flow diagram of SourCat process.

3.3. Chemical Oxidation (SourCat)

The SourCat process (shown in Figure 3) directly converts H_2S to elemental sulfur with SO_2 as a side product as shown in Eqs. (6-7). The catalyst exhibits more than 90% conversion and selectivity. Because of the side product and remaining H2S, a sorbent bed is needed. Similar to the Triazine process, the saturated sour gas can be directly fed to the system without first removing the water. First, the sour gas and oxygen feeds are heated to 200°C at 115 psi and then fed to a solid bed reactor to generate elemental sulfur. The reaction is highly exothermic, so tight temperature control is needed, especially when scaling up the process. Following the reaction, the elemental sulfur is captured by a water quench and then separated by a filter. A 20% water loss is specified for the filter, and the rest of the water along with makeup fresh water is recycled back to the quench system.

The gaseous product can be sent to downstream processing after passing through a sorbent bed.

$$\frac{1}{2}O_2 + H_2S \rightarrow H_2O + S \tag{6}$$

$$\frac{3}{2}O_2 + H_2S \rightarrow H_2O + SO_2 \tag{7}$$

4. Economic Analysis

Following the simulation studies, equipment sizes from Aspen Process Economic Analyzer are input to a process economics tool ECON (Kalakul et al., 2014) to calculate the capital (CAPEX) and operating (OPEX) costs. These values are then used to calculate the desulfurization cost as defined in Eqs. (8-9), where the annual interest (i) is set at 10% and the payoff period (n) is three years.

$$\text{Desulfurization cost before pay off} = \frac{CAPEX \times \frac{i(1+i)^n}{(1+i)^n - 1} + OPEX}{Capacity} \tag{8}$$

$$\text{Desulfurization cost after pay off} = \frac{OPEX}{Capacity} \tag{9}$$

4.1. Validation of Simulation Results

In order to verify the results from the simulation and economic analyses, a comparison with reference data is performed. The LOCAT reference data (Echt et al., 2017; Judd and Eng, 2006) along with the simulation results are shown in Table 1. It can be seen that our results fall within the ranges of the reference data and as such indicates that the simulation and cost estimation models can reasonably represent the actual processes. The same comparison is performed for the triazine absorption process and the results, which have confirmed by our collaborators, are shown in Table 2. It should be noted that the triazine prices can fluctuate significantly, and since the process cost depends almost entirely on the triazine cost, the operating cost in this study should be considered a general case not necessarily the optimal one.

Table 1. Validation of Results for LOCAT process (TPD: tons per day; ST: standard ton).

Parameter	Reference Data	Simulation Data
Capacity (sulfur removal)	0.5 – 20 TPD	3.8 TPD
H_2S concentration	10000 ppm	10000 ppm
Gas flow rate	0.01 – 200 MMSCFD	10 MMSCFD
Iron concentration	250 – 1000 ppm	250 ppm
OPEX (chemicals and electricity)	$250 - $1000 per ST	$436 per ST

Table 2. Validation of Results for Triazine Absorption Process.

Parameter	Reference Data	Simulation Data
H_2S concentration	100 ppm	100 ppm
Gas flow rate	1 MMSCFD	1 MMSCFD
OPEX	$1	$1.1

4.2. Cost Estimation at Different Conditions

After verifying the appropriateness of the simulation and economic models, we can evaluate the three desulfurization processes at different scales. Figure 4 shows the capital and operating costs of the three processes at 0.1 MMSCFD. It can be seen that the LOCAT process has the highest capital and operating cost at this scale. The triazine process has the lowest capital and operating costs, but the latter increases rapidly as the sulfur concentration goes up. The SourCat process exhibits medium capital cost and the operating cost remains fairly stable as a function of sulfur concentration as it uses a solid bed reactor and the primary contributor to the operating costs are utilities.

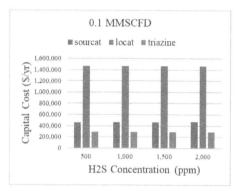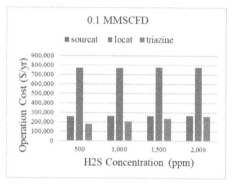

Figure 4. Capital and operating cost of desulfurization processes at 0.1 MMSCFD flow rate.

Next, the process economics are evaluated at flowrates of 1 MMSCFD, 10 MMSCFD, and 100 MMSCFD. Figure 5 shows the desulfurization cost for all three processes at the four different gas flowrates. For small scale conditions (gas flowrate less than 0.1 MMSCFD), the triazine process shows the lowest desulfurization cost, however as the gas flowrate increases (1-10 MMSCFD), the SourCat process shows the best performance. At the largest scale evaluated (100 MMSCFD), the results show that the SourCat and LOCAT processes have similar desulfurization costs, however it would appear that the LOCAT process could be favored if the flowrate was increased even further.

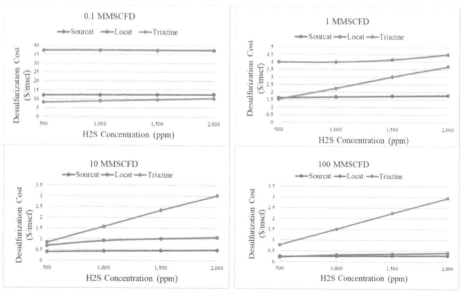

Figure 5. Desulfurization cost (with 3 year payoff) at different gas flowrates.

5. Conclusions

In this work, we have compared the performance of a novel small scale desulfurization process to two commercial industrial implementations. Following a detailed simulation study and subsequent cost estimation of all three processes (and validation against reference data where available), it was found that the triazine absorption process shows the best performance at very small scale (0.1 MMSCFD corresponding to a sulfur removal rate of 0.02 TPD), while the SourCat process has the lowest desulfurization cost at flowrates between 1 and 10 MMSCFD (corresponding to sulfur removal rates of 0.02-2 TPD). Finally, the LOCAT process is found to be better suited for large scale processes (over 100 MMSCFD). As new intensified/modular technologies for GTL and other valorization strategies for stranded gas resources are developed, the ability to remove sulfur from the feed gas will be of critical importance. This study provides a foundation for insightful selection of the appropriate desulfurization technology for small scale natural gas conditioning.

Acknowledgements

The authors are grateful for the financial support provided by the DOE-RAPID Process Intensification Institute under contract DE-EE0007888-10-6.

References

Baldea, M., Edgar, T.F., Stanley, B.L., (2017). Modular manufacturing processes: status, challenges, and opportunities. AIChE journal, 63(10), 4262-4272.

Catalyzing Commercialization: Sour Gas Has a Sweeter Future. (2017). Retrieved from https://www.aiche.org/resources/publications/cep/2017/january/catalyzing-commercialization-sour-gas-has-sweeter-future.

Echt, B., Leppin, D., Mamrosh, D., Mirdadian, D., Seeger, D., Warren, B., (2017). Fundamentals of low-tonnage sulfur removal and recovery. In Proceedings of 2017 Laurance Reid Gas Conditioning Conference.

Faramawy, S., Zaki, T., Sakr, A.A.E., (2016). Natural gas origin, composition, and processing: A review. Journal of Natural Gas Science and Engineering, 34, 34-54.

Judd, B., Eng, P., (2003). Fundamentals - gas sweetening. In Proceedings of 2003 Laurance Reid Gas Conditioning Conference.

Kalakul, S., Malakul, P., Siemanond, K., Gani, R., (2014). Integration of life cycle assessment software with tools for economic and sustainability analyses and process simulation for sustainable process design. Journal of Cleaner Production, 71, 98-109.

Wood, D., Mokhatab, S., Economides, M.J., (2008). Technology options for securing markets for remote gas, In Proceedings of 87th Annual Convention of the Gas Processors Association (GPA).

Sauro Pierucci, Flavio Manenti, Giulia Bozzano, Davide Manca (Eds.)
Proceedings of the 30th European Symposium on Computer Aided Process Engineering
(ESCAPE30), May 24-27, 2020, Milano, Italy. © 2020 Elsevier B.V. All rights reserved.
http://dx.doi.org/10.1016/B978-0-12-823377-1.50249-4

Supply Chain Design Optimization within Planetary Boundaries

Jonathan Wheeler,[a,b] Ángel Galán Martín,[b] Fernando D. Mele,[a] Gonzalo
Guillén-Gosálbez [b].

[a] *Consejo Nacional de Investigaciones Científicas y Técnicas, FACET-UNT, Av.
Independencia 1800, T4002BLR S. M. de Tucumán, Tucumán, República Argentina.*
[b] *Institute for Chemical and Bioengineering, Swiss Federal Institute of Technology in
Zurich, Vladimir-Prelog-Weg 1, Zurich, 8093, Switzerland.*
gonzalo.guillen.gosalbez@chem.ethz.ch

Abstract

The recently emerged Planetary Boundaries framework establishes global limits to human activities in order to avoid highly deleterious events that could shift the current state of the Earth. Here, for the first time we address the strategic design of sustainable supply chains (SCs) considering their absolute sustainability level using PBs. To this end, an MILP model is developed where the mass and energy flows of the network are linked to PBs, thereby enabling the maximization of their absolute environmental sustainability. To illustrate our approach, we studied the supply of sugarcane-based bioethanol in Argentina, considering local policies seeking to increase the gasoline-ethanol blend from 12% to 20% in the upcoming years. We found that none of the SC configurations can meet the eight downscaled PBs concurrently, although their transgression would be reduced significantly in the optimal solution. Our results highlight the need for incorporating PBs in the design of sustainable SCs in a globalized world.

Keywords: Planetary Boundaries, Supply Chain, Optimization, Bioethanol

1. Introduction

The growth in trade of goods and services resulting from increased globalization over the past decades has posed new challenges for the design, planning and operation of value chains. In the area of PSE, the strategic planning of SCs has attracted increasing interest in the last decades. This has led to a plethora of decision-support tools, most of which are based on optimization methods. In essence, the task of optimizing SCs requires: (i) building models for representing the network precisely; (ii) algorithms to solve these models efficiently; and (iii) analysis tools to interpret their optimal solutions insightfully. The latter cover activities from raw materials acquisition to the delivery of final products passing through all manufacturing, transportation and storage stages, which should be coordinated effectively for optimal operation of the network.

Traditional SC models focused on optimizing economic performance as a unique criterion, yet the recent quest for sustainability requires enlarging the scope of the analysis to embrace environmental and societal concerns as well. This has been accomplished through the integration of Life Cycle Assessment (LCA) and optimization tools, which allows covering the three sustainability pillars when optimizing SC decisions (*i.e.*, societal-human health, environmental-ecosystems quality, and economic-resources). The main drawback of the so-called Life Cycle Optimization (LCO) approach is that it allows comparing and optimizing solutions in terms of a set of impact metrics, but as such cannot answer the questions of whether they are "truly" sustainable.

Here we present an approach that overcomes this limitation by integrating the planetary boundaries (PBs) concept (Steffen et al., 2015; Rockström et al., 2009) into SC models to assist in the optimal design of sustainable SCs. In essence, the PBs framework identifies nine biophysical boundaries that define a "safe operating space" (SOS) for the Planet (*e.g.*, climate change, freshwater use or land-use change boundaries). Operating outside the SOS could lead to catastrophic events and a shift from the current Anthropocene state (where humanity flourished) to an unknown (most likely, much less friendly) state.

Our proposed framework provides a theoretical and methodological basis to evaluate SCs considering the carrying capacity of the Earth. This is accomplished by imposing limits on the SC operation, whose activities are linked to impacts on PBs. To illustrate the capabilities of the proposed framework, we applied it to the design of a biomass-to-biofuels SC that produces bioethanol from sugarcane in Argentina. Our framework aims at guiding practitioners, researchers and governments in the design and planning of SCs aligned with global sustainable development.

2. Modelling Framework

A general design problem of sustainable SCs can be mathematically expressed as follows:

$$
\begin{aligned}
&min\ \{f_{econ}, f_{env}, f_{soc}\} \\
&s.t.\quad f(x, y, z) = 0 \\
&\qquad\quad g(x, y, z) \leq 0 \\
&x \in \Re, y \in N, z \in Z^+
\end{aligned}
\tag{M1}
$$

where f_{econ}, f_{env} and f_{soc} are the economic, environmental and societal objective functions, and, x, Y and Z represent continuous, binary and integer decision variables, respectively, related to the design and operation of the SC. In essence, we incorporate PBs into this model by following LCA principles combined with a recently published damage assessment model that converts inventory flows into impacts on PBs. The overall approach is outlined in Figure 1. The PBs, defined globally, are first downscaled to the SC level. Next, LCA is applied to derive equations that link the SC operation to its performance in terms of PBs. Finally, M1 is solved with these equations embedded to find solutions that minimize the PBs transgression.

2.1. Environmental assessment using Planetary Boundaries

A total of 14 global and regional PBs have been defined, including climate change due to energy imbalance and CO_2 emissions, stratospheric ozone depletion, biogeochemical flows of nitrogen and phosphorus (global and regional), land-system change (global and biome), freshwater use (global and basin), atmospheric aerosol loading (global and regional), introduction of novel entities and biosphere integrity. While there is no full consensus on their exact values, there seems to be a general agreement on most of them and their global relevance (Steffen et al., 2015; O'Neill et al., 2018).

Here we are interested in assessing the performance of a SC in terms of these PBs. To this end, we include constraints in the optimization model that link any activity in the SC with its corresponding impact on PBs.

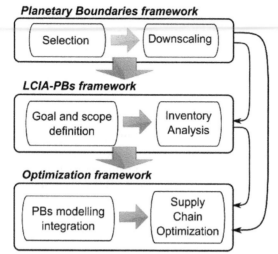

Figure 1. Flowsheet of the proposed modelling framework.

2.1.1. Step 1: Selection of Planetary Boundaries and downscaling

Due to some methodological gaps highlighted in previous work by some of us (Alguinabet et al., 2019), we omit here regional PBs on freshwater use, land system change and phosphorus flow, as well as the one defined on biodiverse integrity. We also omit atmospheric aerosol loading, as current values refer to the Indian subcontinent. Finally, the PB on the introduction of novel entities was also left out of the analysis because it has not been fully defined yet. A partition principle needs to be applied first to define an allowable budget for the SC activities (considering a given functional unit, FU) in each PB (Ryberg et al., 2018a). If the environmental impact of the activity remains below the value of the assigned share, it is deemed fully sustainable, while the converse would imply that it is unsustainable. Assigning a share of the SOS (SoSOS) is controversial. Without loss of generality, an Egalitarian principle is applied to calculate the share assigned (aS) from the final consumption expenditure (FCE) for the functional unit (FU) and the total FCE worldwide:

$$aS = \frac{FCE_{FU}}{FCE_{world}} \tag{1}$$

Next, the SoSOS for a PB b is calculated using the selected sharing principle and the value of the SOS, according to Eq. (2).

$$SoSOS_b = SOS_b \times aS_b \quad \forall b \tag{2}$$

Here $SoSOS_b$ is the quota of the SOS_b assigned to the FU considered following the sharing principle chosen (aS_b). The absolute sustainability level of a system is given by the ratio between the impact score in PBs and the $SoSOS_b$, as shown in Eq. (3).

$$FSoSOS_b = \frac{ES_b}{SoSOS_b} \quad \forall b \tag{3}$$

ES_b is the impact score of the activity measured in the units of a PB b, and $FSoSOS_b$ represents the occupied fraction of the SoSOS. Therefore, if this value is equal to or lower than one, the activity can be considered fully sustainable.

2.1.2. Step 2: Linking SC activities to their performance in PBs

The life cycle inventory entries are linked to PBs using the characterization factors (CF) in (Ryberg et al., 2018b). Therefore, we can calculate the environmental impact of an SC in terms of PBs as in Eq. (4):

$$ES_b = \sum_i F_i \sum_j LCI_{j,i} \cdot CF_{j,b} \quad \forall b \tag{4}$$

where ES_b is the total environmental flow in PB b, F_i is the material flow of product i, $LCI_{j,i}$ is the elementary flow j in the life cycle inventory of activity i (represented by a mass or energy flow) and $CF_{j,b}$ is the characterization factor that links the elementary flow j to PB b. We can define the transgression on a PB (PBT_b) as the difference between the environmental score of the SC (ES_b) and the downscaled value of the PB b ($SoSOS_b$).

2.1.3. Step 3: Solving the optimization model with embedded constraints on PBs
Finally, to solve the sustainable SC optimization problem, we add up the transgression level across PBs, as follows:

$$f_{env} = \sum_b \frac{PBT_b}{SoSOS_b} \tag{5}$$

$$PBT_b \geq 0 \quad \forall b \tag{6}$$

$$EP_b \leq SoSOS_b + PBT_b \quad \forall b \tag{7}$$

In Eq. (5-7), PBT_b is the transgression in PB b. If a PB is transgressed, the transgression level corresponds to the difference between the SC environmental impact EP_b and the downscaled PB ($SoSOS_b$). Otherwise, the transgression in that PB would be zero. Note that here f_{env} quantifies how many times the $SoSOS_b$ is exceeded.

3. Case study

We test the proposed framework by addressing the design of a biomass-to-biofuels SC. Specifically, we search for the optimal design of a three-echelon SC to produce bioethanol from sugarcane in Argentina considering its environmental and economic performance simultaneously and a ten-year time horizon. To this end, we modified a previous model (Wheeler et al., 2018) to introduce current industrial and transport practices as well as the PBs equations required to calculate the environmental performance of the SC .

3.1. Life cycle impact assessment
We adopt a well-to-wheel approach, where the FU is defined as *"the annual passenger transport in conventional cars using a gasoline and sugar cane ethanol blend in Argentina"*. Inventories for the agricultural and ethanol production stages were obtained from previous studies of the sugar-ethanol production in Argentina (Nishihara et al., 2017; Amores et al., 2013). Life cycle inventories to calculate PBs ($LCI_{j,i}$) were acquired from the Ecoinvent LCA database. LCI for ethanol transport and gasoline market were directly obtained from Ecoinvent 3.5®. Elementary flows for passengers transport were taken from GREET® (Wang et al., 2018).

3.2. Share of the safe operating space
We calculated first the SoSOS based on the FCEs in Argentina and the world (Eq. (1) and Eq. (2)). The domestic FCE for passenger transport in Argentina is 24 billion US$, while the FCE of the world is 43900 billion US$. Thus, the share of the SOS for to the FU (aS_{AR}-

Thus, the share of the SOS for to the FU *(aSAR-transp)* is 0.0274%. The values of the PBs studied in this work, their background level and the SOS can be found in Ryberg et al.

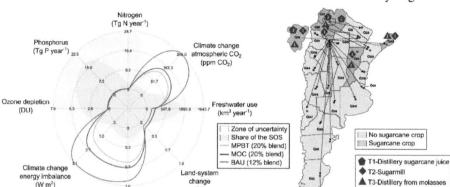

Figure 2. Supply chain performance in PBs for the MPBT, MOC and BAU solutions. Full lines show the environmental performance in eight planetary boundaries; the darker area is the safe operating space and the lighter one, the uncertainty zone. a) Supply chain topology for the MPBT solution.

3.3. Results

Fig. 2 depicts the environmental performance relative to the downscaled PBs of the minimum cost and minimum transgression solutions together with the BAU solution. Although there are significant improvements in the environmental performance in the MPBT solution, no SC configuration meets all PBs concurrently. Three PBs were transgressed beyond the uncertainty zone: climate change (in CO_2 concentration and energy imbalance), and ocean acidification. Here, fossil emissions (gasoline) are the main contribution to the environmental scores, where the amount of bioethanol in gasoline blends is limited to 20%. The score in land system change also transgresses the downscaled PB; meanwhile, values for MOC and MPBT remained in the uncertainty range. The worsening in this PB compared to the BAU solution is mainly related to a more extensive agricultural activity needed to increase bioethanol production.

Concerning the SC design decisions, we find by minimizing the PBs transgression, that the model decides to change the current technologies (T2 and T3) to direct ethanol production from sugar cane (T1), in the central crop regions (G13, G16 and G17). Moreover, in crop regions that only produce sugar (G09 and G18) currently, the model decides to produce ethanol from molasses (T3). This investment scheme for the MPBT solution, reports a 23.12% higher total costs compared to the topology results for the MOC solution, but a 71.56% improvement in the total transgression of PBs.

4. Conclusions

We proposed here a novel framework to assist in the design of SCs within the safe operating space of the Earth System. Our approach relies on the use of optimization models that incorporate equations to link the SC activities with its performance in terms of PBs. We applied our approach to the design of a real SC producing bioethanol from sugarcane in Argentina to satisfy increased fuels demands in the transportation sector. Overall, our results show that despite significant improvements in PBs performance compared with the business-as-usual scenario, there is no configuration capable of meeting all PBs considering a 20% gasoline blend. This highlights the need for higher-blends, which should be promoted through government mandates, or alternative transportation technologies. The proposed framework provides a sound tool to support practitioners and researchers in the development of optimization models for the design of sustainable SCs entirely consistent with the carrying capacity of our Planet.

References

I.M. Algunaibet, C. Pozo, Á. Galán-Martín, M.A. J. Huijbregts, N. Mac Dowell, G. Guillén-Gosálbez. 2019. Powering sustainable development within planetary boundaries. Energy Environ. Sci., 12, 1890.

M.J. Amores, F.D. Mele, L. Jiménez, F. Castells, 2013. Life cycle assessment of fuel ethanol from sugarcane in Argentina. Int J Life Cycle Assess., 18, 1344–1357.

Z. Kravanja, L. Čuček, 2013. Multi-objective optimization for generating sustainable solutions considering total effects on the environment. Appl.Energy 101, 67–80Z.

A.L. Nishihara Hun, F.D. Mele, G.A. Pérez, 2017. A comparative life cycle assessment of the sugarcane value chain in the province of Tucumán (Argentina) considering different technology levels. Int J Life Cycle Assess, 22:502–515.

D.W. O'Neill, A.L. Fanning, W.F. Lamb, J.K. Steinberger. 2018. A good life for all within planetary boundaries. Nature Sustainability,Volume 1, (2), 88-95.

J. Rockstrom, W. Steffen, K. Noone, A. Persson, F. S. Chapin, E. F. Lambin, T. M. Lenton, M. Scheffer, C. Folke, H. J. Schellnhuber, B. Nykvist, C. A. de Wit, T. Hughes, S. van der Leeuw, H. Rodhe, S. Sorlin, P. K. Snyder, R. Costanza, U. Svedin, M. Falkenmark, L. Karlberg, R. W. Corell, V. J. Fabry, J. Hansen, B. Walker, D. Liverman, K. Richardson, P. Crutzen and J. A. Foley, 2009. A safe operating space for humanity. Nature, 461, 472–475

M.W. Ryberg, M. Owsianiak, J. Clavreul, C. Mueller, S. Sim, H. King and M. Z. Hauschild, 2018a. How to bring absolute sustainability into decision-making: An industry case study using a Planetary Boundary-based methodology, Sci. Total Environ., 634, 1406–1416.

M.W. Ryberg, M. Owsianiak, K. Richardson and M. Z.Hauschild, 2018b. Development of a life-cycle impact assessment methodology linked to the Planetary Boundaries framework Ecol. Indic., 88, 250–262.

M.W. Ryberg, M. Owsianiak, K. Richardson, M.Z. Hauschild, 2016. Challenges in implementing a planetary boundaries based life-cycle impact assessment methodology. J. Clean. Prod. 139, 450–459.

W. Steffen, K. Richardson, J. Rockström, S.E. Cornell, E. M. Bennett, R. Biggs, S. R. Carpenter, W. de Vries, C. A. de Wit, C. Folke, D. Gerten, J. Heinke, G. M. Mace, L. M. Persson, V. Ramanathan, B. Reyers, S. Sörlin. 2015. Planetary boundaries: guiding human development on a changing planet. Science 347, 1217.

J. Wheeler, M.A. Páez, G. Guillén-Gosálbez, F.D. Mele, 2018. Combining multi-attribute decision-making methods with multi-objective optimization in the design of biomass supply schains. Computers and Chemical Engineering 113, 11–31.

M. Wang, A. Elgowainy, A., P. T. Benavides, A. Burnham, H. Cai, Q. Dai, ... & U. Lee. 2018. Summary of Expansions and Updates in GREET® 2018 (No. ANl-18/23). Argonne National Lab.(ANL), Argonne, IL (United States).

Sauro Pierucci, Flavio Manenti, Giulia Bozzano, Davide Manca (Eds.)
Proceedings of the 30th European Symposium on Computer Aided Process Engineering
(ESCAPE30), May 24-27, 2020, Milano, Italy. © 2020 Elsevier B.V. All rights reserved.
http://dx.doi.org/10.1016/B978-0-12-823377-1.50250-0

Simultaneous Multiperiod Optimization of Rankine Cycles and Heat Exchanger Networks

Cristina Elsido,[a] Emanuele Martelli,[a*] Ignacio E. Grossmann[b]

[a] Politecnico di Milano, Dipartimento di Energia, Via Lambruschini 4, Milano, IT

[b] Department of Chemical Engineering, Center for Advanced Process Decision-Making, Carnegie Mellon University, Pittsburgh, PA, USA

emanuele.martelli@polimi.it

Abstract

This work addresses the multiperiod synthesis and optimization of integrated Heat Exchanger Networks (HEN) and Rankine cycles for plants with demanding operational flexibility requirements. A general and systematic synthesis methodology has been developed to optimize simultaneously the utility systems, Rankine cycles and HENs considering different expected operating modes, seeking for the solution with the minimum Total Annual Costs (TAC). Heat exchangers have been modelled with different approaches depending on the type of control measure (with/without by-pass) in off-design operation. The problem is formulated as a challenging nonconvex MINLP and solved with a bilevel decomposition method, specifically developed to address this class of problems. We present the results of the proposed methodology applied to an extremely challenging problem, with 35 streams and 2 operating modes (periods), consisting in the design of an Integrated Gasification Combined Cycle (IGCC).

Keywords: Heat integration, Nonconvex MINLP, Bilevel decomposition, Multiperiod, Utility systems, Rankine cycle superstructure.

1. Introduction

Given the increasing share of intermittent renewable energy sources and the use of novel energy technologies, a new challenge for these energy systems and poly-generation plants is to deal with the increased requirement of operational flexibility. This includes the capability of achieving stable and efficient operation in different operating modes. Among the operational issues, when dealing with plants featuring large volumetric flows of high-temperature gases, it is not possible to control the heat exchanger in the off-design conditions by using bypass streams, as typically done in chemical processes. Examples of this issue are the steam tube banks (superheaters and reheaters) of coal-fired boilers and combined cycles, for which it is impractical to install a bypass duct for the stream of flue gases. Moreover, in steam generators, the steam acts as temperature moderator, as it keeps the metal temperature of the tubes exposed to high-temperature flue gases lower than the maximum allowed value of the material (Spliethoff, 2010). Thus, it is not feasible to use a bypass on the steam side, because the reduced flow of steam would cause an excessive increase in the steam outlet temperature and consequent overheating of the tubes. For the same reason, if steam is used as temperature moderator of the heat exchanger tubes and the hot stream (e.g., the flue gases) cannot be bypassed, the heat exchanger must exchange heat for all operating periods. The heat exchanger featuring this kind of operational issue needs to be modelled with ad-hoc constraints called "no-bypass HX" constraints (see Section 2).

In the process system engineering community, the design optimization approaches which can consider different expected operating modes and operating issues (e.g., off-design control measures of heat exchangers) are referred to as "multiperiod" design/synthesis methods. Among these methods, three main categories can be distinguished: multiperiod HEN synthesis approaches, multiperiod utility design/synthesis approaches, multiperiod HEN & utility synthesis approaches. Previous studies mainly focused on the first two approaches, optimizing only the HEN synthesis, or only the utility synthesis. Only recently, some authors started to address both problems simultaneously in the multiperiod version (Mian et al., 2016; Isafiade et al., 2015).

In this work, we propose an MINLP formulation of the multiperiod HEN & utility synthesis problem, starting from an extension of the single-period model proposed by Martelli et al. (2017) and further extended in Elsido et al. (2019), that enables the automated generation of Rankine cycles recovering heat from one or more heat sources, and the HEN of the overall heat integration.

2. Mathematical model

The general problem for the multi-period simultaneous synthesis of utilities, Rankine cycles and HENs, is formulated as follows:

"Given

- *a set of hot/cold process streams to be cooled/heated, with their heat capacity flow rates, input and output temperatures and heat transfer coefficients for different operating conditions,*
- *a set of hot and cold utility streams, with their specific heat capacity, input and output temperatures and heat transfer coefficients,*
- *information on process needs of hot water/liquid and steam/vapor, technical limitations (e.g., forbidden/forced matches, no stream splitting, etc.) and economic data (e.g., price of fuels, price of electricity, cost models of units, etc.),*

determine

- *the optimal arrangement and design of the heat recovery cycle, of the installed energy systems (e.g., gas turbines, boilers, etc.), and the design of the HEN,*
- *the optimal commitment (on/off status) and operation (loads) of the installed utility and energy systems for each period,*
- *the optimal load and mass flow rates of the Rankine cycle in each period,*

while taking into account a finite set of expected operating conditions of the process with their duration".

The model is based on the SYNHEAT superstructure (Yee and Grossmann, 1990) for the optimal design of heat exchanger networks. The SYNHEAT model is extended to include the streams of the heat recovery cycle, with variable mass flow rate. It should be noted that a steady state condition is assumed in each working period (i.e., no dynamics).

The thermodynamic cycles are modelled with a very general "*p-h* superstructure" (Elsido et al., 2017a, 2017b), capable of embedding many configurations of Rankine cycles, both power cycles and inverse cycles (refrigeration cycles or heat pumps), steam cycles or organic Rankine cycles, with single or multiple pressure levels, as well as heat/steam distribution networks. The proposed approach allows to explicitly consider both technical design constraints (i.e., the "no stream splitting" constraint, forbidden matches, etc.), which are extremely important when dealing with the detailed design of power plants and chemical processes, and heat integration equipment costs.

The multiperiod problem can be formulated as a non-convex MINLP problem (P1), that comprises Eqs. (1)-(10), extending the single-period formulation of Elsido et al. (2019) to the multiperiod case. Two types of variables are defined: "operational" variables, depending on the periods, and "design" variables, for the selection of the components of the cycle and the layout of the network of heat exchangers. All the constraints are period-dependent, and they are linked by the design constraints defining the calculation of the installed areas and the logical constraints on the binary variables (i.e., complicating constraints). The multi-period objective function (Eq. (1)) is the sum of the annualized investment costs and the weighted sum of the operational costs and revenues of the plant at the different operating conditions, weighted for their expected duration.

$$
\min TAC = \sum_r C_{F,r} y_r + \sum_{i,j,k} C_{F,i,j} z_{i,j,k} + \sum_i C_{F,CU,i} z_{CU,i} + \sum_j C_{F,HU,j} z_{HU,j}
$$

$$
+ \sum_r C_{S,r} S_{REF,r} \left(\frac{S_r}{S_{REF,r}}\right)^{\alpha_r} + \sum_{i,j,k} C_{A,i,j} A_{REF,i,j} \left(\frac{A_{i,j,k}}{A_{REF,i,j}}\right)^{\beta_{i,j}}
$$

$$
+ \sum_i C_{A,CU,i} A_{REF,CU,i} \left(\frac{A_{CU,i}}{A_{REF,CU,i}}\right)^{\beta_{CU,i}}
$$

$$
+ \sum_j C_{A,HU,j} A_{REF,HU,j} \left(\frac{A_{HU,j}}{A_{REF,HU,j}}\right)^{\beta_{HU,j}}
\tag{1}
$$

$$
+ \sum_{i,p} h_{EQ,p} C_{CU,i,p} q_{CU,i,p} + \sum_{j,p} h_{EQ,p} C_{HU,j,p} q_{HU,j,p}
$$

$$
- \sum_p h_{EQ,p} P_{EL,p} \left(\sum_{r \in TURB} \Gamma_{r,p} \Delta h_{r,p} - \sum_{r \in (PUMP \cup COMPR)} \Gamma_{r,p} \Delta h_{r,p} \right)
$$

$$
\text{s.t. } B_1 \begin{bmatrix} z \\ y_p \end{bmatrix} + B_2 \begin{bmatrix} t_p \\ dt_p \\ \Gamma_p \\ q_p \\ A \\ S \end{bmatrix} - b \leq 0
\tag{2}
$$

$$
(t_{ic,k,p} - t_{ic,k+1,p}) \Gamma_{ic,p} C_{P,ic,p} = \sum_j q_{ic,j,k,p} \quad \forall k, ic \notin ISO, p
\tag{3}
$$

$$
(t_{jc,k,p} - t_{jc,k+1,p}) \Gamma_{jc,p} C_{P,jc,p} = \sum_i q_{i,jc,k,p} \quad \forall k, jc \notin ISO, p
\tag{4}
$$

$$
q_{i,j,k,p} \leq U_{i,j,p} A_{i,j,p} \left(dt_{i,j,k,p} dt_{i,j,k+1,p} \frac{dt_{i,j,k,p} + dt_{i,j,k+1,p}}{2} \right)^{1/3} \quad \forall i,j,k,p
\tag{5}
$$

$$
q_{CU,i,p} \leq U_{i,CU,p} A_{CU,i} \left(dt_{CU,i,k,p} dt_{CU,i,k+1,p} \frac{dt_{CU,i,k,p} + dt_{CU,i,k+1,p}}{2} \right)^{1/3} \quad \forall i, last(k), p
\tag{6}
$$

$$
q_{HU,j,t} \leq U_{HU,j,p} A_{HU,j} \left(dt_{HU,j,k,p} dt_{HU,j,k+1,p} \frac{dt_{HU,j,k,p} + dt_{HU,j,k+1,p}}{2} \right)^{1/3} \quad \forall j, first(k), p
\tag{7}
$$

$$
q_{i,j,k,p} \leq \left(1 + \left(\frac{\Delta A}{A}\right)_{MAX,i,j}\right) U_{i,j,t} A_{i,j,p} \left(dt_{i,j,k,p} dt_{i,j,k+1,p} \frac{dt_{i,j,k,p} + dt_{i,j,k+1,p}}{2} \right)^{1/3}
\tag{8}
$$

$$\forall (i,j) \in MP, p$$

$$\left(1 - \left(\frac{\Delta A}{A}\right)_{MAX,i,j}\right) U_{i,j,t} A_{i,j,k} \left(dt_{i,j,k,p} dt_{i,j,k+1,p} \frac{dt_{i,j,k,p} + dt_{i,j,k+1,p}}{2}\right)^{1/3} \leq q_{i,j,k,p} \qquad (9)$$

$$\forall (i,j) \in MP, p$$

$$z_{i,j,k}, z_{CU,i}, z_{HU,j}, y_{ic}, y_{jc}, y_r \in \{0,1\}$$

$$\Gamma_{ic,p}, \Gamma_{jc,p}, \Gamma_{r,p}, q_{i,j,k,p}, q_{CU,i,p}, q_{HU,j,p}, A_{i,j,k}, A_{CU,i}, A_{HU,j}, S_r, dt_{i,j,k,p} \in \mathcal{R}_+$$

$$t_{i,k}, t_{j,k} \in \mathcal{R}$$

The linear constraints (synthetically represented by Eq. (2)) of the multiperiod model are: the energy balances for each hot and cold stream for each period, the energy balances of non-isothermal process streams in each stage for each period, assignment of inlet temperatures, monotonic temperature variation, load of and utilities, logical constraints on the existence of heat exchangers, calculation of approach temperatures, "no stream splitting" constraint, forbidden matches, restricted/required matches, activation/deactivation of utility streams, mass and enthalpy balances of the "*p-h* superstructure", calculation of nominal size of Rankine cycle units and utility, constraints for thermal energy storage system, logical constraints for heat exchanger areas.

The nonlinear constraints of the multiperiod model are: the objective function (Eq. (1)), the energy balances of non-isothermal "HEN utility" streams in each stage for each period (Eq. (3)-(4)), the calculation of the installed areas of heat exchangers (Eq. (5)-(7)), and the areas for "no-bypass HXs" (Eq. (8)-(9)). Eq. (8) and (9) impose that the areas of the heat exchangers between hot stream i and cold stream j in temperature stage k can only vary within a certain tolerance. This margin of error to the heat transfer rate equation allows avoiding possible numerical issues due to the adopted linearization technique of the equation (i.e., the Taylor expansion) and take into account the fact that in practice the outlet temperatures of streams can vary by some degrees.

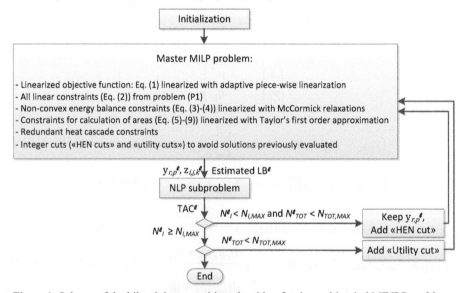

Figure 1: Scheme of the bilevel decomposition algorithm for the multiperiod MINLP problem.

3. Bilevel decomposition

The solution of the challenging nonconvex MINLP problem is tackled with a bilevel decomposition algorithm, extended from the single-period version of Elsido et al. (2019). The algorithm, represented in Figure 1, is based on an upper level (i.e., the "master" problem), comprising a linearized and relaxed version of the original problem (MILP) is solved, to minimize a linearized version of the original objective function; then a lower level problem is solved, in which the binary variables are fixed, and the continuous variables are re-optimized solving a non-convex nonlinear program (NLP). The master problem is obtained by the integration of multiple linearization techniques and the addition of redundant constraints and integer cuts to improve the algorithm convergence.

4. Case study

The methodology is applied to optimize the design and the Heat Recovery Steam Cycle (HRSC) and HEN of an Integrated Gasification Combined Cycle (IGCC) plant with 9 hot and 4 cold process streams in addition to the streams of the superstructure. The HRSC superstructure includes 3 levels of evaporation (HP, MP, LP) and reheating. The single-period analysis of the same process is reported in Elsido et al. (2019).

Here we consider that the IGCC must operate in two different modes:

- "IGCC mode" (5256 h/year): full load condition with gasifier and process at the nominal operating mode;
- "GT-only mode" (2628 h/year): Gas Turbine (GT) is running on natural gas following the electric market/grid requirements, while the gasification island is off (e.g., due to maintenance of the gasifier).

Technical limitations are taken into account as additional constraints in the model: the "no stream splitting" constraint is imposed to the GT flue gases; forbidden matches are imposed so that the high-temperature syngas cooler can be matched only with the HP evaporator or the MP evaporator; the gasifier can be coupled only with the MP evaporator (Elsido, Martelli, & Grossmann, 2019). Besides, the "no-bypass HX" constraints have been imposed to the GT flue gases stream with a critical temperature level of 300°C. The full multiperiod MINLP problem has 30,680 equations and 19,930 variables (3,130 binaries). The proposed algorithm reached convergence to a promising solution in 9,000 s, while BARON, state-of-the-art general purpose MINLP solver, did not provide any feasible solution in 20,000 s. The scheme of the optimal plant is represented in Figure 2.

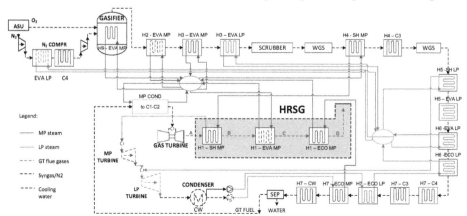

Figure 2: Scheme of the optimal solution of the multiperiod IGCC case study.

The solution obtained by the proposed methodology is a double-level steam cycle (only the MP and LP levels are activated). Thanks to the flexible design, the HRSC can operate 90 % of the yearly hours, both in the "IGCC mode", with net power output equal to 203.7 MW and 31.9 % net electric efficiency, and in the "GT-only mode", with net power output equal to 106.7 MW and 34.0 % net electric efficiency of the HRSC. The MP steam is raised in the Heat Recovery Steam Generator (HRSG) with heat from GT flue gases, the gasifier cooling, and the high-temperature, low-temperature, and post-first WGS syngas coolers. During the "GT-only mode" the MP level flow rate decreases considerably (31.7%) compared to the "IGCC mode", due to the reduction of heat available from the process, and the LP level is de-activated. The outlet temperature of the flue gases is 110°C in "IGCC mode" and 130°C in "GT-only mode".

5. Conclusions

We have presented a multiperiod MINLP model and an ad-hoc bilevel decomposition method to solve complex optimization problems for the simultaneous design of utility systems, Rankine cycles and HEN considering multiple operating conditions. The proposed method is effectively applied to the design of an Integrated Gasification Combined Cycle featuring 10 hot process streams and 14 cold process streams. The design of the HEN and HRSC considers two different expected operating modes ("IGCC mode" and "GT-only mode") making the problem extremely challenging for general purpose MINLP solvers. Nevertheless, the proposed MINLP model can include all the key design and operational constraints, and the ad hoc bilevel decomposition algorithm can find promising solutions within a limited computational time.

Nomenclature

Indices
i, j hot/cold process or utility stream
k index for temperature stage
r component of Rankine cycle
p period
Parameters
T_{IN}, T_{OUT} inlet/outlet temperature of a stream
U heat transfer coefficient
h enthalpy, h_{EQ} duration of periods
C, α, β specific cost and exponent for component/area cost

Binary Variables
z existence of heat exchanger
y existence of utility/Rankine cycle component
Continuous variables
Γ mass flow rates of streams
t temperature of streams at a stage
dt approach temperature difference
q, q_{CU}, q_{HU} heat exchanged
A, A_{CU}, A_{HU} heat transfer areas
S_r nominal size of a Rankine cycle component

References

C. Elsido, A. Mian, F. Marechal & E. Martelli, 2017a. A general superstructure for the optimal synthesis and design of power and inverse Rankine cycles. Computer Aided Chemical Engineering, 40, 2407–2412.
C. Elsido, A. Mian & E. Martelli, 2017b. A systematic methodology for the techno-economic optimization of Organic Rankine Cycles. Energy Procedia, 129, 26–33.
C. Elsido, E. Martelli & I.E. Grossmann, 2019. A Bilevel Decomposition Method for the Simultaneous Heat Integration and Synthesis of Steam/Organic Rankine Cycles. Computers & Chemical Engineering, 228-145.
A. Isafiade, M. Bogataj, D. Fraser & Z. Kravanja, 2015. Optimal synthesis of heat exchanger networks for multi-period operations involving single and multiple utilities. Chemical Engineering Science, 175–188.
E. Martelli, C. Elsido, A. Mian & F. Marechal, 2017. MINLP Model and two-stage Algorithm for the Simultaneous Synthesis of Heat Exchanger Networks, Utility Systems and Heat Recovery Cycles. Computers & Chemical Engineering, 106, 663–689.
A. Mian, E. Martelli & F. Marechal, 2016. Framework for the Multiperiod Sequential Synthesis of Heat Exchanger Networks with Selection, Design, and Scheduling of Multiple Utilities. Industrial & Engineering Chemistry Research, 55, 168–186.
H. Spliethoff, 2010. Power Generation from Solid Fuels. Springer-Verlag Berlin Heidelberg.
T. Yee & I.E. Grossmann, 1990. Simultaneous optimization models for heat integration—II. Heat exchanger network synthesis. Computers & Chemical Engineering, 14(10), 1165–1184.

Sauro Pierucci, Flavio Manenti, Giulia Bozzano, Davide Manca (Eds.)
Proceedings of the 30th European Symposium on Computer Aided Process Engineering
(ESCAPE30), May 24-27, 2020, Milano, Italy. © 2020 Elsevier B.V. All rights reserved.
http://dx.doi.org/10.1016/B978-0-12-823377-1.50251-2

A MILP Model for the Operational Planning of Multi-Energy Systems Accounting for variable Delivery/Return Temperatures and Non-Isothermal Mixing in Headers

Luca Moretti[*], Giampaolo Manzolini, Emanuele Martelli[**]

Politecnico di Milano, Piazza Leonardo da Vinci, 32, Milano, 20133, Italy
*luca1.moretti@polimi.it **emanuele.martelli@polimi.it

Abstract

This work presents a MILP formulation for the optimal operation planning of Multi-Energy Systems serving district heating networks. In particular, the work focuses on Multi-Energy Systems (MES) featuring thermal generation units connected in series and/or parallel, units with limitations on the operating temperature range of inlet/outlet water, and headers in which occurs the non-isothermal mixing of water flows. The model accounts for both dispatchable (e.g. CHP engines) and non-dispatchable (e.g. thermal solar panels) generation units, as well as for the presence of stratified thermal storages. To avoid the nonlinearity and nonconvexity associated to the variable stream temperatures and non-isothermal mixing, each water flow is represented as a linear combination of at most two virtual flows at discrete temperature levels, imposing a Type 2 Special Ordered Set (SOS2) condition to identify the two flows with closest temperatures. The model is used to optimize the operation of an integrated MES designed to serve the electric and thermal loads of a University Campus.

Keywords: Multi-Energy Systems (MES), Unit Commitment and Economic Dispatch, Heating Network, Mixed Integer Linear Programming.

1. Introduction

Multi-Energy Systems (MES) have been identified as a fundamental concept in the undergoing transition of the energy sector towards a more flexible, efficient and greener paradigm [1]. A MES is an integrated energy system utilizing different types of primary energy sources by means of a diversified set of energy conversion and storage technologies, to supply different energy vectors (e.g., electricity, heating, cooling). The heating and cooling power are typically transferred to the final users via a district heating/cooling network (DHN). By exploiting synergies in the energy conversion processes, the coordinated management of the MES units can lead to an overall performance relevantly higher than for a system addressing the supply of the energy vectors independently. MES typically feature various types of generators consuming different forms of internal / external inputs (including poly-generation units such as Combined Heat and Power (CHP) generators), intermittent Renewable Energy Sources (RES), and energy storage system technologies [2]. The large number of units and control degrees of freedom makes the definition of an optimal control strategy non-trivial [3]. Numerous MILP formulations have therefore been proposed in the literature to solve the Unit Commitment (UC) and Economic Dispatch (ED) of these type of systems (e.g. [3]).

However, these approaches do not account for the topology of the hydraulic network connecting thermal generators, Thermal Energy Storage Systems (TESS) and the thermal load, relying on the assumption that all units are placed in parallel (i.e., directly connected to return and delivery water headers). In many plants, units are connected to intermediate headers arranged in series/parallel with respect to the flow of water (i.e., the heat transfer medium to be sent to the thermal users) with the aim of operating each generation technology in the range of temperatures best suited to their technical features (see Figure 1). As an example, Solar Thermal (ST) panels are typically placed to warm-up the water from the return header to an intermediate header so as to maximize their efficiency. Similarly, heat pumps are used to heat-up water to an intermediate temperature (lower than the delivery temperature required by the final user) so as to operate with a high coefficient of performance. Boilers are typically placed in series to heat pumps and ST panels to raise the water temperature from the that of the intermediate headers to the final delivery temperature because their thermal efficiency is not appreciably affected by the water temperature. As a result, units may be placed in series or parallel with respect to the flow of water (heat carrier fluid), each unit may have a different outlet water temperature, non-isothermal mixing of water flows may occur in the headers, and the temperature of the headers may vary in time depending on the water flow rates and temperatures supplied by each unit. Since the flow rate, return and delivery temperatures of the water to be sent to the DHN may vary throughout the day, considering only the thermal power provided by each unit in the operational planning problem may lead to infeasible solutions (e.g., the ST panels or the heat pump may provide all the thermal power required by the users but their maximum water outlet temperature is lower than required by the DHN). This calls for the need of considering also the maximum/minimum inlet/outlet water temperatures and flow rates of each unit as well as the non-isothermal mixing occurring within the headers.

The bilinear terms arising when modelling non-isothermal mixing make the energy balance equations of the headers nonlinear and nonconvex, a well-known problem in the literature [4], leading to a challenging nonconvex MINLP which may not be tractable for operational planning problems due to the large number of time steps. This work proposes a novel linear approach, formulated as a Mixed Integer Linear Program (MILP), for approximating the solution of the non-isothermal mixing occurring in headers and for accounting for the detailed topology of the water network between thermal generation units, limitations on the inlet/outlet temperatures of the units and non-isothermal mixing. Stratified thermal storages (thermoclines) are also accounted for in the model.

2. Problem Statement

The scheme of a typical MES with the connections between the different water headers is shown in Figure 1. Delivery temperature $\tilde{T}_t^D$, return temperature $\tilde{T}_t^R$ and circulating water flow $\tilde{m}_t^{CIRC}$ are linked by the energy balance of the thermal user served by the DHN:

$$\tilde{m}_t^{DHN} \tilde{c}_{H_2O} (\tilde{T}_t^D - \tilde{T}_t^R) = \tilde{Q}_t^{DHN} \tag{1}$$

Considering a MES supplying a heat load through a thermal network as the one depicted in Figure 1, and given:

- the topological description of the water network (connections between units and headers, bypass flows, etc.);
- the profiles of water flow rates, delivery temperature and return temperatures of the DHN;
- the production profiles from the intermittent RES generators;

- the performance maps of all units, including part-load curves of generators, maximum / minimum load constraints and ramping limits, and capacity (in terms of contained water mass) of the thermal energy storage systems (TESS);
- the minimum and maximum inlet / outlet temperatures of the water heated by each generator;
- the value of selling / purchasing energy from external networks (e.g. electric grid);

we aim at determining the optimal Unit Commitment (UC) and Economic Dispatch (ED) of all units for each hour of the day, defined by:

- commitment plan (on/off status), input consumption and energy production rate for all generators;
- elaborated water mass flow (for thermal generators) and corresponding outlet temperature;
- outlet temperature from each header;
- mass of water in the hot and cold region of thermoclines, and their temperature;
- bypass flow rate between connected headers.

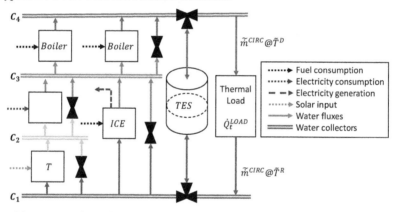

Figure 1: topological scheme of the MES heat generation and supply network.

The typical control strategy of DHNs consists in keeping a fixed water delivery temperature $\tilde{T}^D$ throughout the day while the return temperature $\tilde{T}^R$ changes with time according to the thermal load and to the circulating water mass flow control strategy. It is worth noting, the proposed model is suited for any DHN control strategy.

3. Mathematical Formulation

The general idea of the proposed formulation is to avoid bilinear terms in the energy balance equations of headers and units by defining a set of pre-defined temperature levels for the water flows. Each water flow $\dot{m}$ at temperature T is represented as an ordered set of virtual flows $\dot{m}_{i,h,t}$ at discrete increasing temperature levels $\tilde{T}_h$ spanning the temperature range in which the flow temperature can vary. Streams of water delivered by a unit at an arbitrary temperature T (potentially different from the discrete temperature levels $\tilde{T}_h$) is represented as the linear combination of two or more virtual mass flows of water at discrete temperatures. Each thermal generator is connected to an inlet and an outlet header, C_i^{IN} and C_i^{OUT}. In this formulation, for each unit $\mathcal{M}_i$, for each temperature level $h \in \mathcal{H}_i \backslash last(\mathcal{H}_i^{out})$ (excluding the highest temperature level), the mass flow variable $\dot{m}_{i,h,t}$ denotes the amount of water heated up by the machine from the virtual temperature level h to the subsequent one (h+1). If a generator has limitations on the maximum/minimum inlet/outlet temperatures of the elaborated water flow, it is sufficient to restrict the set of inlet/outlet virtual flows $\dot{m}_{i,h,t}$ to a proper subset encompassing the feasible thermal operating range of the unit (as denoted by the dashed rectangles in Figure 1 for the depicted units).

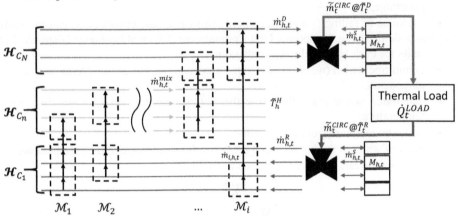

Figure 2: modelling approach for the thermal network of variable temperature headers: the colored group of lines identify the set of virtual headers associated to a physical header. Thermal generators can promote water from their inlet to their outlet set of headers.

Machines can only withdraw water from the inlet headers, and deliver it on the outlet headers: therefore, $\dot{m}_{i,h,t}$ can only increase on $\mathcal{H}_i^{in}$ and decrease on $\mathcal{H}_i^{out}$. The overall thermal power supplied by the generator can then be computed by Eq. (2):

$$\dot{Q}_{i,t}^{out} = \sum_{h \in \mathcal{H}_i \setminus last(\mathcal{H}_i^{out})} \dot{m}_{i,h,t} \tilde{c}_{H_2O} \left(\tilde{T}_{h+1}^H - \tilde{T}_h^H \right) \quad \forall i \in \mathcal{M}^{th}, t \in \mathcal{T} \tag{2}$$

Since each header can receive water at different temperatures (generated by two or more units and/or coming from the by-pass valves), the resulting mixing temperature of the water exiting the header must be modelled. This is done by writing the mass and energy balance equation on the header, in which the header outlet flow (resulting from the perfect mixing of all inbounds flows and either directed to the DHN or available to the units fed by the header) is modelled as at most two flows at discrete temperature levels, by imposing a Type 2 Special Ordered Set (SOS2) condition on the mass flow variables at the discrete temperature levels $\dot{m}_{c,h,t}^{mix}$. The SOS2 condition guarantees that the header outlet stream is represented as at most two flows at adjacent discrete temperature levels. Since the two fractions of water are determined according to the energy and mass balances, they are equivalent to the real outlet flow at a continuous temperature level in terms of energy content. Although introducing a non-physical separation of the flow in a warmer and a colder stream violates the second law of thermodynamics, the proposed approach preserves the energy balance and the entity of approximation can be controlled by adopting a finer temperature discretization (i.e., increasing the number of discrete temperature levels).

Similarly to units and headers, the masses of water associated to the hot and cold zones of TESS are represented by a set of virtual masses $M_{h,t}$ at discrete temperature levels $h \in \mathcal{H}_{c_{TESS}^{IN}} \cup \mathcal{H}_{c_{TESS}^{OUT}}$. To model the average temperature of the hot and cold zones of the TESS, an SOS2 condition ensures that at most two virtual masses with adjacent temperature levels are active. For sake of simplicity, the model presented in this work only considers a single TESS connecting the delivery and return headers, but the approach be easily extended to account for an arbitrary number of TESS placed in between any pair of headers. Each TESS virtual mass $M_{h,t}$ can exchange a virtual water flow $\dot{m}_{h,t}^S$ with the header to which it is connected: $\dot{m}_{h,t}^S$ can assume both positive (outbound) or negative (inbound) value. The total mass stored in the hot and cold storage zone can be computed according to the following mass balance (shown for the cold zone):

$$\sum_{h\in\mathcal{H}_{C_{TESS}^{IN}}} M_{h,t+1} = \sum_{h\in\mathcal{H}_{C_{TESS}^{IN}}} M_{h,t} - \sum_{h\in\mathcal{H}_{C_{TESS}^{IN}}} \dot{m}_{h,t} \quad \forall t \in \mathcal{T} \tag{3}$$

The dynamic evolution of each single virtual $M_{h,t}$ is determined by the energy balance on each TESS zone (assuming a perfect mixing with any inlet flow):

$$\sum_{h\in\mathcal{H}_{C_{TESS}^{IN}}} M_{h,t+1}\tilde{T}_h^H = \sum_{h\in\mathcal{H}_{C_{TESS}^{IN}}} M_{h,t}\tilde{T}_h^H - \sum_{h\in\mathcal{H}_{C_{TESS}^{IN}}} \dot{m}_{h,t}\tilde{T}_h^H \quad \forall t \in \mathcal{T} \tag{4}$$

While the storage can be charged with water at any temperature level, it can discharge water only from the active virtual masses (due to the SOS2 condition):

$$M_{h,t} - \dot{m}_{h,t} \geq 0 \quad \forall t \in \mathcal{T} \tag{5}$$

The storage is always filled with water, therefore discharging a given water flow from the cold zone of the storage implies charging an equivalent flow to the hot zone and vice-versa. As shown in Figure 1, the hydraulic connection considered for the TESS consists in two three-way valves that allow directing part of the delivery (return) flow respectively to the hot (cold) region of the thermal storage, while at the same time mixing an outlet flow from the TESS cold (hot) region with the flow coming from (directed to) the thermal user. Respectively, the two described operating modes correspond to charging / discharging the storage. The values of $\dot{m}_{h,t}^D$ and $\dot{m}_{h,t}^R$ are respectively linked to the mixing balance (both energy and mass) on the delivery header C_N and on the three-way valve.

4. Case Study

The proposed formulation is used to determine the optimal management of an integrated MES designed to supply heat and electricity to the university campus. The system architecture is the one shown in Figure 1 featuring Solar Thermal (ST) panels in series with a Heat Pump (HP), and in parallel with a natural gas CHP Internal Combustion Engine (ICE). A natural gas boiler further increases the water temperature in case of thermal demand peaks. The electricity and heating demand profiles, the delivery temperature (constant at 80°C), return temperature and DHN water flow rate derive from operational data of a real plant. ST and HP both discharge at a constant outlet temperature respectively of 60 and 75°C, whereas the ICE can discharge in the temperature range 60°C to 90°C. The solution yield by the proposed model was compared with the solution yield by a traditional UC and ED formulation, not accounting for the hydraulic connections and the temperature limitations of the units. The new formulation properly foresees the need of using the natural gas boiler to attain the required delivery temperature also during thermal demand peak hours, when the return temperature is lowest and the circulating mass flow higher, therefore making it impossible to ensure the 80 °C delivery temperature relying only on the parallel configuration of ICE and ST + HP. Conversely, the traditional model yields a commitment solution that provides an equivalent amount of thermal energy but at a thermal level lower than the target delivery temperature $\tilde{T}^D$.

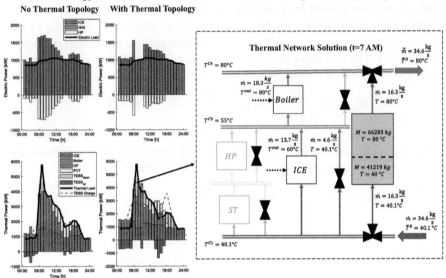

Figure 3: comparison of dispatch profiles when accounting / neglecting thermal topology and units' temperature limitations (left). Temperature and flow distributions are shown for the simulation accounting for thermal topology in a specific timestep (right).

5. Conclusions

This work proposes a formulation of the Unit Commitment and Economic Dispatch problem for the optimal management of a Multi-Energy System featuring units with limited inlet/outlet temperatures, multiple headers and variable return/supply temperatures of the DHN flows. The topology of the water network connecting the units and headers is defined and the nonlinearities (bilinear products due to the non-isothermal mixing) are avoided by representing water flows with variable temperature as linear combinations of virtual flows at discrete temperatures. The mixing temperature in the headers and in the hot/cold regions of the thermoclines are determined by enforcing energy and mass balances and by imposing SOS2 conditions on the virtual water masses / mass flows. The model is tested on a real-life case study, showing how explicitly accounting for the topology and for the temperature limitations of units in terms of inlet/outlet temperature range is essential to avoid infeasible solutions.

Acknowledgements: The authors acknowledge SIRAM for supporting the research activity and for the useful discussions about the operational issues of MESs.

References

[1]   P. Asmus, "Microgrids, Virtual Power Plants and Our Distributed Energy Future," *Electr. J.*, vol. 23, no. 10, pp. 72–82, Dec. 2010.

[2]   P. Mancarella, "MES (multi-energy systems): An overview of concepts and evaluation models," *Energy*, vol. 65, pp. 1–17, Feb. 2014.

[3]   A. Bischi *et al.*, "A detailed MILP optimization model for combined cooling, heat and power system operation planning," *Energy*, vol. 74, pp. 12–26, 2014.

[4]   K. A. Pruitt, S. Leyffer, A. M. Newman, and R. J. Braun, "Optimal Design and Dispatch of Distributed Generation Systems," 2012.

Sauro Pierucci, Flavio Manenti, Giulia Bozzano, Davide Manca (Eds.)
Proceedings of the 30th European Symposium on Computer Aided Process Engineering
(ESCAPE30), May 24-27, 2020, Milano, Italy. © 2020 Elsevier B.V. All rights reserved.
http://dx.doi.org/10.1016/B978-0-12-823377-1.50252-4

Optimal Operation and Control of a Thermal Energy Storage System: Classical Advanced Control versus Model Predictive Control

Cristina Zotica[a], David Pérez-Piñeiro[a], Sigurd Skogestad[a]*

[a]*Department of Chemical Engineering, Norwegian University of Science and Technology, Trondheim, NO-7491, Norway*
Sigurd.Skogestad@ntnu.no

Abstract

The objective of this work is to define the optimal operation and control for a thermal storage system with heat sources and a consumer, which exchange utilities using one hot water thermal energy storage tank. In this work, we compare a decentralized control structure using classical advanced control with PID controllers and logic blocks (split-range control and selectors) and a centralized control structure (model predictive control) to implement optimal operation for a simple thermal energy storage system, which is a multivariable system with constraints. We analyze a varying heat supply profile over a horizon of 24 hours. We show that the supply and demand can be balanced, and we achieve optimal operation by using the energy stored in the tank while minimizing the heat from the market.

Keywords: thermal storage, optimal operation, split range control, model predictive control

1. Introduction

Thermal energy storage has the potential to save energy in many applications by balancing the asynchronous supply and demand of heating and cooling. Furthermore, it can enhance the use of uncertain and highly fluctuating heat sources (e.g., power generation from solar thermal plants and/or re-utilization of industrial waste heat).

A large emphasis in the literature on energy storage has been placed on technology advances, design and applications (Arteconi et al., 2012; International Energy Agency, 2014). From an operational and control perspective, model predictive control has become the multivariable control technique of choice in several papers for controlling thermal energy storage systems in buildings, combined heat and power plants, and solar thermal power plants (Ma et al., 2009; Cole et al., 2012; Knudsen et al., 2019). Although less extensively, classical advanced control structures have also been studied in the context of thermal energy storage in buildings (de Oliviera et al., 2016). In this work, we show how to use classical advanced control using PID controllers and logic blocks (split-range control and selectors) to control a simple thermal energy storage system, which is a multivariable system with constraints. The control performance of the proposed solution is compared with model predictive control (MPC).

This paper is organized as follows. In Section 2, we describe a typical thermal storage system, in Section 3 we describe both a decentralized and a centralized control structure for the system, in Section 4, we present a simulation case study, and we make our final remarks in Section 5.

2. Thermal storage system

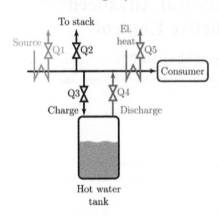

Figure 1. Process flowsheet indicating the five degrees of freedom for operation.

The process studied in this work is a thermal storage system illustrated in Figure 1. For example, this can be a district heating network, or an industrial cluster formed of heat sources and heat sinks. We consider a general system, composed of a variable heat source (Q_0) that utilizes industrial waste heat, an electric boiler that employs electricity from the market (Q_5), one consumer plants with heat demand (Q), and a hot water tank used for energy storage. The tank can either be charged (Q_3) or discharged (Q_4). The tank acts as a buffer between a varying heat supply and demand to minimize electric heating. Note that we may also heat the tank directly with electric heating (not shown in the figure). Excess heat is sent to the stack (Q_2).

Considering the relationship between demand and supply we can identify three cases:

Case 1.   Low demand. No storage tank $\Rightarrow$ send excess heat to the stack (Q_2).
Case 2.   Intermediate demand. Use tank to balance heat demand and supply.
Case 3.   High demand. No storage tank $\Rightarrow$ buy electric heating (Q_5).

We analyse case 2, and we consider a scenario with constant electricity prices. Note that with constant electricity prices we would not gain from charging the tank with electric heating and discharge it subsequently to the consumer. We should instead supply the consumer directly with electric heat to minimize heat losses.

2.1. Process model

We discuss optimal operation on a simple thermal storage example, and we start by deriving a model based on first principle. On the consumer side, we assume that the dynamics are considerable faster compared to the slow tank dynamics, and we write the steady-state energy balance, given by Eq. (1).

$$Q = Q_1 + Q_4 + Q_5 \tag{1}$$

We assume constant density (ρ), heat capacity (c_p), and volume (V). The energy balance in temperature (T) form for the tank is given by Eq. (2).

$$\frac{dT}{dt} = \frac{1}{\rho c_p V}(Q_3 - Q_4) \tag{2}$$

where, Q3 is the excess heat, given by a static energy balance in Eq. (3).

$$Q_3 = \max(0, (Q_0 - Q_1 - Q_2)) \tag{3}$$

3. Optimal operation and control

We analyse the system in the setting of plantwide control (Skogestad 2004), and we systematically define the operational objective, manipulated variables (MVs) (i.e. degrees of freedom for optimal operation), operational constraints, main disturbances and controlled variables (CVs). The operational objective of the system is to keep the heat demand setpoint, while minimizing electric heating. Table 1 shows the MVs (also shown in Figure 1. Process flowsheet indicating the five degrees of freedom for operation., CVs, and main disturbances.

Table 1 Manipulated variables, controlled variables and disturbances

Manipulated variables	Controlled variables	Disturbances
MV1: Heat directly to consumer (Q1)	CV1: Consumer heat demand	D1: Heat supply
MV2: Heat to stack (Q2)	CV2: Tank temperature	D2: Electricity prices (not considered in this work)
MV3: Heat to tank (Q3) (not independent)		
MV4: Heat from tank (Q4)		
MV5: Electric heating (Q5)		

Furthermore, during operation the tank water temperature must satisfy the following constraints, as given by Eq. (4).

$$T^{\min} < T < T^{\max} \tag{4}$$

where $T^{\min}$ is given by the consumer process specifications and $T^{\max}$ is the allowed maximum temperature in the tank given by operation constraints.

With the constant electricity prices assumption, optimal operation is trivial, and three regions can be defined:

R 1. $Q < Q_0$. Charge the tank with surplus heat until $T = T^{\max}$.

R 2. $Q > Q_0$. Discharge the tank.

R 3. $Q > Q_0$ and $Q_3 = 0$ (fully discharged tank). Buy electric heat from the market.

The operational challenge arises from the fact that the degrees of freedom are dynamic, that is, they are not available at all time (i.e. once the tank is discharged is can no longer supply the consumers). The question we want to answer is: what is the simplest way to implement optimal operation? We compare a decentralized control structure using classical advanced control using PID-controllers and logic, and centralized control structure using Model Predictive Control (MPC).

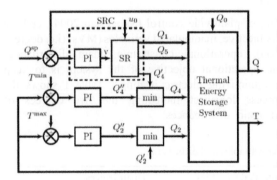

Figure 2 Decentralized control structure with split range control and min selectors. The split range (SR) block is represented in Figure 3

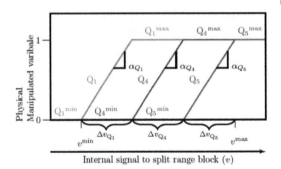

Figure 3 . Split range block

3.1. Decentralized control with classical advanced control structures

Optimal operation can be implemented in practice using classical advanced control structure, i.e. cascade, feedforward, valve position control or split range control together with logic elements (selectors) (Reyes-Lua and Skogestad, 2019). Split range control is a multiple-inputs single-output control structure that allows to use one input at a time and extends the steady-state operating range for the controlled variable. In this work we propose a control structure with split range control (SRC) and selectors, which can be used for active constraints changes (Reyes-Lua et al., 2018). Figure 2 shows the block diagram of the proposed decentralized control structure. The SRC keeps the heat demand setpoint Q^{sp} by manipulated the heat flows Q_1, Q_4, and Q_5. However, when $T \leq T^{min}$, and the active set constraints changes, we use a min selector to give-up discharging the tank. Similarly, when $T \geq T^{max}$, we use a min selector to give-up charging the tank.

Figure 3 shows the split range block. Note that this is not a typical split range controller because of the dynamic degrees of freedom. Consider a case when the tank is fully discharged ($Q_3=0$), there is no heat supply ($Q_0=0$), and we operate on the red line in the split range block in Figure 3. If the heat demand decreases, we could in theory operate on the green line using Q_3, but this is not physically possible because the tank is discharged. To solve this issue, we propose to update the maximum values (Q_1^{max} and Q_3^{max}) in the split range block to reflect the operational constraints. We set $Q_3^{max}=0$, when the tank is discharged (i.e. $T=T^{min}$), and $Q_1^{max} = Q_0$. We follow the systematic design procedure from the work of (Reyes-Lua 2019) to design the split range controller. In the split range block, the split value is set at $v^*=0$, which corresponds to maximum Q_1, and minimum Q_3 and Q_4. The slopes $\pm$ in the split block are equal, because the process gains from MVs to CV are equal. To tune the PI-controllers, we use the SIMC tuning rules (Skogestad2003). Note that Eq. 3 is static, and we need to use a pure I-controller. The tuning parameters for the split range controller are: slope $\pm=3$, and integral gain $K_I=0.033$. The other PI-controllers are tuned following the SIMC rules for integrating processes.

3.2. Centralized control. Model predictive control

Model predictive control solves an open loop control problem subject to constraints with a finite horizon at each sampling time to determine an optimal control sequence, and the first control is applied to the plant (Mayne et al., 2000). It's main advantage it that it handles constraints and interactive processes by design, while it's disadvantage is that it required a details model.

We formulate the optimal control problem as to minimize electric heating (Q_5), heat discharged (Q_3) and heat sent to stack (Q_2) subject to model equations and operational constraints, as given in Eq. (5).

$$\min \sum_{k=1}^{N} \omega_2 Q_{2_k}^2 - \omega_4 Q_{4_k}^2 + \omega_5 Q_{5_k}^2 \tag{5}$$
$$s.t. Q_k - Q_k^{sp} = 0$$
$$Q_k = f(Q_{i_k}), \forall i \in \{1,4,5\}$$
$$T_k = g(Q_{i_k}), \forall i \in \{3,4\}$$
$$0 < Q_{i_k} < Q_{i_k}^{max}, \forall i \in \{1,3,4,5\}$$
$$T_k^{min} < T_k < T_k^{max}$$
$$\forall k \in \{1,...,N\}$$

where, ω_j are the weights in the optimization problem and $Q_1^{max} = Q^0$.

4. Simulation results

We anaylze a varying heat supply profile over a horizon of 24 hours with a constant heat supply, as shown in Figure The tank volume is V = 100, the initial tank temperature is $T_0=105$ °C. The MPC is solved in CasADi (Andersson et al., 2013), and IPOT is used to solve the NLP (Wächter and Biegler, 2005). We use N = 60 control intervals and a sampling time of 60 s and $\omega_2 = 10, \omega_4 = 10^3, \omega_j = 10^4$

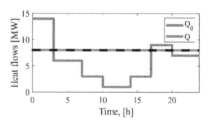

Figure 4. Variable heat supply in pink, and constant heat demand in blue

Figure 4, Figure 5, and 6 show the simulations results. Full lines show SRC and the dotted lines MPC.

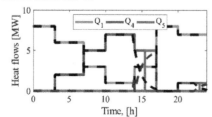

Figure 5. Input usage for SRC and MPC

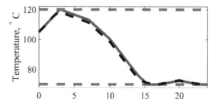

Figure 6. Temperature profile for SRC and MPC

5. Discussion and conclusions

In this work we identify optimal operation for a simple thermal energy storage system with constant electricity prices. We compare a decentralized control structure using PID controllers and logic blocks (split-range control and selectors) and a centralized control structure using MPC to implement optimal operation. For this example, we have shown that a systematically designed advanced control structure using SRC and selectors gives similar performance compared to MPC. The simulation results from Figures 4, 5 and 6 shows that the tank is discharging heat when the heat supply is not enough, and electric heat is used when the tank is fully discharged, while satisfying the operational constraints. Comparing both alternatives, SRC is considerable easier to implement in practice and tune and does not require as full detail model as MPC. However, for a larger scale process, PID-controllers and logic might not provide a simple implementation.

Acknowledgment - This publication has been partly funded by HighEFF - Centre for an Energy Efficient and Competitive Industry for the Future, an 8-years' Research Centre under the FME-scheme (Centre for Environment-friendly Energy Research, 257632). The authors gratefully acknowledge the financial support from the Research Council of Norway and user partners of HighEFF.

References

J. Andersson, 2013. A General Purpose Software Framework for Dynamic Optimization. Phd thesis, KU Leuven.

A. Arteconi, N. J. Hewitt, F. Polonara, 2012. State of the art of thermal storage for demand-side management. Applied Energy 93, 371–389.

W. J. Cole, K. M. Powell, T. F. Edgar, 2012. Optimization and advanced control of thermal energy storage systems, Reviews in Chemical Engineering. 28. 10.1515/revce-2011-0018.

International Energy Agency, 2014. Technology Roadmap. Energy storage. Tech. rep., International EnergyAgency.

B. R. Knudsen, H. Kauko, T. Andresen, 2019. An Optimal-Control Scheme for Coordinated Surplus-Heat Exchange in Industry Clusters. Energies.

Y. Ma, F. Borrelli, B. Hencey, A. Packard, S. Bortoff, 2009. Model predictive control of thermal energy storage in building cooling systems. In: Proceedings of the 48h IEEE Conference on Decision andControl (CDC) held jointly with 2009 28th Chinese Control Conference. IEEE, pp. 392–397.

D.Q. Mayne, J.B. Rawlings, C.V.Rao, and P. O. M Scokaert (2000). Constrained model predictive control: Stability and optimality. Automatica, 36(6):789–814.

A. Reyes-Lua, C. Zotica, S. Skogestad, 2018. Optimal Operation with Changing Active Constraint Regions using Classical Advanced Control. IFAC-PapersOnLine 51 (18), 440–445.

A. Reyes-Lúa, A. and Skogestad, S., 2019. Systematic Design of Active Constraint Switching Using Classical Advanced Control Structures. Industrial & Engineering Chemistry Research (In Press)

A. Reyes-Lúa, C. Zotica, S. Skogestad, 2019. Systematic Design of Split Range. IFAC-PapersOnLine 53 (1), 898–903.

S. Skogestad, 2003. Simple analytic rules for model reduction and PID controller tuning. Journal of Process Control 13 (4), 291–309.

S. Skogestad, 2004, Control structure design for complete chemical plants, Computers and Chemical Engineering 28 (1-2) 219-234.

A. Wächter, L. T. Biegler, Apr. 2005. On the implementation of an interior-point filter line-search algorithm for large scale nonlinear programming. Mathematical Programming 106 (1), 25–57.

Sauro Pierucci, Flavio Manenti, Giulia Bozzano, Davide Manca (Eds.)
Proceedings of the 30th European Symposium on Computer Aided Process Engineering
(ESCAPE30), May 24-27, 2020, Milano, Italy. © 2020 Elsevier B.V. All rights reserved.
http://dx.doi.org/10.1016/B978-0-12-823377-1.50253-6

A Robust Rolling-Horizon Algorithm for the Optimal Operation of Multi-energy Systems with Yearly Constraints and Seasonal Storage

Alessandro Francesco Castelli, Luca Moretti, Giampaolo Manzolini, Emanuele Martelli[*]

Politecnico di Milano, Dipartimento di Energia, Via Lambruschini 4, Milano, IT
emanuele.martelli@polimi.it

Abstract

This work proposes an affinely adjustable robust optimization model and rolling horizon algorithm to optimize the day-ahead unit commitment and economic dispatch problem of Multi Energy Systems (MES) featuring seasonal storage systems and/or yearly basis constraints on the performance of the installed units and/or yearly limits on the electricity import/export. The algorithm is applied to optimize the operation of a MES designed to serve the district heating network of the university campus. Results indicate that the proposed approach is able to operate the MES and the seasonal storage system in an efficient way while meeting the yearly basis constraints.

Keywords: robust optimization, unit commitment, seasonal storage, MILP, CHP.

1. Introduction

Buildings are characterized by thermal demands which vary according to daily path, mainly related to the control strategy of the building internal temperatures (i.e., to guarantee the desired comfort temperature within certain hours of the day) and habits of the users, and a yearly path related to the ambient temperature and sun radiation. In order to reduce fossil fuels consumption and the related CO_2 emissions, three strategies are typically adopted: (i) integrating the use of intermittent renewable sources, such as solar photovoltaic (PV) panels and solar thermal (ST) panels, (ii) adopting efficient Combined Heat and Power (CHP) systems and heat pumps (HP), (iii) use thermal storage (TS) systems. The integrated energy system is referred to Multi-Energy System (MES). For MES featuring a large capacity of solar thermal panels, seasonal TS can be considered so to exploit the heat stored during the warmer months during the colder periods of the year (Shah et al. 2018). On the other hand, the seasonal TS can be used with daily charge/discharge cycles to operate the CHP and HP units in a more efficient/economic way. As a further challenge, in several EU countries the operation of CHP units must meet yearly basis constraints to guarantee that they are operated efficiently (and not just to maximize the revenues from the electricity sales): the total electric energy generated during the year must be smaller than the total consumption of the buildings/users, the average (yearly basis) primary energy efficiency (PES) and first–law efficiency (η_I) must be above certain threshold values (Bischi et al., 2017). In Italy and other EU countries, fiscal incentives are given to the owner of the yearly targets on the average yearly efficiency η_I and PES. Since these incentives have a considerable impact on the economic balance of the MES, meeting the yearly performance targets is of primary relevance.

This paper addresses the Unit Commitment (UC) and Economic Dispatch (ED) problem of MESs featuring CHP with yearly basis performance constraints, intermittent renewable sources and seasonal TS systems by proposing an ad hoc affine adjustable robust optimization MILP model. Uncertainty factors related to short-term (day-head) and long-term (till the end of the year) forecasts are considered. Since the Robust MILP cannot be applied to optimize the whole year of operation, a Rolling Horizon algorithm is adopted. The algorithm has been applied to optimize the operation of a MES designed to serve the university campus.

2. Problem statement

A scheme of the type of MES under investigation is represented in Figure 1.

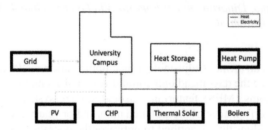

Figure 1. Scheme of the MES under investigation.

The MES may include one or more CHP units (e.g., internal combustion engines), boilers, PV panels, ST panels, Heat Pumps, conventional energy storage systems (hot tanks, batteries, etc.) as well as seasonal storage systems (e.g. Underground Thermal Energy Storage). Being connected to the electric grid, electricity can be sold or bought depending on the electricity balance. The excess heat generated by the CHP unit can be wasted (rejected to the environment). Provided the data of the MES, the general problem is formulated as follows:

"Given:

- *The part-load performance curves and operational limitations (ramp-up rates, start-up time, etc.) of the machine and boilers,*
- *the 24h ahead (short-term) forecasts of daily profiles of heating and electricity demands, PV and Thermal Solar production, electricity selling and buying prices for each day of the year*
- *the estimate for the electricity import/export, the electricity, the useful heat and the fuel consumed by each CHP for the future days of the year (long-term estimates required by the yearly constraints).*

determine for each hour of the following day:

- *the amount of electricity bought and sold to the grid,*
- *the management of the storage system (charge/discharge rate),*
- *the Unit Commitment (on/off) and economic dispatch (loads) of the units,*

which minimize the total operating costs of the MES taking into account:

- *the energy demand of the users*
- *the yearly limit on the amount of electricity which can be exported,*
- *the constraint on the average yearly η_I and PES ("CHP incentive constraints") of the CHP units,*
- *the optimal seasonal management of the seasonal storage system*
- *the uncertainty of the short-term forecast and long-term estimates."*

A robust Rolling-Horizon algorithm for the optimal operation of multi-energy systems with yearly constraints and seasonal storage

1515

3. Rolling Horizon and Forecast generation

The proposed Rolling Horizon algorithm is shown in Figure 2. The basic idea is to proceed optimizing a single day of operation (so as to have a computationally tractable RO MILP), one day after the other, with estimates for the short-term and long-term forecasts and with historical data of the past days. The short-term forecasts are day-ahead forecasts of the profiles of electric consumption, heating demand and production from PV and ST panels while the long-term forecasts are estimates for the optimal management of the seasonal storage system, the fuel consumption, electric energy and heat generated by the CHP unit from the optimized day k to the end of the year (parameters involved in the calculation of the PES, η_I and net electricity export constraints).

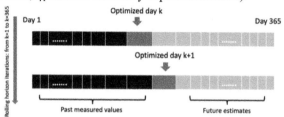

Figure 2. Rolling Horizon algorithm scheme.

The short-term forecasts of energy demand are determined using the Persistence method (properly accounting for weekends and holydays), while the short-term PV and ST previsions are obtained by means of the artificial neural network proposed in Dolara et al. (2015).

As far as the long-term forecast are concerned, it is necessary to determine the optimal management of the seasonal storage and CHP unit from the beginning to the end of the year. The basic idea is to determine the optimal yearly solution considering the past years. For representation of the whole year of operation and modelling of the yearly cycles of the seasonal storage in a computationally tractable way, we adopted the approach proposed by Gabrielli et al. (2018) relying on the definition of. "typical days". First, for each of the past years, twelve typical days are determined by means of the k-means clustering algorithm considering the profiles of solar production, heat and electricity demands and electricity prices. Then, a deterministic MILP UC and ED optimization model is formulated to obtain the yearly operational solution with the lower operational cost. In such MILP, all the yearly constraints on CHP units (PES, η_I and limit on the electricity export) can be easily included while the seasonal variation of the charge of the seasonal storage system can be modelled with the approach proposed by Gabrielli et al. (2018): the storage charge variable is defined for every hour of the year (thus 8760 variables) and a cyclic constraint is imposed to have the same storage charge level at the beginning and end of the year. While the year is represented as a sequence of typical days, this allows having different storage charge levels at the beginning and end of each typical day (needed to allow seasonal variations of the storage state of charge). Unfortunately for the university campus only the energy demand profiles of the years 2017 and 2018 are available, making it difficult to analyze the year-by-year variability of the yearly performance indexes and seasonal storage management. Thus, it has been necessary to reconstruct the heating and electricity demand profiles of the last 10 years (2008-2017) from the measured weather data using a model similar as the one described by Gambarotta et el. (2017). The parameters of the model have been regressed to best fit the thermal demand profiles of the years 2017-2018.

Once optimization is done for all the available past years, it is possible to calculate the profiles of the average expected fuel consumption, electricity and useful heat generated by the CHP unit and average optimal profile of the state of charge of the seasonal TS. Calculating the average over multiple past years allows filtering atypical periods which could have affected some of the past years. Similarly, it is possible to calculate the average cumulative profiles of electricity import/export, fuel consumption and number of operating hours of the ICE from the current day k to the end of the year. The average profiles obtained considering the past 10 years are shown in Figure 3. Since years may differ considerably in terms of average yearly ambient temperature ($\pm 5°C$), the expected (average) profiles of fuel consumption, electricity and heat generation must be treated as uncertain parameters in the robust optimization of the MES operation.

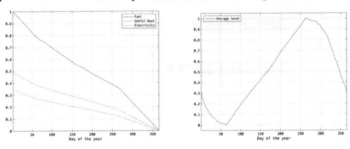

Figure 3. On the left: estimates on the future CHP consumption and generation (normalized to the total fuel consumption), on the right: yearly average profile of the seasonal storage (normalized to the storage capacity).

4. Affinely Adjustable Robust Optimization model

The optimization of the UC and ED of the MES is performed 24h ahead using as input the day-ahead forecasts of heating demand, production from ST, electric demand and PV production for the next day (the k-th day of the year to be optimized), the expected future fuel consumption and operating hours of the CHP unit (from day k+1 to the end of the year), the expected future electricity import/export, and the average optimal charge level of the seasonal storage at the end of day k. All the above listed short-term and long-term forecasted profiles are considered as independent uncertain data for the RO MILP model. It is worth noting that the estimate of future electric energy and useful heat generated by the CHP unit, terms of the yearly incentive constraints, can be expressed as linear functions of the future fuel consumption and operating hours of the CHP unit thanks to the linearity of the performance map of the CHP unit. As a consequence, they must not be considered as independent uncertain parameters. Similarly, to the model recently published by Moretti et al. (2019), for the uncertainty related to the short-term forecasts, an affine piecewise linear recourse decision rule is defined so as to adjust the loads of the units and the management of the storage system depending on the realization of the uncertain data. The model mimics the fact that real MES are operated defining the scheduling of the units on a day-ahead basis (here and now decisions) and then the loads of the units are corrected during operation (recourse) so as to meet the demands. On/off status of the units are "here and now" decision variables (the recourse does not involve any binary/integer decisions) while the loads of the units and the charge level of the storage have a "here and now" component (the expected set point decided the day-ahead) and an adjustable one. As far as the long-term forecasts are considered, the realization of their uncertainty of the forecast does not occur within the optimized day but it is revealed

A robust Rolling-Horizon algorithm for the optimal operation of multi-energy systems with yearly constraints and seasonal storage

1517

only at the end of the year. So, it is not possible to define a recourse decision rule: the operational solution found for the optimized day must meet the yearly operational constraints under any possible realization of the long-term forecast uncertainty. Thus, the proposed RO model is adjustable only for the subset of the uncertain parameters related to the short-term forecasts (energy demands and production from renewables). A polyhedral uncertainty set is defined for the forecasted parameters. As for the short-term forecasted parameters, in addition to the upper/lower bounds, a budget of uncertainty limiting the cumulated absolute error of each forecast is defined so as to encompass the 99th percentile of the forecast errors observed in the past year. For the long-term forecasted parameters, their uncertainty set is a simple box with bounds assessed by looking at the variability of the optimal profiles computed for the past years available. As far as the seasonal storage charge is concerned, the RO model guarantees that at the state of charge at the end of the k-th day is higher or equal to the average optimal storage profile computed for the previous years. This allows storing more heat than expected if the sun radiation or the optimal loads of the ICE turn out to be higher than the same period of the previous years. The piecewise affine decision rules and the polyhedral uncertainty set have been selected because of the possibility of reformulating the affinely adjustable robust counterpart into a tractable MILP (using to the duality theorem of linear programming (Ben-Tal et al., 2009)) and the good results obtained by Moretti et al. (2019) for the operation of MESs.

5. Case study

The rolling horizon algorithm with RO MILP model has been applied to optimize the day ahead UC+ED and real-time operation of an MES designed to serve the district heating network of the university campus. The MES features a CHP ICE unit sized to meet 7% of the peak heating demand and 14% of the peak electricity one, two equal boilers (each covering 32% of the peak demand), PV panels with a capacity equal to the 40% of the peak electricity demand, ST panels with capacity covering 21% of the peak heating demand, and a heat pump sized to provide up to 23% of the peak demand. The CHP unit and the boilers use natural gas. The seasonal storage has a capacity equal to 25% of the total expected yearly heating demand. The university campus is connected to the grid, such that electricity can be sold or bought. For the optimization of a single day, the RO MILP model is solved with an average computational time of 120 sec in an Intel Xeon E5 workstation. The historical data of years 2008-2017 have been used to derive the long-term forecasts and average optimal management strategy of the seasonal storage while the rolling horizon algorithm is tested in the year 2018. Once determined (day-ahead), the optimized affine decision rules are used to adjust the loads of the units to meet the real demand profiles and the simulated system performance are recorded.

6. Results and conclusions

The operational results for the second week of January 2018 are shown in Figure 4. The peak demand is met by using the CHP ICE and the TES (which, according to the optimal seasonal strategy, must be discharged in that period). It is worth noting that the electricity produced by the engine is always smaller than the demand of the campus and the use of the boiler is minimized. Figure 5 shows the comparison between the day-ahead commitment plan (left-hand bars) and the real-time operation (right-hand bars) of the MES. Uncertain variations of the heating demand profiles are a compensated by the affine decision rules by adjusting the discharge rate of the storage and loads of the HP and boiler.

As far as the yearly performance indexes are concerned, the rolling horizon algorithm does not deviate from the average optimal seasonal storage charge profile and it meets all the yearly basis constraints on CHP incentives and electricity export.

The proposed affinely adjustable robust optimization MILP model and rolling horizon algorithm appears to be a promising and effective approach to optimize the day-ahead UC and ED of Multi-Energy Systems featuring seasonal storage systems and/or yearly basis constraints on the performance of the units.

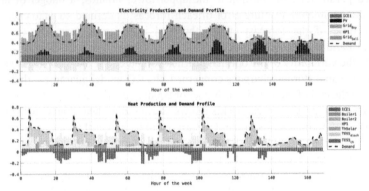

Figure 4. Operation of the second week of January 2018. Dashed black line show the actual demand profiles.

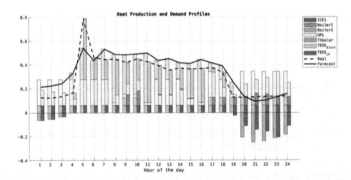

Figure 5. Heat production in a working day of January. Solid black line is the forecast, while the dashed one is the actual demand. For each hour, the bar on the right is the recourse, on the left is the day ahead set point.

References

A. Ben-Tal, L. El Ghaoui, A. Nemirovski, Robust Optimization, Princeton Series in Applied Mathematics, Princeton University Press, 2009.

A. Bischi et al., A rolling-horizon optimization algorithm for the long term operational scheduling of cogeneration systems, Energy, 184, Pages 73-90, 2017.

A. Dolara, F. Grimaccia, S. Leva, M. Mussetta, E. Ogliari, A Physical Hybrid Artificial Neural Network for Short Term Forecasting of PV Plant Power Output, Energies, 8, 2015.

P. Gabrielli, M. Gazzani, E. Martelli, M. Mazzotti, Optimal design of multi-energy systems with seasonal storage, Applied Energy, Volume 219, Pages 408-424, 2018.

A.Gambarotta, M. Morini, M. Rossi, M. Stonfer, A Library for the Simulation of Smart Energy Systems: The Case of the Campus of the University of Parma, En. Proc, 105, 1776-1781, 2017

L. Moretti, E. Martelli, G. Manzolini, An efficient robust optimization model for the unit commitment and dispatch of multi-energy systems and microgrids, Applied Energy, 261, 2020

S. K. Shah, L. Aye, B. Rismanchi, Seasonal thermal energy storage system for cold climate zones: A review of recent developments, Ren. and Sust. En, Rev., 97, 2018, 38-49.

Sauro Pierucci, Flavio Manenti, Giulia Bozzano, Davide Manca (Eds.)
Proceedings of the 30th European Symposium on Computer Aided Process Engineering
(ESCAPE30), May 24-27, 2020, Milano, Italy. © 2020 Elsevier B.V. All rights reserved.
http://dx.doi.org/10.1016/B978-0-12-823377-1.50254-8

Global Sensitivity Analysis for Design and Operation of Distributed Energy Systems

Ishanki De Mel,[a*] Panagiotis Demis,[a] Bogdan Dorneanu,[a,b] Oleksiy Klymenko,[a] Evgenia Mechleri,[a] Harvey Arellano-Garcia[a,b]

[a]*Department of Chemical and Process Engineering, University of Surrey, Guildford GU2 7XH, United Kingdom*
[b]*LS Prozess- und Anlagentechnik, Brandenburgische Technische Universität Cottbus-Senftenberg, Cottbus, Germany*
i.demel@surrey.ac.uk

Abstract

Distributed Energy Systems (DES) are set to play a vital role in achieving emission targets and meeting higher global energy demand by 2050. However, implementing these systems has been challenging, particularly due to uncertainties in local energy demand and renewable energy generation, which imply uncertain operational costs. In this work we are implementing a Mixed-Integer Linear Programming (MILP) model for the operation of a DES, and analysing impacts of uncertainties in electricity demand, heating demand and solar irradiance on the main model output, the total daily operational cost, using Global Sensitivity Analysis (GSA). Representative data from a case study involving nine residential areas at the University of Surrey are used to test the model for the winter season. Distribution models for uncertain variables, obtained through statistical analysis of raw data, are presented. Design results show reduced costs and emissions, whilst GSA results show that heating demand has the largest influence on the variance of total daily operational cost. Challenges and design limitations are also discussed. Overall, the methodology can be easily applied to improve DES design and operation.

Keywords: Distributed energy system, optimisation, design and operation, global sensitivity analysis, mixed-integer linear programming.

1. Introduction

In the UK, the National Grid has predicted that high energy demands can be met through decentralised and local Distributed Energy Systems (DES) and a smart grid using renewable and low-carbon energy resources, leading to a decarbonised energy sector by 2050 (National Grid, 2018). Optimisation-based models are often employed for the design and operation of DES; these usually minimise objective functions related to total cost and/or carbon emissions (Flores and Brouwer, 2018). Design involves selecting suitable distributed technologies and their capacities for energy generation and storage for each user whilst operation involves scheduling these technologies based on the recommended design (Mehleri *et al.*, 2013). Mixed-Integer Linear Programming (MILP) has been commonly used for both design and operation models as it can achieve a good balance between complexity, accuracy and solver-time that is suitable for real-time operation of DES (Nosratabadi, et al., 2017). However, when formulating MILP, modellers tend to assume that input variables can be measured accurately and there is no natural variability. Consequently, when real-time data is fed, uncertainties associated with these variables can lead to unexpected issues such as increased costs that may prevent wider implementation of DES. Identifying these input variables, quantifying their uncertainties, and evaluating the influence of these variables on the outputs can lead to the design of more robust models.

Quantitative methods to analyse uncertainties have been frequently used in DES studies, particularly Local Sensitivity Analysis (LSA) (Di Somma *et al.*, 2018). LSA varies only one parameter at a time whilst remaining parameters are prescribed fixed nominal values. Global Sensitivity Analysis (GSA) has been less frequently used; however, it is generally preferred over LSA because it allows simultaneous variations of multiple uncertain parameters and considers those variations over the joint probability distribution of all uncertain parameters (Saltelli *et al.*, 2008). This provides measures of overall influence of input uncertainties over that of the output. Although a framework to conduct GSA has been presented by Mavromatidis, et al. (Mavromatidis, *et al.*, 2018) for design models, no such methodology exists for operational models. This paper addresses the gap by presenting a methodology that can be easily applied to other DES models, helping modellers identify areas for improvement and limitations within their designs.

2. Methodology

2.1. Overview

The overall methodology is summarised in Figure 1. The design model is formulated using input data from a test case for the lifetime of the DES. The design and input data are then used to formulate an operational model, which is optimised for a smaller period, such as 24 hours, in a given season. Uncertain inputs are identified and quantified by creating empirical models from past data using relevant distributions; this is detailed using data from a case study. Variance-based methods of GSA require the computation of multidimensional integrals, which are estimated using Monte Carlo methods. This is done by employing a sample of random or quasi-random points based on the joint probability distribution of all uncertain parameters (Saltelli *et al.*, 2008). The operational model is updated to feed these random samples as inputs, which then generate random outputs for each sample. Sampled inputs and outputs are then used to conduct GSA, which quantifies the influence of uncertain variables on the variance of the model output, in the form of sensitivity indices. The dashed feedback arrows in Figure 1 represent how results from GSA can be used to make improvements in design and operational models.

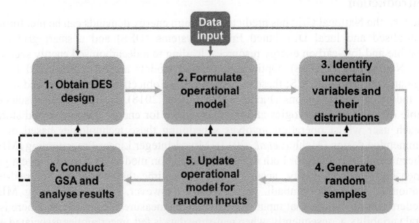

Figure 1. Flow diagram summarising the methodology used in this work.

2.2. Model formulation

The design of the DES is modelled as a Mixed-Integer Linear Programming (MILP) problem, as presented in Mehleri et al. (Mehleri *et al.*, 2012a). Distributed technologies include photovoltaic (PV) arrays, mini combined heat and power (CHP) units and boilers. The objective function minimises total annualised cost. The MILP operational model is based on the work of Mehleri (Mehleri *et al.*, 2012b), where Model Predictive Control (MPC) rolling horizon is used. MPC is a strategy which predicts the current state of the model at each timestep (hourly, in this case) over the total horizon (24 hours). The objective function minimises total daily operational cost. Both design and operational models are tested on the General Algebraic Modelling System (GAMS) (GAMS Development Corporation, 2019).

The operational model has been updated to account for a design limitation, which is applicable to all models, particularly those that do not incorporate heat storage. When heating demand exceeds the maximum generation capacity of the design, the model is rendered infeasible. This is avoided by introducing a set of equations instructing the generation technologies (such as CHPs and boilers) to produce the maximum heat, based on their capacities, whilst the additional demand is recorded for future analysis.

2.3. Uncertain variables

In this study, a subset of model inputs, which include electricity demand, heating demand and solar irradiance, is treated as uncertain. The objective to be optimised, C_{Total}, which is the total daily operational cost in this study, is presented as a function of these uncertain input variables as shown in Eq. 1.

$$minimise \quad C_{Total} \quad where \quad C_{Total} = f(X_{elec,t}, X_{heat,t}, X_{insol,t}) \tag{1}$$

where $X_{elec,t}$, $X_{heat,t}$, and $X_{insol,t}$ are the input variables for electricity, heating and irradiance, respectively. Note that index t has been used to denote a variable or parameter as a function of time.

3. Case study

3.1. Description

Data from nine residential areas at the University of Surrey is used to test the methodology. It is assumed that the DES is operating under the Feed-In-Tariff (FIT) scheme (Ofgem, 2019); design and operational model equations have been updated accordingly. Some model inputs data include electricity consumption, heating consumption, FIT tariffs, current electricity and gas prices, and solar irradiance. Currently residential DES in the United Kingdom are exempt from carbon taxes.

Figure 2 shows real data for $X_{elec,t}$, $X_{heat,t}$, and $X_{insol,t}$ and their means over a 24-hour period for electricity demand, heating demand and irradiance, respectively. Analysis of raw data at each timestep show that electricity and heating demand appear to be normally distributed, whilst irradiance has a beta distribution. Uncertain parameters for each input variable are assigned the corresponding distribution.

Inputs for electricity and heating demand are modelled using the following equations:

$$X_{v,t} = \mu_{v,t} (1 + k_v) \tag{2}$$

$$k_v = \frac{\mu_{v,t}}{\sigma_{v,t}} \tag{3}$$

where k_v is the uncertain parameter (index v indicates for either electricity or heat), $\mu_{v,t}$ is the expected time-dependent variation, $\sigma_{v,t}$ is the standard deviation. A constant relative variance model is assumed. Distribution of k_v, is assumed to be $N(0,\sigma_v)$ as given in Table 1.

Irradiance is modelled by:

$$X_{insol,t} = l_{max,t} * \alpha \tag{4}$$

where $l_{max,t}$ is the maximum recorded irradiance as a function of time in winter. The uncertain parameter α describes the variability of irradiance due to weather conditions; it is modelled using a beta distribution fitted to the data, as seen in Table 1.

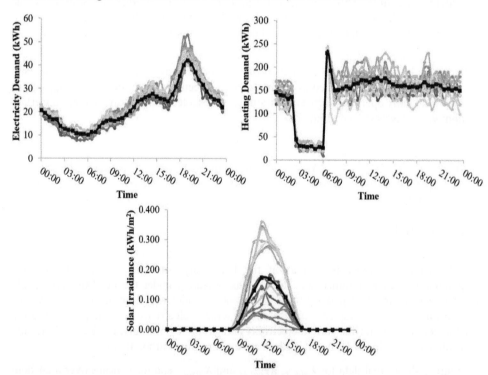

Figure 2. Electricity demand, heating demand and insolation from real data (noise). The mean is shown by the black line.

Random sampling points are generated using SobolGSA (Kucherenko and Zaccheus, 2018), software which was also used to conduct GSA of outputs (total daily operational cost) simulated for each random sample and each scenario. These are fed into the operational model to calculate inputs using Eq. (2) and (4), which then generates the optimised output, total daily operational cost, for each scenario.

Table 1. Uncertain parameters and their distributions. Under distribution parameters, μ, σ, α, β are mean, standard deviation, alpha and beta parameters, respectively.

Uncertain Parameter	Assigned distribution	Distribution parameters
$k_{electricity}$	Normal	μ = 0, σ = 0.14
$k_{heating}$	Normal	μ = 0, σ = 0.12
α	Beta	α = 0.56, β = 0.60

4. Design and operational results

Optimal capacities for solar panels, CHPs and boilers are obtained for each of the nine residential areas. When compared to a conventional design, i.e. electricity from the grid and heat from boilers only, a cost saving of over 30% is obtained for the DES. Carbon emissions are reduced by 4.5% for the same DES design.

The operational model is run for 1,023 scenarios, which take a total computational time of 15 hours and 42 minutes on an Intel® Core™ i3-7130U processor at 2.70 GHz, solved to 5% optimality using the CPLEX solver. Each scenario solves 135 single equations with 171 single variables. Figure 3 presents the results from conducting GSA, in the form of first-order sensitivity indices.

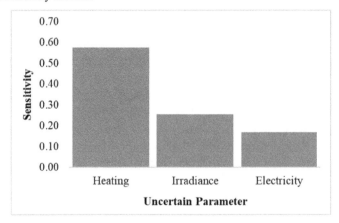

Figure 3. Sensitivity of model output, total daily operational cost, to uncertain input parameters.

5. Discussion and Conclusions

Results from the test case shows that heating demand has the largest influence on the variance of total daily operational cost in winter. Solar irradiance and electricity demand have minor influences (note that these conclusions may not hold for other seasons). With respect to the case study, the large influence of heating demand highlights the need for better heating regulation within the DES.

Key limitations of the study are high computational expense, consideration of data from the recent past only (for the development of empirical models), and lack of energy storage in the DES design.

Despite these limitations, the methodology can be applied to other operational models and a larger number of uncertain inputs. As illustrated through the test case, these findings undoubtedly can help modellers to explore the design limitations and thus lead to the development of more robust DES for the future.

References

R. J. Flores and J. Brouwer, 2018, Optimal design of a distributed energy resource system that economically reduces carbon emissions, Applied Energy. Elsevier, 232, pp. 119–138.

GAMS Development Corporation, 2019, General Algebraic Modeling System (GAMS). Fairfax, VA, USA,. Available at: https://www.gams.com/download/ (Accessed: 14 November 2018).

S. Kucherenko and O. Zaccheus, 2018, SobolGSA Software, Imperial College London. Available at: https://www.imperial.ac.uk/process-systems-engineering/research/free-software/sobolgsa-software/ (Accessed: 10 November 2018).

G. Mavromatidis, K. Orehounig, and J. Carmeliet, 2018, Uncertainty and global sensitivity analysis for the optimal design of distributed energy systems, Applied Energy. Elsevier, 214, pp. 219–238.

E. D. Mehleri, H. Sarimveis, N. C. Markatos, and L. G. Papageorgiou, 2012, A mathematical programming approach for optimal design of distributed energy systems at the neighbourhood level, Energy, 44(1), pp. 96–104.

E. D. Mehleri, L. G. Papageorgiou, N. C. Markatos, and H. Sarimveis, 2012, A Model Predictive Control Framework for Residential Microgrids, Computer Aided Chemical Engineering, 30(June), pp. 327–331.

E. D. Mehleri, H. Sarimveis, N. C. Markatos, and L. G. Papageorgiou, 2013, Optimal design and operation of distributed energy systems: Application to Greek residential sector, Renewable Energy. Elsevier Ltd, 51, pp. 331–342.

National Grid, 2018, Future Energy Scenarios. Available at: http://fes.nationalgrid.com/media/1363/fes-interactive-version-final.pdf (Accessed: 25 May 2019).

S. M. Nosratabadi, R. A. Hooshmand, and E. Gholipour, 2017, A comprehensive review on microgrid and virtual power plant concepts employed for distributed energy resources scheduling in power systems, Renewable and Sustainable Energy Reviews. Elsevier, 67, pp. 341–363.

Ofgem, 2019, About the FIT scheme, Ofgem. Available at: https://www.ofgem.gov.uk/environmental-programmes/fit/about-fit-scheme (Accessed: 18 March 2019).

A. Saltelli, M. Ratto, T. Andres, F. Campolongo, J. Cariboni, D. Gatelli, M. Saisana, and S. Tarantola, 2008, Global sensitivity analysis : The Primer. Online. Chichester, United Kingdom: John Wiley & Sons, Ltd.

M. Di Somma, G. Graditi, E. Heydarian-Forushani, M. Shafie-khah, and P. Siano, 2018, Stochastic optimal scheduling of distributed energy resources with renewables considering economic and environmental aspects, Renewable Energy. Pergamon, 116, pp. 272–287.

Sauro Pierucci, Flavio Manenti, Giulia Bozzano, Davide Manca (Eds.)
Proceedings of the 30th European Symposium on Computer Aided Process Engineering
(ESCAPE30), May 24-27, 2020, Milano, Italy. © 2020 Elsevier B.V. All rights reserved.
http://dx.doi.org/10.1016/B978-0-12-823377-1.50255-X

Retrofit of Heat Exchanger Networks with Temperature and Flowrate Uncertainties

Yossaral Charnkhuang,[b] Jui-Yuan Lee,[a] Dominic Chwan Yee Foo[c,]*

[a]*Chemical Engineering Practice School, King Mongkut's University of Technology Thonburi, 126 Prachautid Road, Bangmod, Thoongkru, Bangkok 10140, Thailand*

[b]*Department of Chemical Engineering and Biotechnology, National Taipei University of Technology, 1, Sec. 3, Zhongxiao E. Rd., Taipei 10608, Taiwan, R.O.C.*

[c]*Department of Chemical & Environmental Engineering/Centre of Excellence for Green Technologies, University of Nottingham Malaysia, 43500 Semenyih, Selangor, Malaysia*
Dominic.Foo@nottingham.edu.my

Abstract

This work presents a fuzzy optimisation model for HEN retrofit design incorporating parametric uncertainties. The basic model is based on a stage-wise superstructure with non-isothermal mixing. Fuzzy set theory is used with max-min aggregation to provide a robust, more conservative design with maximum overall degree of satisfaction of fuzzy constraints. An illustrative example is presented to demonstrate the application of the proposed approach. Results obtained for the deterministic and fuzzy cases are discussed and compared with the literature.

Keywords: process integration, mathematical programming; fuzzy optimisation, energy recovery.

1. Introduction

After four decades of development, process integration techniques are well established for heat exchanger network (HEN) synthesis, particularly for grassroots design, i.e. for new processes at the conceptual design stage. However, a significant breakthrough still remains to be made for the retrofit of HENs in existing process plants. In most cases, HENs not designed using a systematic approach tend to involve cross-pinch heat transfer. This could result in much higher consumption of hot and cold utilities, as compared to the best grassroots design targets. Such ill-designed HENs may thus be retrofitted for better energy efficiency. Also, it is often the case that the existing HEN needs to be retrofitted to accommodate process changes. Retrofitting an existing HEN can entail significant costs, and it is important to ensure a reasonable payback period for a retrofit project. Apart from the economic aspect, uncertainties in process stream data such as flowrates and temperature should also be taken into account.

There have been many research works on HEN retrofit based on pinch analysis and mathematical programming. In the seminal work of Tjoe and Linnhoff (1986), grassroots design targets were used to guide retrofit. More recently, Lal et al. (2018) developed an HEN retrofit method based on bridge analysis. Their method identifies retrofit bridges corresponding to energy saving modifications using the heat surplus-deficit table and the modified energy transfer diagram. Jiang et al. (2018) proposed an HEN retrofit methodology with performance reassessment. The authors incorporated performance simulation into the HEN retrofit model to reassess the performance of reused heat exchange units, and adopted genetic algorithm for the optimization problem.

Most of the works on HEN retrofit do not consider uncertainties in process stream data. Although Monte Carlo simulation can be used to analyse the effect of stream data variations on the performance of retrofitted HENs, and to assess the sensitivity and robustness of the HEN and individual heat exchangers (Lal et al., 2019), uncertainties should be incorporated in retrofit design to better guide the decision making. In this paper, a new mathematical technique is proposed for robust HEN retrofit design under parametric uncertainties. The basic model formulation is based on a stage-wise superstructure with non-isothermal mixing streams. Uncertainties in stream flowrates and supply temperatures are allowed for using fuzzy optimisation, which has been applied to water network synthesis problems (Tan, 2011). An illustrative example is presented to illustrate the proposed approach.

2. Problem statement

The HEN retrofit problem addressed in this paper can be formally stated as follows. A given process has a set of hot streams $i \in \mathbf{I}$ and a set of cold streams $j \in \mathbf{J}$. Hot and cold utilities are available to meet the cooling and heating demands of the process. There has been an existing HEN for the process to reduce its utility consumption. This HEN is, however, to be retrofitted for further energy efficiency improvements. Knowing stream data and parameters for utilities and equipment, the objective is to determine the optimal HEN retrofit design with maximum profit.

3. Model formulation

The basic model for the HEN retrofit problem is adapted from Jiang et al. (2018). Based on the stage-wise superstructure with non-isothermal mixing, the formulation consists mainly of energy balances (for each stream, in each stage and for each heat exchanger), mass balances (for each stream in each stage) and temperature constraints.

To improve energy efficiency whilst ensuring economic feasibility, the objective is to maximise the total retrofit profit (g_{TRP}), which is defined as the difference between the utility cost savings (g_{UCS}) and the annualised capital cost (g_{ACC}), as given in Eq. (1).

$$g_{\text{TRP}} = g_{\text{UCS}} - g_{\text{ACC}} \tag{1}$$

$$g_{\text{UCS}} = AOH \left[C_{\text{CU}} \sum_{i \in \mathbf{I}} \left(Q_{i,\text{CU}}^0 - q_{i,\text{CU}} \right) + C_{\text{HU}} \sum_{j \in \mathbf{J}} \left(Q_{\text{HU},j}^0 - q_{\text{HU},j} \right) \right] \tag{2}$$

$$
\begin{aligned}
g_{\text{ACC}} = AF \sum_{i \in \mathbf{I}} \sum_{j \in \mathbf{J}} \sum_{k \in \mathbf{K}} \left[C_{\text{fix}}^{\text{ex}} z_{ijk}^{\text{ex}} + C_{\text{fix}}^{\text{new}} z_{ijk}^{\text{new}} + C_{\text{var}} \left(a_{ijk}^{\text{add}} \right)^{\beta} \right] \\
+ AF \sum_{i \in \mathbf{I}} \left[C_{\text{fix}}^{\text{ex}} z_{i,\text{CU}}^{\text{ex}} + C_{\text{fix}}^{\text{new}} z_{i,\text{CU}}^{\text{new}} + C_{\text{var}} \left(a_{i,\text{CU}}^{\text{add}} \right)^{\beta} \right] \\
+ AF \sum_{j \in \mathbf{J}} \left[C_{\text{fix}}^{\text{ex}} z_{\text{HU},j}^{\text{ex}} + C_{\text{fix}}^{\text{new}} z_{\text{HU},j}^{\text{new}} + C_{\text{var}} \left(a_{\text{HU},i}^{\text{add}} \right)^{\beta} \right]
\end{aligned} \tag{3}
$$

where AOH is the annual operating hours; C_{CU} and C_{HU} are the costs of cold and hot utilities; $Q_{i,\text{CU}}^0$ and $Q_{\text{HU},j}^0$ are the cold utility load for hot stream i and the hot utility load for cold stream j in the existing HEN; $q_{i,\text{CU}}$ and $q_{\text{HU},j}$ are the cold utility load for stream i and the hot utility load for stream j in the retrofitted HEN; AF is the annualisation factor; $C_{\text{fix}}^{\text{ex}}$ and $C_{\text{fix}}^{\text{new}}$ are the fixed area cost coefficients for existing and new heat exchangers; C_{var} is the variable area cost coefficient; β is the area cost exponent; a_*^{add} (*

$= \{(ijk), (i,\mathrm{CU}), (\mathrm{HU},j)\})$ represents the additional heat transfer area required for the match; z_*^{ex} and z_*^{new} are binary variables indicating the use of an existing heat exchanger or a new one for the match in the retrofitted HEN.

The additional heat transfer areas are calculated using Eqs. (4)-(6).

$$a_{ijk}^{\mathrm{add}} \geq a_{ijk} - A_{ij}^0 z_{ijk}^{\mathrm{ex}} \quad \forall i \in \mathbf{I}, j \in \mathbf{J}, k \in \mathbf{K} \tag{4}$$
$$a_{i,\mathrm{CU}}^{\mathrm{add}} \geq a_{i,\mathrm{CU}} - A_{i,\mathrm{CU}}^0 z_{i,\mathrm{CU}}^{\mathrm{ex}} \quad \forall i \in \mathbf{I} \tag{5}$$
$$a_{\mathrm{HU},j}^{\mathrm{add}} \geq a_{\mathrm{HU},j} - A_{\mathrm{HU},j}^0 z_{\mathrm{HU},j}^{\mathrm{ex}} \quad \forall j \in \mathbf{J} \tag{6}$$

where A_*^0 and a_* ($* = \{(ijk), (i,\mathrm{CU}), (\mathrm{HU},j)\}$) represent the heat transfer areas required for the match in the existing and retrofitted HENs. Furthermore, the binary variables are correlated in Eqs. (7)-(12).

$$z_{ijk} = z_{ijk}^{\mathrm{ex}} + z_{ijk}^{\mathrm{new}} \quad \forall i \in \mathbf{I}, j \in \mathbf{J}, k \in \mathbf{K} \tag{7}$$
$$z_{i,\mathrm{CU}} = z_{i,\mathrm{CU}}^{\mathrm{ex}} + z_{i,\mathrm{CU}}^{\mathrm{new}} \quad \forall i \in \mathbf{I} \tag{8}$$
$$z_{\mathrm{HU},j} = z_{\mathrm{HU},j}^{\mathrm{ex}} + z_{\mathrm{HU},j}^{\mathrm{new}} \quad \forall j \in \mathbf{J} \tag{9}$$
$$\sum_{k \in \mathbf{K}} z_{ijk}^{\mathrm{ex}} \leq Z_{ij}^0 \quad \forall i \in \mathbf{I}, j \in \mathbf{J} \tag{10}$$
$$z_{i,\mathrm{CU}}^{\mathrm{ex}} \leq Z_{i,\mathrm{CU}}^0 \quad \forall i \in \mathbf{I} \tag{11}$$
$$z_{\mathrm{HU},j}^{\mathrm{ex}} \leq Z_{\mathrm{HU},j}^0 \quad \forall j \in \mathbf{J} \tag{12}$$

where z_* ($* = \{(ijk), (i,\mathrm{CU}), (\mathrm{HU},j)\}$) is the binary variable indicating the existence of the match in the retrofitted HEN; Z_*^0 is the binary parameter denoting the match in the existing HEN. It should be noted that this formulation applies to a specific case in which there is at most one match between any pair of hot and cold process streams in the existing HEN.

To allow for uncertainties in process stream flowrates and temperatures, the basic model is extended using fuzzy set theory (Zimmermann, 1978). The objective function of the fuzzy model is to maximise the overall degree of satisfaction (λ) of the fuzzy goals and constraints, as given in Eq. (13).

$$\max \lambda \tag{13}$$
$$0 \leq \lambda \leq 1 \tag{14}$$

Eq. (15) represents the fuzzy profit goal, for which a high value is desirable, assuming a linear membership function. Note that g_{TRP} reaches its lower bound (TRP^{L}) when the degree of satisfaction of the profit goal (λ^{TRP}) is equal to zero (unsatisfactory), and reaches its upper bound (TRP^{U}) when $\lambda^{\mathrm{TRP}} = 1$ (completely satisfactory).

$$g_{\mathrm{TRP}} = TRP^{\mathrm{L}} + \lambda^{\mathrm{TRP}}(TRP^{\mathrm{U}} - TRP^{\mathrm{L}}) \tag{15}$$
$$0 \leq \lambda^{\mathrm{TRP}} \leq 1 \tag{16}$$

The fuzzy parameters are redefined and treated as variables in the fuzzy constraints given in Eqs. (17)-(20).

$$F_i = F_i^{\mathrm{U}} - \lambda_i^{\mathrm{F}}(F_i^{\mathrm{U}} - F_i^{\mathrm{L}}) \tag{17}$$
$$T_i^{\mathrm{in}} = T_i^{\mathrm{in,U}} - \lambda_i^{\mathrm{T}}(T_i^{\mathrm{in,U}} - T_i^{\mathrm{in,L}}) \tag{18}$$
$$F_j = F_j^{\mathrm{L}} + \lambda_j^{\mathrm{F}}(F_j^{\mathrm{U}} - F_j^{\mathrm{L}}) \tag{19}$$
$$T_j^{\mathrm{in}} = T_j^{\mathrm{in,U}} - \lambda_j^{\mathrm{T}}(T_j^{\mathrm{in,U}} - T_j^{\mathrm{in,L}}) \tag{20}$$
$$0 \leq \lambda_i^{\mathrm{F}}, \lambda_i^{\mathrm{T}}, \lambda_j^{\mathrm{F}}, \lambda_j^{\mathrm{T}} \leq 1 \tag{21}$$

where F_i and F_j are the flowrates of hot stream i and cold stream j; T_i^{in} and T_j^{in} are the supply temperatures of hot stream i and cold stream j. For hot streams, lower values of flowrates and supply temperatures are considered more conservative and thus more desirable, whilst higher values are riskier and less desirable. Likewise, for cold streams, higher values of flowrates and lower values of supply temperatures are considered to be more conservative and more desirable.

Eq. (22) ensures that the overall degree of satisfaction is less than all individual degrees of satisfaction. The satisfaction degrees of these fuzzy goal and constraints can be maximised simultaneously using max-min aggregation, where λ is equal to the degree of satisfaction of the least satisfied fuzzy goal/constraint.

$$\lambda \le \lambda^{TRP}, \lambda_i^F, \lambda_i^T, \lambda_j^F, \lambda_j^T \tag{22}$$

4. Illustrative example

A four-stream problem adapted from Lal et al. (2018) is used to illustrate the proposed approach. The models are implemented in GAMS and solved using BARON. Figure 1 shows the existing HEN (Lal et al., 2018). There are two coolers (C1 for stream F2; C2 for stream F4), two process-process heat exchangers (E1 for match F4-F1; E2 for match F2-F1) and one heater (H1 for stream F3). This HEN has a hot utility load of 2,700 kW (H1) and a total cold utility load of 2,950 kW (C1 and C2). Table 1 shows the stream data.

This example assumes a ΔT^{min} of 10 °C. The total utility cost is based on 8,000 h of operation per year. The ACC is calculated using the following parameters: $C_{fix}^{ex} = 2,000$ NZD; $C_{fix}^{new} = 4,000$ NZD; $C_{var} = 500$ NZD/m²; $\beta = 0.83$.

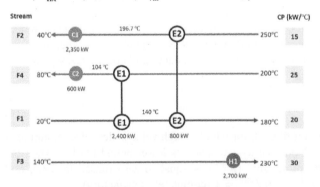

Figure 1. Existing HEN for the Four-stream Example

Table 1. Stream Data for the Illustrative Example

Stream	Supply temperature (°C)	Target temperature (°C)	Heat capacity flowrate (kW/°C)	Cost (NZD/kWh)
F1	20	180	20	-
F2	250	40	15	-
F3	140	230	30	-
F4	200	80	40	-
Steam	250	250	-	0.035
Cold utility	20	40	-	Negligible

$U = 0.25$ kW/m²/°C for all heat exchangers, heaters and coolers.

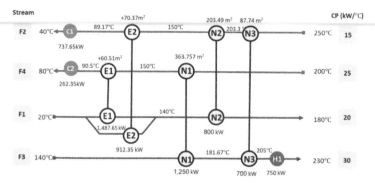

Figure 2. Retrofitted HEN without Considering Parametric Uncertainties

Table 2. Fuzzy Limits for Stream Flowrates and Temperatures

Stream	Heat capacity flowrate (kW/°C)		Supply temperature (°C)	
	Lower bound	Upper bound	Lower bound	Upper bound
F1	19	21	19	21
F2	10	20	240	255
F3	27	32	120	165
F4	15	37	190	210

Solving the basic model gives the retrofit design in Figure 2. The retrofitted HEN uses three new exchangers (N1 for match F4-F3, N2 for match F2-F1 and N3 for match F2-F3) together with the existing units, requiring a total additional area of 758.87 m². Thus, the hot utility and cold utility loads are reduced to 750 kW and 1,000 kW, respectively. The corresponding TRP is about 0.526 million NZD/y.

Table 2 shows the fuzzy range for each of the uncertain parameters in this example. These fuzzy ranges are taken from Lal et al. (2019). Wider fuzzy intervals in these data represent greater parametric uncertainty. The lower and upper limits of the fuzzy profit goal are based on the TRP before HEN retrofit (= 0), and the maximum TRP of 0.5 million NZD/y in the case without considering uncertainties, respectively.

Solving the fuzzy model gives the optimal retrofit design in Figure 3. It can be seen that a new exchanger (N1 for match F2-F3) and a new heater (NH1 for stream F1) are used in the retrofitted HEN, requiring a total additional area of 372.56 m², whilst the existing cooler C2 and exchanger E2 are no longer used. The resulting hot utility and cold utility loads are 1,711.25 kW and 1948.6 kW respectively, with a TRP of 0.269 million UZD/y. This is only half the TRP to be achieved in the deterministic (non-fuzzy) case, with an overall degree of satisfaction of 0.5. The decrease in TRP is the penalty incurred to provide a margin of safety based on process energy balances, particularly with regard to the heating demand.

Table 3 shows the results comparison. When parametric uncertainties are not considered, the solution obtained using the basic model results in a much higher TRP than the solution of Lal et al. (2018). However, the fuzzy model provides a conservative HEN retrofit design, from which the TRP is lower than that reported by Lal et al. (2018). The number of heat exchange units used and hence heat recovery is also reduced with the consideration of parametric uncertainties in stream flowrates and temperatures.

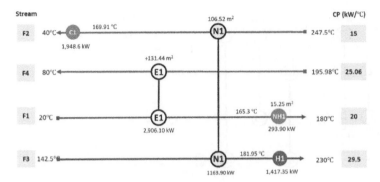

Figure 3. Retrofitted HEN Considering Parametric Uncertainties

Table 3. Results Comparison

Parameter	Existing HEN	Lal et al. (2019)	Basic model	Fuzzy model
Hot utility (kW)	2,700	1,500	750	1,711
Cold utility (kW)	2,950	1,750	1,000	1,948
Utility cost (NZD/y)	7.56×10^5	4.2×10^5	2.1×10^5	4.79×10^5
Additional area (m²)	0	298.3	758.87	372.56
TRP (NZD/y)	0	3.27×10^5	5.26×10^5	2.69×10^5
Number of units	5	6	8	5

5. Conclusions

A fuzzy optimisation model for HEN retrofit design under parametric uncertainties has been developed in this paper, based on a stage-wise superstructure with non-isothermal mixing. An illustrative example was solved to illustrate the proposed approach. Future work will extend the current model to more general HEN retrofit problems with a more detailed evaluation of the cost incurred by HEN retrofits. Monte Carlo simulation may then be performed to verify the results obtained from the improved model.

References

N. S. Lal, T. G. Walmsley, M. R. W. Walmsley, M. J. Atkins, J. R. Neale, 2018, A Novel Heat Exchanger Network Bridge Retrofit Method Using the Modified Energy Transfer Diagram, Energy, 155, 190-204

N. S. Lal, M. J. Atkins, T. G. Walmsley, M. R. W. Walmsley, J. R. Neale, 2019, Energy, 181, 1129-1141

N. Jiang, W. Han, F. Guo, H. Yu, Y. Xu, N. Mao, 2018, A Novel Heat Exchanger Network Retrofit Approach Based on Performance Reassessment, Energy Conversion and Management, 177, 477-492

R. R. Tan, 2011, Fuzzy Optimization Model for Source-sink Water Network Synthesis with Parametric Uncertainties. Industrial and Engineering Chemisrty Research, 50, 3686-3694

T. N. Tjoe, B. Linnhoff, 1986, Using Pinch Technology for Process Retrofit, Chemical Engineering, 93, 47-60

H-J. Zimmermann, 1978, Fuzzy Programming and Linear Programming with Several Objective Functions. Fuzzy Sets and Systems, 1, 45-55

Sauro Pierucci, Flavio Manenti, Giulia Bozzano, Davide Manca (Eds.)
Proceedings of the 30th European Symposium on Computer Aided Process Engineering
(ESCAPE30), May 24-27, 2020, Milano, Italy. © 2020 Elsevier B.V. All rights reserved.
http://dx.doi.org/10.1016/B978-0-12-823377-1.50256-1

Probabilistic Performance Evaluation of Small-Scale Organic Rankine Cycle Power Plants for Waste Heat Recovery

Giuseppina Di Lorenzo* , Ambra Giovannelli

Department of Engineering - University of Roma Tre, via della Vasca Navale 79, Rome 00146, Italy
giuseppina.dilorenzo@uniroma3.it

Abstract

The performance of Organic Rankine Cycles (ORC) plants is subject to uncertainties deriving from several factors. Such uncertainties are unavoidably propagated through the model to the outputs, affecting predictions of the commercial-scale performance and cost of this technology. The aim of this work is to analyse how the uncertainties associated with the performance of the expander, one of the main ORC components, propagate to the relevant thermodynamic and economic outputs and affect their final value. The analysis was performed for three different expander options (a single-stage turbine, a twin screw and a two-stage turbine) to generate a full spectrum of possible outputs rather than exact figures. Overall, a considerable variability of the output metrics was highlighted compared to the results from the deterministic analysis.

Keywords: Monte Carlo simulation, stochastic analysis, mini Organic Rankine Cycle, techno-economic modelling and analysis.

1. Introduction

Organic Rankine Cycle (ORC) plants are a promising technical solution for recovering and converting low-to-medium grade waste heat into electricity, as they present several advantages compared to other technologies in terms of improved thermal performance, flexibility and maintainability (Tchanche et al., 2011). However, the introduction of this advanced solution at a small scale, although technically interesting, is not always economically attractive. As a matter of fact, the small-scale application of ORCs is hindered by their uncompetitive specific cost, which is too high compared to other existing technologies. For this reason, a core issue for the development of the small-scale ORC systems is the assessment and optimization of their techno-economic feasibility. More specifically, considerable research efforts have been channelled into the technical performance optimization of different cycle layouts (including selection of the most appropriate organic fluids) and improvement of the performance of the individual components, with the ultimate aim of maximizing the power production of ORC plants while keeping their specific total capital requirement as low as possible. (Tocci et al., 2017). In all of the existing studies and analyses, however, the models devised and applied are essentially deterministic (i.e., they use best estimates of model input parameters, without inclusion of any uncertainties, and generate exact figures for the output parameters). This is a concern because the input values characterizing such process models can have significant uncertainties, stemming from several factors (e.g., material properties, variable operating conditions, design factors, low technological readiness level). Such uncertainties will be unavoidably propagated through the model to the outputs, thus affecting predictions of the commercial-scale performance and cost of this technology. Combining the techno-economic evaluation of energy conversion systems with a stochastic analysis has proved helpful in dealing with such uncertainties and thus providing a more comprehensive understanding of their technical and economic feasibility and their operation (Di Lorenzo et al., 2012; Maccapani et al., 2014).The aim of this study is to evaluate, by means of a stochastic approach, the impact of uncertainties in model input parameters on the performance of the ORC power plants. In particular, the stochastic method has been used in this work to systematically and explicitly analyse how the uncertainties related to the expander performance propagate to the relevant thermodynamic and economic outputs and affect their final value. The proper selection of the expander for small-scale ORC systems remains an outstanding issue (Tocci et al., 2017), as can be deduced from the existing literature. For small-scale applications different expander options are available, each with its own advantages and disadvantages. The selection process is complicated further by the fact that, among all of the ORC components, the expander is the one whose performance is most negatively affected when downscaling to kW (Tocci et al, 2017). The analysis in this work has been performed on three different expander options that were previously comparatively studied by the authors (Di Lorenzo et al., 2019). By including uncertainties in the techno-economic evaluation, a full spectrum of possible outputs is made available rather than exact figures, thus quantifying the confidence in the results from the previous work.

2. Description of the ORC Plant

The plant considered in this analysis is an ORC plant for Waste Heat Recovery (WHR) applications with a power output of less than 100 kWe based on a subcritical cycle. Three different expanders have been considered, i.e. a one-stage radial turbine (Case A), a twin-screw expander (Case B) and a two-stage radial turbine (Case C). On one hand, the twin-screw expanders display lower speed and higher nominal pressure ratios compared to a single-stage turbomachine, which theoretically fits well ORC requirements. However, the performance of twin-screw expanders for small-scale applications is considerably reduced by under- or over-expansions in off-design conditions, leakage and clearance gap losses, and lubrication issues. On the other hand, radial-inflow turbomachines are robust and reliable machines and could provide higher performances in a wide range of operating conditions, though high rotational speeds, low pressure ratio per stage, clearance and windage losses, and choking conditions hinder the design of an efficient turbine for ORC applications.

In the ORC system considered in this work, a feed pump compresses and pumps the working fluid up to 17.5 bar into the Primary Heat Exchanger (PHE), where the waste heat is transferred to the working fluid, which is pre-heated, evaporated and then super-heated. An expander is connected to a generator, so that the thermal energy of the working fluid is converted into useful work and then into electricity. After the expansion (down to 6 bar for Case A, 4 bar for Case B and 2.2 bar for Case C, according to the expander's features), the thermodynamic cycle is closed by condensing the fluid in the condenser. The resulting three power plants were designed for the same reference waste heat source with the same refrigerant used as the working fluid. They were compared from a thermodynamic and economic performance viewpoint in a previous study by the same authors (Di Lorenzo et al., 2019), using only a deterministic approach and delivering the following key results. Case C, with a two-stage turbine, resulted in efficiency (11.6%) and power output (87.4 kWe) well above those achieved by the plants with a one-stage turbine (7% and 45kWe) and a twin-screw expander (8.5% and 58.5 kWe). The plant specific cost figure for the two-stage turbine plant is also considerably below those for the other two plants ($6188 USD$_{2016}$ against $9889 USD$_{2016}$ and $8221 USD$_{2016}$). These results were obtained assuming exact figures for the input variables with no consideration of their stochasticity. Among these input variables is the efficiency of the expander (Case A: η_{is}=75%; Case B: η_{is}=72%; Case C: η_{is}=75% for the first stage, η_{is}=72% for the second stage), which has a strong impact on the cycle performance.

3. Methodology

In this analysis, the approach adopted was the Monte Carlo method, an established stochastic approach that has been used extensively to model and study uncertainty in engineering system behaviour evaluation. In a Monte Carlo simulation a sufficiently large number of samples of the uncertain input variables are randomly generated based on the defined probability distributions. The samples are input into the model of the system being considered and the resulting output variables chosen as indices of the performance of the system are collected and stored. The analysis of these results ultimately produces a quantitative estimate of the impact of the uncertainty of the input variables on the system behaviour. The three ORC plant variants were modelled with a simulation routine developed in-house (Di Lorenzo et al., 2019), estimating their design-point performance. The thermodynamic and transport properties of the organic fluid were determined using the RefProp database (Lemmon et al., 2002). The stochastic analysis was performed assuming as a stochastic input the isentropic efficiency of the expander. The uncertainty of this input parameter was described by means of triangular and normal distributions with the features presented in Table I. The deterministic on-design value was assumed to be the central value of the distribution, while the standard deviation stemmed from information and data collected from the open literature and critically reviewed: for the single stage turbine the values suggested by (Costall et al., 2015; Kang, 2012; Han et al., 2014; Sung et al., 2016; Wong et al., 2013; Shao et al., 2017; Giovannelli et al., 2019) were examined, while for the twin-screw expander, the figures proposed by (Hsu et al., 2014; Stošić et al., 1997; Lee et al., 2017; Platell, 1993; Astolfi, 2015) were evaluated. For the two-stage turbine, in contrast, not many values are currently available in the literature, apart from the one resulting from the work by Kang (2016). A summary of the other main assumptions used for the calculation of the heat and mass balances of the ORC systems is reported elsewhere (Di Lorenzo et al., 2019). The performance metric that was monitored to evaluate the effect of the uncertainty in the expander performance on the ORC system was the thermal efficiency.

Table I - Probability distributions for the expander efficiency

Case – Expander Type	Distribution	Min and Max Values
Case A – Single Stage Turbine	Triangular	68% - 83%
Case B – Twin Screw	Triangular	70% - 85%
Case – Two Stage Turbine (second stage)	Normal	65% - 79%

[1]For the first stage the probability distribution adopted for the single stage case was used.

Furthermore, the uncertainty in the expander performance was propagated through economic parameters. The Specific Unit Cost ($_{2016}$/kW) was used as an indicator representative of the economic performances of the power plants being investigated. The work aimed primarily to assess the propagation of uncertainty from the expander to the economic parameters. For this reason, the impacts that the variability of expander η_{is} can have on the sizing and design of the other components (e.g., the condenser) were not taken into account, but rather, all of the other components were assumed to be as estimated in the previous work and unchanging. Nevertheless, the final results are yet informative, as they reflect changes in economic expectations based on expander performance variability.

4. Key Results

The results are presented as cumulative probability distributions (Figures 1-3), which provide the analyst with the likelihood of random variable X, evaluated at $\bar{x}$, being equal to or less than the specified value $\bar{x}$; the complement (one minus the cumulative probability) is the probability that the variable will exceed the specified value $\bar{x}$. The deterministic evaluation is represented in the same figures by a vertical dotted line.

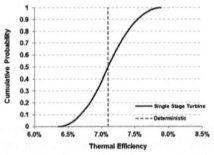

Figure 1 -Cumulative probability distribution for case A

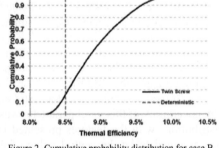

Figure 2 -Cumulative probability distribution for case B

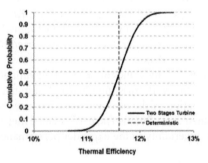

Figure 3 -Cumulative probability distribution for case C

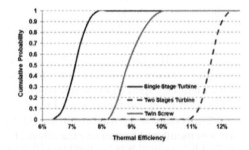

Figure 4 -Cumulative probability distribution for the three cases

According to the simulation results, the probability that the thermal efficiency for Case A could be less than the deterministic value of 7.1% is approximately 50%. It could range between 6.3% and 7.9% with a standard deviation of 0.003 and a relative standard deviation of 0.045. The median value was equal to 7.1% in line with the deterministic prediction. For Case B, the resulting efficiency displays a median value of 8.9% close to the deterministic value of 8.5%. It could vary within a range of 8.2% to 10.1%, with a standard deviation of 0.004 and a relative standard deviation of 0.048. The probability that the final figure of plant efficiency could exceed the deterministic value is quite high (85%). The results indicate that a considerable level of uncertainty is also associated with the variation of the expander performance in Case C. The likelihood that the forecast efficiency value can exceed the deterministic value is approx. 52%, with a remaining 48% probability that the final value could be lower than the deterministic one. The variation in the expander efficiency in Case C causes the plant efficiency to vary between 10.6% and 12.6%, with a median value of 11.6% (well aligned with the deterministic result), a standard deviation of 0.003 and a relative standard deviation of 0.025. It is of paramount importance to highlight that these results (like the results of any Monte Carlo simulation analysis) rely on the initial assumptions, especially the statistical distributions selected and assigned to the uncertain input variables. A deterministic analysis only provides the decision maker with information on deterministic efficiencies, with no suggestion of the above-mentioned likelihood of a higher (or lower) value. Figure 4 shows the cumulative probability distributions of the plant efficiency for the three cases. It is evident that there are not any intersection points among the three curves; therefore, Case C (the two stage turbine) should be selected, as its probability distribution curve spreads further to the right (higher values of efficiency), although the results (i.e., same chance of observing a lower or higher value compared to the deterministic one) suggest that additional research should be undertaken in order to reduce uncertainty in the expander performance.

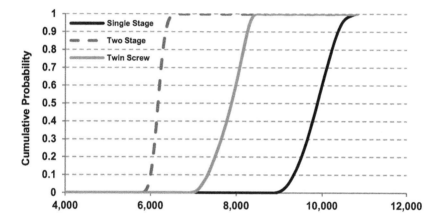

Figure 5 -Cumulative probability distribution for the three cases for the economic results

Figure 5 reports the cumulative probability distributions for the Specific Unit Cost for the three cases. Like the plant efficiency results, the three cumulative probability distributions do not intersect at any point, confirming the superior economic performance of Case C already highlighted by the deterministic analysis.

5. Conclusions

The research effort presented in this paper focuses on the inclusion of uncertainties in the techno-economic evaluation of ORC power plants. The Monte Carlo simulation technique was employed to quantify the impact of uncertainties associated with three different expanders on key techno-economic performance outputs (plant efficiency and specific unit cost). By including uncertainties in the techno-economic evaluation of the three plant options, it was found that the plant efficiency was equally likely to be lower or higher than the deterministic value for Cases A and C, while it could exceed the forecasted value with an 85% probability in Case B. The economic results are indicative of how the probability distribution of specific unit cost is affected by the uncertainty in the expander performance and confirm that the two-stage turbine outperforms the other two cases. Overall, a considerable variability of the output metrics was highlighted compared to the results from the deterministic analysis. A full spectrum of possible outputs was made available, rather than exact figures. This type of analysis allows the decision-maker to make more informed decisions on the evaluation of the ORC technology and, in particular, on what options to pursue for further R&D activities by establishing the least expensive and the best-performing solution among those analysed.

References

M. Astolfi, 2015, Techno-economic Optimization of Low Temperature CSP Systems Based on ORC with Screw Expanders, Energy Procedia, 69, 1100-1112.

A.W. Costall, A. Gonzalez Hernandez, P.J. Newton, R.F. Martinez-Botas, 2015, Design methodology for radial turbo expanders in mobile organic Rankine cycle applications, Applied Energy, 157, 729-743.

G. Di Lorenzo, P. Pilidis, J. Witton, D. Probert, 2012, A Framework for the Evaluation of Investments in Clean Power-Technologies, Computer Aided Chemical Engineering, 30, 492-496.

G. Di Lorenzo, A. Giovannelli, P. Bartocci, F. Fantozzi, 2019, Comparison of Mini Organic Rankine Cycle Plants for Waste Heat Recovery, AIP Conference Proceedings 2191, 020066.

A. Giovannelli, E.M. Archilei, C. Salvini, 2019, Full-admission radial turbine for waste heat recovery organic Rankine cycles, Energy Reports, https://doi.org/10.1016/j.egyr.2019.09.043.

S. Han, J.B. Seo, B.-S. Choi, 2014, Development of a 200 kW ORC radial turbine for waste heat recovery, Journal of Mechanical Science and Technology, 28, 12, 5231-5241.

S.-W. Hsu, H.-W.D. Chiang, C.-W. Yen, 2014, Experimental investigation of the performance of a hermetic screw-expander organic rankine cycle, Energies, 7, 9, 6172-6185.

S.H. Kang, 2012, Design and experimental study of ORC (organic Rankine cycle) and radial turbine using R245fa working fluid, Energy, 41, 1, 514-524.

S.H. Kang, 2016, Design and preliminary tests of ORC (organic Rankine cycle) with two-stage radial turbine, Energy, 96, 142-154.

Y.-R. Lee, L.-W. Liu, Y.-Y. Chang, J.-C. Hsieh, 2017, Development and application of a 200 kW ORC generator system for energy recovery in chemical processes, Energy Procedia, 129, 519-526.

E. W. Lemmon, M. O. McLinden and M. L. Huber, 2002, NIST Reference Fluid Thermodynamic and Transport Properties – REFPROP, NIST Standard Reference Database 23, Version 7.0.

M. Maccapani, R.S.R. Khan, P.J. Burgmann, G. Di Lorenzo, S.O.T. Ogaji, P. Pilidis, I. Bennett, 2014, A TERA based comparison of heavy duty engines and their artificial design variants for liquified natural gas service, Journal of Engineering for Gas Turbines and Power, 136, 2, 022001.

P. Platell, 1993, Displacement expanders for small-scale cogeneration, Lic. Thesis, KTH Stockholm.

L. Shao, J. Zhu, X. Meng, X. Wei, X. Ma, 2017, Experimental study of an organic Rankine cycle system with radial inflow turbine and R123, Applied Thermal Engineering, 124, 940-947.

N. Stošić, I.K. Smith, A. Kovačević, C.A. Aldis, 1997, The Design of a Twin-screw Compressor Based on a New Rotor Profile, Journal of Engineering Design, 8, 4, 389-399.

T. Sung, E. Yun, H.D. Kim, S.Y. Yoon, B.S. Choi, K. Kim, J. Kim, Y.B. Jung, K.C. Kim, 2016, Performance characteristics of a 200-kW organic Rankine cycle system in a steel processing plant, Applied Energy, 183, 623-635.

B.F. Tchanche, G. Lambrinos, A. Frangoudakis, G. Papadakis, 2011, Low-grade heat conversion into power using organic Rankine cycles–a review of various applications, Renewable and Sustainable Energy Reviews, 15, 8, 3963-3979.

L. Tocci, T. Pal, I. Pesmazoglou and B. Franchetti, 2017, Small Scale Organic Rankine Cycle (ORC): A Techno-Economic Review, Energies, 10, 4, 413.

C. S. Wong, D. Meyer, S. Krumdieck, 2013, Selection and conversion of turbo-expander for organic Rankine cycle (ORC), 35th New Zeland Geothermal Workshop Proceedings, 17-20 November 2013, Rotorua, New Zeland.

Sauro Pierucci, Flavio Manenti, Giulia Bozzano, Davide Manca (Eds.)
Proceedings of the 30th European Symposium on Computer Aided Process Engineering
(ESCAPE30), May 24-27, 2020, Milano, Italy. © 2020 Elsevier B.V. All rights reserved.
http://dx.doi.org/10.1016/B978-0-12-823377-1.50257-3

Optimum Installation of Heat Recovery Devices in Biomass Boiler

Somchart Chantasiriwan

Department of Mechanical Engineering, Thammasat University, Pathum Thani 12121, Thailand
somchart@engr.tu.ac.th

Abstract

Biomass boiler uses thermal energy from the combustion of biomass fuel and air to produce superheated steam from feed water. Biomass fuel usually has a high moisture content, which leads to low boiler efficiency. The boiler efficiency can be increased by using heat recovery devices to decrease the temperature of flue gas before it is exhausted from the boiler. Three heat recovery devices found in a typical installation of biomass boiler are economizer, air heater, and flue gas dryer. Economizer increases feed water temperature, air heater increases air temperature before combustion, and flue gas dryer decreases the moisture content of fuel. Limited available thermal energy of flue gas means that a decision must made in selecting the sizes of these devices. The main objective of this paper is to use a biomass boiler model, in which the boiler consists of as a furnace and a set of heat exchangers, to determine the optimum sizes of economizer, air heater, and flue gas dryer that minimize the total cost of installing them in biomass boiler system.

Keywords: Heat exchangers, Biomass drying, Energy system, Modelling

1. Introduction

Biomass fuels are usually characterized by high-moisture content. Combustion of a moist fuel in a biomass boiler results in low boiler efficiency because a large amount of thermal energy released from fuel combustion is required for the evaporation of moisture in the fuel. Drying of fuel requires an energy source. A high-temperature source like flue gas seems to be ideal for this purpose. Flue gas dryer is a heat recovery device that may be installed in a boiler to decrease flue gas temperature and increase boiler efficiency. Other heat recovery devices that are normally installed in a boiler are economizer and air heater. Thermal energy from flue gas increases feed water temperature in economizer and air temperature in air heater. All three heat recovery devices can effectively increase boiler efficiency. However, since all three devices require thermal energy from flue gas, there are limits to their sizes if they are installed together in a biomass boiler.

Studies of integrating flue gas dryer into biomass boiler system have been carried out by several investigators. Andersson et al. (2006) evaluated different methods of drying biomass in a pulp mill, and found that flue gas dryer was the most attractive. Sosa-Arnao and Nebra (2009) analyzed different energy recovery configurations in boilers fired by bagasse, and showed that the configuration consisting of economizer, air heater, and flue gas dryer had the lowest optimized cost. Li et al. (2012) compared energy saving resulting from the integration of flue gas dryer in a power plant that used pine chips as fuel and the cost of drying, and concluded that 3 - 4 years of operation was expected to give a return on the investment. Gebreegziabher et al. (2014) proposed a multi-stage process for biomass drying that combines hot air dryer, superheated steam dryer, and flue gas dryer. Liu (2017) determined the limit for the cost of flue gas dryer under which the integration of the dryer was economically justified. Although some previous works have considered the economic aspect of the integration of flue gas dryer and the comparison between flue gas dryer and other dryers, none of the previous works have considered the constraint of flue gas dryer installation in presence of economizer and air heater and the optimum installation of these devices.

In this paper, a model of biomass boiler is used to determine the optimum installation of heat recovery devices in biomass boiler. The boiler is required to generate superheated steam at specified flow rate, pressure, and temperature. It is shown that, under the constraint that boiler efficiency is fixed, there are the optimum sizes of economizer, air heater, and flue gas dryer that minimize the total cost of installing these devices.

2. Biomass boiler system

Analysis of a thermal energy system usually requires a boiler model. A widely used model is the black-box model. This model considers only the inputs to the boiler, which are feed water, fuel, and air, and the outputs, which are superheated steam and flue gas. Using this model requires that either boiler efficiency or flue gas temperature is known. Although the black-box model is sufficient in an analysis that does not consider effects of heating surface areas, it is insufficient for the current investigation. A more suitable model must take into account components of the boiler. An illustration of biomass boiler system with flue gas dryer is shown in Fig. 1. Solid lines denote fuel, air, and flue gas, whereas and dashed lines denote feed water and steam. The main components of the system are furnace (F), evaporator (EV), steam drum (SD), superheater (SH), boiler bank (BB), economizer (EC), air heater (AH), and flue gas dryer (FD).

Combustion of fuel in F results in thermal energy that is used to evaporate water in EV and increase steam temperature in SH from the saturated steam temperature (T_v) to T_s. Flue gas leaving F at T_{g1} flows successively SH, BB, EC, AH, and FD, and its temperature is reduced, respectively, to T_{g2}, T_{g3}, T_{g4}, T_{g5}, and T_{g6}. Heat transfer from flue gas causes the increase of feed water temperature from T_{wi} to T_{we} in EC, the increase of air temperature from T_{ai} to T_{ae} in AH, the increase of fuel temperature from T_{ai} to T_f, and the reduction of fuel moisture content from x_{Mi} to x_M in FD. Subcooled feed water at a mass flow rate m_w from EC and saturated steam at mass flow rates m_{s1} and m_{s2} from EV and BB enter SD, which returns saturated liquid water at the same mass flow rates to EV and BB, and sends saturated steam at a mass flow rate m_s to SH. Water evaporation in EV is due to radiative heat transfer from flue gas in F, whereas water evaporation in BB is due to convective heat transfer from flue gas. In order to maintain the concentration of dissolved solids in feed water at a safe level, it is assumed that some of the feed water is blowdown water. It should be noted that, in an actual operation, the inputs to SD from EV and BB are mixtures of saturated steam and saturated liquid water, which are separated in SD. In other words, most saturated liquid water is recirculated through SD. In this simplified model, the recirculated saturated liquid water is ignored, and inputs to SD from EV and BB are assumed to be saturated steam. Mathematical models for F, EV, SD, SH, BB, EC, and AH are provided by Chantasiriwan (2019).

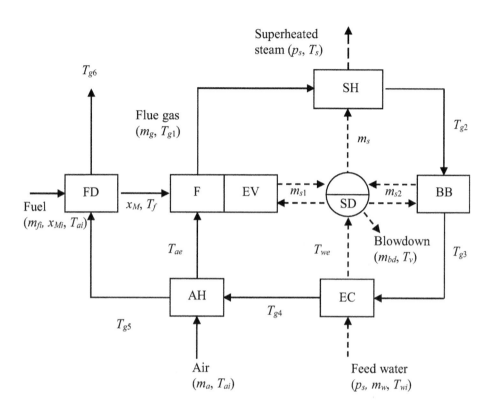

Figure 1. Bagasse boiler model.

The model of FD is shown in Fig. 2. Assume that fuel is divided into 2 parts with mass fractions y and $(1-y)$. The mass fraction y of fuel is completely dried in FD, as reported in Eq. (1).

$$y = \frac{m_g c_{pg}\left(T_{g5} - T_{g6}\right)}{m_{fi}\left\{\left(1 - x_{Mi}\right)c_{pf} + x_{Mi}c_{pw}\right]\left(T_{g6} - T_a\right) + x_{Mi}\left[c_{pw}\left(T_r - T_{g6}\right) + \Delta i_r + c_{pv}\left(T_{g6} - T_r\right)\right]\right\}} \tag{1}$$

where c_{pg}, c_{pf}, c_{pw}, and c_{pv} are specific heat capacities of flue gas, fuel, water, and vapor, T_r is the reference temperature (25°C), and Δi_r is the latent heat of evaporation at the reference temperature. The dried fuel is then mixed with the rest of the fuel. The mass flow rate, the moisture content, and the temperature of fuel at the dryer outlet are determined from Eqs. (2) – (4).

$$m_f = m_{fi} - y m_{fi} x_{Mi} \tag{2}$$

$$x_M = \frac{(1-y)x_{Mi}m_{fi}}{m_f} \tag{3}$$

$$T_f = \frac{m_{fi}\left\{c_{pf}\left(1-x_{Mi}\right)\left[yT_{g6}+(1-y)T_a\right]+c_{pw}(1-y)x_{Mi}T_a\right\}}{m_f\left[c_{pf}\left(1-x_M\right)+c_{pw}x_M\right]} \tag{4}$$

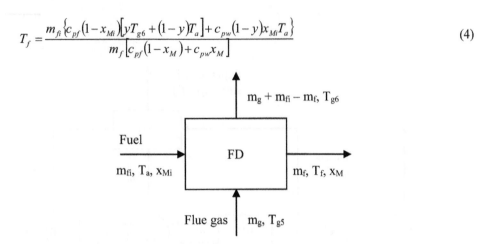

Figure 2. Flue gas dryer model.

Heating surface areas of F are A_v and A_t, whereas A_{SH}, A_{BB}, A_{EC}, and A_{AH} are, respectively, heating surface areas of SH, BB, EC, and AH. Unlike these heat exchangers, which are characterized by heating surface areas, FD is characterized by the amount of moisture removed from fuel (M) in kg/h, which is determined from Eq. (5).

$$M = 3600\,yx_{Mi}m_{fi} \tag{5}$$

3. Optimization procedure

The 25 primary variables in this boiler system are A_v, A_t, A_{SH}, A_{BB}, A_{EC}, A_{AH}, M, p_s, T_s, m_s, m_{s2}, m_{fi}, m_a, x_{Mi}, x_M, T_{ai}, T_{ae}, T_{wi}, T_{we}, T_{g1}, T_{g2}, T_{g3}, T_{g4}, T_{g5}, and T_{g6}. The other variables are secondary variables, which may be expressed in terms of primary variables. The system is governed by 12 energy and heat transfer equations. Therefore, the values of 13 primary variables must be specified values so that the solution of the system can be found. Known variables are A_v, A_t, A_{SH}, A_{BB}, A_{EC}, A_{AH}, M, p_s, m_{fi}, m_a, x_{Mi}, T_{ai}, and T_{wi} in a boiler system analysis. In a boiler design for the minimum installation cost of heat recovery devices, however, A_{EC}, A_{AH}, and M are unknown, and must be determined for given design conditions, which include a fixed value of boiler efficiency. Boiler efficiency (η) is defined in Eq. (6).

$$\eta = \frac{m_s\left(h_s - h_{fw}\right)}{m_f HHV} \tag{6}$$

where m_s is the mass flow rate of steam, h_s is the enthalpy of superheated steam at pressure p_s and temperature T_s, h_{fw} is the enthalpy of feed water, m_f is the mass flow rate of fuel, and HHV is the fuel higher heating value. This design requires the specified values of m_s and T_s. The other known variables are A_v, A_t, A_{BB}, A_{EC}, M, p_s, m_a, x_{Mi}, T_{ai}, and T_{wi}. In order to find the minimum installation cost, only A_{EC} and M are allowed to vary. As a result, heating surface area A_{AH} becomes a function of A_{EC} and M. It is assumed that the nominal unit installation costs of economizer and air heater are, respectively, 120 \$/m², and 100 \$/m². Furthermore, the unit installation cost of flue gas dryer is assumed to be 50 $/(kg/h). Therefore, the total installation cost of heat recovery devices is determined from Eq. (7).

$$C_{total} = 120 A_{EC} + 100 A_{AH} + 50M \tag{7}$$

The minimum value of C_{total} corresponds to the optimum values of A_{EC} and M.

4. Results and discussion

The fuel for the boiler system is bagasse of which composition is provided by Rein (2017). The boiler design parameters are $p_s = 4.5$ MPa, $T_s = 500°C$, and $m_s = 100$ kg/s. The fuel moisture content is 52%. The inlet air and fuel temperatures are 30°C. The inlet feed water temperature is 120°C.

By fixing η at 70%, it is found that A_{AH} decreases as either A_{EC} or M increases. Further-more, C_{total} varies with only A_{EC} and M. The minimum value of C_{total} may be found by using a line-search method. First, the optimum value of A_{EC} that yields the minimum installation cost at a specified value of M ($C_{min,M}$) is determined. Figure 3 shows variations of C_{total} with A_{EC} for four values of M. $C_{min,M}$ is found to be $1.144 × 10^6$, $1.128 × 10^6$, $1.124 × 10^6$, and $1.132 × 10^6$ for $M = 0$, 2000, 4000, and 6000 kg/h, respectively. Next, $C_{min,M}$ is plotted as a function of M as shown in Fig. 4. It can be seen that the minimum installation cost (C_{min}) of $1.125 × 10^6$ results from the optimum value of 3550 kg/h for M. The corresponding values of A_{EC} and A_{AH} are, respectively, 4685 m² and 3844 m². Therefore, the installation of flue gas dryer in addition to economizer and air heater results in 1.7% less total installation cost than the installation of only economizer and air heater. It should be noted that this result is obtained for the value of 50 $/(kg/h) for the unit cost of flue gas dryer. The minimum installation cost is quite sensitive to the unit cost of flue gas dryer. When the unit cost reaches 61 $/(kg/h), the installation of flue gas dryer is not justified because C_{min} is equal to $C_{min,0}$, and the installation of flue gas dyer increases the total installation cost.

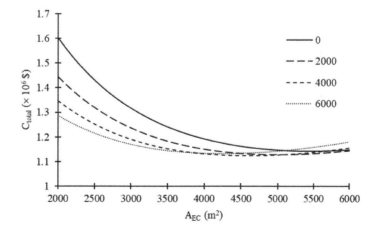

Figure 3. Variations of total installation cost (C_{total}) with the economizer surface area (A_{EC}) and the amount of removed moisture (M).

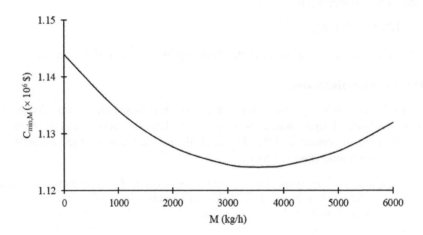

Figure 4. Variation of minimum installation cost at a fixed *M* value (*Cmin,M*) with *M*.

5. Conclusion

Three heat recovery devices that may be installed in a biomass boiler are economizer, air heater, and flue gas dryer. They decrease flue gas temperature, and increase boiler efficiency. Since all three devices require thermal energy from high-temperature flue gas that results from combustion of biomass fuel, there are limits to the sizes of these devices under given boiler operating conditions if they are installed together. For a fixed value of 70% for the boiler efficiency, a boiler model can be used to demonstrate that there are the optimum sizes of these devices that result in the minimum installation cost. Simulation results indicate that the optimum installation of economizer, air heater, and flue gas dryer can reduce the installation cost by 1.7% compared with a non-optimum installation, in which there are only economizer and air heater. Cost reduction increases with decreasing unit cost of dryer.

References

E. Andersson, S. Harvey, T. Berntsson, 2006, Energy efficient upgrading of biofuel integrated with a pulp mill, Energy, 31, 1384-1394.

S. Chantasiriwan, 2019, Effects of heating surface areas on the performance of bagasse boiler, Chemical Engineering Transactions, 74, 139-144.

T. Gebreegziabher, A. O. Oyedun, Z. Yu, W. Maojian, Z. Yi, L. Jin, C. W. Hui, 2014, Biomass drying for an integrated power plant: Effective utilization of waste heat, Computer Aided Chemical Engineering, 33, 1555-1560.

H. Li, Q. Chen, X. Zhang, K. N. Finney, V. N. Sharifi, J. Swithenbank, 2012, Evaluation of a biomass drying process using waste heat from process industries: A case study, Applied Thermal Engineering, 35, 71-80.

M. Liu, X. Zhang, X. Han, G. Li, J. Yan, 2017, Using pre-drying technology to improve the exergetic efficiency of bioenergy utilization process with combustion: A case study of a power plant, Applied Thermal Engineering, 127, 1416-1426.

P. Rein, 2017, Cane Sugar Engineering, 2nd Ed., Verlag, Berlin.

J. H. Sosa-Arnao, S. A. Nebra, 2009, Bagasse dryer role in the energy recovery of water tube boilers, Drying Technology, 27, 587-594.

Sauro Pierucci, Flavio Manenti, Giulia Bozzano, Davide Manca (Eds.)
Proceedings of the 30th European Symposium on Computer Aided Process Engineering
(ESCAPE30), May 24-27, 2020, Milano, Italy. © 2020 Elsevier B.V. All rights reserved.
http://dx.doi.org/10.1016/B978-0-12-823377-1.50258-5

Thermogravimetric Analysis of Individual Food Waste Items and their Blends for Biochar Production

Samar Elkhalifa,[a] Omar Elhassan,[c] Prakash Parthasarathy,[a] Hamish Mackey,[a] Tareq Al-Ansari, [a,b] , Gordon McKay[a]*

[a]Divison of Sustainable Development, College of Science and Engineering, Hamad Bin Khalifa University, Qatar Foundation, Doha, Qatar.

[b]Division of Engineering Management and Decision Sciences, College of Science and Engineering, Hamad Bin Khalifa University, Doha, Qatar.

[c]Qatar Environment and Energy Institute, Doha, Qatar.

gmckay@hbku.edu.qa

Abstract

Food waste is generated in enormous quantities globally. Due to its organic- and nutrient-rich composition, food waste is a potential feedstock for the production of energy and value-added products. In many countries, food wastes are currently landfilled or incinerated together with other combustible municipal wastes for possible recovery of energy, but these two approaches are facing more and more economic and environmental pressures. Moreover, food waste can be converted into energy using waste to energy technologies. The use of thermochemical technologies has become an acceptable practice that is undergoing widespread research. The ultimate goal of the current research work is to produce value-added biochar products from food waste, hence providing an option to tackle the previously addressed problems of effective waste management. Prior to the production of biochars, three selected food items are studied under Thermogravimetric analysis (TGA). The analysis involves the single food items, a binary mixture, and a blend of the three. The studied food wastes are tomatoes, cucumbers, and carrots. Moreover, TGA revolves around measuring the weight of sample continuously in a controlled temperature program. This, in turn, allows the physical and chemical properties of the sample to be obtained based on the variation of sample weight with respect to time and temperature using the DTG curve resulting from a differential TGA curve. The TGA technique can be helpful in determining the proximate analysis of food waste and to find out the thermal characteristics like ignition, burnout temperature and chemical kinetics of food waste by using the pyrolysis process. The results of TGA are of key importance as they suggest the thermal degradation patterns of food waste, and bio-char under air or an inert environment for succeeding kinetic studies. The configurations explain the response of heating rate, food waste properties, stability and compatibility of food waste to different processes. Furthermore, the results of the different experimental runs and TGA modelling are presented, analyzed and discussed. Very little information is available on the pyrolysis and understanding of individual food waste components.

Keywords: TGA, Food Waste, Modelling, Pyrolysis, Biochar.

1. Introduction

Thermogravimetric analysis (TGA) is based on the weight loss and the heat transfer rate of material and therefore the derivative difference peaks of each specific elements (e.g. C or N) are not available, which are key components for the characterization of biochar (Li & Chen, 2018).

Previous studies have investigated the TGA of different biomass waste like food waste (Jo et al., 2017), apricots stones (Nocera et al., 2016), and biosolids and plant-based biomass waste (Li & Chen, 2018). However, the use of mixed food items and binary mixtures have not been fully explored. The motivation behind the use of food waste is the huge quantities generated (Elkhalifa et al., 2019a), in addition to the unique properties of the value-added products produced from their conversion using waste to energy conversion methods such as pyrolysis (Elkhalifa et al., 2019b). Thus, this paper aims to investigate the TGA of different widely used food waste products and their different interactions and behavior. In particular, the study looks at tomatoes, cucumbers and carrots and their single, binary and ternary blends and mixtures.

2. Materials and Methods

In order to study the interaction between the components, all permutations of binary and tertiary mixture of components, which are mixed in an equal proportion by weight are prepared for TG analyses. Slow pyrolysis, which occurs at low heating rates, moderate temperatures and long residence times, was carried out in the presence of a nitrogen atmosphere until a temperature of 800 °C was reached. The effect of different heating rates (5 and 10 °C/min) has been studied.

2.1. Feedstock and Production of Biochar

The raw feedstock samples (i.e. carrots, cucumber and tomatoes) were oven-dried at 140 °C for 24 h before being chopped into smaller chunks. The dried samples were then ground to finer particles making them ready for TGA.

2.2. Thermogravimetric Analysis (TGA)

Both the feedstock and products of the pyrolysis were analyzed under inert atmosphere using a TA Discovery thermogravimetric analyzer with a continuous nitrogen flow of 100 ml/min. The TG analyzer was used to obtain the simultaneous mass loss and differential mass profile of the samples with respect to time and temperature.

Around 10 mg of the sample was weighed for the thermal weight-change analysis. Additionally, the temperature ramp was set as follows: (1) temperature equilibrium at 30 °C linearly heated to 100 °C at two different constant heating rates: 5 and 10 °C/min; (2) isotherm at 100 °C for 10 min; (3) two ramping rate of ramping of 5 and 10 °C/min from 100 °C to 800 °C.

An attached mass spectrometer was able to monitor the evolving gas samples while the TGA measured the thermal decomposition of the feedstock and biochar by monitoring the weight loss.

2.3. Kinetics Analysis Using the Friedman Method

The TGA/DTGA curves were then evaluated using the Friedman kinetics method that is described in White et al. (2011). The method determines the Arrhenius kinetic parameters from the non-isothermal TGA measurements as follows in Eq. (1):

$$\ln\left(\frac{d\alpha}{dt}\right) = \ln\left[HR\left(\frac{d\alpha}{dT}\right)\right] = \ln\left(A(1-\alpha)\right) - \frac{Ea}{RT} \tag{1}$$

Where α is the conversion degree of biomass and is computed from the TGA measurement of mass; t is the time, HR(dT/dt) is a linear heating rate; T is the absolute temperature; A is the frequency factor; Ea is the activation energy, and R is the universal constant of the ideal gases. Plotting ln(dα/dt) as a function of 1/T produces a straight line from which the activation energy can be obtained from the slope while the frequency factor can be obtained from the intercept of the equation.

3. Results and Discussion

Mass loss profiles, temperature ranges, and kinetic parameters of the decomposition of each component are presented in this section along with the approximate analysis that was also generated using TGA. Figure 1-3 show, for both food products and their blends, the mass loss (TGA) and the derivative of mass loss (DTGA) as a function of the pyrolysis temperature. The 3 figures are constructed based on the use of 2 different heating rates: 5 °C/min and 10 °C/min. Moreover, the approach for the kinetics analyses was demonstrated on the same selected food waste samples and for the hemicellulose decomposition region only.

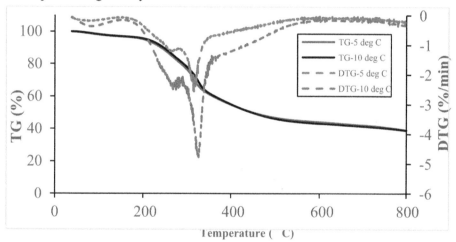

Figure 1. TGA/DTGA of the cucumber sample at heating rates of 5 °C/min and 10 °C

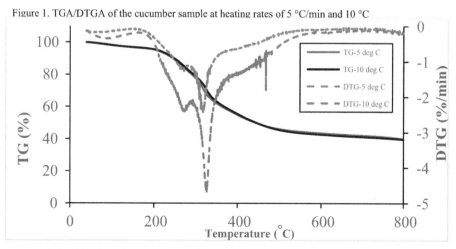

Figure 2. TGA/DTGA of the tomato sample at heating rates of 5 °C/min and 10 °C/min

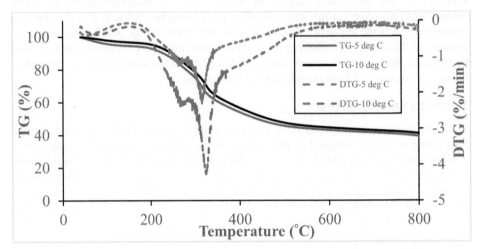

Figure 3. TGA/DTGA of the cucumber and tomato sample at heating rates of 5 °C/min and 10 °C/min

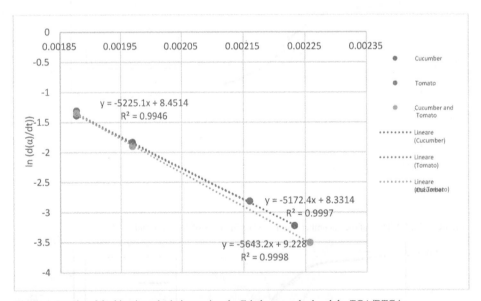

Figure 4. Results of the kinetics calculations using the Friedman method and the TGA/DTGA

Table 1. Proximate analysis of the raw materials (air-dried basis)

Vegetables	Moisture content (wt. %)	Volatile matter (wt. %)	Fixed carbon[*] (wt. %)	Ash content (wt. %)
Cucumber	8.32	63.97	25.87	1.84
Tomato	5.24	76.24	14.00	4.52
Carrot	8.75	80.14	5.87	5.24

*calculated by difference

Table 2. The kinetic parameters for hemicellulose decomposition region for selected samples

Sample	T_1 (°C)	T_2 (°C)	Conversion	Ea (kJ/mol.K)	A (min^{-1})
Cucumber	175.0	260.0	8.3-28.3%	43.0	4151.5
Tomato	190.0	260.0	8.3-25.0%	43.4	4680.9
Cucumber and Tomato	170.0	260.0	8.3-25.0%	46.9	10177.4

As can be seen from the figures, for both heating rates, the total weight loss at the final temperature is approximately 60-72%, however the larger part of biomass volatilization occurs between 200 °C and 500 °C. The volatilization of biomass can be attributed to the presence and thermal decomposition of three main biomass components, namely: lignin, cellulose and hemicellulose. These components are known to have a great influence on the behavior of the pyrolysis process (Hu et al., 2007).

Moreover, the occurrence of some peaks is observed in the DTGA curves, which represent maximum points of the reaction rates for both heating rates. The first peak is observed around 100 °C and is attributed to the moisture evaporation, which is associated with very low weight loss around 2-4%. The second peak of DTGA occurs at around 260 °C for both 5 °C/ min and 10 °C/min. This peak is primarily associated with hemicellulose pyrolysis. According to other studies that are found in the scientific literature, hemicellulose decomposes in the range 160 °C and 300 °C for orange peel residues (Aguiar et al., 2008), olive oil pomace (Özveren & Özdoğan, 2013), and biomass residuals mixtures with lignite (Vamvuka et al., 2003). The third peak of interest occurs at around 310 °C for both heating rates. This peak is mainly associated with cellulose, which normally degrades at high temperatures around 300 °C – 400 °C (Yang et al., 2007). Additionally, lignin is the first biomass component to decompose at low temperatures, however the degradation of this component takes place at very low rates and hence it continues for 800 °C. This indicates that a very small part of the second and third peaks of the DTGA curves are associated with the decomposition of lignin (Font et al., 2009). Furthermore, the results of the studies indicated some similarities between the two heating rates used in this study. The mass loss trends, amounts and peaks were very similar throughout all the samples. Differences in the DTGA peaks, for both heating rates, are negligible. According to the literature, however, varying the heating rate has a major influence on DTGA curves (Ounas et al., 2011). It should be noted that these low heating rates were chosen to study the slow pyrolysis which produces higher yields of the desired biochar product. The findings indicate that both heating rates are capable of producing the same TGA and DTGA curves. Hence, it is recommended to explore the effect of lower heating rates (e.g. 1 °C/min) and higher heating rates (e.g. 20 °C/min) to arrive at a better understanding of the behavior of the pyrolysis process in relation to the heating rates that are employed in the study.

With respect to the kinetics results, the Friedman method allowed the computation of both the activation energy and frequency factors as shown in Table 2 when assuming a first order reaction. In order to demonstrate the approach, the kinetics were only evaluated at the region of hemicellulose decomposition until the maximum decomposition is reached. As can be noticed, the activation energy was almost constant for the three samples with slight variations for the binary mixture, while the frequency factor increased significantly in the mixed binary sample. The activation energies of the two single component systems are 43 kJ/mol, but for the binary system there appears to be some form of interaction as the Ea value is slightly higher at 47 kJ/mol.

4. Conclusion

The current work is concerned with the understanding of the pyrolysis process and the production of biochars from food waste. The TGA is a convenient method that facilitates the understanding of such systems. The results of the use of two distinct heating rates indicated that further research is required employing higher and lower heating rates since both heating rates for slow pyrolysis generated identical TGA/DTGA results. According to the results, the peaks of hemicellulose and cellulose decomposition occurred at ranges typical to those reported in the literature. Finally, the kinetics analysis revealed that the interactions between the binary mixtures resulted in an activation energy of a similar magnitude to the energies of the individual food wastes, while the frequency factor was almost doubled.

References

L. Aguiar, F. Márquez-Montesinos, A. Gonzalo, J. L. Sánchez, & J. Arauzo, 2008, Influence of temperature and particle size on the fixed bed pyrolysis of orange peel residues. Journal of Analytical and Applied Pyrolysis, 83, 124–130. https://doi.org/10.1016/j.jaap.2008.06.009

S. Elkhalifa, T. Al-Ansari, H. R. Mackey, & G. McKay, 2019a, Food waste to biochars through pyrolysis: A review. Resources, Conservation and Recycling, 144. https://doi.org/10.1016/j.resconrec.2019.01.024

S. Elkhalifa, A. AlNouss, T. Al-Ansari, H. R. Mackey, P. Parthasarathy & G. Mckay, 2019b, Simulation of Food Waste Pyrolysis for the Production of Biochar: A Qatar Case Study. In Computer Aided Chemical Engineering (pp. 901–906). https://doi.org/10.1016/B978-0-12-818634-3.50151-X

R. Font, J. Moltó, A. Gálvez, & M.D. Rey, 2009, Kinetic study of the pyrolysis and combustion of tomato plant. Journal of Analytical and Applied Pyrolysis, 85, 268–275. https://doi.org/10.1016/j.jaap.2008.11.026

S. Hu, A. Jess, & M. Xu, 2007, Kinetic study of Chinese biomass slow pyrolysis: Comparison of different kinetic models. Fuel, 86, 2778–2788. https://doi.org/10.1016/j.fuel.2007.02.031

J. H. Jo, S. S. Kim, J. W. Shim, Y.E. Lee, & Y.S. Yoo, 2017, Pyrolysis characteristics and kinetics of food wastes. Energies. https://doi.org/10.3390/en10081191

S. Li, & G. Chen, 2018, Thermogravimetric, thermochemical, and infrared spectral characterization of feedstocks and biochar derived at different pyrolysis temperatures. Waste Management, 78, 198–207. https://doi.org/10.1016/j.wasman.2018.05.048

F. Nocera, A. Gagliano, F. Patania, M. Bruno, & S. Scirè, 2016, Slow pyrolysis kinetics of apricots stones by thermogravimetric analysis. In IREC 2016 - 7th International Renewable Energy Congress. https://doi.org/10.1109/IREC.2016.7478945

A. Ounas, A. Aboulkas, K. El harfi, A. Bacaoui, & A. Yaacoubi, 2011, Pyrolysis of olive residue and sugar cane bagasse: Non-isothermal thermogravimetric kinetic analysis. Bioresource Technology, 102, 11234–11238. https://doi.org/10.1016/j.biortech.2011.09.010

U. Özveren, & Z. S. Özdoğan, 2013, Investigation of the slow pyrolysis kinetics of olive oil pomace using thermo-gravimetric analysis coupled with mass spectrometry. Biomass and Bioenergy, 58, 168–179. https://doi.org/10.1016/j.biombioe.2013.08.011

D. Vamvuka, E. Kakaras, E. Kastanaki, & P. Grammelis, 2003, Pyrolysis characteristics and kinetics of biomass residuals mixtures with lignite. In Fuel (pp. 1949–1960). https://doi.org/10.1016/S0016-2361(03)00153-4

J.E. White, W. J. Catallo, & B.L. Legendre, 2011, Biomass pyrolysis kinetics: A comparative critical review with relevant agricultural residue case studies. Journal of Analytical and Applied Pyrolysis. https://doi.org/10.1016/j.jaap.2011.01.004

H. Yang, R. Yan, H. Chen, D. H. Lee, & C. Zheng, 2007, Characteristics of hemicellulose, cellulose and lignin pyrolysis. Fuel, 86, 1781–1788. https://doi.org/10.1016/j.fuel.2006.12.013

Sauro Pierucci, Flavio Manenti, Giulia Bozzano, Davide Manca (Eds.)
Proceedings of the 30th European Symposium on Computer Aided Process Engineering
(ESCAPE30), May 24-27, 2020, Milano, Italy. © 2020 Elsevier B.V. All rights reserved.
http://dx.doi.org/10.1016/B978-0-12-823377-1.50259-7

Analyzing Hydrogen Production Capacities to Seize Renewable Energy Surplus

Mariana Corengia, Nicolás Estefan, Ana I. Torres[*]

Instituto de Ingeniería Química, Facultad de Ingeniería, Universidad de la República, Montevideo, Uruguay
aitorres@fing.edu.uy

Abstract

Modern renewable energy sources such as wind or sunlight cannot be programmed to be available when needed. A robust design of electrical grids with high penetration of these usually imply the existence of energy surplus. This surplus can be taken advantage of by seeking integration with fuel hydrogen production systems. However, the surplus is neither constant nor periodic, hence there is a trade-off between usage resource and economic goals. For a given energy surplus vs time curve, this paper presents three different decision-making problems to find the optimal hydrogen production capacity that needs to be installed, and the associated hydrogen prices.

Keywords: renewable energy surplus, power to hydrogen, green fuels, optimization

1. Introduction

Decarbonization of the energy mix has two main objectives: one is the displacement of the fossil fuels from the electricity generation sector, the other one is their displacement from the transportation sector. The former can be considered at a mature stage: in many regions, electricity from wind and sunlight is already integrated into the power grid, and in some cases (e.g. Norway, Costa Rica, Uruguay) the power mix is now close to 100 % renewable (Kroposki et al., 2017; MIEM, 2018). Replacement of liquid fuels within the transportation sector lags behind. For short distance applications battery electric vehicles seem to be the most suitable solution. However, for medium-long distance or heavy load applications, battery sizes and their weight become a barrier; in these cases, electric vehicles fueled by hydrogen are promising alternatives (Hydrogen Council, 2017).

Hydrogen produced by electrolysis has several advantages over hydrogen produced by other means. First, it requires little downstream processing to be suitable for fuel cell electric vehicles (i.e. does not contain CO and other contaminants that are poisonous to the fuel cells). Second, as electrolyzers usually have fast on-off dynamics (Corengia and Torres, 2018), they can run intermittently.

The presence of large energy surplus is common in regions in which the power mix is now close to 100 % renewable, as to avoid failures due to the non-programmable nature of wind and sun, generation capabilities are usually oversized by design. In these regions, using the surplus to operate electrolyzers has been proposed to valorize the surplus. The overall renewable energy to hydrogen process is schematized in Figure 1. Power from non-programmable sources is incorporated into the electric grid when available; if the power required by users (households, industries, etc.) is larger than the amount produced, programmable sources (such as hydroelectrical) are turned on. If users do not consume all the power produced by the non-programmable sources, the electrolyzer is turned on.

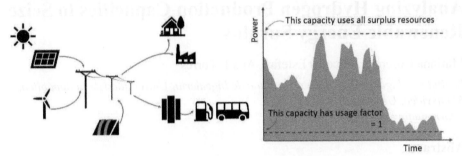

Figure 1. Schematic of the renewable energy (RE) to fuel-hydrogen process. RE is delivered to the grid whenever it is available, the electrolyzer is turned on in case of surplus.

Figure 2. Energy surplus (dark area) is variable during time.

Questions pertinent to the design of hydrogen production systems include which technology to use, how many electrolyzers to install and which capacity to select. Among the technologies alkaline electrolyzers, proton exchange membranes and solid oxide cells are the most mature ones. The number of the electrolyzers to be installed and their capacity depends on the (expected) demand for hydrogen and the amount of energy that will be available. The latter largely depends on the climatic conditions as well as the consumption patterns of the region of interest. Figure 2 shows an example of variation of energy surplus with time, which, given a region, more or less cyclically repeats. As seen, there are two limiting design cases: one that takes maximum advantage of the energy surplus (low usage factor of the electrolyzer), the other takes maximum advantage of the installed capacity (low resource use).

The goal of our research is to design optimal grid-connected H_2 production plants. The novelty of the work lies in considering the energy surplus as a limiting factor, thus there is a trade-off between maximum usage of the resource and maximum usage of installed capacity. We focus on this trade off and analyze its effect on H_2 selling price and economic performance of the plant.

2. Mathematical model and relevant problem formulations

As mentioned above we will seek for economic solutions; we have chosen the Net Present Value (*NPV*) as the economic indicator. As usual, *NPV* is computed in terms of the installed equipment cost (*IC*), future revenues (*REV*) and operational expenditures (*OPEX*), assuming N years of operation and a discount rate r.

Installed equipment costs: mainly include the cost of the electrolyzer and the cost of the compressor(s) required to pressurize the hydrogen exiting to the electrolyzer to the standard vehicle charging pressures: 350 or 700 bars. These costs can be modeled as having a linear/piecewise linear dependence with production capacity (M_{H2} mass/time units) with factors to correlate H_2 mass with power ($f_{pwr,el}$ and $f_{pwr,comp}$) and investment factors ($f_{IC,el}$ and $f_{IC,comp}$) for the electrolyzer and compressor.

Revenues: are computed as the product of the hydrogen selling price ($\$_{H2}$ in USD/mass) and the total hydrogen produced during a year of operation. The latter is in turn computed as the sum of the amount of hydrogen generated at each time step ($\dot{m}_{H2,t}$ and Δt respectively).

Operational expenditures: include the cost of energy and maintenance. Energy is consumed by the electrolyzer and the compressor(s) and depends on the amount of hydrogen generated. Maintenance costs are estimated as a fraction (f_M) of the installed equipment cost. Note that the price of energy ($\$_{energy,t}$) may be a time-dependent parameter, that varies according to local electricity tariffs.

Eqs. (1)-(4) present the mathematical formulation of these statements.

$$NPV = -IC + \sum_{i=1}^{N} \frac{REV - OPEX}{(1+r)^i} \tag{1}$$

$$IC = M_{H_2} \cdot \left(f_{pwr,el} \cdot f_{IC,el} + f_{pwr,comp} \cdot f_{IC,comp} \right) \tag{2}$$

$$REV = \$_{H_2} \cdot \sum_{t} \Delta t \cdot \dot{m}_{H_2,t} \tag{3}$$

$$OPEX = \sum_{t} \left(\Delta t \cdot \dot{m}_{H_2,t} \cdot \$_{energy,t} \cdot \left(f_{pwr,el} + f_{pwr,comp} \right) \right) + f_M \cdot IC \tag{4}$$

In addition, the designs have to guarantee that:
- At each time t the amount of H$_2$ produced has to be below the installed capacity.

$$\dot{m}_{H_2,t} \leq M_{H_2} \tag{5}$$

- The power used for production of hydrogen and its compression cannot exceed the power that is available from the surplus of non-programmable sources (RE_t).

$$\dot{m}_{H_2,t} \cdot \left(f_{pwr,el} + f_{pwr,comp} \right) \leq RE_t \tag{6}$$

- Achievement of hydrogen production targets ($H_{2,trgt}$) if required.

$$H_{2,trgt} \leq \sum_{t} \Delta t \cdot \dot{m}_{H_2,t} \tag{7}$$

Based on these equations our interest lies in finding the answer for the following problems:

Problem 1: For a given target of H$_2$ selling price, find capacity and mode of operation that maximizes *NPV*.

$$\min_{M_{H_2}, \dot{m}_{H_2,t}} - NPV \tag{8}$$

$$\text{s.t. Eqs}: 1, 2, 3, 4, 5, 6$$

$$IC, OPEX, REV, M_{H_2}, \dot{m}_{H_2,t} \geq 0$$

Problem 2: For a given target of H$_2$ selling price, find capacity and mode of operation that maximizes surplus usage.

This problem formulation intends to capture the case of policy makers that would like to make maximum use of the resource without losing money.

$$\min_{M_{H_2}, \dot{m}_{H_2,t}} \sum_{t} RE_t - \dot{m}_{H_2,t} \cdot \left(f_{pwr,el} + f_{pwr,comp} \right) \tag{9}$$

$$\text{s.t. Eqs}: 1, 2, 3, 4, 5, 6$$

$$NPV, IC, OPEX, REV, M_{H_2}, \dot{m}_{H_2,t} \geq 0$$

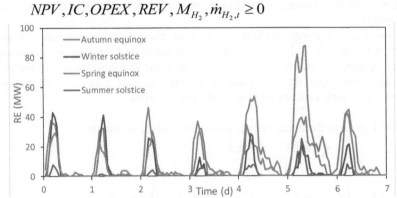

Figure 3. Surplus of renewable energy in four representative weeks.

Problem 3: Find capacity and mode of operation that minimizes the selling price of hydrogen and achieves a certain production goal.

This problem formulation again captures the case of policy makers. In this case we study the need to achieve a certain share of substitution of fossil-based fuels for long-distance transportation.

$$\min_{M_{H_2}, \dot{m}_{H_2,t}} \$_{H_2} \qquad (10)$$

$$\text{s.t. Eqs}: 1, 2, 3, 4, 5, 6, 7$$

$$NPV, IC, OPEX, REV, M_{H_2}, \dot{m}_{H_2,t} \geq 0$$

The optimization problems described above were implemented in GAMS 24.8.5. It is easy to see that the first two problems are linear; the third problem is not linear as written as in this case both terms in Eq. (3) contain decision variables (price of hydrogen and flux rate). However, this problem can be linearized by considering that Eq. (7) will be always be satisfied as an equality thus the term $H_{2,target}$ (a parameter) can substitute the sum. Then, all problems are LP and were solved using CPLEX.

3. Case Study

The case study focuses in Uruguay, a country in which 98% of the electricity is generated from renewable sources: 26 % is eolic 2 % is solar (MIEM, 2018), and the next milestone is decarbonization of the transportation sector. Pilot projects for production of hydrogen for heavy duty and long-distance fleet have recently been approved.

Figure 3 shows the surplus of renewable energy in the country. The surplus was obtained in the following way: (1) we generated 100 year-long random scenarios of production of electricity from wind and solar sources using the software SimSEE version iee19.193: a locally built software that loads historical data of solar irradiance, wind speed and precipitations and simulates probable renewable electricity generation with current installed capacities; (2) we considered a representative electric energy demand for the country which is available in ADME (2019); (3) for each of the 100 scenarios we computed the non-programmable renewable energy surplus by adding wind and solar generation at each hour and subtracting the power consumed (demand) at the same time, if demand was larger than generation, a zero was placed; (4) The average of the 100 scenarios was considered. Overall, we found that the mean value of the surplus is 10

MW, with a maximum of 130 MW (in spring), and that periods without any surplus account for 37 % of the time. As expected, larger surplus usually occurs at night.

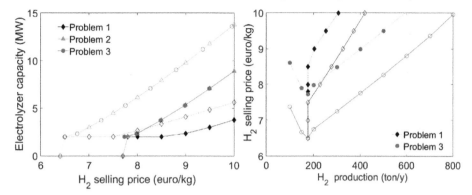

Figure 4: Optimal installed capacity vs H_2 prices. Filled/empty symbols indicate 0.022/0 euro/kWh surplus cost.

Figure 5: H_2 selling price an annual production. Filled/empty symbols indicate 0.022/0 euro/kWh surplus cost.

In terms of technologies, PEMs were selected as they provide the most flexible operation due to faster start-ups and the possibility of working under different loads. Hydrogen produced in PEMs is already partially pressurized; for design purposes we have assumed that PEM stacks self-pressurize up to 15 bar, which is conservative. The compression system was designed offline using the software Aspen Plus. From the two standard pressures used to fuel H_2-based vehicles, in this article, we have assumed service at 350 bar, as this is the most favorable situation in terms of the economics. From the compression system designs analyzed so far, a three-stage compressor with intermediate cooling provided the best performance.

4. Results and discussion

Simulations of the problems were run by considering surplus data for ten years with an hourly time step. Surplus costs in the 0-0.022 € /kWh range (usual lowest energy prices for current day-ahead Uruguayan tariffs (UTE, 2019)) were assumed. Following the electrolyzer costs in Proost (2019) we proved that the 6/10th rule is satisfied for the cost/capacities pairs up to 2 MW reported in the paper. For multiple stacks, i.e. when more than 2 MW are needed, it can be shown that a linear relation that considers a cost of 1238 € per kW installed reasonably approximates the composite cost. Note that as mentioned in Proost (2019) this cost already includes the water demineralizer, the gas separators and vessels, the purifying system and the required peripherals. Investment costs for the compressor were estimated with Aspen Process Economics Analyzer. In both cases we assumed a location factor of 1.14. Energy consumptions were assumed as 58.2 kWh/kg H_2 for the electrolyzer (Proost, 2019) and 77 kW/kg H_2 for the compressor (Aspen simulations).

The results of the simulations are shown in Figures 4, 5 and 6. As expected H_2 selling price is the key parameter. As seen in Figure 4, the program choses to install capacity only if the H_2 selling price is above 6.5 €/kWh, this is the most favorable case and assumes that the surplus of energy is available at no cost. This threshold implies installation of a single 2 MW electrolyzer. Beyond this threshold, Problem 1 can initially increase its NPV without increasing its production rate. whereas Problem 2 and 3 are required to increase their production. The latter is achieved by providing a solution at the

NPV=0 restriction. When hydrogen price becomes large enough, Problem 1 has an incentive to install more capacity to increase its NPV.

Figure 5 shows a particular feature of Problem 3. As this problem needs to satisfy a set production target, when the target is lower than that of a single 2 MW equipment, small and costly units are installed, which result in larger H_2 selling price, whereas Problems 1 and 2 just cannot produce for low capacities. In addition, note that the minimums in the curves for Problem 3 coincide with the capacity production threshold for the other problems.

Figure 6 shows the fraction of usage of

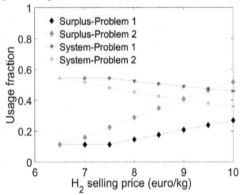

Figure 6: Optimal usage factors for both resource and installed capacity at several H_2 prices. Surplus cost = 0 euro/kWh.

electrolyzer and compressor (i.e. amount of hydrogen produced in a year over the maximum they can produce based on their capacity), and the fraction of usage of the renewable energy surplus (amount of energy used in a year over what was available). The curves indicate that as H_2 price increases, it is more favorable to capture the resource, which is achieved by installing more capacity. On the other hand, large capacities imply lower usage of the system due to the natural fluctuation of the surplus. In all cases, it should not be forgotten that 37 % of the time there is no energy available, hence the usage is capped at 63 %. This cap was not achieved in any of these problems due to effects of the capital cost. This discussion is left out of this paper due to space restrictions.

5. Conclusions

Three different decision-making problems to produce fuel hydrogen from surplus of renewable energy were presented and appropriate optimization problems proposed for their solution. For the numerical demonstration, Uruguay was taken as the case study. For these instances we found that H_2 prices are too high to compete with classical fuels, mainly due to the intermittence of the resource, that tends to install large capacities which even at the optimal have an usage factor of less than 55 %.

References

ADME (Administración del mercado eléctrico). https://adme.com.uy/ acceded on Oct. 2019.

M. Corengia, A. I. Torres, 2018. Two-phase dynamic model for PEM electrolyzer. In: 13th International Symposium on Process Systems Engineering (PSE 2018). Elsevier, 1435–1440.

Hydrogen Council, 2017. How hydrogen empowers the energy transition.

B. Kroposki, B. Johnson, Y. Zhang, V. Gevorgian, P. Denholm, B.-M. Hodge, B. Hannegan, 2017. Achieving a 100% renewable grid: Operating electric power systems with extremely high levels of variable renewable energy. IEEE Power and Energy Magazine 15 (2), 61–73.

MIEM (Ministerio de Industria, Energía y Minería), Dirección Nacional de Energía, 2018. Energy Balance 2017. Historical Series 1965-2017.

J. Proost, 2019. State-of-the art CAPEX data for water electrolysers, and their impact on renewable hydrogen price settings. International Journal of Hydrogen Energy 44 (9), 4406–4413.

UTE. Plan 24 horas. https://portal.ute.com.uy/ Last access Nov.

Sauro Pierucci, Flavio Manenti, Giulia Bozzano, Davide Manca (Eds.)
Proceedings of the 30th European Symposium on Computer Aided Process Engineering
(ESCAPE30), May 24-27, 2020, Milano, Italy. © 2020 Elsevier B.V. All rights reserved.
http://dx.doi.org/10.1016/B978-0-12-823377-1.50260-3

Characterizing the Dynamic Behaviour of a WtE Plant through Start-up Data

Elisa Magnanelli,[a]* Jostein Mosby,[b] Cansu Birgen,[a] Per Carlsson,[a] Michaël Becidan[a]

[a]*SINTEF Energy Research, Sem Sælands vei 11, Trondheim 7034, Norway*
[b]*Returkraft AS, Setesdalsveien 205, Kristiansand 4618, Norway*
elisa.magnanelli@sintef.no

Abstract

Municipal Solid Waste is a highly heterogenous fuel, with physical and chemical properties that change over time. When describing the dynamic behaviour of a waste-to-energy plant, physical parameters such as thermal inertia of the different plant components play an important role when determining the plant response to fluctuations in waste properties. In this work, we used process data collected during plant start-ups to experimentally determine these parameters for an existing plant. Identification of these parameters during normal operation is challenging due to lack of information on physical and chemical properties of waste entering the process. However, fossil fuels are burned during start-up due to EU regulations. By using process data from a plant start-up where a chemically and physically defined fuel was used, we could establish mass and energy balance over the whole system and estimate plant specific parameters. The parameters were further validated using data from a second start-up. The error between model prediction and experimental data was below 6%, and prediction was better for conditions closer to plant normal operation.

Keywords: Waste-to-Energy, Dynamic modelling, Start-up.

1. Introduction

One of the main factors that challenges stable operation of waste-to-energy (WtE) plants is the feedstock properties. Municipal Solid Waste (MSW) is a highly heterogenous fuel, with physical and chemical properties that change over time. Hence, despite advanced control systems, the process remains subject to large fluctuations in both heat production and emissions. Different works in the literature have focused on modelling steady state operation of WtE plants, e.g. Yang et al. (2004) described steady state combustion in grate furnace, while Shin and Choi (2000) modelled waste particle combustion. However, this approach is not suitable when the goal is to identify measures to improve process stability, and a dynamic model should be used instead (Alobaid et al. 2018). In the dynamics of a system, parameters such as components' thermal inertia play an important role. Due to fluctuations in MSW properties, it is difficult to estimate these parameters during normal plant operation. However, to satisfy current EU regulation, conventional fuel is burned during plant start-ups (Directive 2010). In this work, we developed a dynamic model that describes the boiler of a WtE plant and use process data to estimate plant specific parameters. Since the start-up fuel has known chemical and physical properties, data from start-up are used to determine plant parameters that describe the dynamic behaviour of the process. A second set of start-up data is used to validate the dynamic model.

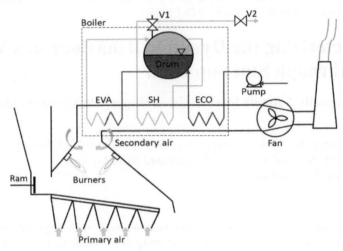

Figure 1: A schematic illustration of the Returkraft WtE plant in Kristiansand, Norway. Burners warm up the air and materials in the combustion chambers. Thanks to the fan, the flue gas leaves the combustion chamber passing through the boiler section. In the boiler, heat is recovered from the flue gas by a series of heat exchangers (EVA, SH, and ECO), and accumulated in the drum.

2. System

The dynamic model is based on Returkraft WtE plant in Kristiansand, Norway. It is a grate-fired plant with a capacity of 130,000 t/y (Figure 1). During normal operation, MSW is incinerated to produce electricity and/or heat. To comply with regulations, during start-ups, fossil fuel is burned instead. To minimize fuel usage, neither electricity nor district heating are produced during start-up, and a smaller number of components can hence be considered when modelling the start-up.

2.1. Process overview

During start-up, oil-burners heat the combustion chamber and boiler circuit in a controlled and gradual way. Well-established procedures must be followed depending on the nature of the stop and on the state of the system when start-up is initiated. A general and simplified procedure can be described as follows:

P1. The combustion chamber and flue gas system are vented to ensure that no combustible gas is present. If the boiler circuit is cold and not under pressure, steam system drainage and ventilation valves are opened (valve V1 in Figure 1 is opened and V2 is closed) before starting the burners, so that water/vapor can only circulate in the evaporator circuit (EVA).

P2. Burners are started to achieve the desired temperature increase in the drum.

P3. Once the boiler reaches 100 °C, the boiler is kept at 100 °C for at least 1 hour.

P4. Valve V1 is closed and V2 is opened to let steam circulate in the superheater (SH).

P5. When the steam production equals the heat recovered from the flue gas, valve V2 is regulated to allow the pressure in the drum and boiler circuit to build up at a predefined rate.

P6. When the pressure has reached the desired value and the temperature of the flue gas in the combustion chamber is such to satisfy regulations, MSW can be introduced in the combustion chamber.

During the whole procedure, water is pumped in the drum to keep the water level constant. Figure 2 shows the temperature evolution in the boiler drum during a start-up.

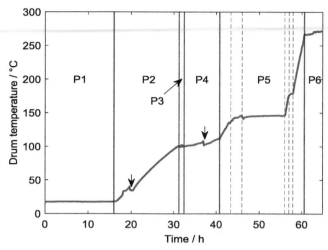

Figure 2: Temperature evolution in the boiler drum during a start-up procedure. The vertical solid lines delimit the startup phases described in Section 2 (P1-P6). The vertical arrows point at the effect of sudden water level drop in the drum and subsequent pumping of water.

The temperature profile during each phase is linear. Deviations from the linear behaviour are caused by sudden water level drop and subsequent pumping of water (the two vertical arrows in Figure 2 point at two such instances). The profile that the drum temperature follows in P5 is piecewise linear, as in the illustrated case a more cautious warming up was carried out to reduce stress on the plant.

3. Model description

The model was implemented in Matlab Simulink® using a set of differential and/or algebraic equations describing each sub-process.

3.1. Combustion chamber

The mass of flue gas in the freeboard, M_{fg}, results from a balance of the flue gas from the burners, F_b, the combustion air entering the combustion chamber, F_a, and the flue gas flow that leaves the system thanks to the flue gas fan, F_{fg}:

$$\frac{dM_{fg}}{dt} = F_b + F_a - F_{fg}. \tag{1}$$

The temperature of the flue gas, T_{fg}, is given by:

$$M_{fg}c_{p,fg}\frac{dT_{fg}}{dt} = F_b c_{p,fg}(T_b - T_{fg}) + F_a c_{p,a}(T_a - T_{fg}) + Q_{rad} \tag{2}$$

where $c_{p,fg}$ and $c_{p,a}$ are the specific heat capacity of the flue gas and of the air respectively, T_b is the temperature of the flue gas from the burners, T_a is the temperature of the incoming air, and Q_{rad} is the heat exchanged by radiation between the flue gas and the walls of the combustion chamber. In order to account for the large thermal inertia of the combustion chamber materials, a separate energy balance was established:

$$M_c c_{p,c}\frac{dT_c}{dt} = -Q_{rad} \tag{3}$$

where T_c, M_c and $c_{p,c}$ are the temperature, mass and heat capacity of the combustion chamber materials, respectively.

3.2. Boiler drum

Boiler drum dynamics was modelled as described by Åström and Bell (2000). The global mass balance in the drum is given by the water flow entering the drum, F_w, and the steam leaving it, F_{st}:

$$\frac{d}{dt}(M_{st} + M_w) = -F_{st} + F_w \qquad (4)$$

where M_{st} and M_w are the mass of steam/air and liquid water in the drum. The energy balances for the water inside the drum and for the materials of the drum are:

$$\frac{d}{dt}(M_{st}h_{st} + M_w h_w - pV) = -F_{st}h_{st} + F_w h_w + Q_{EVA} + Q_{wall} \qquad (5)$$

$$M_{wall}c_{p,wall}\frac{dT_{wall}}{dt} = -Q_{wall} - Q_{loss,drum} \qquad (6)$$

where h_{st} and h_w are the enthalpy of the steam/air and liquid water, p is the pressure in the drum, V is the drum volume, Q_{EVA} is the heat transferred to the water in the evaporator, Q_{wall} is the heat exchanged between the water and the drum walls, $Q_{loss,drum}$ is the heat lost to the environment, and M_{wall}, $c_{p,wall}$ and T_{wall} are the mass, heat capacity and temperature of the boiler drum materials.

3.3. Superheater, evaporator and economizer

The heat exchanged between a fluid and the walls of a heat exchanger, Q_{ex}, can be described as (Incropera et al. 2007):

$$Q = H_{ex}(T - T_{wall,ex}) \qquad (7)$$

where H_{ex} is an empirical overall heat transfer coefficient between the fluid and the wall, and T and $T_{wall,ex}$ are the fluid and wall temperatures, respectively. To reduce the complexity of the model, the outlet temperature of the fuel was calculated as:

$$T_{out} = T - \frac{Q}{c_p F} \qquad (8)$$

where the c_p is the specific heat capacity of the fluid and F is the fluid mass flow in the heat exchanger. To take into account the thermal inertia offered by the heat exchanger materials, a dynamic energy balance for the heat exchanger walls, where the temperature was given by a balance between the heat exchanged with the cold fluid, Q_c, and the heat exchanged with the hot fluid, Q_h was established:

$$M_{wall,ex}c_{p,wall}\frac{dT_{wall,ex}}{dt} = Q_c + Q \qquad (9)$$

3.4. Flue gas fan

The angular velocity of the flue gas fan, ω, is controlled to maintain the pressure in the combustion chamber at a desired value. Its dynamic response was described as:

$$I\frac{d\omega}{dt} = \tau_M - \tau_D \qquad (10)$$

where I is the moment of inertia, and τ_M and τ_D are the motor and drag torque. The flue gas mass flow through the fan, F_{fg}, can be calculated from the fan angular velocity as:

$$F_{fg} = \rho_{fg} k \omega \tag{11}$$

where ρ_{fg} is the flue gas density and k is a fan constant.

4. Results

Two sets of start-up data were collected from Returkraft WtE plant. These data were used as calibration and validation data set, respectively. The plant start-ups considered were so-called *warm start-ups*, where the plant had been stopped for less than one day and the boiler drum temperature was above 100 °C. Phase P2 (see Section 2.1) was therefore not part of these start-ups. The parameters to be estimated were the mass of the different components, M_i, and the heat transfer coefficients between fluid and component walls, H_i. The parameters were estimated through an optimization procedure based on nonlinear least-squares algorithms, where the error between simulated and measured output was minimized. A sensitivity analysis was carried out to identify the parameters that had the largest influence on the model outputs and to find appropriate starting values for the optimization procedure (not reported in this work). Figure 3 shows some of the experimental data used for parameter estimation (solid lines) and the respective simulated response of the model with the calibrated parameters (dashed lines). Figure 4 shows the experimental data used for validation (solid lines) and the corresponding model response (dashed lines). The relative error between experimental and simulated data lies within 6% of the output absolute value. The good match between model prediction and validation data indicates that the model has not been overfitted and describes the dynamic behaviour of the plant well. In addition, the error is lower in the second part of the start-up (below 2 %). The larger discrepancy during the initial part of start-up is due to the fact that there are no data on the amount of steam being vented out through valve 1 (see Fig.1). This lack of information introduced some uncertainties on the mass and energy balance of the drum.

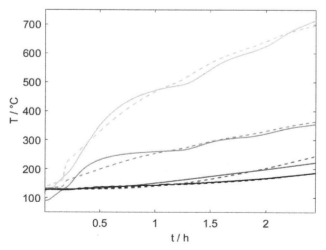

Figure 3: Temperature measurements during start-up (solid lines) and model response (dashed lines) for the boiler drum (black) and for the flue gas at 3 different positions (shades of gray). Calibration set: start-up on 12.03.19.

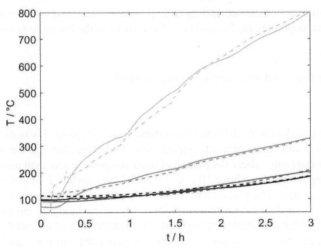

Figure 4: Temperature measurements during start-up (solid lines) and model response (dashed lines) for the boiler drum (black) and for the flue gas at 3 different positions (shades of gray). Validation set: start-up on 18.07.18.

On the other hand, complete mass and energy balance could be established when valve 1 was closed. For this reason, the model prediction was more accurate in the second part of start-up. Conditions during the final part of start-up are closer to those under normal plant operation, which indicates that the model can be used to describe MSW combustion.

5. Conclusions

In this work, a dynamic model describing the boiler of a WtE plant was developed. Data from a plant start-up, where conventional fuel is combusted, were used to determine plat specific parameters that describe the dynamic response of important plant components. The resulting dynamic model with calibrated parameters was further validated using data from a different start-up at the same plant. The good agreement between process data and model response suggests that the model describes the system dynamics well and that it can be used to simulate and study plant operation under normal conditions.

Acknowledgment

This work is part of the Waste-to-Energy 2030 project co-funded by industry partners and the Research Council of Norway under EnergiX program (WtE 2030, 280949).

References

F. Alobaid, W.A.K. Al-Maliki, T. Lanz, M. Haaf, A. Brachthäuser, B. Epple, I. Zorbach, 2018, Dynamic simulation of a municipal solid waste incinerator. Energy, 149, 230-249.

C. Directive, 2010. Directive 2010/75/EU of the European Parliament and of the Council. Official Journal of the European Union, 334, 17-119.

F.P. Incropera, A.S. Lavine, T.L. Bergman, D.P. DeWitt, 2007, Fundamentals of Heat and Mass Transfer, Wiley, Hoboken, New Jersey.

D. Shin, S. Choi, 2000, The combustion of simulated waste particles in a fixed bed, Combustion and flame, 121, 1, 167-180.

Y. Yang, C. Ryu, J. Goodfellow, V. N. Sharifi, J. Swithenbank, 2004, Modelling waste combustion in grate furnaces, Process Safety and Environmental Protection, 82, 3, 208-222.

K.J. Åström, R.D. Bell, 2000, Drum-Boiler Dynamics, Automatica, 36, 363-378.

Sauro Pierucci, Flavio Manenti, Giulia Bozzano, Davide Manca (Eds.)
Proceedings of the 30th European Symposium on Computer Aided Process Engineering
(ESCAPE30), May 24-27, 2020, Milano, Italy. © 2020 Elsevier B.V. All rights reserved.
http://dx.doi.org/10.1016/B978-0-12-823377-1.50261-5

Evaluating the Cleaning Routines in a Norwegian WtE Plant by Principal Component Analysis

Cansu Birgen[a], Elisa Magnanelli[a], Per Carlsson[a], Michaël Becidan[a], Jostein Mosby[b]

[a]SINTEF Energy Research, 7034, Trondheim, Norway
[b]Returkraft AS, 4618 Kristiansand, Norway
cansu.birgen@sintef.no

Abstract

Principal components analysis was performed using process data from a waste-to-energy plant (WtE), together with Hotelling's T^2 statistics and Q statistics, to evaluate the effect of maintenance routines on the performance of different units. The results showed that shower cleaning of evaporator units improves their efficiency while decreasing the heat exchanged in superheater and economizer. Q statistic detected the effects of maintenance earlier than Hotelling's T^2 statistics. The analysis could indicate which of the cleanings were less effective. Therefore, the proposed method can contribute to the design of a more effective cleaning strategy to prevent failures due to particle deposition. All in all, the fault detection and diagnosis proposed in this work can provide operational improvements, increased efficiency and reliability in WtE plants.
Keywords: Waste-to-Energy, Principal component analysis, fault detection, fault diagnosis, plant maintenance

1. Introduction

Heat or power can be produced from MSW that cannot be recycled. In 2016, the number of Waste-to-Energy (WtE) plants in Europe reached 512, with a potential for 248 new plants (Scarlat et al. 2019). WtE plants are confronted with strict regulations (Makarichi et al. 2018) as well as requirements for efficiency and reliability due to increasing load demands and strong process fluctuations. These can be attained by improving efficiency in steam boilers, which are critical units for heat recovery (Yu et al. 2017).

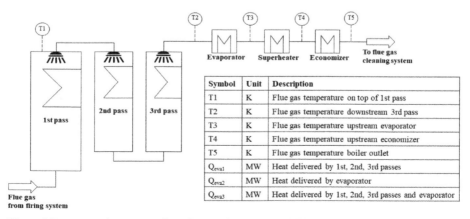

Symbol	Unit	Description
T1	K	Flue gas temperature on top of 1st pass
T2	K	Flue gas temperature downstream 3rd pass
T3	K	Flue gas temperature upstream evaporator
T4	K	Flue gas temperature upstream economizer
T5	K	Flue gas temperature boiler outlet
Q_{eva1}	MW	Heat delivered by 1st, 2nd, 3rd passes
Q_{eva2}	MW	Heat delivered by evaporator
Q_{eva3}	MW	Heat delivered by 1st, 2nd, 3rd passes and evaporator

Figure 1 Representative process flow sheet with process variables (in table).

Heat transfer efficiency deteriorates due to deposition of particles transported with the flue gas onto the boiler walls. To prevent this, a shower cleaning system is employed at the Returkraft WtE plant in Kristiansand, Norway (Fig.1). The evaluation of the boiler cleaning strategy will allow us to quantify its effectiveness and to propose improvements.

In this paper, Principal Component Analysis (PCA) was employed to study the effects of cleaning on the performance of the steam boiler unit. PCA is an advantageous method, since it provides robust performance due to elimination of random noise and uncontrollable disturbances by dimensionality reduction (Gao et al. 2016).

2. Methodology

The data used in PCA consisted of 8 variables and 11520 observation samples, which were recorded every minute for 8 days from 04.11.2019 to 12.11.2019 in Returkraft WtE plant. Temperature data (T1, T2, T3, T4 and T5) are direct sensor measurements, while heat delivered in evaporator units are calculated using sensor measurements.

First, the data was standardized using their median and median absolute deviation (Boudt et al. 2012), then PCA was performed. The amounts of heat delivered by the evaporator units were calculated using Eq. (1) to Eq. (3).

$$Q_{evap1} = F_{fg} Cp_{fg} (T1-T2) \tag{1}$$

$$Q_{evap2} = F_{fg} Cp_{fg} (T2-T3) \tag{2}$$

$$Q_{evap3} = F_{fg} Cp_{fg} (T1-T3) \tag{3}$$

where F_{fg} and Cp_{fg} are mass flow rate (kg/s) and specific heat capacity of the flue gas (J/kg/K). Raw data plots of the eight variables used in PCA are shown in Figure 2.

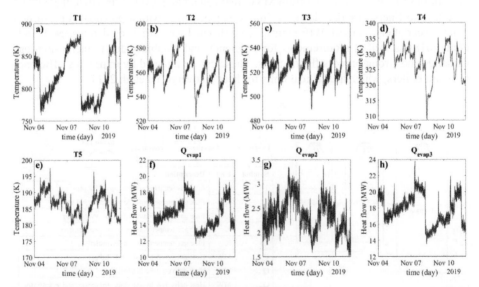

Figure 2 Raw data plots of the eight variables used in PCA (a-h).

2.1. Principal Component Analysis

The aim of PCA is to find latent variables called Principal Components (PCs) that capture important variations in the data that cannot be observed and measured directly; therefore, PCs should be chosen to preserve original information as much as possible (Yu et al. 2017). Let $X = [x_1 \ldots x_n]^T \in R^{n \times m}$ be an original data matrix composed of n observations, where each observation consists of m correlated variables, $x_n \in R^m$. The matrix X is decomposed as in Eq. (4).

$$X = T P^T \tag{4}$$

where the matrices $T = [t_1 \ldots t_m] \in R^{n \times m}$ and $P = [p_1 \ldots p_m] \in R^{m \times m}$ are composed of m score vectors $t_m \in R^n$ and m orthogonal loading vectors $p_m \in R^m$, respectively. The matrix P consists of eigenvectors of covariance matrix Σ, given in Eq. (5).

$$\Sigma = \frac{1}{n-1} X^T X = P \Lambda P^T \tag{5}$$

where $P P^T = P^T P = I_m$, I_m is a m×m identity matrix, and Λ is a diagonal matrix where the components consist of m eigenvalues sorted in descending order, $\lambda_1 > \lambda_2 > \ldots > \lambda_m$, and $\Lambda = \text{diag}(\lambda_1, \ldots, \lambda_m)$. Λ is given in Eq. (6).

$$\Lambda = \frac{1}{n-1} T^T T = \text{diag}(\lambda_1, \ldots, \lambda_m) \tag{6}$$

2.2. Hotelling's T^2 statistic

Hotelling's T^2 statistic is a measure of variation in each sample within the PCA model (Bro & Smilde, 2014). Eq. (7) shows calculations of T^2.

$$T^2_n = \sum_{m=1}^{M} \frac{t^2_{nm}}{\lambda_m} \tag{7}$$

where T^2_n and t_{nm} are the Hotelling's T^2 value and the score value of the nth sample on the mth component. The Hotelling's T^2 contribution for a specific sample indicates variables causing the sample to have extreme score values, shown in Eq. (8).

$$Tcont_{nm} = \sum_{m=1}^{M} \frac{t_{nm} p_{nm}}{\sqrt{\lambda_m}} \tag{8}$$

where $Tcont_{nm}$ is the Hotelling's T^2 contribution of the mth variable on the nth sample.

2.3. Q statistic

The lack of fit statistic in PCA models can be provided by Q statistics, which is a measure of how well each sample conforms to the PCA model and a measure of residuals, e_n. Eq. (4) can be written as Eq. (9) to include the residuals. Then Q for the nth sample (Q_n) is calculated as the sum of squares of the nth row of E(e_n) as shown in Eq. (10).

$$X = T P^T + E \tag{9}$$

$$Q_n = e_n e^T_n \tag{10}$$

e_n represents the Q contributions, which define how much each variable contributes to the overall Q statistic for the sample. Confidence limits for both Q statistic and Hotelling's T^2 statistic are calculated for a significance level of $\alpha=0.01$ by using the formulas given in Yu et al. (2017).

3. Results and Discussions

3.1. Principal Component Analysis
PCA results are summarized in Figure 3 in terms of explained variances. It is typical to decide on the number of PCs with a minimum cut-off point of explaining 70% variance (Yu et al. 2016). Figure 3.a shows that the first 4 PCs explain almost all the variance, and the first 3 PCs, which we selected as the number of PCs in our analysis, can explain more than 91% of variance in the system. Figure 3.b shows that the most important variable is T4, thus it can be beneficial to improve its measurement. For the model with 3 PCs, the most important variables are T5 and Q_{eval}, while T3 and Q_{eva2} are the least important. Figure 3.b illustrates that PCA models with different number of PCs have different variable importance ranking.

3.2. Fault Detection and Diagnosis
Shower cleaning of the boiler walls affects the process; therefore, we refer to this disturbance as a "fault", to remain consistent with PCA terminology. Information on the cleaning strategy was obtained from the plant operators, while the data were received from the sensors in the plant. Table 1 shows the faults, i.e. cleaning locations and times. Cleaning location was determined using the cleaning hose position data.

Table 1 Fault descriptions in terms of hose cleaning locations and times.

	Fault1	Fault2	Fault3	Fault4	Fault5	Fault6	Fault7	Fault8
Location	3rdpass	1stpass	2ndpass	3rdpass	1stpass	2ndpass	3rdpass	1stpass
Time	Nov4	Nov4	Nov5	Nov7	Nov8	Nov9	Nov10	Nov11
	08:55	13:13	10:59	08:14	07:37	12:19	14:02	14:14

As described in the methodology section, T^2 and Q statistics are complementary to provide information about faults observed in the system. 99% confidence limits are calculated for both statistics to define criteria for fault detection. The results are given in Figure 4.

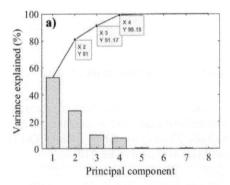
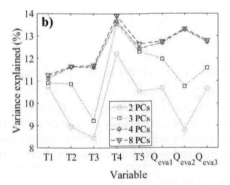

Figure 3 Variance explained by each principal component (a) and by each process variable (b).

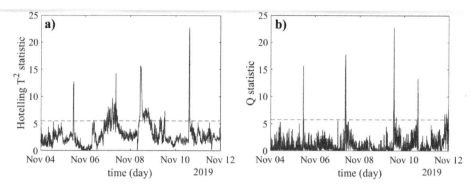

Figure 4 T² (a) and Q statistics (b) with 99% confidence limits shown by the dashed lines.

Figure 4 shows that Faults 1, 2, 5 and 8 are not detected (see Table 1); it seems that cleaning of 1st pass (i.e. Faults 2, 5 and 8) does not provide sufficient cleaning to result in a significant change in the system. This result is in line with the observations done in the plant, where there seems to be less deposit formation on the walls of the 1st pass compared to the 2nd and 3rd. Fault 1 was not detected since the cleaning did not actually take place; hose was placed but water was not sprayed. A fault on 08.11 at 11:11 is wrongly detected by T². Fault 3, 4, 6 and 7 are detected by both T² and Q. Moreover, Q statistic detected these 3 faults earlier than T². Because, the variances explained by Q and T² are composed of different process variables, and the effect of cleaning is observed in process variables measured by different sensors having different physical locations. This information becomes critical when a monitoring or a control system is installed in the plant.

Figure 5 shows the fault diagnosis results explaining the root causes of the faults happening in the system. T5 is the largest contributor to T² statistics for Fault 3. Q_{eval} and Q_{eva3} have positive contributions due to improved the heat transfer efficiency.

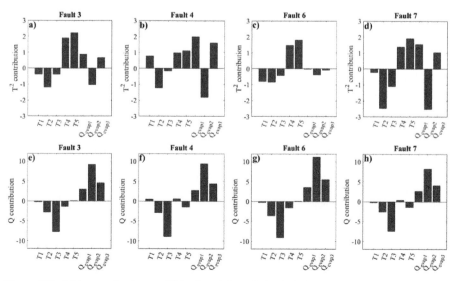

Figure 5 Variable contributions to T² (a-d) and Q statistics (e-h) for faults 3, 4 ,6 and 7.

Similarly, the larger the amount of heat exchanged in the evaporators, the lower their outlet temperatures become, as apparent in the negative contributions of T1, T2 and T3. However, T4 and T5 have large positive contributions to Fault 3, since the driving force to heat exchange in superheater and economizer (temperature difference between inlet hot and cold streams) becomes lower. Q statistic covers the rest of fault diagnosis showing that all Qeva1, Qeva2 and Qeva3 are positive contributors to Fault 3 (Figure 5.e). Other faults show a similar contribution trend for both Q and T^2 statistics. Practically, this means that shower cleaning of the 2nd and 3rd pass of the evaporator unit improves its efficiency, consequently decreasing the heat exchanged in superheater and economizer. It is important to note that Q statistic detects the faults earlier, with the largest contributors being Qeva1, Qeva2 and Qeva3, while T4 and T5 have the largest contributions to T^2 statistics. This trend can be explained by the physical locations of sensors; cleaning impacts are seen first on the evaporator temperatures (T1, T2 and T3), then on Qeva1 Qeva2 and Qeva3 and lastly on T4 and T5. Therefore, the variable contributions to the overall variance needs to be combined with considerations on sensors' location in the system to effectively detect and diagnose faults.

4. Conclusions

Fault (i.e. cleaning) detection and diagnosis show that the proposed methodology can successfully identify the effect of maintenance on different units in the WtE process. Shower cleaning of 2nd and 3rd passes of the evaporator unit improves its efficiency while decreasing the heat exchanged in superheater and economizer. The analysis could indicate which of the cleanings were less effective. Therefore, the proposed method can help to design a more effective cleaning strategy, helping to prevent severe failures due to deposits on the evaporator walls. Moreover, Q statistic detects the faults earlier than Hotelling's T^2 statistics as a result of the physical locations of sensors. All in all, the fault detection and diagnosis proposed in this work can lead to operational improvements, increased reliability and better understanding of WtE plants.

Acknowledgements

This work is part of the Waste-to-Energy 2030 project co-funded by industry and public partners and the Research Council of Norway under the EnergiX program (WtE 2030 - 280949).

References

Boudt, K., Cornelissen, J., & Croux, C. (2012). The Gaussian rank correlation estimator: robustness properties. Statistics and Computing, 22(2), 471-483.
Bro, R., & Smilde, A. K. (2014). Principal component analysis, Analytical Methods.
Gao, Y., Wang, X., Wang, Z., & Zhao, L. (2016). Fault detection in time-varying chemical process through incremental principal component analysis. Chemometrics and Intelligent Laboratory Systems, 158, 102-116.
Makarichi, L., Jutidamrongphan, W., & Techato, K. A. (2018). The evolution of waste-to-energy incineration: A review. Renewable and Sustainable Energy Reviews, 91, 812-821.
Scarlat, N., Fahl, F., & Dallemand, J. F. (2019). Status and opportunities for energy recovery from municipal solid waste in Europe. Waste and Biomass Valorization, 10(9), 2425-2444.
Yu, J., Yoo, J., Jang, J., Park, J. H., & Kim, S. (2017). A novel plugged tube detection and identification approach for final super heater in thermal power plant using principal component analysis. Energy, 126, 404-418.Z.
Yu, H., Khan, F., & Garaniya, V. (2016). A sparse PCA for nonlinear fault diagnosis and robust feature discovery of industrial processes. AIChE Journal, 62(5), 1494-1513.

Sauro Pierucci, Flavio Manenti, Giulia Bozzano, Davide Manca (Eds.)
Proceedings of the 30th European Symposium on Computer Aided Process Engineering
(ESCAPE30), May 24-27, 2020, Milano, Italy. © 2020 Elsevier B.V. All rights reserved.
http://dx.doi.org/10.1016/B978-0-12-823377-1.50262-7

Circular Economy in Banana Cultivation

Nicole Gehring[a], Bogdan Dorneanu[a,b], José José Manrique Silupú[c],

William Ipanaqué Alama[c], Harvey Arellano-Garcia[a,b,*]

[a]*LS Prozess- und Anlagentechnik, Brandenburgische Tecnische Universität Cottbus-Senftenberg, Cottbus, D-03046, Germany*
[b]*Department of Chemical and Process Engineering, University of Surrey, Guildford, GU2 7XH, United Kingdom*
[c]*Departamento de Ingeneria Mecánico Eléctrica, Universidad de Piura, Piura, Peru*
arellano@b-tu.de

Abstract

This paper examines the most important approaches that could be applied for the introduction of circular economy strategies for the banana production process in the region of Piura (Peru). Based on this, a framework for an optimized economic cycle that is able to conserve resources and minimize the capital investments of farmers, while simultaneously increasing their production, can be created. Challenges and potential solutions are discussed for the production stages.

Keywords: Circular economy, Banana production, Biomeiler, Digestor.

1. Introduction

Peru has experienced success in developing a strong export market for its organic bananas. This success has been built on a strategy for developing a strong niche market, especially in the European Union (Donahue, et al., 2011), in the face of large competitors in the non-organic market, such as Ecuador. Almost all of Peru's exported bananas are organic, accounting for around 3% of the global production. The region of Piura, in the north of the country, produces about 80 % of the national organic bananas. The production is characterized by small producers with farms of less than 3 ha of farmland, over a total of almost 170,000 ha.

The current approach in the production of bananas in Piura is that the trees are cut off after harvesting and left in the field. The fertilizer is expensive and is usually not dosed correctly, since measurements are scarce, hence a danger of under- or overfertilization exists, which can lead to a large loss of fruit. The water used for irrigation is taken from nearby rivers and fed into catchment basins and the plantation is flooded by means of joints in the soil, which are distributed over the field and connected to the basin. The water from giant washbasins used for washing the fruits is discarded, as it cannot be reused, being polluted.

Maintaining a strong growth in organic banana exports is important, as the industry is providing additional employment opportunities in rural areas of Peru. In order to access global markets, the farmers are required to meet demands for quality of produce, as well as for quantity and quality of supply. Organic producers in Peru face several challenges (FAO, 2017): providing an appropriate level of nutrients, in particular nitrogen, phosphorus and potassium; securing an adequate supply of quality planting material; securing sufficient water supply for irrigation; access to improved production technologies to increase yields. Moreover, organic bananas are more subject to disease and insects than the conventional counterparts grown with herbicides and pesticides. To prevent insects, the organic banana bundles are covered in plastic bags until they are ready to be harvested.

The main costs for the banana producers relate to inputs and labour. The main inputs are manure and other organic fertilizers (island guano, sulfomag and potassium sulfate). The cost of fertilizers represents 43% of the total costs in a year (ODI, 2009). Although Piura has an excellent dry tropical climate and fertile soil for growth of the organic bananas, allowing the fruits to be produced year-round, the country is vulnerable to the effects of climate change. For these reasons it is important to keep focusing on sustainable practices to keep the organic banana sector a successful one. Efforts should be made to enhance investments leading to implementing modern farming techniques and improving the infrastructure around the plantations.

In the context of the agri-food chain, the circular economy (CE) aims to reduce waste while also making best use of the agricultural wastes, by-products and co-products produced, by using innovative technologies and profitable business practices to increase their value (Toop, et al., 2017). The development of CE requires the adoption of closed loop systems which work towards the goals of improved economic and environmental sustainability (Winkler, 2011).

The next sections present various CE approaches that can be applied in the organic banana sector that could significantly increase production, and the way they could be applied specifically to the farms in Piura. These include ways in which valuable resources, such as water or nutrients (Bertolucci Paes, et al., 2019; James Sherwood) can be protected or recycled, (Ngan, et al.,2019; Del Borghi, et al., 2020).

2. Methods

2.1. Parameter monitoring

How can these objectives be achieved? On one hand, by closely monitoring the plantations in order to record the necessary influencing variables, as shown in Table 1, and to be able to intervene if necessary.

Table 1. Parameters of optimal banana production

Parameter	Best conditions	Bad conditions	Measure with
Temperature	26 °C-30 °C	Less than 14 °C, more than 34 °C	Thermometer
Air humidity	50-80 %		Sensor Hygrometer
Sunshine hours		Less than 3 hours	
Soil moisture	Humidity	Not too wet for too long, as it is very sensitive to root rot.	Sensor Hygrometer
pH	5,6-7 pH	Die at more 7.5 pH	Measuring strips Sensor
Lime		Not too much because it's too bad for the plant.	Electrical conductivity Sensor
Nitrogen			Sensor
Phosphors			Sensor

Potassium			Sensor
Zinc			Sensor
Chlorine			Sensor
CO_2 or O_2 (presence of insects)			Sensor

Smart farming is important for tackling the challenges of agricultural production in terms of productivity, environmental impact, food security and sustainability. To address these challenges, the agricultural ecosystem needs to be better understood by monitoring, measuring and analysing it continuously. This implies analysis of big agricultural data and the use of new ICT technologies.

It is therefore necessary to develop comprehensive monitoring solutions of banana cultivation in order to achieve maximum yields with minimum use of resources. This not only makes sense for optimizing the use of resources, but also for saving capital. The aim of a CE approach is to ensure the optimal supply of resources to the plantations and to redesign existing processes in order to achieve better results with higher yields and minimal waste.

2.2. Waste (re)utilization

Currently, the banana plant waste remains in the field after harvest, to decompose, spreading diseases and polluting water supplies. This raises the question of whether there are no better alternatives or use for the banana plants waste, such as developing low-cost solutions to capitalize the banana waste through transformation into useful products such as solid or liquid fuels (Nazari, et al., 2019), organic fertilizers (Mohiuddin, et al., 2014), or precursors to other high value-added products (Tarrés, et al., 2017). This offers a possibility for a paradigm shift in the development of technological approaches for a complete conversion of the banana waste.

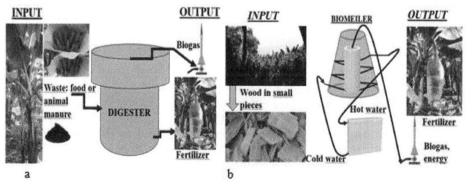

Figure 1. a) Digestor; b) Biomeiler

A low cost, stand-alone process to generate electricity for production and packing stations and at the same time, to produce a very good fertilizer for the plants would provide additional gain for the rural agricultural communities of Peru. A digestion tank (Figure 1a), or a Biomeiler (Figure 1b), could be used here.

In the digestion tank, the biological residues, such as bananas not suitable for trade and the harvested banana plant, can be disposed of. As a product for the recycling industry, fertilizer is obtained and biogas that can be further processed as electricity for the packaging station near the plantation.

In the Biomeiler the stem of the banana tree can be used as feed to produce fertilizers, as well as biogas. A further advantage of the Biomeiler is that a water pipe can be integrated into the system, which enables the automatic production of hot water through various biological processes.

2.3. Water treatment

The average water footprint of bananas produced in Peru corresponds to 11.4 m3 per standard 18.14 kg box (Clercx, et al., 2016). Approximately 1% of the blue water footprint corresponds to the washing, processing and packaging stage. Yet, the predominant irrigation practices in Peru imply a waste of water in the context of severe water scarcity. In order to increase the sustainability and the efficiency of the production process, the water resulting from the processing of bananas should be treated for reuse. This could be achieved with the aid of activated carbon filters, which can be produced from banana peels waste (Baloch & Mangi, 2019). Thus, the dirty washing water is treated and either used again for washing the bananas or for irrigation.

Furthermore, the recovery of the various nutrients, in particular of phosphorus, is very important as this resource is limited (Greuling, 2011). This could be achieved with the Stuttgart or the Gifhorn processes (Amann, et al., 2018). Thus, the phosphorus is recovered from digested sludge, with the aid of acid leaching.

3. Implementation

So how can the methods presented in the previous section be applied to improve the production of organic bananas in Peru?

3.1. Parameter monitoring

As can be seen in Table 1, there are several parameters that should be monitored more closely, in order to create optimal conditions for the plants' growth, especially with regard to nutrients such as:

- Phosphorus – essential in the DNA of all life on Earth

- Potassium – plants low in potassium are stunted in growth and have lower yields

- Nitrogen – important for photosynthesis and a significant component for amino acids, building blocks of proteins

Temperature and humidity have also great influence on the crops, as well as on the diseases and insects, hence affordable and reliable monitoring of these parameters is important as well. The recent developments in the Internet of Things and communication technologies enable the implementation of reliable, affordable wireless sensor networks, including RFID able to transmit stored information on various parameters such as soil, water, light, precipitation, temperature, humidity, etc., enabling producers to make better decision on how to handle the crops, when to add fertilizers or pest control, or when to irrigate.

3.2. Waste (re)utilization

The idea of using technologies such as the digestion tower is to supply energy to the plantation independently, without generating extra costs and to use the resulting biowaste profitably. This can be done with both methods. Fig.2 shows the implementation of these processes in the context of CE for the banana production process. Thus, all data from the sensors should be evaluated in order to compile the amounts of fertilizer and nutrients required. The nutrients or fertilizers should be produced from the biomass waste of the biomass resulted on the plantation, so that no further costs are incurred. To achieve this, after harvesting, the plants' unused parts are cut into small pieces and fed into the digestion tower. Fruit not suitable for sale can be added as well. The biological processes produce both fertilizer and biogas. The biogas can be used to produce energy that can be used to produce hot water or to power various stages of the production process.

In case a Biomeiler is used, the unit can be equipped with a pipe that heats the water flowing through this pipe up to 55 °C. However, to start the fermentation process, the Biomeiler needs some water to be added to the shredded banana waste.

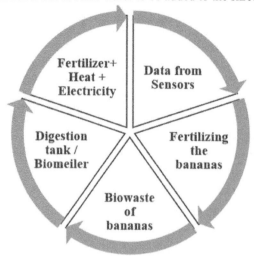

Figure 2 Circular economy in banana production

Both technologies do not require a lot of space and are not very expensive, which makes them suitable for any banana plantation, no matter how small.

3.3. Water treatment

As already mentioned in the Introduction section of this paper, the Piura region is an arid region in the north of Peru. Due to this fact the efficient use of water is of outmost importance.

The banana production, however, already requires a lot of water during cultivation, not to mention the post-harvest stage, when the banana bunches are taken directly to the packaging station, where they are first divided into the appropriate portions, and then washed in a very large basin filled with water. The bananas are then treated and packed in cartons and prepared for transport. For these reasons, it is particularly important to treat the used washing water appropriately so that the treated water can then be reused either as washing water, for soaking the banana plants or for irrigation. Sensors can be used to check the water quality and enable decisions on when to use treatment methods. Activated carbon filters can be used here as they remove chlorine and dirt from the water. A method has been developed in which the banana shells (Mahindrakar, et al, 2018) have been processed into activated carbon filters. Thus, the farmers have an opportunity for an extra income, by selling banana peels to the manufacturers of these filters, as well as having the possibility to acquire them to treat the waste water on their plantation.

The recovery of nutrients is also an important task, so that future generations can use it, as there is currently no alternative for this vital component in the DNA. The easiest way to recover it is to use technologies such as the digestion tower of the Biomeiler. Since phosphorus is found in the organic bananas and their residues, it can be recovered in the fertilizers produced from these feedstocks through composting. By fertilizing the plants, the phosphorus is returned to the natural cycle, and the plants can grow according to expectations. If more phosphorus is needed, there are further possibilities of phosphorus recycling from the sewage sludge (Amann, et al., 2018). However, some of these processes (e.g., the Stuttgart process) are very complex and require appropriately trained personnel and an expensive technical system.

4. Conclusions

Circular economy attempts to eliminate waste and reduce the impact of human activity on the environment. This paper explored several options for applying the CE concepts to optimize the banana cultivation in Peru, and showed that novel technologies could have an important impact in the activity of the banana producers. Furthermore, in the context of the unique conditions of the banana production in Peru (small-size farms, organic, low precipitation), parameter monitoring, waste (re)utilization and water treatment can offer solutions that can be realized with little effort and at low cost.

Thus, higher profits can be achieved by improving the control of the production, obtaining better crops, and additionally producing energy from the waste that can be used to decrease the operating costs.

Other technologies can be examined further to close the circle, among them the use of thermal processes on the banana biowaste, or the possibilities to replace the plastic used during the cultivation, which is currently not recycled due to its insignificant cost.

In this way, all materials introduced into the banana production process can be used several times, or nearly endlessly, with the ultimate goals not only to improve the quality of the crops while also protecting the environment for future generations, but also the livelihood of the rural communities where it takes place.

Furthermore, the CE would not be only limited to the banana cultivation, but it can also be transferred to other agricultural processes that may take place on the same farm (e.g., cocoa is often produced on many Peruvian banana plantations), or in other regions in Peru.

References

Amann, et al., 2018, Resources, Conservation and Recycling 120, pp. 127-139

Baloch & Many, 2019, Journal of Materials and Environmental Sciences 10 (10), pp. 966-986

Bertolucci Paes, et al., 2019, Journal of Cleaner Production 239, 118086

Clercx, et al., 2016, Acta Hortic. 1112, DOI: 10.17660/ActaHortic.2016.1112.1

Del Borghi, et al., 2020, Current Opinion in Environmental Science & Health, Volume 13, pp. 23-28

Donahue, et al., 2011, An examination of expanding Peru's organic banana exports to the United States, 21st Annual International Food and Agribusiness Management World Symposium, Frankfurt, Germany

FAO, 2017, Organic banana production in Peru, http://www.fao.org/3/a-i6870e.pdf

Greuling, 2011, Die Welt Bewegen, https://www.welt.de/dieweltbewegen/article13585089/Am-Phosphor-haengt-das-Schicksal-der-Menschheit.html

James Sherwood, Bioresource Technology

Mahindrakar, et al., 2018, Environmental Technology and Innovation 11, pp. 371-383

Mohiuddin, et al., 2014, The Agriculturists 12 (1), pp. 148-158

Nazari, et al., 2019, International Journal on Advanced Science Engineering Information Technology 9 (2), pp. 455-460

Ngan, et al., 2019, Renewable and Sustainable Energy Reviews 111, pp. 314-331

ODI, 2009, Organic banana cultivation and fair trade in Peru, https://www.odi.org/sites/odi.org.uk/files/odi-assets/publications-opinion-files/5652.pdf

Tarrés, et al., 2017, Industrial Crops and Products 99, pp. 27-33

Toop, et al., 2017, Energy Procedia 123, pp. 76-80

Winkler, 2011, CIRP Journal of Manufacturing Science and Technology 4 (3), pp. 243-246

Sauro Pierucci, Flavio Manenti, Giulia Bozzano, Davide Manca (Eds.)
Proceedings of the 30th European Symposium on Computer Aided Process Engineering
(ESCAPE30), May 24-27, 2020, Milano, Italy. © 2020 Elsevier B.V. All rights reserved.
http://dx.doi.org/10.1016/B978-0-12-823377-1.50263-9

The Value of Bioenergy with CO_2 Capture and Storage in an Electrified UK Heat Sector

Mathilde Fajardy[a], Vasileios Charitopoulos[b], David Reiner[a]

[a]*Energy Policy Research Group, Judge Business School, University of Cambridge, Trumpington Street, Cambridge CB2 1AG, UK.*
[b]*Department of Chemical Engineering, Centre for Process Systems Engineering, University College London, Torrington Place, London WC1E 7JE, UK.*
d.reiner@jbs.cam.ac.uk

Abstract

The electrification of heat in the UK offers an alternative to a heating system dominated by natural gas, but poses significant challenges for the current energy supply, both in terms of meeting peak heat demand, and in decommissioning existing infrastructure. The UK's recent adoption of a net zero target by 2050 signals an increase in ambition in heat decarbonisation targets. On the other hand, negative emissions from the power sector, in the form of bioelectricity with carbon capture and storage (BECCS), could provide both low-carbon firm power and CO_2 removal, to assist in this transition. Our study explores the role of CO_2 removal in least cost electrification pathways to net zero, using a spatially explicit hourly unit operation and capacity expansion optimisation model of the UK heat and power sectors. We model the full biomass and CCS value chains to account for potential geo-physical, sustainability and financial constraints to BECCS deployment at the regional level. Our contribution introduces the methodology to derive the biomass supply curve and CO_2 storage capacity and injectivity cost curves for the UK.

Keywords: electrification of heat, negative emissions, biomass supply curve, carbon capture and storage

Acronyms

AR: Agricultural Residues; BECCS: Bioenergy with CO_2 capture and storage; CCS: CO_2 capture and storage; DEC: Dedicated Energy Crop; FR: Forestry Residues; LDZ: Local Distribution Zone; SRF: Short Rotation Forestry; T&S: Transport and Storage; UK-GBRM: UK and Global Bioenergy Resource Model.

1. Introduction

The heat sector accounts for 37% of UK greenhouse gas emissions and will be instrumental in achieving the UK net zero target by 2050 (BEIS 2018a). However, the timing, approach (hydrogen, electrification, or hybrid), and extent to which CO_2 removal will be required to decarbonise the UK heat sector, remain unknown (CCC 2019). A range of CO_2 removal methods have been proposed (Royal Society 2018). One option, bioenergy with carbon capture and storage (BECCS), has been consistently featured in UK-level power systems modelling as a way to provide both low-carbon firm power and CO_2 removal to decarbonise the power sector (Daggash *et al.* 2019). This role could become increasingly important with the electrification of other sectors of the economy (*e.g.*, see Heuberger *et al.,* 2020 for the impact of electric vehicles). Knowing how much biomass can be sustainably produced in or imported to the UK, and at what cost, is therefore key to quantifying the value of BECCS in the UK energy system. Studies have quantified the indigenous biomass potential by 2050 between 100 and 240 TWh (ETI 2018; Zhang *et al.* 2019; BEIS 2018b), depending on land availability, yield assumptions, and the range of feedstocks included. Open-access assessments of bioenergy potential at the regional level are, however, not readily available. While Zhang *et al.* (2019) curated biomass availability values for a range of feedstock types at a high resolution, this dataset did not account for potential competition with other biomass uses, and sustainability constraints restricting this supply, as included in the UK and Global Bioenergy Resource Model (UK-GBRM) (BEIS 2018b). Where, how much, at which rate, and at which cost, can the UK store CO_2, is also likely to impact the optimal investment decision to deploy BECCS (and fossil CCS) capacity across the UK. While the UK boasts ample CO_2 storage reserves in the North Sea, the affordability, capacity and injectivity of this reserve is not evenly distributed (ETI 2013). It is therefore important to integrate a spatially explicit CO_2 storage cost curve, for both capacity and injectivity, in the modelling framework. Our study aims to explore the potential role for BECCS in heat electrification scenarios, by integrating spatially-explicit biomass and CO_2 storage supply curves in a UK heat and power systems model, which operates at a high spatial and temporal resolution, using an actual hourly heat demand profile (Charitopoulos *et al.*, *under review*). This particular contribution presents the methodology to derive the biomass and CO_2 storage supply curves (Section 2), and discusses the spatial distribution of the UK's geophysical constraints on BECCS deployment (Section 3).

2. Derivation of supply curves

2.1 Biomass supply curve

In our modelling framework, the UK is divided into thirteen local distribution zones (LDZ) of the natural gas network (National Grid 2016). A biomass supply curve for each UK LDZ was derived based on local and imported biomass. The archetype chosen for the BECCS technology is a large scale (500 MW) biomass pulverised combustion plant combined with amine-based post-combustion CO_2. The following feedstock types were considered suitable for the use in a large scale BECCS plant: 1) dedicated energy crops (DEC) including miscanthus and short rotation coppice, 2) short rotation forestry (SRF), 3) wood forestry residues (FR), 4) agricultural residues (*e.g* cereals straw) (AR), and 5) wood pellet imports. The UK-GBRM was used to obtain the availability of these different feedstock at the national scale (BEIS 2018b). In assessing local bioenergy availability, the UK-GBRM accounts for competing uses and potential sustainability constraints. For imports, the model quantifies the availability of wood pellets from forestry in different producer countries, and assumes a share of that biomass will be available to the UK (based on the UK share of global energy use). The biomass is assumed to be sourced in the same proportions as the UK's current biomass imports are sourced. We find that the amount of global biomass available for imports to the UK decreases over time, from 240 TWh/yr in 2015 to 37 TWh/yr in 2050, as global demand for bioenergy increases.

In order to allocate these national assessments by UK region, we adopted tailored approaches for different feedstock types. For virgin biomass (DEC and SRF), regional marginal land availability for deploying energy crops and short rotation forestry was obtained using a 30 arc second resolution world map of "marginal mixed crop and vegetation land" (Cai *et al.* 2011). Such assessments are naturally highly uncertain and dependent on definitions of "marginal" land, and a sensitivity analysis will need to be performed to assess the robustness of the model outcomes. With this method, we find that marginal land availability in the UK is primarily concentrated in Scotland and southern

England, and sums up to 1.2 Mha. These findings are consistent with a previous assessment by the Energy Technology Institute (ETI), in which total land availability amounted to 1.4 Mha (ETI 2018). This map was then overlayed with a miscanthus, poplar and short rotation forestry yield map by Hastings *et al.* (2014). For each parcel of marginal land, the crop with the highest yield potential was selected. With this method, total DEC and SRF potentials were found to be 83 TWh/yr and 12 TWh/yr respectively. These values are considerably higher than in the UK-GBRM, where DEC availability ranges from 0.4 (2015) to 31 (2050) TW/yr, and SRF between 0 (2015) and 6 (2050) TWh/yr. Regional availability ratios were derived and applied to the more conservative national value obtained in the UK-GBRM model. For agricultural and forestry residues, cereal straw (Copeland and Turley 2008) and forestry residue (di Maio and Turley 2014) estimates were calculated by LDZ. Similarly, regional ratios were derived and applied to the national assessment value in the UK-GBRM. Costs and carbon footprint data from earlier calculations by DECC, curated by Element Energy and E4Tech (2018), were used for each biomass type. Pelleting and transport costs derived from Mobini *et al.* (2013) were added to obtain the cost of virgin biomass pellets at the point of use. The same methodology was applied for the carbon footprint. The biomass pellets can be used locally in each LDZ – in which case the transport distance is assumed to be 50 km (Bonilla and Whittaker 2009; DECC 2014) – or transported to another region. The cost and carbon footprint associated with biomass road transport from one LDZ to another were computed based on the Euclidean distance between the centroid of each LDZ, and emissions and cost factors from Lu *et al.* (2015). For biomass imports, the eight largest UK ports were represented in the model. For each LDZ, biomass imports are assumed to be available from the nearest port, with an added carbon and financial cost associated with biomass transport from the port to the centroid of the LDZ. Regional biomass availability are represented in *Figure 1*, while biomass supply curves in 2030 and 2050 are represented in *Figure 2*.

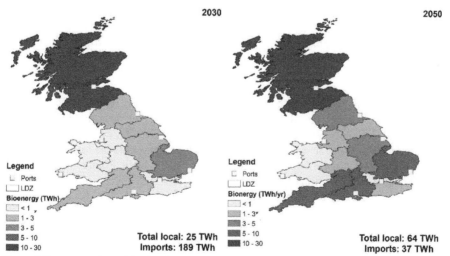

Figure 1 Representation of the UK in local distribution zones (cells), featuring ports for biomass imports (yellow squares) and regional bioenergy potential in TWh/yr (colouring).

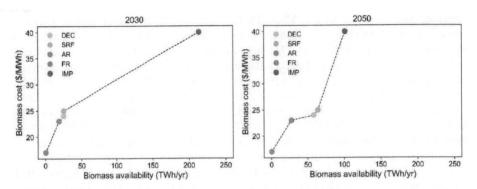

Figure 2 Representation the UK biomass cost curves in 2030 and 2050.

2.2 CO_2 storage

The British Geological Survey and ETI estimated the UK CO_2 storage capacity to 78 $GtCO_2$ with 50% confidence across 505 potential storage sites distributed around the UK in the North Sea and Irish Sea (Bentham *et al.* 2014). Out of 505 storage sites, ETI selected 20 sites for pre-feasibility studies (ETI 2013), and conducted economic analysis on 186 sites. We populated our CO_2 storage database with these 186 units, along with their characteristics, including latitude and longitude of storage centroid (assumed to be injection point), storage capacity (50% probability estimate), storage lifetime, storage injection rate, offshore CO_2 transport (T) capital and operating costs, and storage (S) capital and operating costs. For some of the storage units, T&S capital and operating costs were available for a range of injection rates (2 to 60 $MtCO_2$/yr) and lifetimes (10 to 40 years) in the database. When possible, the costs calculated for a lifetime of 30 years and the highest injection rate possible, were collected. When not available, costs for a lower lifetime (10-20 years) were used. Based on the lifetime and injection rate chosen, the undiscounted T&S cost for each selected storage site was calculated. The transport cost data in the CO_2Stored database only includes offshore CO_2 transport from an inland CO_2 terminal to the storage site. ETI identified 10 CO_2 terminals to cluster different incoming CO_2 flows and send the CO_2 offshore to the different CO_2 storage areas (ETI 2013). To account for inland CO_2 transport cost, the cost of transporting CO_2 between the centroid of each LDZ and the nearest CO_2 terminal was calculated based on pipeline capital and operating cost data from Johnson *et al.* (2014). A 26% (higher heating value) efficient 500 MW BECCS plant typically captures 3-4 $MtCO_2$/yr[1]. The CO_2 transport cost data for a flow rate of 3 $MtCO_2$/year was thus chosen. Figure 3a represents the location, capacity and undiscounted cost of the 186 CO_2 storage sites selected, while Figure 3b provides the cost of CO_2 T&S as a function of capacity and injectivity.

---

[1]Assuming 5 MWh/ton biomass (50% carbon content), 90% capture rate and 75% capacity factor.

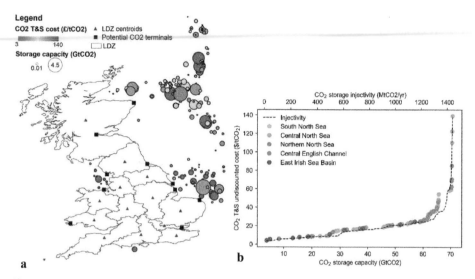

Figure 3 (a) Representation of the UK in local distribution zones (cells), featuring on-shore CO_2 terminals (black squares) and offshore CO_2 storage sites (coloured dots) selected for this analysis. (b) CO_2 storage capacity (each storage area is denoted by a different colour circle) and injectivity (line) cost curve. Data from the CO_2Stored database (Bentham *et al.* 2014).

3. Conclusions

Owing to the decrease in biomass imports over time, we find that bioenergy supply decreases between 2015 and 2050. This decline could be reversed if lower quality feedstock, particularly wastes (*e.g.,* municipal solid wastes, waste food) would be considered for use in smaller scale conversion plants (*e.g.,* combined heat and power) or in gasifiers. In terms of regional distribution, we observe that the primary bioenergy supply regions for the UK are Scotland followed by South East England. By 2050, the South West also becomes a key provider of bio-resources. These are also the regions with the highest installed renewable capacity today (National Grid 2018), and could therefore benefit from BECCS deployment, which would help balance the intermittency of renewables with firm load generation. By examining the CO_2 storage supply curve, we find that approximately 30 GtCO2 of storage capacity and an injectivity of 600 MtCO2/yr is available at a cost below £20/tCO2, which is likely to be enough for the UK to meet its CCS needs by 2050 – in its 'Further Ambition' scenario, the Committee on Climate Change (CCC) estimates that achieving net zero would require up to 175 MtCO2 to be captured annually (CCC 2019). Finally, we observe that 38% of CO_2 storage capacity with a cost below £20/tCO2 is located in the Central and Northern North Sea areas, close to the main bioenergy providers. The spatial distribution of biomass resources and low cost CO_2 storage sites therefore offer, *a priori*, a good opportunity for biomass source and sink matching with CO_2 storage sites, which could have a determining impact on the optimal location of BECCS and fossil-CCS plants.

References

BEIS. 2018a. "Clean Growth - Transforming Heating, Overview of Current Evidence."
    https://assets.publishing.service.gov.uk/government/uploads/system/uploads/attachment_da
    ta/file/766109/decarbonising-heating.pdf.
———. 2018b. "The UK and Global Bioenergy Resource Model." 2018. Department for
    https://www.gov.uk/government/publications/uk-and-global-bioenergy-resource-model.

Bentham, M., J. Lowndes, and A. Green. 2014. "CO2 STORage Evaluation Database (CO₂Stored). The UK's Online Storage Atlas." *Energy Procedia* 63 (0): 5103–13.

Bonilla, D., and C. Whittaker. 2009. "Freight Transport and Deployment of Bioenergy in the UK," no. December: 1–23. http://www.tsu.ox.ac.uk/pubs/1043-bonilla-whittaker.pdf.

Cai, X., X. Zhang, and D. Wang. 2011. "Land Availability Analysis for Biofuel Production." *Environmental Science and Technology* 45 (January): 334–39.

CCC. 2019. "Net Zero - The UK's Contribution to Stopping Global Warming." https://www.theccc.org.uk/publication/net-zero-the-uks-contribution-to-stopping-global-warming/.

Charitopoulos, V., C. K. Chyong, and D. Reiner. (under review). "The Prospect of Electrification for the Decarbonisation of Heat in the UK." *EPRG Working Paper*.

Copeland, J., and D. Turley. 2008. "National and Regional Supply/Demand Balance for Agricultural Straw in Great Britain." http://www.ruraldevelopment.org.uk/northwoods/files/2012/12/StrawAvailabilityinGreatBritain.pdf.

Daggash, H A, C F Heuberger, and N Mac Dowell. 2019. "The Role and Value of Negative Emissions Technologies in Decarbonising the UK Energy System." *International Journal of Greenhouse Gas Control* 81: 181–98.

Element Energy and E4Tech. 2018. "Cost Analysis of Future Heat Infrastructure Options Report for National Infrastructure Commission March 2018." https://www.nic.org.uk/wp-content/uploads/Element-Energy-and-E4techCost-analysis-of-future-heat-infrastructure-Final.pdf.

Energy Technology Institute (ETI). 2013. "A Picture of CO₂ Storage in the UK: Learnings from the ETI's UKSAP and Derived Projects." https://www.eti.co.uk/library/ccs-a-picture-of-co2-storage-in-the-uk.

Energy Technology Institute (ETI). 2018. "The Evidence for Deploying Bioenergy with CCS (BECCS) in the UK." *Energy Technologies Institute*. https://www.eti.co.uk/insights/the-evidence-for-deploying-bioenergy-with-ccs-beccs-in-the-uk.

Hastings, A., M. J. Tallis, E. Casella, R. W. Matthews, P. A. Henshall, S. Milner, P. Smith, and G. Taylor. 2014. "The Technical Potential of Great Britain to Produce Ligno-Cellulosic Biomass for Bioenergy in Current and Future Climates." *GCB Bioenergy* 6 (2): 108–22.

Heuberger, C. F., P. K. Bains, and N. Mac. 2020. "The EV-Olution of the Power System : A Spatio-Temporal Optimisation Model to Investigate the Impact of Electric Vehicle Deployment." *Applied Energy* 257 (June 2019): 113715.

Johnson, N., N. Parker, and J. Ogden. 2014. "How Negative Can Biofuels with CCS Take Us and at What Cost? Refining the Economic Potential of Biofuel Production with CCS Using Spatially-Explicit Modeling." *Energy Procedia* 63: 6770–91.

Lu, X., M. R. Withers, N. Seifkar, R. P. Field, S. R. H. Barrett, and H. J. Herzog. 2015. "Biomass Logistics Analysis for Large Scale Biofuel Production: Case Study of Loblolly Pine and Switchgrass." *Bioresource Technology* 183: 1–9.

Maio, D. di, and D. Turley. 2014. "Lignocellulosic Feedstock in the UK." www.nnfcc.co.uk.

Mobini, M., T. Sowlati, and S. Sokhansanj. 2013. "A Simulation Model for the Design and Analysis of Wood Pellet Supply Chains." *Applied Energy* 111: 1239–49.

National Grid. 2016. "Gas Demand Forecasting Methodology," https://www.nationalgrid.com/sites/default/files/documents/8589937808-Gas%20Demand%20Forecasting%20Methodology.pdf

National Grid. 2018. "Future Energy Scenarios." http://fes.nationalgrid.com/fes-document/.

Royal Society and Royal Academy of Engineering. 2018. *Greenhouse Gas Removal*. https://royalsociety.org/-/media/policy/projects/greenhouse-gas-removal/royal-society-greenhouse-gas-removal-report-2018.pdf.

DECC. 2014. "Life Cycle Impacts of Biomass Electricity in 2020." https://assets.publishing.service.gov.uk/government/uploads/system/uploads/attachment_data/file/349024/BEAC_Report_290814.pdf

Zhang, D., M. Bui, M. Fajardy, P. Patrizio, F. Kraxner, and N. Mac Dowell. 2019. "Unlocking the Potential of BECCS with Indigenous Sources of Biomass at a National Scale." *Sustainable Energy & Fuels*. (*advance article*).

Sauro Pierucci, Flavio Manenti, Giulia Bozzano, Davide Manca (Eds.)
Proceedings of the 30th European Symposium on Computer Aided Process Engineering
(ESCAPE30), May 24-27, 2020, Milano, Italy. © 2020 Elsevier B.V. All rights reserved.
http://dx.doi.org/10.1016/B978-0-12-823377-1.50264-0

Strategic Biorefining Supply Chain Design for Novel Products in Immature Markets

Anna Panteli,[a] Sara Giarola,[b*] Nilay Shah [a]

[a]*Chemical Engineering Department, Imperial College London, SW7 2AZ, UK*
[b]*Earth Science & Engineering Department, Imperial College London, SW7 2AZ, UK*
s.giarola10@imperial.ac.uk

Abstract

Castor oil is a key intermediate in the chemical and pharmaceutical industry, but its use as energy vector is hindered by high feedstock costs. However, it become a competitive fuel if a full market is also created for the by-products. Mixed Integer Linear Programs are effective tools to drive investment decisions in bio-based supply chains.

This paper proposes a Mixed Integer Linear Fractional Programming (MILFP) with the objective to minimise the levelised cost of the examined supply chain. Results produce the most economical supply chain solution which maximises the unit value of the supply chain feedstock rather than just proposing a solution where the system fulfills the demand at the minimum size possible.

Keywords: MILFP, castor oil, supply chain optimisation.

1. Introduction

Environmental and societal concerns regarding the mitigation of climate change (IPCC, 2007) have driven the research in renewable sources as they can improve energy security and reduce greenhouse gas (GHG) emissions. Biorefineries relying on processes and technologies producing high added value bio-fuels, chemicals and polymers can play a remarkable role in delivering energy security and emissions reduction.

With a yield of about 2,000 kg per ha, castor seeds have high oil potentials and lower plantation costs compared to competing crops. Being composed for about 90 % of rinoleic acid, castor oil has also an extraordinary purity compared to the majority of the bio-oils. The fluctuations of the castor seeds price due to biomass availability, has boosted the interest in assessing potentials for castor seeds to produce plant lipids for both energy and industrial applications (Severino et al., 2012).

The application of a system approach, embracing the entire supply chain (SC), is essential in the design of advanced biorefining networks over the long-term. The approach requires that every step, from biomass cultivation to delivery of the final bioproducts to the customers, should be considered, while integrated with a technology superstructure for the biomass transformation (Santos et al., 2019).

Most of the existing works considering the planning and optimizing of novel infrastructures, use an absolute (extensive) economic performance metric, such as maximizing the total profit or minimizing the total cost or a combination of absolute environmental and economic metrics (Patel et al, 2016). In the design of completely novel systems, multi-objective formulations are also widely used. Huang et al. (2019) proposed a multi-objective formulation including greenhouse gas emissions and systems cost minimization in the design of a renewable jet fuel SC in US. Mandade et al. (2019) presented a multi-objective optimization approach to select the feedstock mix for ethanol production in India showing the trade-off among life cycle greenhouse gas emissions, energy return on investment, life cycle water use, and land use. All these approaches, implying the minimisation of an extensive metric, constrain the product demands with lower bounds, thus giving a SC configuration which would produce and sell the lowest quantity of biofuels as possible to reduce costs. The solution is not necessarily the most economical one. The advantage of unit objective is rarely acknowledged in the literature (Gao & You, 2017). In the past, only a few studies used intensive metric to support a supply chain design. In one of the most recent applications, Yue et al. (2013) proposed an optimization for (bio)-refining systems with two fractional objective functions. An economic objective guarantees the optimal sales amount between the demand upper and lower bounds to guarantee the lowest unit cost per functional unit. The environmental objective guarantees the lowest environmental impact per functional unit.

This paper addresses the problem of biorefining planning, specifically applied to a castor oil biorefinery, whose profitability might vary depending on the selling price of the bioproducts, which is unknown as there market is not developed yet. To plan a sustainable biorefinery, an optimization framework is proposed which maximises the bioproducts throughput and controls their costs through minimising the levelized costs. The rest of this article is organised as follows. The general problem statement is first presented followed by the mathematical formulation. A Romanian case study with modelling assumptions, numerical results and final considerations is then discussed.

2. Methods

2.1. Problem statement

Here we examine a bio-based supply chain system, involving the production of castor oil from castor seeds in Romania to meet the demand of oil in Marseille. The case study is based on a real industrial application with a focus on determining where the castor seeds transformation sites would be located and how the products would be channeled to the market, via either truck or ship. The SC optimization problem applies to 12 months of the biorefinery planning and operation.

2.2. Mathematical formulation

A multi-echelon multi-product biorefining supply chain is modelled as proposed in Panteli et al. (2018) where the upstream supply chain steps (such as biomass production, storage, transport, and processing) are optimized alongside the downstream supply chain steps (such as including bioproduct storage and transport to the market). The objective function (Eq. (1)), also known as the cost of goods per gram (COG/g), is equal to the total annualised cost, comprising of both capital and operating costs divided by the total annual demand of products.

The Mixed Integer Linear Programming (MILP) model proposed by Panteli et al. (2018) was reformulated into a MILFP, substituting the profit-based objective function with the levelised cost-based one, as given in Eq. (1).

$$min\, LC = \frac{TAC}{TAD} \tag{1}$$

$$s.t.\; TAC = TCC + \sum_t TOC_t \tag{2}$$

$$TAD = \sum_c \sum_t D_{c,g,t} \tag{3}$$

$$D_{c,g,t} \geq 0.15 \cdot MD_{c,g,t} \tag{4}$$

where LC (€M/kt of products) stands for the levelised cost, TAC (€M/y) refers to the total annualised costs, and TAD (kt of products/y) represents the total annual demand of bioproducts. As reported in Eq. (2), TAC includes the annualized capital costs (TCC) and the operating cost per month t (TOC_t). TAD is the total demand across all the commodities c, all the geographical subdivisions g, and time period t (Eq. (3)). Moreover, an additional demand-related constraint, Eq. (4), is included in the mathematical formulation, introducing a lower bound for the demand of the bioproducts $D_{c,g,t}$ equal to the 15% of the market demand value $MD_{c,g,t}$ by commodity c, region g, and time period t. As there is no consideration of potential profit to motivate the production of bioproducts, in this case a minimum level demand restriction is needed to enforce the production procedure.

The MILFP model is solved using the Dinkelbach algorithm (Liu et al., 2014). This solution procedure began as an application of the classical Newton method to solve convex non-linear fractional programming (NFP) models by solving a sequence of non-linear programming (NLP) models successively, and recently it has been implemented to solve MILFP optimisation problems.

The implementation of the Dinkelbach algorithm, relies on transforming the MILFP model as in EQ. (1) into an MILP model, by modifying the fractional objective function as:

$$min\ TAC - f \cdot TAD \tag{5}$$

Overall, the above MILP model is solved iteratively for different values of f, based on each iteration optimal solutions, until a termination criterion, based on the absolute objective value, is satisfied. The scheme of the employed Dinkelbach algorithm is presented in Figure 1.

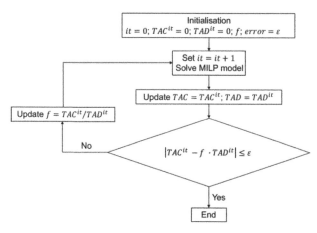

Figure 1. Flowchart for the Dinkelbach algorithm.

3. Case study

The EuroBioRef project (EuroBioRef, 2016) and Tsagkari et al. (2016) were the sources used for the agronomic and costs data. In the remaining part of the section, each SC step is further described.

3.1. Spatially-explicit features

The Romanian area of Constanța (i.e., 150,000 ha) has been discretised into a grid of 60 square cells of equal size, i.e., 5 km of length. An additional cell represents the demand centre in Marseille. The fraction of cultivation area and fraction of arable land devoted to castor seeds were assumed based on the soil conditions and altitude differences of the examined region. As disaggregated data at the spatial scale of analysis were not available, the fraction of the arable land density was randomly distributed while the cultivation yield of castor seeds was assumed constant geographically, although available only two months in a year.

3.2. Transport
The model specifies whether and, if presents, what kind of transport link is available between two cells. Specifically, truck only was allowed within the Romanian area while trans-shipping was allowed between Romanian and Marseille ports.

3.3. Processing
A seed pressing followed by oil extraction technology was modelled. The technology produces castor oil and meal. The biorefining process consists of two sections. In the first section, the castor seeds undergo pretreatment through continuous dehulling, conditioning and flaking. In the second section, crude oil is separated from the seeds by hexane (solvent) extraction and the de-oiled meal is desolventised and toasted. Due to the small surface of the Romanian region and the low demand of castor oil, the installation of only one conversion facility was examined: the capacity of the investigated SC is assumed to be 150 kt/y.

3.4. Storage
Castor seeds were assumed to be stored on-fields, whereas castor meal and castor oil in drums. The cost and the maximum capacity of storage were calculated from Panteli et al. (2018).

3.5. Demand

Marseille is the market for the products and where the consumption of the bioproducts is assumed. In addition to castor oil, the by-product (i.e., castor meal) can be further utilised for field fertilisation or for power generation, and subsequently, contribute to the total profit of the examined SC system.

4. Results and discussion

The results obtained with the MILFP approach are presented and commented in comparison with the solution obtained solving the problem as a profit maximisation MILP. The MILFP with the use of several non-linear solvers failed, so that the MILP reformulation of the MILFP in CPLEX 12.7.0.0 was adopted. The optimality gap for each run was set to 0%.

4.1. Planning decisions

The obtained minimum levelised cost of 0.733 €M/kt of products resulted in 16.3 €M/y profit. As shown in Figure 2 the required processing plant is installed in Marseille (i.e., in cell g=61). As the maximum level of demand was set equal to the maximum capacity of the examined conversion facility, only one plant was expected to be installed for the conversion of castor seeds into castor oil and castor meal. Aiming at satisfying the targeted castor oil and meal demand in Marseille, the SC configuration showed that the optimal location to build the examined seeds pressing and oil extraction plant would be in the port cell in Marseille. In addition, castor seeds were cultivated in the Romanian region. Except a 5 kt/y castor oil and a 22 kt/y castor meal storage facility in Marseille (i.e., in cell g=61, where the conversion facility would be planned), most of the storage would occur next to the biomass production fields. All the biomass stored in Romania would be then transhipped to Marseille. The relatively higher unit cost of transporting liquid compared to solids, explains the preference for moving solid biomass for most of the freights envisaged in the final solution.

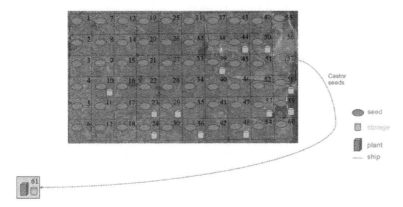

Figure 2. Optimal SC system configuration.

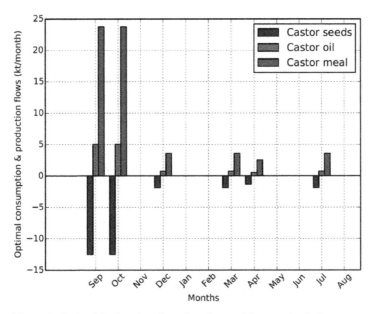

Figure 3. Optimal feedstock and product flows of the examined plant.

Figure 3 illustrates the optimal monthly flows of castor seeds, oil and meal of the facility. The plant of the current case would operate for four months (i.e., September, October,

December, March, April and July), and at full capacity just for the first two periods. The cost breakdown for the MILFP shows a dominant role of cultivation (49 % of total) and biomass pretreatment (37 %) costs. Transport and storage, 13 % and 1% of the total costs respectively, play a minor role.

4.2. Comparison between the MILFP and the MILP solution

The MILP and MILFP solutions appear very close in term of SC configuration, where the optimisation driven MILP sets all the storage facilities in the Romanian region. The cost breakdown between the MILP and the MILFP solutions is also comparable. The relative proximity in the results can be mainly explained with the constraints set on the SC demand due to the limits on biomass availability. However, the MILFP case produces a 2 % less profitable supply chain system than the MILP profit maximisation, where the difference depends on the implications of the assumptions on the product selling price.

5. Conclusions

A Mixed Integer Linear Fractional Programming (MILFP) approach is used to minimise the levelized cost of a castor seeds-to-oil supply chain and solved using the Dinkelbach approach. The methodology has the benefit that no assumptions would be required on product selling prices, which are hard to define when novel infrastructures introduce products for yet-to-developed markets. Overall, the examined castor seeds-to-oil supply chain network produces an interesting business case for investments even when land usage restrictions regarding plant allocation are applied.

Acknowledgements

The FP7 RENESENG project under grant agreement 607415 is acknowledged for funding this research.

References

EuroBioRef (2014). Available from: http://www.eurobioref.org/index.php/dissemination.

Gao, J., & You, F. (2017). Computers and Chemical Engineering, 107, 221–236.

Huang, E., Zhang, X., Rodriguez, L., Khanna, M., de Jong, S., Ting, K. C., Lin, T. (2019). Renewable and Sustainable Energy Reviews, 115, 109403.

IPCC. Intergovernmental Panel on Climate Change (IPCC) [online]. Available from: http://www.ipcc.ch/,page, 2017.

Liu, S., Simaria, A. S., Farid, S., and Papageorgiou, L. G. (2014). Computers & Chemical Engineering, 68:151–164, 2014. doi: 10.1016/j. compchemeng.2014.05.005.

Mandade, P. and Shastri, Y. (2019). Journal of Cleaner Production. Elsevier, 231, pp. 1226–1234. doi: 10.1016/J.JCLEPRO.2019.05.311.

Panteli, A., Giarola, S., and Shah (2018). Industrial & Engineering Chemistry Research, 57(30):9849–9865, 2018. doi: 10.1021/acs.iecr.7b05228

Patel, V. R., Dumancas, G. G., Viswanath, L. C. K., Maples, R., & Subong, B. J. J. (2016). Lipid Insights, 9(1), 1–12. https://doi.org/10.4137/LPI.S40233.

Santos, A., Carvalho, A., Barbosa-Póvoa, A. P., Marques, A., & Amorim, P. (2019). Forest Policy and Economics, 105, 112–135. https://doi.org/10.1016/J.FORPOL.2019.05.026.

Severino, L. S., Auld, D. L., Baldanzi, M., Cândido, M. J. D., Chen, G., Crosby, W., Zieler, H. (2012). Agronomy Journal, 104(4), 853–880. https://doi.org/10.2134/agronj2011.0210.

Tsagkari, M., Couturier, J. L., Kokossis A., and Dubois, J. L. ChemSusChem, 9(17): 2284–2297, 2016. doi: 10.1002/cssc.201600309

Yue, D., Kim, M. A., & You, F. (2013). ACS Sustainable Chemistry and Engineering, 1(8), 1003–1014. https://doi.org/10.1021/sc400080x

Sauro Pierucci, Flavio Manenti, Giulia Bozzano, Davide Manca (Eds.)
Proceedings of the 30th European Symposium on Computer Aided Process Engineering
(ESCAPE30), May 24-27, 2020, Milano, Italy. © 2020 Elsevier B.V. All rights reserved.
http://dx.doi.org/10.1016/B978-0-12-823377-1.50265-2

Optimization of Biomass Circulating Fluidized Bed Gasifier for Synthesis Applications using Simulation and Response Surface Methodology

Ingrid L. Motta, Andressa N. Marchesan, Rubens Maciel Filho, Maria Regina Wolf Maciel

Laboratory of Optimization, Design and Advanced Control, School of Chemical Engineering, University of Campinas, Av. Albert Einstein 500, Campinas, 13083-852, Brazil

ingridmotta2@gmail.com

Abstract

Biomass gasification is a complex process that uses heat and catalysts to convert biomass into syngas, which can be applied in Fischer-Tropsch (FT) synthesis to produce liquid fuels. As FT requires specific syngas compositions, this work performs an optimization of the operating conditions of a pressurized circulating fluidized bed (CFB) gasifier for such purposes. The CFB operated with sugarcane bagasse as a feedstock and steam as a gasifying agent and was simulated in Aspen Plus v8.6 based on Gibbs free energy minimization with restricted equilibrium. The optimization followed the response surface methodology (RSM), consisting of central composite designs performed in Statistica 7.0 at a 99.0 % confidence level to obtain simplified mathematical models between input factors (temperature, T; steam-to-biomass ratio, S/B; and moisture content, MC) and output factors (cold gas efficiency, CGE; H_2/CO ratio; gasifier heat duty, $Q_{gasifier}$; higher heating value, HHV; and H_2, CO, CO_2, and CH_4 contents). The models were used to generate four optimized cases of pressurized CFBs that returned H_2/CO ratios of 2.15, required for FT reactors. The optimized CFB operates at 916 °C, 15 bar, S/B of 1.12, and 10 wt.% moisture, generating a syngas stream of low CO_2 and CH_4 contents, which may reduce the syngas cleaning and conditioning costs downstream the gasifier. The results agree with optimizations using other feedstocks and sets of objectives, showing the validity of the models.

Keywords: optimization, response surface methodology, biomass gasification, fluidized bed, Aspen Plus

1. Introduction

Biomass gasification is the conversion of biomass using heat and catalysts mainly into syngas, a gas mixture composed of H_2, CO, CO_2, CH_4, water, and light hydrocarbons (Sadhwani et al., 2017). Syngas can hold a variety of applications, from low-added-value uses in gas turbines to high-added-value uses in Fischer-Tropsch (FT) synthesis (Bain and Broer, 2011).

FT synthesis is an important group of catalytic reactions in which syngas polymerizes into a wide range of long-chain hydrocarbon fuels. To yield certain hydrocarbon fractions, the FT reactor must operate with specific catalysts (usually Fe and Co-based) (Bukur et al., 2016), temperatures, and pressures (Graves et al., 2011), and the syngas must have specific compositions. Thus, the first step consists of obtaining strict syngas compositions via the optimization of the biomass gasifiers' operating conditions.

This chapter continues a previous study on sugarcane bagasse gasification (Motta et al., 2019) and performs an optimization of a pressurized circulating fluidized bed (CFB) gasifier using simulation and response surface methodology (RSM) tools to achieve H_2/CO ratios of 2.15, suitable for FT synthesis. The results show the direct correlation between syngas composition and possible downstream applications.

2. Methodology

The CFB was simulated in Aspen Plus v8.6, and its flowsheet is depicted in Figure 1. The simulation includes a sugarcane bagasse dryer and a gasification stage based on Gibbs free energy minimization with restricted equilibrium. Details on the bagasse characterization and simulation parameters are described elsewhere (Motta et al., 2019).

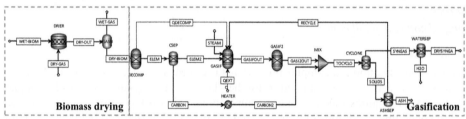

Figure 1 – Simulation flowsheet. Reproduced with permission from Elsevier (Motta et al., 2019).

In the RSM optimization, 2^4 face-centered central composite analyses were run in Statistica 7.0 at a 99 % confidence level. The analyses used coded input factors (Table 1) to ensure that the orders of magnitude of the latter did not influence the obtained models. The analyses were performed for each output factor: higher heating value (HHV), cold gas efficiency (CGE), gasifier heat duty ($Q_{gasifier}$), H_2/CO ratio, as well as H_2, CO, CO_2, and CH_4 contents.

Table 1 – Design matrix used in the RSM for CFB gasifier.

Input factor	2^4 face-centered central composite designs levels		
	-1	0	+1
T (°C)	750	850	950
P (bar)	1	8	15
S/B	0.5	1.0	1.5
MC (%)	10	20	30

In each analysis, the statistically significant parameters were determined using Pareto charts of effects, and full mathematical quadratic models using coded input factors were estimated. Later, the backward elimination methodology was used to obtain simplified models. If a parameter does not contribute to a model's description, its elimination will increase R^2_{adj} (adjusted R-squared). Therefore, the least significant parameters of each Pareto chart were removed one by one until R^2_{adj} no longer increased. The models were then tested for the F-test with 99.0 % confidence to verify their statistical significance.

The models were used to generate four optimized cases (max HHV, min $Q_{gasifier}$, max H_2 content, and min CH_4 content) that returned an H_2/CO ratio of 2.15 at a 15-bar pressure. The optimization cases represent desirable features for either gasifiers or FT reactors: higher HHV means that the syngas streams may also be used for efficient combustion purposes, increasing the process flexibility; minimum $Q_{gasifier}$ implies higher energy efficiencies and lower costs; higher H_2 and lower CH_4 contents are both desirable for FT synthesis. The H_2/CO ratio of 2.15 was selected because it is a typical syngas ratio for FT synthesis. A 15-bar pressure was fixed because, as the FT reactor downstream of the gasifier works at high pressures, higher gasifier pressures will result in lower syngas compression costs (Spath et al., 2005). All cases had additional restrictions: H_2, CO, CO_2, and CH_4 concentrations must be higher than 0 to avoid negative values; and T, S/B, and MC must vary in the ranges defined for the central composite design ($-1 \leq X \leq 1$). Finally, the optimization was run using the SOLVER tool at Microsoft Excel using the GRG nonlinear solving method.

3. Results and Discussion

Table 2 presents the models obtained via RSM for a CFB at 15-bar pressure. Quadratic models were selected because they provide more accurate adjustments than linear models, as also experienced by Yusup et al. (2014). All models passed the F-test at a 99 % confidence level, indicating that they are statistically significant equations.
All models except for CGE present R^2 values higher than 0.97 and R^2_{adj} higher than 0.96, which shows satisfactory adjustment between the values simulated in Aspen Plus and those calculated by the mathematical models.
Table 3 presents the results obtained for the optimization scenarios. Max HHV and min $Q_{gasifier}$ require lower temperatures (~750 °C) and S/B (0.6–0.7), leading to gas mixtures of low H_2 and CO concentrations and high CH_4 contents. Such cases are comparable because extra gasifier heat duty is necessary to reform CH_4 and other hydrocarbons, and CH_4 is the component of the highest contribution to HHV. The syngas mixtures of max HHV and min $Q_{gasifier}$ are unsuitable for synthesis purposes but can find application in heat and power plants. On the other hand, max H_2 and min CH_4 require higher temperatures (> 900 °C) and S/B (1.12), producing syngas mixtures of appropriate composition for FT synthesis. Such scenarios are equivalent because high temperatures and steam feeds (S/B) shift the chemical equilibrium towards H_2 production and CH_4 consumption in the water-gas shift and steam-methane reforming reactions (Motta et al., 2019). In all cases, low moisture contents were obtained, being 18.4 wt.% advised for the max HHV case and values below 12 wt.% moisture for the other cases.
Figure 2 demonstrates the good agreement between predicted and simulated results of the selected scenarios (max H_2, min CH_4) for compositions (H_2, CO, CO_2, CH_4), H_2/CO ratios, HHV, and $Q_{gasifier}$. Slightly higher deviations for CGE are observed due to the model's lower regression coefficients (R^2 and R^2_{adj}), as shown in Table 3.
Figure 3 shows the response profiles for T, S/B, and some gasification parameters at 10-wt.% moisture content and 15-bar pressure. In the response profiles, dashed lines were used to highlight the areas in which the optimal values of max H_2 and min CH_4 (see Figure 2) could occur. The H_2/CO response profile shows a narrow region (highlighted with dashed lines) that leads to H_2/CO ratios of 2.15, occurring along the entire T range and at S/B values of 0.6 – 1.2. The overlapping of this H_2/CO region onto the other charts, represented by a transparent solid area, shows that the input conditions necessary to achieve the optimal parameters are much stricter and that the gasifier operation is sensitive to changes in parameters.
The response profiles also demonstrate the relationship between the parameters. Even though the T levels for higher H_2 production are opposite to those of higher CH_4 generation, both response profiles present similar shapes. H_2/CO ratios and $Q_{gasifier}$ present opposing effects in terms of S/B, but also similar shapes.

Table 2 – Mathematical coded models obtained via RSM.

Output factor and mathematical model	Eq.	R^2	R^2_{adj}
$CGE(\%) = 77.09 + 0.75T - 2.19S/B - 1.63MC + 0.84MC^2$	(1)	0.988	0.978
$H_2/CO = 2.37 - 0.57T + 0.39T^2 + 0.96S/B - 0.16(S/B)^2 - 0.25MC - 0.32T \times S/B - 0.09T \times MC$	(2)	0.889	0.843
$Q_{gasifier}(MJ/h\ kg_{bagasse}) = 5.74 + 1.09T - 0.62T^2 + 0.86S/B + 0.22(S/B)^2 + 0.61MC + 0.28MC^2$	(3)	0.992	0.985
$HHV(MJ/m^3) = 14.05 - 2.19T + 1.72T^2 - 0.97S/B - 0.34(S/B)^2 - 0.29MC - 0.64MC^2$	(4)	0.991	0.978
$H_2(vol.\%) = 32.69 + 14.68T - 11.45T^2 + 5.42S/B + 2.56(S/B)^2 + 1.64MC + 4.23MC^2$	(5)	0.976	0.961
$CO(vol.\%) = 14.03 + 8.81T - 6.49T^2 - 2.23S/B + 3.36(S/B)^2 - 1.00MC + 2.37MC^2 - 1.55T \times S/B - 0.47T \times MC$	(6)	0.977	0.962
$CO_2(vol.\%) = 30.84 - 10.18T + 7.65T^2 + 0.26S/B - 3.14(S/B)^2 + 0.35MC - 2.81MC^2 + 1.33T \times S/B + 0.39T \times MC$	(7)	0.992	0.982
$CH_4(vol.\%) = 22.25 - 13.27T + 10.25T^2 - 3.30S/B - 2.77(S/B)^2 - 0.98MC - 3.78MC^2 + 0.92T \times S/B$	(8)	0.989	0.978

Table 3 – RSM optimization results for a 15-bar CFB gasifier. P (predicted), S (simulated), *wet basis

Case	T (°C)	P (bar)	S/B	MC (%)	H_2/CO P	H_2/CO S	CGE (%) P	CGE (%) S	$Q_{gasifier}$ (MJ/h kg$_{bagasse}$*) P	$Q_{gasifier}$ S	HHV (MJ/m³) P	HHV S	H_2 (vol.%) P	H_2 S	CO (vol.%) P	CO S	CO_2 (vol.%) P	CO_2 S	CH_4 (vol.%) P	CH_4 S
Max HHV	750	15	0.60	18.4	**2.15**	1.98	75.6	73.6	3.4	4.8	18.6	17.5	3.7	10.3	1.6	5.2	47.5	42.9	47.4	41.3
Min $Q_{gasifier}$	750	15	0.68	11.3	**2.15**	1.95	77.1	73.9	3.2	4.7	18.2	17.5	5.9	10.2	3.1	5.2	46.0	42.9	45.3	41.4
Max H_2	916	15	1.12	10.0	**2.15**	2.14	78.5	78.5	6.1	8.3	13.1	13.1	41.4	39.3	20.0	18.4	24.1	26.0	14.4	16.2
Min CH_4	915	15	1.12	10.0	**2.15**	2.14	78.5	78.5	6.1	8.3	13.1	13.1	41.4	39.1	20.0	18.3	24.1	26.1	14.4	16.3

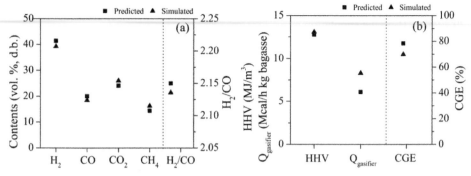

Figure 2 – Comparison of predicted (P) and simulated (S) gasification results of the selected optimization cases: (a) syngas composition; (b) HHV, $Q_{gasifier}$, and CGE.

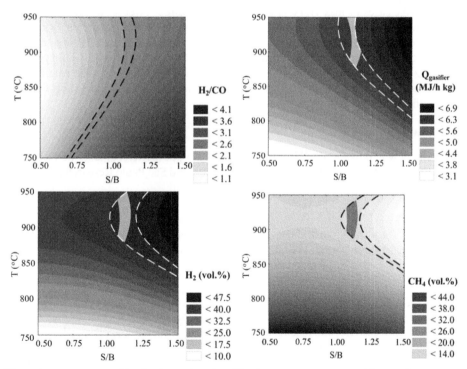

Figure 3 – Response profiles for the analyzed gasification parameters. Dashed lines and transparent areas refer to T and S/B for optimal values at any H_2/CO ratio and 2.15, respectively.

Although several simulation and experimental works have used RSM to optimize syngas composition, yields, heating values, and gasifier performances, none have optimized steam-blown CFB gasifiers for FT synthesis and with the same objective functions of our study. Therefore, the results obtained here can be compared to the literature only in part. In the optimization of an entrained-flow gasifier with rice husk as a feedstock, Gao et al. (2019) aimed at maximizing CO production and CGE, obtaining a 25.15 % CO content and 65.34 % CGE, similar to the results of max H_2 and min CH_4 of this work. In the attempt to maximize H_2 yield and CGE, Silva and Rouboa (2014) found that and S/B of 1, temperature of 777 °C, and O content of 25 vol.% may produce 29.2 vol.% H_2 in the simulation o

f a steam-air-blown BFB gasifier operating with forest residues. Such an S/B is close to the one obtained in the selected optimized cases of our study. Yusup et al. (2014) found that, to produce syngas containing 82.11 vol.% H_2 in a pilot-scale fluidized bed gasifier, a much higher S/B of 2.0 was necessary.

Thus, the optimization of a biomass gasifier for a specific syngas downstream application requires the understanding of the correlation between input parameters (such as biomass properties and operating conditions) and output parameters (CGE, heating value, syngas composition).

4. Conclusions

The optimization of a sugarcane bagasse pressurized CFB gasifier for downstream synthesis purposes via RSM was performed in this work, analyzing scenarios of max HHV, min gasifier heat duty ($Q_{gasifier}$), max H_2 production, and min CH_4 generation. Although the cases of max HHV and min $Q_{gasifier}$ required lower temperatures and S/B, they resulted in low H_2 and CO concentrations and high CH_4 contents, which are unsuitable for synthesis purposes. On the other hand, the cases of max H_2 and min CH_4 levels produced syngas mixtures of appropriate starting composition for FT synthesis, requiring 916 °C, 15 bar, S/B of 1.12, and 10 wt.% moisture content. The results agree with other optimization studies and propose a new application for circulating fluidized bed gasifiers.

Acknowledgments

The authors would like to thank CNPq, Coordenação de Aperfeiçoamento de Pessoal de Nível Superior - Brasil (CAPES) - Finance Code 001, and São Paulo Research Foundation (FAPESP) grant #2015/20630-4 for the financial support.

References

R.L. Bain, K. Broer, 2011, Gasification, Thermochemical Processing of Biomass: Conversion into Fuels, Chemicals and Power, 1st ed, Chichester, John Wiley & Sons, 47-77.

D.B. Bukur, B. Todic, N. Elbashir, 2016, Role of water-gas-shift reaction in Fischer-Tropsch synthesis on iron, Catal Today, 275, 66-75.

X. Gao, F. Xu, F. Bao, C. Tu, Y. Zhang, Y. Wang, B. Li, 2019, Simulation and optimization of rice husk gasification using intrinsic reaction rate based CFD model, Renew Energy, 139, 611-620.

C. Graves, S.D. Ebbesen, M. Mogensen, K.S. Lackner, 2011, Sustainable hydrocarbon fuels by recycling CO_2 and H_2O with renewable or nuclear energy,Renew Sustain Energy Rev,15,2-23.

I.L. Motta, N.T. Miranda, R. Maciel Filho, M.R. Wolf Maciel, 2019, Sugarcane bagasse gasification: simulation and analysis of different operating parameters, fluidizing media, and gasifier types, Biomass Bioenergy, 122, 433-445.

N. Sadhwani, P. Li, M.R. Eden, S. Adhikari, 2017, Process Modeling of Fluidized Bed Biomass-CO_2 Gasification using ASPEN Plus, Computer Aided Chemical Engineering, 40, 2509-2514.

V. Silva, A. Rouboa, 2014, Optimizing the gasification operating conditions of forest residues by coupling a two-stage equilibrium model with a response surface methodology, Fuel Process Technol, 122, 163-169.

P. Spath, A. Aden, T. Eggeman, M. Ringer, B. Wallace, J. Jechura, 2005, Biomass to Hydrogen Production Detailed Design and Economics Utilizing the Battelle Columbus Laboratory Indirectly- Heated Gasifier, Golden, National Renewable Laboratory.

S. Yusup, Z. Khan, M.M. Ahmad, N.A. Rashidi, 2014, Optimization of hydrogen production in in-situ catalytic adsorption (ICA) steam gasification based on response surface methodology, Biomass Bioenergy, 60, 98-107.

Sauro Pierucci, Flavio Manenti, Giulia Bozzano, Davide Manca (Eds.)
Proceedings of the 30th European Symposium on Computer Aided Process Engineering
(ESCAPE30), May 24-27, 2020, Milano, Italy. © 2020 Elsevier B.V. All rights reserved.
http://dx.doi.org/10.1016/B978-0-12-823377-1.50266-4

Modelling and Analysis of Microbial Fuel Cells with a Two-species Anode Biofilm

Ziming Yang, Aidong Yang*

Department of Engineering Science, University of Oxford, Parks Road, Oxford, OX1 3PJ, United Kingdom

aidong.yang@eng.ox.ac.uk

Abstract

A mathematical model for continuous Microbial Fuel Cells (MFCs) with a two-species anode biofilm was developed, taking either Mediator-Based Extracellular Electron Transfer (MET) or Direct Conduction-Based Extracellular Electron Transfer (DET) as the electron transfer mechanism. The results of numerical simulation revealed the impact of key parameters on biofilm composition and current generation, several optimal settings for current generation, and a number of trade-offs between the impacts of different factors. These findings offer new insights on multi-species biofilms governed by bioelectrochemical kinetics and mass and electron transfer, and have the potential to guide the design and operation of multi-species MFCs or other similar systems.

Keywords: Microbial fuel cells, Two-species biofilm modelling, Extracellular electron transfer, Biofilm composition; Current generation

1. Introduction

Climate change and other environmental issues associated with the use of fossil fuels call for urgent exploration of green and renewable energy options, including bioelectrochemical systems such as Microbial Fuel Cells (MFCs). An MFC relies on the biofilm attached on the anode to convey electrons from substrate. The microorganisms that produce electrons in the biofilm and carry out Extracellular Electron Transfer (EET) are called Electron Active Bacteria (EAB). There are two EETs widely accepted so far: Mediator-Based Extracellular Electron Transfer (MET) and Direct Conduction-Based Extracellular Electron Transfer (DET). In MET, electron transfer is realised through the reduction and the oxidisation of soluble mediators at the EAB and the anode surface, respectively. In DET, electrons are transferred directly from the EAB to the anode surface by exchanging with the conductive biofilm matrix.

While an anode biofilm may comprise a single microbial species, it has been proven that synergy exists in a multispecies biofilm which enhances electron transfer efficiency and power output compared to pure culture (Logan, 2009; Liu et al., 2017). A particular type of multispecies consortium is "fermenter-EAB", where the EAB achieves electrons generation and transportation, which relies on the Fermentative Bacteria (FB) as a fermenter to digest the primary substrate to an intermediate substrate that the EAB can consume.

In general, the spatial heterogeneity across a biofilm, the electron transfer mechanism and interactions between different microbial species ultimately determine the maximum power output of an MFC. However, the interplay between these factors under different process settings has not been systematically studied, particularly in the continuous MFCs. This study is therefore aimed at analysing the impact of key parameters on the composition of the multispecies anode biofilm and power generation with two alternative EET mechanisms in continuous MFCs.

2. Mathematical model

A 1-D, time-dependent model for an MFC with a two-species 'fermenter-EAB' biofilm is established. The model constructed only considers the growth and characteristics of the biofilm in the x-axis, which is perpendicular to the anode surface. The higher-dimensional aspect is not considered as biofilm heterogeneity was reported to be higher in the direction proportional to substratum than in the horizontal direction (Zhou et al., 2009). The whole model comprises three domains: bulk liquid, biofilm and electrode. The model focuses on the biofilm; planktonic biomass (i.e. biomass in the bulk liquid) is not considered. In the following, the main kinetics and conservation equations are presented.

2.1. Bulk liquid

It is assumed that the bulk liquid sub-domain is well-mixed and the volumetric flowrates of the inlet (feeding) and outlet streams are identical. For a soluble component, mass balance that includes diffusion and convection is applied:

$$\frac{dC_{S,B}}{dt} = -\frac{1}{V_B} \cdot n_{S,F} \cdot A_F + \frac{V_I}{V_B} \cdot (C_{S,in} - C_{S,B}) \tag{1}$$

where $C_{S,B}$, $C_{S,in}$ are the concentration of a soluble component in the bulk liquid and inlet flow, respectively; V_B is the volume of the bulk liquid; V_I is the volumetric flowrate of inlet/outlet flow; $n_{S,F}$ denotes the molar flux of a soluble component across the biofilm/bulk liquid interface, of which area is A_F. According to the Fick's law and the assumption of constant concentration gradient in the diffusion layer, $n_{S,F}$ is expressed as:

$$n_{S,F} = -D_{S,F} \frac{\partial C_{S,F}}{\partial x} |_{x=L_F} = (\frac{D_{S,B}}{L_D}) \cdot (C_{S,B} \cdot \varepsilon - C_{S,F} |_{x=L_F}) \tag{2}$$

where $D_{S,F}$ is the diffusivity of a soluble component in the biofilm; $C_{S,F}$ is the concentration of a soluble component in the biofilm; L_F, L_D are the thickness of biofilm and diffusion layer, respectively; the biofilm porosity, ε is introduced to modify and indicate the actual soluble concentration at the biofilm/bulk liquid interface.

2.2. Biofilm

2.2.1. Growth kinetics

For FB, its specific growth rate, μ_{FB} can be modelled by the Monod Equation:

$$\mu_{FB} = \mu_{max,FB} \cdot (C_{P,F}/(C_{P,F} + K_P)) \tag{3}$$

where $\mu_{max,FB}$ is the maximum specific growth rate for FB; $C_{P,F}$ represents the concentration of primary substrate in the biofilm and K_P denotes half-saturation constant.

For EAB, its specific growth rate is controlled by both the substrate concentration and the concentration of the Electron Acceptor (EA). In MET, the oxidised mediator (*Mo*) serves as the primary EA and the EAB's specific growth rate, $\mu_{EAB,M}$ therefore can be given by the double Monod equation (Bae and Rittmann, 1996):

$$\mu_{EAB,M} = \mu_{max,EAB} \cdot \frac{C_{I,F}}{C_{I,F} + K_I} \cdot \frac{C_{Mo,F}}{C_{Mo,F} + K_{Mo}} \tag{4}$$

where $\mu_{max,EAB}$ is the maximum specific growth rate for EAB; $C_{I,F}$ and $C_{Mo,F}$ represent the concentration of intermediate substrate and *Mo* in the biofilm, respectively; K_I and K_{Mo} correspond to the half-saturation constant for intermediate substrate and *Mo*, respectively. As for the DET mechanism, the only EA is the anode surface, which is non-soluble. In order to model the EAB's specific growth rate with DET, $\mu_{EAB,C}$, the Nernst-Monod equation is applied, using the anode potential, V_a to substitute the soluble EA's concentration (Marcus et al., 2007):

$$\mu_{EAB,C} = \mu_{max,EAB} \cdot \frac{C_{I,F}}{C_{I,F} + K_I} \cdot \frac{1}{1 + \exp(-F(V_a - E_{KA})/RT)} \tag{5}$$

where E_{KA} is the anode potential corresponding to the half $\mu_{max,EAB}$; F is the Faraday constant; R is the ideal gas constant; T is the operating temperature.

2.2.2. Mass balance

Mass balance for any soluble component in the biofilm (including primary substrate, intermediate substrate and for MET case, oxidised and reduced forms of the mediator) is:

$$\frac{\partial C_{S,F}}{\partial t} = \frac{\partial}{\partial x}(D_{S,F} \frac{\partial C_{S,F}}{\partial x}) - R_{S,F} \tag{6}$$

where $R_{S,F}$ represents the consumption rate of a soluble component in the biofilm. At the biofilm/bulk liquid interface, Eq. (2) is applied. The boundary condition for the anode/biofilm interface is established by stating the equality between the production rate (per unit anode surface area) and the diffusion flux (Picioreanu et al., 2007).

For biomass, its mass balance is (Wanner and Gujer, 1986; Marcus et al., 2007):

$$\frac{\partial C_{X,F}}{\partial t} + \frac{\partial(vC_{X,F})}{\partial x} = R_{X,F} \tag{7}$$

where $C_{X,F}$ is the biomass concentration of any type of microbial species in the biofilm; $R_{X,F}$ is the net reaction rate of biomass in the biofilm, which is the product of biomass yield from its corresponding substrate and $R_{S,F}$; v is the advective velocity due to the growth of the biofilm, which is determined by the sum of $R_{X,F}$ (Wanner and Gujer, 1986; Marcus et al., 2007).

2.3. Electrode

In the case of MET, the current density, i_M is proportional to the net reaction rate of the mediator conversion process at the anode surface, r_E, which itself is given by the Butler-Volmer equation:

$$r_E = k_a C_{Mr,F} \mid_{x=0} \exp((1-\beta)nFV_a/RT) - k_c C_{Mo,F} \mid_{x=0} \exp(-\beta nFV_a/RT) \tag{8}$$

where k_a, k_c are the rate constant for oxidisation and reduction processes, respectively; $C_{Mr,F} \mid_{x=0}$, $C_{Mo,F} \mid_{x=0}$ denote the concentration of reduced and oxidised forms of the mediator at the anode surface, respectively; β is the transfer coefficient; n is the number of electrons transferred per redox mediator reaction.

With DET, the current density i_C is obtained based on the electron conservation and Ohm's law (Marcus et al., 2007; Renslow et al., 2013):

$$k \frac{\partial^2 V_a}{\partial x^2} = F \cdot R_c \qquad\qquad\qquad (9)$$

where R_c is the electron generation rate via DET, which is proportional to the specific growth rate of EAB (see Eq. (5)).

2.4. Model implementation

The model is applied for the anodic biofilm with *Shewanella oneidensis* (as known as MR1) and *E. coli*. *E. coli* as a fermentor converts glucose to formate; the latter is treated as the only intermediate substrate to be utilised by MR1, the EAB in this case. All simulations were carried using COMSOL Multiphysics Software.

3. Results and discussion

3.1. The effect of feeding flowrate

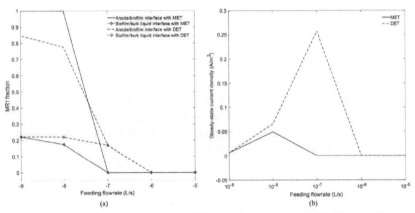

Figure 1 Impacts of the feeding flowrate. (a) MR1 fraction at the anode/biofilm interface (without 'diamond') and biofilm/bulk liquid interface (with 'diamond') via MET (solid line) and DET (dashed line) at the steady state; (b) Steady-state current density profiles with MET and DET.

As shown in Figure 1(a), with either MET or DET, there is more MR1 at the anode surface end of the biofilm than the end interfacing with the bulk liquid when flowrate is sufficiently low to allow MR1 to exist in the biofilm. In those cases, the combination of decreasing *Mo* (V_a for DET) and increasing glucose concentration weakens the competitiveness of MR1 from anode/biofilm interface, hence the level of MR1 fraction drops. The increase in the feeding flowrate generally leads to the decrease of MR1 fraction across the biofilm and eventually causes MR1 to disappear. The decline of MR1 is due to the dilution effect of a higher feeding flowrate, which results in a lower formate concentration that restricts the growth of MR1. On current generation, Figure 1(b) shows that current density in the case of DET is much higher compared to MET, which is due to the higher overall growth rate of MR1. However, the tendencies of steady-state current density change with the feeding flowrate are similar between the two cases: the current density initially rises as more formate is produced and subsequently descends due to the decrease in MR1 fraction. The above results suggest that biofilm composition and current density are affected by the trade-offs between substrate supply and dilution along with the changing feeding flowrate. The respective values of $1 \times 10^{-8} L / s$ and $1 \times 10^{-7} L / s$ for the flowrate with MET and DET are shown to be optimal for the maximization of the steady-state current density.

3.2. The effect of feed primary substrate (glucose) concentration

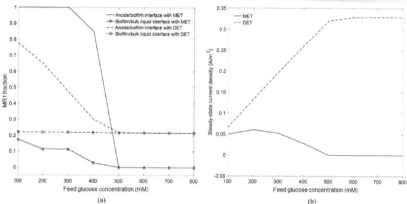

(a)   (b)

Figure 2 Impacts of the feed glucose concentration. (a) MR1 fraction at the anode/biofilm interface (without 'diamond') and biofilm/bulk liquid interface (with 'diamond') via MET (solid line) and DET (dashed line) at the steady state; (b) Steady-state current density profiles with MET and DET.

As shown in the Figure 2(a), for MET, overall MR1 fraction drops when the biofilm is fed with more concentrated glucose. There are two causes: (1) the specific growth rate of *E. coli* in the biofilm is promoted by reducing the glucose limitation. When glucose concentration is 500mM or higher, even the *E. coli* at the most remote location (i.e. anode/biofilm interface) grows faster than MR1 and eventually repels MR1 completely; (2) the specific growth rate of MR1 is restricted by the lower level of *Mo*, which will be illustrated in the following section. In the case of DET, the fraction of MR1 at the anode/biofilm interface has the similar declining trend with MET. It is noticeable, however, that the biofilm composition at the biofilm/bulk liquid interface almost remains constant. This is because of the identical specific growth rate of the two species at this interface (revealed by simulation results, not shown here). As mentioned in the *section 3.1*, the current generated via MET is determined by both biofilm composition and substrate supply. For feed glucose concentration, an optimal value corresponding to the maximum steady-state current density exists at 200mM in this case. With DET, Figure 2(b) shows that current density is primarily governed by the substrate concentration until it reaches a plateau.

3.3. The effect of initial concentration of Mo in the bulk liquid

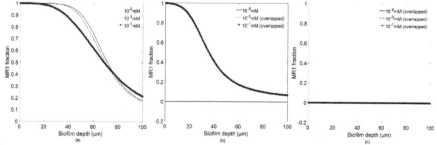

Figure 3 Impact of initial concentration of *Mo* in the bulk liquid on steady-state MR1 fraction, with the feed glucose concentration at (a) 100mM; (b) 300mM; and (c) 500mM.

The simulations with MET reveal that the impact of initial concentration of *Mo* in the bulk liquid on the steady-state biofilm composition varies with the values of the feed glucose concentration. As shown in the Figure 3(a) and (c), the overall biofilm composition is independent of the initial concentration of *Mo* in the bulk liquid when the level of the feed glucose concentration is either the lowest (i.e. 100mM) or the highest (i.e. 500mM). With the lowest feed glucose concentration, *Mo* is consumed slowly and thus the specific growth rate of MR1 is maintained and it is able to co-exist with *E. coli*. Conversely, *Mo* is exhausted rapidly in the case of the higher feed glucose concentration. Coupled with the faster specific growth rate of *E. coli* resulting from better substrate (glucose) supply, MR1 is repelled completely from the biofilm. When the 'middle' value of the feed glucose concentration (i.e. 300mM) is selected, the increase of the initial concentration of *Mo* in the bulk liquid can change the steady-state biofilm from the '*E. coli only*' type to the '*E. coli*-MR1 co-existence' type. The value of $1 \times 10^{-3} mM$ marks this transition, being the lowest initial level of *Mo* to be able to sustain MR1 in the biofilm.

4. Conclusion

A two-species, 'fermenter-EAB' anode biofilm, modelled in this work as part of a continuous MFC, was shown by our simulation studies to be shaped by a number of factors, including the kinetics of microbial growth and electrochemical reactions, mass and electron transfer mechanisms. The modelling outcomes particularly implied that the biofilm composition would change with the feeding flowrate, feed concentration of the primary substrate and the initial concentration of mediators in the bulk liquid. Our results also showed the trade-offs between the impacts of various factors, and the existence of optimal settings for the purpose of improving current generation.

Acknowledgement

The financial support from China Scholarship Council (CSC) to Z. Y. is greatly appreciated

References

Andrew Kato Marcus, Ce´sar I. Torres, Bruce E. Rittmann. 2007. "Conduction-Based Modeling of the Biofilm Anode of a Microbial Fuel Cell." *Biotechnology and Bioengineering* 98 (6): 1171–82.

Bae, Wookeun, and Bruce E. Rittmann. 1996. "A Structured Model of Dual-Limitation Kinetics." *Biotechnology and Bioengineering* 49 (6): 683–89.

Liu, Ting, Yang Yang Yu, Tao Chen, and Wei Ning Chen. 2017. "A Synthetic Microbial Consortium of Shewanella and Bacillus for Enhanced Generation of Bioelectricity." *Biotechnology and Bioengineering* 114 (3): 526–32.

Logan, Bruce E. 2009. "Exoelectrogenic Bacteria That Power Microbial Fuel Cells." *Nature Reviews Microbiology* 7 (5): 375–81.

Picioreanu, Cristian, Ian M Head, Krishna P Katuri, Mark C M van Loosdrecht, and Keith Scott. 2007. "A Computational Model for Biofilm-Based Microbial Fuel Cells." *Water Research* 41 (13): 2921–40.

Renslow, Ryan, Jerome Babauta, Andrew Kuprat, Jim Schenk, Cornelius Ivory, Jim Fredrickson, and Haluk Beyenal. 2013. "Modeling Biofilms with Dual Extracellular Electron Transfer Mechanisms." *Physical Chemistry Chemical Physics* 15 (44): 19262–83.

Wanner, O., and W. Gujer. 1986. "A Multispecies Biofilm Model." *Biotechnology and Bioengineering* 28 (3): 314–28.

Zhou, Xiao-Hong, Yu-Qin Qiu, Han-Chang Shi, Tong Yu, Miao He, and Qiang Cai. 2009. "A New Approach to Quantify Spatial Distribution of Biofilm Kinetic Parameters by in Situ Determination of Oxygen Uptake Rate (OUR)." *Environmental Science & Technology* 43 (3): 757–63.

Sauro Pierucci, Flavio Manenti, Giulia Bozzano, Davide Manca (Eds.)
Proceedings of the 30th European Symposium on Computer Aided Process Engineering
(ESCAPE30), May 24-27, 2020, Milano, Italy. © 2020 Elsevier B.V. All rights reserved.
http://dx.doi.org/10.1016/B978-0-12-823377-1.50267-6

Development of Systems Modelling Framework for Waste-to-Resource Transformation

Ivan Robles[a], Miao Guo[a, b, *]

[a] *Department of Chemical Engineering, Impeiral College London, SW7 2AZ, UK*

[b] *Department of Engineering, Strand Campus, King's College London, WC2R 2LS, UK*

miao.guo@kcl.ac.uk

Abstract

Due to complex composition e.g. carbohydrates, lipids, protein, lignin, cellulose and hemicellulose, organic fraction municipal solid waste (OFMSW) represent nutrient and carbon rich resources. Full utilisation of OFMSW resources requires a value chain transformation towards pro-active resource recovery. This study focuses on the waste value chain optimisation to recover value added products from OFMSW.

Our research presents a systems modelling approach, which integrates spatial data analyses, mixed integer linear programming (MILP) optimisation and technology performance evaluation to inform the waste-to-resource value chain design. Variation in OFMSW quantity and composition across the UK and over 600 existing anaerobic digestion (AD) operational plants in the UK have been accounted for in the model. Based on the 2018 UK land cover map, potential sites for new waste-recovery facilities have been identified and the transportation and logistics were modelled based on the network analyses of existing UK road transport infrastructures. Furthermore, OFMSW generation scenarios were constructed, where the probability was estimated based on OFMSW correlation with environmental variables. The optimisation problems were solved to provide insights into the economically optimal design of OFMSW-recovery value chains, which highlight the spatially-explicit solutions on technology choice, sizing, location, and logistics of AD and thermochemical treatment facilities.

Keywords: OFMSW, waste recovery, MILP, value chain optimisation, anaerobic digestion

1. Introduction

Global municipal solid waste (MSW) growth is projected to exceed 11 million tons per day (59%-68% organic fraction (OFMSW)) by 2100 under 'business as usual' and a significant amount (330km^3 per year) of municipal wastewater (WW) is generated. Increasing waste trends are particularly intense in less developed countries and contribute to resource stress, greenhouse gases and environmental degradation. The transition from a linear fossil-based economy to a circular bio-based economy offers a mechanism to tackle environmental changes and degradation.

In conventional waste management value chains, OFMSW and WW along with other waste streams have been regarded as by-products (carrying zero or low-value). In fact, OFMSW and WW streams are not only carbon-rich resources as energy carrier but also contain high nutrient values. The waste sector represents promising opportunities for resources to be converted to value-added products under circular economy. To exploit waste resource value requires a transformative value chain, which calls for robust projection of waste quantity and composition and waste recovery planning from whole systems perspectives. Efficient planning (e.g. sizing and logistics) and operation of waste recovery facilities requires continuous and consistent waste feedstock supply. However, it is complex to quantity waste feedstock due to highly varying composition and low traceability. These are dependent on spatially-explicit socio-economic factors and seasonally environmental variables. Despite the increasing interests in waste volume forecast by using material flow models, regression analysis, machine learning and artificial intelligence techniques, projection of waste composition remains open.

By far the most widespread resource recovery in the WW and OFMSW sector is anaerobic digestion (AD). The generated biogas i.e. carbon recovery, is often used for onsite combined-heat-and-power generation (CHP), but could be upgraded and injected into the natural gas grid (BtG), or used for methanol and biodegradable plastic production, or reformed to hydrogen. Other recovery technologies e.g. nutrient recovery and digestate utilization are also of interest. To maximize the waste resource recovery, existing AD facilities could be further optimized via systems design integrating biogas conversion with value-added carbon and nutrient resource recovery.

This study presents an OFMSW supply chain optimization model considering the existing AD plants and waste supply variability where the model application in UK case study is demonstrated.

2. Methodology

2.1. Spatial data analyses

Geographic Information Systems (GIS) is recognized as an efficient approach to analyze complex spatial phenomena and has been used to model various applications at multiple levels spanning from waste resource potential to conversion technologies. In this study, the UK was divided into 70 grid cells; ArcGIS v10.7 was applied to analyze spatial data to 1) map out OFMSW resource availability and existing AD facilities; 2) screen and identify the potential AD locations; 3) analyze networks and logistic data.

2.2. Deterministic optimization

For a given set of technology options and spatially explicit OFMSW resource distribution, this study aims to design the economic optimal strategies for technology integration, logistics and resource flows. A mixed integer linear programming (MILP) model is developed to solve the optimization problem.

The objective function (Eq. (1)) is to maximize the profit J, which is determined by the revenue (Rev^{Tot}), and the total costs including the capital costs (Cap^{Total}), operational costs (Opt^{ProDry}), and transport costs (Opt^{trans}).

$$J = Rev^{Tot} - Opt^{trans} - Opt^{ProDry} - Cap^{Total} \tag{1}$$

The transport cost is defined as Eq.(2), where variable $trans_{sp}^{Tot}$ denotes total transport costs for each chemical species present in waste stream sp. The total operational cost (Eq.(3)) is dependent on two variables i.e. operational costs of each technology Opt_{θ}^{Proc} and costs for drying digestate Opt_{g}^{Dry} in cell g. The operational costs of existing AD plant, new AD plants with BtG and CHP as well as post-treatment of digestate are determined by amount of products generated from resource recovery ($Prd_{\theta,sp}$) and operational costs ($\delta_{\theta,sp}^{op}$) of each technology θ (Eq. (4)). The total cost of digestate drying in each cell prior to being transported to post-treatment is defined as Eq.(5), where variable $Prd_{g,sp}$ represents chemical species produced in cell g. The total capital cost for new AD (JN) and posttreatment facilities (K) is defined in Eq.(6), where binary variable $y_{\theta,st}^{st}$ indicates the presence of a type/size (st) of a given technology (θ) and parameter δ_{st}^{cap} denotes the annualised capital costs for a given technology type st. As given in Eq. (7) the total revenue generated by selling the products is calculated by amount of products from waste recovery and unit price (δ_{sp}) of chemical specie sp.

$$Opt^{trans} = \Sigma_{sp\in\{W,D\}} \, trans_{sp}^{Tot} \qquad (2)$$

$$Opt^{ProDry} = \Sigma_{\theta\in\vartheta} Opt_{\theta}^{Proc} + \Sigma_{g\in G} Opt_{g}^{Dry} \qquad (3)$$

$$Opt_{\theta}^{Proc} = \Sigma_{sp} Prd_{\theta,sp}\delta_{\theta,sp}^{op} \, , \qquad (4)$$

$$Opt_{g}^{Dry} = Prd_{g,sp}\delta^{dry} \qquad (5)$$

$$Cap^{Total} = \Sigma_{\theta\in JN\cup K} \Sigma_{st\in St} \, y_{\theta,st}^{st} \, \delta_{st}^{cap} \qquad (6)$$

$$Rev^{Tot} = \Sigma_{sp\in Pr} \Sigma_{\theta\in\vartheta} Prd_{\theta,sp} \, \delta_{sp} \qquad (7)$$

A range of constraints have been introduced in the developed MILP model to bound the selection of technology locations, size and types and constrain transport network and resource and chemical species flows. The model was parameterized using the costs database we developed based on the publicly available information.

2.3. Stochastic optimization

A two-stage stochastic optimization model was developed to optimize the OFMSW supply chain under uncertainty, where Benders decomposition method was applied (Benders, 1962; Birge and Louveaux, 1988). Two sets of decision variables have been defined. The first-stage variables include selection of technology capacity and type and second-stage variables cover the flows of resource and chemical species and transport network. The objective function under master problem is to minimize the total capital costs of new AD plants (JN) as defined by Eq.(8), where STJ denotes the new AD subset of size/type. The new plant locations are constrained by Eq.(9) and Eq.(10), which define that only one location exists for any technology and new technologies can only be present in the potential cells identified by GIS analyses (binary parameter φ_g). The selection of size/type (st) of each technology (θ) is determined by binary variable $y_{\theta,st}^{st}$ (Eq.(11)). The continuous variable $Cpct_{sp,g,st}$ defines the capacity selected for each technology type and sp recovery, which is determined by given maximum capacity $(Cpt_{\theta,st,sp}^{max})$ of technology θ type st to recover sp and binary variable $z_{\theta,g,st}^{cpct}$ (Eq.(12)). By solving master problem, the optimal solution for capacity variable $(Cpct_{sp,g,st})$ is sent to the sub-problem as a constant. A set of logical constraints Eq.(13-15) were introduced to bound the capacity solution consistent with the type and location of technologies. In addition constraints were introduced in the master problem to bound 1) the operating capacity lower than the waste feedstock availability; 2) maximum landfilled waste not exceeding environmental regulation and non-negative.

$$Cap^{Total} = \Sigma_{\theta\in JN} \Sigma_{st\in STJ} y_{\theta,st}^{st} \, \delta_{st}^{cap} \qquad (8)$$

$$\Sigma_{g\in G} \, y_{\theta,g}^{\theta} \leq 1 \, , \, \theta \in JN \qquad (9)$$

$$y_{\theta,g}^{\theta} \leq \varphi_g, \, \theta \in JN, g \in G \qquad (10)$$

$$\sum_{st \in STJ} y_{\theta,st}^{st} = \sum_{g \in G} y_{\theta,g}^{\theta}, \ \theta \in JN \tag{11}$$

$$Cpct_{sp,g,st} = \sum_{\theta \in JN} Cpt_{\theta,st,sp}^{max} \ z_{\theta,g,st}^{cpct}, \ g \in G, sp \in \{elec, bgs\}, st \in STJ \tag{12}$$

$$z_{\theta,g,st}^{cpct} \leq y_{\theta,g}^{\theta} \qquad \theta \in JN, st \in STJ, \ g \in G \tag{13}$$

$$z_{\theta,g,st}^{cpct} \leq y_{\theta,st}^{st} \qquad , \theta \in JN, st \in STJ, \ g \in G \tag{14}$$

$$z_{\theta,g,st}^{cpct} \geq y_{\theta,st}^{st} + y_{\theta,g}^{\theta} - 1 \ , \theta \in JN, st \in STJ, \ g \in G \tag{15}$$

The objective function of sub-problem (Eq.(16)) is to maximize the profit, which is determined by the revenue, Rev^{Tot}, operational costs, Opt^{Pro}, transport costs Opt^{trans}, landfill cost, Lnd^{TX}, and the penalisation of the slack variable $Slck^{Pen}$. The landfill costs and slack variables are given in Eq.(17) and Eq.(18), where NP_g represents landfilled waste in cell g, δ^{LndTX} denotes the landfill tax, $Slck^{Pen}$ is the summation of all slack variables$(Slck_g)$ in a given cell. A set of constraints were introduced to constrain the technology capacities and resource flow balances and transport network.

$$J = Rev^{Tot} - Opt^{trans} - Opt^{Pro} - Lnd^{TX} - Slck^{Pen} \tag{16}$$

$$Lnd^{TX} = \sum_{g \in G} NP_g \ \delta^{LndTX} \tag{17}$$

$$Slck^{Pen} = \sum_{g \in G} Slck_g \ \mathcal{M} \tag{18}$$

3. Results

3.1. Spatial data analyses

OFMSW can be categorised as garden waste, food waste or other organic waste. The weighted averages waste composition produced under each categories in each authority were calculated (as shown in Figure 1) based on the 12-year data (April 1st 2006 to January 1st 2018) derived from (WDF, 2019). AD plants were categorised into five types based on the feedstock as shown in Figure 1.

To prevent issues with the installation of the new facilities, steep and elevated terrain was identified and excluded from the set of potential areas for plant construction (areas which have an incline larger than >10-15° and an elevation over 250m (Lovett et al., 2014). To achieve this, a digital elevation model (DEM) of the UK (EROS, 1996) is used. Numerous sample areas were constructed within each cell the elevation measurements from the DEM were extracted; only those under 250m were selected. The sensitive areas including forests, reserves, urban areas and water bodies are also identified and excluded as potential areas for waste-treatment site construction, where the CORINE land cover data were used. As plotted in Figure 2, the locations of the existing AD facilities correspond to feasible regions denoted by the black color, which verify the spatial data analyses. The road transport network was developed based on the UK road map obtained from Ordnance Survey (OS OpenData, 2019).

3.2. Deterministic optimization results

To obtain an optimal configuration of the technologies and distribution for OFMSW processing, the model presented in Section 2.2 was solved using the PuLP 1.6.9 library for Python 3.5. The optimal solution for baseline (waste generation remaining constant in future) is plotted out in Figure 3 as an example. Our results suggested that the optimal solutions are sensitive to the quantity of waste produced in the future, where three scenarios were constructed to represent waste generation ranging from 50% to 150% of the 2018 level. For the baseline scenario (100% of 2018 level), the total cost for the system operation including annualized capital costs is 155.7 Million £/year, while the total revenue for selling the products made is 179.85 million £/year. This leads to a whole system profit of 24.1 million £/year and a specific profit of 13.7 £/tonne of waste processed. The cost of transporting waste and digestate, is relatively small (1.79 Million £/year) in comparison to operational and capital inputs for AD facilities. The ratio of OPEX to CAPEX decrease with the increase in future waste generation (4.59:1, 3.89:1 and 2.96:1 for 50%, 100% and 150% waste generation scenarios respectively).

3.3. Stochastic optimization results

We developed a projection model for waste generation considering environmental variables and building OFMSW scenarios for stochastic optimization. The effects of technology minimum capacity and landfilled waste threshold and landfill tax rates have been investigated. Our previous research has identified a strong correlation between temperature and OFMSW generation in the UK (Adeogba et al., 2019). In this study, based on the correlation between OFMSW and temperature, we estimated OFMSW production throughout the year 2018 with an equal time spacing of 1.2 million sample points (Figure 4A); a histogram with 5000 bins was then constructed to represent the probability distribution functions (Figure 4b) and used to calculate the probability of OFMSW generation scenarios (Figure 4 c) for stochastic optimization modelling.

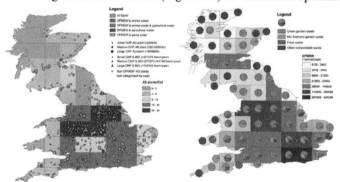

Figure 1 Characterization of anaerobic digestion plants which use OFMSW as feedstock in Great Britain and percentage category of OFMSW per area

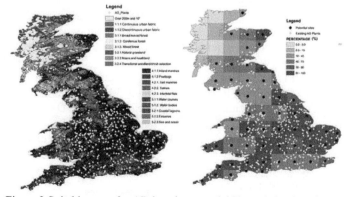

Figure 2 Suitable areas for AD locations overlaid by existing locations

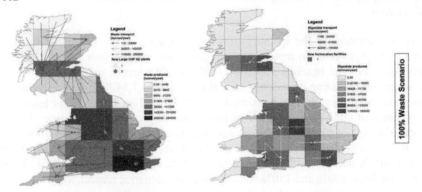

Figure 3 Spatially-explicit new technologies solutions and resource flow

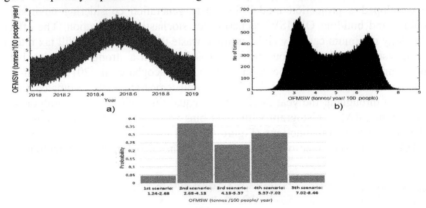

Figure 4: a) 2018 OFMSW estimation. b) OFMSW generation histogram (1.2 million samples and 5000 bins). c) probability for the 5 waste scenarios

Our modelling results suggested that i) waste generation variability has a negative impacts on OFMSW value-chain economic performances with profit decrease to 11.49 £/tonne OFMSW (13.78 £/tonne OFMSW in deterministic optimization). ii) despite that minimum capacity constraints avoid the competition of AD facilities for OFMSW supply, this leads to a cost-ineffective value chain design and loss in waste recovery. iii) constraining the maximum waste landfilled decrease profit; iv) 2018 landfill tax would lead to an optimal value chain design with 1.1% of the OFMSW ending in landfill.

References

Adeogba E, Barty P, O'Dwyer E, Guo M. Waste-to-Resource Transformation: Gradient Boosting Modelling for Organic Fraction Municipal Solid Waste Projection. 2019.

Benders, J. F. (1962) 'Partitioning procedures for solving mixed-variables programming problems', Numerische Mathematik, 4(1), pp. 238–252.

Birge, J. and Louveaux, F. (1988) 'A multicut algorithm for two-stage stochastic linear programs', European Journal of Operational Research, 34(3), pp. 384–392.

WDF, 2019. Data on organic fraction municipal solid waste. Waste Data Flow, Available at: http://www.wastedataflow.org/ (Accessed: 5 June 2019).

Lovett, A., Sünnenberg, G., Dockerty, T., 2014. The availability of land for perennial energy crops in Great Britain. GCB Bioenergy 6, 99–107.

EROS, 1996. 30 arc-second DEM of Europe (GTOPO30). U.S. Geological Survey's Center for Earth Resources Observation and Science (EROS)

OS OpenData, 2019. OS Open Roads. Ordenance Survey.

Sauro Pierucci, Flavio Manenti, Giulia Bozzano, Davide Manca (Eds.)
Proceedings of the 30th European Symposium on Computer Aided Process Engineering
(ESCAPE30), May 24-27, 2020, Milano, Italy. © 2020 Elsevier B.V. All rights reserved.
http://dx.doi.org/10.1016/B978-0-12-823377-1.50268-8

Time Scale Analysis and Optimization of a Continuous Microbial Bioprocess

Peter Sinner, Christoph Herwig, Julian Kager,[*]

Institute of Chemical, Environmental and Bioscience Engineering, Technische Universität Wien, Gumpendorfer Straße 1a, 1060 Vienna, Austria
julian.kager@tuwien.ac.at

Abstract

Continuous bioprocesses are widely used for quantitative strain characterization and industrial fermentations aiming for high space time yields and constant productivity. However, due to the presence of different biochemical reaction dynamics these processes can exhibit slow system behavior under certain conditions. This leads to extended start up times to reach a targeted steady state and impedes to detect and act on process disturbances. We applied a model-based approach to determine the time scale of a continuous *Corynebacterium glutamicum* bioprocess utilizing a lignocellulosic waste stream in dependence of operational parameters. Time scales were derived by Jacobian linearization of the nonlinear process model and used as an input for multi-objective process optimization. Hereby, operational points with high productivity as well as fast system response upon process disturbances could be obtained. In this way, model-based time scale analysis delivers valuable input for the design of efficient and robust bioprocesses.

Keywords: Bioprocess, dynamic modelling, time scale analysis, multi-objective optimization

1. Introduction

Model-based methods enable a targeted development of bioprocesses. Especially for continuous processes, quantitative understanding is important to select stable operational points. Besides of its relevance in biomanufacturing, continuous cultivation processes are also an important experimental method for the characterization of microbial strains. A three-residence-times rule of thumb is commonly used to reach a hypothetical steady state approximation of 95 % and to derive the corresponding process characteristics. However, this assumption is based on non-reactive tracer experiments and is only proven to be applicable to non-autocatalytic reactions (Heinrichs and Schneider, 1980; Zhang et al., 2007). For different chemical (Zhang et al., 2007) and biochemical systems (Lachmann and Schneider, 1983; Sonnleitner and Hahnemann, 1994) slow system behaviour was reported in the literature, showing a higher number of hydraulic residence times needed to reach a targeted steady state. Methods for time scale analysis based on eigenvalue analysis are well-established in the fields of systems biology (Kremling, 2013) and chemical engineering (Isaac et al., 2013). However, time scale analysis is so far not systematically included in bioprocess design applications. To show the potential and possible effects of time scale analysis within bioprocess development, a continuous *C. glutamicum* bioprocess utilizing the lignocellulosic waste stream spent sulfite liquor is analyzed in this work. *C. glutamicum* is a platform organism with high industrial importance and a wide potential product spectrum (Becker et al., 2018). Time scales of this example process are analyzed in dependence of operational parameters and used as input for process design. In the first part of this work, the applied process model and the methodology for time scale analysis and model-based process design are outlined. Then, the effect of operational parameters on the time scale is shown. The practical relevance of time scale analysis for bioprocess design applications is discussed subsequently, with a focus on system response upon process disturbances.

2. Material and Methods

2.1. Dynamic Process Model

A dynamic process model describing the growth of wild-type *C. glutamicum* ATCC 13032 on spent sulfite liquor was used for simulations. The spent sulfite liquor composition of this study is typical for softwood pulping (Niemelä and Alén, 1999). A general vector form of a dynamic system of mass concentrations $\underline{c}$, inputs $\underline{u}$, parameters $\underline{\theta}$ and disturbances $\underline{d}$ is shown in Eq. (1).

$$\underline{\dot{c}} = \underline{f}(\underline{c}, \underline{u}, \underline{d}, \underline{\theta}, t) \tag{1}$$

The model describes biomass (X) growth on the two main carbon substrates glucose (S_1) and mannose (S_2), as well as conversion of xylose (S_3) without detectable contribution to biomass formation. The ODEs describing mass concentrations (g L^{-1}) of biomass c_X and sugar states $c_{S,1}$, $c_{S,2}$, $c_{S,3}$ in a CSTR with constant reactor volume V_R (L) are shown in Eq. (2) and Eq. (3).

$$\dot{c}_X = \left(\sum_{i=1}^{3} q_{S,i} Y_{XS,i} - \frac{F_{in}}{V_R} \right) c_X \tag{2}$$

$$\dot{c}_{S,i} = \frac{F_{in}}{V_R} \left(c_{S,i,in} - c_{S,i} \right) - q_{S,i} c_X \tag{3}$$

Sugar uptake $q_{S,i}$ (gs,i gx^{-1} h^{-1}) is governed by competitive interaction between different sugars and a non-competitive inhibitory effect (inhibition constant $K_{I,SSL}$ in g L^{-1}) of spent sulfite liquor concentration $c_{I,SSL}$ (g L^{-1}), see Eq. (4). Biomass growth and sugar uptake are linked by constant yield coefficients $Y_{XS,i}$ (gx gs,i^{-1}). The model parameters were previously determined using experimental data (Sinner et al., 2019). All calculations were performed in MATLAB R2017b (The MathWorks, Inc., United States).

$$q_{S,i} = q_{Smax,i} \frac{c_{S,i}}{K_{S,i}(1+\sum_{j=1,j\neq i}^{3} \frac{c_{S,j}}{K_{S,j}})+c_{S,i}} \frac{K_{I,SSL}}{K_{I,SSL}+c_{I,SSL}} \tag{4}$$

2.2. Time Scale Analysis

For time scale analysis, the Jacobian matrix J is used to linearize the nonlinear vector function f around a steady state operating point of interest, see Eq. (5). Hereby, $\underline{c}'$ denotes a deflection of the process variables around the steady state values $\underline{c}_{eq}$. The entries j_{ij} of the Jacobian are calculated according to Eq. (6).

$$\underline{\dot{c}}' = J\underline{c}' \tag{5}$$

$$j_{ij} = \left. \frac{\partial f_i}{\partial c_j} \right|_{c=c_{eq}} \tag{6}$$

By decomposing the Jacobian its eigenvalues λ_n are derived. The absolute value of the real part (*Re*) of the eigenvalue describes the reciprocal time scale τ_n (h) of a mode, see Eq. (7). The largest time scale τ_{max} was selected as the dominating time scale among τ_n.

$$\tau_n = |Re(\lambda_n)|^{-1} \tag{7}$$

As a reference, hydraulic residence times needed to approach a steady state with a certain accuracy were calculated numerically by nonlinear model simulations.

2.3. Model-based Process Optimization

Optimal process inputs for dilution rate (D) and spent sulfite liquor concentration in the feed medium ($c_{I,SSL}$) were selected using a multi-objective optimization procedure. Biomass space time yield was defined as a typical objective to be maximized in bioprocess development, see Eq (8). In addition to that, time scale of the system, see Eq (9), was included as an additional objective function to obtain regions with high biomass productivity and fast equilibration kinetics. Time scales at operating points of interest were scaled by the maximum time scale of the process design space.

$$\min_{D,c_{I,SSL}} J_1 = -c_{X,steady\ state}D \tag{8}$$

$$\min_{D,c_{I,SSL}} J_2 = \frac{\tau_{max,operating\ point}}{\tau_{max,design\ space}} \tag{9}$$

Pareto-optimal solutions were computed using a genetic algorithm (gamultiobj, MATLAB R2017b) based on NSGA-II (Deb et al., 2002).

3. Results and Discussion

3.1. Influence of Process Parameters and Reaction Kinetics on Time Scale

Time scales were determined based on eigenvalue analysis of the linearized process model. Figure 1 shows the effect of two main operational parameters for CSTR processes, dilution rate and feed concentration, on the time scale of the analyzed process. Each Jacobian eigenvalue corresponds to the time scale of a mode, as depicted by dashed lines in Figure 1. The mode with the largest time scale at a certain operating point dominates the time scale of the process in the respective region, as can be seen by comparison to the numerically calculated residence times needed to approach a steady state in Figure 1 (solid line). When the dilution rate of the CSTR is approaching the washout of the system, in the region around 0.05 h^{-1} in Figure 1, time scale is considerably increasing. This is in accordance with the phenomenon of critical slowing down of nonlinear systems close to phase transitions (Jähnig and Richter, 1976; Lachmann and Schneider, 1983).

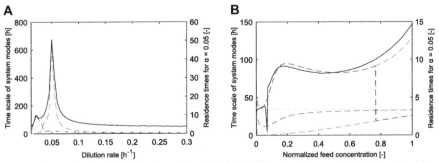

Figure 1: Eigenvalue based time scales of modes (dashed lines) and numerically derived residence times (solid line) needed to approach steady state with α = 0.05 in dependence of CTSR operational parameters dilution rate (A) and feed concentration (B).

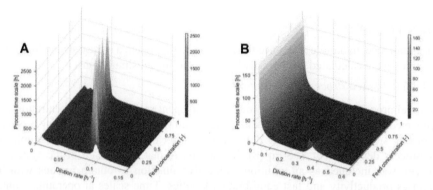

Figure 2: Eigenvalue based process time scale in dependence of CSTR operational parameters dilution rate and normalized feed concentration for different reaction systems. A: Multi-substrate process (spent sulfite liquor). B: Single carbon substrate process without inhibitory effects.

The concentration of spent sulfite liquor in the feed influences the time scale of the process as well. Different substrate and inhibitor levels can shift the boundary of the CSTR washout equilibrium and thereby the region of slow time scales. In general, it can be stated that residence times significantly above the commonly applied three-residence-times rule of thumb are necessary to approach a steady state in most operational regions of the studied CSTR process. 10 residence times are sufficient for a wide range of the design space. However, close to the washout state up to 100 theoretical residence times are necessary to fully reach a steady state. Equilibration of the CSTR bioprocess is not governed by hydraulic equilibration but by the time scale of the biochemical reaction system. In Figure 2 A the process time scale is visualized for the entire process design space, depicting critical slowing down in the region close to washout. In comparison to that, a single substrate CSTR without inhibitory effects as described in Doran (2013) is shown in Figure 2 B. For this simpler reaction system, lower time scales and a less pronounced slowing down close to washout can be observed. The type of underlying reaction mechanisms, such as substrate competition, strongly influences the reaction velocity of a bioprocess, making time scale analysis a necessity to determine steady state stabilization timepoints during strain and bioprocess characterization.

3.2. Time Scale Analysis in Model-based Optimization

Time scale analysis can be included as an objective function within an optimization problem. By defining a multi-objective optimization problem, maximum space time yields for biomass productivity and minimal time scales for fast system responses were defined for the examined bioprocess. In Figure 3 A the process design space based on the sum of equally weighted objective function values is shown. In accordance to the critical slowing down of the system, undesirably high objective function values are obtained close to washout equilibrium. Washout regions are excluded from the process design space. To obtain optimal operating conditions among the conflicting objective functions for high biomass formation rates and fast system response, Pareto optimal solutions were computed by a genetic algorithm, see Figure 3 B. A time scale threshold below 80 h was set as constraint. Thereby, a dilution rate of 0.018 h^{-1} and a normalized spent sulfite liquor feed concentration of 0.51 were selected as optimal process parameters yielding a CSTR bioprocess with predicted 0.70 g L^{-1} h^{-1} biomass space time yield and a time scale of 68.8 h. This corresponds to 8.4 residence times needed to reach a steady state when simulating the nonlinear process.

3.3. Dynamic Response to Process Disturbances

The dynamic behavior during CSTR process start up as well as upon process disturbances was analyzed for the operating point optimized in section 3.2. Variability in lignocellulosic raw material characteristics is an important challenge for industrial biotechnology (Kenney et al., 2013). Therefore, the transitory behavior after disturbances in the substrate feed composition (25 %) is simulated for the optimized (dilution rate 0.018 h^{-1}, normalized feed concentration 0.51, productivity 0.70 g L^{-1} h^{-1}) as well as for a time-scale suboptimal but equally productive operational point (dilution rate 0.018 h^{-1}, normalized feed concentration 0.84, productivity 0.71 g L^{-1} h^{-1}). The startup phase until steady state and behavior after disturbance in the feed composition are displayed in Figure 4 A for the biomass and B for the substrate concentration. The optimized operational point (black line) reaches its initial steady state faster than the operational point with comparable productivity (grey line). Also, its response upon process disturbances and the subsequent return to its targeted operational point is considerably faster. This shows that time scale information can be used to define process conditions leading to a stable and productive process.

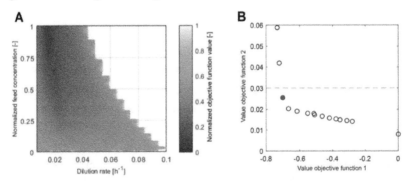

Figure 3: Multi-objective bioprocess optimization. A: Projection of surface plot of normalized sum of objective function value for equally weighted J_1 (productivity) and J_2 (time scale) in dependence of dilution rate and normalized feed concentration. B: Pareto-optimal solutions (black, circle) for objective functions J_1 and J_2 with maximum time scale threshold of 80 h (dashed lined), the selected point is highlighted (filled circle).

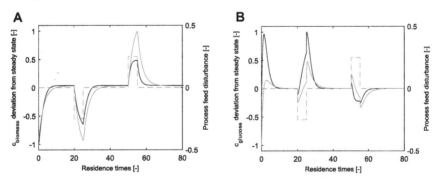

Figure 4: Dynamic response of CTSR states (left axis) upon process start up and subsequent disturbances in the substrate feed concentration level of glucose (dashed line, right axis) for the optimized operational point (black line) and a time scale suboptimal but equally productive operational point (grey line). A: Scaled biomass state deviation. B: Scaled carbon substrate state (glucose) deviation.

4. Conclusions

Time scale analysis delivered valuable insights into the dynamics of a wild-type *C. glutamicum* bioprocess utilizing lignocellulosic waste as a substrate. It could be shown that a high amount of residence times can be necessary to approach a steady state under certain operational parameters. This has implications for CSTR cultivations for strain characterization as well as industrial operations subject to process disturbances due to raw material fluctuations. Multi-objective optimization was performed to select operational points combining high productivity with fast steady state convergence. Time scale analysis is a straightforward, quantitative methodology and its inclusion within process design and development can help to correctly plan strain characterization experiments and to determine robust process conditions.

Acknowledgements

This project has received funding from the Bio Based Industries Joint Undertaking under the European Union's Horizon 2020 research and innovation program under grant agreement No 790507 (iFermenter).

References

J. Becker, C. M. Rohles, C. Wittmann, 2018, Metabolically engineered Corynebacterium glutamicum for bio-based production of chemicals, fuels, materials, and healthcare products, Metab. Eng., 50, 122-141

K. Deb, A. Pratap, S. Agarwal, T. Meyarivan, 2002, A fast and elitist multiobjective genetic algorithm: NSGA-II, IEEE Trans. Evol. Comput., 6 (2), 182-197

P. M. Doran, 2013, Chapter 14 - Reactor Engineering, In P. M. Doran (Ed.), Bioprocess Engineering Principles (Second Edition), London, UK, Academic Press, 761-852

M. Heinrichs, F. W. Schneider, 1980, On the Approach to Steady States of Reacting Systems in the Continuous Stirred Tank Reactor, Ber. Bunsenges. Phys. Chem., 84 (9), 857-865

B. J. Isaac, A. Parente, C. Galletti, J. N. Thornock, P. J. Smith, L. Tognotti, 2013, A Novel Methodology for Chemical Time Scale Evaluation with Detailed Chemical Reaction Kinetics, Energy Fuels, 27 (4), 2255-2265

F. Jähnig, P. H. Richter, 1976, Fluctuations in spatially homogeneous chemical steady states, J. Chem. Phys, 64 (11), 4645-4656

K. L. Kenney, W. A. Smith, G. L. Gresham, T. L. Westover, 2013, Understanding biomass feedstock variability, Biofuels, 4 (1), 111-127

A. Kremling, 2013, Systems biology: mathematical modeling and model analysis, Boca Raton, USA, CRC Press Taylor & Francis Group

H. Lachmann, F. W. Schneider, 1983, Phenomenon of slowing down in the autocatalytic trypsinogen to trypsin conversion in a continuous-flow stirred-tank reactor, J. Am. Chem. Soc., 105 (9), 2898-2900

K. Niemelä, R. Alén, 1999, Characterization of Pulping Liquors, In E. Sjöström & R. Alén (Eds.), Analytical Methods in Wood Chemistry, Pulping, and Papermaking, Berlin and Heidelberg, Springer, 193-231

P. Sinner, J. Kager, S. Daume, C. Herwig, 2019, Model-based Analysis and Optimisation of a Continuous Corynebacterium glutamicum Bioprocess Utilizing Lignocellulosic Waste, IFAC-PapersOnLine, 52 (26), 181-186

B. Sonnleitner, U. Hahnemann, 1994, Dynamics of the respiratory bottleneck of Saccharomyces cerevisiae, J. Biotechnol., 38 (1), 63-79

M. Zhang, T. W. Karjala, B. W. S. Kolthammer, 2007, Delayed Dynamics of Polymer Properties in Continuous Stirred Tank Polymerization Reactors, Ind. Eng. Chem. Res., 46 (18), 5922-5935

Sauro Pierucci, Flavio Manenti, Giulia Bozzano, Davide Manca (Eds.)
Proceedings of the 30th European Symposium on Computer Aided Process Engineering
(ESCAPE30), May 24-27, 2020, Milano, Italy. © 2020 Elsevier B.V. All rights reserved.
http://dx.doi.org/10.1016/B978-0-12-823377-1.50269-X

Integrated Design of Biopharmaceutical Manufacturing Processes: Operation Modes and Process Configurations for Monoclonal Antibody Production

Sara Badr,[a] Kozue Okamura,[a] Nozomi Takahashi,[a] Vera Ubbenjans,[b] Haruku Shirahata,[a] Hirokazu Sugiyama[a*]

[a]*Department of Chemical System Engineering, The University of Tokyo, 7-3-1 Hongo, Bunkyo-ku, 113-8656, Tokyo, Japan*
[b]*Faculty of Mechanical Engineering, RWTH Aachen University, Kackertstraße 9, 52072 Aachen, Germany*
sugiyama@chemsys.t.u-tokyo.ac.jp

Abstract

The market for monoclonal antibodies (mAb)s is rapidly expanding. They are however expensive, with complicated lengthy production processes. Process models for two bottleneck operating units up- and downstream of the production chain are presented. The models are validated using pilot scale and experimental literature data. Dynamic simulations of batch, continuous, and mixed mode operations are used to compare economic performance and productivity. A qualitative discussion of risk factors and possible operational hurdles is presented. Results show that continuous operations have a significant advantage in terms of processing times, but not regarding operating costs. To realize a cost advantage, careful consideration of process conditions and parameters is required. These simulations can be used to map the design space and show the range of favourable operating modes and conditions in a thorough sensitivity analysis study.

Keywords: Process design, Continuous operation, Techno-economic assessment, Upstream, Downstream

1. Introduction

Monoclonal antibodies (mAb)s are dominating the biopharmaceutical market, which is the fastest growing sector in the pharmaceutical industry (Butler and Meneses-Acosta, 2012; Walsh, 2018). They are used to treat, among others, certain types of cancer and auto-immune diseases and often with less side effects than available alternative treatments. The market for monoclonal antibodies has been rapidly expanding and is expected to double again over the next five years (Grilo and Mantalaris, 2019). These drug products are often expensive and have complicated lengthy production processes. To facilitate the expansion of the mAb market, to face the competition from biosimilars, and to ensure the availability of the required demand volume, the production process needs to be optimized to allow for higher production flexibility and lower costs. The production of mAbs is typically conducted through upstream cell cultivation processes and downstream purification processes to obtain the desired mAb product. Figure 1 shows a typical mAb production process.

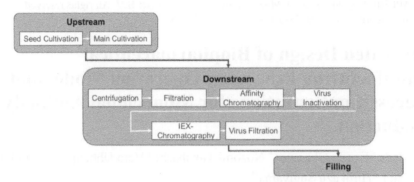

Figure 1: Typical mAb upstream cultivation and downstream purification processes

Generally, continuous production of biopharmaceuticals can offer significant advantages in terms of increased production efficiency. However, continuous production can also suffer from higher operational problems. Many factors affect the performance of the production process. This work aims to explore the available design options and map favourable production modes at different production scales and sizes. Process models are developed and validated with experimental data from literature and pilot scale runs in Japan. Two process units: the main cultivation unit, and the capture chromatography unit are chosen as the main focus of this work. These units represent bottleneck operations in terms of time and cost requirements. Dynamic simulations of batch, continuous, and mixed mode operations are used to compare economic performance and productivity. The impact of different process configurations and operating modes is evaluated in terms of operating costs and production time with a qualitative discussion of risk factors and possible operational hurdles.

2. Process modelling and simulation

Upstream processes comprise activities of cell cultivation. Three cultivation modes are commonly employed: conventional batch cultivation; fed-batch, where nutrients are fed throughout the production batch to maintain glucose concentrations thus increasing batch periods and productivity; and perfusion mode where the cultivation media is constantly fed and the reactor output is removed at the same rate with cell retention in the system achieving continuous operation. Multi-column processes, e.g. periodic counter current chromatography (PCC) with alternating column loading and regeneration stages can be used to simulate continuous flow in downstream capture chromatography processes. Simulated moving bed (SMB) operation can reduce the required number of columns to two (Angarita et al., 2015; Karst et al., 2018). Interconnected columns can thus provide longer loading times and higher column utilizations.

Production data has been obtained from a pilot scale research facility in Japan for the production of mAbs from Chinese hamster ovary (CHO) cells. Different models for the large-scale cultivation and chromatography have been fitted against the production data and the appropriate models were selected and further validated with more experimental data from literature. The obtained parameters were then used to simulate and assess further production scenarios.

2.1. Cultivation models

Cultivation models were developed based on mass balances of key process components and Monod type model for cell growth and death rates as previously presented in literature

(Kornecki and Strube, 2018; Xing et al., 2010). The models were adjusted based on pilot scale fed-batch production data and then validated with perfusion mode experimental data from Xu and Chen (2016) and from Zhang et al. (2015), which employed a temperature downshift within the process operation. Equations (1-7) show the perfusion model equations used:

$$\frac{d(VX_V)}{dt} = (\mu - \mu_d)VX_V - F_{bleed}X_V \tag{1}$$

$$\frac{d(VP)}{dt} = Q_P VX_V - (F_{harvest} + F_{bleed})P \tag{2}$$

$$\frac{d(V[GLC])}{dt} = -\left(\frac{\mu - \mu_d}{Y_{X_V/glc}} + m_{glc}\right)VX_V + F_{in}C_{in} \mp F_{suppl}C_{suppl} \\ - (F_{harvest} + F_{bleed})[GLC] \tag{3}$$

$$\frac{d(V[LAC])}{dt} = Y_{lac/glc}VX_V - (F_{harvest} + F_{bleed})[LAC] \tag{4}$$

$$\frac{d(V)}{dt} = F_{in} + F_{suppl} - F_{harvest} + F_{bleed} \tag{5}$$

$$\mu = \mu_{max}\left(\frac{[GLC]}{K_{glc}+[GLC]}\right)\left(\frac{KI_{lac}}{KI_{lac}+[LAC]}\right) \tag{6}$$

$$\mu_d = k_d\left(\frac{[LAC]}{KD_{lac}+[LAC]}\right)\left(\frac{KD_{glc}}{KD_{glc}+[GLC]}\right) \tag{7}$$

where, X_V is the viable cell density and V is the culture volume. F_{bleed}, $F_{harvest}$, F_{in}, and F_{suppl} are the bleed, harvest, main, and supplementary feed flows rates, respectively. P, $[GLC]$, and $[LAC]$ represent the antibody product, glucose and lactate concentrations, respectively. C_{in} and C_{suppl} are glucose concentrations in the main and supplementary feed streams, respectively. μ and μ_d are cell growth and death rates respectively, while μ_{max} and k_d are their corresponding maximum values. Y is the yield coefficient, where $Y_{x/y}$ for example represents the change in the value of x with respect to variations in values of y. m_{glc}, KI_{lac}, K_{glc}, KD_{lac}, KD_{glc} are the Monod model parameters representing the glucose maintenance coefficient, the lactose and glucose half maximum rate concentrations for cell growth and cell death, respectively.

The pilot facility implemented single-use equipment for its runs. Changeover time was therefore calculated to be 1 day and changeover costs represented the costs of new reactor bags used. Run durations were assumed to be 7, 14, and 60 days for batch, fed-batch, and perfusion operations, respectively. The operating cost was calculated as the cost of media (basal and feed) and utilities (water, gas, and electricity) in addition to changeover costs (cost of reactor bags).

2.2. Capture chromatography models

The lumped kinetic model was used for the chromatography column (Felinger and Guiochon, 2004; Guélat et al., 2016). Equations (8-9) show the model equations:

$$\varepsilon\frac{\partial c_i}{\partial t} + (1-\varepsilon)\frac{\partial q_i}{\partial t} + u_{sf}\frac{\partial c_i}{\partial x} = u_{sf}d_{ax}\frac{\partial^2 c_i}{\partial x^2} \tag{8}$$

$$\frac{\partial q_i}{\partial t} = k_m \left(q_i^{eq} - q_i \right) \tag{9}$$

where, c_i and q_i are the concentrations of component i in the mobile liquid phase and in the resin, respectively. ε is the total porosity. x is the distance travelled along the column length, and u_{sf} is the superficial velocity. d_{ax} is the axial dispersion coefficient. k_m is the lumped mass transfer coefficient, while q_i^{eq} is the equilibrium concentration of component i in the resin.

Model parameters were fitted using data obtained from the pilot scale facility. Optimal superficial velocities and column lengths are determined based on input conditions from upstream operations in terms of total volume to be treated and product titer. In the pilot facility, approximately 200 loadings are assumed per column before it is disposed of. The required cost of resin is then accordingly calculated. Operating time for batch columns include: loading, washing, elution, and regeneration. Multiple column operations (PCC and SMB) take into account the parallel execution of the columns, but add the interconnected loading time.

3. Results and discussion

Figure 2 shows the model fit to two experimental perfusion runs. The figure shows the viable cell density, Glucose and lactate concentrations, in addition to the mAb product. In the experiment of Zhang et al. (2015) the total produced mAb was reported, while in the experiment of Xu and Chen (2016), the produced titer. Zhang et al. (2015) implemented a temperature shift in the experiment. Lowering temperatures in perfusion culture to inhibit cell growth has been shown to enhance productivity. The model developed and used here is independent of operating conditions. Therefore, three different phases are modelled for such an operation, the initial batch phase, the initial growth phase in perfusion mode, and the production phase after a temperature downshift. Model performance is reported independently for each phase. The model results match well to the experimental values, especially for viable cell density and produced mAb concentrations/amounts. Lactate concentrations are not well modelled in the perfusion growth phase though. Nevertheless, the fed-batch model (fitted to the pilot scale data) performed better for lactate prediction yielding an R^2 value of 0.75.

Figure 3 shows the simulated results of a comparison of the different cultivation modes in terms of operating costs and production time in a 200 L reactor. Perfusion simulation assumed conditions closer to those presented by Xu and Chen (2016), which resulted in a higher titer compared to Zhang et al. (2015). No scale-up effects were assumed in this work. Perfusion mode shows a definite advantage in terms of productivity. However, due to the higher costs of media in perfusion, it can also lead to higher costs with longer operation times as compared to the fed-batch operation. Further analysis of this result can show the sensitivity of the produced results to operating conditions and model assumptions.

Figure 4 shows the results of the comparison of batch and a 3-column PCC operation of chromatography columns in terms of the cost of resin needed and the processing time for a small, pilot and large-scale operation at an inlet titer of 3 g/L. PCC columns were assumed to be one third of the length of the batch. The higher column utilization observed in PCC can be seen at pilot and larger scales as benefits in operating costs. Continuous column operation once again shows a major advantage in processing time.

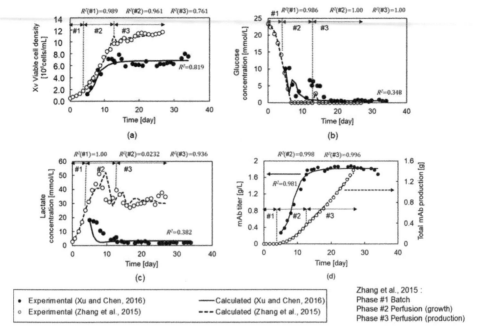

Figure 2: Model fitting results to perfusion experiments form Xu and Chen (2016) and Zhang et al. (2015)

Since column dimensions were not changed among scales, the processing time/g-mAb remains the same. The total processing time will then accordingly change with the scale; or the cost can change as more columns become needed at larger scales.

For the operation of an integrated continuous process, flowrates and productivities of upstream and downstream units need to be unified. Intermediate buffer tanks will be required to maintain flexibility, or in the case of implementing hybrid mode operations. Considerations of operational difficulties might also be encountered at larger scales for continuous operation. In cultivation mode, clogging might impede longer operation times, while in chromatography valve reliability will be a key issue for smooth operations.

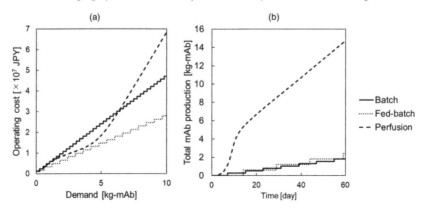

Figure 3: comparison of operating modes in terms of (a) operating cost and (b) production time using a 200 L reactor volume.

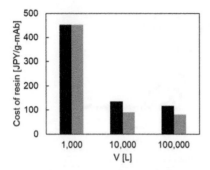 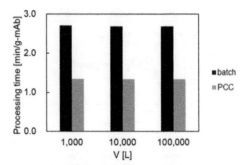

Figure 4: (a) cost of resin and (b) processing time for batch and PCC capture chromatography for a 3 g/L inlet titer

4. Conclusions

This work presents models developed for the main cultivation unit. The models are fitted and validated using pilot scale fed-batch data and experimental scale perfusion data from literature. Models for chromatography units are also fitted using pilot scale data. The produced models are used to simulate and compare different operating modes in terms of operating costs and processing times. Continuous operation was shown to have a clear advantage in terms of productivity, but the advantage in terms of costs still needs to be fully investigated and verified. A sensitivity analysis to model assumptions is still required to map out and characterize the design space.

Acknowledgements

This work was supported by the Japan Agency for Medical Research and Development (AMED) [grant No. JP19ae0101064, JP17ae0101003, JP18ae0101058].

References

Angarita, M., Müller-Späth, T., Baur, D., Lievrouw, R., Lissens, G., Morbidelli, M., 2015, Twin-column CaptureSMB: A novel cyclic process for protein A affinity chromatography. J. Chromatogr. A 1389, 85–95.

Butler, M., Meneses-Acosta, A., 2012, Recent advances in technology supporting biopharmaceutical production from mammalian cells. Appl. Microbiol. Biotechnol. 96, 885–894.

Felinger, A., Guiochon, G., 2004, Comparison of the kinetic models of linear chromatography. Chromatographia 60, 175–180.

Grilo, A.L., A. Mantalaris, 2019, The Increasingly Human and Profitable Monoclonal Antibody Market. Trends Biotechnol. 37, 9–16.

Guélat, B., Khalaf, R., Lattuada, M., Costioli, M., Morbidelli, M., 2016, Protein adsorption on ion exchange resins and monoclonal antibody charge variant modulation. J. Chromatogr. A 1447, 82–91.

Karst, D.J., Steinebach, F., Morbidelli, M., 2018, Continuous integrated manufacturing of therapeutic proteins. Curr. Opin. Biotechnol. 53, 76–84.

Kornecki, M., Strube, J., 2018, Process analytical technology for advanced process control in biologics manufacturing with the aid of macroscopic kinetic modeling. Bioengineering 5.

Walsh, G., 2018, Biopharmaceutical benchmarks 2018. Nat. Biotechnol. 36, 1136–1145.

Xing, Z., Bishop, N., Leister, K., Li, Z.J., 2010, Modeling kinetics of a large-scale fed-batch CHO cell culture by markov chain monte carlo method. Biotechnol. Prog. 26, 208–219.

Xu, S., Chen, H., 2016, High-density mammalian cell cultures in stirred-tank bioreactor without external pH control. J. Biotechnol. 231, 149–159.

Zhang, Y., Stobbe, P., Silvander, C.O., Chotteau, V., 2015, Very high cell density perfusion of CHO cells anchored in a non-woven matrix-based bioreactor. J. Biotechnol. 213, 28–41.

Sauro Pierucci, Flavio Manenti, Giulia Bozzano, Davide Manca (Eds.)
Proceedings of the 30th European Symposium on Computer Aided Process Engineering
(ESCAPE30), May 24-27, 2020, Milano, Italy. © 2020 Elsevier B.V. All rights reserved.
http://dx.doi.org/10.1016/B978-0-12-823377-1.50270-6

Robust Monitoring of Lactic Acid Bacteria with Sequential Monte Carlo

Ergys Pahija,[a] Robert Spann,[b] Gürkan Sin[a,*]

[a]*Process and Systems Engineering Research Center (PROSYS), Department of Chemical and Biochemical Engineering, Technical University of Denmark, 2800 Kgs. Lyngby, Denmark*
[b]*Chr. Hansen A/S, Hørsholm, Denmark*
gsi@kt.dtu.dk

Abstract

Lactic Acid Bacteria (LAB) are commonly utilised in the dairy industry. Although the process is well established, the conditions in which the fermentation process takes place can strongly influence the production of LAB.

The objective of this manuscript is to apply the Sequential Monte Carlo (SMC) method for monitoring the fermentation process. The online monitoring system is based on a statistical method for the estimation of model parameters using importance sampling technique, making use of limited data and predicting a number of relevant but unmeasured process variables such as biomass and product yields. The SMC technique was evaluated using two case studies one a simulation study and the other is a pilot-scale data from LAB fermentation. To describe the process, a mechanistic fermentation model was developed and validated comprehensively before being used in SMC for online monitoring. The results show the application of SMC makes effective use of online data as batch progress and the quality of the predictions (for unmeasured state variables) improve as more information becomes available. This indicates the principle of Bayesian update of prior information on model parameters through importance sampling successfully works. In addition to process monitoring using limited online knowledge, the SMC technique allows convergence to the real value of the parameters of interest in the model. In fermentation studies with a limited online sensor, SMC offers a flexible alternative to traditional soft-sensors especially when the measurement errors are not necessarily normally distributed.

Keywords: Lactic acid bacteria, fermentation, monitoring, sequential Monte Carlo.

1. Introduction

Parameter estimation problems are very common in engineering and science applications (Beck and Arnold, 1977). Possible approaches to solve the problem are the trial and error, the frequentists approach (e.g., MLE) and the Bayesian approach (e.g., Monte Carlo methods (Sin et al., 2008)). In our case, we will focus on the latter approach, being the application of Sequential Monte Carlo (SMC) method for updating of model parameters as a function of online data with an application for fermentation processes. The main motivation is that in fermentation process models, the biokinetic parameters are subject to vary hence motivating the application of online update/parameter estimation. The end application is to use the online update model as a soft-sensor/process monitoring purpose. Several approaches can be followed when applying sequential Monte Carlo for on-line monitoring, such as defining an extended state that includes state and parameters, and then apply standard particle methods (Kantas et al., 2015). We present the methodology of applying SMC based on importance sampling which is a Bayesian inference/update method. We first demonstrate the concept of the SMC methodology using a simulation/test study by studying the effect of several degrees of freedom of the methodology. To this end, we use a biological process focusing on the ammonia-oxidizing bacteria. After the implementation of the methodology is demonstrated step by step for online updating and process monitoring, we present the application of the methodology for a LAB fermentation process.

2. Methodology

The ammonia-oxidizing bacteria represent the first step of the two-step nitrification process. The model has a total of 6 ODE equations, which corresponds to one mass balance for each variable of interest. The objective is to determine [Y_{AOO} μ_{maxAOB} $K_{s,AOB}$ $K_{o,AOB}$]. For a complete description of the model refer to the paper from Sin et al. (2010). Using matrix notation, each ODE can be formulated as shown by System of Equations (1).

$$\begin{cases} \dfrac{dC_{NH4}}{dt} = -\dfrac{1}{Y_{AOB}}\mu_{AOB} \\[2mm] \dfrac{dC_{NO2}}{dt} = \dfrac{1}{Y_{AOB}}\mu_{AOB} - \dfrac{1}{Y_{NOB}}\mu_{NOB} \\[2mm] \dfrac{dC_{NO3}}{dt} = \dfrac{1}{Y_{NOB}}\mu_{NOB} \\[2mm] \dfrac{dC_{DO}}{dt} = \left(1 - \dfrac{3.43}{Y_{AOB}}\right)\mu_{AOB} - b_{AOB}C_{AOB} + \left(1 - \dfrac{1.14}{Y_{NOB}}\right)\mu_{NOB} - b_{NOB}C_{NOB} + k_{la}\left(O_{2,sat} - C_O\right) \\[2mm] \dfrac{dC_{AOB}}{dt} = \mu_{AOB} - b_{AOB}C_{AOB} \\[2mm] \dfrac{dC_{NOB}}{dt} = \mu_{NOB} - b_{NOB}C_{NOB} \end{cases} \tag{1}$$

where AOB and NOB represent the ammonia-oxidizing bacteria and nitrite oxidizing bacteria performing the nitrification process.

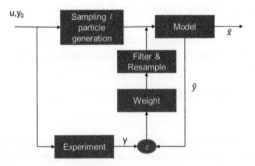

Figure 1 Schematic representation of the SMC for parameter estimation, x: unmeasured state variables, y: measured variable(s), epsilon is an error (different between model and measurements). The hat indicates it is an estimated value.

In order to follow the scheme shown in Figure 1, the following points have been implemented in MATLAB:
- Step 1 Initialization
- Step 2 Select experimental data and select the subset of parameters of interest
- Step 3 Select the sample size and apply a sampling technique

- Step 4 Apply the model of the defined problem
- Step 5 Compare (weight) the measured variable and compare to the ones estimated by the model
- Step 6 Overall weight, apply the filter
- Step 7 Update the parameters value and their uncertainty

In our case, we will make use of the importance sampling algorithm for updating the prior information on model parameters after new data/information becomes available (Gelman et al., 2013) (Doucet et al., 2006). We make use of the importance sampling as shown in Equation (3), where the weights are updated at each iteration by comparing the available data to the estimated variable. Note that in our case, the resampling is applied on the same initial particles.

$$E\big(f(x)\big) \approx \frac{1}{n}\Sigma_i f(x_i)\frac{p(x_i)}{q(x_i)} \tag{2}$$

where the estimation of a function *f(x)* depends on the number of particles (*n*) and on the "weight" obtained through the $p(x_i)/q(x_i)$ ratio, which allows a better convergence to the real solution at each iteration. The weight given to specific particle *i*, based on a certain measurement at time *j*, is calculated by using the likelihood function $1/_{\sqrt{2\pi\varepsilon}}\exp\left(-\Sigma_i \frac{(\hat{y}_{i,j}-Data_{i,j})^2}{2\varepsilon}\right)$, where ε represents the measurement error.

Below, we briefly introduce the LAB problem, that is currently under investigation and that will be included in the final version of this manuscript.

LAB is commonly used in the dairy industry for the production of yoghurt. This work focuses on *Streptococcus thermophilus*, which is gram-positive, aerotolerant, non-motile and used for the production of yoghurt, together with *Lactobacillus bulgaricus*, among others. The production process is well established, and mechanistic models can be found in the literature (Spann et al., 2018).

However, only a limited number of variables is commonly available at industrial scale. In our case, only pH and ammonia flowrate measurements are available. Temperature is kept constant, while other variables need to be calculated using the available models. Hence, it arises the necessity in having a robust monitoring system. The reaction defining lactic acid production is shown below.

Lactose + Ammonia + Phosphoric acid → Biomass + Lactic acid + Galactose

The dynamic model that is used to determine the change of state variables like biomass, lactose and lactic acid is shown below in Equation (3) and Equation (4). The biomass growth rate is calculated as a function of the maximum specific growth rate μ_{max}, lag time f_{lag}, lactose limitation and inhibition f_s, lactate inhibition f_p and pH f_{pH}.

$$\frac{dC_x}{dt} = \mu_{max}f_{lag}f_sf_pf_{pH}C_x \tag{3}$$

$$\frac{dC_x}{dt} = \mu_{max}\cdot\left(1-e^{-\frac{t}{t_{lag}}}\right)\cdot\left(\frac{C_s}{C_s+K_s+\frac{C_s^2}{K_I}}\right)\cdot\left(\frac{1}{1-e^{K_{P,La}(C_{LA}-K_{La})}}\right)\cdot\left(e^{-\left(\frac{(pH_{opt}-pH)^2}{\sigma_{pH}^2}\right)}\right)\cdot C_x \tag{4}$$

For additional information on the applied model, refer to the paper written by Spann et al. (2018).

3. Results

3.1. Case study 1: Model parameter estimation/update using online data

For the first case study, a sample of 300 particles was randomly selected for each parameter of interest. The initial parameter values are assumed uniform as shown in Figure 3 (a). As data are collected over time, the information is updated on the prior with importance sampling, and the uncertainty on the monitored state variables decreases.

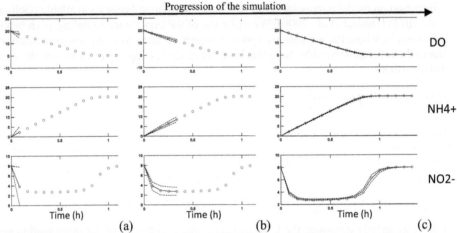

Figure 2 Representation of the model output at different times. (a) Time interval 1, (b) time interval 4, (c) time interval 16. Circles: measurements (based on a single set of data – benchmark); line: model predictions.

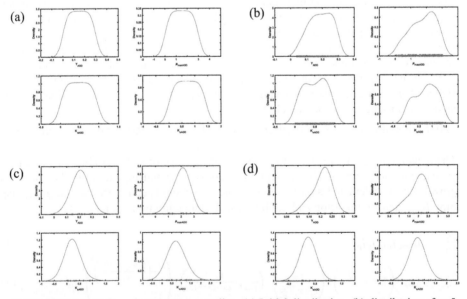

Figure 3 Representation of parameters sampling. (a) Initial distribution, (b) distribution after 5 time steps, (c) distribution after 9 time steps and (d) distribution after 15 time steps.

Figure 3 shows the effect of applying the filter. In our case, we assume that after the filter is applied to the initial distribution, the resampling is performed on the same set of numbers which was randomly sampled in the first place. It is possible to observe that the distribution of the particles starts with flat distributions and it converges to much sharper distributions, indicating that the value is converging. The red dots in Figure 3 represent the MC samples. They start from being uniformly distributed (flat distribution – a) to being concentrated around a specific value (bell-shaped distribution – d).

The covariance matrix of the evaluated parameters is shown below in Table 1. As a comparison, the estimated value of parameters by applying MLE ($\hat{\theta}_{MLE}$).

Table 1 Covariance matrix.

	$\hat{\theta}$	$\hat{\theta}_{MLE}$	Y_{AOO}	μ_{maxAOB}	$K_{s,AOB}$	$K_{o,AOB}$
					Correlation matrix	
Y_{AOO}	0.1983	0.14	1.0000	0.9897	-0.2992	0.3775
μ_{maxAOB}	2.0368	1.45	0.9897	1.0000	-0.2120	0.5022
$K_{s,AOB}$	0.5279	0.5	-0.2992	-0.2120	1.0000	0.4803
$K_{o,AOB}$	0.7950	0.69	0.3775	0.5022	0.4803	1.0000

3.2. Case study 2: Effect of considering only one measurement when calculating the weight in the importance sampling

Differently from Case study 1, in which we made use of all three measurements for the weight of particles, we are considering only the measurement from the dissolved oxygen. As shown in Figure 4, the results are still acceptable, and very similar to applying the MLE method, for the proposed problem.

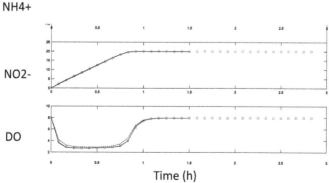

Figure 4 Concentration of ammonia, nitrite and dissolved oxygen over time (sample size: 300 particles).

Sensitivity analysis with the effect of the sample size of particles and the prior distribution of parameters (initial range of values) is studied and it is determined that it is better to start with relatively large uninformative prior (so that importance sampling can sample and generate particles from a broader space). On the other hand, if the particle size is too small and the initial distribution (prior range) is wide, the model will tend to converge very quickly to a single value, which can diverge from actual measured values.

In the case of LAB monitoring, only pH and ammonia can be measured while all other variables are calculated and rely on the quality of the model and its parameters. Hence, the SMC provides an update on the unmeasured state variables. Figure 5 shows some preliminary results of the LAB monitoring. The model is applied to two sets of data.

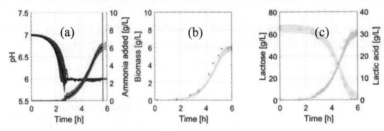

Figure 5 Monitoring of LAB, model prediction and data. (a) Online measurements: pH and ammonia addition, Offline measurements: (b) biomass and (c) lactose and lactic acid. Symbols: on- and off-line (time-delayed) measurements, filling: model prediction with 90% uncertainty interval.

4. Conclusions

The SMC is applied to the two-steps nitrification process. The SMC implementation is adapted for updating information on the model parameters, which is then used to estimate future states of the system and unmeasured outputs (this is different than the state space implementation, where particle filters are defined on the states themselves). When a parameter is unknown, one can start with a large uninformative prior (giving a "small" sampling range is not advised, as it risks limiting the input space covered during successive importance sampling). However, it is possible to define some limitations when applying such methodology: the sample size needed to have a good estimate of the problem can be quite large if the value of the required parameters is not known, and the number of parameters that need to be determined may affect the computational time.

The proposed work will be applied to LAB and several investigations on the effect of different filtering techniques as well as on the sample size will be investigated in future.

References

J. V. Beck, & K. J. Arnold, 1977, Parameter estimation in engineering and science.

A. Doucet, M. Briers, and S. Sénécal, 2006, Efficient block sampling strategies for sequential Monte Carlo methods. Journal of Computational and Graphical Statistics, 15(3), 693-711.

A. Gelman, J. B. Carlin, H. S. Stern, D. B. Dunson, A., Vehtari, & D. B., Rubin, 2013, Bayesian data analysis. Chapman and Hall/CRC.

N. Kantas, A. Doucet, S.S. Singh, J. Maciejowski, and N. Chopin, 2015, On particle methods for parameter estimation in state-space models. Statistical science, 30(3), 328-351.

G. Sin, D. J. De Pauw, S. Weijers, and P.A. Vanrolleghem, 2008, An efficient approach to automate the manual trial and error calibration of activated sludge models. Biotechnology and bioengineering, 100(3), pp.516-528.

G. Sin, A.S. Meyer, K.V. Gernaey, 2010, Assessing reliability of cellulose hydrolysis models to support biofuel process design—Identifiability and uncertainty analysis. Computers & Chemical Engineering, 34(9):1385-92.

R. Spann, C. Roca, D. Kold, A. E. Lantz, K. V. Gernaey, and G. Sin, 2018, A probabilistic model-based soft sensor to monitor lactic acid bacteria fermentations. Biochemical Engineering Journal, 135, 49-60.

Sauro Pierucci, Flavio Manenti, Giulia Bozzano, Davide Manca (Eds.)
Proceedings of the 30th European Symposium on Computer Aided Process Engineering
(ESCAPE30), May 24-27, 2020, Milano, Italy. © 2020 Elsevier B.V. All rights reserved.
http://dx.doi.org/10.1016/B978-0-12-823377-1.50271-8

Solvent Selection using CAMD for the Solid-liquid Extraction of Bioactive Compounds from Agroindustrial Waste from Avocado (Persea Americana)

Jorge Rodríguez-Iniesta,[a] Nancy Medina-Herrera,[a*] Guillermo Martínez-Ávila,[a] Romeo Rojas-Molina,[a] Salvador Tututi-Avila[b]

[a] *Universidad Autonoma de Nuevo León, Agronomy School, Francisco Villa s/n, Ex Hacienda el Canadá, General Escobedo, N.L., 66451, Mexico*

[b] *Universidad Autónoma de Nuevo León, Department of Chemical Engineering, Av. Universidad s/n, Ciudad Universitaria, San Nicolas de los Garza, N.L., 66455, Mexico*

nancy.medinahr@uanl.edu.mx

Abstract

The extraction of bioactive compounds is an interesting alternative to add value to agroindustrial waste, due to its demand in the pharmaceutical and food industry. The extraction of these compounds is highly dependent on the solvent used. The extraction of these compounds is limited by a small variety of solvents. Currently, there is no extraction model that accounts for thermodynamic behaviour. This manuscript presents a methodology to design a solid-liquid extraction system for bioactive compounds, from solvent selection generating candidates via computer aided molecular design (CAMD), model generation and process simulation in Aspen Custom Modeler (ACM). The approach was applied to a case study, which examines the extraction of bioactive compounds from avocado (*Persea americana*) agroindustrial waste. Results show how the extraction performance varies according to selected solvent, for instance conventional solvent (methanol) differs to the candidate solvent (1,2-propylene glycol) tested by process simulation. From simulation results, the candidate solvent presented flexible operating conditions, extracting 90.72% of the initial bioactive compound present in the agroindustrial waste in a single equilibrium stage. While working at a higher temperature, the solvent feed flowrate was decreased. The proposed strategy allows obtaining composition and temperature profiles for the extraction to select a proper solvent and operating conditions, although, it is still necessary to validate the results with experimental data.

Keywords: Bioactive compounds, CAMD, waste added value, solid-liquid extraction, solvent selection.

1. Introduction

Due to the population growth rate of the last decades, there has been a dramatic increment of agroindustrial waste worldwide. Thus, several works have reported that the agroindustrial waste is a valuable source of bioactive compounds, which are important on the pharmaceutical and food industry due to their antioxidant potential and their uses in therapeutic treatments and nutrition (Morais, et al., 2015).

Currently, the extraction of this compounds is limited to just a few solvents, which do not perform optimally, resulting in a high solvent consumption in the extraction process (Jannatul, et al., 2013). Thus, a proper solvent selection is crucial for the extraction process, because the solvent determine the overall extraction yield, as well as product safety (de Matos, et al., 2018). Accordingly, there is an increasing need for a proper solvent selection for the extraction of bioactive compounds present in agroindustrial waste. A useful tool to achieve this goal is the implementation of CAMD to determine the optimal solvent candidates (Fedorova, et al., 2015).

Besides, a proper model for the extraction of this kind of compounds has not been fully developed in process simulators, limiting the evaluation of the extraction using different solvents. Therefore, there is a need to develop proper models and evaluate them within process simulators in order to save time and resources in experimental designs.

The goal of this work is to study the mathematical model for bioactive compounds extraction from agroindustrial waste and evaluate different potential solvents generated via CAMD in the software ICAS and extraction simulation in ACM on ASPEN Tech software.

2. Methodology

The proposed methodology uses ICAS 20.0 and AspenTech software, as illustrated on Figure 1. Based on literature survey, the main bioactive compounds present in agroindustrial waste tissue are identified. The ICAS 20.0 software is used for the generation of the candidate solvents for the extraction of bioactive compounds. Bioactive compounds are separated by families for optimal solvent selection. First, thermodynamic properties were estimated via the Marrero & Gani model for each bioactive compound, for better property estimation, experimental data can be added if it is available in literature.

Then, a solvent preselection is performed on ProCAMD tool within ICAS. The solvent design was carried out selecting the bioactive compounds of interest in such a way that there were no azeotropes between the selected compounds and the generated solvents. In the last step, the solvents are selected by analyzing the highest selectivity coefficients (β), and the lowest Octanol/Water partition coefficient, also the normal boiling point (T_b) was considered.

Finally, the model for the extraction of bioactive compounds is solved considering a single solid-liquid extraction (SLE) stage by means of simulation. By using Aspen Custom Modeler V11.0, the model was developed for the evaluation of the candidate solvents generated in ProCAMD. A comparison is made between the conventional solvents and the candidate solvents.

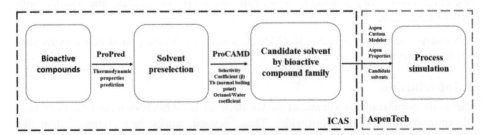

Figure 1 Methodology for the solid-liquid extraction.

Solvent Selection using CAMD for the solid-liquid extraction of bioactive compounds from agroindustry waste from avocado (Persea Americana)

1623

3. Case of study

Avocado (*Persea americana*) is a tropical or subtropical fruit native from Mexico and South America, which has been referred as one of the most nutritious of all fruits. It is highly valuated due to its taste and healthy properties. Because of this it has gained worldwide recognition and its consumption has increased in the last years (Hurtado, et al., 2018).

It has been reported that their agroindustrial waste (seed and peel) are a rich source of bioactive compounds. The most abundant families present in *Persea americana* are phenolic acids, quinic acids, tyrosol derivatives, carboxylic acids and flavonoids. One of the most valuable is the carboxylic acids, due to their application in the pharmaceutical and food industry, such as anti-inflammatory, antioxidant, anti-microbial, food stabilizer and food flavouring.

The extraction of this compounds has been reported by typical conventional solvents, such as ethanol, methanol, acetone, chloroform, dioxane, which do not show very promising experimental yields.

It has been reported that for every 100 g of dry matter (DM), there are around 911 mg of this bioactive compounds (López, et al., 2016) as it is shown in Table 1. A bioactive compound was selected to represent each family according to the experimental properties data availability, expecting similar behaviour for compounds present in each chemical family, their economic and industrial potential. In this manuscript only carboxylic acids will be evaluated and presented.

Table 1 Bioactive compounds present in *Persea americana*.

Bioactive compound family	Weight per 100 g of DM (mg)	Compound of interest
Carboxylic acids	0.5189	Citric acid
Quinic acids	126.42	1-caffeoylquinic acid
Flavonoids	325.53	Rutin
Tyrosol derivatives	262.61	Hydroxytyrosol glucoside
Phenolic acids	196.79	3,4-Dihydroxybenzoic acid

4. Results

4.1. Candidate solvents for bioactive compounds extraction.

Solvent screening was performed by evaluating each family of bioactive compounds separately accordingly to Table 1 using the UNIFAC model. Conventional solvents were also considered for the analysis. Solvent selection criteria were based on safety of usage and operational thermodynamic properties, such as the normal boiling temperature (Tb), selectivity coefficient (β) and Octanol/Water partition coefficient as a safety coefficient. Regarding Tb, the upper limit was 175 °C to avoid thermal degradation of the desired bioactive compounds. Regarding to β coefficient, an indicator of optimal solvent affinity with the bioactive compound, the lower limit was fixed at 1, this value was obtained on a preliminary selection of candidate solvents. Octanol/Water coefficient was considered in an interval of -2 and 2 as an indicator for health safety. Thus, final candidate solvents were selected considering a higher Tb, a higher β coefficient and lower Octanol/Water coefficient values. The final candidate solvent list takes into consideration the potential solvent performance with other bioactive compound families. As well, commercial availability was considered for industrial scale.

The candidate solvents for the extraction of bioactive compounds found by ProCAMD are shown in Table 2. It should be noted that the CAMD was performed considering no azeotropes formation. From results, it should be noted that only the acetone has been reported as a conventional solvent for bioactive compound extraction, whereas 1,2-Propylene glycol, succinic acid and cyclohexanol has not been reported to our knowledge for the extraction of these compounds.

4.2. Solid-Liquid extraction model in ACM.

Currently there is not an extraction model that consider thermodynamic behaviour within ASPEN Plus. Thus, for developing the SLE model, the extraction was considered in a single equilibrium stage, as it is shown in the flowsheet (Figure 2).

Table 2 Candidate solvents for the solid-liquid extraction for the selected bioactive compounds

Candidate solvent	Bioactive compound family	Selectivity coefficient (β)	Octanol/Water coefficient	Tb (°C)
1,2-Propylene glycol	Tyrosol derivatives	2.58	-0.43	172.34
	Phenolic acids	130.87		
	Carboxylic acids	1.14		
Acetone	Quinic acids	1.37	0.0674	32.22
	Tyrosol derivatives	3.69		
Cyclohexanol	Phenolic acids	7.85	1.93	162.53
	Quinic acids	1.03		
Succinic acid	Flavonoids	5.85	-0.347	258.92

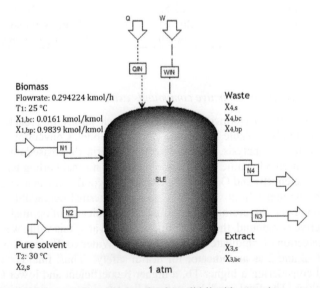

Figure 2 Process flow diagram for the solid-liquid extraction

Solvent Selection using CAMD for the solid-liquid extraction of bioactive compounds from agroindustry waste from avocado (Persea Americana)

1625

The equations for the SLE model for bioactive compounds are presented in this section. Molar material balances represent that the sum of the inlet flowrates is equal to the sum of outlet flowrates (Equation 1-3).

$$n_1 * x_{1,i} + n_2 * x_{2,i} - n_3 * x_{3,i} - n_4 * x_{4,i} = 0 \qquad \forall i \in N \tag{1-3}$$

Where the solvent (s), the bioactive compound (bc) and the biopolymer (bp) represent the set N. The sum of composition fractions in the outlet streams are considered as well.

The energy balance considers the inlet and outlet enthalpy and heat and work required to perform the extraction, Equation 4.

$$n_3{}^*h_3 + n_4{}^*h_4 - n_1{}^*h_1 - n_2{}^*h_2 - Q - W = 0 \tag{4}$$

According to Nevers (2016) the solid-liquid equilibrium in extraction can be represented by Equation 5. Where it is considered the activity coefficient, enthalpy of fusion, operating and melting temperatures.

$$\ln\left(\frac{1}{x_{3,bc}\gamma_{3,bc}}\right) = \left(\frac{H_{fus,bc}}{R}\right)\left(\left(\frac{1}{T_3}\right) - \left(\frac{1}{T_{m,bc}}\right)\right) \tag{5}$$

Additionally, thermal equilibrium was considered on the outlet streams. Enthalpies and activity coefficients are calculated through calling ASPEN Properties. Thus, the model has four degrees of freedom, the design specifications were the molar bioactive compound composition of extract stream and waste stream, the molar solvent composition fraction on the waste stream and the power of agitator. The model was codified within ACM and evaluated for solvent candidates.

4.3. Extraction process simulation.

A sensitivity analysis for 1,2-propylene glycol was performed with the design specification of molar bioactive compound composition of bioactive compounds for carboxylic acids can be seen at Figure 3.

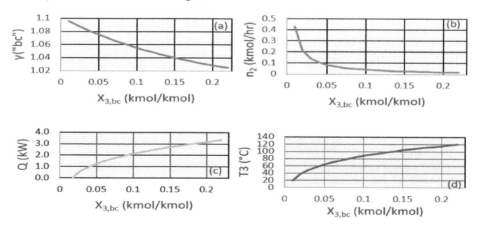

Figure 3 Sensitivity analysis for molar bioactive compound composition of extract stream for carboxylic acids. Results for (a) activity coefficient; (b) solvent feed flowrate; (c) heat duty; and (d) extraction temperature

The following design specifications were fixed: agitator power (0.00027 kW); molar solvent composition fraction on the waste stream (0.005 kmol/kmol); molar bioactive compound composition on the waste stream (0.0015 kmol/kmol).

The candidate solvent (1,2-propylene glycol) presented an activity coefficient greater than one. The amount of solvent used for the extraction decreases by increasing the operation temperature. This would require greater heat duty into the system. In comparison with conventional solvent (methanol), the trend is similar regarding solvent feed flowrate, operating temperature, and heat duty. However, the activity coefficient for the conventional solvent was calculated between 0.4-0.6. The operating temperature using the conventional solvent limits the extract composition of bioactive compounds, due to after a value of 0.09 the normal boiling point of methanol is reached. Therefore, operation using the candidate solvent is more flexible.

5. Conclusions

This methodology has the potential to be extrapolated to other agroindustrial waste. Potential candidate solvents can be obtained for the solid-liquid extraction of bioactive compounds present in *Persea americana* using CAMD. A solid-liquid extraction model has been developed for the simulation of the extraction process. The simulation performed in ACM showed promising results for the extraction of carboxylic acids, although a more reliable model considering mass and energy transfer is still required. The usage of candidate solvents may reduce the solvent consumption and ease of purification, on the other hand, extraction process may be performed into higher temperatures, consequently it should be performed a more detailed analysis for the energy consumption on the process in order to evaluate economic feasibility.

Acknowledgements

The authors acknowledge the software license support for ICAS 20.0 provided by Dr. Rafiqul Gani.

References

A. Jannatul, et al. 2013. Techniques for extraction of bioactive compounds from plant materials: A review. Journal of Food Engineering. 117. 10.1016/j.jfoodeng.2013.01.014.

A. López, et al. 2016.. HPLC-DAD-ESI-QTOF-MS and HPLC-FLD-MS as valuable tools for the determination of phenolic and other polar compounds in the edible part and by-products of avocado. LWT, 73, pp.505-513.

application. Computers & Chemical Engineering, 83, pp.232-247.

D. Morais, et al. 2015. Antioxidant activity, phenolics and UPLC–ESI(–)–MS of extracts from different tropical fruits parts and processed peels. Food Research International, 77, pp.392-399.

E. Hurtado, A. Fernández, A. Carrasco. 2018. Avocado fruit— Persea americana. Exotic Fruits, pp.37-48.

M. Fedorova, G. Sin, R. Gani. 2015. Computer-aided modelling template: Concept and

N. Nevers. 2013. Physical and chemical equilibrium for chemical engineers. Hoboken, N.J.: Wiley..

R. de Mattos, et al. 2018. Solvent use optimization on polyphenols extraction from grape marc involving economical aspects.

Sauro Pierucci, Flavio Manenti, Giulia Bozzano, Davide Manca (Eds.)
Proceedings of the 30th European Symposium on Computer Aided Process Engineering
(ESCAPE30), May 24-27, 2020, Milano, Italy. © 2020 Elsevier B.V. All rights reserved.
http://dx.doi.org/10.1016/B978-0-12-823377-1.50272-X

Development of a Computational Intelligence Framework for the Strategic Design and Implementation of Large-scale Biomass Supply Chains

Ahmed AlNouss,[a] Rajesh Govindan,[b] Gordon McKay,[a] Tareq Al-Ansari [a,b*]

[a] *Division of Sustainable Development, College of Science and Engineering, Hamad Bin Khalifa University, Qatar Foundation. Doha, Qatar*

[b] *Division of Engineering Management and Decision Sciences, College of Science and Engineering, Hamad Bin Khalifa University, Qatar Foundation. Doha, Qatar*

talansari@hbku.edu.qa

Abstract

Biomass utilisation has witnessed growing attention as a promising alternative to fossil fuels. However, the biomass supply chain is generally unstable due to the fluctuation of the supply and the difficulty to accommodate all the available biomass feedstock and utilisation pathways. This has made the optimisation of the supply chain a challenging task due to the complexities of modelling the different interconnected systems consisting of various production sources, intermediate processing methods, and utilisation sinks. The objective of this study is to develop a geospatial information systems (GIS)-based decision framework integrated with statistical learning and heuristic optimisation capabilities in order to establish the design solutions for biomass supply chains on a national scale and subsequent strategic decision-making. The artificial neural network (ANN)-based surrogate models for the biomass processing system were developed and validated to predict the synthesis gas flowrate and composition linked to the input parameters of biomass attributes in terms of their proximate and ultimate analysis, as simulated in previously developed Aspen Plus models. The surrogate models were then coupled with GIS, including information about biomass sources, candidate plant locations, and utilisation sinks. The optimal biomass utilisation routes were subsequently solved using the genetic algorithm (GA). The framework implementation is illustrated through a biomass gasification case study in the state of Qatar. The results demonstrate the importance of domestic biomass resources to support the local economy through the production of methanol as a final product, and utilising primarily manure-based biomass feedstock in an optimal blend with sludge and date pits. The economic optimisation of the biomass processing-plant locations reveals production routes supporting the generation of methanol and the utilisation of manure feedstock in Qatar.

Keywords: Biomass Supply Chain, Biorefinery Plant, Biomass Gasification, Artificial Neural Network, Genetic Algorithm, GIS

1. Introduction

Biomass gasification is witnessing growing attention as a result of the promising production of high-energy syngas from renewable sources and the reduction in carbon dioxide emissions (AlNouss et al., 2018). Nevertheless, the investment risk in biomass conversion is largely due to the complex nature of the process and the requirement of quality biomass feedstock and cost-efficient biomass handling facility (Sharma et al., 2013). Moreover, the requirement of safely-operated experiments that are highly time-consuming hinders the progression in analysing the effect of key gasification parameters on the overall process performance. Mathematical simulation and modeling have the capabilities to mimic real operational processes and help in understanding the operational performance of complex natural processes (Salah et al., 2016). The highly integrated sequential operational processes involved in the conversion of biomass into value-added products that hinder its modelling using simple closed-form equations. Though, machine learning techniques (Salah et al., 2016) coupled with geospatial analysis methods (Rodríguez et al., 2017) can help in data-driven model induction for complex systems that aid in making decisions to solve the problems related to supply chain routing, productivity, resource efficiency and risk management. The state of Qatar depends purely on natural gas to run its entire power and petrochemical production sector. The national strategy supports the utilisation of the high waste per capita generation approximated at 7,000 tons per day of food waste only to diversify the energy mix and reduce the significant greenhouse gas (GHG) emissions (AlNouss et al., 2020). This research described in this paper looks at the development of a geospatial information systems (GIS)-based decision framework integrated with statistical learning and heuristic optimisation capabilities in order to establish the design solutions for biomass supply It is envisaged that the proposed framework will enable stakeholders to rapidly assess alternative designs under different scenarios for the biomass supply chains, in both the local and international context. The implementation of the framework is illustrated through a biomass gasification case study in the state of Qatar.

2. Methodology

The methodological framework developed in this study is illustrated in Figure 1. This framework combines the capabilities of GIS analysis, artificial neural network (ANN) modelling, and process simulation and optimization. In addition, it takes into account several important components in the biomass supply chain as illustrated in Figure 2. These components include: (a) procurement of biomass feedstock from the sources; (b) transportation of biomass raw material; (c) processing of biomass; (d) transportation of the intermediate product; and (e) processing of the value-added products.

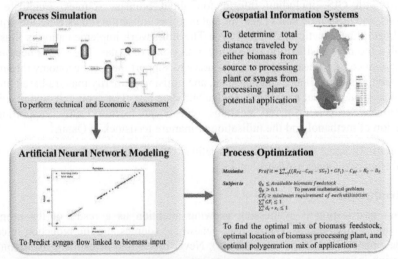

Figure 1: Methodological framework developed in this study.

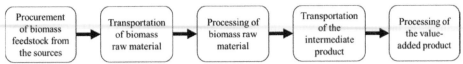

Figure 2: Biomass supply chain stages considered in this study.

The biomass feedstocks are first procured from the different sources. The biomass types involved in this study include date pits, manure, sludge and foodwaste. The prices associated with the biomass sources available in Table 1 are used to calculate the cost of raw materials through Eq (1).

$$B_c = \sum_{i=1}^{4} Q_{B,i} * B_{p,i} \tag{1}$$

Where Q_B = Biomass Quantity, and $B_{P,i}$ = Biomass price for each biomass type. The transportation of biomass raw material from the different biomass sources to the processing plant is assumed to take place using trucks. The cost associated with biomass transportation is calculated using Eq (2) through (4).

$$B_T = \sum_{i=1}^{4} n_{B_{T,i}} * T_{P,i} \tag{2}$$

$$T_{p,i} = d_i * C_d \tag{3}$$

$$n_{B_{T,i}} = \frac{Q_{B,i}}{C_T} \tag{4}$$

Where n_{BT} = number of biomass transportation, $T_{P,I}$ = price of one transportation, d = distance, C_d = cost per distance travelled, and C_T = Capacity of one biomass transportation. The cost of biomass processing plant is retrieved from previously simulated Aspen Plus models in (AlNouss et al., 2019b). The models are based on the gasification of the same biomass feedstock considered in this study using oxygen and steam as gasification agents to generate high-energy syngas. The cost of the processing plant is accounted for in the network using Eq (5).

$$C_{BP} = Cost\ of\ Biomass\ processing \tag{5}$$

The transportation of the intermediate syngas product from the biomass processing plant to the different utilisation applications is assumed to take place using a pipeline network. The cost of the pipeline construction to transport syngas based on a pipeline corridor specific to Qatar is calculated using Eq (6) through (8).

$$SG_T = Q_{SG} * C_Q \tag{6}$$

$$C_Q = C_{Seg} * n_{seg} \tag{7}$$

$$n_{seg} = \frac{d}{CP_{Seg}} \tag{8}$$

Where Q_{SG} = quantity of syngas, C_Q = cost per quantity, C_{Seg} = cost of one segment of pipline, n_{Seg} = number of segments needed, d = total distance, and CP_{Seg} = capacity of one segment. The prediction of syngas production quantity is governed through the use of ANN-based surrogate models. The ANN-based surrogate models for the biomass processing system are trained and validated to predict the synthesis gas flowrate and composition linked to the input parameters of biomass attributes in terms of their proximate and ultimate analyses as illustrated in Figure 3. The feed-forward back propagation technique is used to develop the network. A multi-layer perceptron (MLP) one of the classes of feed-forward neural network is utilised to model the network. It comprises three layers i.e. input layer, hidden layers and the output layer. The model utilises a non-linear least squares approach called the Levenberg-Marquardt (LM) algorithm to determine the weights Biomass types, attributes and flowrate represent neurons in the input layer, while the effluent flowrate of CO_2, CO, H_2, CH_4, and N_2 represent neurons in the output layer. Before the training of the network, the data for input and output variables are normalised to improve the network efficiency. For the training of the network, 60% data points are used, while the remaining 40% of the data are used for the testing and the validation of the network respectively for the better indication of the model's performance on unseen data.

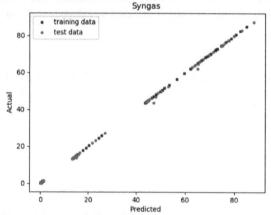

Figure 3: Training and test plots for ANN model.

The syngas in the case study is utilised in four different applications that include, urea, methanol, power, and liquid fuels production. The costs associated with product generation for each application are supplied from the simulated Aspen Plus models (AlNouss et al., 2019) and Eq (9) to demonstrate the representation of these costs in the model.

$$C_{PG} = Cost\ of\ product\ generation \quad (9)$$

Moreover, the revenue of from products generation is accounted using Eq (10).

$$R_{PG} = \sum_{i=1}^{4} Q_{Product,i} * P_{Product,i} \quad\quad\quad\quad\quad (10)$$

Where R_{PG} = revenue from product generation, Q = quantity of a certain product, and P_i = selling price of each product. The optimisation objective is then formulated to maximise the summation of the different costs subtracted from the revenue of each application as indicated in Eq (11).

Maximise $Profit = \sum_{i=1}^{4}((R_{PG} - C_{PG} - SG_T) * GF_i) - C_{BP} - B_C - B_T$ (11)

Where GF_i = Generation fraction of each product based on the required minimum quantity. These fractions limit the minimum requirement of each utilisation technique to the national needs where for the case of Qatar, urea is represented by 0.032, methanol by 0.0085, liquid fuels by 0.00032 and power by 0.042 (AlNouss et al., 2019a). The optimisation problem is subject to different constraints as specifiedby Eq (12) through (14).

Subject to $Q_B \leq Available\ biomass\ feedstock$ (12)
$\quad\quad\quad\quad\quad\quad Q_B \geq 0.1$ To prevent mathematical problems   (13)
$\quad\quad\quad\quad\quad\quad GF_i \geq minimum\ requirement\ of\ each\ utilisation$ (14)
$\quad\quad\quad\quad\quad\quad \sum_{i}^{n} GF_i \leq 1$ (15)
$\quad\quad\quad\quad\quad\quad \sum_{i}^{n} d_i * x_i \leq 1$ (16)

Where x_i represents the applicability of this distance in the geospatial information systems for a minimum distance to be traveled by either biomass source using the expressway and road network or syngas intermediate product using the service pipeline corridors. This is achieved through calculating the shortest distance between latitude and longitude points on the available network map over the earth's surface.

3. Case Study

The integrated (GIS)-based decision framework with statistical learning and heuristic optimisation capabilities is implemented in the case study of Qatar. Table 1 summarises the main raw data used in the case study.

Table 1: Raw data of Qatar's case study.

Parameter	Value	Unit
Biomass Price ($B_{p,i}$)	10	\$/Ton
Cost per distance (biomass) (C_d)	1	\$/km
Capacity of one transfer (C_T)	1000	Ton
Cost of one segment of pipline (syngas) (C_{Seg})	2	\$/km
Capacity of pipe (CP_{Seg})	1000	kg/s

The local biomass sources are identified by several map locations that include 11 locations for date pit procurement, 3 locations for manure procurement, 4 locations for sludge procurement and 1 location for food waste procurement. The potential biomass processing plant locations are located in the expressway and road network or in the service pipeline corridors where 2453 location points were identified and included in the optimization. The utilisation applications are identified by 2 locations for current gas to liquid (GTL) plants located in Ras Laffan industrial city (RLIC), 1 location for urea and 1 location for methanol located in Mesaieed industrial city (MIC), and 3 locations for power located in RLIC, MIC and Ras Abu Fontas power station. The optimisation problem is formulated as a mixed integer nonlinear programming (MINLP) and solved using the genetic algorithm (GA) in Matlab. The formulation consists of 63,786 decision variables, 2453 integers/binary and 44 constraints.

4. Results

The results of the optimisation problem are in the from of optimum biomass blended feedstock, optimum polygeneration mix and optimum locations of biomass sources, processing plant and application sinks. The optimum biomass blended feedstock presented in Figure 4 demonstrates a domination of manure-based biomass with around 60,118 kg/h. Whereas the optimum polygeneration mix illustrated in Figure 5 suggests methanol as the optimal biomass utilisation technique with more than 93%. The overall objective function highlights a net revenure \$6.5M per year coming mainly from methanol and power production. These results demonstrate the potential of manure utilisation and methanol production in supporting the national waste utilisation and emissions reduction in Qatar. The optimum locations of biomass sources, processing plant and application sinks are highlighted in the network map of Qatar in Figure 6. The location of the biomass processing plant is placed near to the manure procurement source. The applications sinks are mainly selected in MIC with only the GTL plant located in RLIC.

Figure 4: Optimum biomass blends.

■ Manure ■ Dates ■ Sludge ■ Food Waste

■ Urea ■ Methanol ■ Power ■ BTL

Figure 5: Optimum polygeneration mix.

Figure 6: Optimum locations map.

5. Conclusions

This paper study the development of a geospatial information systems (GIS)-based decision framework integrated with statistical learning and heuristic optimisation capabilities in order to establish the design solutions for biomass supply chains on a national scale and subsequent strategic decision-making. The proposed framework potentially enables stakeholders to rapidly assess alternative designs under different scenarios of the biomass supply chains, in both the local and international context. The implementation of the framework is illustrated through a biomass gasification case study in the state of Qatar where manure utilisation and methanol production dominated the national biomass supply chain.

Acknowledgment

The authors acknowledge the support of Qatar National Research Fund (QNRF) (a member of Qatar Foundation) by GSRA grant No GSRA4-1-0518-17082.

References

A. AlNouss, G. McKay, and T. Al-Ansari, 2018, Optimum utilization of biomass for the production of power and fuels using gasification, Computer Aided Chemical Engineering, 43, 1481-86.

A. AlNouss, G. McKay, and T. Al-Ansari, 2019a, Superstructure Optimization for the Production of Fuels, Fertilizers and Power using Biomass Gasification, Computer Aided Chemical Engineering, 46, 301-06.

A. AlNouss, G. McKay, and T. Al-Ansari, 2019b, A techno-economic-environmental study evaluating the potential of oxygen-steam biomass gasification for the generation of value-added products, Energy Conversion and Management, 196, 664-76.

A. AlNouss, G. McKay, and T. Al-Ansari, 2020, Production of syngas via gasification using optimum blends of biomass, Journal of Cleaner Production, 242, 118499.

R. Rodríguez, P. Gauthier-Maradei, and H. Escalante, 2017, Fuzzy spatial decision tool to rank suitable sites for allocation of bioenergy plants based on crop residue, Biomass and Bioenergy, 100, 17-30.

A. Salah, L. Hanel, M. Beirow, and G. Scheffknecht, 2016, Modelling SER Biomass Gasification Using Dynamic Neural Networks, Computer Aided Chemical Engineering, 38, 19-24.

B. Sharma, R.G. Ingalls, C.L. Jones, and A. Khanchi, 2013, Biomass supply chain design and analysis: Basis, overview, modeling, challenges, and future, Renewable and Sustainable Energy Reviews, 24, 608-27.

Sauro Pierucci, Flavio Manenti, Giulia Bozzano, Davide Manca (Eds.)
Proceedings of the 30th European Symposium on Computer Aided Process Engineering
(ESCAPE30), May 24-27, 2020, Milano, Italy. © 2020 Elsevier B.V. All rights reserved.
http://dx.doi.org/10.1016/B978-0-12-823377-1.50273-1

Optimising Multi Biomass Feedstock Utilisation Considering a Multi Technology Approach

Tareq Al-Ansari [a,b*], Ahmed AlNouss[a], Mohammad Alherbawi , Nayla Al-Thani[a], Prakash Parthasarathy[a], Samar ElKhalifa[a], Gordon Mckay[a]

[a]Divison of Sustainable Development, College of Science and Engineering, Hamad Bin Khalifa University, Qatar Foundation, Doha, Qatar.
[b]Division of Engineering Management and Decision Sciences, College of Science and Engineering, Hamad Bin Khalifa University, Doha, Qatar.
talansari@hbku.edu.qa

Abstract

As effects of climate change and resource scarcity disturb the modern world, there is an urgent need to shift from the traditional fossil fuel-based economy towards a more sustainable future. Transitioning towards a bio-economy can serve waste reduction and energy diversification objectives. Whilst technologies continue to develop that are capable of processing a wide array of wastes as feedstock, it is necessary to devise methodologies that optimise strategic decisions within bio-economies and increase the competitiveness with traditional fossil fuel-based industries. As such, the objective of this study is to develop an integrated framework that can inform optimal technological pathways for the conversion of various biomass waste into value-added products. The biomass feedstock include: date seeds, municipal solid waste, food waste, camel manure, and sludge. To achieve this objective, a two stage optimisation framework is developed based on three technologies; gasification, pyrolysis, hydrothermal liquefaction. Outputs of process specific models are used in a multi-objective mathematical formulation model to identify optimal pathways that encompass technology pathways and corresponding value-added product for each waste type. The mathematical model maximises the total revenue and minimises total emissions within the waste to value added product pathways. The simulation results demonstrate that the process yield of syngas production using gasification is higher than the pyrolysis for the date seeds, MSW, food wastes, and camel manure by about 58.67%, 69.81%, 60.38%, and 58.32% respectively. The results of the optimisation indicate the need to improve the efficiency of the hydrothermal liquefaction process, which is the optimal pathway to produce bio-oil from date seeds alone. However, for the other waste types, the gasification process is the preferred technology discarding bio-oil quality.

Keywords: Bioenergy, Aspen Plus, Gasification, pyrolysis, hydrothermal liquefaction

1. Introduction

Extracting value from biomass, which would have otherwise been disposed of as waste is an important component of circular and bio-economies. By extension, bio-economies involve the sustainable transformation of renewable organic resources into food, energy, and other essential products. There are various types of waste that are produced from both urban and industrial ecosystems that have potential to be recycled into valued added products such as food waste, animal manure, municipal solid waste, sewage sludge. As such, the objective of this paper is to explore the optimal pathways for which particular feedstock can be converted into value-added products through various technology options. However, the challenge is identify optimum technology pathway for the different feedstock determined by the quality of products, environmental and economic dimensions. The three processes considered in this study include gasification, pyrolysis, and hydrothermal liquefaction as illustrated in Figure 1 and will form the basis of process models developed. Pyrolysis is the thermal decomposition of biomass in the absence of oxygen to form bio-char and bio-oil. It has the potential to produce highly porous solids used as adsorbents and catalytic support materials (Elkhalifa et al., 2019). In this process, the pseudo-biomass components; hemicellulose, cellulose, and lignin, undergo thermal decomposition in the temperature ranges of 220-315 ℃, 314-400 ℃ and 160-900 ℃, respectively, to yield varying composition of the gaseous components (Yang et al., 2007). Gasification is a promising technique in the utilisation of biomass for the generation of high-energy combustible gas (Sikarwar et al., 2016). It is defined as the process of converting carbon-based materials thermochemically into synthesis gas using a gasifiying agent such as oxygen and steam. It can also generate pyrolysis products such as bio-fuels and bio-char. The gasification processes are usually distinguished by reactor conditions that ranges from low temperature (425-650 ℃) to medium and high temperatures of (900-1050 ℃) and (1250-1600 ℃), respectively, and atmospheric pressure to high pressurised gasifiers. These conditions influence the oxygen and steam demand of the gasification process along with the H_2:CO ratio in syngas and the presence of the pyrolysis products (AlNouss et al., 2020). Hydrothermal Liquefaction (HTL) is a thermochemical conversion of wet biomass into liquid bio-crude using pressurised hot water operating at high temperatures between 250 – 400 °C and pressures between 50 – 200 bar (Ramirez et al., 2015). During HTL, water acts as a reactant, therefore, biomass can be converted directly without the need to the energy-intensive drying step as in pyrolysis technology (Toor et al., 2011).

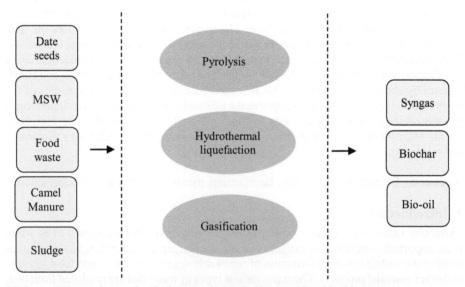

Figure 1: Biomass thermochemical conversion pathways considered in this study.

2. Methodology

2.1 Process descriptions

The gasification model in this paper is simulated using on the basis of atmospheric pressure with medium temperature gasification at 850 °C, isothermal and steady state operations. The fluid package is selected to be Peng-Robinson with Boston-Mathias modification to account for nonpolar and real components presented in the model. The main operation units considered in the model include a decomposition rector that uses a calculator block to convert the nonconventional attributes presented in Table 1 into conventional components. The stream is then introduced into a solid separator to remove ash content from the gaseous mixture that is sent to the gasification reactor. Steam is introduced in the gasifier as a gasifying agent with a steam to biomass ratio of 0.75. The gasifier is simulated as a Gibbs reactor where the equilibrium is restricted through minimisation of Gibbs free energy. The model is valeted against available literature models (AlNouss et al., 2019; 2018). Whereas, the pyrolysis model is simulated based on the assumptions of kinetic-free equilibrium, steady state operation, 500 °C decomposition temperature and atmospheric pressure. After decomposing the nonconventional attributes presented in Table 1 into conventional components, the stream enters a cyclone unit to separate ash and char solids from the gaseous species. The gaseous stream is cooled to separate the condensable components and yield the two products; syngas and bio-oil. The solid stream enters another solid separator to purify char product from ash (Elkhalifa et al., 2019).

Table 1: Feedstock Characteristics.

Biomass	Date seeds	MSW	Food waste	Camel manure	Sludge
Proximate analysis (%)	Air dried-basis	As-received	As-received	Air dried-basis	As received
Moisture	0.33	7.56	10	4.34	39.29
Fixed carbon	14.99	24.21	33.07	28.51	19.49
Volatile matter	83.61	57.99	61.14	51.56	18.07
Ash	1.40	17.80	5.79	19.94	62.44
Ultimate analysis (%)	Dry-basis	Dry-basis	Dry-basis	Dry-basis	Dry-basis
Ash	1.4	16.45	5.8	19.94	62.44
Carbon	46.48	49.02	43.99	36.73	7.63
Hydrogen	6.54	5.24	4.9	5.55	1.54
Nitrogen	0.89	1.23	2.07	2.62	1.2
Cl	0	0	0	0	0
Sulphur	0	0.3	0.19	0.42	0.28
Oxygen	44.69	27.76	43.05	34.74	26.91

Aspen Plus (V.9) ® is used to develop the different thermochemical conversion models. Whereby, biomass feeds are defined as nonconventional components based on their proximate and elemental values presented in Table 1. Biomass is defined based on Aspen's built-in enthalpy and density correlations of coal, identified as HCOALGEN and DCOALIGT respectively. Char is defined as 100% carbon. Biomass feeds initially undergo decomposition to breakdown nonconventional components into their corresponding conventional elements. Prediction of resulted elements' yield is calculated based on the Fortran code introduced by (AlNouss et al., 2018). Ash is then separated from the mixture before processing the stream into the main reactors. In the HTL model, a slurry is created via mixing the biomass feed with a hot and pressurized water before being pumped into the HTL reactor. Besides, sodium hydroxide alkali catalyst is added to biomass slurry to increase the possibility of oil-like products formation (Cao et al., 2017). Block "RGibbs" is used to represent the HTL reactor, which operates based on the principle of minimizing Gibbs free energy. The reactor is operated at 300°C and 150 bars. At these reaction conditions, water is preserved in sub-critical state, thus, has lower viscosity and higher solubility of organic compounds. Possible products of the process are defined based on earlier reports (Pedersen et al., 2017). The downstream process is initiated with solids separation. Consecutively, gases are separated by partial cooling of products, while the aqueous phase is separated from the bio-crude using a distillation column that consists of 6 stages and operates at atmospheric pressure with a reflux ratio of 1.

2.2 Optimsation framework

The optimisation framework determines the optimum technology to treat each waste type into useful products i.e. syngas, char, and bio-oil. The problem was formulated as 0-1 integer programming with two objectives which were solved sequentially. The first objective is an economical objective that aims to maximise the profit, while the second objective in an environmental objective which aims to minimise the total emissions represented as tonnes of CO_2 equivalent per year. The problem is subject to a logical constraint which ensures that each waste type will be treated by only one technology.

Table 2: Optimisation variables.

	indices
K = 1,2, ..., k	technology types
J = 1,2, ..., j	product types
I = 1,2, ..., i	waste types
	Parameters
C_{jki}	the cost associated with producing product j from waste i using technology k
P_{ijk}	the selling price of the product j from waste I using technology k
E_{jki}	the emissions associated with producing product j from waste i using technology k
	Decision Variable
x_{jki}	$\begin{cases} 1, & \text{if technology } k \text{ will be used to produce product } j \text{ from waste} \\ 0, & \text{otherwise} \end{cases}$

Objective function:

$$Economic:\ \max \sum_{I=1}^{i} \sum_{K=1}^{k} \sum_{J=1}^{j} [(P_{ijk}x_{jki}) - (C_{jki}x_{jki})]$$

$$Envirnomental:\ \min \sum_{I=1}^{i} \sum_{K=1}^{k} \sum_{J=1}^{j} (E_{jki}x_{jki})$$

Subject to:

$$\sum_{K=1}^{k} x_{jki} \leq 1 \qquad \forall\, I = 1,2,\dots,i;\, J = 1,2,\dots,j$$

3. Results

The results of the economical objective maximization illustrated in Figure 2 suggest that for the date seeds the gasification is the best option to produce syngas, while for the char and bio-oil, pyrolysis and HT liquefaction are the optimal conversion pathways, respectively. Additionally, gasification turned out to be the optimal option to produce both syngas and bio-oil from MSW, food waste, and the camel manure, while pyrolysis is the optimal option for the production of char. However, the results from the environmental objective maximisation illustrated in Figure 3 suggest that bio-oil is to be produced by pyrolysis while syngas and char to be produced by HT liquefaction for all waste types in order to minimise the environmental effect of the processes. These results represent overall production pathways discarding products quality, hence further analysis shall be done to explain and improve the results.

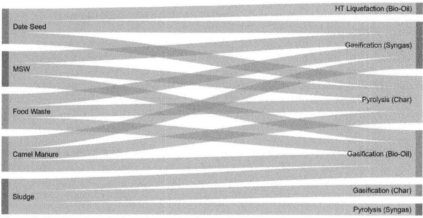

Figure 2: Feedstock and tehcnology selection pathways considering economic objective.

Figure 3: Feedstock and tehcnology selection pathways considering environmental objective.

4. Conclusion

Considering the development of multiple technologies that can treat similar feedstock, it is important to devise decision tools that determine the best pathway for a particular feedstock in terms of environmental impact and economic feasibility. Preliminary work introduced in this study formulated the problem using a 0-1 integer programming where the two objectives were solved sequentially. The results demonstrate that the gasification dominate the conversion pathway from economic prespective to produce syngas and bio-oil while pyrolysis is the optimal technology to produce char. From environmental perspective, HT liquefaction was found to be the optimal pathway to produce syngas and char, while pyrolysis is the optimal pathway to generate bio-oil. Future work will include development of the optimisation solver to solve environmental and economic objectives concurrently and study the effect on the technology selection. In addition, the model could be expanded to include more constraints such as water, and energy requirements for the processes and to pay more attention to the quality of generated products from the different conversion pathways.

References

A. AlNouss, G. McKay, and T. Al-Ansari, 2018, Optimum utilization of biomass for the production of power and fuels using gasification, Computer Aided Chemical Engineering, 43, 1481-86.

A. AlNouss, G. McKay, and T. Al-Ansari, 2019, A techno-economic-environmental study evaluating the potential of oxygen-steam biomass gasification for the generation of value-added products, Energy Conversion and Management, 196, 664-76.

A. AlNouss, G. McKay, and T. Al-Ansari, 2020, Production of syngas via gasification using optimum blends of biomass, Journal of Cleaner Production, 242, 118499.

L. Cao, C. Zhang, H. Chen, D.C.W. Tsang, G. Luo, S. Zhang, and J. Chen, 2017, Hydrothermal liquefaction of agricultural and forestry wastes: state-of-the-art review and future prospects, Bioresource technology, 245, 1184-93.

S. Elkhalifa, A. AlNouss, T. Al-Ansari, H.R. Mackey, P. Parthasarathy, and G. McKay, 2019, Simulation of Food Waste Pyrolysis for the Production of Biochar: A Qatar Case Study, Computer Aided Chemical Engineering, 46, 901-06.

T.H. Pedersen, C.U. Jensen, L. Sandström, and L.A. Rosendahl, 2017, Full characterization of compounds obtained from fractional distillation and upgrading of a HTL biocrude, Applied Energy, 202, 408-19.

J.A. Ramirez, R.J. Brown, and T.J. Rainey, 2015, A review of hydrothermal liquefaction bio-crude properties and prospects for upgrading to transportation fuels, Energies, 8, 7, 6765-94.

V.S. Sikarwar, M. Zhao, P. Clough, J. Yao, X. Zhong, M.Z. Memon, N. Shah, E.J. Anthony, and P.S. Fennell, 2016, An overview of advances in biomass gasification, Energy & Environmental Science, 9, 10, 2939-77.

S.S. Toor, L. Rosendahl, and A. Rudolf, 2011, Hydrothermal liquefaction of biomass: A review of subcritical water technologies, Energy, 36, 5, 2328-42.

H. Yang, R. Yan, H. Chen, D.H. Lee, and C. Zheng, 2007, Characteristics of hemicellulose, cellulose and lignin pyrolysis, Fuel, 86, 12, 1781-88.

Sauro Pierucci, Flavio Manenti, Giulia Bozzano, Davide Manca (Eds.)
Proceedings of the 30th European Symposium on Computer Aided Process Engineering
(ESCAPE30), May 24-27, 2020, Milano, Italy. © 2020 Elsevier B.V. All rights reserved.
http://dx.doi.org/10.1016/B978-0-12-823377-1.50274-3

Data-Driven Model Development for Cardiomyocyte Production Experimental Failure Prediction

Bianca Williams[a], Caroline Halloin[b], Wiebke Löbel[b],Ferdous Finklea[a], Elizabeth Lipke[a], Robert Zweigerdt[b], Selen Cremaschi[a]*

aAuburn University, Department of Chemical Engineering, Auburn, AL, USA
bLeibniz Research Laboratories for Biotechnology and Artificial Organs (LEBAO), Department of Cardiac, Thoracic, Transplantation, and Vascular Surgery, Hannover Medical School, 30625 Hannover, Germany
selen-cremaschi@auburn.edu

Abstract

Cardiovascular diseases (CVD) are the leading cause of death worldwide. Engineered heart tissue produced by differentiation of human induced pluripotent stem cells may provide an encompassing treatment for heart failure due to CVD. However, considerable difficulties exist in producing the large number of cardiomyocytes needed for therapeutic purposes through differentiation protocols. Data-driven modeling with machine learning techniques has the potential to identify factors that significantly affect the outcomes of these differentiation experiments. Using data from previous cardiac differentiation experiments, we have developed data-driven modeling methods for determining which experimental conditions are most influential on the final cardiomyocyte content of a differentiation experiment. With those identified conditions, we were able to build classification models that can predict whether an experiment will have a sufficient cardiomyocyte content to continue with the experiment on the seventh (out of 10) day of the differentiation with a 90% accuracy. This early failure prediction will provide cost and time savings, as each day the differentiation continues requires significant resources.

Keywords: cardiac differentiation, machine learning, random forests

1. Introduction

Cardiovascular diseases (CVD) are the leading cause of death worldwide, meaning there are more deaths annually due to CVD than any other cause. These diseases can lead to heart attacks, which can result in the loss of more than one billion heart cells, leading to congestive heart failure (Kempf, Andree, et al., 2016). Patients who suffer from advanced stages of heart failure have a poor prognosis for survival, and the large disparity between numbers of donors and recipients leaves few viable treatments. Artificial prosthetic hearts and heart assist devices have demonstrated some success in prolonging the lives of patients receiving treatment, but their development is slow and clinical trials have seen limited. Due to the nature of heart transplants and the stigma surrounding artificial organs, engineered heart tissue may provide an encompassing treatment for heart failure (Kempf, Andree, et al., 2016).

Mature cardiomyocytes, the contracting cells in the heart, are some of the least regenerative cells in the body. This characteristic carries over into the laboratory environment and thus limits in vitro expansion capabilities of cardiomyocytes.

Difficulties in direct culture of cardiomyocytes can be overcome by differentiation from human pluripotent stem cells (hiPSCs) (Kempf, Andree, et al., 2016). The indefinite turnover potential of pluripotent cells allows for the expansion of large quantities for differentiation into therapeutic engineered tissues. However, the differentiation of hiPSCs into specific cell types is a highly complex and costly process that is sensitive to the impact of a high number of factors (Gaspari et al., 2018), and significant difficulties exist in reliably and consistently producing the large number of cardiomyocytes needed for therapeutic purposes (Kempf, Andree, et al., 2016).

Data-driven modeling with machine learning techniques has the potential to identify factors and patterns that most significantly affect the outcomes of these differentiation experiments. Previously, machine learning techniques have successfully been used to identify key factors and assist in optimization for production of several proteins and cell lines (Sokolov et al., 2017; Zhou et al., 2018). The goal of this work is to use machine learning techniques to identify key process parameters to be used in predictive modeling of bioreactor cardiac differentiation outcomes. The high number of experimental factors that influence the differentiation results in a large set of possible inputs to be considered for modeling. This high data dimensionality, in addition to the low number of data points due to the time-consuming nature of these experiments, represent significant challenges for modeling the differentiation process. Our aim is to use machine learning models to predict whether or not the cardiomyocyte content at the end of differentiation process will be sufficiently high. We define insufficient production as having a cardiomyocyte content on the tenth day of differentiation (dd10) that is less than 90%, meaning less than 90% of the cells produced at the end of the differentiation are cardiomyocytes. Predicting if the cardiomyocyte content will be insufficient before the end of the differentiation will provide cost and time savings, as each day the differentiation continues requires significant resources.

Using existing data from bioreactor experiments, we have applied feature selection techniques, including correlations, principal component analysis, and built-in feature selection in machine learning models, to identify the conditions in the bioreactor, which we define as bioreactor features, are the most influential on and predictive of the cardiomyocyte content. Bioreactor features considered include values related to the cell concentration, size of cell aggregates, pH, dissolved oxygen concentration, and concentrations and timings of certain nutrients, such as glucose, and small molecules known to direct the differentiation. We then used the identified features as inputs to build models to classify the resulting cardiomyocyte content of a particular bioreactor run as being sufficient or insufficient to justify continuing with the differentiation.

2. Machine Learning Techniques for Cardiomyocyte Content Prediction

2.1. Multivariate Adaptive Regression Splines (MARS)

Multivariate adaptive regression spline (MARS) models are made up of a linear summation of basis functions. The three types of possible basis functions are a constant, a hinge function (or "spline"), or a product of two or more hinge functions. The training of a MARS model starts with an initial model that is a constant value equal to the mean of the data outputs. On its initial training pass, the model is overfit to the data using a greedy algorithm, adding basis functions to reduce the sum of the squared errors (SSE) between the given and predicted outputs. Then, a backward, pruning pass is performed to remove terms that have little effect on the SSE until the best model is identified based on generalized cross validation (GCV) criteria (Friedman, 1991). In order to make cardiomyocyte content classifications, MARS models were trained to predict the value of the cardiomyocyte content using the selected bioreactor features as inputs, and a classification was assigned based on the predicted value.

2.2. Random Forests (RF)

Random forest (RF) models are machine learning models that make output predictions by combining outcomes from a sequence of regression decision trees. Each tree is constructed independently and depends on a random vector sampled from the input data, with all the trees in the forest having the same distribution. The predictions from the forests are averaged using bootstrap aggregation and random feature selection. RF models have been demonstrated to be robust predictors for both small sample sizes and high dimensional data (Biau & Scornet, 2016). RF classification models were constructed that directly classified bioreactor runs as having sufficient or insufficient cardiomyocyte content.

2.3. Gaussian Process Regression (GPR)

Gaussian process regression (GPR) is a method of interpolation where interpolated values are modeled by a Gaussian process governed by prior covariances. Under suitable assumptions on the priors, GPR gives the best linear unbiased prediction of the intermediate values (Rasmussen & Williams, 2005). It uses a kernel function as measure of similarity between points to predict the value for an unseen point from the training data. This method has been successfully used with small dataset sizes. In order to make cardiomyocyte content classifications, GPR models trained were similarly to the MARS models.

3. Data Collection and Feature Selection Methods

3.1. Experimental Data

Experimental data was generated and collected from 58 cardiac differentiation experiments performed by (Halloin et al., 2019). The differentiation experiments were carried out in chemically defined conditions in stirred tank bioreactors. Details of the experiments are described in Halloin et al. (2019). The set of independent variables include experimental conditions such as the rotation speed in the bioreactor and measurements such as differentiation day dependent cell densities and aggregate sizes, and continuous time measurements of dissolved oxygen (DO) concentration and pH. The set of independent variables measured from the experiments was expanded to include engineered features such as estimated gradients in cell densities and DO concentrations, resulting in a total of 101 variables, which we refer to as bioreactor features. The dependent variable is the percentage of the cells in the bioreactor that have differentiated into cardiomyocytes, or the cardiomyocyte content, on the last day of the differentiation experiment, dd10. Data from 42 of the experiments was designated as training data and used for feature selection and classification model construction. The remaining experiments were reserved as test data for testing the classification models.

3.2. Feature Selection Methods

We performed feature selection using the training data set in order to discover which of the bioreactor features were most influential on the cardiomyocyte content. The set of features considered consists of all the collected bioreactor features measured up until the seventh day of differentiation (dd7).

3.2.1. Correlations

The Pearson and Spearman correlations (Bonett & Wright, 2000) between the collected bioreactor features and the cardiomyocyte content were calculated. The Pearson correlation measures the strength of the linear relationship between two variables. It has a value between -1 to 1, with a value of -1 meaning a total negative linear correlation, 0 being no correlation, and +1 meaning a total positive correlation. The Spearman correlation measures the strength of a monotonic relationship between two variables with the same scaling as the Pearson correlation.

3.2.2. Principal Component Analysis
Principal component analysis (PCA) converts a set of possibly correlated variables into a set of linearly uncorrelated ones through an orthogonal transformation (Hotelling, 1933). The resulting principal components (PCs) are linear combinations of the original set of variables.

3.2.3. Machine Learning Technique Built-In Feature Selection
Each of the machine learning techniques applied has its own method for selecting features and ranking their predictive importance. During the MARS model construction, a pruning pass is performed over the model that removes terms and features based on the level of their effect on GCV criteria. For RF models, features are selected based on how well they improve the separation of the data at each decision node. GPR selects features using its built-in automatic relevance determination method.

4. Classification Performance Metrics

The metrics used to evaluate the performance of the classification models (i.e., the classification of insufficient/sufficient cardiomyocyte content) are accuracy, precision, (Sokolova & Lapalme, 2009), and the Matthews correlation coefficient (MCC) (Matthews, 1975). The accuracy is the proportion of the classifications made by the models that were correct. Given that the classification model predicts an insufficient cardiomyocyte content for a bioreactor run, precision is the probability that the cardiomyocyte content of that run will actually be insufficient. The MCC is the correlation between actual and predicted classifications. It has the same range and scale of the Pearson and Spearman correlations. Figure 1 depicts the workflow of the process taken to construct the models and calculate the performance metrics.

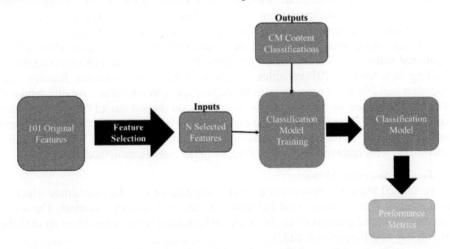

Figure 1-Feature selection and model training process (CM = cardiomyocyte)

5. Results and Discussion

5.1. Feature Selection Results

PCA of the collected feature set yielded five principal components that explained 94% of the variance in the input data. Correlations and PCA did not yield any results for significant features, with the strongest linear correlation between a feature and the cardiomyocyte content being -0.51, with the time that the IWP2 molecule remained in the bioreactor. The strongest linear correlation between the PCs and the cardiomyocyte content was 0.16. However, we had success in reducing the feature set using the built-in feature selection methods of each of the machine learning approaches investigated. From the original 101 features, MARS, RF and GPR identified 12, 12, and 7 significant features, respectively. Common features that were selected as significant include the cell densities and their gradients during the first two days of the differentiation protocol (dd0 and dd1). This selection agrees with previous experimental studies concluding that cell density during early differentiation influences differentiation into specific cell lineages (Kempf, Olmer, et al., 2016).

5.2. Classification Model Results

Results for classification model performance are summarized in Tables 1 and 2. The performance metrics in Table 1 were calculated using the leave one out (LOO) cross validation (Wong, 2015) on the training data. Two classification models were trained for each method. One model utilized the bioreactor features selected by the built-in feature selection as the inputs, and the other employed the PCs obtained from PCA as the inputs.

Table 1 – Performance of classification models on training data evaluated using LOO cross validation

	MARS		RF		GPR	
	Features	PCA	Features	PCA	Features	PCA
Accuracy	0.74	0.64	**0.90**	0.74	**0.90**	0.67
Precision	0.81	0.66	**0.90**	0.74	**0.93**	0.67
MCC	0.55	-0.11	**0.78**	0.36	**0.79**	0

For all of the machine learning techniques tested, the classification models using the model-selected features yielded better performance (Table 1). This suggests that while the principal components successfully explain the variance in the data, they fail to accurately characterize the relationship between the features and the cardiomyocyte content. RF models and GPR had similar performance with an accuracy and precision both of about 90%, while MARS models did not perform as accurately.

Table 2 – Performance of classification models on test data

	RF	GPR
Accuracy	0.89	0.89
Precision	0.92	0.87
MCC	0.72	0.72

The performances of the RF and GPR classification models trained using the model-selected features were evaluated on the test data (Table 2). Both classification models performed comparably for the test data with an accuracy of 89%, precisions near 90%, and MCC values of 0.72. The results obtained for the test data are comparable to those obtained from LOO cross validation on the training data, indicating that the models accurately captured the relationship between the features and the cardiomyocyte content, while avoiding overfitting.

6. Conclusions and Future Directions

Using existing data from previously conducted cardiac differentiation experiments, we were able to identify on dd7 if an experiment would have an insufficient final cardiomyocyte content of less than 90% with accuracy and precision of about 90% with both RF and GPR models. We were able to make these predictions using less than 16% of the collected features. Future work with this data will focus on predicting the experimental outcomes at earlier timepoints in the differentiation. This modeling will enable the early interruption of failing experiments, providing cost and time savings.

Acknowledgements

This work was partially funded by Department of Education GAANN grant #P200A150075 and NSF grant #1743445.

References

Biau, G., & Scornet, E. (2016). Rejoinder on: A random forest guided tour. Test, 25, 264-268.

Bonett, D. G., & Wright, T. A. (2000). Sample size requirements for estimating Pearson, Kendall and Spearman correlations. Psychometrika, 65, 23-28.

Friedman, J. H. (1991). Multivariate Adaptive Regression Splines - Rejoinder. Annals of Statistics, 19, 123-141.

Gaspari, E., Franke, A., Robles-Diaz, D., Zweigerdt, R., Roeder, I., Zerjatke, T., & Kempf, H. (2018). Paracrine mechanisms in early differentiation of human pluripotent stem cells: Insights from a mathematical model. Stem Cell Res, 32, 1-7.

Halloin, C., Schwanke, K., Lobel, W., Franke, A., Szepes, M., Biswanath, S., Wunderlich, S., Merkert, S., Weber, N., Osten, F., de la Roche, J., Polten, F., Wollert, K., Kraft, T., Fischer, M., Martin, U., Gruh, I., Kempf, H., & Zweigerdt, R. (2019). Continuous WNT Control Enables Advanced hPSC Cardiac Processing and Prognostic Surface Marker Identification in Chemically Defined Suspension Culture. Stem Cell Reports.

Hotelling, H. (1933). Analysis of a complex of statistical variables into principal components. Journal of Educational Psychology, 24, 417-441.

Kempf, H., Andree, B., & Zweigerdt, R. (2016). Large-scale production of human pluripotent stem cell derived cardiomyocytes. Advanced Drug Delivery Reviews, 96, 18-30.

Kempf, H., Olmer, R., Haase, A., Franke, A., Bolesani, E., Schwanke, K., Robles-Diaz, D., Coffee, M., Gohring, G., Drager, G., Potz, O., Joos, T., Martinez-Hackert, E., Haverich, A., Buettner, F. F. R., Martin, U., & Zweigerdt, R. (2016). Bulk cell density and Wnt/TGFbeta signalling regulate mesendodermal patterning of human pluripotent stem cells. Nature Communications, 7.

Matthews, B. W. (1975). Comparison of Predicted and Observed Secondary Structure of T4 Phage Lysozyme. Biochimica Et Biophysica Acta, 405, 442-451.

Rasmussen, C. E., & Williams, C. K. I. (2005). Gaussian Processes for Machine Learning. Adaptive Computation and Machine Learning, 1-247.

Sokolov, M., Ritscher, J., MacKinnon, N., Souquet, J., Broly, H., Morbidelli, M., & Butte, A. (2017). Enhanced process understanding and multivariate prediction of the relationship between cell culture process and monoclonal antibody quality. Biotechnol Prog, 33, 1368-1380.

Sokolova, M., & Lapalme, G. (2009). A systematic analysis of performance measures for classification tasks. Information Processing & Management, 45, 427-437.

Wong, T. T. (2015). Performance evaluation of classification algorithms by k-fold and leave-one-out cross validation. Pattern Recognition, 48, 2839-2846.

Zhou, Y., Li, G., Dong, J., Xing, X. H., Dai, J., & Zhang, C. (2018). MiYA, an efficient machine-learning workflow in conjunction with the YeastFab assembly strategy for combinatorial optimization of heterologous metabolic pathways in Saccharomyces cerevisiae. Metab Eng, 47, 294-302.

Sauro Pierucci, Flavio Manenti, Giulia Bozzano, Davide Manca (Eds.)
Proceedings of the 30th European Symposium on Computer Aided Process Engineering
(ESCAPE30), May 24-27, 2020, Milano, Italy. © 2020 Elsevier B.V. All rights reserved.
http://dx.doi.org/10.1016/B978-0-12-823377-1.50275-5

Simulation of Multi-stage Lactic Acid Salting-out Extraction using Ethanol and Ammonium Sulfate

Andressa N. Marchesan, Ingrid L. Motta, Rubens Maciel Filho, Maria Regina W. Maciel

Laboratory of Optimization, Design and Advanced Control, School of Chemical

Engineering, University of Campinas, Av. Albert Einstein 500, Campinas,

13083-852, Brazil

marchesan.andressa@gmail.com

Abstract

Lactic acid obtained through fermentation is an important chemical in the bioeconomy, especially for the production of the biodegradable polymer polylactic acid. However, its production in a larger scale is hindered by its low concentration in the fermentation broth, low volatility, and temperature sensitivity. These characteristics result in high cost for vacuum evaporation and distillation for water removal. Therefore, alternative methods for lactic acid separation have been studied in the literature, including liquid-liquid extraction methods. Salting-out extraction uses the addition of an inorganic salt to reduce the mutual solubility between water and a solvent, thus resulting in a two-phase system. In this work, salting-out extraction of lactic acid using ethanol as solvent and ammonium sulfate as salt was studied using process simulation to define the process conditions that lead to maximum lactic acid recovery and water removal at one-stage and multi-stage extraction scenarios. The simulations were performed using the electrolyte NRTL activity coefficient model (ELECNRTL) in Aspen Plus v8.6, and one-stage simulation was validated with experimental results published in the literature. The results demonstrate that one-stage extraction can yield up to 87 % lactic acid recovery with 35 % of water removal, while counter-current multi-stage extraction can provide more than 96 % recovery with water removal ranging from 47 % to 57 %, and yet requiring lower ethanol volumes, which demonstrates the need for multi-stage experiments in salting-out extraction to validate its performance.

Keywords: lactic acid, salting-out extraction, biorefinery, Aspen Plus, simulation

1. Introduction

The demand for bio-based and biodegradable materials has stimulated the growth of the lactic acid fermentative production and the research on methods to improve the economic competitiveness of this bioproduct. To that end, different approaches have been studied in the literature, including microbial technology, cheaper substrates (Méndez-Alva et al., 2018), and alternative separation methods (Gasca-González *et al.*, 2019). The latter is motivated by the low product concentration, lactic acid's high affinity for water, and low volatility, which result in high purification costs. In this context, salting-out extraction has been studied as an alternative separation method for bioproducts, which is based on the reduced mutual solubility of a solvent and water due to the presence of a salt. However, lactic acid salting-out extraction studies reported in the literature (Ayodogan *et al.*, 2011; Fu *et al.*, 2015) were limited to one-stage separation, which is not very attractive from a large-scale perspective. Considering that, the objective of this work is to use process simulation to assess the performance of multi-stage salting-out extraction.

2. Methods

2.1. Process Simulation

Simulations were performed in Aspen Plus v8.6 using the Electrolyte NRTL activity coefficient model (ELECNRTL) using the equilibrium reaction in Eq. (1), and its equilibrium constant as represented in Eq. (2) (Rumpf *et al.*, 1997) in the liquid-liquid equilibrium calculations. For the ethanol/ion pair parameters, these were assumed to be symmetric (GMELCC = 5), as per the software manual. The non-volatile characteristic of the salt was accounted for in the simulation by setting its natural log of the vapor pressure in N/m² (PLXANT) to -15 and the heat of vaporization (DHVLWT) to zero. To obtain the liquid-liquid equilibrium, the apparent components approach was used. However, in this approach, the salt saturation is not calculated. Therefore, to account for salt precipitation in the aqueous phase, the true components approach was used in the raffinate stream with the reaction represented in Eq. (1) and the salt equilibrium constant in Eq. (3). This approach allows the identification of unfeasible operating conditions.

$$(NH_4)_2 SO_4 \; = \; 2NH_4^+ + SO_4^{2-} \tag{1}$$

$$\ln K = 8.7 \tag{2}$$

$$\ln K = -216.55 + 4262.38/T + 37.52 \cdot \ln(T) - 0.08 \cdot T \tag{3}$$

For model validation, a single equilibrium-stage separator (DECANTER) was used to generate the binodal curve and tie-lines for the system water + ethanol + ammonium sulfate and also single-stage extraction of lactic acid using the same components, which were used for comparison with experimental results reported in the literature.

2.2. Multi-stage extraction and Statistical analysis

Multi-stage extraction simulations were performed using a liquid-liquid extractor model (EXTRACT) at a constant temperature of 25 °C – the temperature has little effect on the lactic acid partition coefficient up to 60 °C for the system under study (Fu *et al.*, 2015). A face-centered composite design was used to assess the effects of the initial lactic acid concentration (**LA**), the mass ratios of ammonium sulfate (**SULF**) and hydrous ethanol (93 wt % ethanol) to water (**ETOH**) in the feed stream, and the number of equilibrium stages (**N-ST**) at a 95.0 % confidence level. This intends to maximize the lactic acid recovery (**LA REC**) and the amount of water removed (**WAT REM**). The mass fraction of precipitated salt (**W SULF**) is also calculated as a model output so that it can be used as a restriction in the optimization studies. Figure 1 presents the simulation flowsheet and the levels used in the statistical analysis. The statistical models were determined through backward elimination, assessed as per the F-test and applied for optimization using the GRG Nonlinear method.

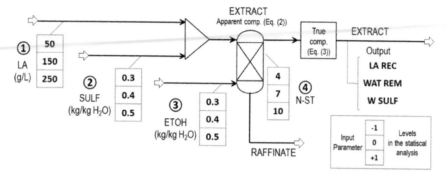

Figure 1: Simulation flowsheet and parameters. 1) Lactic acidc oncentration (g/L); 2) Sulfate to water mass ratio (kg/kg); 3) Ethanol to water mass ratio (kg/kg); 4) Number of equilibrium stages.

3. Results

The validation of results for the one-stage separation demonstrates a good agreement between simulation and experimental results, as shown in Figure 2. Although the LLE calculations underestimate the mass fraction of sulfate in the ethanol-rich phase (Figure 2a), it still provides good acid recovery estimates (Figure 2b).

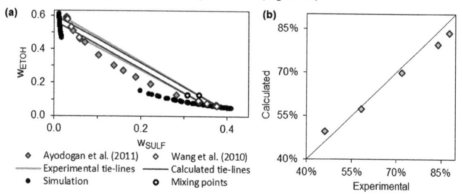

Figure 2: Validation of results: (a) LLE for the system ethanol + ammonium sulfate + water at 298.15 K (Wang *et al.*, 2010; Ayodogan *et al.*, 2011); (b) Lactic acid recovery in one-stage extraction for a 25 g/L solution, experimental results from Fu *et al.* (2015).

Figure 3 presents the simplified Pareto charts of the effects of parameters. The results show that the parameters studied have opposite effects on acid recovery and water removal, which are largely affected by the ethanol-to-water ratio (ETOH). Eq. (4) describes the model for each output (LA REC, WAT REM, W SULF), with their respective parameters listed in Table 1, and the models are illustrated by the response profiles in Figure 4. For each response profile, the other parameters were fixed at the central point. All models presented R^2 and R^2_{adj} above 0.96 and 0.95, respectively, and were significant to the F-test with 95 % confidence. Although ethanol- and sulfate-to-water ratios and lactic acid initial concentration have positive effects on acid recovery, it is possible to observe from Figure 4(c) that higher values for these parameters result in the precipitation of salt (W SULF) and, therefore, result in an unfeasible area of operation.

$$OUTPUT = a_0 + \sum_{i=1}^{4} a_i x_i + \sum_{i=1}^{4} b_i x_i^2 + \sum_{i=1}^{3} \sum_{j=i+1}^{4} c_{ij} x_i x_j \qquad (4)$$

Standardized Effect Estimates

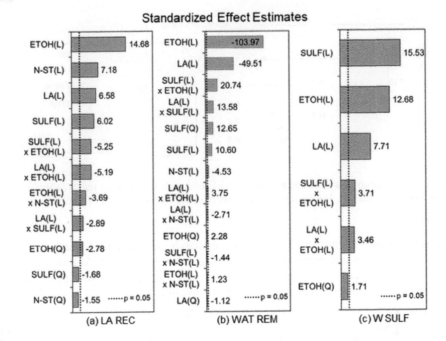

(a) LA REC   (b) WAT REM   (c) W SULF

Figure 3: Pareto charts of parameters` effects on (a) Lactic acid recovery; (b) Water removal; (c) Mass fraction of salt precipitate.

Table 1: Parameters for statistical model (x_1 = LA, x_2 = SULF, x_3 = ETOH, x_4 = N-ST).

Param.	LA REC	WAT REM	W SULF	Param.	LA REC	WAT REM	W SULF
a_0	0.975	0.557	0.048	c_{12}	-0.019	0.018	0
a_1	0.041	-0.062	0.018	c_{13}	-0.035	0.005	0.009
b_1	0	-0.004	0	c_{14}	0	-0.004	0
a_2	0.038	0.013	0.037	c_{23}	-0.035	0.027	0.009
b_2	-0.027	0.040	0	c_{24}	0.000	-0.002	0
a_3	0.092	-0.129	0.030	c_{34}	-0.025	0.002	0
b_3	-0.045	0.007	0.008	R^2	0.973	0.999	0.965
a_4	0.045	-0.006	0	R^2_{adj}	0.951	0.998	0.953
b_4	-0.025	0.000	0				

The output models in Table 1 were used to maximize the acid recovery for each concentration level (50, 150, 250 g/L) with the restriction of a maximum fraction of precipitated salt in the raffinate (W SULF) of 0.01. For comparison, the same approach was used for a single-stage extraction. In this situation, the highest recovery (86.6 %) was obtained for a 50 g/L solution, with a water removal of 35.3 %, requiring the sulfate and ethanol to water ratios of 0.2 and 0.77, respectively. The results for the optimization in Table 2 demonstrate that multi-stage extraction yields higher acid recovery and water removal with lower ethanol use. Although higher recoveries are achieved for more dilute solutions, Case 1 requires larger volumes of salt and ethanol and also produces a more dilute extract (mass percentages: lactic acid – 5 %, water – 51 %, ethanol – 43%). On the other hand, Case 3 produces an extract with 30 wt % lactic acid, 43 wt % water, and 25 wt % ethanol, thus reducing heat duty for further extract concentration.

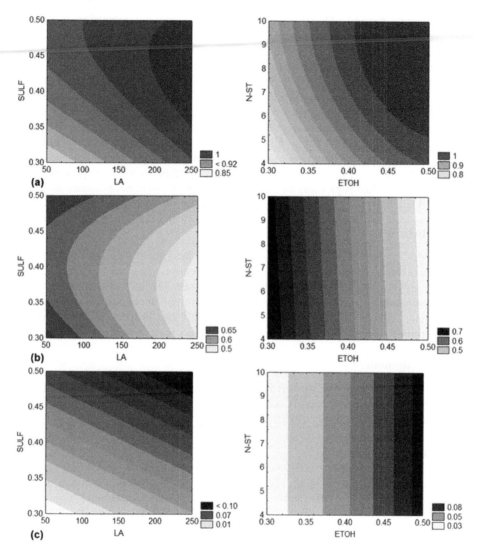

Figure 4: Response profiles of (a) Lactic acid recovery; (b) Water removal (c); Mass fraction of salt precipitate. For each response profile, the other parameters were fixed at the central point.

Table 2: Optimization results (M – statistical model outputs, S – simulation results).

Case	LA	SULF	ETOH	N-ST	LA REC (%)		WAT REM (%)		W SULF	
					M	S	M	S	M	S
1	50	0.3	0.491	8	96.5	98.6	51.9	47.2	0.01	0.03
2	150	0.3	0.395	10	92.6	98.0	58.4	54.4	0.01	0.00
3	250	0.3	0.317	10	90.4	96.0	62.4	57.0	0.01	0.00

To produce high-purity lactic acid, reactive distillation is employed to convert the acid in a more volatile ester by reaction with an alcohol, that is evaporated and then hydrolyzed back to the acid to reach a mass purity of 88 wt % (Gasca-González *et al.*, 2019). However, it requires a pre-concentration step to remove part of the water and drive the reaction equilibrium towards the products, and the entire reactive distillation process has a high energy demand. Therefore, assuming that salting-out extraction is able to selectively separate the acid from fermentation residues, it could be employed as a pre-evaporation step, and simplify the following downstream steps. To illustrate this, a simple four-effect evaporation of the extract from Case 3 to obtain an 88 wt % lactic acid solution was simulated. Without heat integration, the multiple-effect evaporation, the ethanol recovery from the raffinate, and the hydrous ethanol distillation require a reboiler duty of 7235 kJ per kg of lactic acid final product, starting from 24 wt % (250 g/L) in the fermentation broth. For comparison, the reactive distillation process with ethanol reported by Su *et al.* (2013) for a 30 wt % initial lactic acid solution requires ca. 16300 kJ/kg. Although salting-out extraction of a real fermentation broth has been published in the literature (Ayodogan *et al.*, 2011), the distribution of other components present in the broth, such as residual sugars and metabolites were not assessed. Such studies should be performed to allow more detailed simulations and designs of salting-out processes.

4. Conclusions

In this work, process simulation was used to assess lactic acid multi-stage salting-out extraction in terms of the influence of initial acid concentration, salt and solvent amounts, and the number of stages. The results show that it is possible to obtain more than 96 % acid recovery while removing more than 50 % of the initial amount of water in the feed. A preliminary analysis also demonstrates the potential gains in terms of energy savings if such a process could replace more traditional options such as reactive distillation.

Acknowledgments

This work was executed with support from CNPq, Coordenação de Aperfeiçoamento de Pessoal de Nível Superior - Brasil (CAPES) - Finance Code 001, and São Paulo Research Foundation (FAPESP) grant #2015/20630-4.

References

Ö. Aydoğan, E. Bayraktar, Ü. Mehmetoğlu, 2011, Aqueous two-phase extraction of lactic acid: Optimization by response surface methodology, Sep. Sci. Technol., 46, 1164–1171.

H. Fu, Y. Sun, H. Teng, D. Zhang, Z. Xiu, 2015, Salting-out extraction of carboxylic acids, Sep. Purif. Technol., 139, 36–42.

R. Gasca-González, O. A. Prado-Rubio, F. I. Gómez-Castro, J. Fontalvo-Alzate, E. S. Pérez-Cisneros, R. Morales-Rodriguez, 2019, Techno-economic analysis of alternative reactive purification technologies in the lactic acid production process, Computer Aided Chemical Engineering, 46, 457-462.

J. A. Méndez-Alva, E. S. Perez-Cisneros, D. Rodriguez-Gomez, O. A.Prado-Rubio, B. Ruiz-Camacho, R. Morales-Rodriguez, 2018, Computer-aided process simulation, design and analysis: lactic acid production from lignocellulosic residues, Computer Aided Chemical Engineering, 44, 463-468.

B. Rumpf, F. Weyrich, G. Maurer, 1997, Enthalpy of dilution in aqueous systems of single solutes ammonia, sodium sulfate and ammonium sulfate: Experimental results and modeling, Therrnochimica Acta, 303, 77-91.

C. Y. Su, C. C. Yu, I. L. Chien, J. D. Ward, 2013, Plant-wide economic comparison of lactic acid recovery processes by reactive distillation with different alcohols, Ind. Eng. Chem. Res., 52, 11070–11083.

Y. Wang, Y. Yan, S. Hu, J. Han, X. Xu, 2009, Phase diagrams of ammonium sulfate + ethanol/1-propanol/2-propanol + water aqueous two-phase systems at 298.15 K and correlation, J. Chem. Eng. Data, 55, 876–881.

Sauro Pierucci, Flavio Manenti, Giulia Bozzano, Davide Manca (Eds.)
Proceedings of the 30th European Symposium on Computer Aided Process Engineering
(ESCAPE30), May 24-27, 2020, Milano, Italy. © 2020 Elsevier B.V. All rights reserved.
http://dx.doi.org/10.1016/B978-0-12-823377-1.50276-7

Improving the Calibration of Kinetic Growth Models using Dynamic Time Warping

Mhd Adnan Jouned[a,b], Julian Kager[a,c], Judit Aizpuru[b], Christoph Herwig[a,c], Tilman Barz[b]

[a] *ICEBE, TU Wien, Gumpendorfer Straße 1a 166/4, 1060 Wien, Austria*
[b] *AIT Austrian Institute of Technology GmbH, Giefinggasse 2, 1210 Wien, Austria*
[c] *CD Laboratory on Mechanistic and Physiological Methods for Improved Bioprocesses, TU Wien, Gumpendorfer Straße 1a 166/4, 1060 Wien, Austria*
tilman.barz@ait.ac.at

Abstract

Off-gas measurements give valuable information on the respiratory activity of organisms during fermentation processes. Measured oxygen consumption and carbon dioxide production is usually linked to the overall metabolic activity of the cultivated cells. Together with offline measured nutrient and metabolite concentrations reaction parameters of growth models can be determined. Standard algorithms for parameter estimation use the least-squares (LSQ) error criterion for fitting model predictions to measured data. However, their application does not necessarily yield off-gas representative model predictions and parameters. This is especially true for off-gas signals with rapid variability and corresponding sharp bends and kinks. Off-gas signals include clear indicators for nutrient limitations and metabolic shifts of the culture. Using the LSQ error criterion the fitting tends to smooth out these informative details leading to poor model predictions and parameter estimates.

This contribution presents a comparative analysis of the performance of standard nonlinear LSQ algorithms and an adapted algorithm using the Dynamic Time Warping (DTW) criterion. Both algorithms are applied to fit off-gas signals for the calibration of the kinetic model of *Saccharomyces cerevisiae* (Sonnleitner and Käppeli 1986) on three experimental datasets. The data represents high dynamics with rapid variations and covers yeast fermentation through Batch and Fed-Batch phases including time windows where the organisms are forced to produce ethanol through the "Crabtree effect" by overfeeding. It turns out that, compared to results using LSQ criterion, the application of the DTW criterion yields a better shape matching of the data. In addition, results are also discussed comparing the performance in terms of convergence to the best fitting parameters and the robustness of algorithms against structural modelling errors.

Keywords: dynamic programming, signals matching, parameter estimation, kinetic modelling

1. Introduction

Kinetic modeling plays an essential role in bioprocess development because it provides not only information about changing quantities and rates, but also gives valuable insights about the underlying reactions scheme. Hence, the parameters reflect biological meaning apart from being mathematical coefficients. Model calibration is considered to be a complex task especially for problems with a high number of interdependent parameters and a low number of samples. In addition to that, available information is often concentrated in certain time ranges or only available at distinct time points. For example, for practical reasons it is often the case that offline samples are concentrated in the Fed-batch phase while no/less data is available for the Batch-phase. The parameters estimated in these cases may not reveal the actual underlying behavior and may result in "Observation Biased" models where the quality of the model in experimental design and control can be questionable. This issue can be improved when semi-/continuous (online) data resources are introduced such as off-gas information or spectral information (Golabgir and Herwig 2016).

In yeast fermentations processes off-gas information proved to be used to identify different metabolic pathways and to provide information, like maximum growth rate (Petkov and Davis 1996, Anderlei et al. 2004, Gollmer and Posten 1996). On the other hand, off-gas signals are usually more complex than other states and contain both low and high frequency information where rapid changes represent mostly certain limitations or metabolic shifts and slower changes are usually corelated to the respiration of the culture. Moreover, off-gas signal errors arise completely from different sources compared to other states such as component concentrations. While for concentration samples, variance in the measurements is witnessed, off-gas signal suffers - among different errors types - from shifts, offsets and drifts. These usually caused by different factors including possible sensors delay, not-proper accounting for humidity and high interactions with other conditions/states such as pH and temperature (Frick and Junker 1999). Fitting criteria able to account for these characteristics are necessary to obtain representative model parameters.

Parameter estimation algorithms using Least-Squares (LSQ) as a criterion to fit off-gas signals, could potentially perform better if another criterion that accounts for these characteristics is used. The reason is that the standard criterion evaluates the quadratic fitting error by comparing measurements and predictions point-by-point. Interesting features like kinks and sharp bends in the measured signals are not in the focus. Accordingly, in the presence of structural model simplifications and measurement noise, off-gas signals are usually fitted by smooth curves (which are optimal in the sense of the quadratic error criterion, but do not mimic the shape of the measured signals). A possible solution to this is parameter estimation implementing an error criterion derived from Dynamic Time Warping (DTW) method (Gollmer and Posten 1996) (Srinivasan and Qian 2007). The method is applied in shape recognition. It has a high potential for yielding model predictions, which mimic the interesting features in the measured signals, and to overcome the limitations of algorithms using LSQ error criterion.

The applicability of DTW as a non-linear mapping tool between signals, which reduces the distance and matches the shape, has been shown in the field of chemistry and bioprocessing (Srinivasan and Qian 2007; González-Martínez, Ferrer, and Westerhuis 2011). (Gollmer and Posten 1996) actually used DTW to identify different phases of off-gas signals in *S. cerevisiae* fermentation two decades ago, but according to author knowledge, this concept has not been exploited to match simulation/observation signals to improve model parameters estimation consequently. This work exemplarily validates this improvement by a comparative analysis of the performance of standard nonlinear LSQ algorithms and an adapted algorithm using the Dynamic Time Warping (DTW) criterion.

2. Materials and Methods

To understand the effect of using an error criterion derived from DTW on parameters estimation, two algorithms with different error criteria are used to fit three different experimental datasets. The well-known model for baker's yeast fermentation (Sonnleitner and Käppeli 1986) is used where we try to get best parameter-set $(q_{s,max}, \mu_{ethanol,max}, q_{O_2,max}, K_s, Y_{biomass/glucose}^{oxidative}, Y_{biomass/glucose}^{reductive}, Y_{biomass/ethanol})$. The selection of the parameters and initial values has been done recursively based on importance ranking and sensitivity information (López et al. 2013) (Ulonska et al. 2018). Details on the model structure, nomenclature and parameter values are shown in the original paper (Sonnleitner and Käppeli 1986).

Around thousand initializations with various initial guesses of selected parameter-set were established, passed to an optimizer *("fminsearch", MATLAB R2017b,* stopping criterion is set to 100 iterations, all other options are set to default) to find parameter values yielding lowest error criterion.

In order to find a reference base to compare both results, the solutions from both algorithms are accepted among best fitting parameters-set, when the metabolic states calculated back from the model match the ones that have been pre-identified by experts, error of the state estimation is between 0-5% NRMSD and the error of off-gas signals estimation is between 0-50% NRMSD of any off-gas signal of each metabolic state.

The three fermentation experiments consist of Batch and Fed-Batch phases where overfeeding is applied after some hours in the Fed-Batch phase to force the cells deliberately to produced ethanol through "Crabtree effect". Data presented in Figure 1 shows clearly high dynamics in the off-gas signals with some rapid changes reflecting the time-varying behavior of the cells.

2.1. S. cerevisiae fermentation model

In this model derived from (Sonnleitner and Käppeli 1986) the growth is described on two substrates glucose and ethanol with fermentative and oxidative pathways, based on three metabolic pathways with correspondent yield parameters $Y_{biomass/glucose}^{oxidative}, Y_{biomass/glucose}^{reductive}$ and $Y_{biomass/glucose}$. Total growth is the growth based on all forms of biomass specific intake ($q_s^{oxidative}, q_s^{reductive}, q_{ethanol}$) as:

$$\mu_{total} = Y_{biomass/glucose}^{oxidative} \cdot q_s^{oxidative} + Y_{biomass/glucose}^{reductive} \cdot q_s^{reductive} + Y_{biomass/ethanol} \cdot q_{ethanol} \quad (1)$$

Mass balances equations are (*x: biomass, s: glucose, e: ethanol, V: volume and F: feed*)

$$\frac{dV}{dt} = F_S + F_{Base} + F_{Acid} - F_{Gas}$$

$$\frac{d\,C_x}{dt} = \mu_{total} \cdot C_x - \frac{F_S}{V} \cdot C_x$$

$$\frac{d\,C_s}{dt} = -(q_s^{reductive} + q_s^{oxidative}) \cdot C_x - \frac{F_S}{V} \cdot C_s + \frac{F_S}{C_{s,in} \cdot V} \quad (2)$$

$$\frac{d\,C_e}{dt} = (q_s^{reductive} - q_e) \cdot C_x - \frac{F_S}{V} \cdot C_e$$

Additionally, off-gas equations of Carbon Dioxide Evolution Rate (CER) and Oxygen Uptake Rate (OUR) can be derived from the original model taking into consideration elemental balance, which can be derived from oxidative and reductive reaction stoichiometry:

$$CER = (q_s^{oxidative} \cdot Y_{s,ox}^{CO_2} + q_{ethanol} \cdot Y_e^{CO_2} + q_s^{reductive} \cdot Y_{s,Red}^{CO_2}) C_x \cdot V \quad (4)$$

$$OUR = (q_s^{oxidative} \cdot Y_s^{O_2} + q_{ethanol} \cdot Y_e^{O_2}) C_x \cdot V \quad (3)$$

2.2. Objective functions

Two objective functions are formulated, in which the first uses standard LSQ. The second uses a combination of LSQ and DTW derived terms. The two functions differ from each other by how they calculate the similarity of the off-gas signals, i.e. the sampled and simulated OUR, CER.

2.2.1. LSQ criterion

For M samples, $N = N_L + N_G$ liquid and gas states, and θ as unknown parameter vector, LSQ is defined as ϕ^{LSQ}. Assuming all model states have the same weight in the objective function the fitting problem reads:

$$\min_\theta \phi_{L+G}^{LSQ}(\theta); \quad \text{with} \quad \phi_{L+G}^{LSQ}(\theta) = \sum_{i=1}^{M} \sum_{j=1}^{N_L+N_G} (Y_{i,j}^m - Y_{i,j}(\theta))^2 \tag{5}$$

2.2.2. Combined LSQ and DTW criterion

Replacing $\phi_G^{LSQ}(\theta)$ by $\phi_G^{DTW}(\theta)$ where all deviations from off-gas measurements are calculated based on DTW. For both, $OUR, CER,$ two sequences are needed to build DTW distance matrix. The matrix size is defined by the sizes of both sequences Y_G^m and $Y_G(\theta)$, in which each matrix element $\varepsilon_{i,j}$ represents the distance according to the chosen metric, which is in our case the squared Euclidian distance. To get shape preserved matching between two sequences DTW seeks an optimal path k through the matrix which minimize the warping cost (Ratanamahatana and Keogh 2004)

$$\phi_G^{DTW} = \min_k \left(\sum^{I,J} \gamma_{i,j}\right)_k \tag{6}$$

Where γ are the elements of the warping path. The optimal path is found by calculating the minimum cumulative distance of the current element and the other three adjacent cells in DTW matrix

$$\gamma_{i,j} = \varepsilon_{i,j} + \min(\gamma_{i-1,j-1}, \gamma_{i-1,j}, \gamma_{i,j-1}) \tag{7}$$

Using α as a weighting coefficient to scale the DTW term to the same magnitude of the LSQ term, the combined objective function reads

$$\min_\theta \left(\phi_L^{LSQ}(\theta) + \alpha \cdot \phi_G^{DTW}(\theta)\right) \tag{8}$$

3. Results and discussion

Figure 1 shows model estimation results of two experiments after 100 optimization iterations. While the fitting of the states is similarly good for both objectives, larger differences can be seen when examining the off-gas signals and by comparing the active metabolic states. We can notice that the metabolic states sequence differs. It can be seen that with standard LSQ criterion the optimizer overlooks some intermediate details in order to get a good fitting along the whole time horizon.

This is problematic, as different metabolic states are assigned along the process, where metabolic states are indicated by sharp changes in the off-gas signal.

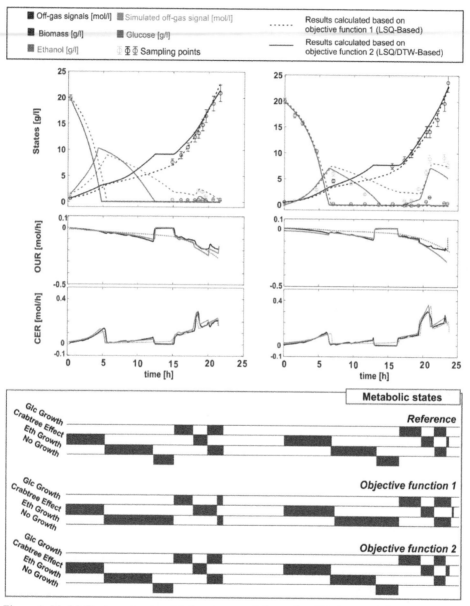

Figure 1: Model fits two experimental datasets out of three after 100 optimization iterations with standard LSQ-based objective function (dashed line) and LSQ/DTW-based objective function (solid line). The corresponding metabolic states are presented below with the reference solution (identified by an experienced field expert based on the visual inspection of CER, OUR signals and offline measurements).

The length of a metabolic state is strongly determined by the parameters related to maximum reaction rates and the corresponding conversion coefficients (yields), which needed to be correctly assigned during model parametrization. Figure 2 shows clearly that the algorithm using DTW/LSQ criterion had a twice higher success rate in finding the exact parameters out of 1000 model calibrations, each with differently perturbed initial parameter sets.

4. Conclusion

Using DTW (Dynamic Time Warping) as a fitting criterion for the identification of *S. cerevisiae* fermentation models clearly leads to more reliable parameters estimates compared with the standard LSQ fitting approach. This has been quantitatively proved for three experimental

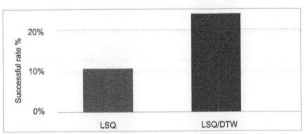

Figure 2: Success rate implementing the LSQ and the combined LSQ/DTW objective functions for parameter identification from off-gas and sampling data.

datasets with different metabolic states. For the presented case study, it is shown that model predictions generated by LSQ fitting tend to smooth out measured off-gas signals losing specific details of the signals shape that might represent important metabolic changes. The results clearly indicate a superior performance using DTW, i.e. the more accurate shape matching of the signals yields improved model predictive performance and provides more accurate model parameters.

Acknowledgment

This work was partially funded by the Austrian Research Funding Association (FFG) within the program Bridge 1 in the project "AdaMo" (No. 864705).

References

Frick, and Junker. 1999. "Indirect Methods for Characterization of Carbon Dioxide Levels in Fermentation Broth." *J. Biosci. Bioeng.* 87 (3): 344–51.

Golabgir, and Herwig. 2016. "Combining Mechanistic Modeling and Raman Spectroscopy for Real-Time Monitoring of Fed-Batch Penicillin Production." *Chemie Ing. Tech.* 88 (6): 764–76.

Gollmer, and Posten. 1996. "Supervision of Bioprocesses Using a Dynamic Time Warping Algorithm." *Control Eng. Pract.* 4 (9): 1287–95.

González-Martínez, Ferrer, and Westerhuis. 2011. "Real-Time Synchronization of Batch Trajectories for on-Line Multivariate Statistical Process Control Using Dynamic Time Warping." *Chemom. Intell. Lab. Syst.* 105 (2): 195–206.

López, Barz, Peñuela, Villegas, Ochoa, and Wozny. 2013. "Model-Based Identifiable Parameter Determination Applied to a Simultaneous Saccharification and Fermentation Process Model for Bio-Ethanol Production." *Biotechnol. Prog.* 29 (4): 1064–82.

Ratanamahatana, and Keogh. 2004. "Everything You Know about Dynamic Time Warping Is Wrong." *Third Work. Min. Temporal Seq. Data*, no. January 2004: 22–25.

Sonnleitner, and Käppeli. 1986. "Growth of Saccharomyces Cerevisiae Is Controlled by Its Limited Respiratory Capacity: Formulation and Verification of a Hypothesis." *Biotechnol. Bioeng.* 28 (6): 927–37.

Srinivasan, and Qian. 2007. "Online Temporal Signal Comparison Using Singular Points Augmented Time Warping." *Ind. Eng. Chem. Res.* 46 (13): 4531–48.

Ulonska, Kroll, Fricke, Clemens, Voges, Müller, and Herwig. 2018. "Workflow for Target-Oriented Parametrization of an Enhanced Mechanistic Cell Culture Model." *Biotechnol. J.* 13 (4): 1–11.

Sauro Pierucci, Flavio Manenti, Giulia Bozzano, Davide Manca (Eds.)
Proceedings of the 30th European Symposium on Computer Aided Process Engineering
(ESCAPE30), May 24-27, 2020, Milano, Italy. © 2020 Elsevier B.V. All rights reserved.
http://dx.doi.org/10.1016/B978-0-12-823377-1.50277-9

Dynamic Simulation and Visualisation of pH-Modulated Fed-batch Fermentation for mAb Production from CHO Cell Cultures

Samir Diab[a], Sara Badr[b], Hirokazu Sugiyama[b], Dimitrios I. Gerogiorgis[a*]

[a] *Institute for Materials and Processes (IMP), School of Engineering, University of Edinburgh, The Kings Buildings, Edinburgh, EH9 3FB, United Kingdom*
[b] *Department of Chemical System Engineering, University of Tokyo, Tokyo, 113-8656, Japan*
D.Gerogiorgis@ed.ac.uk

Abstract

Monoclonal antibodies (mAbs) are therapeutic proteins used for treating cancer, autoimmune diseases and many other critical ailments, thus constituting essential biopharmaceutical products in global healthcare. The mAb market turnover is predicted to significantly increase, with numerous new products and processes being developed each year. Current mAb processes often rely on Chinese Hamster Ovary (CHO) cell cultures, which are commonly implemented in batch and fed-batch modes, with some demonstrations of continuous/perfusion cultures in pursuit of much leaner manufacturing. Modelling and simulation can allow optimisation of different design and operating parameters towards achieving the most promising process configurations. The dynamic model for mAb fed-batch production from CHO cell cultures employed in this study describes cell growth and death, mAb production and culture volume as a function of time and pH, allowing for systematic simulation in order to elucidate promising dynamic pH modulations. Dynamic pH and state profiles for fed-batch production of mAbs from CHO cells via systematic simulation are presented. Comparisons of attained productivities, resulting concentration profiles and culture volumes are visualised and compared in order to quantitatively elucidate trade-offs in mAb production with a view to manufacturing.

Keywords: Dynamic simulation; monoclonal antibodies (mAbs); fed-batch production; Chinese Hamster Ovary (CHO) cells; pH modulation; comparative evaluation.

1. Introduction

Monoclonal antibodies (mAbs) represent approximately 50% of the rapidly growing biopharmaceuticals market and are important Drug Substances (DS) for their applications in cancer treatment, autoimmune diseases and many other therapies (Grilo and Mantalaris, 2019). The production of mAbs is most commonly implemented via fermentation of Chinese Hamster Ovary (CHO) cells in either batch, fed-batch or perfusion modes (Shukla et al., 2017), with the latter being pushed towards continuous mode by numerous recent research efforts towards leaner manufacturing campaigns (Schofield, 2019; Papathanasiou et al., 2019). Fed-batch mode is the industrial standard mode of operation for mAb manufacturing due to the ability to tune the nutrient dosing policy throughout the batch runtime (Bunnak et al., 2016). Optimisation of manipulation trajectories during fed-batch operation pinpoints promising process improvements over current experimental demonstrations, and foster manufacturing (Dafnomilis et al., 2019).

Dynamic simulation and optimisation of fermentation operations in bioprocessing is a useful tool in screening promising operating policies while circumventing time and financial investments in laborious experimental campaigns (Shirahata et al. 2019). A recently published dynamic model for the fed-batch production of mAb from a CHO cell culture utilised pH manipulation in order to control fermentation process performance (Hogiri et al., 2018); implementation of the model for optimisation subject to different process constraints can highlight improved pH control policies and trade-offs in performance vs. product quality. This study implements the published dynamic model for mAb production from CHO cells via pH variation for systematic comparative evaluation of different dynamic pH modulations to meet different production objectives. Dynamic pH profiles for fed-batch production of mAbs from CHO cells via systematic simulation are presented. Comparisons of productivities, concentration profiles, and culture volumes are visualised and compared to quantitatively elucidate trade-offs in mAb production.

2. Dynamic model for mAb production from CHO cells

The dynamic model for pH-dependent production of mAb from CHO cells is presented in Fig. 1 (Hogiri et al., 2018). The model describes the production of the mAb immunoglobulin G (IgG) from a CHO cell culture, where X_n, X_a and X_d are concentrations of viable, apoptotic and dead cells, respectively. The mAb is produced from viable (X_n) and apoptotic (X_a) cells, which consume nutrient and dictate the amount of dosing required vs. operation time, t, which affects the culture volume, V. The kinetic model equations are also presented in Fig. 1 (Eqs. 1–6). Here, ρ_1 and ρ_2 are production rate constants and g_1 and g_2 are production kinetic orders from viable and apoptotic cells, respectively. Parameters v_0, v_1, v_2, v_3 and v_4 describe cell growth, apoptosis onset, apoptotic cell death, viable cell death and cell lysis rates, respectively; μ and μ_{max} are specific cell growth rate as a function of cell concentration and its maximum value, respectively and x_{max} = maximum total cell density. Parameters x_{max}, μ_{max}, k_1, k_2, k_3, k_4, r_1, r_2 and r_3 are functions of $pH(t)$, which can be found in the literature (Hogiri et al., 2018).

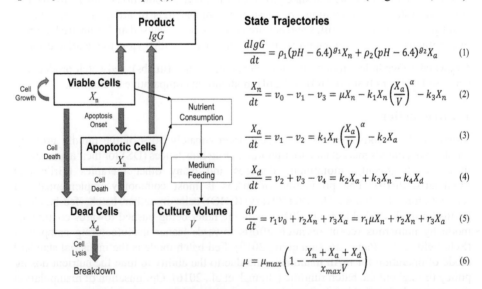

State Trajectories

$$\frac{dIgG}{dt} = \rho_1(pH - 6.4)^{g_1}X_n + \rho_2(pH - 6.4)^{g_2}X_a \quad (1)$$

$$\frac{X_n}{dt} = v_0 - v_1 - v_3 = \mu X_n - k_1 X_n\left(\frac{X_a}{V}\right)^\alpha - k_3 X_n \quad (2)$$

$$\frac{X_a}{dt} = v_1 - v_2 = k_1 X_n\left(\frac{X_a}{V}\right)^\alpha - k_2 X_a \quad (3)$$

$$\frac{X_d}{dt} = v_2 + v_3 - v_4 = k_2 X_a + k_3 X_n - k_4 X_d \quad (4)$$

$$\frac{dV}{dt} = r_1 v_0 + r_2 X_n + r_3 X_a = r_1 \mu X_n + r_2 X_n + r_3 X_a \quad (5)$$

$$\mu = \mu_{max}\left(1 - \frac{X_n + X_a + X_d}{x_{max}V}\right) \quad (6)$$

Figure 1: Dynamic model for mAb (IgG) production $= f(pH)$ (Hogiri et al., 2018).

3. Dynamic simulation of static pH operation

Dynamic simulation of the published model for mAb production is performed for varying $pH(t)$ = constant, as per the published experimental results (Hogiri et al., 2018); the dynamic model is valid within the range $6.6 \leq pH(t) \leq 7.2$ and thus constant values of $pH(t)$ = {6.6, 6.8, 7.0, 7.2} are considered for a maximum batch duration of t_f = 350 hr. As $pH(t)$ is increased, the final amount of mAb produced increases and then decreases beyond some intermediate pH value. Production of mAb is slow at first and then increases around t = 50 hr for all considered pH values. As pH is increased, dead cell concentrations increase. Viable cell concentrations reach a peak at different points during the batch run and then decrease; as pH is increased from 6.6 to 7.0, the time at which this is reached becomes later and the value and final viable cell concentration are higher, whereas for pH = 7.2, these values occur earlier and lower, respectively. Specific growth rates decrease and then increase to a plateau over the batch duration with final values decreasing with increasing pH. Culture volumes vary with cell densities, which both increase with pH.

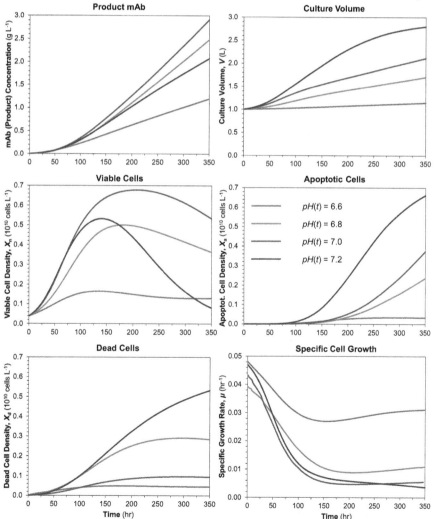

Figure 2: Dynamic simulation of different constant $pH(t)$ profiles on state trajectories.

4. Dynamic pH manipulation: process performances and trade-offs

From the previous static simulations, it is shown that there are trade-offs between variables in the considered system. The model can be used to investigate the effect of dynamic pH profile implementation on different production objectives. Previous work investigated dynamic manipulation to maximise mAb production (Hogiri et al., 2018), but did not consider effects on other variables, such as cell concentrations and culture volume, which can inform the design of more efficient processes, e.g., implementing recycle. Here, we consider the effect of dynamic pH on different process variables and then visualise production trade-offs. The considered pH profiles assume initial $pH(t = 0)$ = 6.8, as per experimental demonstrations, and ΔpH = {0.0, +0.2} within each 24 hr period; the maximum possible batch duration is 384 hr. All considered limitations are in accordance with literature demonstrations (Hogiri et al., 2018). The number of time domain discretisation elements, $N = 16$; thus the number of considered pH profiles = 2^{16}.

Fig. 3 shows the considered pH profile attaining the highest final mAb concentration (IgG $(t_f = 384$ hr) = 3.35 g L^{-1}) and corresponding state variables. A gradual increase from the initial pH $(t = 0) = 6.8$ to pH $(t = 168$ hr) attains the maximum final mAb concentration of those pH profiles considered. The best pH profile of those considered lies in the middle of the applicable pH range, i.e. above the lower bound, (pH$_L$ = 6.6) and below the upper (pH$_U$ = 7.2). The likely reason for pH plateauing at this time is the decrease of viable cells producing mAb thereafter, which implies a concurrent increasing quantity of dead cells. Investigating the region of attainable production performance over the range of possible implemented pH manipulations gives an indication of where process improvement can be achieved, with excessive cell death (reduction in viable cell concentration) thus avoided.

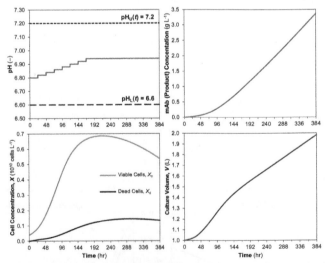

Figure 3: Manipulation (pH) and state profiles attaining maximum mAb concentration.

Fig. 4 visualises process variables vs. batch time for all pH profiles considered. While batch time increases productivity, the culture volume increases; although the considered scale is relatively small (initial volume, V $(t = 0) = 1$ L), increasing culture volumes at larger scales of operation may be undesirable due to the larger material handling requirements post-batch as well as the higher capital expenditures associated with larger equipment. With ongoing batch duration, viable cell concentrations begin to decrease as dead cell quantities increase; this makes potential cell recycling/separation less feasible.

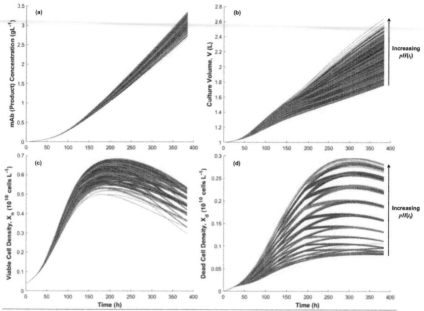

Figure 4: Trade-offs: (a) Product, (b) Volume, (c) Viable cells, (d) Dead cells vs. time.

Fig. 5 shows trade-offs between variables for all pH profiles. Banding is observed due to the constraints on the pH. Increasing productivity leads to lower viable and higher dead cell densities. There is a trade-off between viable and dead cell densities that must be considered if deciding to recycle. The considered pH profiles are limited in their pH step size, temporal discretisation, initial pH and their piecewise constant variation; piecewise linear variation is also possible. Formulation of a dynamic multiobjective optimisation problem of pH for optimal production will further elucidate productivity benefits.

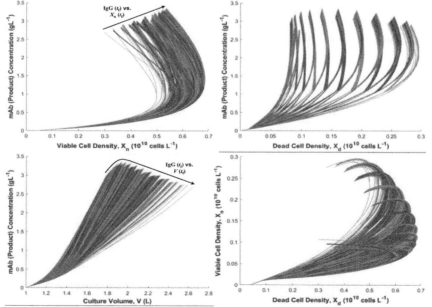

Figure 5: Pareto fronts exhibiting different trade-offs between different process variables.

5. Conclusions

The dynamic modelling and simulation of mAb production from CHO cell cultures can elucidate potential improvements in biopharmaceutical production compared to static pH culture conditions in terms of productivity, cell viability, culture volume and total batch duration. This study has visualised and compared trade-offs between mAb production, cell concentrations and culture volume. The pH manipulation attaining maximum productivity steadily increases until halfway through the batch and then remains steady for the remaining half. This manipulation profile lies in the middle of the applicable pH range of the model. Consideration of the effects of different pH manipulations on other state variables is also important for efficient process design. Trade-offs between mAb productivity as well as viable and dead cell concentrations elucidate the need for dynamic optimisation of pH variation, in order to design biopharma processes of high efficiency.

Acknowledgements

The authors acknowledge the support of the Engineering and Physical Sciences Research Council (EPSRC)/IAA, the Japan Society for the Promotion of Science, the Great Britain Sasakawa and Nagai Foundations and the Royal Academy of Engineering (RAEng).

References

P. Bunnak, R. Allmendinger, S.R. Ramasamy, P. Lettieri and N.J. Titchener-Hooker, 2016, Life-cycle and cost of goods assessment of fed-batch and perfusion-based manufacturing processes for mAbs, *Biotechnol. Prog.*, 32, 5, 1324–1335.

A. Dafnomilis, S. Diab, A.D. Rodman, A.G. Boudouvis and D.I. Gerogiorgis, 2019, Multiobjective dynamic optimization of ampicillin batch crystallization: sensitivity analysis of attainable performance vs product quality constraints, *Ind. Eng. Chem. Res.*, 58, 40, 18756–18771.

A.L. Grilo and A. Mantalaris, 2019, The increasingly human and profitable monoclonal antibody market, *Trends Biotechnol.*, 37, 9–16.

T. Hogiri, H. Tamashima, A. Nishizawa and M. Okamoto, 2018, Optimization of a pH-shift control strategy for producing mAbs in Chinese hamster ovary cell cultures using a pH-dependent dynamic model, *J. Biosci. Bioeng.*, 125, 2, 245–250.

C.D. Kappatou, A. Mhamdi, A.Q. Campano, A. Mantalaris and A. Mitsos, 2018, Model-based dynamic optimization of monoclonal antibodies production in semibatch operation—use of reformulation techniques, *Ind. Eng. Chem. Res.*, 57, 30, 9915–9924.

M.M. Papathanasiou, B. Burnak, J. Katz, N. Shah and E.N. Pistikopoulos, 2019, Assisting continuous biomanufacturing through advanced control in downstream purification, *Comput. Chem. Eng.*, 125, 232–248.

M. Schofield, 2019, Current state of the art in continuous bioprocessing, *Biotechnol. Lett.*, 40, 9–10, 1303–1309.

H. Shirahata, S. Diab, H. Sugiyama and D.I. Gerogiorgis, 2019, Dynamic modelling, simulation and economic evaluation of two CHO cell-based production modes towards developing biopharmaceutical manufacturing processes, *Chem. Eng. Res. Des.*, 150, 218–233.

A.A. Shukla, L.S. Wolfe, S.S. Mostafa and C. Norman, 2017, Evolving trends in mAb production processes, *Bioeng. Transl. Med.*, 2, 1, 58–69.

F. Steinebach, N. Ulmer, M. Wolf, L. Decker, V. Schneider, R. Wälchli, D. Karst, J. Souquet and M. Morbidelli, 2017, Design and operation of a continuous integrated monoclonal antibody production process, *Biotechnol. Prog.*, 33, 5, 1303–1313.

Sauro Pierucci, Flavio Manenti, Giulia Bozzano, Davide Manca (Eds.)
Proceedings of the 30th European Symposium on Computer Aided Process Engineering
(ESCAPE30), May 24-27, 2020, Milano, Italy. © 2020 Elsevier B.V. All rights reserved.
http://dx.doi.org/10.1016/B978-0-12-823377-1.50278-0

Surrogate Modelling Based Uncertainty and Sensitivity Analysis for the Downstream Process Design of a Xylitol Biorefinery

Nikolaus I. Vollmer,[a]* Krist V. Gernaey,[a] Solange I. Mussatto,[b] Gürkan Sin[a]

[a]*Process and Systems Engineering Center (PROSYS), Department of Chemical and Biochemical Engineering, Technical University of Denmark, Søltofts Plads, Building 229, 2800 Kgs. Lyngby, Denmark*
[b]*Biomass Conversion and Bioprocess Technology Group, Novo Nordisk Foundation Center for Biosustainability, Technical University of Denmark, Kemitorvet, Building 220, 2800 Kgs. Lyngby, Denmark*
nikov@kt.dtu.dk

Abstract

A rising number of diabetes patients and the urgent need for novel biotechnological process solutions are the instigation for this work. A biorefinery concept based on the valorization of the hemicellulosic sugar fraction is proposed by producing the sugar substitute xylitol. Its process design is supposed to be performed via superstructure optimization (SSO). In order to assess the viability, the downstream process unit operations are analyzed by a comprehensive uncertainty and sensitivity analysis. Monte Carlo methods and the *easyGSA* framework are applied. The output is twofold: the uncertainty in the output is assessed and shows improvement potential for the xylitol yield by serial crystallization and the sensitivity analysis of operational parameters indicates a serial crystallization in the downstream process. Overall, the biorefinery concept is viable and can contribute to the development of sustainable value chains.

Keywords: Biorefinery, Monte Carlo Methods, Surrogate Modelling, Process Design, Optimization.

1. Motivation and Outline

1.1 Motivation

By 2045, over ten percent of the human population will suffer from type II diabetes, while this group grows by around two percent per year (International Diabetes Federation, 2019). This is promoted enormously by the availability of sugar-rich convenience food and a general transition towards an unhealthy lifestyle (International Diabetes Federation, 2019). Hence, it is of major importance for the affected to facilitate a suitable diabetic nutrition with the use of sugar substitutes and to prevent the further build-up of insulin resistances in the population to stop the increase of the number of diabetics (Mussatto, 2012).

A good candidate for this is xylitol: it is a pentose sugar alcohol, showing anticariogenic properties and a low glycemic index, making it perfectly suitable for diabetic nutrition. In addition, it has a similar sweetening power to sucrose but 40% less calories (Mussatto, 2012). Currently, xylitol is produced in a chemical conversion process from wood biomass or corn, but due to exhaustive purification steps, this process is very expensive (Hernandez et al., 2019).

Because of this, amongst other reasons, the US Department of Energy lists xylitol as one of the top 12 bio-based molecules, indicating a high potential for biotechnological production (Hernandez et al., 2019).

The biorefinery concept describes the utilization of a single feedstock for the production of multiple biochemicals, biofuels and energy. Second-generation biorefineries aim to use agricultural or forestal residues as feedstock. This lignocellulosic biomass contains a lot of sugars in different fractions, which can be used as substrate for fermentation processes. In particular, the main fractions are the hemicellulosic fraction (HF) with xylose as main component, the cellulosic fraction (CF) with glucose as main component and the lignin fraction (LF) with different phenolic macromolecules as main compounds (Mussatto, Dragone, 2016). All of the fractions show a macromolecular structure. The major challenge in designing and operating these second-generation biorefineries in an economically viable way derives from the pretreatment of the biomass in order to break down the polymeric structure into monomers for their use in the fermentation processes (Mussatto, Dragone, 2016).

Therefore, we propose a strategy in order to surmount these economic hurdles: The production focus in the biorefinery is shifted towards the valorization of the HF sugars by producing xylitol in a biotechnological process. As the chemical production process is expensive, a viable biotechnological production indicates a promising economic potential. Building up on this, the CF can be valorized by producing bioethanol or another value-added product as e.g. succinic acid. Lastly, lignin is either used as energy source for the supply of heat in both downstream processes or valorized by producing high-value energy carriers as e.g. sustainable aviation fuels. In order to conceptually perform the process design for this biorefinery and to find an optimal overall design, a SSO approach is chosen (Gargalo et al., 2017). For this, mechanistic models for all the relevant unit operations in the refinery are developed, which guarantee flexibility and scalability due to their parametrization.

The US DoE state in their report that the major issue for a biotechnological production is the separation from other sugars (Hernandez et al., 2019). In order to assess this, the uncertainty and sensitivity of the models in the downstream process (DSP) of the suggested biorefinery concept is investigated. By quantifying this uncertainty, a robust process design in the SSO can be guaranteed, which ultimately is supposed to yield an economically resilient biorefinery.

1.2 Outline

First, the models employed in the DSP of xylitol are described, i.e. an evaporation and a crystallization unit. Other unit operations are not considered to have a crucial influence on the robustness of the design. Following this, the applied methods in uncertainty analysis and sensitivity analysis are presented, as well as the results from the model assessment. This ultimately allows drawing conclusions, which give necessary indications on how to best perform the process design as mentioned in 1.1.

2. Models and Surrogates

The employed main unit operations in the downstream operation are an evaporation unit and a crystallization unit. For the successful recovery of xylitol, these units become crucial in order to remove residual sugars and other impurities. Both models are mechanistic models and are described in detail in the following section.

2.1. Evaporation Model

The evaporation unit mainly serves the purpose of upconcentrating the fermentation broth, but also helps removing more volatile compounds from the bulk phase as e.g. ethanol which is inherently produced in the fermentation process, or acetic acid. Due to the high separation factor of water and xylitol, a single-stage evaporation is sufficient to fulfil this task. The employed model here is a simple evaporator model of the ASPEN Plus process simulation package. The underlying thermodynamic model for the modelling of the phase behavior in order to simulate the evaporation is NRTL.

2.2. Crystallization Model

The crystallization unit both yields the final product and also serves to remove less soluble compounds from the bulk phase. As xylitol shows an extraordinarily high solubility in comparison to other sugars (C=1.6 g/g H_2O), the assumption holds that all other present sugars will crystallize before xylitol.

The model itself is based on previous work (Öner et al., 2018): it is a mechanistic model based on mass and energy balances, as well as a population balance which is solved by the method of classes. The incorporated phenomena in the population balance are crystal nucleation and crystal growth. Both the operation as cooling crystallization or as anti-solvent crystallization are implemented. The underlying thermodynamic model for the modelling of the phase behavior for different solvent/anti-solvent ratios is based on experimental work measuring solubility curves. Equally, kinetic parameters for the population balance are determined from experimental data as described by Bandit and Pari (Bandit, Pari, 2018). The model is implemented in MATLAB.

2.3. Surrogate Models

In order to facilitate the performed analyses, a surrogate model of the evaporation unit in ASPEN Plus is created. For the generation and cross-validation of the surrogate models the *easyGSA* framework is used (Al et al., 2019). Different types of surrogate modelling techniques as e.g. Gaussian Process Regression (GPR), Artificial Neural Networks (ANN) or Polynomial Chaos Expansion (PCR) can be utilized by the toolbox.

3. Uncertainty and Sensitivity Analysis

Models have inherent uncertainties. Especially the propagation of these uncertainties when using several models in series of a simulation may lead to meaningless result. Therefore the uncertainties have to be assessed, which happens classically by a combined uncertainty and sensitivity analysis. The uncertainty analysis quantifies the influence of uncertainties in the model input on the model output, whereas the complementary sensitivity analysis quantifies the individual and combinatorial contribution of input parameters on the output uncertainty. A suitable technique for the named analysis are Monte Carlo methods. They are based on large random sampling numbers, which derive a numerical solution for the underlying deterministic problem by processing the random numbers in a stochastic process. In the case of the uncertainty and sensitivity analysis, the input space of the model is sampled and then the model output for each sample is calculated (Sin et al., 2009). For both analyses, the first step is the definition of the input uncertainty for the set of m subjected parameters. The parameters can be input parameters to the model, the model parameters itself or also design parameters.

3.1. Uncertainty Analysis

In the Uncertainty Analysis, a sampling technique is chosen in order to randomly sample the input space. The here applied methodology is Latin Hypercube sampling (LHS). The sampling number N has to be sufficiently high in order to guarantee randomness. The output is a sampled input space $\boldsymbol{x}_{N \times m}$. By evaluating the model for every input in the input space, the output space $\boldsymbol{y}_{N \times n}$ for the set of n outputs is created. With this output space, the mean value μ_{y_i} and standard deviation σ_{y_i} of each respective output y_i are calculated (Sin et al., 2009)

3.2. Sensitivity Analysis

The applied Sensitivity Analysis is a variance-based method, assuming that a higher dimensional model representation (HDMR) for the underlying model $\boldsymbol{y} = f(\boldsymbol{x})$ exists. With this HDMR, the variance of the model output can be decomposed, which allows the calculation of first-order and total sensitivity indices (S_i and S_{Ti}) of each input x_i as described by (Saltelli et al., 2010). The first-order sensitivity index describes the reduction in the output variance by fixing parameter x_i, the total sensitivity index equivalently describes the reduction in the output variance by fixing all parameters but x_i. With this, the first-order sensitivity index helps identifying important model parameters, whereas the total sensitivity index helps detecting parameters, which possibly can be discriminated. In practice, the sampling technique applied here is quasi-random Sobol sampling, which provides four specific input space matrices being subsequently used for the Monte Carlo simulations as described by Sobol (Al et al., 2019). The sensitivity indices are calculated by the methodology described by Jansen et al. (Saltelli et al., 2010). The analysis itself is performed through the easyGSA framework (Al et al., 2019).

4. Model Assessment

By assessing both downstream models with the named Monte Carlo methods, two things can be investigated: the first is the model uncertainty in predicting the output yield of xylitol which helps classifying the viability of the downstream concept. Secondly, by assessing the operational parameters for both models by sensitivity analysis, important parameters for the implementation and the scale-up of this process can be detected. This yields answers to all the questions arising in section 2.

4.1. Output yield

As the downstream process is commonly the most cost-intensive process part, a high output yield becomes crucial in order to guarantee economic viability. In the upstream process, in the biomass pretreatment yields of around $Y_{Pret} = 90\%$ can be achieved. In the actual fermentation process, the yield is highly dependent on the employed cell factory. Hernandez et al. indicate an average yield $Y_{Ferm} = 70\%$ for different *Candida* species, including also engineered and evolved cell factories (Hernandez et al., 2019).

For the evaporation unit, it is assumed, that the yield of xylitol is $Y_{Evap} = 100\%$, as the separation factor of water and xylitol is sufficiently high. Furthermore the parameter uncertainties for the NRTL model implemented in ASPEN Plus are assumed to have low uncertainty, so that the model output can be considered robust.

The crystallization model uses solubility and kinetic parameters, which were estimated from experimental data. A realistic simulation scenario for a batch crystallization with ethanol as anti-solvent is selected. The simulation parameters are the nominal values μ in table 2. A sampling number of $N = 100$ is chosen for the simulations. The uncertainty bounds of the parameters are set according to the mean values and the standard deviations from the parameter estimation. The results on the xylitol concentration in the solute for only assuming the kinetic parameters uncertain, as well as assuming both kinetic and solubility parameters uncertain are illustrated in the following figure 1:

Surrogate Modelling Based Uncertainty and Sensitivity Analysis for the Downstream Process Design of a Xylitol Biorefinery

1667

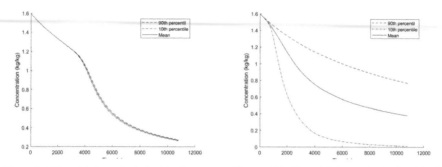

Figure 1a) Uncertainty analysis for kinetic parameters

Figure 1b) Uncertainty analysis for kinetic and solubility parameters

The direct comparison of both analyses illustrates very clearly that the uncertainty in the kinetic parameters is very low compared to the uncertainty in the solubility parameters. The yield for both cases is $Y_{Cryst,a} = 65\%$ and $Y_{Cryst,b} = 51\%$.

4.2. Importance of Operational Parameters

For performing SSO in order to properly design a biotechnological production process of xylitol in a biorefinery, it is imperative to possess knowledge of the sensitivity of operational parameters of the employed models in order to define an expedient objective function. Therefore the operational parameters of both models are analyzed.

4.2.1. Sensitivity Analysis of the Evaporation Model

In order to perform the proposed analysis, a surrogate model is created. The considered operational parameters and their bounds are the feed rate F, the xylitol concentration according to the mentioned yields, the preheating temperature T_{Pre} and the vapor fraction γ within the range σ around their nominal value μ. Each parameter is sampled with $n = 4$ points. From this sampling, surrogate models are fitted to the data. With this, a sensitivity analysis as described in section 3.2 is performed with $N=2000$ sampling points. The results for a GPR surrogate model are shown in the following table:

Table 1: Sensitivity of the operational parameters of the evaporation unit model

Parameter	μ	σ	S_i	S_{Ti}
F	$1000\ kg/s$	50 %	−0.0052	0
x_{XyOH}	0.08	62.5 %	0.8058	0.8209
T_{Pre}	80 °C	12.5 %	−0.0052	0
γ	0.75	10 %	0.1791	0.1942

4.2.2. Sensitivity Analysis of the Crystallization Model

The sensitivity analysis for the crystallization model as described in section 3.2 is equally performed with $N = 2000$ samples. All parameters are sampled within the range σ of their nominal values μ. The ranges and results are displayed in the following table 2:

Table 2: Sensitivity of the operational parameters of the crystallization unit model

Parameter	μ	σ	S_i	S_{Ti}
F_{AS}	$0.01\ kg/s$	10%	0.0106	0.0118
F_C	$1.6\ kg/s$	10%	0.0075	0
m_S	$0.0025\ kg$	10%	0.0075	0
t_B	$10800\ s$	25%	0.1847	0.2401
H	$0.5\ m$	10%	0.0072	0.0003
$C_{XyOH,0}$	$1.6\ kg/kg$	25%	0.7479	0.7902
$T_{C,0}$	10 °C	10%	0.0076	0
T_0	40 °C	25%	0.0078	0

5. Conclusion and Outlook

5.1. Conclusion

When assessing the yield of the downstream process, the following points become clear: as the yield for the pretreatment is very high and the yield in the fermentation process can only be elevated by engineering more compelling cell factories, it is crucial to increase the yield of the downstream process. Firstly, the solubility parameters should be improved by including more measurement data. Secondly, the superstructure should be set up including more than one crystallizer in series as a trade-off against uncertainties in the upstream units. The sensitivity analysis with the *easyGSA* framework proves to be a simple yet effective tool for the analysis. It shows for both unit operations, that the most important operational parameter on the output yield is the input concentration. This directly indicates further potential in developing a new cell factory, paving the way for higher recovery rates and also the employment of a serial crystallization in order to increase the overall yield. Overall, the performed Monte Carlo based analyses provide valuable insight into the downstream process design, show possible potential for improvement and prove the general viability of this setup for the downstream process.

5.2. Outlook

The following step now is the final implementation of the surrogate models created by the *easyGSA* framework in a superstructure in order to validate the concept by optimizing towards the objective of a maximum xylitol production under minimum capital and operational costs. Further research will study the effect of including a process train for the utilization of the CF and the LF on the optimal biorefinery concept. The overall aim is to improve the economic potential of integrated biorefineries for the biotechnological production of xylitol and creating more sustainable value chains as demanded by the sustainable development goals of the United Nations.

References

International Diabetes Federation, 2019, IDF Diabetes Atlas 9th Edition, acces: 19.11.2019.

S. Mussatto, in: D-Xylitol, S. da Silva, A. Chandel (Eds.), Springer, Heidelberg, Berlin; 2012; 309-323.

A. Hernandez et al., 2019, Xylitol bioproduction: state-of-the-art, industrial paradigm shift and opportunities for integrated biorefineries, *Critical Reviews in Biotechnology*, 39, 7, 924-943.

S. Mussatto, G. Dragone, 2016, Biomass Pretreatment, Biorefineries, and Potential Products for a Bioeconomy Development, in: Biomass Fractionation Technologies for a Lignocellulosic Feedstock Based Biorefinery, S. Mussatto (Ed.), Elsevier, 1-22.

C. Gargalo et al., 2017, Optimal Design and Planning of Glycerol-Based Biorefinery Supply Chains under Uncertainty, *Industrial & Engineering Chemistry Research*, 56, 41, 11870-11893.

M. Öner et al., 2018, Scale-up Modeling of a Pharmaceutical Crystallization Process via Compartmentalization Approach, *Computer Aided Chemical Engineering*, 44, 181-186.

A. Bari, A. Pandit, 2018, Sequential Crystallization Parameter Estimation Method for Determination of Nucleation, Growth, Breakage, and Agglomeration Kinetics, *Industrial & Engineering Chemistry Research*, 57, 5, 1370-1379.

R. Al et al., 2019, Meta-modeling based efficient global sensitivity analysis for wastewater treatment plants – An application to the BSM2 model, *Computers & Chemical Engineering*,

G. Sin et al., 2009, Good Modeling Practice for PAT Applications: Propagation of Input Uncertainty and Sensitivity Analysis, *Biotechnology Progress*, 25, 4, 1043-1053.

A. Saltelli et al., 2010, Variance based sensitivity analysis of model output. Design and estimator for the total sensitivity index, *Computer Physics Communications*, 181, 2, 259-270.

Sauro Pierucci, Flavio Manenti, Giulia Bozzano, Davide Manca (Eds.)
Proceedings of the 30th European Symposium on Computer Aided Process Engineering
(ESCAPE30), May 24-27, 2020, Milano, Italy. © 2020 Elsevier B.V. All rights reserved.
http://dx.doi.org/10.1016/B978-0-12-823377-1.50279-2

Process Modelling and Sensitivity Analysis of Roller Mill and Lauter Tun Subsystem Operation

Eduardo Andres Morales, Dimitrios I. Gerogiorgis

*Institute for Materials and Processes (IMP), School of Engineering, University of
Edinburgh, The Kings Buildings, Edinburgh, EH9 3FB, United Kingdom*
D.Gerogiorgis@ed.ac.uk

Abstract

Industrial beer production faces many technical as well as economic challenges, with
increased competition and trends towards craft beers and non-alcoholic beverages posing
new challenges to brewers, who strive to minimise production costs and processing times
whilst improving product quality. Milling, mashing and lautering are a major bottleneck
in sweet wort production; however, mathematical models describing these unit operations
remain elusive. This study focuses on modelling these unit operations as a subsystem,
using a dataset compiled from a brewhouse pilot plant. A first-principles model using
batch filtration theory is conceived for the lauter tun, with another statistical model based
on Partial Least Squares (PLS) regression describes the milling and mashing operations.
The first-principles model describes reasonably well lautering data; the PLS model offers
reasonable accuracy for batch time prediction. A holistic view on the brewhouse is then
emphasised through a sensitivity analysis, in which variables such as mashing agitation
speed and pre-mashing, resting and mash-out temperatures have been found to have the
greatest influence on subsystem batch time. Strategies for improved operating protocols
are also presented, highlighting the strengths and limitations of the models proposed.

Keywords: Process modelling; Partial Least Squares (PLS); roller mill; lauter tun; beer.

1. Introduction

Beer is one of the most globally consumed alcoholic beverages, accounting for 74% of
alcohol consumption in 2016. However, consumption per capita has decreased over the
past 50 years in traditionally beer-drinking (mainly European) countries while
consumption in the US has plateaued. These trends may be due to increased globalisation
and competition, the rise of microbreweries and craft beer and the emergence of health-
oriented drinks, which has shifted consumer preferences (Conen and Swinnen, 2016).

Milling, mashing and lautering operations in beer brewing are strongly linked due to the
complex interactions and trade-offs arising between them. A very fine grist will increase
starch conversion and sugar extraction rates, but at the cost of undesirable flavours such
as bitterness in the finished beer. Moreover, it could lead to a "stuck mash" condition in
the separation vessel, where the mash filter becomes clogged and cannot filter the wort
and thus hindering its collection rate. On the other hand, coarser grists increase wort
flowrates and reduce filtration times but with lower extraction yields. A balance must be
struck between grist particle size and the obtained extraction efficiency (Crescenzi, 1987).

This study aims to analyse the milling-mashing-lautering operations in an industrial UK
brewery, and improve their performance by means of formulating a mathematical model
describing the subsystem and the main drivers behind wort separation. To this end,
operational parameters and process variables contained in datasets collected from a pilot

plant are used to develop a validated model for the subsystem. The ultimate goal is to improve brewhouse efficiency via superior operating protocols towards minimising batch time whilst not compromising high product quality (Rodman and Gerogiorgis, 2019).

2. Roller Mill and Lauter Tun Subsystem Modelling

Model formulation for brewhouse subsystems must be pursued in accordance with plant size, sensor availability and process variables obtained or inferred from industrial data. The experimental data in this study is acquired from a pilot plant consisting of a roller mill, a mash conversion vessel and a lauter tun. Process variables are recorded at one-second (1 s) intervals over the entire subsystem batch duration. The experimental data has been compiled over 12 different days, with one batch produced per day. Process variables associated with the mashing and lautering operations (and raw material weights used) have also been recorded over the batch duration for each batch. The subsystem is therefore considered as two connected sub-processes, presented in Fig. 1; milling and mashing are described via the statistical (PLS) model and the lautering via a physics-based model.

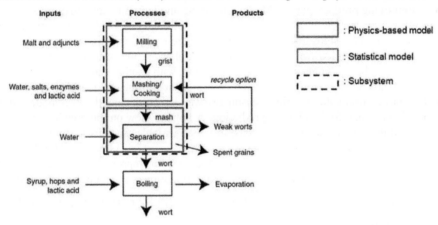

Figure 1: Modelling strategy for the sweet wort subsystem.

For the milling and mashing sub-process PLS model, 14 variables were chosen in order to develop the statistical model. The general linear regression model can be written in a compact form as Eq. 1, where y is the response vector, X is the process matrix, β is the regression coefficient vector and ε the residuals vector. PLS regression is based on the idea that while many predictor variables could be present, only a few variables, i.e., components or latent variables, account for most of the variation in the response, measured by the coefficient of determination, R^2. By projecting the information present to low-dimensional spaces as delineated by the number of PLS variables (n_{comp}), data redundancy is eliminated, giving structure to the process matrix formulated. To obtain the PLS components, initially the variables in X and y are normalised. Afterwards, a linear transformation for the original variables is performed, using an appropriate weight matrix W, such that the covariance between the PLS components from the T matrix and the response variable y is maximised. Using the new latent variables obtained, OLS regression is performed to solve for the vector Q (Eq. 2), which represents the loading vector for the response variable. The original coefficients β are then determined (Eq. 4).

$$y = X\beta + \varepsilon \tag{1}$$

$$y = TQ + \varepsilon \tag{2}$$

$$T = XW \tag{3}$$

$$\beta = WQ \tag{4}$$

The PLS model (MacGregor et al., 1994) was implemented in MATLAB using a modified version of the SIMPLS algorithm (de Jong, 1993). To assess the PLS model, the cumulative R^2 vs. the number of PLS components was plotted to determine the range of optimal latent variables. Then, a detailed PLS regression was performed for the selected components, making use of the cross-validation technique, to test its capability against future observations. Following best practice and prior experience, the 'leave-one-out' cross-validation method has been selected. Along with the R^2 coefficient, the Root Mean Squared Error of Prediction (RMSEP) was also considered as a performance indicator.

Lauter tun vessels can be described by Darcy's law (Eq. 5), where Q : the volumetric flowrate, k the permeability constant, A: the filter area, ΔP the pressure differential, μ: the wort viscosity, and L: the filter bed thickness. The resulting differential form of the filtration equation is given by Eq. 6, defining α_{av}: average specific resistance accounting for compressible cake filtration, c: the corrected dry solids concentration in the filter cake, V: the cumulative filtrate volume, R: the medium resistance. To ensure optimal flowrate and to avoid filter blocking in a lauter tun, the differential pressure through the filter cake is often selected as the controlled variable. When ΔP is kept constant during filtration, Eq. 6 can be integrated analytically, assuming constant α_{av}, c and R to obtain Eq. 7: K_1 and K_2 are the cake and medium resistance factors, respectively. For the sake of filter size scaling, the cake resistance factor K_1 is converted to a filterability coefficient F_k (Eq. 8). A plot of t/V vs. V yields a linear trend if the Darcy model adequately fits industrial data.

$$Q = \frac{kA\Delta P}{\mu L} \tag{5}$$

$$\frac{1}{A}\frac{dV}{dt} = \frac{A\Delta P}{\mu(\alpha_{av}cV + AR)} \tag{6}$$

$$\frac{t}{V} = \frac{K_1}{2}V + K_2 \tag{7}$$

$$F_k = K_1 A^2 \tag{8}$$

3. Subsystem Model Validation

The PLS model results for the mashing-milling sub-process vs. industrial data for different numbers of PLS variables (n_{comp}) are shown in Fig. 2. With 6 or 7 PLS components, the PLS model does not accurately represent the data; however, when 9 components are used, the model represents the data accurately but may exhibit significant deviation when fitted to new data. Generally, one should avoid having too many variables (MacGregor et al., 1994; Shen et al., 2019). Thus, a selection of $n_{comp} = 8$ is used here, in order to ensure an adequately descriptive but not overly complex statistical formulation.

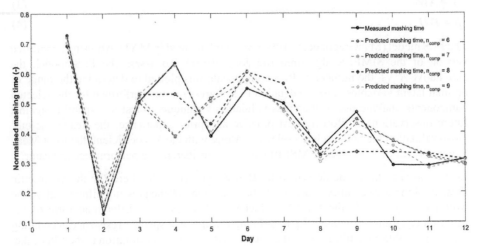

Figure 2: PLS components (n_{comp}) predictive assessment.

Lautering modelling results from the first-principles model are presented in Fig. 3. Experimental points from individual days follow a linear trend, as per the $R^2 = 0.654$–0.993 in this work, indicating reasonable fit. The variation may be attributed to equipment design or gradual filter blocking due to insufficient wort recirculation time. The resulting model coefficients K_1, K_2 and F_k and their standard deviations are listed in Table 1.

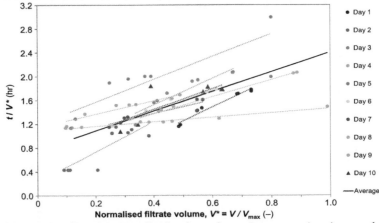

Figure 3: Lautering time vs. normalised volume for various operation days, and average.

4. Sensitivity Analysis

To detect the main drivers for the overall subsystem, a sensitivity analysis was performed, under a ±10% scenario. Following the method of Jørgensen and Fath (2011), sensitivity indices S were calculated. The values of S-indices remain constant regardless of the parameter relative perturbation if the model is linear. The perturbed subsystem variables, x_i, are listed in Table 2. Sensitivity analysis results are presented in Fig. 4 by illustration of S-values (Fig. 4a) and the effect of a ±10% variable deviation on the overall subsystem batchtime. The subsystem batch time is highly sensitive towards changes in the pre-mashing temperature (x_8), third resting temperature (x_{11}), mash-out temperature (x_{13}), mashing agitation speed (x_{14}) and moderately sensitive to the amount of malted grain weight (x_1–x_4) and the wort volume collected (x_{15}), providing valuable hints for operation.

Table 1: Lautering model statistics summary.

Stats	K_1		K_2		F_k
Units	10^{-7} hr L^{-2}	10^{-4} hr m^{-6}	hr L^{-1}	hr m^{-3}	hr m^{-2}
Average	8.24	3.79	0.824	0.379	2.57
Std. dev.	3.26	1.84	0.326	0.184	1.02
Variation (%)	85.1	92.9	85.1	92.9	85.1

Fig. 4b shows an increase mash-out temperature (x_{13}), agitation speed (x_{14}) and wort volume (x_{15}) also increases the batch processing time. On the lower end of the tornado plots, increasing the malted grain weight (x_1), the pre-mashing temperature (x_8) and the third resting temperature (x_{11}) decrease the subsystem batch time significantly. Implementing a speed control system would improve mash filterability, because excessive stirring leads to increased batch times because of the increased shear forces exerted on the mash, in agreement with brewing theory (de Rouck et al., 2013). The wort volume can thus be controlled via a composition loop system so as to stop its collection and reduce batch times, once the sweet wort has achieved a desired sugar composition.

Table 2: Milling, mashing and lautering: subsystem process variables.

Variable	Name	Units	Unit Op.	Variable	Name	Units	Unit Op.
x_1	Material Weight 1	kg	Milling	x_9	Resting T_1	°C	Mashing
x_2	Material Weight 2	kg	Milling	x_{10}	Resting T_2	°C	Mashing
x_3	Material Weight 3	kg	Milling	x_{11}	Resting T_3	°C	Mashing
x_4	Material Weight 4	kg	Milling	x_{12}	Resting T_4	°C	Mashing
x_5	Initial tank T	°C	Mashing	x_{13}	Mash-out T	°C	Mashing
x_6	Pre-mash water volume	L	Mashing	x_{14}	Agitation speed	rpm	Mashing
x_7	Strike water volume	L	Mashing	x_{15}	Wort volume	L	Lautering
x_8	Pre-mash T	°C	Mashing				

Not all sensitive variables mentioned can be used as manipulations for process control. The mass of malted grain (MW1) and the wort volume are defined as design parameters for a specific brewing recipe and cannot change under normal conditions. The rest of the sensitive variables (x_3, x_8, x_{11}, x_{14}) can be conveniently used for batch process regulation.

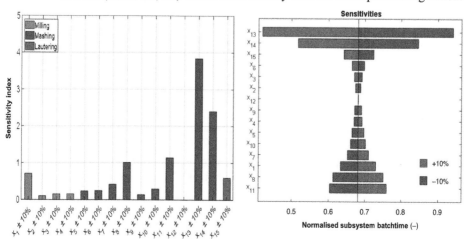

Figure 4: (a) Parameter sensitivity indices, (b) Batch times vs. ±10% parameter variation.

5. Conclusion

The modelling strategy conceived in this study resulted in the formulation of two mathematical models capable of capturing mashing and lautering behaviour, giving rise to operational protocols aimed at reducing batch times and increasing plant productivity. To gain mechanistic understanding of the wort separation processes, a first-principles model based on filtration theory has been formulated to describe lauter tun operation. Correlation of the coefficients K_1 and K_2 to other process parameters may further increase the fidelity of the presented model and the accuracy of the modelling results vs. the considered industrial datasets which can be analysed. This model can be used to predict lautering times as a function of the wort volume only, which is a key operating parameter. The optimal number of PLS latent variables for mashing-milling modelling is a compromise between model accuracy and reliability for future predictions. This model predicts milling-plus-mashing times with adequate accuracy for performance monitoring. The sensitivity analysis clearly indicates that significant reductions in batch time can be achieved by increasing the malted grain weight, pre-mashing temperature, resting temperature and decreasing the mash-out temperature, agitation speed and wort volume.

Acknowledgements

The authors acknowledge the support of the Engineering and Physical Sciences Research Council (EPSRC)/IAA, the Japan Society for the Promotion of Science, the Great Britain Sasakawa and Nagai Foundations and the Royal Academy of Engineering (RAEng). Previous discussions with Molson Coors colleagues are also gratefully acknowledged.

References

A.M. Crescenzi, 1987, Factors governing the milling of malt, *J. I. Brewing*, 93, 193–201.

L. Colen and J. Swinnen, 2016, Economic growth, globalisation and beer consumption, *J. Agric. Econ.*, 67, 1, 186-207.

S. de Jong, 1993, SIMPLS: An alternative approach to partial least squares regression, *Chemometr. Intell. Lab.*, 18, 3, 251–263.

G. de Rouck, B. Jaskula, B. de Causmaeckerm, S. Malfliet, F. van Opstaele, J. de Clippeleer, J. de Brabanter, L. de Cooman and G. Aerts, 2013, The influence of very thick and fast mashing conditions on wort composition, *J. Am. Soc. Brew. Chem.*, 71, 1, 1–14.

S.E. Jørgensen and B.D. Fath, Concepts of modelling. In *Fundamentals of Ecological Modelling*, S.E., Jørgensen, B.D. Fath, Eds. *Developments in Environmental Modelling*, Elsevier: 2011; 23, 19-93.

J.F. MacGregor, C. Jaeckle, C. Kiparissides and M. Koutoudi, 1994, Process monitoring and diagnosis by multiblock PLS methods, *AIChE J.*, 40, 5, 826–838.

A.D. Rodman and D.I. Gerogiorgis, 2019, An investigation of initialisation strategies for dynamic temperature optimisation in beer fermentation, *Comput. Chem. Eng.*, 124, 42–61.

Q. Shen, M. Weaser, L. Griffiths and D.I. Gerogiorgis, 2019, Statistical modelling for optimisation of mash separation efficiency in industrial beer production, *Comput. Aided Chem. Eng.*, 46, 1465–1470.

Sauro Pierucci, Flavio Manenti, Giulia Bozzano, Davide Manca (Eds.)
Proceedings of the 30th European Symposium on Computer Aided Process Engineering
(ESCAPE30), May 24-27, 2020, Milano, Italy. © 2020 Elsevier B.V. All rights reserved.
http://dx.doi.org/10.1016/B978-0-12-823377-1.50280-9

Dynamic Modelling and Simulation of Cold Contact Fermentation (CCF)

Dylan Pilarski, Dimitrios I. Gerogiorgis

Institute for Materials and Processes (IMP), School of Engineering, University of Edinburgh, The Kings Buildings, Edinburgh, EH9 3FB, United Kingdom
D.Gerogiorgis@ed.ac.uk

Abstract

The increased commercial presence and comparative health benefits of alcohol-free beer (AFB) provide a substantial impetus for research, particularly in the field of dynamic simulation whereby the development of accurate models can help reduce costs of experimentation. Cold Contact Fermentation (CCF) is an existing method of industrial-scale AFB production that utilises reduced fermentor temperatures and altered contact times compared to Warm Fermentation (WF), though requiring continual attention given the production of non-optimal organoleptic compositions, which drastically affect taste. In order to better understand the differences between Warm Fermentation (WF) and CCF, a DAE system is constructed based on previous WF studies whose responses are compared vis-à-vis to simulations of the same model under industrial CCF conditions. Given the significant discrepancies between dynamic results, industrial data can be for the parametrisation of a new CCF model, in order to accurately portray plant operation. Further to these simulations, the sensitivity of final species concentrations to parameter variation and the effect of hypothetical temperature profiles are studied with the aim of evaluating model system flexibility and opportunities for improvement based on changes to fermentor temperature profiles. Overall, disparate relative ethyl acetate sensitivity and clustering of hypothetical CCF responses reflect existing challenges with flavour composition but highlight opportunities for remarkable process improvements.

Keywords: Cold Contact Fermentation (CCF); Cold Contact Process (CCP); Alcohol-Free Beer (AFB); dynamic modelling; multivariate constrained dynamic optimisation.

1. Introduction

Cold Contact Fermentation (CCF) or Cold Contact Process (CCP) emerged in 1983 as novel method of producing beer with a reduced alcohol content by altering both fermentation duration and temperature from the conditions utilised in standard brewing practice (Perpète and Collin, 1999). Since that time, interest in alcohol-free beer (AFB) has surged, with an estimated global increase in consumption of 80% from 2007 to 2012 corresponding to an amount of $2.2 \cdot 10^9$ L yr^{-1} (Liguori et al., 2018). Despite this increase in consumption, the production of AFB is still beset by concerns with the issue of maintaining the balance between flavours such as butter/butterscotch (due to vicinal diketones, frequently denoted as VDKs, such as diacetyl), bitterness (due to aldehydes such as acetaldehyde) and fruitiness (due to esters, such as ethyl acetate) while retaining a consistent flavour profile with regard to sweetness (residual extract) and beer aroma.
While numerous research efforts regarding CCF at a laboratory scale have been undertaken since its inception, its dynamic modelling has not received the same attention

as the produced beverage. Dynamic modelling and optimisation have been applied for beer manufacturing (Rodman and Gerogiorgis, 2016); this work steers towards the implementation of not only a robust model but a sound platform for future optimisation on a broader industrial scale aimed at process cost reduction and flavour improvement. This study uses the kinetic model of de Andrés-Toro et al. (1998) as the basis for describing state responses under CCF conditions of suspended biomass (X_S), ethanol (C_E), sugar (C_S), diacetyl (C_{DY}) and ethyl acetate (C_{EA}) (see Fig. 1). This model splits the fermentation process into an initial lag phase and, upon adequate lag cell activation, transition to a fermentation phase where secondary flavour products are generated. The kinetic model equations (Eqs. 1–12) describing species profiles are shown in Fig. 1.

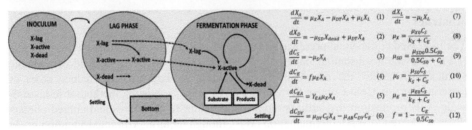

Figure 1: Kinetic model for Warm Fermentation (WF) (de Andrés-Toro et al., 1998).

Arrhenius factors (μ_i) denote formation or consumption of corresponding model species while the stoichiometric factor (Y) and inhibition factor (f) guide ethyl acetate and ethanol formation, respectively. The full mathematical model has been expressed as a Differential Algebraic Equation (DAE) system and solved in MATLAB, to simulate key responses.

2. CCF Model Parameterisation

A comparison of dynamic simulation responses for the de Andrés-Toro et al. (1998) model ($T = 13$ °C) and implementation of new CCF operating ($T = 5–6.5$ °C) and initial conditions (CCFIC) demonstrated severe differences in model dynamic behaviours, i.e., differing trends aside from the differing initial (imposed via the CCFIC) and final species concentration values (Fig. 2). Because of anticipated response discrepancies between simulations of WF and CCF in respect to assumed initial conditions, final concentrations from industrial CCF batches were incorporated as numerical benchmarks for parameterisation of de Andrés-Toro (1998) kinetic model, now under CCF conditions.

Reparameterisation of temperature-dependent parameters of specific rates (μ_i, Eq. 13) has therefore been systematically conducted, and it was achieved through an algorithm targeting least squares regression (Eq. 14) with respect to each of the state variables $\theta_{i,\text{measured}}$ (for a total of N) and corresponding model responses, $\theta_{i,\text{model}}$ (Pilarski, 2019).

$$\mu_i = \exp\left(A_i + \frac{B_i}{T}\right) \tag{13}$$

$$\min_{\theta_i} J(\theta_i) \tag{14}$$

$$J = \sum_{i=1}^{N} \left(\theta_{i,\text{measured}} - \theta_{i,\text{model}}\right)^2 \tag{15}$$

Minimisation was performed using the Nelder-Mead direct search algorithm, whereby a subset of DAE parameters were allowed to vary in order for the algorithm to converge and produce a solution set of parameters that diverged minimally from the WF parameters presented by de Andrés-Toro et al. (1998). Plausible industrial operating conditions and/or data encompassing processing, initial conditions and final concentrations for CCF simulations and parameterisation can be considered in this computational framework.

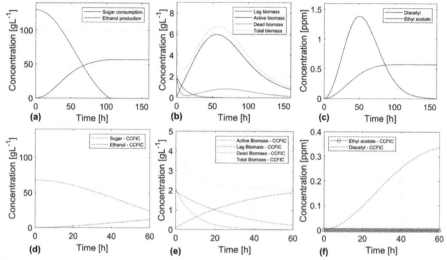

Figure 2: Key dynamic response comparisons between WF (a–c) and CCFIC (d–f).

Values of A_i and B_i for explicit kinetic model parameters which have properly converged have been then reparameterised to constrain the scope of the problem. This successfully allowed for parameterisation with respect to C_S, C_E, C_{EA} and C_{DY} based on limited pilot plant data, with all biomass responses remaining unconstrained (Fig. 3). Reparameterised CCF values, but also those kept as per the WF model, have been summarised in Table 1.

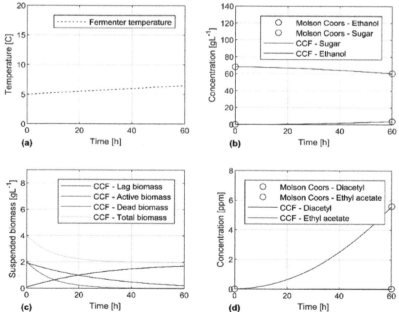

Figure 3: A plausible CCF temperature profile (a); parameterised CCF responses (b–d).

Table 1: Resulting CCF model parameters with * denoting values original to this study (our results).

Rates / Parameters	Description	A_i	B_i
μ_{SD0}	Maximum dead cell settling rate	33.820	−10,033.280
μ_{X0}	Maximum cell growth rate	37.450*	−31,934.090
μ_{S0}	Maximum sugar consumption rate	−41.920	11,754.776*
μ_{E0}	Maximum ethanol production rate	4.125*	−1,267.240
μ_{DT}	Specific cell death rate	130.160	−38,313.000
μ_L	Specific cell activation rate	30.720	−9,501.540
$k_E = k_S$	Affinity constant for sugar and ethanol	−119.630	35,203.709*
Y_{EA}	Stoichiometric factor - ethyl acetate production	169.130*	−26,589.000
		Value	
μ_{DY}	Rate of diacetyl production	$7.590 \cdot 10^{-6}$*	
μ_{AB}	Rate of diacetyl consumption	$1.138 \cdot 10^{-3}$	

3. Sensitivity Analysis

Sensitivity analyses offer great insight for batch and semi-batch processing that may require control policies of varying flexibility based on production progress/completion. Process response sensitivity S can be quantified in relation to the measured change in a state variable θ based on an intended change in a parameter P according to Eq. 15.

$$S = \frac{\partial \theta}{\theta} \bigg/ \frac{\partial P}{P} \qquad (15)$$

Parameter variations of ±5% were implemented and the resulting sensitivities of state variables (model responses) visualised for clarity (Fig. 4). Variations in parameters A_{kes} and B_{kes} produced large perturbations for all state variables, though final C_{EA} sensitivity to variation (particularly for A_{YEA}, B_{YEA}, $A_{\mu x0}$ and $B_{\mu x0}$) was most significant and a reflection of 'fruity' flavour issues described for AFB as a result of over or uncontrolled ester expression (Verstrepen et al., 2003). Thus, process variations (parameter values being a function of processing conditions) have the greatest impact on C_{EA}.

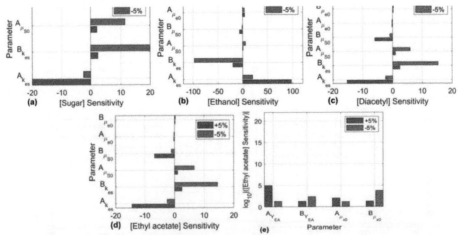

Figure 4: Sensitivities for (a) final sugar, (b) ethanol, (c) diacetyl and (d–e) ethyl acetate concentrations under ±5% variation for all parameters of non-negligible process impact.

4. Course Grid Enumeration of Hypothetical Temperature Profiles

Previous CCF industrial results were garnered via consideration of a 1.5 °C temperature band. However, it is known that CCF processes can make use of temperatures between 0–8 °C (Perpète and Collin, 1999; Montanari et al., 2009). In addition, by using existing cooling jackets, the fermentor temperature can be controlled provided the CCF progresses, through the exothermic reactions in the fermentor, or with future implementation of external heating. The effect of temperature variation was studied via coarse grid discretisation of the computational time (10 hr sub-grids for $t \in [t_0, t_f] = [0, 60]$ and temperature domains (1 °C sub-grids for 1–7 °C). Furthermore, different temperature profiles have been selected on the basis of ease of industrial implementation (Pilarski, 2019). This resulted in 29 hypothetical temperature profiles, ranked by total theoretical heat Q (Eq. 16). Here, m is the fermentation broth mass and C_P is the specific heat capacity at constant pressure. Results for all temperature profiles are given in Fig. 5.

$$Q = mC_P \int_{t_0}^{t_f} T(t)\mathrm{d}t \tag{16}$$

Of all enumerated results, C_{EA} and C_{DY} represent the largest and smallest spans of hypothetical outcomes, respectively. In addition, a general increase in consumption of final C_S and increased formation of C_E, C_{EA} and C_{DY} is noted. However, general trends for rates of change of each response are very different. When coupled with evident clustering (e.g., Trials 26–29) these trends show the potential for improvement based on changes to fermentor temperatures. Although the number of temperature profiles considered here is limited in comparison to the full scope of possibilities that could be implemented industrially, comparison of the effects of the theoretical Q limits the number of temperature profiles that allow one to stay within product specifications. Each Q may have multiple associated temperature profiles; the optimal manipulation may be established via dynamic optimisation attain target ethanol concentrations while also ensuring critical flavour component concentration constraints (Rodman et al., 2019).

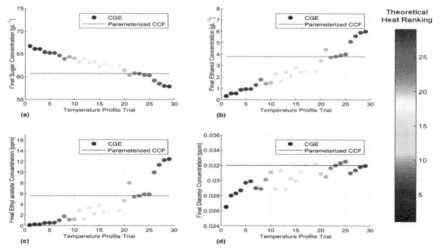

Figure 5: (a) Sugar, (b) ethanol, (c) ethyl acetate and (d) diacetyl final concentrations based on T- profile variation and ranking by a Q metric (CGE: Coarse Grid Enumeration).

5. Conclusion

This study used industrial data to formulate a newly parameterised model for CCF using the published de Andrés-Toro et al. (1998) kinetic model to compare model responses between WF and CCF. Differences in dynamic behaviour, aside from different initial and final species concentration values inherent of the different processing requirements of WF and CCF operations, necessitated reparameterisation of the Andrés-Toro model to accurately describe CCF. Subsequent parameterisation regarding industrial data points provided a solution set of parameters to follow the dynamic behaviour of the WF model. Sensitivity analyses based on a ±5% variation elucidated the most important model parameters with the highest sensitivity to changes in temperature-dependence, with ethyl acetate concentrations being the most impacted. Enumeration of CCF responses based on hypothetical temperature profiles confirmed that increased theoretical heat increased formation of ethanol, ethyl acetate and diacetyl during CCF, albeit at different rates. Future work will implement the newly parameterised CCF model for dynamic optimisation of temperature profiles in order for low-alcohol content beer subject to different end-point (related to flavour species) and interior-point (related to temperature boundaries and gradient limitations associated with controllers) constraints as well as heat transfer dynamics to account for different scales of fermentor operation and production.

Acknowledgements

The authors acknowledge the support of the Engineering and Physical Sciences Research Council (EPSRC)/IAA, the Japan Society for the Promotion of Science, the Great Britain Sasakawa and Nagai Foundations and the Royal Academy of Engineering (RAEng). Previous discussions with Molson Coors colleagues are also gratefully acknowledged.

References

B. de Andrés-Toro, J.M. Girón-Sierra, J.A. Lopez-Orozco, C. Fernández-Conde, J.M. Peinado and F. Garcia-Ochoa, 1998, A kinetic model for beer production: simulation under industrial operational conditions, *IFAC Proceedings Volumes*, 48, 65–74.

L. Liguori, P. Russo, D. Albanese and M. Di Matteo, 2018, Production of low-alcohol beverages: current status and perspectives, in *Food Processing for Increased Quality and Consumption*, Grumezescu, A.M.; Maria, A (eds.), Cambridge, USA, Academic Press, 347–382.

L. Montanari, O. Marconi, H. Mayer and P. Fantozzi, 2009, Production of alcohol-free beer, *Beer Heal. Dis. Prev.*, 274, 2016, 61–75.

P. Perpète and S. Collin, 1999, Fate of the worty flavours in a cold contact fermentation, *Food Chem.*, 66, 3, 359–363.

D. Pilarski, 2019, *Dynamic Modelling and Simulation of Cold Contact Fermentation*, Masters Thesis, The University of Edinburgh, UK.

A.D. Rodman and D.I. Gerogiorgis, 2016, Multi-objective process optimisation of beer fermentation via dynamic simulation, *Food Bioprod. Process.*, 100, 255–274.

A.D. Rodman, M. Weaser, L. Griffiths and D.I. Gerogiorgis, 2019, Dynamic optimisation and visualisation of industrial beer fermentation with explicit heat transfer dynamics, *Comput. Aided Chem. Eng.*, 46, 1459–1464.

K.J., Verstrepen, G., Derdelinckx, J-P., Dufour, J., Winderickx, J.M., Thevelein, I.S., Pretorius and F.R., Delvaux, 2003, Flavor-active esters: adding fruitiness to beer, *J. Biosci. Bioeng.*, 96, 2, 110–118.

Sauro Pierucci, Flavio Manenti, Giulia Bozzano, Davide Manca (Eds.)
Proceedings of the 30th European Symposium on Computer Aided Process Engineering
(ESCAPE30), May 24-27, 2020, Milano, Italy. © 2020 Elsevier B.V. All rights reserved.
http://dx.doi.org/10.1016/B978-0-12-823377-1.50281-0

Application of the "Distance to Target" Approach to the Multiobjective Optimization of Nutritional and Economic Costs due to Food Loss and Waste

Ricardo Abejón,[a] Ian Vázquez-Rowe,[b] Alba Bala,[c] Pere Fullana-i-Palmer,[c]
María Margallo,[a] Rubén Aldaco[a*]

[a]*Departamento de Ingenierías Química y Biomolecular, Universidad de Cantabria.
Avda. de Los Castros s/n, 39005, Santander, Spain*
[b]*Peruvian LCA Network, Department of Engineering, Pontificia Universidad Católica
del Perú, Av. Universitaria 1801, 15088 San Miguel, Lima, Peru*
[c]*UNESCO Chair in Life Cycle and Climate Change ESCI-UPF. Pg. Pujades 1, 08003
Barcelona, Spain*
aldacor@unican.es

Abstract

Since about one third of all food produced worldwide is lost or wasted throughout the
supply chain, measures to reduce food loss and waste (FLW) must be fostered to meet the
increasing challenge of sustainable feeding of the world's population. In addition to the
minimization of the total amount of FLW, two additional relevant aspects must be taken
into account: the nutritional and economic costs caused by these losses. This point of view
defines a more complex scenario with multiple sustainability targets, with different
minimization objectives. A "distance to target" approach, based on the definition of a
normalized weighted distance, has been selected to provide practical and effective
optimization guidelines by measuring the magnitude towards the quantitative sustainable
targets in the minimization of economic and nutritional costs associated to FLW. The
results revealed that vegetables were the food category that showed the worst
performance in terms of nutritional and economic costs due to the great amount of loss
and waste generated, which highlights the importance of providing measures in this
category.

Keywords: Multiobjetive optimization, Distance, FLW, Economic costs, Nutritional
costs.

1. Introduction

The food supply chain is a key aspect to be considered for sustainable development of the
Water-Food-Energy nexus. In addition, wastes must be integrated in this context, since
food supply chains are particularly wasteful (García and You, 2018). About 30% of all
food produced is lost or wasted worldwide throughout the supply chain. These losses have
important consequences on the environment, implying significant impacts in terms of
inefficient use of natural resources and energy, biodiversity and habitat loss, soil and
water degradation, and climate change (Hoehn et al., 2019).

Efficient measures and future strategies are required to decrease FLW. In order to identify
the most critical aspects, the simple quantification of the losses in terms of mass are
insufficient and further tools to include the nutritional and economic characteristics of
these losses must be taken into account (Vázquez-Rowe et al., 2019). Indexes that

consider the nutritional quality and economic cost of lost and wasted food can assist policy-makers, because these more complex metrics include additional relevant aspects to support the decision-making processes.

Although the definition of this type of indexes helps to measure the performance of different solutions, a high number of case studies related to sustainability assessment and impact reduction that must manage with multiple objectives are based on a "direction to target" approach, which defines the improving direction to a sustainable objective without quantitative guidelines. However, a "distance to target" approach results more effective, since it provides practical guidelines by measuring and quantifying the magnitude toward a previously defined sustainable target. This approach was applied to the minimization of the economic and nutritional costs due to FLW attributable to different food categories.

2. Case study

FLW along the supply chain of the Spanish food system was selected as the case study (García-Herrero et al. 2018). This work does not consider the nature of the supply chain models, since a previous study, which evaluated the economic and nutritional efficiency of 13 food categories, was used as the reference database (Vázquez-Rowe et al., 2019). This previous work applied a life cycle perspective to define two indexes that characterize the economic and nutritional losses: the economic FLW index (EFLW) and the nutrient-rich foods index (NFR9.3). In the current study, however, these indexes were transformed to normalized economic and nutritional factors (X_{EC} and X_{NUTR}, respectively) by dividing each value by the corresponding maximal value. The factors obtained are presented in Figure 1.

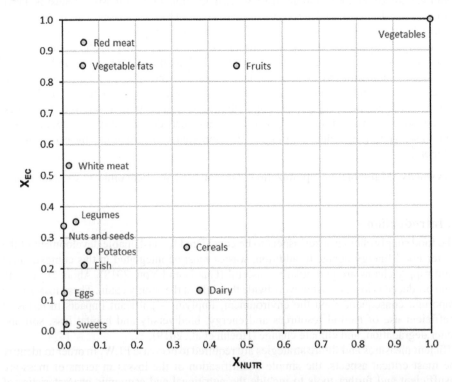

Figure 1. Economic factor X_{EC} versus nutritional factor X_{NUTR} for the food categories.

Application of the "distance to target" approach to the multiobjective optimization of nutritional and economic costs due to food loss and waste

1683

3. Modelling

The use of a "distance to target" approach provides some advantages when compared to standard multiobjective optimization methods like ε-constraints (Abejón et al., 2012). For instance, it provides a single Pareto solution, rather than a Pareto front of solutions. Moreover, it can be applied to identify the best way to improve suboptimal solutions by finding minimal projections onto the Pareto front (Limleamthong and Guillen-Gosálbez, 2017). The Euclidean distance between the individual solutions and the optimization targets can be used as base (Schadler et al., 2016). The Euclidean distance D in a n-dimension space can be defined by the following equation:

$$D = \overline{\sum_{i=1}^{n} |f_i(x) - g_i|^2} \qquad (1)$$

where $f_n(x)$ is the vector to be optimized and g_n the specified target vector. In the current study, a normalized weighted distance D_n was employed as the main indicator to identify minimal nutritional and economic costs of different categories of food products:

$$D_n = \frac{\sqrt{\sum_{i=1}^{n} k_i |F_i(x) - G_i|^2}}{\sqrt{n}} \qquad (2)$$

where $F_n(x)$ is the normalized vector to be optimized and G_n the normalized specified target vector, while k_n represents the weighting factor of each objective. This definition of D_n implies that the distance values are normalized in the range between 0 (closest to the target) and 1 (furthest to the target), so a direct and easily comparable outlook of the results is provided (another clear advantage over conventional multiobjective optimization methods). In this case, since both objectives must be minimized, the normalized target vector is the null vector (all components are equal to 0).

4. Results

First, normalized distances of each category were assessed when the contributions of both objectives were considered equally important ($k_{EC} = k_{NUTR} = 1$). The results obtained can be observed in Table 1 ($D_{n \, eq}$ column). Sweets appeared as the optimal category, with minimal distance to the defined sustainability target. In contrast, vegetables was the most distant category to the target due to the higher economic and nutritional factor values. Then, GAMS software was employed to manage the formulated NLP models using CONOPT3 solver (Abejón et al., 2016) to calculate the minimal and maximal values that the normalized distance could take ($D_{n \, min}$ and $D_{n \, max}$ respectively in Table 1). These optimization programs were subject to restrictions: the weighting factors were ranged between 0.2 and 1.8, and the sum of the weighting factors was equal to the number of objectives (i.e., 2):

$$\min D_n = f(k_i) \quad \text{or} \quad \max D_n = f(k_i)$$
$$\text{s.t.} \qquad h(k_i) = 0$$
$$g(k_i) \le 0$$
$$k_i \in \Re$$

Once again, when the minimal values were compared, sweets were the optimal category. When white meat, as the best example of a category with uncompensated economic and nutritional values, was compared to cereals, with more compensated values, different patterns were identified. White meat presented lower minimal distance because it was favored by its low X_{NUTR} value and high weighting factor of this objective improved its performance when compared to cereals. However, the range between minimal and maximal distances was lower for cereals. In addition to sweets, other two categories (i.e., eggs and nuts and seed) resulted non-dominated and these three categories formed the standard Pareto front (Figure 2). Therefore, the rest of categories can be considered sub-optimal points.

Table 1. Economic and nutritional factors, normalized distance under equal weighting factors (D_n eq), minimal (D_n min) and maximal (D_n max) normalized distances, and the normalized projection distances onto the Pareto front (D_n Front) or the distance to form a new front (D_n Pareto)

	X_{EC}	X_{NUTR}	$D_{n\,eq}$	$D_{n\,min}$	$D_{n\,max}$	$D_{n\,Front}$	$D_{n\,Pareto}$
Sweets	0.021	0.006	**0.016**	0.009	0.020	-	-
Eggs	0.123	0.002	**0.087**	0.039	0.117	-	-
Fish	0.212	0.057	**0.155**	0.086	0.202	0.039	0.039
Potatoes	0.256	0.069	**0.187**	0.104	0.244	0.048	0.048
Nuts and seeds	0.338	0.000	**0.239**	0.107	0.321	-	-
Legumes	0.351	0.033	**0.249**	0.115	0.333	0.025	0.023
Dairy	0.130	0.373	**0.279**	0.171	0.356	0.262	0.077
Cereals	0.268	0.338	**0.305**	0.276	0.332	0.239	0.175
White meat	0.532	0.015	**0.377**	0.169	0.505	0.138	0.010
Vegetable fats	0.853	0.055	**0.604**	0.275	0.809	0.366	0.039
Red meat	0.927	0.058	**0.657**	0.298	0.880	0.419	0.041
Fruits	0.850	0.476	**0.689**	0.526	0.820	0.494	0.336
Vegetables	1.000	1.000	**1.000**	1.000	1.000	0.848	0.692

These sub-optimal categories can be projected onto the Pareto front to establish the best improvement route to make them Pareto optimal. These projection distances (D_n Front) were assessed as the minimal normalized distance between a category and the front formed by the three Pareto optimal categories (Table 1). Legumes, which had a higher D_n eq value when compared to fish or potatoes, resulted with a lower D_n Front value because it was relatively close to an optimal category (i.e., seeds and nuts). Instead of becoming optimal solutions by projection onto the existing Pareto front, a sub-optimal category could be a new optimal point to extend the front. In this case, this situation resulted from the reduction of the X_{NUTR} value below that of sweets or the reduction of the X_{EC} value below that of seeds and nuts. These minimal distances (D_n Pareto) are also included in Table 1. In most cases, the D_n Pareto values were lower than D_n Front values. The case of the categories with uncompensated factors (white meat as example) must be highlighted, because a slight decrease of the factor with lower value (X_{NUTR} in this case) resulted in a close transformation to optimal solution (0.010 is the lowest Dn Pareto value).

Finally, a detailed analysis of Figure 2 revealed that under particular weighting factor conditions, each of the three optimal categories could be those with the lowest distance to target.

Application of the "distance to target" approach to the multiobjective optimization of nutritional and economic costs due to food loss and waste

1685

However, as demonstrated in the results compiled in Table 1, the minimizationof these distances subject to restriction in the weighting factors (limited between 0.2 and 1.8) displayed sweets as the best option.

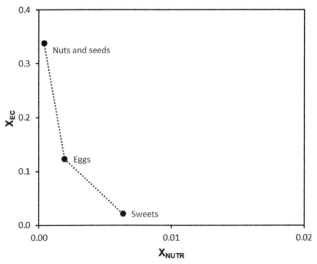

Figure 2. Detailed view of the Pareto front of optimal categories.

Therefore, a more complete sensitivity analysis of the influence of the weighting factors without restrictions was carried out. As observed in Figure 3, only extreme values of the weighting factors resulted in the discarding of sweets as the best performing category. When the k_{NUTR} value was higher than 1.995, the distance value of eggs was lower than that of sweets and it became the best performing category. To get nuts and seeds as the best category a more extreme situation was required: the k_{EC} value had to be lower than $7.8 \cdot 10^{-5}$ to overpass eggs and attain the lowest distance. Consequently, the robustness of sweets as the optimal category according to the distance to target approach was clear.

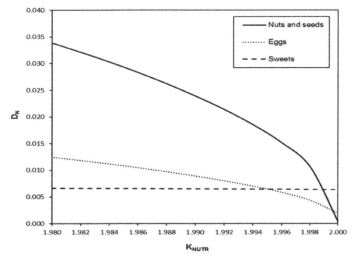

Figure 3. Evolution of the normalized distant of the three Pareto categories as a function of the weighting factors.

5. Conclusions

A "distance to target" approach, based on a normalized weighted distance, was applied to the simultaneous minimization of the nutritional and economic costs of FLW. On the one hand, the analysis of the different food categories demonstrated that vegetables resulted as the worst performing category, requiring urgent measures. On the other hand, sweets appeared as the best performer. Only the consideration of extreme weighting factors that practically cancel the economic costs made possible the transformation of eggs or nuts and seeds into the most preferable categories. This study can assist the decision-making process to design and select effective strategies and policies for the most adequate management of FLW. The applied approach is a useful tool to prioritize the most critical food categories and to measure the efficacy of the implementation of the proposed measures.

Acknowledgements

The authors are grateful for the funding of the Spanish Ministry of Economy and Competitiveness through the Ceres-Procom Project: Food production and consumption strategies for climate change mitigation (CTM2016-76176-C2-1-R) (AEI/FEDER, UE).

References

R. Abejón, A. Garea, A. Irabien, 2012, Multiobjective optimization of membrane processes for chemicals ultrapurification, , Computer Aided Chemical Engineering, 30, 542-546.

R. Abejón, A. Abejón, M.P. Belleville, J. Sánchez-Marcano, A. Garea, A. Irabien, 2016, Multiobjective optimization of membrane networks for fractionation of protein hydrolysate from fish by-products, Computer Aided Chemical Engineering, 38, 415-420.

D.J. Garcia, F. You, 2018, Including agricultural and organic waste in Food-Water-Energy-Waste nexus modelling and decision-making, Computer Aided Chemical Engineering, 43, 1475-1480.

I. García-Herrero, D. Hoehn, M. Margallo, J. Laso, A. Bala, L. Batlle-Bayer, P. Fullana, I. Vázquez-Rowe, M.J. González, M.J. Durá, C. Sarabia, R. Abajas, F.J. Amo-Setién, A. Quiñones, A. Irabien, R. Aldaco, 2018, On the estimation of potential food waste reduction to support sustainable production and consumption policies, Food Policy, 80, 24-38.

D. Hoehn, M. Margallo, J. Laso, I. García-Herrero, A. Bala, P. Fullana-i-Palmer, A. Irabien, R. Aldaco, 2019, Energy embedded in food loss management and in the production of uneaten food: seeking a sustainable pathway, Energies, 12, 767.

P. Limleamthong, G. Guillen-Gosálbez, 2017, Rigorous analysis of Pareto fronts in sustainability studies based on bilevel optimization: Application to the redesign of the UK electricity mix, Journal of Cleaner Production, 164, 1602-1613.

P. Schadler, J.D. Berdugo, T. Hanne, R. Dornberger, 2016, A distance-based Pareto evolutionary algorithm based on SPEA for combinatorial problems, 4th International Symposium on Computational and Business Intelligence Proceedings, 112-117.

I. Vázquez-Rowe, J. Laso, M. Margallo I. Garcia-Herrero, D. Hoehn, F. Amo-Setién, A. Bala, R.aAbajas, C. Sarabia, M. J. Durá, P. Fullana-i-Palmer, R. Aldaco, 2019, Food loss and waste metrics: a proposed nutritional cost footprint linking linear programming and life cycle assessment, The International Journal of Life Cycle Assessment, in press.

Sauro Pierucci, Flavio Manenti, Giulia Bozzano, Davide Manca (Eds.)
Proceedings of the 30th European Symposium on Computer Aided Process Engineering
(ESCAPE30), May 24-27, 2020, Milano, Italy. © 2020 Elsevier B.V. All rights reserved.
http://dx.doi.org/10.1016/B978-0-12-823377-1.50282-2

A Step Closer to the Market for Poly-hydroxy-alkanoates (PHAs) through their Bacterial Production in Continuous Bioreactors in Series: a Model Investigation of Novel Operating Strategies

Christos Chatzidoukas,[a,*] Evgenios Karasavvas[b]

[a]*Department of Chemical Engineering, Aristotle University of Thessaloniki (AUTH), P.O. Box: 472, 54124, Thessaloniki, Greece*

[b]*Chemical Process & Energy Resources Intitute (CPERI), Centre for Research and Technology Hellas (CERTH), P.O. Box: 60361, 57001, Thermi, Thessaloniki, Greece*
chatzido@auth.gr

Abstract

The current work explores the dynamic optimization of a sequence of two continuous stirred-tank bioreactors for the production of poly-3-hydroxybutyrate (PHB) in *Azohydromonas lata* cultures using a credible and sophisticated mathematical model. The cumbersome problem of operating a microbial fermentation process continuously in a consistent, systematic and controllable manner is uncovered at its full dimension and addressed, pursuing in parallel the efficient substrate utilization and the optimization of the fermentation stage. Advanced optimization algorithms and well-posed optimization strategies with different subsets of control variables are implemented A notable improvement on the performance of the continuous optimal operating bioreactors is demonstrated via the maximization of key process factors, such as productivity, biopolymer content, final product concentration etc., under three different strategies

Keywords: Dynamic optimization of microbial processes, fermentation process design, bio-based polymer production, optimal operating profiles, fermentation modelling.

1. Introduction

The stiffness of the biochemical industry to change the operating mode of fermentation processes from a batch-wise profile to a continuous one is a well-known reason blamed for the large production cost of highly promising, green, renewable products with novel applications, deficient though to compete the respective fossil-based counterparts, massively fabricated in continuous chemical processes. This is currently the status quo of polyhydroxyalkanoates (PHAs), a group of biopolymers gaining global importance across different sectors (e.g., packaging, automotive, pharmaceutical, medical industry, etc.) due to their thermoplastic and mechanical properties (similar to polyolefins) combined with biocompatibility, biodegradability, and sustainability, holding though a modest position in the global polymer market ranking (Spierling et al., 2018). The large production cost is definitely the major drawback of PHAs, which suspends their commercialization. The complexity of the bio-processes and the interdependence of the decisions that should be taken simultaneously (Koller et al., 2017) to take care fermentation aspects make the development of reliable and rigorous mathematical models for dynamic simulation and model-based optimization of the PHAs production process indispensable. In the present study, the dynamic problem of the continuous operation of two bioreactors in series for the production of poly-3-hydroxybutyrate (PHB) in *Azohydromonas lata* cultures is investigated. It is demonstrated that the establishment of a steady-state operation of the system is feasible, thus the continuous process operation guarantees a substantially productivity enhancement and provides the means for a truly sustainable production of PHB.

2. Dynamic Mathematical Model of Bioprocess

A two-compartment, structured, non-segregated macroscopic/kinetic and oxygen mass transfer model (Chatzidoukas et al., 2013, Papapostolou et al., 2019) is used in the present study for the fermentative intracellular production of PHB by *A. lata* bacteria. The integrated model enables the simulation and prediction of the time evolution of the residual biomass, X; the polymer intracellular content, w_p; the accumulation of polymer, P; the carbon (S) and nitrogen (N) source utilization, as well as the dynamic profile of oxygen concentration in both gas phase ($O_{2,g}$) and liquid culture phase ($O_{2,l}$). The derived validated model is employed as a rigorous and reliable mathematical tool for the optimal decision making towards the mitigation of the PHAs production cost, through the design of novel efficient continuous operating strategies of a two-bioreactor system.

3. Dynamic Optimisation Strategies

Continuous operation of a fermentative PHB production process practically means a continuous feeding of fresh nutrient medium to the culture with a simultaneous removal of culture broth, while holding the entire process at the desired steady state. The optimisation of the continuous two-stage process operation is practically meant as the investigation of the optimal steady state. However, the settlement of the optimal steady state cannot be sought independently of the selection of the optimal dynamic trajectory towards this *'static'* operation. Thus, the design of optimal operating policies of PHB-producing fermentation reactors, operating in continuous mode, is practically attained through the intelligent handling of the nutrient feeding, and the initial concentration of substrates as a means of regulating both the size of the cell population and their physiological state towards the efficient production of the product of interest. Properly formulated equality and/or inequality constraints representing rational and operational restrictions of the fermentation process are employed for a realistic statement of the dynamic optimization problem. Then the problem of the optimal continuous operation of the two bioreactors in series is explored via the design of three continuous operating scenarios (*CO1-CO3*) of gradually increasing number of control variables (CVs) summarized in Table 1. It is noted that for all three continuous operating policies a stock of sucrose aqueous solution and ammonium sulphate aqueous solution of fixed concentration (i.e., 50 g/l and 20 g/l, respectively) is employed for the feeding of both bioreactors. Primarily, the optimal initial substrates concentrations ($[S]_{0,i}$, $[N]_{0,i}$) as well as the respective optimal substrates feeding profiles and broth outflow rates, ($Q_{S,in,i}$, $Q_{N,in,i}$, $Q_{out,i}$) are sought separately for each bioreactor (i=1,2), under the scenario *CO1*. Then *CO2* has been designed similarly to the first one, but the air flow rate, ($F_{air,i}$) and the set point value ($D.O_{sp,i}$) of the controller for the dissolved oxygen concentration in the medium, which is cascaded to the rate of agitation ($N_{r,i}$), supplement the set of CVs. Finally, *CO3* is identical to *CO2* and differs only in terms of the working volume of the second bioreactor. In *CO1* & *CO2* both bioreactors are of equal working volumes (i.e., 3 l), while in *CO3* the respective volume V_2 is 5 l, allowing for greater flexibility in culture's residence time in the reactor where polymer cellular accumulation is built.

Table 1: Set of control variables for the continuous operating scenarios of two bioreactors (i=1,2).

Scenarios	$[S_{o,i}]$ (g/L)	$[N_{o,i}]$ (g/L)	$Q_{S,in,i}$ (l/h)	$Q_{N,in,i}$ (l/h)	$Q_{out,i}$ (l/h)	$F_{air,i}$ (l/h)	$D.O_{sp,i}$ (-)	$t_{f,i}$ (h)
CO1	✓	✓	✓	✓	✓	—	—	✓
CO2 & CO3	✓	✓	✓	✓	✓	✓	✓	✓

The objective function employed to address the dynamic optimisation of the PHB production process operating in a continuous mode, is mathematically defined as:

$$Obj = w_1[P_2(t_f)]Q_{out,2}(t_f) + w_2 w_{p,2}(t_f) - w_3 \int_0^{t_f} Q_{out,2}(t)[S_2(t)]dt$$

The first two terms in the objective function clearly express the polymer mass rate exiting from the second bioreactor, and the respective polymer content in the cells. The last term though contributed detractively to the objective function and practically represents the cumulative amount of sucrose removed from the process (via the 2nd bioreactor outlet stream) and thus is wasted. Thus, the mathematical statement of the multi-objective dynamic optimization problem of the continuously operating process is written as shown below, while the entire problem is solved using the generic simulation platform gPROMS® (Process Systems Enterprise, Ltd.) combined with the embedded gOPT optimization tool.

$$\max_{[S_{0,i}],[N_{0,i}],Q_{s,in,i},Q_{N,in,i},Q_{out,i},F_{air,i},D.O_{sp,i},t_f} Obj$$

w.r.t. *process* mod *el equations*

$0 \le Q_{out,i}(t) \le 0.5 \ l/h; \ i = 1,2$

$V_{l,i}(t) \le 2.5 \ l; \ i = 1,2 \ (for \ CO1, \ CO2) \ or \ V_{l,1}(t) \le 2.5 \ l, \ V_{l,2}(t) \le 4.5 \ l, \ (for \ CO3)$

$0 \le D.O_{sp,i}(t) \le 100; \ i = 1,2$

$100 \le N_{r,i}(t) \le 1000 \ rpm; \ i = 1,2$

$t_j \ge 0.5 \ h; \ j = 1,...10$

$-10^{-7} \le \dfrac{dY_i(t_f)}{dt} \le 10^{-7}; \ i = 1,2 \ where \ Y_i = \{[X_i],[P_i],[S_i],[N_i],[O_{2g,i}],[O_{2l,i}],[V_{l,i}],[V_{g,i}]\}$

4. Results and Discussion

Analysing the optimal policies calculated for the system of the two bioreactors in series it is important to illuminate the scope of each reactor unit in a continuous PHB production process and the pathway followed towards the establishment of the optimal steady state. High priority target for the optimizer is to build immediately a sufficiently dense population in the first reactor unit, which successively feeds the second reactor unit. This need unambiguously requires a culture medium rich in nitrogen source and adequacy in carbon source. At the same time avoidance of culture suffocation conditions, due to the high level of demanded oxygen and given the process limitations in culture aeration and mixing, is a major issue that an optimal strategy should take care of. On the other hand, the role attributed by the optimiser to the second bioreactor is mainly to raise the polymer content of the bacterial population and maintain (or ideally further increase) the population density. The reported values of the optimal initial bioreactor loadings (see Table 2) and the respective optimal control trajectories displayed in Fig. 1-3 for the three operating scenarios, demonstrate this operating plan.

Table 2. Optimal initial loadings of the two bioreactors and steady-state values of state variables for the 2nd reactor unit for each continuous operating scenario.

Scenarios	$[S_{0,1}]$ (g/l)	$[N_{0,1}]$ (g/l)	$[S_{0,2}]$ (g/l)	$[N_{0,2}]$ (g/l)	$[P_2]$ (g/l)	$[X_2]$ (g/l)	$[S_2]$ (g/l)	$[N_2]$ (g/l)	$[w_{p,2}]$ (%)	$D.O_2$ (%)	$V_{l,2}$ (l)
CO1	16.14	2.28	6.61	3.19	10.36	3.68	6.93	1.10	73.78	13.79	2.50
CO2	8.20	1.31	3.06	3.10	16.08	4.69	4.51	0.99	77.40	14.95	2.50
CO3	21.90	2.84	25.00	0.02	17.12	3.39	3.73	1.07	83.43	14.30	4.50

Note that in *CO1* & *CO2* operating scenarios, different initial loadings of the first reactor unit with the nitrogen source (resulted from our capacity to adjust in addition the F_{air} and $D.O_{sp}$, in the case of *CO2*) are combined with different complementary feeding policies of this nutrient to guarantee its sufficiency in the culture medium, throughout the transition period and at the final steady state. In the second reactor unit the respective initial loadings are even larger combined though with more conservative feeding policies, since for this unit the outflow stream is held close to zero (in order to minimise the wasted carbon) and only towards the completion of the transition strategy it is raised to its steady state value. In line with this tactic is the sucrose initial loading and feeding implemented in the process. In case though of the *CO3* operating scenario, where all the available CVs are employed, the larger volume of the second reactor unit steers the optimization problem towards a totally different solution approach (see Table 2 & Fig.3). Null nitrogen initial loading in the second reactor unit is applied and its repletion in the nitrogen source is practically regulated by the outflow stream from the first reactor. It is worth of pointing out that similar to *CO1* & *CO2* in this operating scenario the optimal profile of the bioreactor outlet stream, $Q_{out,2}$, is held zero throughout the transient period and only in the last time interval raises to its maximum allowed value, driving the bioreactor to the optimal steady state. Finally, it should be emphasized

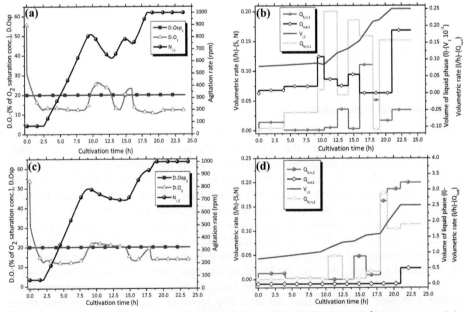

Figure 1: Dynamic transition to the optimal steady state of the 1st (a, b) and 2nd bioreactor (c, d) in a process of two continuously operating bioreactors in series under the optimized scenario *CO1*.

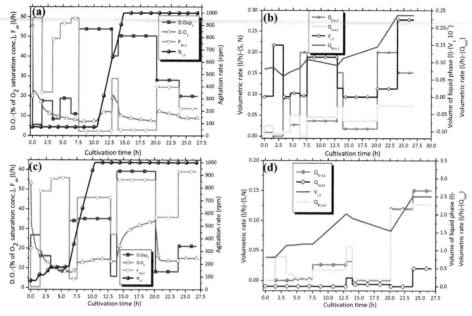

Figure 2: Dynamic transition to the optimal steady state of the 1st (a, b) and 2nd bioreactor (c, d) in a process of two continuously operating bioreactors in series under the optimized scenario *CO2*.

that the large culture needs in oxygen, restrains the optimal process performance no matter which one of the three operating scenarios is applied since in all cases, in both reactor units the agitation speed is bound to the maximum allowed value (i.e., 1000 rpm) in the final steady state, while the value of the D.O. in the culture cannot be fixed to the desired set point.

For the comparison of the three operating scenarios with respect the objective function and key performance indicators, their values are summarised in Table 3. The predominance of the operating scenario *CO3* against the other two is evident in terms of either the polymer production rate (8.56 g/h against 5.18 & 8.04 g/h) or yield or polymer content or even sucrose wasted rate ($Q_{out,2}[S_2]$). The only performance index where the *CO3* scenario is inferior is the productivity (1.9 g/(l h) against 2.07 & 3.21 g/(l h)) and this is because a larger working volume for the 2nd reactor (4.5 l) has been decided by the optimiser to increase the cells residence time and thus PHB content.

Table 3: Optimal values of objective function and individual performance indices for *CO1-CO3*.

Scenarios	$Q_{out,2}$ (1/h)	$[P_2]Q_{out,2}$ (g/h)	$Q_{out,2}[S_2]$ (g/h)	$\int Q_{out,2}[S_2]dt$ (g)	Productivity (g/(l h))	Yield (g/g)	t_f (h)	Obj (-)
CO1	0.5	5.18	3.46	3.46	2.07	0.62	22.0	12.33
CO2	0.5	8.04	2.25	5.01	3.21	0.62	25.6	15.44
CO3	0.5	8.56	1.86	5.43	1.90	0.74	28.5	16.54

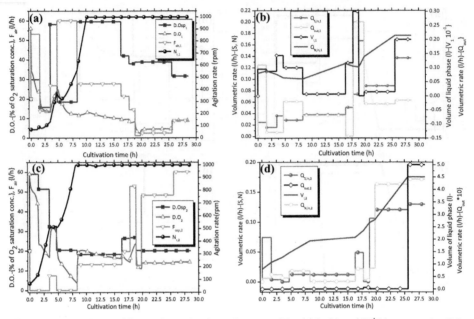

Figure 3: Dynamic transition to the optimal steady state of the 1st (a, b) and 2nd bioreactor (c, d) in a process of two continuously operating bioreactors in series under the optimized scenario *CO3*.

5. Conclusions

In the present study, a highly non-linear, sophisticated and validated dynamic mathematical model of *A. lata* bacterial culture was employed to develop a systematic optimization methodology and launch an innovative continuous PHB production strategy. For the first time, a configuration of two stirred tank bioreactors in series was modelled and optimized under three different policies seeking for the optimal steady state in terms of key process factors such as productivity, biopolymer content and final product concentration, which explicitly reflect prosperous financial indexes of the process operation. It was demonstrated that the decision of this optimal steady state is in essence not a matter of identifying the final optimal steady-stated culture conditions, but of dynamically optimising the system's operation during the transition from the initial loading and inoculation of the two reactor units up to the point where the process performance is stable (i.e., a steady state has been reached). The most promising among these strategies enabled the system operation at steady state values of PHB concentration and intracellular content in the outflow stream equal to 17.12 g/L and 83.43 % wt., respectively and a minimum substrate loss rate of 1.86 g/h. The proposed operating strategy is a strong evidence of the potential of continuous production processes of PHAs, of their restrictions and their capacity to help towards the commercial advancement of PHAs.

References

S. Spierling, E. Knüpffer, H. Behnsen, M. Mudersbach, H. Krieg, S. Springer, S. Albrecht, C. Herrmann, H. J. Endres, 2018, J. Cleaner Product. 185, 476-491

M. Koller, K. Maršálek, M.M. de Sousa Dias, G. Braunegg, 2017, N. Biotechnol. 37, 24-38.

C. Chatzidoukas, G. Penloglou, C. Kiparissides, 2013, Biochem. Eng. J., 71, 72-80.

A. Papapostolou, E. Karasavvas, C. Chatzidoukas, 2019, Biochem. Eng. J., 148, 224-238.

Sauro Pierucci, Flavio Manenti, Giulia Bozzano, Davide Manca (Eds.)
Proceedings of the 30th European Symposium on Computer Aided Process Engineering
(ESCAPE30), May 24-27, 2020, Milano, Italy. © 2020 Elsevier B.V. All rights reserved.
http://dx.doi.org/10.1016/B978-0-12-823377-1.50283-4

Modelling Ontologies for Biorefinery Processes - A Case Study

Robert Pujan,[a,b] * Roy Nitzsche,[a] Jakob Köchermann,[a] Heinz A. Preisig[b]

[a]*DBFZ Deutsches Biomasseforschungszentrum gemeinnützige GmbH, Torgauer Straße 116, 04347 Leipzig, Germany*
[b]*NTNU Norwegian University of Science and Technology, Høgskoleringen 5, 7491 Trondheim, Norway*
robert.pujan@dbfz.de

Abstract

This study introduces the systematic modelling approach of "visual modelling" to biorefinery processes by applying it to a concept from the demonstration project *KomBiChem[PRO]*. The process consists of a hydrothermal conversion of hemicellulose-derived oligo sugars into monomeric C5 sugars, combined with purification steps of adsorption and nanofiltration. The experimental studies determine on model effluents hydrothermal conversion kinetics, adsorption isotherms and kinetics, as well as separation efficiencies of the nanofiltration. The paper shows an efficient graphical representation of the process topology, which is combined with an equation ontology.
Keywords: process modelling, ontology, topology, biorefinery

1. Motivation

Research and development in modern biorefinery concepts require the combination of multiple disciplines such as physics, biology, chemistry, and engineering. Correspondingly, one has to utilise the same large pool of interdisciplinary expertise when designing biorefinery models. That is a collection of fundamental principles, relations, and definitions taken from the different scientific roots - an equation ontology. Introducing the ontology- and topology-based approach to biorefinery modelling minimises modeller-caused errors and enables rapid design. The modelling suite *ProMo*, currently in development at the NTNU (Elve and Preisig, 2017), implements this approach. *ProMo* also compiles the equations into several target languages and generates with the help of a graph-based reasoner executable program code based on the user-defined topology. Due to this, the modeller has to only focus on the structural design. This paper presents the systematic modelling methodology implemented in *ProMo* and provides a first equation ontology for the discussed process. As a biorefinery-representative example, one of the concepts developed in the demonstration project *KomBiChem[PRO]* is used. The model's performance is out of the scope of this methodology paper and will be assessed in a future study.

2. The process concept

Within a lignocellulose biorefinery, a pulping process separates the biomaterial into its main components cellulose, hemicellulose, and lignin. Due to relatively mild process conditions and easy to recover solvents, organosolv pulping with ethanol-water is a promising technology (Laure et al., 2014). During this pulping, a process stream rich in oligomeric and monomeric sugars, as well as other hemicellulose degradation products accrues - the so-called hemicellulose hydrolysate (HH). This stream is currently not recovered due to its low concentration and inhomogeneity. However, utilizing the HH can be important for making lignocellulose processes economic feasible. Therefore, a part of *KomBiChem*[PRO] focused on the development of processes for the hemicellulose conversion into C5 sugars for further processing. The result is the process concept shown in Figure 1, designed for the valorization and purification of xylose from HH. The process removes via adsorption residual lignin and its phenolic degradation products from the HH, which would otherwise cause impurities and inhibitors downstream. A continuous hydrothermal process hydrolyses the oligomeric xylose in the HH to monomeric xylose, while keeping the yield of products, like furfural and acetic acid, low. Finally, membrane nanofiltration removes furans and carboxylic acids from the treated solution and increases the concentration of xylose up to 12 %.

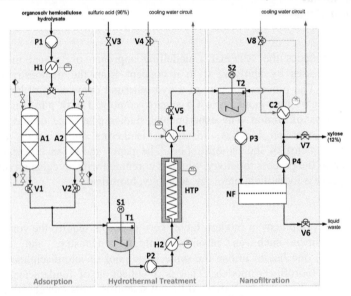

Figure 1: The exemplary process concept from *KomBiChem*[PRO]

3. Experimental methods

While fundamental process parts like pipes, pumps, and heat exchangers can be modelled by theoretical methods, complex processes often require models to be fitted to experimental data. This paragraph discusses the experiments conducted for this purpose.

3.1. Adsorption

Batch experiments were carried out on the resin *SEPABEADS SP700* (*Mitsubishi Chemical Corporation*) to determine adsorption isotherms and kinetics. A binary-component model solution consisting of 3.1 g/L phenol and 4.2 g/L xylose was used. Detailed information of experimental setup, analytics, isotherm modelling, and preliminary desorption studies are given by Nitzsche et al. (2019). The adsorption of phenol and xylose is best described by the extended Freundlich isotherm in the model feed (Table 1, Eq. (37)). Hence, multi-layer adsorption, with non-uniform distribution of adsorption heat and affinities, seems to be predominant (Nitzsche et al., 2019).

3.2. Hydrothermal treatment

Hydrothermal conversion was performed in a continuous coiled tube reactor using HH with 70 g/L xylose as real substrate. To determine the best conditions, experiments covered different reaction temperatures (160, 180, 200 °C) and residence times of 2.5 to 23 min. A back pressure valve at the reactor outlet regulated the process to 50 bar. The reaction model found best-fitting is represented in Eq. (1)-(4). The experiments are comprehensively described by Köchermann et al. (2018) and (2019).

$$\dot{c}_{Xos} = -k_0 c_{Xos} \tag{1}$$

$$\dot{c}_{Int} = k_1 c_{Xy} - k_2 c_{Int} - k_3 c_{Int} c_{Fu} \tag{3}$$

$$\dot{c}_{Xy} = k_0 c_{Xos} - k_1 c_{Xy} \tag{2}$$

$$\dot{c}_{Fu} = k_2 c_{Int} - k_3 c_{Int} c_{Fu} - k_4 c_{Fu} \tag{4}$$

3.2.1. Nanofiltration

The experimental set-up consisted of an *Alfa Laval LabStak M20* plate-and-frame membrane module, an *Alfa Laval NF* flat-sheet membrane, a feed tank, a diaphragm pump, and a shell-and-tube heat exchanger. A model solution of 50 g/L xylose, 6 g/L glucose, 2 g/L furfural, and 8 g/L acetic acid was used. In parameter screenings, transmembrane pressure (10-40 bar), temperature (25-55 °C) and cross-flow velocity v_z (0.5-1.5 m/s) were varied at pH = 2.5 and in total reflux mode. 40 bar, 25 °C, and 1.1 m/s were identified to be appropriate. The permeate flux J (Table 1, Eq. (24)) was measured by collecting permeate for 1 min at predetermined time intervals. With feed, retentate, and permeate samples (10 mL), the component concentrations c_i and the observed retention R_{obs} (Eq. (5)) were determined. At the appropriate process parameters and a filtration area A_M of 0.036 m², a J of 78.1 L/(m²h) and R_{obs} of 100 % for glucose, 93.6 % xylose, 14.1 % furfural, and 2.4 % acetic acid were achieved. 70 % of the feed solution was transferred into the permeate, yielding 20 g/L glucose, 159 g/L xylose, 2.7 g/L furfural, and 8.5 g/L acetic acid in the retentate. The average frictional pressure drop $\Delta p_{f,av}$, determined according to Jönsson et al. (2009), is 1.18 bar.

$$R_{obs} = \left(1 - \frac{c_{Perm}}{c_{Feed}}\right) \cdot 100\% \tag{5}$$

4. Topology and ontology design

The topology in Figure 2 is generated based on the plant sketch in Figure 1 by applying the methods established in (Preisig, 2014). In addition to the depiction of mass and energy balances, the graph also includes a process control domain and the pressure distribution model discussed by Pujan and Preisig (2020). Due to space limitations, we place the focus on the description of the physical domain.

The model is equipped with the equation ontology presented in Table 1, covering everything from pipe flows, heat transfer, adsorption, hydrothermal reactions, nanofiltration and pressure distribution. $\underline{F}$ is the incidence matrix of the directed graph from Figure 2, while $\underline{D}$ and $\underline{R}$ refer to capacity-intern transport processes and internal reactions respectively. The state vectors are written as $\underline{x}$, while a dot decorator indicates accumulation and a hat a flow. The ontology also considers heat transfer and the thermal effect of reactions. Usually, the introduction of energy as a state variable requires the Legendre transformations, linking internal energy U, enthalpy H, and Helmholtz energy. In this case however, constant volume is the modus operando in the energy-exchanging parts of the model. Thus, only U is required. To convert reaction enthalpies into U, Eq. (32) is used. Eq. (31) uses the stoichiometry $\underline{N}$ and reaction coefficients $v_{i,r}$ found in section 3.2.

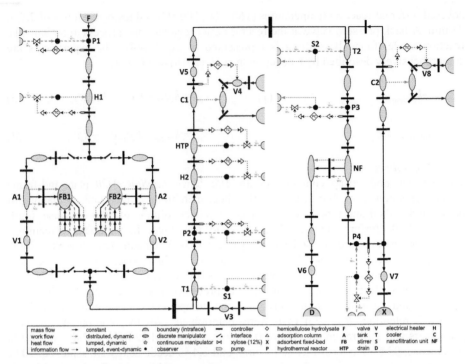

Figure 2: The initial topology of the exemplary process

Table 1: Equation ontology of the physical domain

Description	Equation	
Integrals		
Mass	$\underline{m} = \int_0^t \underline{\dot{m}}(\tau)d\tau + \underline{m}(0)$	(7)
Energy	$\underline{E} = \int_0^t \underline{\dot{E}}(\tau)d\tau + \underline{E}(0)$	(8)
Component mass	$\underline{m}_i = \int_0^t \underline{\dot{m}}_i(\tau)d\tau + \int_0^t \underline{\tilde{m}}_i(\tau)d\tau + \underline{m}_i(0)$	(9)
Component concentration	$\underline{c}_i = \int_0^t \underline{\dot{c}}_i(\tau)d\tau + \int_0^t \underline{\tilde{c}}_i(\tau)d\tau + \underline{c}_i(0)$	(10)
Balances		
Mass conservation	$\underline{\dot{m}} = \sum \underline{\dot{m}}_i$	(11)
Component conservation	$\underline{\dot{m}}_i = \underline{\underline{F}}\hat{m}_i + \underline{\underline{D}}\hat{m}_i^D + \underline{\underline{R}}\tilde{m}_i$	(12)
Energy conservation	$\underline{\dot{E}} = \underline{\underline{F}}\hat{U} + \underline{\underline{R}}\tilde{U}_T^R + \underline{\underline{F}}\hat{K} + \underline{\underline{F}}\hat{P} + \underline{\underline{F}}\hat{w}^y + \underline{\underline{F}}\hat{w}^f$	(13)
Flows		
Mass flow	$\hat{m} = \sum \hat{m}_i$	(14)
Component mass flow	$\hat{m}_i = \underline{c}_i \underline{\hat{V}}$	(15)
Component adsorption	$\hat{m}_i = \underline{m}_{Ads}\dot{q}_i$	(16)
Diffusional flow	$\hat{m}_i^D = \underline{J}_i^D \underline{A}$	(17)

Table 1: Equation ontology of the physical domain (continued)

Description	Equation	
Internal energy flow	$\hat{U} = C_V \hat{m} \underline{T}$	(18)
Kinetic energy flow	$\hat{K} = \frac{1}{2} \hat{m} \underline{v}^2$	(19)
Potential energy flow	$\hat{P} = \hat{m} \underline{h} g$	(20)
Volume work flow	$\hat{\underline{w}}^y = \underline{p} \hat{\underline{V}}$	(21)
Friction work flow	$\hat{\underline{w}}^f = \Delta \underline{p}^f \hat{\underline{V}}$	(22)
Volume flow	$\hat{\underline{V}} = \hat{m} \underline{\rho}^{-1}$	(23)
Permeate volume flow	$\hat{\underline{V}} = \underline{J}^{NF} \underline{A}_{Mem}$	(24)
Cross-sectional velocity	$\underline{v} = \hat{\underline{V}} \underline{A}^{-1}$	(25)
Material properties		
Cylindrical cross-section	$\underline{A} = \pi \left[\underline{r}(l) \right]^2$	(26)
Liquid level	$h_L := root[\underline{F}_l \underline{V} = \pi \int_0^{h_L} \left\{ \underline{F}_l \underline{r}(l) \right\}^2 dl]$	(27)
Voluminous property	$\underline{V} = \underline{m} \underline{\rho}^{-1}$	(28)
Component accumulation	$\underline{\dot{m}}_i = \dot{\underline{c}} \underline{V}$	(29)
Component transposition	$\tilde{\underline{m}}_i = \tilde{\underline{c}} \underline{V}$	(30)
Concentration transposition	$\tilde{\underline{c}}_i = \underline{N}^T \underline{k} \underline{c}_i^{|v_i|}$	(31)
Internal energy transposition	$\tilde{\underline{U}}_T^R = \left(C_V C_p^{-1} \underline{H}_m \right)_T$	(32)
Length of cylindrical body	$\underline{l} = \underline{V} \underline{A}^{-1}$	(33)
Void fraction fixed-bed	$\underline{\varepsilon} = \underline{V}_L \left(\underline{V}_L + \underline{V}_{Ads} \right)^{-1}$	(34)
Adsorption pseudo-2nd order kinetic model	$\underline{q}_i = \dfrac{q_{e,i}^2 \underline{k}_{P2} t}{1 + q_{e,i} \underline{k}_{P2} t} = \int_0^t \dot{\underline{q}}_i(\tau) d\tau + \underline{q}_i(0)$	(35)
Adsorption intra-particle diffusion kinetic model	$\underline{q}_i = \dfrac{3 \underline{q}_{e,i}}{\underline{d}_{Ads}} \sqrt{\dfrac{D_P}{\pi}} t + \underline{B} = \int_0^t \dot{\underline{q}}_i(\tau) d\tau + \underline{q}_i(0)$	(36)
Multi-component extended Freundlich isotherm model	$\underline{q}_{e,i} = \dfrac{\underline{K}_{F,i} \underline{c}_{e,i}^{n_i + x_i}}{\underline{c}_{e,i}^{x_i} + \underline{y}_i \underline{c}_{e,j}^{z_j}}$	(37)
Fick's 1st law	$\underline{J}_i^D = -D_L \cdot \nabla \underline{c}_i$	(38)
Darcy-Weisbach model	$\Delta \underline{p}^f = \frac{1}{2} \underline{f}^i \underline{v}^2 \underline{\rho} \underline{l} \left[2 \underline{r}(l) \right]^{-1}$	(39)
Friction factor (laminar)	$f^i := f^{la} = 64 \mathrm{Re}^{-1} \qquad \text{if } \mathrm{Re} \leq 2,100;$	(40)
Friction factor (turbulent)	$f^i := f^t = f(\mathrm{Re}, \in) \qquad \text{if } \mathrm{Re} > 2,100$	(41)
Reynolds number	$\mathrm{Re} = 2 \rho v r(l) \eta^{-1}$	(42)

Pujan and Preisig (2020) discuss extensively how to derive a reduced plant model from the ontology. Substituting Eq. (7), (9)-(12), (14)-(17), (25), (26), (29) and (33)-(38), as well as common assumptions, yields for example the mass balance for the fixed-bed adsorption in Eq. (6):

$$\dot{c}_i = D_L \frac{\partial^2 c_i}{\partial z^2} - v_z \frac{\delta c_i}{\delta z} - \rho_{Ads} \frac{(1-\varepsilon)}{\varepsilon} \dot{q}_i \tag{6}$$

5. Conclusions

Based on experimental studies and the process flowsheet, a model design was performed by applying the systematic methodology. This study shows that the introduced methodology enables rapid process modelling, also for multi-disciplinary, complex biorefinery processes like the one discussed. At this point, only assumptions, initial and boundary conditions to the ontology equations, and the implementation of a numerical solver are required, what will be the focus of future work to conclude with model fitting and a simulation study.

Acknowledgments

The process concept as well as the experiments were conducted as part of the demonstration project *KomBiChem^{PRO}*, funded by the *German Federal Ministry of Education and Research* (*BMBF*) under the grant number FKZ 031B0083B. The modelling was executed within the research centre *Bio4Fuels*, funded by the *Research Council of Norway* (*RCN*) under the support code 257622.

References

A.T. Elve, H.A. Preisig, 2019, From ontology to executable program code, Comput. Chem. Eng., 122, 383-394

A.-S. Jönsson, O. Wallberg, 2009, Cost estimates of kraft lignin recovery by ultrafiltration, Desalination, 237, 254-267

J. Köchermann, J. Mühlenberg, M. Klemm, 2018, Kinetics of Hydrothermal Furfural Production from Organosolv Hemicellulose and D-Xylose, Ind. Eng. Chem. Res., 57, 14417-14427

J. Köchermann, J. Schreiber, M. Klemm, 2019, Conversion of d-Xylose and Hemicellulose in Water/Ethanol Mixtures, ACS Sustain. Chem. Eng., 7, 12323-12330

S. Laure, M. Leschinsky, M. Fröhling, F. Schultmann, G. Unkelbach, 2014, Assessment of an organosolv lignocellulose biorefinery concept based on a material flow analysis of a pilot plant, Cell. Chem. Technol., 48, 793–798

R. Nitzsche, A. Gröngröft, M. Kraume, 2019, Separation of lignin from beech wood hydrolysate using polymeric resins and zeolites – Determination and application of adsorption isotherms, Sep. Purif. Technol., 209, 491-502

H.A. Preisig, 2014, Visual Modelling, Comput. Aided Chem. Eng., 34, 729-734

R. Pujan, H.A. Preisig, 2020, Systematic Modelling of Flow and Pressure Distribution in a Complex Tank, Proceedings of the 30th European Symposium on Comput. Aided Process Eng.

Sauro Pierucci, Flavio Manenti, Giulia Bozzano, Davide Manca (Eds.)
Proceedings of the 30th European Symposium on Computer Aided Process Engineering
(ESCAPE30), May 24-27, 2020, Milano, Italy. © 2020 Elsevier B.V. All rights reserved.
http://dx.doi.org/10.1016/B978-0-12-823377-1.50284-6

Life Cycle Assessment for Carbon Balance of a Wastewater Treatment Integrated Microalgae Biofuel Production Process

Peiyao Li,[a] Xigang Yuan, [a,b,c]*Yiqing Luo[a,c]

[a]School of Chemical Engineering and Technology, Tianjin University, Tianjin 300350, China
[b]State Key Laboratory of Chemical Engineering, Tianjin University, Tianjin 300350, China
[c]Chemical Engineering Research Center, Tianjin University, Tianjin 300350, China
yuanxg@tju.edu.cn

Abstract

Recent technology advances in carbon fixation via microalgae have shown increasing potentials in reducing net greenhouse gas emission. Carbon in the greenhouse gas is assimilated by photosynthesis in algal cell during the cultivation process, which can be carried out in wastewater environment as an alternative to conventional fertilizer feedstock-based processes. To improve the environmental performance of microalgae biofuel production process as well as increase the efficiency of nutrient biomass uptake in microalgae activities, the carbon balance is investigated by using the Life Cycle Assessment (LCA) for a separated nutrient delivery configuration in this study. In the proposed configuration, sewage sludge from wastewater treatment segment is reclaimed as supporting mediums to improve microalgae biogas production and a stream of pretreated nutrient-enriched wastewater is introduced to high rate algal ponds to satisfy the demand of microalgae-derived lipid productivities. Combined with the downstream process converting algal biomass into biofuel, the system termed as wastewater treatment integrated microalgae biofuel production process is formed. Our analysis showed the advantage of the separated nutrient delivery configuration in improving microalgae carbon fixation performance and the environmental impact of the biofuel production process. In the analysis, the mass and energy balances are achieved by process simulation, and the background data are taken from available databases and the literature. The LCA results show that the system proposed in this work can generate biofuel in energy self-sufficient condition with the carbon fixation effect.

Keywords: microalgae biofuel; life cycle assessment; wastewater treatment; carbon fixation

1. Introduction

Microalgae has been regarded as a promising approach to address climate change and greenhouse effect because of the carbon fixation capability in the microalgae photosynthesis activities (Enamala et al. 2018). Attempts to develop algal biomass conversion technologies and biofuel products to utilize the rich content of lipids, carbohydrates and proteins in algal cells as a cleaner and lower carbon footprint algal biofuel have been reported (Maria et al. 2019). However, the current technical pathways of microalgae biofuel production are in the limitation of nutrient resources from ecological system. To address this challenge, nutrient loaded wastewater has been introduced to microalgae cultivation system as an alternative of make-up nutrient fertilizers to satisfy nutrient demands of algae culture.

As reported by Whitton et al. (Whitton et al. 2016), algae species are in high nutrient removal capacity of wastewater via biomass uptake to algal cells. Besides, lipid content and lipid accumulation rate of algae species could be regulated and controlled by adjustment of nutrient ratio. However, the wastewater-based microalgae cultivation is in risk of low nutrient recovery potentials. The previous researches have mainly focused on microalgae culture processes and the profitability in environmental impacts of wastewater integration to reduce eutrophication, whereas the issue of greenhouse gas (GHG) emissions improvement of the wastewater-integrated microalgae production design has been barely discussed.

Inspired by the work of de Wilt et al. (de Wilt et al. 2016) concerning different technological pathways of integration with algae cultivation for wastewater collected from different sources loaded with different concentrations of nutrient contents, the separated nutrient delivery configuration we proposed for the analysis are shown in figure 1. This configuration includes the primary and secondary treatment of wastewater, tertiary microalgae treatment, biomass conversion and combined heat and power unit. Municipal wastewater and urine influents are treated via microalgae from different pathways. To show the potential advantages of the separated nutrient delivery design in improving microalgae carbon fixation performance, the Life Cycle Assessment (LCA) method is employed in this study to make assessments on the environmental impacts of the integrated biofuel production process. The mass and energy balances are achieved by process simulation software Aspen Plus v8.6, and the background data are taken from Ecoinvent3.5 Database(Frischknecht 2011) and the literatures.

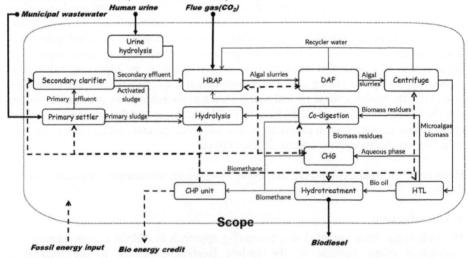

Figure 1 Configuration of the WWTP integrated microalgae biofuel production process.

2. Methods

2.1. Lifecycle inventory (LCI)

2.1.1. LCA goal, scope and function unit

The goal of this study is to reveal the potential impacts of source-separated nutrient delivery strategy to carbon balances in wastewater treatment integrated with microalgae biofuel production process. The GHG emissions of each part in the whole process is quantified as the output of LCI results. Besides, the LCA scope is from gate to gate, which includes the primary and secondary treatment of wastewater, algal tertiary treatment, algal biomass harvesting conversion, combined heat and power unit. The function unit in this LCA study is 1 MJ energy.

The main parameters of lifecycle inventory are shown in Table 1.

2.1.2. Lifecycle impact assessment

ReCiPe(Huijbregts et al. 2017) method is introduced in this study to evaluate global warming potentials (GWP). The GHG emission results, associated with the 100-year global warming equivalence factors, which, for carbon dioxide, methane and nitrogen oxide is 1,34 and 298 in turn, are involved to calculate the GWP index in g $CO2_{-eq}$ MJ^{-1}. This midpoint impacts in ReCiPe could explicitly show the GHG emissions of each section in the wastewater-microalgae integration process. In the analysis, the mass and energy balances are achieved by process simulation via Aspen Plus 8.6 software, and the background data are taken from Ecoinvent3.5 database(Wernet et al. 2016) and literatures.

Table 1: Background data of wastewater treatment integrated microalgae biofuel production process

Sub-process	Parameter	Value	Units
Cultivation			
Growth	Pond circulation energy	1.42	$kwh \cdot ha^{-1}$
	Biomass productivity	25	$g \cdot m^{-2} \cdot day^{-1}$
	Cultivation Area	2000	ha
Harvest/Dewatering			
Bio flocculation	Biomass concentration	2%	wt.%
Dissolved air flotation	Biomass concentration	6%	wt.%
Centrifuge	Biomass concentration	20%	wt.%
Conversion & Upgrading			
Hydrothermal Liquefaction (HTL)	Bio-oil yield	35%	wt.%
Catalytic Hydrothermal Gasification (CHG)	Biogas yield	4%	wt.%
Hydrotreating	Diesel yield	61.90%	wt.%
	Naphtha yield	12.10%	wt.%
	Biogas yield	9.10%	wt.%
Combined Heat &Power Unit (CHP)	Electricity	35	%
	Heat	12	%
Primary wastewater treatment			
Primary settler	Electricity demand	0.00441	$kwh \cdot m^{-3}$
Urine precipitation	Electricity demand	0.0004	$kwh \cdot m^{-3}$
Pumping	Electricity demand	0.5	$kwh \cdot m^{-3}$
Secondary wastewater treatment			
Secondary settler	Electricity demand	0.00252	$kwh \cdot m^{-3}$
Thermal hydrolysis	Heat demand	0.000108	$kwh \cdot m^{-3}$
Digester	Heat demand	0.0417	$kwh \cdot m^{-3}$
	Electricity	0.015	$kwh \cdot m^{-3}$

2.2. Scenario design

The plant layout of our study is partly based on the baseline assumptions of the carbon delivery engineering model given by Somers and Quinn (Somers and Quinn 2019). This study underlies the integration design with wastewater treatment to utilize separated alternative nutrient resources from municipal wastewater and urine instead of make-up nutrient. Primary and secondary treatment of wastewater are designed in this study as the upstream sub-processes of the whole process, biomass harvesting and dewatering, biomass conversion and upgrading, and combined heat and power unit in this study are designed as the downstream sub-processes of the whole process.

2.2.1. Primary and secondary treatment

In the primary treatment, hydrolyzed urine is mixed with primarily treated municipal wastewater as nutrients feedstock to supplement microalgae cultivation in high rate algae ponds (HRAPs). The primary treatment settles down the girds suspended in municipal wastewater influent and the primary influent is then further clarified in the secondary settler to remove sludge. The sewage sludge from primary and secondary settlers go through thermal hydrolysis and then enters anaerobic digestor to generate biogas, which is composed of CH_4 and CO_2 that could be utilized in combined heat and power unit to generate heat.

2.2.2. Algae tertiary treatment

Microalgae *Galdieria sulphuraria* biomass productivity in HRAPs is 25 $g \cdot m^{-2} \cdot day^{-1}$ with nutrient contents from wastewater influent and CO2 supply from flue gas injection. The HRAPs with paddle wheel circulation in electricity demand of 1.42 $kw \cdot ha^{-1}$, for on-site material flow, the pumping energy demand is 1.6 kJ kg^{-1}, for flue gas delivery is 37.1 $kJ \cdot kg^{-1}$.

2.2.3. Algae biomass harvesting and conversion

Algae harvesting and dewatering in this study is achieved by the state of art technology: bio-flocculation-dissolved air flotation-centrifuge. The biomass separation efficiencies of the three sections in algae harvesting and dewatering are 90 %, 95 %, and 95 % respectively, and the harvested biomass concentrations are 2 %, 6 % and 20 % (wt) respectively. The concentrated biomass is converted to bio oil via hydrothermal liquefaction (HTL), and then upgraded by hydrotreatment to generate final products: biodiesel and naphtha fuel. According to Somers and Quinn (Somers and Quinn 2019), the energy demand of HTL is 3 $kJ \cdot kg^{-1}$ AFDW algae. Slurries dehydrated from algal harvesting and dewatering are reclaimed to HRAPs to recover nutrients and freshwater. The gas co-generated with fuel products is sent to the combined heat and power unit to generate heat and electricity.

3. Results and discussion

3.1 Carbon balance results

Carbon balance relationship is based on the mass and energy balance relationship of the process configuration in this study. The results show that unit GHG emissions of the whole process are 0.09357 $kgCO2$-eq.$\cdot MJ^{-1}$, and 0.1913 $kgCO2$-eq.$\cdot MJ^{-1}$ GHG assimilation in function unit, so the unit credit of GHG emissions 0.09773 $kgCO2$-eq.$\cdot MJ^{-1}$ of GHG emissions credit, as shown in Table 2. The result in the carbon credit shows that although the downstream biomass harvesting, biomass dewatering, biomass conversion and upgrading are carbon-discharging processes, the carbon balance in our study comes across the neutral point and to reach positive carbon credit, in other words, the process of the designed separated nutrient delivery configuration in this study could significantly reduce carbon emissions to environment. Comparing to GHG emissions reported in LCA research on conventional wastewater treatment (Rodriguez-Garcia et al. 2012), the microalgae-based wastewater treatment is notably more sustainable to ecosystem.

Table 2 :GWP results of wastewater treatment integrated microalgae biofuel production process.

Sub-process	Unit GHG emissions / $kgCO_2$-eq. $\cdot MJ^{-1}$
Cultivation	3.1681E-02
Harvest/Dewatering	5.1888E-04
Conversion & Upgrading	2.4665E-02
Primary WWTP	3.5529E-02
Secondary WWTP Electricity	1.2031E-03
Unit GHG emission	9.3597E-02
Unit GHG assimilation	1.9133E-01
Unit GHG credit	9.7737E-02

For the wastewater pretreatment, primary treatment is the biggest contributor to the GHG emissions, approximately 0.03553 kgCO2-eq.$\cdot MJ^{-1}$. The high carbon emission is the result of the highest fossil energy demand in wastewater influent pumping, which leads directly to the increase of the carbon emission. The secondary treatment only contributes less than 8 % of total GHG emissions, and the co-digestion of sludge and microalgal residues is accounted for a lower GHG emission, as it converts the organic carbon in sludge and algal residues to the biogas by co-digestion. Comparing to conventional secondary treatment of wastewater such as aerobic or anoxic digestion (Bonton et al. 2012), the separated nutrient recovery in secondary treatment in this study is significantly more sustainable. Among the downstream sub-processes, the biomass conversion and upgrading is the biggest fossil energy consumer, it generates thus approximately 27 %, the highest, of the total GHG emissions.

3.2 Separated nutrient delivery strategy impacts to carbon balance

Comparing to the high GHG emissions 0.40-1.18 kgCO2-eq.$\cdot MJ^{-1}$ of conventional treatment reported (Bonton et al. 2012), the separated nutrient delivery shows significantly more sustainable due to positive carbon credit result. Compared with sole source of nutrient delivery of microalgae-wastewater integration process presented in literature (Colzi Lopes et al. 2018), 0.1322 kgCO2-eq.$\cdot MJ^{-1}$ of the separated nutrient delivery is lower than the reported 0.1947 kgCO2-eq.$\cdot MJ^{-1}$. The comparison results show the advantages of separated-nutrient delivery not only in improving sustainability performance of wastewater treatment, but also in microalgae biofuel production.

In LCA methodology, the GHG emission could be divided into two categories: direct GHG emissions and indirect GHG emissions. The separated nutrient delivery strategy proposed in this study reduces GHG emissions by recycling the direct and indirect GHG emissions. Direct GHG emissions, which is composed of $bioCH_4$ and $bioCO_2$, is generated from co-digestion and biomass conversion and upgrading. $BioCO_2$ is recovered by HRAPs as carbon resource for microalgae cultivation and $bioCH_4$ is recycled in CHP unit for energy supply. As for the indirect GHG emissions discharged by fossil energy usage of the whole system as flue gas, although unavoidable, it could be recycled and assimilated by microalgae in HRAPs.

4. Conclusion

In this study, we employed the LCA methodology to show the effectiveness of a separated nutrient delivery configuration of wastewater treatment integrated microalgae biofuel production in improving microalgae carbon fixation performance and the environmental impact of the biofuel production process. The LCA result shows that the primary treatment of wastewater is a major contributor to the carbon emission, and the carbon emission of secondary treatment could be significantly reduced by separated nutrient delivery design. Even though the carbon emission of the downstream process of biofuel production could not be avoided, the carbon utilization in the wastewater-based microalgae cultivation could make the carbon balance come across a neutral point achieving a positive effect in carbon credit.

References

Bonton, Alexandre, Christian Bouchard, Benoit Barbeau, and Stéphane Jedrzejak, 2012, Comparative Life Cycle Assessment of Water Treatment Plants, Desalination, 284, 42-54

Colzi Lopes, Alexandre, Antonio Valente, Diego Iribarren, and Cristina González-Fernández, 2018, Energy Balance and Life Cycle Assessment of a Microalgae-Based Wastewater Treatment Plant: A Focus on Alternative Biogas Uses, Bioresource Technology, 270, 138-146

Enamala, Manoj Kumar, Swapnika Enamala, Murthy Chavali, Jagadish Donepudi, Rajasri Yadavalli, Bhulakshmi Kolapalli, Tirumala Vasu Aradhyula, Jeevitha Velpuri, and Chandrasekhar Kuppam, 2018, Production of Biofuels from Microalgae - A Review on Cultivation, Harvesting, Lipid Extraction, and Numerous Applications of Microalgae, Renewable and Sustainable Energy Reviews, 94, 49-68

Huijbregts, Mark A. J., Zoran J. N. Steinmann, Pieter M. F. Elshout, Gea Stam, Francesca Verones, Marisa Vieira, Michiel Zijp, Anne Hollander, and Rosalie van Zelm, 2017, ReCiPe2016: A Harmonised Life Cycle Impact Assessment Method at Midpoint and Endpoint Level, International Journal of Life Cycle Assessment, 22, 2, 138-147

Maria Solé-Bundó, Fabiana Passos, Maycoll S. Romero-Güiza, Ivet Ferrera, Sergi Astalsd, 2019, Co-digestion strategies to enhance microalgae anaerobic digestion: A review, Renewable and Sustainable Energy Reviews, 112, 471–482

Rodriguez-Garcia, G., A. Hospido, D. M. Bagley, M. T. Moreira, and G. Feijoo, 2012, A Methodology to Estimate Greenhouse Gases Emissions in Life Cycle Inventories of Wastewater Treatment Plants, Environmental Impact Assessment Review, 37, 37-46

Somers, Michael D. and Jason C. Quinn, 2019, Sustainability of Carbon Delivery to an Algal Biorefinery: A Techno-Economic and Life-Cycle Assessment, Journal of CO2 Utilization, 30, 193-204

Wernet, Gregor, Christian Bauer, Bernhard Steubing, Jürgen Reinhard, Emilia Moreno-Ruiz, and Bo Weidema. 2016, The Ecoinvent Database Version 3 (Part I): Overview and Methodology, The International Journal of Life Cycle Assessment, 21, 9, 1218–1230

Whitton, Rachel, Amandine Le Mével, Marc Pidou, Francesco Ometto, Raffaella Villa, and Bruce Jefferson, 2016, Influence of Microalgal N and P Composition on Wastewater Nutrient Remediation, Water Research, 91, 371-378

de Wilt, Arnoud, Andrii Butkovskyi, Kanjana Tuantet, Lucia Hernandez Leal, Tânia V. Fernandes, Alette Langenhoff, and Grietje Zeeman, 2016, Micropollutant Removal in an Algal Treatment System Fed with Source Separated Wastewater Streams, Journal of Hazardous Materials, 304, 84–92

Sauro Pierucci, Flavio Manenti, Giulia Bozzano, Davide Manca (Eds.)
Proceedings of the 30th European Symposium on Computer Aided Process Engineering
(ESCAPE30), May 24-27, 2020, Milano, Italy. © 2020 Elsevier B.V. All rights reserved.
http://dx.doi.org/10.1016/B978-0-12-823377-1.50285-8

Economics of Climate Change: a Sensitivity Analysis Study Applied to Integrated First- and Second-Generation Ethanol Biorefinery

Roymel R. Carpio[a,*], Simone C. Miyoshi[b], Andrew M. Elias[b], Felipe F. Furlan[b], Roberto C. Giordano[b], Argimiro R. Secchi[a]

[a]Chemical Engineering Program, Universidade Federal do Rio de Janeiro (UFRJ), Rio de Janeiro - RJ, 21941-914, Brazil
[b]Chemical Engineering Department, Universidade Federal de São Carlos (UFSCar), São Carlos - SP, 13565-905, Brazil
roymel@peq.coppe.ufrj.br

Abstract

According to the Brazilian federal program called Renovabio, biofuels producers will earn a number of carbon credits, known as CBios, proportionally to the reduction of greenhouse gases emissions. These CBios will be sold by biorefineries to fuel distributors in Brazil. Thus, the environmental performance will have a direct impact on the economic profitability of the biorefinery. In this work we compared the sensitivity of the overall economic performance for ten key parameters of the second generation ethanol process, considering the current conditions and future scenarios with additional incomes of CBios selling. The most influent parameters for all scenarios were hydrolysed bagasse fraction, enzyme loading and pre-treatment solid fraction. The relative relevance of parameters does not change when considered the CBios selling incomes, but the absolute relevance of the hydrolysed bagasse fraction decreases significantly, especially for the optimist CBios price. The residence times of hydrolysis, pre-treatment and fermentation, and the xylose concentration have negligible effects for both current and future scenarios.

Keywords: Sugarcane biorefinery, sensitivity analysis, economical and environment evaluation.

1. Introduction

In a low-carbon economy and increasing energy demanding society, concerns about climate change and energy security are shifting the global energy matrix towards renewable energy technologies. In Brazil, as result of Paris agreement (COP 21, 2016), a federal program called Renovabio was issued. Thus, carbon credits, called CBios, will be sold by biofuels producers and the environmental performance will have an impact on the economic evaluation of the process.

Sugarcane biorefineries play an important role in this economic scenario due to the production of biofuel and bioelectricity. The quantification of how the application of Renovabio Program will affect the relative importance of operational parameters in an integrated first and second generation ethanol Biorefinery has not been sufficient assessed yet. Therefore, this work compares the sensitivity of the overall economic performance for ten key parameters of the second generation ethanol process, considering the current conditions and a future scenario with the additional incomes of CBios selling.

2. Methodology

2.1. Process modelling and simulation

The biorefinery was modelled based on a standard autonomous Brazilian distillery, with a process capacity of 500 t/h of sugarcane. The modelled biorefinery can produce first generation ethanol (E1G) from sugarcane juice, second-generation ethanol (E2G) from bagasse, and electricity from residues in an integrated process. The process data used in the base case simulation were based on Carpio et al. (2019). A simplified process diagram is presented in Figure 1.

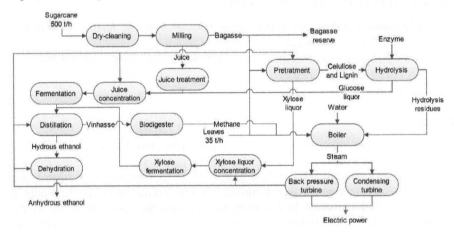

Figure 1. Simplified process diagram of the integrated biorefinery.

The bagasse obtained after milling is diverted into two fractions. The first one is fed in the boiler and the second one is used for E2G production. The bagasse diverted to E2G production undergoes a liquid hot water pre-treatment. After that, the liquid fraction, rich in xylose is separated from the solid fraction containing the cellulose. The xylose liquor is used for ethanol production by fermentation. On the other hand, the solid fraction containing cellulose is fed to the enzymatic hydrolysis. The coupling of the kinetic model of Angarita et al. (2015) into the whole steady-state simulation was made as described in Carpio et al. (2018).

After hydrolysis period, the solid fraction (mostly lignin) is sent to the boiler and the liquid fraction (glycose liquor) is mixed to the 1G treated juice and undergoes the traditional stages of E1G. The cogeneration system includes a boiler, a back-pressure turbine and a condensing one, and produces steam and electricity to supply process demands. The electricity surplus is sold to the grid. EMSO software (Soares and Secchi, 2003) was used to perform the modelling and simulation of the biorefinery.

2.2. Economic analysis

The economic analysis was also implemented in EMSO, coupled to the process model. This allows instant calculation of economic indexes for any feasible operational condition simulated, without requiring external or auxiliary sheet calculations. The main economic premises considered in this study are shown in Table 1.

The capital cost (CAPEX), operating costs (OPEX), cash flows (CF) and net present value (NPV) were calculated based on the methodology of Peters et al. (2003). The main

*Economics of Climate Change: a Sensitivity Analysis Study Applied to
Integrated First- and Second-Generation Ethanol Biorefinery*

1707

equipment purchase costs were estimated from industrial information (personal communication) and the literature (Humbird et al., 2011).

Table 1. Main premises considered in the economic analysis

Parameter	Value	Reference
Ethanol selling price (US$/m^3$)	584.61	MAPA (2018)
Electricity selling price (US$/MWh)	71.19	CCEE (2018)
CBios selling price (US$/CBio)	10 / 30	Conservative/Optimist estimates
Sugarcane costs (US$/t)	22.15	UDOP (2018)
Leaves cost (US$/t)	15	Bechara et al. (2016)
Enzyme cost (US$/kg)	1.25	Bechara et al. (2016)
Fresh water cost (US$/t)	0.06	Bechara et al. (2016)
Refrigeration cost (US$/kW)	0.04	Bechara et al. (2016)
Operation time (h/year)	4732	Furlan et al. (2013)
Project life time (years)	25	Longati et al. (2018)
Construction period (years)	2	Furlan et al. (2013)
Tax Rate (%)	34	Longati et al. (2018)
Discount rate (%)	10	Bechara et al. (2016)
Depreciation strategy (%/year)	10	Longati et al. (2018)

2.3. Life cycle assessment (LCA)

The Life Cycle Assessment considered the climate change impact category using the Global Warming Potential under a horizon of 100 years – GWP 100 (Myhre et al., 2013). It was performed an inventory of inputs, outputs and emissions based on process simulation and ethanol agricultural data (Seabra et al., 2011) under a cradle to grave scope. The characterization factor data base considered was IPCC (2006) for emissions in fuels burning and agricultural emissions and the Ecoinvent 3.1 (Wernet et al., 2016) database for raw materials inputs. The applied allocation method was energy based and the bagasse, as it is an agricultural residue, was considered to have zero emission as input. The quantity of CBios was determined by the annual tonnes of CO_2 equivalent savings of ethanol compared with gasoline.

2.4. Sensitivity analysis

A global sensitivity analysis was performed applying the modified method of Morris (Campolongo et al., 2007) with 200 trajectories and 8 levels. Ten parameters of E2G process were chosen as input variables, as shown in Table 2. Since E2G process is not fully developed, all selected parameter are related to different subareas of this process.

Table 2. Parameter considered in the sensitivity analysis

Parameter	Range	Parameter	Range
1 Hydr. bagasse fraction (wt %)	10-50	6 Pre-treat. yield (%)	40-60
2 Hydr. enzyme loading (FPU/g)	10-30	7 Pre-treat. residence time (min)	10-20
3 Hydr. solid fraction (wt %)	10-20	8 Xylose concentration (g/L)	40-60
4 Hydr. residence time (h)	48-72	9 Xylose ferment. yield (%)	60-80
5 Pre-treat. solid fraction (wt %)	10-20	10 Ferment. residence time (h)	12-24

3. Results and discussion

The indices μ, μ^*, e σ were calculated as described in Campolongo et al. (2007). The impact of opposite signs in the elementary effects, which may occurs when the model is non-monotonic, were negligent, i.e., $|\mu|\approx\mu^*$. Thus, the measure μ can be used without affecting the factors' ranking. Figure 2 shows the results of the sensitivity analysis of NPV without considering CBios selling.

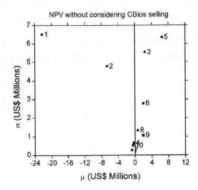

Figure 2. Result of the sensitivity analysis of NPV without considering CBios selling.

The parameter hydrolysed bagasse fraction (P1) has the greatest impact on NPV (highest absolute value of μ). The negative sign indicates an inversely proportional behaviour of NPV to P1, i.e., the NPV decreases as P1 increases. This behaviour may suggests that, in the studied configuration, it is more advantageous to produce electric energy (a larger proportion of bagasse going to cogeneration) than E2G.

The sensitivity of NPV to pre-treatment solid fraction (P5) and hydrolysis enzyme loading (P2) is approximately the same, being these parameters in the second place of importance. Nevertheless, they have opposite signs and consequently, an increase on P5 or/and a decrease on P2 will improve the NPV. All the cited parameters have nonlinear effects or/and interactions represented by the high value of σ.

The sensitivity analysis also indicates which parameters have non-significant effects. In this case, the influence of parameters residence times of hydrolysis (P4), pre-treatment (P7) and fermentation (P10), and xylose concentration (P8) on NPV is practically negligible. This information provides feedback to R&D teams, indicating the parameters which the efforts should focus on.

The results for the future scenarios, which consider additional incomes due to CBios selling, are shown in Figure 3. Two sale prices (conservative and optimist) of CBios were used.

When considered the additional incomes from CBios selling, the relative importance of the parameters does not change significantly, but it is notable that the absolute relevance of the hydrolysed bagasse fraction (P1) decreases sensibly, especially when the optimist price of CBios is used. This behaviour is caused by the trade-off between the economic and environmental performance, thus the CBios incomes tend to compensate the sensitivity of NPV on hydrolysed bagasse fraction.

Economics of Climate Change: a Sensitivity Analysis Study Applied to Integrated First- and Second-Generation Ethanol Biorefinery

1709

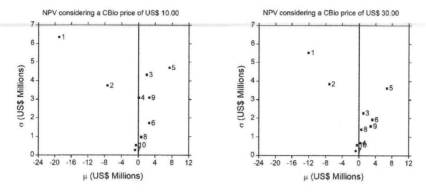

Figure 3. Result of the sensitivity analysis of NPV considering CBios selling.

4. Conclusions

For all scenarios, the most influent parameter is the hydrolysed bagasse fraction, showing a high sensitivity of NPV to 2G ethanol and bioelectricity production. When the higher CBios price is considered, the environmental impact of E2G production reduces significantly the effect of the bagasse fraction on economic results. These results indicate that the decision towards ethanol 2G and bioelectricity production has a key conflicting impact on both environmental and economic aspects: an improve on the NPV frequently implies an increase on the environmental impact of the E1G2G process.

The relative relevance of the analysed parameters does not change significantly when considered the implementation of Renovabio Program with two different CBios prices. Nevertheless, the absolute relevance of the hydrolysed bagasse fraction decreases significantly, particularly when the higher price of CBios is considered. Some parameters such as residence times of hydrolysis, pre-treatment and fermentation, and xylose concentration have negligible effects on NPV for both current and future scenarios.

Acknowledgements

Financial support from FAPERJ (grant #E012018-236117), FAPESP (grants #2017/13993-9, #2014/21252-0 and #2016/10636-8), and CAPES (finance Code 001) are gratefully acknowledged.

References

J. Angarita, R. Souza, A. Cruz, E. Biscaia, A. Secchi, 2015, Kinetic modeling for enzymatic hydrolysis of pretreated sugarcane straw, Biochemical Engineering Journal, 104, 10-19.

R. A. Bechara, A. Gomez, V. Saint-Antonin, J.-M. Schweitzer, F. Maréchal, 2016, Methodology for the optimal design of an integrated first and second generation ethanol production plant combined with power cogeneration, Bioresource Technology, 214, 441-449.

F. Campolongo, J. Cariboni, A. Saltelli, 2007, An effective screening design for sensitivity analysis of large models, Environmental Modelling & Software, 22, 1509-1518.

R. R. Carpio, F. F. Furlan, R. C. Giordano, A. R. Secchi, A kriging-based approach for conjugating specific dynamic models into whole plant stationary simulations, 2018, Computers & Chemical Engineering, 119, 190-194.

R. R. Carpio, R. C. Giordano, A. R. Secchi, 2019, Optimization of an Integrated First- and Second-Generation Ethanol Production Plant with Focus on Hydrolysis Parameters, Computer Aided Chemical Engineering, 46, 241-246.

CCEE, 2018, Public auction electricity prices, Electric Energy Commercialization Chamber, www.ccee.org.br.

F. F. Furlan, R. T. Filho, F. H. Pinto, C. B. Costa, A. J. Cruz, R. L. Giordano, R. C. Giordano, 2013, Bioelectricity versus bioethanol from sugarcane bagasse: is it worth being flexible?, Biotechnology for Biofuels, 6 (1), 142.

D. Humbird, R. Davis, L. Tao, C. Kinchin, D. Hsu, A. Aden, P. Schoen, J. Lukas, B. Olthof, M. Worley, D. Sexton, D. Dudgeon, 2011, Process design and economics for biochemical conversion of lignocellulosic biomass to ethanol, Tech. rep., NREL/TP-5100-47764.

IPCC. 2006 IPCC guidelines for national greenhouse gas inventories: v. 2-3 agriculture, forestry and other land use and industrial processes and product use. Prepared by the National Greenhouse Gas Inventories Programme, Eggleston H.S., Buendia L., Miwa K., Ngara T., and Tanabe K. Japan: IGES, 2006.

G. Myhre, D. Shindell, F.M. Bréon, W. Collins, J. Fuglestvedt, J. Huang, D. Koch, J.F. Lamarque, D. Lee, B. Mendoza, T. Nakajima, A. Robock, G. Stephens, T. Takemura and H. Zhang, 2013, Anthropogenic and Natural Radiative Forcing. In: Climate Change 2013: The Physical Science Basis. Contribution of Working Group I to the Fifth Assessment Report of the Intergovernmental Panel on Climate Change [Stocker, T.F., D. Qin, G.-K. Plattner, M. Tignor, S.K. Allen, J. Boschung, A. Nauels, Y. Xia, V. Bex and P.M. Midgley (eds.)]. Cambridge University Press, Cambridge, United Kingdom and New York, NY, USA. https://www.ipcc.ch/site/assets/uploads/2018/02/WG1AR5_Chapter08_FINAL.pdf

A. A. Longati, A. R. Lino, R. C. Giordano, F. F. Furlan, A. J. Cruz, 2018, Defining research & development process targets through retro-techno-economic analysis: The sugarcane biorefinery case, Bioresource Technology, 263, 1-9.

MAPA, 2018, Brazilian annual ethanol exports, Ministry of Agriculture, Cattle and Supply, www.agricultura.gov.br.

M. S. Peters, K. D. Timmerhaus, R. E. West, 2003, Plant design and economics for chemical engineers, 5th Edition, Vol. 5, McGraw-Hill.

J.E. Seabra, I.C. Macedo, H.L. Chun, C.E. Faroni, C.A. Sarto, 2011, Life cycle assessment of Brazilian sugarcane products: GHG emissions and energy use. Biofuels Bioprod. Bioref. 5, 519-532. https://doi.org/10.1002/bbb.289

R. P. Soares, A. Secchi, 2003, EMSO: A new environment for modelling, simulation and optimisation, Computer Aided Chemical Engineering, Vol. 14, pp. 947-952.

G. Wernet, C. Bauer, B. Steubing, J. Reinhard, E. Moreno-Ruiz, B. Weidema, 2016, The ecoinvent database version 3 (part I): overview and methodology. The International Journal of Life Cycle Assessment, 21(9), 1218-1230. http://doi.org/10.1007/s11367-016-1087-8

UDOP, 2018, Sugarcane prices, Union of Biofuel Producers, www.udop.com.br.

Sauro Pierucci, Flavio Manenti, Giulia Bozzano, Davide Manca (Eds.)
Proceedings of the 30th European Symposium on Computer Aided Process Engineering
(ESCAPE30), May 24-27, 2020, Milano, Italy. © 2020 Elsevier B.V. All rights reserved.
http://dx.doi.org/10.1016/B978-0-12-823377-1.50286-X

Assessing Parameter Relative Importance in Bioprocesses Mathematical Models through Dynamic Sensitivity Analysis

Julio Cesar Sánchez-Rendón [a], Ricardo Morales-Rodriguez [b], Luis Gerónimo Matallana-Pérez [c], Oscar Andrés Prado-Rubio [a*]

[a]*Departamento de Ingeniería Química, Universidad Nacional de Colombia, Km 9 vía al Aeropuerto La Nubia, 170003, Colombia.*
[b]*Departamento de Ingeniería Química, División de Ciencias Naturales y Exactas, Campus Guanajuato, Universidad de Guanajuato, Noria Alta S/N, Guanajuato, Gto. 36050, México*
[c]*Departamento de Ingeniería, Facultad de Ingeniera, Universidad de Caldas, Cl. 65 #26-10, Manizales, 170004, Colombia*
oaprador@unal.edu.co

Abstract

Fast global population growth has imposed an increasing demand for feedstock, food, energy and commodities; therefore, the industries are in constant development to optimize their processes. From the Process System Engineering (PSE) perspective this problem could be addressed employing mathematical models that describe the processes behaviour. However, it is common that mathematical models have parameters that must be estimated from experimental data, leading to the propagation of experimental uncertainty into the model. Several methods have been designed and used for uncertainty quantification and sensitivity analysis over the whole model output. In this work, the Standardized Regression Coefficient method has been applied for quantification of parameter relative importance profiles (PRIP) along the simulation time. The results show that parameter importance changes dynamically and the relevance of one parameter could be different for different state variables, which gives insights of the relevant processes taking place at one specific point in time. This methodology could also be used in experimental design and data selection to improve parameter estimation and parameter interpretability.

Keywords: mathematical models, bioprocess, parameter estimation, uncertainty analysis, sensitivity analysis.

1. Introduction

The fast-growing world population imposes an increasing demand on feedstock, food, energy and commodities (Jones & O'Neill, 2016). Therefore, industries are constantly under pressure to optimize and upgrade technology in order to have safer, cleaner, environmentally friendly and more profitable production to cope with the demand. From Process System Engineering (PSE) perspective, process optimization and more recently process intensification offer a systematic way to address the above-mentioned challenge (Prado-Rubio *et al.*, 2016). Current methodologies highly rely on process models and system understanding, in order to achieve a substantial breakthrough in technology design and operation. Thus, there is a constant need to improve process mathematical models towards developing high fidelity representations with high parameter significance. This task is particularly complex for bioprocesses due to the lack of process understanding and diverse sources of uncertainty.

In literature, there are several methods for quantifying the effect of uncertainty has over the model output such as differential sensitivity analysis, sensitivity index, subjective sensitivity analysis, the importance index, relative deviation methods, factorial design methods and regression methods (Hamby, 1994). Typically, sensitivity analysis has been applied to the whole model output, as like a stationary state, but the following question arises: is the importance of a parameter the same throughout the simulation time? Or does it changes dynamically according to the model dynamics? Therefore, this paper aims to identify and analyze the parameter relative importance over the simulation time, in order to identify the impact related with the physical interpretation, aiming to improve the process performance.

2. Methodology

2.1. Mathematical model

Xylitol is a highly versatile molecule with several uses like dental creams, sweeteners, pharmaceutics compounds, dietary supplements and has even been pointed out as a chemical building block for chemical or biochemical industries (Prado-Rubio et al., 2015). For this reason, the mathematical model of diauxic xylitol production from glucose and xylose proposed by Tochampa et al.,(2015) was analyzed. The experimental data used for parameter estimation was extracted from Sirisansaneeyakul et al. (2013).

2.2. Parameter estimation

The particle swarm optimization algorithm found in the Global optimization Toolbox of Matlab was used to obtain the parameter values of the above mentioned mathematical model. Additionally, these optimization algorithm was calibrated using the "IRACE" package available in R software.

2.3. Experimental design

To explore the sensitivity of the mathematical model to perturbations in its parameters it is necessary to analyze the totality of the parameter space of the mathematical model, considering all the possible combinations of parameter values. However, it is required an experimental design that leads to a finite set of experimental points that represent the whole parameter space. One approach to solve this problem consist in Latin Hypercube Sampling method (LHS) (Sheikholeslami & Razavi, 2017), followed by a Monte Carlo simulation to obtain the output of the models due to parameter perturbations.

2.4. Sensitivity analysis

Regression methods are often used to represent the complex behavior of the system in a simplified way through a response surface (Hamby, 1994). This representation is simply a regression equation that approximates the model output using only the most sensitive model parameters. Commonly the regression equation is of the form:

$$Y = b_0 + \sum_{i=1}^{p} b_i Z_i \tag{1}$$

where Z_i is predictor variable and a function of the parameters, b_i are the regression coefficients. The equation (1) corresponds to multiple linear regression. This technique allows the calculation of the sensitivity ranking based on the relative magnitude of the regression coefficients. These values are a measure of the amount of influence that a parameter has on the whole model output. However, because of differences in the numeric scale of the parameters, a standardization process is required. Standardized Regression Coefficients (SRC) (Morales-Rodriguez *et al.*, 2012) then uses the standard deviation of the model output σ_Y and the standard deviation of the uncertain parameters σ_{θ_i} according to the following equation:

$$B_i = \left(\frac{\sigma_{\theta_i}}{\sigma_Y}\right) b_i \qquad (2)$$

3. Results and discussion

The parameter values obtained for the diauxic fermentation model for xylitol are listed in Table 1 and the model fitting is shown in Figure 1. Even though the glucose is consumed first, the growth of the biomass appears to be in a latent state, only when the glucose has been completely consumed the xylose is actively consumed by the microorganism as expected of a diauxic fermentation. However, the growth in the presence of xylose overcome this latent state and the exponential growth phase begin.

Table 1. Estimated parameter values for diauxic fermentation model for xylitol production

Parameter	Estimated value	Parameter	Estimated value
μ_{glu}^{max}	0.01907 h^{-1}	q_{xyl}^{max}	0.23987 g xylose/DWG h
μ_{xyl}^{max}	0.99999 h^{-1}	q_{glu}^{max}	1.81202 g glucose/DWG h
$K_{S,glu}$	2.38313 g/L	$K_{i,xyl}$	13.3963 g/L
$K_{S,xyl}$	0.02636 g/L	$K_{i,glu}$	0.00558 g/L
$K_{S,xyt}$	0.93634 g/L	P_{xyl}	9.5185x10^{-9} m/s
K_r	0.46133 g/L		

The global sensitivity of the diauxic fermentation model is shown on Figure 2. The bars represent the dispersion of the model output due to aleatory changes up to 25% in the model parameters. The uncertainty in the model output increase with time, except for glucose concentration. This is because both, the initial and the final state of this variable, are well known as the glucose is completely depleted before the active consumption of xylose. On the other hand, xylitol concentration has the mayor effect of uncertainty, this could be due to the high interaction of this molecule with the other metabolites through the metabolic pathway represented by the model.

The dynamic sensitivity analysis was performed on a diauxic fermentation model for xylitol production. This analysis was carried out through the calculation of the SRC in each experimental point, thought it could be done at any part of the integration time. This led to a profile of relative importance of the parameter in the model for that specific point. The calculated profiles are shown in Figures 3-5. A positive value in PRIP indicates that a parameter contributes to increase the variable value and vice versa.

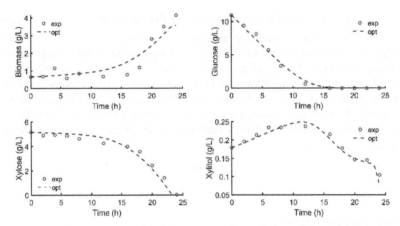

Figure 1. Diauxic fermentation model fitting to experimental data with particle swarm algorithm in MATLAB.

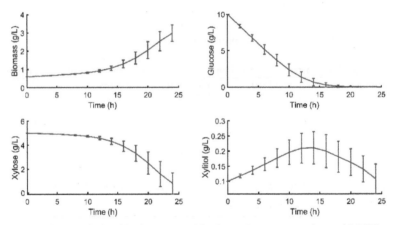

Figure 2. Uncertainty analysis with aleatory combinations of parameter values with LHS.

Figure 3 shows the effect to μ_{glu}^{max}, μ_{xyl}^{max}, $K_{S,glu}$ and $K_{S,xyl}$ on the system states. For biomass concentration, μ_{glu}^{max} was the most important parameter with a relative weight of 1 at the beginning of simulation time but this value dropped at 12 h of fermentation when the glucose was completely depleted of the system. For the case of glucose concentration, the most important parameter was $K_{S,glu}$ whose value increased slowly through simulation time, the remainder parameters were not explanatory for this state. For xylose concentration $K_{S,glu}$ and $K_{S,xyl}$ were the most relevant parameters and exhibit a shift in their value when glucose was depleted, indicating metabolic shift required for a change in the substrate uptake. Interestingly, the dynamic behavior of these parameters showed to have influence in the model output even after the first substrate is consumed, indicating the high interaction between parameters within the model. In the case of xylitol concentration, μ_{xyl}^{max} and $K_{S,xyl}$ were the most relevant since xylose is consumed for biomass growth.

Fig 4 shows the PRIP for $K_{S,xyt}$, K_r, q_{glu}^{max} and q_{xyl}^{max}. For the four state variables, q_{glu}^{max} and q_{xyl}^{max} are the most significant parameters as expected, since the substrates uptake are the fuel for the metabolic engine. K_r and $K_{S,xyt}$ are also important for xylitol concentration, as they are related to xylitol consumption for biomass production after glucose depletion.

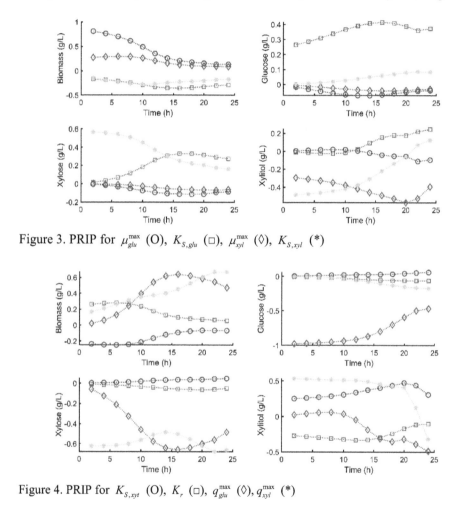

Figure 3. PRIP for μ_{glu}^{max} (O), $K_{S,glu}$ (□), μ_{xyl}^{max} (◊), $K_{S,xyl}$ (*)

Figure 4. PRIP for $K_{S,xyt}$ (O), K_r (□), q_{glu}^{max} (◊), q_{xyl}^{max} (*)

Fig 5 shows the relative parameter importance profiles for $K_{i,glu}$ $K_{i,xyt}$ and P_t. It can be seen that these parameters are not relevant for biomass and glucose states but $K_{i,glu}$ is relevant for xylose and xylitol states. Once again, there is a shift in the parameter relevance after glucose depletion. $K_{i,glu}$ is relevant because it is linked to biomass production and represents the effect of the internal switch between glucose and xylose metabolism uptake(Lebeau *et al.*, 2007).

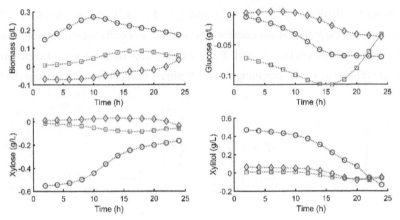

Figure 5. PRIP for $K_{i,glu}$ (O), $K_{i,xyl}$ ($\square$), P_{xyl} ($\Diamond$).

4. Conclusions

The relative parameter importance profiles shown in this work contradict the hypothesis that the influence of a certain parameter inside a mathematical model remains constant during the simulation time. Also, these results lead to a deeper level of understanding of the behavior of the system with the phenomena described by the mathematical model, thereby, improving parameter interpretability. Additionally, this methodology could be extended to be used in experimental design and data selection to optimize the information packed in the parameters, to analyze the model structure and then improve model accuracy.

References

Hamby, D. M. (1994). A review of techniques for parameter sensitivity analysis of environmental models. Environmental monitoring and assessment, 32(2), 135-154.

Jones, B., & O'Neill, B. C. (2016). Spatially explicit global population scenarios consistent with the Shared Socioeconomic Pathways. Environmental Research Letters, 11(8), 084003.

Lebeau, T., Jouenne, T., & Junter, G. A. (2007). Long-term incomplete xylose fermentation, after glucose exhaustion, with Candida shehatae co-immobilized with Saccharomyces cerevisiae. Microbiological Research, 162(3), 211-218.

Morales-Rodriguez, R., Meyer, A. S., Gernaey, K. V., & Sin, G. (2012). A framework for model-based optimization of bioprocesses under uncertainty: Lignocellulosic ethanol production case. Computers & Chemical Engineering, 42, 115-129.

Prado-Rubio, O.A., Morales-Rodriguez, R., Andrade-Santacoloma, P., Hernández-Escoto, H. (2016). "Process Intensification in Biotechnology Applications". In book "Process Intensification in Chemical Engineering", J.G. Segovia-Hernández, A. Bonilla-Petriciolet (eds.). Springer editorial ISBN: 978-3-319-28392-0. pp. 183-219.

Sheikholeslami, R., & Razavi, S. (2017). Progressive Latin Hypercube Sampling: An efficient approach for robust sampling-based analysis of environmental models. Environmental modelling & software, 93, 109-126.

Sirisansaneeyakul, S., Wannawilai, S., & Chisti, Y. (2013). Repeated fed- batch production of xylitol by Candida magnoliae TISTR 5663. Journal of Chemical Technology & Biotechnology, 88(6), 1121-1129.

Tochampa, W., Sirisansaneeyakul, S., Vanichsriratana, W., Srinophakun, P., Bakker, H. H., Wannawilai, S., & Chisti, Y. (2015). Optimal control of feeding in fed-batch production of xylitol. Industrial & Engineering Chemistry Research, 54(7), 1992-2000.

Sauro Pierucci, Flavio Manenti, Giulia Bozzano, Davide Manca (Eds.)
Proceedings of the 30th European Symposium on Computer Aided Process Engineering
(ESCAPE30), May 24-27, 2020, Milano, Italy. © 2020 Elsevier B.V. All rights reserved.
http://dx.doi.org/10.1016/B978-0-12-823377-1.50287-3

Multi-objective Optimization of Co-processing of Bio-oil and Vacuum Gas Oil: a Survey of Gasoline Selling Price and Bio-oil Co-processing Ratio

Le Wu*, Zhaowei Qi, Yuqi Wang, Lan Zheng

School of Chemical Engineering, Northwest University, Xi'an 710069, China
lewu@nwu.edu.cn

Abstract

The prices of the bio-diesel and bio-gasoline are generally higher than those of petroleum based fuels. The co-processing of bio-oil and vacuum gas oil in a fluid catalytic cracker has been proposed to utilize the existing refinery infrastructures and decrease the prices of bio-fuels. According to our previous study, the techno-economic analysis of the co-processing process, there is a contradiction between the minimum gasoline selling price and bio-oil co-processing ratio. In this work, the relations between the two factors (objectives) are investigated via a multi-objective optimization. Two co-processing scenarios, fast pyrolysis scenario using fast pyrolysis make bio-oil and catalytic pyrolysis scenario adopting catalytic pyrolysis produce bio-oil, are proposed to obtain the trade-off solution between the two objectives using the evaluation function method. The minimum gasoline selling price is approximately $3.1/gal if 20% bio-oil is co-processed for the two scenarios. The price is only about $1.9/gal if the bio-oil ratio is 1%. The trade-off solution between the two objectives is strongly depended on the weight factor. Therefore, the relation and the compromise between the bio-oil co-processing ratio and the minimum selling price should be considered and determined before the co-processing technology industrializes.

Keywords: Co-processing, Multi-objective optimization, Bio-oil co-processing ratio, Minimum selling price

1. Introduction

The co-processing of bio-oil and vacuum gas oil (VGO) in a fluid catalytic cracker (FCC) to transportation fuels has been proposed for a decade to lower the production cost of bio-fuels (Bui et al. 2009). The modeling and analysis of the co-processing process has gained increased attention in recently years (Al Jamri et al. 2018 and 2019). Cruz et al. (2017) proposed a kinetic model for the co-processing in FCC. Wu et al. (2019a) built a superstructure model to obtain the optimal integration process between the bio-oil production process and the existing refining process. The techno-economic analysis of the co-processing product was carried out to attain the minimum selling price (MSP) of co-processing product, gasoline (Wu et al. 2019b). Furthermore, the sensitivity analysis was also conducted to investigate the effects of relevant parameters on MSP. It was found that there is a contradiction between the MSP and bio-oil co-processing ratio. A higher MSP as well as a higher bio-carbon content of gasoline would be obtained if more bio-oil and less VGO were co-processed. That is to say, a higher bio-carbon content of co-processing product usually has a higher price. Thus, the best compromise and the trade-off between the bio-carbon content i.e. bio-oil co-processing ratio and the price should be determined when design the process.

In this work, a multi-objective model is proposed to investigate the relation between the bio-oil co-processing ratio and MSP of co-processing product for the co-processing of bio-oil and VGO in an FCC. The evaluation function method is used to obtain the trade-off solution between the two objectives. The effect of the weight factor on trade-off solution is also discussed.

2. Mathematical model

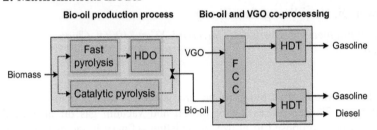

Figure 1 The co-processing flowsheet

According to Figure 1, the biomass is pyrolysised by a fast pyrolysis (FP) or a catalytic pyrolysis (CP) to produce bio-oil. The fast pyrolysis bio-oil is hydrotreated to remove extra oxygen impurities in a hydrodeoxygenation reactor (HDO). The obtained catalytic pyrolysis oil or the HDO bio-oil is then co-fed with VGO into an FCC to make gasoline and diesel with bio-carbon, which are hydrotreated in hydrotreators(HDT).

2.1. Objective functions
The main purpose of this work is to investigate the relations between the minimum selling price (MSP) of the co-processing product gasoline and the bio-oil co-processing ratio. Thus, the objectives are directly set as the minimization of the minimum gasoline selling price and the maximization of the bio-oil co-processing ratio as more bio-carbon would be detected in the products if more bio-oil were co-processed with VGO in an FCC.

$$\min MSP \tag{1}$$

where MSP denotes the minimum selling price of gasoline, in $/gal.
The calculation of the MSP of gasoline is mainly according to our previous work (Wu et al. 2019b), which contains the mass balance and energy balance of the co-processing process, capital investment, operating cost, net present value (NPV), internal interest of rate (IRR) and double declining balance (DBB) for depreciation. The relevant equations are not shown in this work due to the page limitation.

$$\max BCR \tag{2}$$

where BCR is the bio-oil co-processing ratio, in %.

2.2. Constraints
The constraints in this work are the mass balance, which is shown as follows:

$$\sum_i m_i^{in} = \sum_j m_j^{out} \tag{3}$$

$$m_j^{out} = \sum_j \sum_i m_i^{in} y_j \tag{4}$$

where m is the mass flowrate of a stream, in t/h; Subscripts i and j denote the ith inlet streams and the jth outlet stream of a device; Superscripts in and out represent the inlet and outlet streams, respectively.

2.3. Trade-off between the MSP of gasoline and the bio-oil co-processing ratio

For a multi-objective optimization problem, each optimal solution on the Pareto fronts can be considered as the trade-off solution of the two objectives. The evaluation function method is used to obtain the trade-off solution. The summation of all the weight factors equals to one. The minimum value of u^s is the trade-off solution.

$$u_o^s = \left(f_o^s - f_o^{min} \right) \Big/ \left(f_o^{max} - f_o^{min} \right) \tag{5}$$

$$u^s = \sum_o \varpi_o u_o^s \tag{6}$$

where u denotes the value of the evolution function; f is the value of the objective function; Superscript s, min and max are the sth solution, the minimum solution and the maximum solution, respectively; Subscript o represents the oth objective function; ω is the weight factor.

3. Case study

3.1. Basic data

The bio-oil and VGO are co-processed in an FCC with annual processing capability of 1.2 million tonnes. Different bio-oil co-processing ratio are used to obtain the corresponding minimum selling price (MSP) of gasoline. Two scenarios are proposed, as there are two bio-oil production technologies, fast pyrolysis and catalytic pyrolysis. Pulpwood is used as the biomass feedstock to make bio-oil. The product yields for the related processes (Wu et al. 2019b) are listed in Table 1.

Table 1 Yields for pyrolysis, FCC and HDT processes

Yield/%	FP	FP oil HDT	CP	FCC	Gasoline HDT	Diesel HDT
Bio-oil	52.5	/	33.0	/	/	/
Bio-gas	26.0	/	53.0	/	/	/
Bio-char	21.5	/	12.5	/	/	/
HDO oil	/	66.0	/	/	/	/
Gasoline	/	/	/	48.1	99.5	7.6
Diesel	/	/	/	23.0	/	91.2

3.2. Optimal results of fast pyrolysis scenario

3.2.1. Pareto fronts of fast pyrolysis scenario

The Pareto fronts of the bio-oil co-processing ratio and MSP of gasoline are shown in Figure 2. The MSP is increased with the increase of the bio-oil co-processing ratio. The MSP is $3.08/gal when 20% bio-oil is co-processed while the MSP is only $1.9/gal when the bio-oil co-processing ratio is 1%. That is to say, the co-processing product, gasoline, can be competed with the petroleum-based gasoline even the bio-oil ratio is

20%. The reason for the only \$1.9/gal gasoline is that the capital costs of the refinery existing infrastructures, FCC and hydrotreators, are ignored.

According to the breakdown of the gasoline price shown in the right figure of Figure 2, the raw material VGO contributes the largest proportion while the biomass is the least part. The tax takes about 40% to the price as the tax rate is set to 39%. The annual capital cost is strongly linked to the bio-oil co-processing ratio as the ratio decides the capital costs of the pyrolysis process and the HDO process, which are the only capital costs considered in the co-processing system.

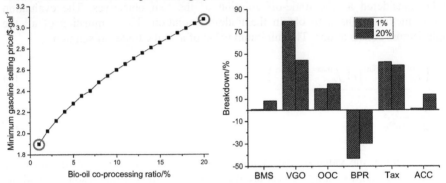

Figure 2 The Pareto fronts and the breakdowns of MSPs with 1% and 20% bio-oil co-processed (BMS=biomass, OOC=other operating cost, BPR=byproduct revenue, ACC=annual capital cost)

The Pareto fronts between the bio-oil co-processing ratio and the MSP of gasoline is not similar as usual. The reason is that the bio-oil co-processing ratio is preferred to be maximized while the gasoline selling price is to be minimized, the two different trends may lead to the curve as it is presented. The usual curve of traditional Pareto fronts would be obtained if the axis X was started from 20 to zero.

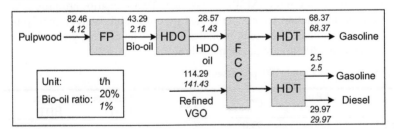

Figure 3 Mass balances of situations of the minimized MSP and the maximized bio-oil ratio

According to Figure 3 with bio-oil co-processing ratio of 20%, 82.46 t/h pulpwood is pyrolysised and hydrotreated to obtain 28.58 t/h HDO oil which is then co-fed with 114.29 t/h VGO into an FCC, gasoline HDT and diesel HDT. Finally, 70.88 t/h gasoline and 29.97 t/h diesel with bio-carbon are produced. For the situation of the minimum selling price with bio-oil co-processing ratio of 1%, 1.43 t/h bio-oil is produced by consuming 4.12 t/h pulpwood, which is then co-processed with 141.43 t/h VGO to make gasoline and diesel of 70.88 and 29.97 t/h, respectively.

3.2.2. Effect of the weight factor on the trade-off solution

The effect of the weight factor on the trade-off solution is also investigated. The result are shown in Table 2. The trade-off solution should be bio-oil ratio of 20% corresponding to the MSP of \$3.08/gal when the weight factor is less than 0.4. If the

Multi-objective optimization of co-processing of bio-oil and vacuum gas oil: a survey of gasoline selling price and bio-oil co-processing ratio

1721

factor is more than 0.7, the bio-oil of 1% and the MSP of $1.9/gal should be the trade-off solution. The optimal bio-oil co-processing ratios should be 8% and 3% if the weight factors are 0.5 and 0.6, respectively.

Table 2 Effect of weight factor on the trade-off solution

Weight factor	0	0.1	0.2	0.3	0.4	0.5	0.6	0.7	0.8	0.9	1
Bio-oil ratio/%	20	20	20	20	20	8	3	1	1	1	1
MSP/$·gal⁻¹	3.08	3.08	3.08	3.08	3.08	2.48	2.12	1.90	1.90	1.90	1.90

3.3. Optimal results of catalytic pyrolysis scenario

3.3.1. Pareto fronts of catalytic pyrolysis scenario

The Pareto fronts for the catalytic pyrolysis scenario is shown in Figure 4. Similar to the fast pyrolysis scenario, the MSP is also raised with the increase of the bio-oil co-processing ratio. The MSP is $1.85/gal when 1% bio-oil is co-processed while the MSP is $3.15/gal when the bio-oil co-processing ratio is 20%. No matter for which scenario, the co-processing product, gasoline, can be competed with the petroleum-based gasoline even the bio-oil ratio is 20%.

As for the breakdown of the gasoline price in the catalytic pyrolysis scenario, it is similar to the one in the fast pyrolysis scenario.

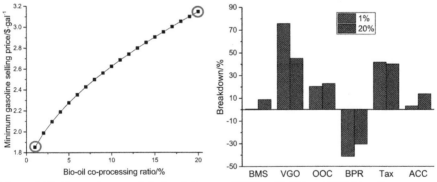

Figure 4 The Pareto fronts and the breakdowns of MSPs with 1% and 20% bio-oil co-processed (BMS=biomass, OOC=other operating cost, BPR=byproduct revenue, ACC=annual capital cost)

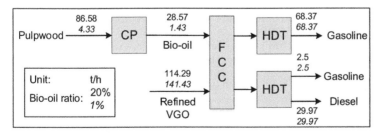

Figure 5 Mass balances of situations of the minimized MSP and the maximized bio-oil ratio

According to Figure 5 with bio-oil co-processing ratio of 20%, 86.58 t/h pulpwood is consumed to attain the bio-oil of 28.57 t/h in a catalytic pyrolysis. The 28.57 t/h bio-oil and 114.29 t/h VGO are then co-processing in an FCC to produce the gasoline and diesel with bio-carbon, which are hydrotreated in HDT to make gasoline of 70.88 t/h and diesel of 29.97 t/h. As for the 1% bio-oil co-fed with 99% VGO into an FCC, the pulpwood consumption is 4.33 t/h, the product (gasoline and diesel) flowrates are the same with the one of 20% bio-oil co-processing ratio as the same yield data is used.

3.3.2. Effect of the weight factor on the trade-off solution

Table 3 Effect of weight factor on the trade-off solution

Weight factor	0	0.1	0.2	0.3	0.4	0.5	0.6	0.7	0.8	0.9	1
Bio-oil ratio/%	20	20	20	20	20	8	3	1	1	1	1
MSP/$·gal^{-1}	3.15	3.15	3.15	3.15	3.15	2.50	2.10	1.85	1.85	1.85	1.85

The effect of the weight factor on the trade-off solution in the catalytic pyrolysis scenario is same with the effect in the fast pyrolysis scenario.

4. Conclusions

A multi-objective optimization of the co-processing of bio-oil and VGO was proposed in this work. Two scenarios, fast pyrolysis scenario and catalytic pyrolysis scenario, were used to investigate the relation between MSP of gasoline and the bio-oil co-processing ratio. The MSP was increased with the increase of the bio-oil co-processing ratio. The MSP of gasoline was approximately $3.1/gal if 20% bio-oil was co-processed for the two scenarios. The MSP was only about $1.9/gal if the bio-oil ratio was 1%. The trade-off solution was strongly affected by the weight factor. Therefore, the best compromise between the MSP and bio-oil co-processing should be determined when designing the co-processing process.

Acknowledgments

The authors gratefully acknowledge funding by the project (No. 21808183) sponsored by the National Natural Science Foundation of China (NSFC) and the project (No. 20190602) sponsored by Young Talent Fund of University Association for Science and Technology in Shaanxi, China.

References

M. Al Jamri, R. Smith and J. Li, 2018, Integration of Renewable Resources into Petroleum Refining, Computer Aided Chemical Engineering, Elsevier, 43, 1439-1444.

M. Al Jamri, R. Smith and J. Li, 2019, Molecular Modelling of Co-processing Biomass Pyrolysis Oil with Vacuum Gasoil in an Oil Refinery Fluid Catalytic Cracking Unit, Computer Aided Chemical Engineering, Elsevier, 46, 991-996.

V. N. Bui, G. Toussaint, D. Laurenti, C. Mirodatos and C. Geantet, 2009, Co-processing of pyrolisis bio oils and gas oil for new generation of bio-fuels: Hydrodeoxygenation of guaïacol and SRGO mixed feed, Catalysis Today, 143, 1-2, 172-178.

P. L. Cruz, E. Montero and J. Dufour, 2017, Modelling of co-processing of HDO-oil with VGO in a FCC unit, Fuel, 196, 362-370.

L. Wu, Y. Wang, L. Zheng, M. Shi and J. Li, 2019, Design and optimization of bio-oil co-processing with vacuum gas oil in a refinery, Energy Conversion and Management, 195, 620-629.

L. Wu, Y. Wang, L. Zheng, P. Wang and X. Han, 2019, Techno-economic analysis of bio-oil co-processing with vacuum gas oil to transportation fuels in an existing fluid catalytic cracker, Energy Conversion and Management, 197, 111901.

Sauro Pierucci, Flavio Manenti, Giulia Bozzano, Davide Manca (Eds.)
Proceedings of the 30th European Symposium on Computer Aided Process Engineering
(ESCAPE30), May 24-27, 2020, Milano, Italy. © 2020 Elsevier B.V. All rights reserved.
http://dx.doi.org/10.1016/B978-0-12-823377-1.50288-3

From Screening to Production: a Holistic Approach of High-throughput Model-based Screening for Recombinant Protein Production

Niels Krausch,[a] Sebastian Hans,[a] Felix Fiedler,[b] Sergio Lucia,[b] Peter Neubauer,[a] Mariano N. Cruz Bournazou[c*]

[a]*Technische Universität Berlin, Bioprocess Engineering, Ackerstrasse 76, 13355 Berlin, Germany*
[b]*Technische Universität Berlin, Internet of Things for Smart Buildings, Einstein Center Digital Future, Einsteinufer 17, 10587 Berlin, Germany*
[c]*DataHow AG, Vladimir-Prelog-Weg 1, 8093 Zurich, Switzerland*
n.cruz@datahow.ch

Abstract

Efficient and robust screening of production strains in early bioprocess development is usually hampered by the limited cultivation resources and identification of dynamical cell parameters for the complete design space. Even though High-Throughput (HT) liquid handling stations enable a large number of strains to be tested, these experiments provide no insight into the dynamical phenotype of the strains. This is especially critical in scale-up, since cultivations in industrial bioreactors expose the microbial cell factories to significant stresses due to substrate, oxygen, and pH gradients among others. In an effort to address this challenge and reduce the risk of failure during scale-up, new HT scale down systems based on model-based operation strategies have been developed and extended to conditional screening experiments.

In this work we further extend the existing platform to enable a feedback control of the 24-parallel mini-bioreactor setting, using a recursive moving horizon parameter estimation combined with a model-predictive control approach to calculate an optimal feeding regime, which exposes the cells to stress conditions similar to those present in large-scale bioreactors. We present a case study showing the advantages of the framework by screening a set of *E. coli* strains for obtaining highest biomass at the end of the process. The results show that the prediction and selection of the most suitable strain for industrial production is significantly improved.

Keywords: High-throughput, MPC, bioprocess development, adaptive robot operation.

1. Challenges in early bioprocess development

The development of a process to produce e.g. a new chemical entity in biotechnology is characterized by long developmental times and high costs. The risk of failure is also high, especially in the early phases when screening for a potential producer strain (Neubauer et al., 2013). Hence, novel tools to shorten product development times are required in biomanufacturing. An important step to tackle this issue has been the introduction of High-Throughput (HT) liquid handling stations, which are able to perform several cultivations in parallel, using micro-well plates or even Mini-Bioreactors (MBR) (Hemmerich et al., 2018; Nickel et al., 2017). These MBRs share geometric similarities to large scale bioreactors and can be used to screen a fair number of possible strains at low costs and effort. Consideration of specific cultivation conditions such as pulse-based glucose feeding regimes enables furthermore to perform scale-down studies with conditions also present in large scale bioreactors, characterized by significant oxygen and glucose gradients (Neubauer and Junne, 2016). Several studies have shown that intermittent feeding regimes with oscillating conditions regarding substrate and oxygen supply are an easy to implement yet powerful way of studying organisms under industrial-like stress conditions.

Successful bioprocess cultivations require a careful and well-tuned operation of the system which is currently performed with continuous manual tuning of the cultivation setpoints, while MBR systems are operated without exploiting state-of-the-art optimization and control methods. Model-based methods for process simulation, design, optimization, and control are required to maximize experimental efficiency and bioprocess understanding. Additionally, keeping conditions comparable to the production scale and promoting a consistent information flow while going through the developmental stages ensures robustness and decreases the risk of failure during scale-up (Haringa et al., 2018). The use of mechanistic models has proven to support and increase efficiency of experimental campaigns (Barz et al., 2018; Cruz Bournazou et al., 2017).

However, during the early screening stage, little is known about the phenotype and dynamical behavior of the mutants. This poses a challenge in the operation of fed-batches since the optimal feeding strategy is not known beforehand. The typical solution to this problem in parallel cultivations is a unique and very conservative feeding profile for all mutants. Using this strategy, it is not possible to compare the performance of each mutant at its optimal process conditions. By this, it is difficult to consider important differences between the mutants like the specific growth rate. Furthermore, relevant constraints are easily violated as would be strict aerobic conditions for all cultivations or avoiding cell starvation.

We tackle these issues implementing a Model Predictive Control (MPC) framework that assures a feeding strategy as close as possible to optimality for each individual mutant. A reduced macro-kinetic growth model with adaptive parameters for qSmax (maximum substrate uptake rate), pAmax (maximum specific acetate production rate), Yem (yield of biomass on glucose, excluding maintenance), and Yaof (yield of acetate on all other products of overflow routes), is used to compute the feeding strategy. The framework can interact with the robotic facility to run fed-batch like cultivations for different strains simultaneously.

As a proof of concept, we present a screening experiment of eight *E. coli* K 12 strains in 24 mini bioreactors in parallel, six of them knockout strains obtained from the well-known Keio collection of *E. coli* knockout strains. For all knockout strains there exists only very limited information regarding the growth behavior and no kinetic model parameters are available.

2. Problem Formulation

Eight different *E. coli* K-12 strains were cultivated in parallel with an industrial process-relevant feeding design consisting of batch and exponential fed-batch phases using a total of $n_r = 24$ mini bioreactors. Each one of the bioreactors $r \in \Re = \{1, \ldots, n_r\}$ can be described by the dynamics:

$$\dot{x}_r(t) = f\left(x_r(t), u_r(t), \theta\right)$$
$$x_r(t_0) = x_{0,r}$$
(1)

Where the dynamic states are denoted by $x_r \in \square^{n_x}$ and include biomass, substrate, dissolved oxygen tension (DOT) as well as acetate. The control inputs for each mini bioreactor are $u_r \in \square^{n_u}$ and $\theta \in \square^{n_\theta}$ denotes the unknown parameters of the reactor and the strains. The available measurements for all the states can be obtained at each sampling time: this is 30 seconds for DOT, and 20 min for the remaining. At each iteration of the proposed framework, the inputs of the system (the optimal feeding rate for each mini bioreactor) is computed using an MPC controller (Rawlings and Mayne, 2009), that uses the dynamical model defined in (1) using the current estimation of the uncertain parameters $\hat{\theta}$. By using the MPC controller, it can be assured that all strains are cultivated based on their maximum capabilities to assure that the best performing strain is selected for further upscaling.

The optimization problem that the MPC controller with prediction horizon N_{mpc} needs to solve at each sampling time can be written as:

$$\min_{u_r} \sum_{r=1}^{n_r} -X_r\left(t_{end}\right) \tag{2}$$

$$\text{s.t.: } \begin{array}{l} \dot{x}_r\left(t\right) = f\left(x_r\left(t\right), u_r\left(t\right), \hat{\theta}\right) \forall r \in \Re \\ x_r\left(t_0\right) = x_{0,r} \\ \text{DOT}_r\left(t\right) \geq 20\% \end{array} \tag{3}$$

Since the estimation of the parameters plays an important role in the computation of the optimal inputs and they are known to vary throughout the cultivation, we iteratively estimate the parameters using a moving horizon approach, which uses a sliding time window and only considers the N_{mhe} last measurements (Haseltine and Rawlings, 2005). The optimization problem that needs to be solved at each sampling time to obtain a new estimate of the parameters can be written as:

$$\min_{\theta} \left\| \hat{\theta}_{old} - \hat{\theta} \right\|_{W_p}^2 + \sum_{k=0}^{N_{mhe}} \left\| h\left(x\left(k\right)\right) - y\left(k\right) \right\|_{W_y}^2 \tag{4}$$

$$\text{s.t.: } \begin{array}{l} \dot{x}_r\left(t\right) = f\left(x_r\left(t\right), u_r\left(t\right), \hat{\theta}\right) \forall r \in \Re \\ x_r\left(t_0\right) = x_{0,r} \\ \theta_{min} \leq \theta \leq \theta_{max} \end{array} \tag{5}$$

Where $h\left(x\left(k\right)\right)$ denotes the measurement equations, $y\left(k\right)$ denotes the measurement at time point k, $\hat{\theta}_{old}$ is the previously estimated parameters and the two terms that penalize the change in parameters and the residuals are weighted by the parameters W_p and W_y.

An overview of the iterative process is given in Figure 1. Based on the sampled measurements, the MHE parameter estimation is performed to generate an updated set of parameters $\hat{\theta}$. Based on this parameter set, an optimal glucose feed is calculated which yields the highest biomass, subject to the constraint that anoxic conditions (DOT < 20 %) should be avoided.

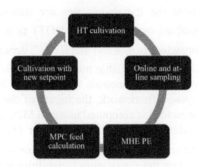

Figure 1: The high-throughput robotic facility (left) and the iterative workflow of the cultivation

3. Methods

3.1. HTBD facility

The results presented in this work are based on *in silico* data generated from 8 models validated with real experimental data, for further details on the experimental procedure the reader is referred to Hans et al. (2020). The framework has been developed to operate the high throughput bioprocess development facility, comprising of two liquid handling stations (Freedom Evo 200, Tecan, Switzerland; Microlab Star, Hamilton, Switzerland), a mini-bioreactor system (48 BioReactor, 2mag AG, Munich, Germany) and a Synergy MX microwell plate reader (BioTek Instruments GmbH, Bad Friedrichshall, Germany). Cultivations are carried out at 37 °C with 5 g L^{-1} initial glucose in the batch phase at a constant stirring speed of 3,000 rpm. Glucose is added as substrate in a pulse-based manner every 5 min after end of the batch. pH and Dissolved Oxygen Tension (DOT) are measured online, while measurements of glucose, acetate and OD600 are performed at-line on the Hamilton LHS using enzymatic kits. The reader is referred to Haby et al. (2019) for a detailed description of the facility and sampling procedure.

3.2. Computational methods

The *E. coli* macro-kinetic growth model used in this framework consists of 6 ordinary differential equations describing biomass, glucose, acetate oxygen, and enzymatic glucose release. The model contains 18 parameters from which 13 have been shown to vary with mutations and cultivation conditions. The reader is referred to the paper by Anane et al. (2017) for a detailed description of the model and to Anane et al. (2019) for a description of the procedure followed for the parameter estimation.

To allow for easier parameter identification, a subset of 4 important parameters (qSmax, pAmax, Yem, Yaof) is used, while the others are kept at constant values. All scripts were written in Matlab R2019a and ODEs were solved using the sundials CVODE solver.

4. Results

After an initial batch phase, the feed was started with 5 min pulses until the end of the process which was set to 11 h. Every hour, the framework performed an MHE based on the data generated during the previous hour. When the feed had started, the MPC part of the framework calculated the optimal feed rate based on the current parameter set $\hat{\theta}$ to obtain the highest biomass based on the different parameters for each strain. Moreover, it is assured that the cells are not overfed, considering that the substrate uptake capacity of the cells is decreasing over time. To give a better insight into the procedure at this stage, we performed simulations based on the parameters obtained from fitting the model to the data of the experiment and describe the process based on *in silico* data. In Figure 2, the process is shown without usage of an MPC framework or MHE parameter adaption (dashed orange line), with usage of the MPC framework, but without parameter estimation (purple dash-dotted line). The blue dotted line represents the output of the simulation with adapted parameters and usage of the MPC framework, while the green solid line represents the simulation output based on the actual parameters that were estimated from the process data. It can be seen clearly, that with a predefined feed, the cells are overfed, glucose accumulates and acetate (an indicator for overflow feeding) is produced in large amounts. In contrast, within the MHE/MPC framework, optimal feeding regimes are calculated, so that overfeeding is prevented. It can be seen clearly, that the MPC approach ensures optimal feeding conditions which are close to the maximum growth capacity and excel traditional approaches with a predefined growth rate. Figure 2 clearly depicts that the constraint (DOT lower than 20 %) are maintained by the MPC framework.

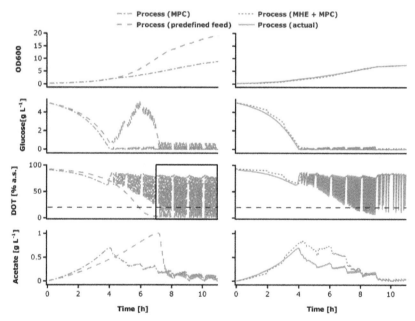

Figure 2: Exemplary results of mutant strain 1. Comparison of the process data, the simulation with the parameter set from the MHE and the simulation without parameter estimation. The black rectangle indicates a time frame in which the process without MHE violates the constraint.

5. Conclusions

In this work we present an adaptive framework comprising of an MHE for computational inexpensive parameter estimation and an MPC controller for optimal feeding calculation. The screening procedure is drastically improved by cultivating the strains at their maximum growth rates while at the same time ensuring that they will not be exposed to anoxic conditions. The results demonstrate the importance advanced control strategies in the operation of parallel dynamical cultivations due to the low *a priori* information of the mutants and the large variations in their phenotypes.

References

Anane E, García ÁC, Haby B, Hans S, Krausch N, Krewinkel M, et al. A model-based framework for parallel scale-down fed-batch cultivations in mini-bioreactors for accelerated phenotyping. Biotechnology and bioengineering 2019;116(11):2906–18. https://doi.org10.1002/bit.27116.

Anane E, López C DC, Neubauer P, Cruz Bournazou MN. Modelling overflow metabolism in Escherichia coli by acetate cycling. Biochemical Engineering Journal 2017;125:23–30. https://doi.org10.1016/j.bej.2017.05.013.

Barz T, Sommer A, Wilms T, Neubauer P, Cruz Bournazou MN. Adaptive optimal operation of a parallel robotic liquid handling station. IFAC-PapersOnLine 2018;51(2):765–70. https://doi.org10.1016/j.ifacol.2018.04.006.

Cruz Bournazou MN, Barz T, Nickel DB, Lopez Cárdenas DC, Glauche F, Knepper A, et al. Online optimal experimental re-design in robotic parallel fed-batch cultivation facilities. Biotechnology and bioengineering 2017;114(3):610–9. https://doi.org10.1002/bit.26192.

Haby B, Hans S, Anane E, Sawatzki A, Krausch N, Neubauer P, et al. Integrated Robotic Mini Bioreactor Platform for Automated, Parallel Microbial Cultivation With Online Data Handling and Process Control. SLAS technology 2019;24(6):569–82. https://doi.org10.1177/2472630319860775.

Hans S, Haby B, Krausch N, Barz T, Neubauer P, Cruz Bournazou MN. Automated conditional screening of Escherichia coli knockout mutants in parallel adaptive fed-batch cultivations. Microbial Cell Factories 2020 (submitted).

Haringa C, Mudde RF, Noorman HJ. From industrial fermentor to CFD-guided downscaling: what have we learned? Biochemical Engineering Journal 2018;140:57–71. https://doi.org10.1016/j.bej.2018.09.001.

Haseltine EL, Rawlings JB. Critical Evaluation of Extended Kalman Filtering and Moving-Horizon Estimation. Industrial & Engineering Chemistry Research 2005;44(8):2451–60. https://doi.org10.1021/ie034308l.

Hemmerich J, Noack S, Wiechert W, Oldiges M. Microbioreactor Systems for Accelerated Bioprocess Development. Biotechnology journal 2018;13(4):e1700141. https://doi.org10.1002/biot.201700141.

Neubauer P, Cruz N, Glauche F, Junne S, Knepper A, Raven M. Consistent development of bioprocesses from microliter cultures to the industrial scale. Engineering in Life Sciences 2013;13(3):224–38. https://doi.org10.1002/elsc.201200021.

Neubauer P, Junne S. Scale-Up and Scale-Down Methodologies for Bioreactors. In: Mandenius C-F, editor. Bioreactors. Weinheim, Germany: Wiley-VCH Verlag GmbH & Co. KGaA; 2016. p. 323–354.

Nickel DB, Cruz-Bournazou MN, Wilms T, Neubauer P, Knepper A. Online bioprocess data generation, analysis, and optimization for parallel fed-batch fermentations in milliliter scale. Eng. Life Sci. 2017;17(11):1195–201. https://doi.org10.1002/elsc.201600035.

Rawlings JB, Mayne DQ. Model predictive control: Theory and design. Madison, Wis.: Nob Hill Publ; 2009.

Sauro Pierucci, Flavio Manenti, Giulia Bozzano, Davide Manca (Eds.)
Proceedings of the 30th European Symposium on Computer Aided Process Engineering
(ESCAPE30), May 24-27, 2020, Milano, Italy. © 2020 Elsevier B.V. All rights reserved.
http://dx.doi.org/10.1016/B978-0-12-823377-1.50289-5

Techno-economic Assessment of a Hydrothermal Liquefaction Process for Energy Recovery from Food Waste

Enrique Medina-Martos[a*], Pablo Miranda-Rey[a,b], José-Luis Gálvez-Martos[a], Javier Dufour[a,b]

[a] *Systems Analysis Unit, IMDEA Energy. Avenida Ramón de la Sagra, 3. 28935 Móstoles, Madrid (Spain).*
[b] *Chemical and Environmental Engineering Group, Rey Juan Carlos University. Calle Tulipán s/n. 28933 Móstoles, Madrid (Spain).*
enrique.medina@imdea.org

Abstract

Hydrothermal technologies have been extensively studied over the last decade as promising pathways for energy recovery from bioresources. Feedstocks with a high moisture content, such as food waste, are particularly suitable to undergo hydrothermal conversion. In this work, we addressed a techno-economic study of the production of food-waste-derived biofuels via Hydrothermal Liquefaction (HTL), in a commercial scale facility. To that end, a simulation model encompassing the HTL conversion step (including the combination of two kinetic models from bibliography), bio-oil upgrading and products separation was implemented in Aspen Plus® V10. Results show that both the predicted biocrude mass yield in HTL (37 %) and its composition are consistent with those of previous experimental studies. Amongst the products, the annual volumetric production of gasoline triples that of diesel. In terms of the economic viability, under the studied assumptions, we found the project would only be profitable if a fee (27-39 €/t) accounting for waste treatment is adopted.

Keywords: Hydrothermal liquefaction, Techno-economic assessment, Process simulation, Aspen Plus.

1. Introduction

A better utilization of resources is currently a global concern. One aspect on this statement is related to exploring innovative uses for waste (Elkhalifa et al., 2019). Within the European Union (EU) context, the Circular Economy package includes diverse actions to that end. Municipal solid waste (MSW) management is one target of such policies. Within MSW, Food Waste (FW) represents a significant fraction, which has been estimated to amount 1.3 billion t/y globally. Thus, a great potential for energy production is associated if a proper management of FW is promoted (Elkhalifa et al., 2019; Pham et al., 2015). The conversion of FW to energy has been previously addressed by the application of thermochemical (incineration, pyrolysis, gasification) or biochemical (anaerobic digestion) technologies. First ones are energetically unfavorable due to high expenses for feedstock drying and the latter involve high investment costs due to extensive conversion times (Pham et al., 2015). As an alternative to these, hydrothermal technologies, which are performed in an aqueous medium and have shorter reaction times, arise as suitable alternatives. In particular, Hydrothermal Liquefaction (HTL) yields a crude-like viscous liquid (biocrude) which can be further refined to produce biofuels. HTL is usually developed at 200-400 °C and 40-220 bar (Gollakota et al., 2018). Together with the biocrude (30-50 %), an aqueous phase (~50 %), a carbonaceous solid called char (~10 %), and little gas (<5 %) are obtained. In this work we approach the conversion of food waste into biofuels (gasoline and diesel) via HTL by assessing economic implications for the deployment of a commercial scale facility. A process simulation model in AspenPlus® V10 served as the basis to retrieve meaningful parameters for such evaluation.

2. Process Description

The considered feedstock composition is reported in Table 1. Plant capacity was set to 161,000 t/y, similar to that reported for the anaerobic digestion facilities owned by the municipality of Madrid (Spain). Figure 1 depicts the studied process, whose main equipment specifications are summarized in Table 2.

Food waste is initially mixed with water so as to obtain a pumpable mixture (85 % moisture) and then sent to the HTL reactor, where it is isothermally converted. Required heating is provided by the exhaust gas resulting from the combustion of heavy hydrocarbons from bottom product of C-302. Afterwards, the produced char is separated in a cartridge filter, which operates at high pressure (Knorr et al., 2013). The liquid stream, made up by the biocrude and the aqueous phase, is headed to a decanter (S-101), where both phases separate. The aqueous phase leaves the process to wastewater treatment. The biocrude follows to the upgrading section to undergo deoxygenation. Such operation is performed in a fixed-bed type hydrotreating reactor (R-201). Most of the required H_2 is freshly introduced, but a certain amount is recovered H_2 which comes from a Pressure Swing Adsorption (PSA) unit (C-201), which is placed after light gases separation in flash unit S-201. The converted hydrocarbons continue to the refinery section, which comprehends two distillation columns, C-301 and C-302, where light gases, gasoline, diesel and heavier hydrocarbons (C_{20+}) are recovered. As previously stated, the latter fraction is combusted to furnish the heat for R-101. The combustion takes place in a furnace (R-401) where 10 % stoichiometric air excess is introduced. Due to environmental concerns, the NO_x concentration needs to be reduced (<0.5 ppm) in order to attain the Spanish national legislation. To that end, a Selective Catalytic Reduction (SCR) unit (R-402) is included, where NO_x reacts with NH_3 to give N_2 and H_2O.

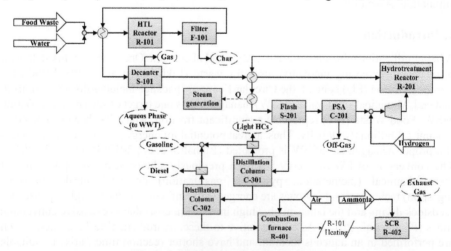

Figure 1. Block chart of studied process.

Table 1. Considered FW composition.

Fraction	Mass % (d.a.f)	Compound used in Aspen Plus®
Moisture	74.00	
Ash	1.15	
Organic Matter	24.85	
Protein	26.46	$CH_{1.57}O_{0.31}N_{0.29}S_{0.07}$ (Davis et al., 2014)
Carbohydrates	52.54	$C_6H_{12}O_6$ (Dextrose)
Lipids	2.00	$C_6H_{32}O_2$ (Palmitic acid)
Lignin	19.00	$C_{22}H_{29}O_9$ (LIG-H, Faravelli et al., (2010))

Table 2. Operating conditions for main process equipment.

Unit equipment	ID	Operating Condition
HTL Reactor	R-101	$T = 300$ °C; $P = 100$ bar; $t_r = 30$ min. (Knorr et al., 2013)
Filter	F-101	$T = 300$ °C; $\Delta P = 3.5$ bar; (Knorr et al., 2013)
Decanter	S-101	$T = 60$ °C; $P = 40$ bar
Hydrotreatment Reactor	R-201	$T = 400$ °C; $P = 138$ bar; Catalyst: Co/Mo (Elliott, 2007)
Pressure-Swing Adsorption	C-201	$T = 30$ °C; $P = 1 - 13$ bar
Distillation Column	C-301	$T_{reboiler} = 217$ °C; $P = 1$ bar; Stages = 10; Feed stage = 4; Reflux ratio = 0.5; Condenser: part.
Distillation Column	C-302	$T_{reboiler} = 337$ °C; $P = 0.8$ bar; Stages = 10; Feed stage = 5; Reflux ratio = 0.86; Condenser: part.
SCR Reactor	R-402	$T = 350$ °C; $P = 3.3$ bar; (Sorrels et al., 2019)

3. Methodology

3.1. Process simulation

The process, as described in Section 2, was implemented in software Aspen Plus® V10 in order to obtain the most relevant design parameters to perform the economic analysis. Utilized property methods were *SOLIDS* for the HTL reaction (due to the presence of char), Non-Random Two-Liquid with the Redlich-Kwong equation of state (*NRTL-RK)* for the upgrading section and the Peng-Robinson equation of state with Boston-Mathias correction (*PR-BM)* for the distillation section.

The core of the simulation i.e. the HTL reactor, was based on the combination of two literature kinetic models. The first one (Sheehan and Savage, 2017; Valdez et al., 2014), describes the formation of the bio-crude, the aqueous phase and gas by taking as input the biochemical composition of the considered feedstock. Yet, this model lacks a description for the degradation of lignin and char formation. To fix this, we incorporated the model by Zhang et al. (2008), in which lignin kinetics are explained. The reactor was simulated by means of a *RYIELD* unit ruled by a *calculator block* in which the cited kinetics are developed. Products from the HTL reaction are further assigned, attending to the elemental composition, to common families of compounds reported in Wądrzyk et al. (2018).

The hydrotreating reactor was also simulated with a *RYIELD* block. Typical process yields and hydrogen consumption were set from those reported in previous works (Elliott, 2007; Peters, 2015). For the PSA unit, we utilized an ideal separator model with assumed efficiency of 85 % for H_2 separation (Spath et al., 2005). We simulated the SCR by a *RGIBBS* block in which the consumption of NH_3 is adjusted through a *DesignSpec* feature to meet the environmental limits on NO_x emissions. Finally, the distillation columns were both implemented as *RADFRAC* blocks, with internal parameters fitted so as to achieve optimized separation of gasoline and diesel.

3.2. Techno-economic assessment

Process economics were assessed with reference on the general methodology described in Towler and Sinnott (2013). Cost data were all updated to Euros (€) of year 2018. First, we estimated the individual equipment purchase cost by using either cost correlations or applying a capacity ratio (Williams' rule). Factors were applied to account for equipment construction in stainless steel and plant location in Spain. Then, the Total Investment Cost (TIC) was estimated by the Lang method. Fixed contributions to the Operating Expenditure (OPEX) were calculated as percentages of the Capital Expenditure (CAPEX). Revenues were obtained by multiplying the annual production of each product by its market price in Spain in late 2018. Based on this, a discounted cash flow analysis was performed assuming a 15-year plant lifespan. Inflation was set to 1.02 %, the assumed tax rate was 35 % and depreciation was calculated by considering the straight line method along project years from 1 to 10. We evaluated the influence of the selected discount rate (DR) on the Net Present Value (NPV) of the project and determined the Minimum Treatment Cost of Waste (MTCW) for it to be profitable.

4. Results and discussion

4.1. Process results

The evolution of mass composition in the HTL reactor is shown in
Figure **2**. We roughly obtained 10 % char, 35 % biocrude, 55 % aqueous phase and a negligible quantity of gas. Such results are in good concordance with those reported in previous works (Kruse et al., 2013), also when attending to the elemental composition of the biocrude and its characterization by families of compounds (Not shown).
For the upgrading section, a comparison between the elemental composition of the biocrude before and after the stage is shown in Table 3. Please note that light nitrogen and sulfur compounds are considered to leave the process by the off-gas stream.
Finally, the calculated annual production of gasoline and diesel was respectively of 5.74 and 1.94 ML/y.

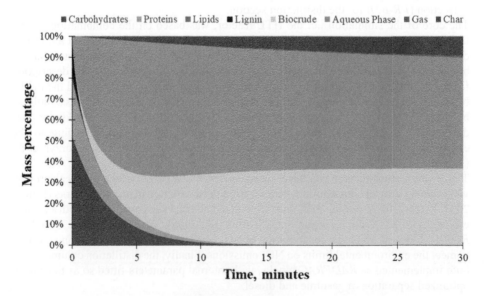

Figure 2. Kinetic profile of the simulated HTL reactor (R-101).

Table 3. Comparison of elemental composition (mass %) of biocrude before and after upgrading.

	C %	**H %**	**O %**	**N %**	**S %**
Before	69.32	9.73	13.83	6.41	0.71
After	85.2	13.5	1.3	-	-

4.2. Economic results

The economic breakdown of plant investment and operation are gathered in Table 4. OPEX is similarly participated by fixed and variable expenses, the latter being 70 % due to natural gas purchase, which is required to fill the heating necessities from the plant, and 14 % H_2 utilized in the upgrading section.

Results for NPV at the final year of the project for DR values between 6-12 % are presented in Figure 3. As proposed, the project is not profitable for any DR. To overcome this, a royalty accounting for the treatment cost of waste was adopted. The calculated MTCW (those values which make NPV=0) range 27-39 €/t. However, note that these are the values that would make the project neutral from an investor's perspective. If we took NPV=30 M€ as the minimum desired profit for investment, the required FW treatment cost would be >54 €/t.

Table 4. Estimated CAPEX, OPEX and revenues of simulated process.

Item	Value (€2018)	Item	Value (€2018)
CAPEX		**OPEX (annual)**	
Working capital	2,551,728	Fixed	2,963,363
ISBL	14,581,301	Variable	2,426,082
Purchased equipment	5,131,003	(If catalyst in SCR replaced – 3 years)	2,441,614
OSBL	5,832,520	**Revenues (annual)**	
Design & engineering	3,645,325	Gasoline (@ 0.533 €/L)	3,057,939
Contingency	1,458,130	Diesel (@ 0.587 €/L)	1,141,359
Total investment cost (TIC)	25,517,277	Steam (@) 7.3 €/t)	98,660

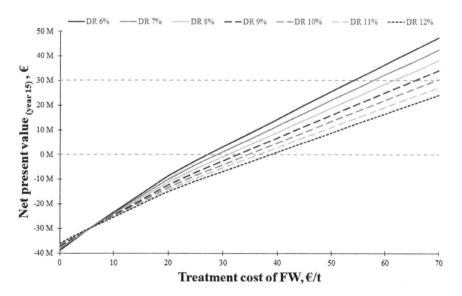

Figure 3. NPV (at final year of project lifespan) as a function of DR and FW treatment cost.

5. Conclusions

A techno-economic study based on process simulation has proven the economic feasibility of the hydrothermal conversion of food waste to biofuels in a commercial scale facility. The simulation of hydrothermal liquefaction and biocrude hydrotreating have shown good consonance with previous literature data. To ensure economic profitability, we calculated a Minimum Treatment Cost for Waste of 27-39 €/t.

Acknowledgements

The authors would like to thank financial support by the Spanish Ministry of Science, Innovation and Universities through the REDEFINERY project (RTI2018-097227-B-I00, AEI-FEDER/Retos Investigación 2018).

References

Davis, R., Kinchin, C., Markham, J., Tan, E.C.D., Laurens, L.M., 2014. Process Design and Economics for the Conversion of Algal Biomass to Biofuels: Algal Biomass Fractionation to Lipid- and Carbohydrate-Derived Fuel Products. Renewable Energy 110.

Elkhalifa, S., Al-Ansari, T., Mackey, H.R., McKay, G., 2019. Food waste to biochars through pyrolysis: A review. Resources, Conservation and Recycling 144, 310–320. https://doi.org/10.1016/j.resconrec.2019.01.024

Elliott, D.C., 2007. Historical Developments in Hydroprocessing Bio-oils. Energy Fuels 21, 1792–1815. https://doi.org/10.1021/ef070044u

Faravelli, T., Frassoldati, A., Migliavacca, G., Ranzi, E., 2010. Detailed kinetic modeling of the thermal degradation of lignins. Biomass and Bioenergy 34, 290–301. https://doi.org/10.1016/j.biombioe.2009.10.018

Gollakota, A.R.K., Kishore, N., Gu, S., 2018. A review on hydrothermal liquefaction of biomass. Renewable and Sustainable Energy Reviews 81, 1378–1392. https://doi.org/10.1016/j.rser.2017.05.178

Knorr, D., Lukas, J., Schoen, P., 2013. Production of Advanced Biofuels via Liquefaction - Hydrothermal Liquefaction Reactor Design: April 5, 2013 (No. NREL/SR-5100-60462, 1111191). https://doi.org/10.2172/1111191

Kruse, A., Funke, A., Titirici, M.-M., 2013. Hydrothermal conversion of biomass to fuels and energetic materials. Current Opinion in Chemical Biology 17, 515–521. https://doi.org/10.1016/j.cbpa.2013.05.004

Peters, J.F., 2015. Pyrolysis for biofuels or biochar? A thermodynamic, environmental and economic assessment. Rey Juan Carlos Univeristy, Madrid.

Pham, T.P.T., Kaushik, R., Parshetti, G.K., Mahmood, R., Balasubramanian, R., 2015. Food waste-to-energy conversion technologies: Current status and future directions. Waste Management 38, 399–408. https://doi.org/10.1016/j.wasman.2014.12.004

Sheehan, J.D., Savage, P.E., 2017. Modeling the effects of microalga biochemical content on the kinetics and biocrude yields from hydrothermal liquefaction. Bioresource Technology 239, 144–150. https://doi.org/10.1016/j.biortech.2017.05.013

Sorrels, J.L., Randall, D.D., Schaffner, K.S., Fry, C.R., 2019. Cost Reports and Guidance for Air Pollution Regulations - Section 4 - NOx Controls - Chapter 2 Selective Catalytic Reduction. US Environmental Protection Agency.

Spath, P., Aden, A., Eggeman, T., Ringer, M., Wallace, B., Jechura, J., 2005. Biomass to Hydrogen Production Detailed Design and Economics Utilizing the Battelle Columbus Laboratory Indirectly-Heated Gasifier (No. NREL/TP-510-37408, 15016221). https://doi.org/10.2172/15016221

Towler, G.P., Sinnott, R.K., 2013. Chemical engineering design: principles, practice, and economics of plant and process design, 2nd ed. ed. Butterworth-Heinemann, Boston, MA.

Valdez, P.J., Tocco, V.J., Savage, P.E., 2014. A general kinetic model for the hydrothermal liquefaction of microalgae. Bioresource Technology 163, 123–127. https://doi.org/10.1016/j.biortech.2014.04.013

Wądrzyk, M., Janus, R., Vos, M.P., Brilman, D.W.F., 2018. Effect of process conditions on bio-oil obtained through continuous hydrothermal liquefaction of Scenedesmus sp. microalgae. Journal of Analytical and Applied Pyrolysis 134, 415–426. https://doi.org/10.1016/j.jaap.2018.07.008

Zhang, B., Huang, H.-J., Ramaswamy, S., 2008. Reaction Kinetics of the Hydrothermal Treatment of Lignin. Appl Biochem Biotechnol 147, 119–131. https://doi.org/10.1007/s12010-007-8070-6

Sauro Pierucci, Flavio Manenti, Giulia Bozzano, Davide Manca (Eds.)
Proceedings of the 30th European Symposium on Computer Aided Process Engineering
(ESCAPE30), May 24-27, 2020, Milano, Italy. © 2020 Elsevier B.V. All rights reserved.
http://dx.doi.org/10.1016/B978-0-12-823377-1.50290-1

A Simulation Case Study for Bio-based Hydrogen Production from Hardwood Hemicellulose

Ville Tuppurainen[a]*, Jani Kangas[a], Juha Ahola[a], Juha Tanskanen[a], Atte Aho[b], Henrik Grénman[b], Dmitry Yu. Murzin[b], Tapio Salmi[b]

[a]Chemical Process Engineering, University of Oulu, P.O. Box 4300, FI-90014 University of Oulu, Finland
[b]Laboratory of Industrial Chemistry and Reaction Engineering, Johan Gadolin Process Chemistry Center, Åbo Akademi University, Biskopsgatan 8, FI-20500 Åbo, Finland
ville.tuppurainen@oulu.fi

Abstract

A novel bio-based hydrogen production process concept is simulated using Aspen Plus software. In the concept, hemicellulose is first extracted from birch wood using aqueous formic acid (FA). The dilute FA is then decomposed and used synergistically as a source of H_2. The hemicellulose monosaccharides in the dilute aqueous hydrolysate are hydrogenated to their corresponding sugar alcohols, which are further processed to H_2, various alkanes and carbon dioxide using aqueous phase reforming (APR). In addition to H_2 and electricity, cellulose and lignin rich solid wood fraction is produced. However, the case study revealed high heating requirements of dilute aqueous hydrolysate stream to APR reaction temperatures. High degree of APR effluent recycling to the extraction stage is considered, resulting in a relatively high concentration of the required fresh FA stream in the process concept.

Keywords: Bio-based Hydrogen, Hemicellulose Extraction, Aqueous Phase Reforming

1. Introduction

Hydrogen is an important raw material for chemical industry and is also considered as a potential energy carrier. H_2, used for various on-site hydrotreatment processes, is predominantly produced by steam reforming of fossil based natural gas and thus inherently producing nonrenewable carbon dioxide emissions. H_2 is an essential reagent in many lignocellulosic feedstock (LCF) valorization processes and its production from wood based raw material streams within an integrated biorefinery has been a subject of considerable interest. (Schüth 2014)

Hot water extraction of hemicellulose from hardwood typically produces a dilute aqueous mixture of mono- and oligosaccharides, furans, dissolved lignin and extractive derived compounds as well as acetic acid released from hemicellulose acetyl groups. However, usage of FA in the extraction of hemicellulose from hardwood has been shown to increase monosaccharide yields (Goldmann et al. 2017, van Heiningen et al. 2017). In addition, FA has been shown to suppress the formation of fouling lignin precipitates, a major bottleneck in the industrial recovery of hydrolysates during prehydrolysis in dissolving pulp production (van Heiningen et al. 2017). In APR, first introduced by Dumesic and colleagues (Davda et al. 2005), oxygenated biomass hydrocarbons are catalytically processed in liquid phase at relatively low temperatures (around 225 °C) and high pressure to H_2, various alkanes and CO_2. Kinetic studies with sugar alcohols, e.g. sorbitol

(Kirilin et al. 2012) and xylitol (Murzin et al. 2017, Kirilin et al. 2012, 2014), have highlighted the feedstock potential of these components for APR, which can be obtained from monosaccharides by commercial hydrogenation processes.

In this study, the concept of combining FA aided hemicellulose extraction (HCE) with APR to a complete integrated process concept is investigated using a simulation software. In the concept, FA, the catalyst of the HCE, is decomposed and used synergistically as an additional source of H_2. APR in turn enables the subsequent conversion of polyols to H_2. In addition to being an alternative source of bio-based H_2, the process concept enables more efficient use of hemicellulose hydrolysate. The aim of this paper is to evaluate the feasibility of the novel process concept by assessing its mass balance of the preliminary heat integrated flowsheet.

2. Methodology

The simulation case study was conducted using Aspen Plus. NRTL was used as the thermodynamic model, except in flash units NRTL-HOC was used to account for the non-idealities caused by the presence of carboxylic acids. H_2, CO and CO_2 were set as Henry components. Detailed description of the components in the birch and decomposition products formed in the HCE was based on the well-known National Renewable Energy Laboratory (NREL) report by Humbird et al. (2011). Palmitic and pimaric acids were used as model components for wood extractives. Solid 4-O-methylglucuronic acid substituent and its soluble monomer were defined by using the same solid enthalpy of formation as for cellulose and defining the molecular structure, respectively.

The simulation process flowsheet is described in Fig. 1. Solid debarked birch wood chips (stemwood composition compiled from Alakangas et al. (2016) with hemicellulose fraction based on Alén (2000)) with 50 wt-% moisture are fed to FA aided HCE reactor. The reactor is modeled using the R-STOIC model based on the fractional conversions of individual components. The fractional conversions were adjusted based on laboratory scale experiments done within this study using a Dionex ASE350 extractor (T=160 °C, t=60 min, Wood-to-solvent (W/S) mass ratio 1:4, 2 wt-% aqueous FA as the solvent) and analysed by HPLC, so that equal concentrations of the measured components in the hydrolysate are obtained. The behavior of unquantified components present in the hydrolysate in small amounts, most notably uronic acids and wood extractives, are subject to high uncertainty. It was assumed that 50 % of these components are solubilized. Oligosaccharides recycled back to the HCE from the APR section are completely hydrolysed to their corresponding monosaccharides. It must be noted that in the absence of detailed kinetic model, possible condensation or other degradation reactions of these components are not considered in the case study.

The HCE reactor outlet is flashed to 1 atm with the flash vapor recycled back to process feed. The solid fraction of the hemicellulose extracted wood is recovered completely but only 60 % of wood hydrolysate is recovered when draining by gravity as proposed by Saeed et al. 2012, while the rest is retained with the solid fraction. FA in the hydrolysate is first completely decomposed to H_2 and CO_2 in decomposition reactor. FA decomposition was experimentally tested to occur in the presence of a Pd/C catalyst for 2 wt-% FA aqueous solution during the study (T=150 °C, P=14 bar). The formed gas is directed to gas-liquid-separation (GLS) and pressure swing adsorption (PSA), from where the amount of H$_2$ required to completely hydrogenate hemicellulosic monosaccharides to the corresponding sugar alcohols is circulated back to the hydrogenation reactor.

APR reactor is modelled as a RPLUG reactor model. The base of the APR reaction stoichiometries and kinetics of sugar alcohols was from Murzin et al. (2017). The kinetic parameters were adjusted to yield approximately the same product distribution and conversion of xylitol as observed in Murzin et al. (2017). The kinetics were extended to other sugar alcohols using the data of Duarte et al. (2017) and Kirilin et al. (2012, 2014). The heating requirements of the APR reactor are met with latent heat of condensing saturated high pressure steam (HPS).

As shown in Fig. 1, the APR reactor outlet stream is used as a heat source in the front end of the process before feeding it to GLS. The separated liquid is flashed to 1 atm to purge most of the dissolved gases before being recycled back to the HCE. The gas is directed to PSA, modelled as a simple component splitter, where 85 % of the H$_2$ is recovered. The alkane containing PSA tail gas is combusted together with birch bark, considered here as an available supplementary fuel. Combustion is modelled as a coupled system of RYIELD, where nonconventional component bark (attributes compiled from Alakangas et al. (2016)) is broken down to conventional components, and RGIBBS, where the most typical combustion products are specified as possible products. Superheated HPS is expanded through a turbine (isentropic, with 0.72 efficiency). Cooling water network was not rigorously simulated in the study, but was assessed using Aspen Plus utility estimates.

Due to the need of estimating formation enthalpies for wood and some products of extraction, reaction enthalpy values have significant uncertainties in HCE. In addition, the net heat formation was relatively low compared to other parts of the process. Thus, the HCE reactor duty was not included in the heat integration.

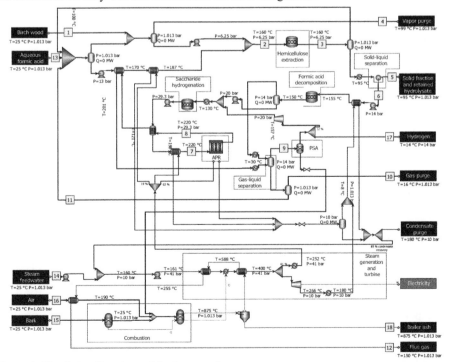

Figure 1. Simulation flowsheet of the integrated process

3. Results and discussion

Simulation results of the main process streams are presented in Table 1.

Table 1. Main process streams (numbered in Figure 1). Similar component groups are lumped.

Streams	1	2	3	4	5	6
Temperature [°C]	25.0	159.7	160.0	99.1	95.0	95.0
Pressure [bar]	1.013	6.25	6.25	1.013	1.013	1.013
Vapor frac	0	0	0	1	0	0
Total flow [kg/h]	134,460	346,637	346,637	6,893	153,702	150,069
Water	0.5	0.76	0.76	0.90	0.58	0.89
Monosaccharides	0	$3 \cdot 10^{-8}$	0.024	$2 \cdot 10^{-20}$	0.021	0.033
Oligosaccharides	0	0.0058	0.0097	$7 \cdot 10^{-16}$	0.0088	0.013
Soluble lign+extr	0	0.0063	0.010	$4 \cdot 10^{-7}$	0.009	0.015
Furans	0	0.0074	0.0106	0.042	0.0052	0.0080
Acetic acid	0	0.011	0.017	0.0013	0.014	0.021
Formic acid	0	0.016	0.016	0.0004	0.014	0.021
Cellulose	0.226	0.088	0.087	0	0.197	0
Hemi polysac	0.132	0.051	0.022	0	0.049	0
Lignin	0.104	0.040	0.040	0	0.090	0
Acetyl	0.016	0.0063	$1 \cdot 10^{-4}$	0	$3 \cdot 10^{-4}$	0
Extractives	0.020	0.0076	0.0038	0	0.0086	0
Ash+tar	$2 \cdot 10^{-3}$	$8 \cdot 10^{-4}$	0.0017	0	0.0039	0
CO_2	0	$4 \cdot 10^{-6}$	$4 \cdot 10^{-6}$	0.0382	$4 \cdot 10^{-9}$	$6 \cdot 10^{-9}$
APR liquids	0	0.0022	0.0022	0.0174	$1 \cdot 10^{-3}$	$2 \cdot 10^{-3}$
APR gases	0	$5 \cdot 10^{-8}$	$5 \cdot 10^{-8}$	$4 \cdot 10^{-4}$	$1 \cdot 10^{-10}$	$2 \cdot 10^{-10}$

Streams	7	8	9	10	11	12
Temperature [°C]	219.9	220.0	16.6	16.0	16.0	150.4
Pressure [bar]	29.3	29.3	14	1.013	1.013	1.013
Vapor frac	0.0027	0.241	1	1	0	1
Total flow [kg/h]	145,270	145,270	8,555	982	140,597	84,470
Water	0.904	0.891	0.0016	0.0078	0.933	0.156
Oligosaccharides	0.014	0.014	$2 \cdot 10^{-14}$	$2 \cdot 10^{-13}$	0.014	0
Soluble lign+extr	0.015	0.015	$3 \cdot 10^{-9}$	$1 \cdot 10^{-8}$	0.016	0
Furans	0.0079	0.0079	$1 \cdot 10^{-4}$	$4 \cdot 10^{-4}$	0.0086	0
Acetic acid	0.022	0.022	$1 \cdot 10^{-5}$	$7 \cdot 10^{-5}$	0.023	0
Sugar alcohols	0.034	$6 \cdot 10^{-5}$	$5 \cdot 10^{-18}$	$4 \cdot 10^{-17}$	$6 \cdot 10^{-5}$	0
H_2	$1 \cdot 10^{-5}$	0.0035	0.075	0.0025	$1 \cdot 10^{-7}$	$3 \cdot 10^{-7}$
CO	0	$1 \cdot 10^{-7}$	$2 \cdot 10^{-6}$	$7 \cdot 10^{-8}$	$3 \cdot 10^{-12}$	$3 \cdot 10^{-6}$
CO_2	0.0010	0.041	0.883	0.974	0.0019	0.280
O_2	0	0	0	0	0	$9 \cdot 10^{-8}$
N_2	0	0	0	0	0	0.564
APR alkanes	$2 \cdot 10^{-11}$	$2 \cdot 10^{-3}$	0.040	0.015	$2 \cdot 10^{-5}$	$4 \cdot 10^{-25}$
APR liquids	$1 \cdot 10^{-3}$	$3 \cdot 10^{-3}$	$5 \cdot 10^{-5}$	$2 \cdot 10^{-4}$	0.0035	0

Stream 13 T [°C] = 25, P [bar] = 1.013, vfrac = 0, total flow [kg/h] = 35,608, massfr: H_2O = 0.85, FA = 0.15
Stream 14 T [°C] = 25, P [bar] = 1.013, vfrac = 0, total flow [kg/h] = 9,575, massfr: H_2O = 1
Stream 15 T [°C] = 25, P [bar] = 1.013, vfrac = 0, total flow [kg/h] = 14,560, specified HHV_{dry} [MJ/kg] = 24.2, [wt-%]: C = 56.6, H = 6.8, O = 34.166, S = 0.034, N = 0.8, ash = 1.6, moisture = 50, FC = 19.68, VM = 78.72
Stream 16 T [°C] = 25, P [bar] = 1.013, vfrac = 0, total flow [kg/h] = 62,020, massfr: O_2 = 0.233, N_2 = 0.767
Stream 17 T [°C] = 14, P [bar] = 14, vfrac = 1, total flow [kg/h] = 483, massfr: H_2 = 1
Stream 18 T [°C] = 875, P [bar] = 1.013, vfrac = 0, total flow [kg/h] = 116 massfr: ash = 1

The main results of the overall process are depicted in Fig. 2. The studied HCE step aims to selectively extract only hemicellulose from wood while maintaining the cellulose and lignin fraction mostly intact for further refining. Thus the amount of the cellulose and lignin rich solid fraction is clearly the largest process output and H_2 can be considered as a side product in the overall process concept. As can be seen in Fig. 2, in the HCE, 21 % of the total dry mass of wood is converted to soluble products present in the hydrolysate, corresponding to 62 % conversion of hemicellulosic material (glucan, mannan, xylan, uronic acids, acetyl groups). H_2 molar yield in APR is 70 % (calculated with an APR reforming ratio of 11/5 for C5 and 13/6 for C6 polyols), while the carbon of polyols is converted to alkanes and CO_2 with the yields of 15 % and 80 %, respectively.

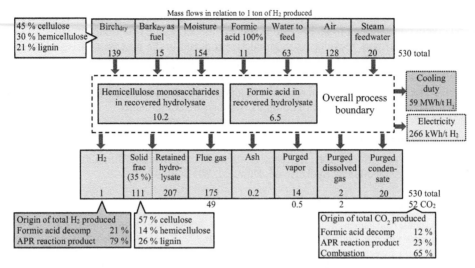

Figure 2. Overall process mass balance and summary of the most important findings.

40 % of FA and hemicellulosic saccharides in the hydrolysate are retained within the porous wood fraction, representing the most significant loss of potentially H_2 forming raw material. The needed amounts of FA and hemicellulose monosaccharides in the recovered dilute hydrolysate for processing them to H_2 through FA decomposition and APR are shown within the process boundary in Fig. 2. It is noteworthy that a relatively large fraction of the produced H_2 (21 %) originates from the FA decomposition.

Assuming 14 % of bark content in dry birch wood and perfect debarking, the bark requirement would correspond to 69 % of the bark that would be present in the total birch feedstock. Total electricity production from the turbine is 1,087 kWh/t H_2, of which 76 % is consumed by the pumps and compressors identified in Fig. 1. Total cooling duty in Fig. 2 corresponds to an estimated 10,200 t/t H_2 of cooling water utility requirement.

Due to the high degree of water recycle and relatively high feedstock moisture content, the minimum aqueous FA feed concentration to achieve the specified FA concentration and W/S ratio in the extraction reactor is 15 wt-% FA (stream 13, Table 1). Lower effluent recycling could permit the use of a more dilute, potentially waste based FA feed stream, but could, in turn, result in increased waste water treatment requirements.

4. Conclusions

A novel process concept for the production of bio-based hydrogen from wood hemicellulose was evaluated by a simulation case study focusing on the mass balance of the process. The largest product output of the process is the cellulose and lignin rich solid wood fraction, potentially suitable as a raw material for other biorefinery processes. H_2 produced originates both from FA used as the HCE catalyst and from hydrogenated hemicellulosic sugars through APR. In addition, net electricity is produced in the process. The APR reactor is operated at higher temperatures compared to HCE stage and thus heat integration of APR outlet stream is beneficial from the energy balance point of view. However, combustion of the alkanes produced in the APR does not provide enough heat to run the overall process and birch bark is exemplified as a supplementary fuel. The main drawbacks hindering the process performance according to this study is high heating requirements of dilute aqueous hydrolysate stream to APR reaction temperatures. Due to the high degree of water recycle and relatively high feedstock moisture content, a relatively concentrated fresh FA feed is needed, hindering the economic attractiveness of the aqueous effluent recycle. As the total H_2 produced in the process consists also from H_2 produced from FA decomposition, the FA fed to the process should also be of bio- or waste-based origin for truly sustainable H_2 output. General development targets of the applied technologies are to increase the recovery of hydrolysate after the HCE and yield of H_2 and alkanes in the APR of complex hydrolysate components.

Acknowledgments

The authors are grateful for the financial support from Business Finland (Biohydrogen from wood hemicellulose hydrolysate, HemiH2, 2017-2019).

References

E. Alakangas, Hurskainen M., J. Laatikainen-Luntama, J. Korhonen, 2016, Properties of indigenous fuels in Finland, VTT Technology report 272, Espoo, Finland, 53, 54, 61

R. Alén, 2000, Structure and chemical composition of wood, In: P. Stenius (Eds.) Papermaking Science and Technology: Forest Products Chemistry, 11-57, Helsinki, Finland

R.R. Davda, J.W. Shabaker, G.W. Huber, R.D. Cortright, J.A. Dumesic, 2005, A review of catalytic issues and process conditions for renewable hydrogen and alkanes by aqueous-phase reforming of oxygenated hydrocarbons over supported metal catalysts, Applied Catalysis B: Environmental, 56, 1-2, 171-186

H.A. Duarte, M.E. Sad, C.R. Apesteguía, 2017, Production of bio-hydrogen by liquid processing of xylitol on Pt/Al2O3 catalysts: Effect of the metal loading, International Journal of Hydrogen Energy, 42 (7), 4051-4060

W.M. Goldmann, J. Ahola, M. Mikola, J. Tanskanen, 2017, Formic acid aided hot water extraction of hemicellulose from European silver birch (Betula pendula) sawdust, Bioresource Technology, 232, 176-182

D. Humbird, R. Davis, L. Tao, C. Kinchin, D. Hsu, A. Aden, P. Schoen, J. Lucas, B. Olthof, M. Worley, D. Sexton, D. Dudgeon, 2011, Process Design and Economics for Biochemical Conversion of Lignocellulosic Biomass to Ethanol: Dilute-Acid Pretreatment and Enzymatic Hydrolysis of Corn Stover, United States.

A.V. Kirilin, A.V. Tokarev, L.M. Kustov, T. Salmi, J-P. Mikkola, D.Y. Murzin, 2012, Aqueous phase reforming of xylitol and sorbitol: Comparison and influence of substrate structure, Applied Catalysis A: General, 435-436, 172-180

A.V. Kirilin, B. Hasse, A.V. Tokarev, L.M. Kustov, G.N.Baeva, G.O. Bragina, A.Y. Stakheev, A-E. Rautio, T. Salmi, B.J.M. Etzold, J-P. Mikkola, D.Y. Murzin, 2014, Aqueous phase reforming of xylitol over Pt/C and Pt/TiC-CDC catalysts: Catalyst characterization and catalytic performance. Catalysis Science & Technology, 4 (2), 387-401

D.Y. Murzin, S. Garcia, V. Russo, T. Kilpiö, L.I. Godina, A.V. Tokarev, A.V. Kirilin, I.L. Simakova, S. Poulston, D.A. Sladkovskiy, J. Wärnå, 2017, Kinetics, Modeling, and Process Design of Hydrogen Production by Aqueous Phase Reforming of Xylitol, Industrial and Engineering Chemistry Research, 56 (45), 13240-13253

A. Saeed, M.S. Jahan, H. Li, Z. Liu, Y. Ni, A. van Heiningen, 2012, Mass balances of components dissolved in the pre-hydrolysis liquor of kraft-based dissolving pulp production process from Canadian hardwoods, Biomass and Bioenergy, 39, 14-19

F. Schüth, 2014, Hydrogen: Economics and its Role in Biorefining, In: R. Rinaldi (Eds.) Catalytic Hydrogenation for Biomass Valorization, 1-21, Royal Society of Chemistry, Cambridge, UK

A. van Heiningen, Y. Yasukawa, K. Dido, R. Francis, 2017, Minimizing Precipitated Lignin Formation and Maximizing Monosugar Concentration by Formic Acid Reinforced Hydrolysis of Hardwood Chips, In: H.A. Ruiz, M.H. Thomsen, H.L.Trajano (Eds.) Hydrothermal Processing in Biorefineries, 421-441, Springer International Publishing

Sauro Pierucci, Flavio Manenti, Giulia Bozzano, Davide Manca (Eds.)
Proceedings of the 30th European Symposium on Computer Aided Process Engineering
(ESCAPE30), May 24-27, 2020, Milano, Italy. © 2020 Elsevier B.V. All rights reserved.
http://dx.doi.org/10.1016/B978-0-12-823377-1.50291-3

Computational Intelligence for Process-optimization Software

Paola P. Oteiza[a,b], Juan I. Ardenghi[a], Nélida B. Brignole[a, c]

aLaboratorio de Investigación y Desarrollo en Computación Científica (LIDECC)-Departamento de Ciencias e Ingeniería de la Computación (DCIC), Universidad Nacional del Sur (UNS), Bahía Blanca, Argentina.
bDepartamento de Ingeniería Química (DIQ), Universidad Nacional del Sur (UNS), B8000 Bahía Blanca, Argentina
cPlanta Piloto de Ingeniería Química (Universidad Nacional del Sur - CONICET) Camino La Carrindanga km. 7 - 8000 Bahía Blanca – Argentina
dybrigno@criba.edu.ar

Abstract

This work describes a general algorithm for a cooperative hyper-heuristics that enables the optimization of systems of nonlinear algebraic equations with algebraic constraints. The hyper-heuristics comprises the following agents: Genetic Algorithms, Simulated Annealing and Particle Swarm Optimization. Information exchanges take place effectively among them since the immediate incorporation of solution candidates speeds up the search. Algorithmic performance is illustrated with general test models, most of them corresponding to process systems that have currently been employed in PSE. When running in parallel, numerical results demonstrate that the collaborative hybrid structure with embedded intelligent learning contributes to improve results in terms of effectiveness and accuracy. The combination of several heuristic optimization approaches into a hyper-heuristics provides enhanced benefits over traditional strategies since this method helps to find proper comprehensive solutions, also contributing to achieve and accelerate convergence.

Keywords: optimization, meta-heuristics, hyper-heuristics, parallel programming.

1. Introduction

Computational Intelligence provides solutions for complex real-world problems by means of many biologically inspired computational approaches, which are known as Evolutionary Computation. Nature-inspired algorithms have recently become popular due to their simplicity and flexibility. The state-of-the-art for these algorithms is summarized in Yang (2015), while Huang (2019) has provided a survey of automatic parameter tuning methods for meta-heuristic algorithms. Though the quick advances in Evolutionary Algorithms (EAs) have resulted in a richer literature, there has been little emphasis on its application for large industrial problems. Therefore, a challenging promising topic is the exploration of the potential value of computational intelligence in process-engineering applications, aiming at the creation of alternative methods, such as hyper-heuristics, that can cope with tough problems.

An up-and-coming approach to solve complex optimization problems is the one of hyper-heuristics, whose agents can be posed as combinations of nature-inspired techniques. Regarding pipelining, Oteiza et al.(2018) presented a hyper-heuristic that employed a genetic algorithm (GA), an ant colony optimization (ACO) and a simulated annealing algorithm (SA). It was noticed that when running SA and GA jointly, GA contributed to diversify the search by enlarging the search space. Later, Liu et al. (2019) analysed the case of West-East Natural Gas Pipeline II by optimizing this problem with the following meta-heuristics: GA, SA and particle swarm optimization (PSO). Their merits and drawbacks were discussed based on their optimization results. In their case they showed that although SA was the slowest algorithm, it yielded the best optimization results. The fastest behaviour was exhibited by GA, while in PSO each optimization problem was treated as a particle and an adaptive value was determined by the optimization function. Compared with GA, the information sharing mechanism was different in PSO and all the particles tended to converge to the best solution quickly in most cases (Lhotska et al., 2006).

Taking everything into consideration, GA, SA and PSO look like the three best candidates for team work. In turn, from an individual point of view, meta-heuristic algorithms have extensively been recognized as effective approaches for solving complex optimization problems (Mahdavi et al., 2015). Besides, it is widely accepted that the performance of EAs can be improved by parameter tuning (Karafotias et al., 2014). This task, which is sometimes very time consuming and tedious, has been carried out manually in the literature to suit specific problems. Moreover, parallel methods are also enticing for time-consuming meta-heuristics. In this sense, parallel computing together with meta-heuristic techniques are increasingly powerful to find swiftly solutions located near optimality.

Decision-making processes that involve optimization strategies play a vital role for modern industry, where there is a pervading trend towards the introduction of more realism in industrial modelling. In consequence, large constrained optimization problems, which can even be NP-hard, often arise since the integrated models usually become bigger when more details are introduced. Hence, efficient optimization procedures may help to maximise profitability. Therefore, an intelligent hyper-heuristics has been designed aiming at obtaining a high-quality solution with an emphasis on both problem search-space diversity and reasonable execution times. As to the strategy of generalisation pursued in this paper, parameter retuning has been automated in order to find adequate settings for efficient processing. In this sense, a generalised cooperative hybrid strategy with a novel learning technique is presented. It has the ability to explore and exploit the problem search space more effectively to solve any problem whose model can be defined as a system of nonlinear algebraic equations with algebraic constraints.

2. Fundamentals

In this optimizer we have employed the following well-known meta-heuristics: GA,SA and PSO. As explained in the introduction, their judicious combination looks promising when a general-purpose optimizer is desired. Figure 1 shows a schematic diagram of the proposed Master-Worker approach, where the Master is a central node and n meta-heuristics (Workers) are running. Hence, $p=n+1$ threads are being used. The Workers (agents) are heterogeneous and only communicate with the Master, who organises the cooperativism.

The computational process of the proposed hyper-heuristic algorithm is illustrated in Figure 1 for three agents: GA, SA and PSO. Firstly, the input is adapted to fit the model information needed by each agent. Then, all of them start working. During the whole procedure, a cooperative learning technique is applied to improve the search. Whenever a candidate solution has been found, all agents should be informed. The meta-heuristics that has succeeded in finding a new candidate solution, i.e. the winner, keeps its settings, while the other agents are retuned. Then, the ranking, which is an ordered list based on fitness values, is updated with the new candidate. The process continues until 30 outer iterations are completed. It is important to remark that each agent carries out 15 inner runs, internally administrating his own termination criteria. Finally, the Master reports the best solution found. Moreover, optional inputs of suggested solutions have also been contemplated in the proposed algorithm, since in many cases the experienced user can envisage the approximate location of the optimum point from an engineering viewpoint.

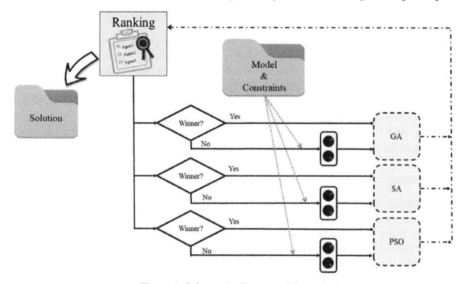

Figure 1. Schematic diagram of the optimizer.

Since the performance of EAs greatly depends on the values of their parameters and operators, on-line selection is carried out to adaptively choose them during the search. From a practical perspective, this strategy contributes to favor diversity. Whenever an agent has failed to be the winner, some of his settings are retuned based on his latest performance for the same problem. In the proposed algorithm the tunable parameters are the temperature for SA and the inertial weight for PSO. As to GA, Figure 2, which is an enlargement of a part of Fig.1, shows that both the crossover rate and the crossover mechanism are automatically adapted during GA evolution.

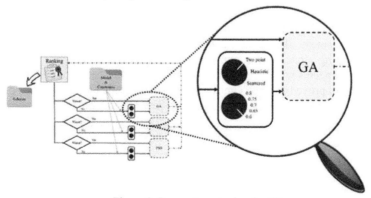

Figure 2. Parameter retuning for GA.

How the information is shared establishes the degree of cooperation among the agents. The update policy depends on the meta-heuristics. For PSO and GA the population is conveniently updated, whereas the initial point is changed for SA. Depending on its input, each meta-heuristics adopts a different behavior in order to include the best discovery so far. It should be taken into account that, in general terms, the shared information provides an idea of where the good areas of the space are. Hence, a new set of samples can be generated. Since the potential parent (i.e., the recently informed candidate solution) is more promising, the enriched set will provide diversity in the initial population for GA, thus favoring convergence.

In particular, SA iterates using a tunable parameter, always calculating energy values (i.e., fitness values) in order to keep the better solution. Given a newly-informed better candidate, the existing solution should be replaced so that the random walk continues from a newly-created point. In this way, the restart might potentially help to escape local optima. If SA remained stuck running towards a local optimum, restarting would be beneficial since both computational speed might be accelerated and the search would be guided to find the global optimum. In turn, for PSO the fitness of each particle is assessed and the best-discovered location is updated.

3. Discussion

For this testing $n=3$ (GA, SA and PSO) and $p=4$ were chosen. Based on their intrinsic features and their potential for complementary behaviour, GA, PSO and SA have been adopted in order to evaluate the strengths and weaknesses of the hyper-heuristics. The results presented in Fig. 3 and Table 1 are based on 48 problems. For software testing all these problems were extracted from the traditional collections by Floudas and Pardalos (1990), Adjiman et al. (1998) and Hock and Schittkowski (1981) in order to have comparable results. These collections are useful for benchmarking purposes because they provide best-known solutions of the optimization problems. First of all, the initial strategy adopted is the cooperative learning technique explained in Section 2. When it was applied to 48 problems, the best-known solution was found for 19 problems. For the rest of them, the algorithm could reach a feasible non-optimal solution, having only two of those cases approached the optimum (i.e., $d \leq 1$). The distance d between points was calculated as the Euclidean norm of the difference between the best-known solution and the one given as final result by the hyper-heuristics. Then, an improvement became necessary.

As shown in Figure 1, the initial strategy implies that there is always a winner in every iteration and for the following outer run the winning agent will only modify his initial point without retuning his method. In fact, there is a tie whenever at least two agents obtain simultaneously the same fitness value. To take this case into account, an improved learning strategy was implemented. It consists in keeping the winner site vacant while all agents without exceptions retune their parameters or operators. Figure 3 shows that the improved strategy contributed to augment the number of solved problems to 25, while for other 6 problems the solutions were feasible points that approached the optimum ($d \leq 1$).

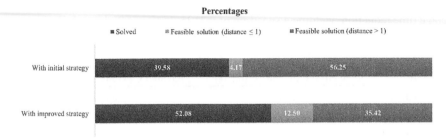

Figure 3 Performance analysis: percentages of successful executions.

Figure 4 shows the optimization results for problems where a braid has ensued in the plots, thus representing competitiveness. Problems 2V, 3V, 6V and 7V have 2, 3, 6 and 7 optimization variables, respectively. In all cases the improved learning strategy was applied and the best-known solution was satisfactorily reached. The best fitness values for all the agents is displayed for each execution. In general terms, it can be observed there is a braid behavior, which means that all the agents become competitive while the algorithm is running. How the learning strategy works can be noticed whenever the fitness value falls down suddenly overtaking the other agents. For example, in iteration 4 for problem 6V, GA exhibited the worst performance, whereas in the next iteration GA became the winner after a judicious retuning of his parameters. The braid behavior shows that all agents compete and learn, jumping out towards distinct fitness values to cope with different situations in the search space. Nevertheless, according to the results for all these problems, the best fitness value was reached between executions 10 and 20.

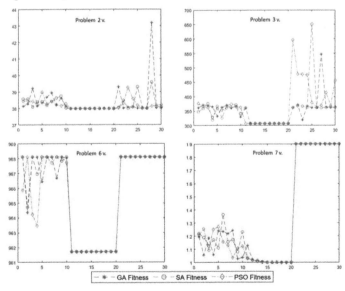

Figure 4. Disaggregated algorithmic performance: best fitness vs. number of executions.

Table 1 shows the average of the CPU times required by 48 test problems. For this analysis, forty-five medium-size (i.e., up to 20 degrees of freedom) problems and three large cases, which respectively involved 22, 30 and 48 degrees of freedom, were evaluated. It was noticed that the coarse-grain parallel implementation led to a 20% average time reduction, yielding a speed-up of 0.3125. If more efficiency is desired, it is possible to increase the attainable speed-up by refining task distribution among workers.

Table 1. Average execution times expressed in seconds

Size	Sequential CPU mean time (s)	Paralell CPU mean time (s)
Medium	316.5	256.8
Large	1284.6	1025.4

4. Conclusions

The general framework of a parallel hyper-heuristic optimizer was developed and implemented. It solves predefined problems by means of various meta-heuristics working collectively and cooperatively. It was tested by using GA, SA and PSO, which contributed to the search with their intrinsic features. The results provided by each agent are administrated by means of an innovative learning mechanism, where improvements of the optimizer intelligence are achieved by including self-adaptive features in every meta-heuristics. General testing was carried out and the hyper-heuristics proved to be accurate and efficient due to the incorporation of self-adaptability.

In chemical engineering applications, this topic is nowadays open for active research. There are plenty of opportunities in Industry 4.0 mainly regarding process control and plant-wide design that might profit from the employment of hyper-heuristic methods. The hyper-heuristic strategy is innovative as a modelling tool. An adequate ad-hoc implementation of this approach may enrich the optimization platforms of traditional PSE packages in order to contribute to next-generation advanced process modelling environments. Aiming at an efficient optimizer to tackle with time-demanding problems, it would be interesting to explore how to combine traditional equation-oriented methods with the hyper-heuristics so that the new solver helps to find improved solutions and/or initializations in competitive CPU times. Moreover, since the prediction of properties can also be posed as problems of error minimization, the proposed algorithm might be useful as an efficient computational tool to provide accurate predictions in this field.

References

C.S. Adjiman, I.P. Androulakis, C.A. Floudas (1998). A global optimization method, αBB, for general twice-differentiable constrained NLPs-II. Implementation and computational results. Computers Chemical Engineering, 22 (9), 1159-1179.

C. A. Floudas, P. M. Pardalos, (1990). A collection of test problems for constrained global optimization algorithms Springer Science & Business Media. Vol. 455.

W. Hock, K. Schittkowski, (1981). Test examples for nonlinear programming codes. Lecture Notes in Economics and Mathematical Systems. Berlin: Springer-Verlag.

C. Huang (2019). A survey of automatic parameter tuning methods for meta-heuristics, IEEE Transactions on Evolutionary Computation.

G. Karafotias, M. Hoogendoorn, A.E. Eiben. (2014). Parameter control in evolutionary algorithms: Trends and challenges. IEEE Transactions on Evolutionary Computation, 19(2), 167-187.

L. Lhotska, M. Macaš, M. Burša, (2006) PSO and ACO in optimization problems. In: International Conference on Intelligent Data Engineering and Automated Learning, Springer, 1390-1398

E. Liu, L. Lv, Y. Yi, P. Xie, (2019) Research on the steady operation optimization model of natural gas pipeline. IEEE Access. 7, 83251-83265.

S. Mahdavi, M. E. Shiri, S. Rahnamayan, (2015). Meta-heuristics in large-scale global continues optimization: A survey. Information Sciences, 295, 407-428.

P.P. Oteiza, D.A. Rodriguez, N.B. Brignole, (2018). A parallel hyper-heuristic algorithm for the design of pipeline networks. Industrial & Engineering Chemistry Res., 57(42), 14307-14314.

X. S. Yang, (2015). Recent advances in swarm intelligence and evolutionary computation. Springer.

Sauro Pierucci, Flavio Manenti, Giulia Bozzano, Davide Manca (Eds.)
Proceedings of the 30th European Symposium on Computer Aided Process Engineering
(ESCAPE30), May 24-27, 2020, Milano, Italy. © 2020 Elsevier B.V. All rights reserved.
http://dx.doi.org/10.1016/B978-0-12-823377-1.50292-5

Identification and Localization of Cyber-Attacks in Industrial Facilities

Kathrin Reibelt, Jörg Matthes, Hubert B. Keller , Veit Hagenmeyer

*Karlsruhe Institute of Technology, Hermann-von-Helmholtz-Platz 1, D-76344
Eggenstein-Leopoldshafen, Germany*
kathrin.reibelt@kit.edu

Abstract

A new method for improving cyber-security of interconnected smart components of industrial systems is introduced and evaluated. Since usual informational security measures are often bypassed (in spite of existing IT security measures), the new proposed method is based on physical models for detecting manipulations resulting from cyber-attacks. The method builds on and goes beyond traditional ways of Data Reconciliation used in chemical facilities by extending it using prior knowledge on informational properties of components. Thereby, our approach is not restricted to a specific attacker model, which is a significant advantage for the detection of unknown cyber-attacks. The attack detection using the new method is demonstrated using the example of a cooling circuit - as it may be found in chemical processing facilities. Receiver operating characteristics (ROC-curves) are used to show and to quantify the improvement provided by our new method over the performance of traditional Data Reconciliation.

Keywords: cyber-security, Data Reconciliation, industry 4.0, cyber-physical systems

1. Cyber-Security for Cyber-Physical Systems

Cyber-attacks on cyber-physical systems are not new, already in 1986, a few years after the introduction of early internet technologies, a malicious software was discovered in the controlling system of a bevatron accelerator [Bellovin, 2019]. Since then several countermeasures were developed and introduced, always in competition with new attack technologies [Bellovin, 2019]. Until today almost all of the defence measures are based on informational technologies, e.g. monitoring of traffic and restriction of access [Bellovin, 2019]. The ongoing digitalization increases the number of targets. Most attacks target on cyber-physical systems like industry 4.0 facilities or components of the new energy system [Kaspersky Lab, 2018]. Attacker models, describing the limited abilities of the attacker, are not sufficient as attacks are today driven with almost unlimited capabilities, sometimes supported by governments. Hence, new approaches are needed that utilize physical constraints and component properties - that cannot be altered - instead of informational measures that are evadable by design [Cherepanov, 2017]. These new approaches should evidently surpass the very basic countermeasures on cyber-attacks utilizing physical properties using constant and uncorrelated constraints for variables.

One of these approaches could be e.g. using error models that describe patterns of errors. Traditionally these error models are set-up and tuned by experts knowledge. A new version of error models is pattern classification by neural networks. For the set-up of error models the effect of dedicated known errors are determined and described. Using neural networks, data of attacks has to be included and named in training datasets. Hence, for both cases detection using error models is always restricted to known types of errors, which is very suitable for early detection of wearing, but does not work for complex and unknown cyber-attacks [Katipamula et al. 2005].

Furthermore, a possible detection method utilizing physical properties could be classic Data Reconciliation [Narasimhan et. al., 2000], in which the values of the systems variables are adjusted to the model. Deviations between measured and model values, arising for both set values at captured controls and measured values at false data injection for influencing controls are used for error detection and localization of the faults. However this detection is not sufficient for any system, as the sensor equipment may not be set-up for this use and - with few redundancy - some faults may not be distinguishable. In order to address this, the proposed model-based method for detection of cyber-attacks in the present paper is an extension of Data Reconciliation: The existing detection methods are extended by prior knowledge regarding properties related to cyber-attacks like exposition and commonalities in order to detect efficiently and suitably respective cyber-attacks.

The present paper is organized as follows: In section 2, the new detection method is introduced based on with Data Reconciliation. Section 3 shows the application using a standard example and section 4 gives an evaluation of the performance and the improvement by the extension using Receiver Operating Characteristic Curves (ROC-Curves).

2. Data Reconciliation with Extension for Cyber-Security

Data Reconciliation is based on a mathematical system model, which contains redundancy w.r.t. the information gained by respective measurements [Narasimhan et al., 2000; Schladt et al., 2007]. Considering all system variables y, a system matrix A is determined that represents the conservation laws fitting the system equation $A \cdot y = 0$. Due to statistical errors, real measurement will not fulfil the system equation exactly. This is utilized by Data Reconciliation to optimize the measurements by adjusting them to the equation. For this adjustment different methods are available, the one used in the present paper is the utilization of Lagrange multipliers. The difference between measured values y and adjusted values $\hat{y}$ is minimized satisfying the constraint of fulfilling the system equation. In this case the measurement deviation is scaled by the variance of the respective variable in order to take different accuracies of the variables into account. The optimization gives a closed solution for calculating $\hat{y}$ from the measured y [Narasimhan et al., 2000].

Based on Data Reconciliation several gross error detection methods are available. Three methods are chosen in view of their adaptability for different systems, their sensitivity to different types of errors (especially to multiple errors), and their ability to localize errors:

1. The measurement test analyses the measurement deviation $d = V_y^{-1} \cdot (y - \hat{y})$ with variance matrix V_y [Tahamhane, 2010].
2. The global test evaluates the sum of the residuals $r = A \cdot y$ and its reduction if measurements of suspected variables are removed and calculated as virtual sensors [Madron, 1985].
3. The hypotheses test compares the residuals to patterns prepared for every possible gross error and gross error combination [Narasimhan et al., 1987].

For normalization the variance matrices for residuals r and normalized deviation d have to be calculated by projecting the variance matrix V_y of the variables y to the basis of r respectively d.

For conventional error detection applied in order to detect sensor outages the probability is decreasing with the number of conjointly affected sensors. For detection of cyber-attacks multiple manipulations have to be expected. The similar structure of many sensors and actors leads to effects on several components by one attack. Vice versa the attacks utilize properties of a component that might also be properties of other components. This is why multiple manipulations for combinations with similar components are more probable than for combinations without commonalities. Subsets $X_i = \{Y|P_i\}$ of variables Y with commonalities P_i like common communication protocols, connection to the same network layer, same measurement principle, same operation system for smart sensors, common manufacturer of the software, high exposition to the network and so on are defined and associated with their common property P_i, an impact factor I_i expressing the weakness of the commonality or the grade of exposition and a class of countermeasures C_i referring to the commonality: $X_i \rightarrow (P_i, I_i, C_i)$. For manipulation detection, the tested combinations $T_k \in Y$ are compared to all predefined subsets X_i, and in case $T_l = X_j$, the threshold for manipulation detection is adapted by factor I_j to be fulfilled more easily. If a group with commonalities is detected to be manipulated, the information about their commonality gives information on possible attack vectors. The class of countermeasures C_i contains targeted measures like blocking certain communication gates as well as safe measures like a shut-down. For every element, it defines conditions regarding system state as well as certainty of knowledge on system state. This enables targeted countermeasures and allows safe further operation during an attack in some cases.

3. Examples

Figure 1 shows the standard example of Data Reconciliation [Narasimhan et al., 2000], a cooling circuit with six devices, one fork and one join. The flow rate of the cooling liquids in the devices is measured. The total amount of cooling liquids is considered to be constant, which leads to conservation equations [Narasimhan et al., 2000]. With the array of 'real' variable values y, a system matrix A is determined that represents the conservation laws fitting the system equation $A \cdot y = 0$.

$$A = \begin{bmatrix} 1 & -1 & -1 & 0 & 0 & 0 \\ 0 & 1 & 0 & -1 & 0 & 0 \\ 0 & 0 & 1 & 0 & -1 & 0 \\ 0 & 0 & 0 & 1 & 1 & -1 \end{bmatrix}$$

Figure 1: Standard example, cooling circuit with six connected devices.

Based on this cooling circuit example, the different detection methods and the effect of the adaption for cyber-attacks is used in the following scenario. The manipulation increases variables 1 and 5 with an amplitude of 5 additional to statistical errors (Table 1).

Table 1: Measurements of example.

Variable	True value	Measurement (with statistical errors)	Measurement manipulated	Reconciled values
1	100	100.54	105.54	102.37
2	36	37.83	37.83	37.09
3	64	61.74	61.74	65.28
4	36	36.31	36.31	37.09
5	64	64.32	69.32	65.28
6	100	98.69	98.69	102.37

For demonstrating the effect of adjusted thresholds high exposition to the internet is assumed for variables 1;3;6 and common properties are considered for combinations [4,6]; [1,5]; [2,3]; [1,2,3]; [3,5,6]; [2,4,6]; [3,4,5]. Note that in the following, thresholds for the detection of manipulated variables and combinations, as well as for the decision, if a tested variable or combination could be part of a manipulated combination with more variables are determined in section 4 using Receiver Operating Characteristic Curves (ROC-Curves). In the example, for all properties the same impact factor of 0.7 is used.

3.1. Measurement Test

For the measurement test the test statistics $z = V_d^{-1} \cdot d$ is evaluated [Tahamhane, 2010]. High test statistics result from high deviations and indicate the presence of a gross error. For single manipulations a threshold of 19.76 is used. The adapted threshold is reduced by impact factor of 0.7 to 5.928. The difference to the individual threshold, given in the right column of Table 2, should be positive in case of a detection. A different threshold of 2.83 is used to decide whether single variables could be part of manipulated combinations. In this case no single manipulation is detected and combinations of 1, 3, 5 and 6 are further investigated.

For the detection of multiple errors, suspected variables are removed and the other variables are tested. Therefore test statistics for combination [3,6] is different from the one of [6,3]. Due to space limitation, in Table 2 only a few combinations are listed.

Table 2: Test statistics and difference to adapted threshold by measurement test.

Var	z	Δ	Var	z	Δ
1	3.8804	-2.0476	5 1	5.2862	0.48623
2	0.9065	-18.8535	5 2	0.3423	-15.6577
3	4.3288	-1.5992	5 3	2.1396	-13.8604
4	0.2836	-19.4764	5 4	1.5714	-14.4286
5	4.9518	-14.8082	5 6	3.3725	-12.6275
6	4.5034	-1.4246	6 1	1.8807	-14.1193
3 1	2.8900	-13.1100	6 2	0.2265	-15.7735
3 2	2.0540	-2.7460	6 3	5.6336	-10.3664
3 4	0.8248	-15.1752	6 4	1.4556	-3.3444
3 5	3.2186	-12.7814	6 5	3.9514	-12.0486
3 6	5.7688	-10.2312			

For the detection of double combinations, a threshold of 16 and adapted threshold of 4.8 is used. This leads to a detection in combination [5,1]. For investigation for being part of triple manipulations, a threshold of 4.22 is used. The combinations [3,6] and [1,5] are qualified to be further investigated, whether they are part of triple combinations. For triple combinations the threshold 16 respective 4.8 is again used. However, none of the triple manipulations fulfils the detection criteria. Hence, for this example the measurement test would only detect the combination [5,1] that was manipulated indeed.

3.2. Global Test

For the global test the suspected variables are removed and the test statistics $\gamma = r^T \cdot V_r^{-1} \cdot r$ is calculated [Madron, 1985]. As the tested combination is removed, the test statistics for the remaining variables should be small. The thresholds are 0.3 for single manipulations, 0.07 for double manipulations and 0.02 for triple manipulations. For adaption the thresholds are increased by impact factor of 0.7 to 0.51, 0.119 and 0.034.

Table 3: Test statistics and difference to adapted threshold by global test.

Var	γ	Δ	Var	γ	Δ
0	52.9998	53.1198	2 4	52.1395	52.0695
1	37.9422	37.4322	2 5	28.3622	28.2922
2	52.1780	51.8780	2 6	32.6679	32.5979
3	34.2610	33.9610	3 4	33.5807	33.5107
4	52.9194	52.4094	3 5	23.9016	23.8316
5	28.4793	28.1793	3 6	0.9821	0.9121
6	32.7192	32.2092	4 5	26.0100	25.9400
1 2	34.1856	34.1156	4 6	30.6003	30.4813
1 3	25.9091	25.8391	5 6	17.1053	17.0353
1 4	37.4394	37.3694	1 2 3	18.6932	18.6592
1 5	0.5351	0.4161	1 2 4	28.7101	28.6901
1 6	29.1822	29.1122	1 2 5	0.0026	-0.0174
2 3	30.0422	29.9232	...	...	...

The global test only identifies the combination [1,2,5] as manipulated (Table 3). Indeed variable 2 has a high statistical error compared to the other not manipulated variables.

3.3. Hypotheses Test

The hypotheses test compares the residuals to expectation values of residuals F_k for hypotheses k of manipulations in the tested variables. The test statistics [Narasimhan et al., 1987]

$$T = sup_{F_k} \frac{(F_k^T \cdot V_r^{-1} \cdot r)^2}{F_k^T \cdot V_r^{-1} \cdot F_k} \qquad (1)$$

is normalized and is high for high similarity. The thresholds used for detection are 34 for single manipulations, 80 for double manipulations and 160 for triple manipulations. The reduced thresholds are 23.8, 56 and 112. According to Table 4 variables 1, 3, 6 and combinations [1,5] and [3,5,6] are considered to be manipulated. The highest difference to the individual threshold is shown by combination [1,5].

Table 4: Test statistics and difference to adapted threshold by hypotheses test.

Var	T	Δ	Var	T	Δ
1	15.0576	4.8576	2 5	24.6376	-55.3624
2	0.8218	-33.1782	2 6	20.3319	-59.6681
3	18.7387	8.5387	3 4	19.4191	-60.5809
4	0.0804	-33.9196	3 5	29.0982	-50.9018
5	24.5205	-9.4795	3 6	52.0177	-27.9823
6	20.2806	10.0806	4 5	26.9898	-53.0102
1 2	18.8142	-61.1858	4 6	22.3995	-1.6005
1 3	27.0907	-52.9093	5 6	35.8945	-44.1055
1 4	15.5604	-64.4396	1 2 3	34.3066	-13.6934
1 5	52.4647	28.4647	1 2 4	24.2897	-135.7103
1 6	23.8176	-56.1824	...	...	...
2 3	22.9575	-1.0425	3 5 6	52.5277	4.5277
2 4	0.8602	-79.1398	4 5 6	41.1488	-118.8512

4. Evaluation

For objectively evaluating the performance of the three detection methods and calculation of optimal thresholds that are already used for the examples, the receiver operating characteristics are determined [Fawcett, 2005]. In order to show the effect of the adaption for cyber-security and to quantify the improvement provided by our new method over the performance of the traditional Data Reconciliation, the ROC-curves are calculated for different shifts of the adapted threshold. Thereby shift of 0% represents the curve without adaption, which means incorporating no prior knowledge. For the determination, if the tested variables could be part of a manipulated combination, the ROC-curves a calculated by considering all subsets of the manipulated combination as 'true' manipulation. The referring curves are plotted in dark colour.

As high sensitivity as well as high specificity is desirable, the area between the curves and the diagonal determines the value of the test. The diagonal itself represents random results. Thresholds can either be determined by boundary conditions, e.g. a required specificity where the referring threshold can be read out at the ROC-curve, or by using the optimal threshold, that has the highest distance to the diagonal. The optimal thresholds are inscribed in the plots. The specificity decreases with higher numbers of involved variables. For hypotheses test and measurement test an extra threshold for the decision of investigating higher combinations including the referred variables is useful, for the global test this threshold is not meaningful as the ROC-curve almost follows the diagonal.

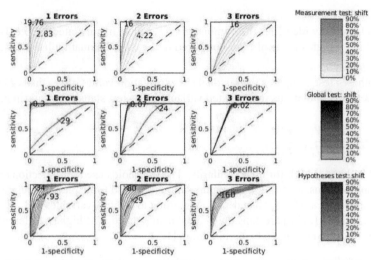

Figure 2: ROC-Curves for the three tests for different numbers of manipulated variables and different threshold shifts for commonalities. Optimal thresholds for detection and for examination for higher combinations are marked.

5. Conclusions

In this paper we introduce a new model-based method for detection of cyber-attacks. The new detection method extends Data Reconciliation by prior knowledge on informational properties of components. It is thus able to detect and localize cyber-attacks in a cyber-physical system. This adds a second layer of defence to industry 4.0 facilities, enables targeted countermeasures and reduces the risk of damages, outages and misproduction.

References

Steven M. Bellovin, 2019, 30 Years of Defending the Internet, Talk, Newark, Delaware, USA, https://www.cs.columbia.edu/~smb/talks/30-years-udel.pdf [Accessed 25 Nov. 2019]

Anton Cherepanov,2017, WIN32/INDUSTROYER, A new threat for industrial control systems, techreport, ESET

Tom Fawcett, 2005, An introduction to ROC analysis, Pattern Recognition Letters 27, pp. 861–874

Kaspersky Lab ICS CERT, 2018, Threat Landscape for Industrial Automation Systems in H2 2017, Moscow, Russia, ics-cert.kaspersky.com

Srinivas Katipamula, Michael R. Brambley, 2005, Methods for Fault Detection, Diagnostics, and Prognostics for Building Systems—A Review, Part I and II. HVAC&R RESEARCH. 11(1) pp. 3 – 26, 11(2) pp. 169 – 187

Frantisek Madron, 1985, ANew Approach to the Identification of Gross Errors in Chemical Engineering Measurements, Chemical Engineering Science - CHEM ENG SCI 40 (1985), pp. 1855–1860

Shankar Narasimhan, Cornelius Jordache, 2000, Data Reconciliation & Gross Error Detection, An Intelligent use of Process Data, Gulf Publishing Company, Houston Texas

Shankar Narasimhan, Richard S. H. Mah, 1987, Generalized Likelihood Ratio Method for Gross Error Detection, AIChE Journal 33 (1987), p. 1514 – 1521

Markus Schladt, Bei Hu, 2007, Soft sensors based on nonlinear steady-state data reconciliation in the process industry. Chemical Engineering and Processing: Process Intensification, 46(11), pp. 1107-1115

Ajit C. Tahamhane, 2010, A Note on the Use of Residuals for Detecting an Outlier in Linear Regression, Biometrika 69(2), pp. 488–489

Sauro Pierucci, Flavio Manenti, Giulia Bozzano, Davide Manca (Eds.)
Proceedings of the 30th European Symposium on Computer Aided Process Engineering
(ESCAPE30), May 24-27, 2020, Milano, Italy. © 2020 Elsevier B.V. All rights reserved.
http://dx.doi.org/10.1016/B978-0-12-823377-1.50293-7

Online Condition Monitoring: Sensors, Models and Software for a Safe Management of Aged Process Plants

Paolo Bragatto[a], Patrizia Agnello[a], Canio Mennuti[a], Maria Francesca Milazzo[b]

[a]INAIL Dipartimento Innovazione Tecnologica, Via Fontana Candida,1; Monteporzio Catone 00078 Italy

[b]Università di Messina Dipartimento di Ingegneria, C.da di Dio, Sant'Agata, Messina 98166 Italy

Abstract

The paper discusses a software application aiming at the dynamic assessment of the remaining useful life (RUL) of critical equipment in process plants. A number of advanced integrity sensors, including *ultrasound thickness* (UT) and *acoustic emissions* (AE) systems, are installed on vessels and pipe throughout the plant. They are able to detect in advance cracks and corrosion and gather continuous data, which feed a simple prognostic model and, in turn, is able to continuously update the information about the expected RUL, in order to support reasonable decisions about equipment life extension as well as inspection scheduling and stops planning. The software exploits an existing platform for communication, database and user interface. The prognosis module uses an easy model, which could be replaced by a more sophisticated algorithm, keeping the other modules.

Keywords: Remaining Useful Life, Major Accident Hazard, Equipment Ageing, Smart Sensors.

1. Context

The control of equipment integrity along the plant lifetime has been a major concern in process industries since a couple of decades ago. For this purpose, operators of major hazard establishments adopt successfully the Risk Based Inspection (RBI) techniques, which determine, based on the results of risk assessment, time and modes of integrity inspections, in order to prevent losses due to deteriorated equipment. The knowledge of deterioration mechanisms and related testing techniques is the core of the RBI methods. The RBI techniques are defined by different national and international standards and represent recognized industrial practices, which are implemented in a number of commercial software products. The main limit of most RBI implementations is the lack of a continuous dynamic update.

Risks related to aged equipment is an emerging concern in European major hazard industries, due to the evidences of many equipment related accidents (Wood & al. 2013), as well as to a few specific requirements of the legislation for the prevention of major accidents. This concern pushes the operators to adopt RBI techniques even with the known limits.

The recent development of innovative sensor technologies is providing the operators new instruments, able to gather and transmit data about material deterioration, allowing a real time monitoring of equipment conditions. The present technologies are able to provide continuous data for a number of deterioration mechanisms, but in the next future, further sensors will be ready for industrial use. They have the potential to provide a real time control of the conditions of most critical equipment (Bragatto & al. 2018). The exploitation of such data is a new challenge, which involves different disciplines, including chemical engineering, corrosion science, electronic engineering and computer science.

2. Objectives

The use of innovative sensors could become very important to extent the equipment lifecycle at Seveso establishments, assuring a higher level of safety with low costs. In this way, the process industry could successfully face the challenge to continue the safe operating of aged plants. Innovative sensors are able to operate in a continuous way and create a huge a huge amount of data, for which special attention is required. The RBI procedures, as present in the recognized guidelines, were developed to deal data coming from punctual measurements, in most case performed just during periodical programmed stops. To evolve towards a new RBI, able to integrate also continuous monitoring data, a few problems have to be solved. The aim of the paper is to focus on these problems and propose a few solutions. In the detail, the objectives of the paper include a) the review of the emerging sensors technologies, b) the definition of a conceptual framework to use the data provided by these technologies for improving the present RBI techniques and c) the development of a simple application for the safe management of ageing in process plants.

3. Innovative sensors for equipment integrity monitoring

The present section discusses a few advanced sensors, based on non-destructive testing techniques, which have been demonstrated suitable to be used to monitor, even in a continuous way, the integrity of primary containment systems. A generic monitoring system is featuring a sensor and a few electronic components or subsystems, which provide services for identification, transmission, and processing of data. These systems can be used in many different contexts of process industry for monitoring the integrity and functionality of critical equipment, including vessels, pipes and rotating machines. The sensors suitable for monitoring system must be low cost, non-invasive, flexible, scalable and user friendly.

3.1. Vibration Monitoring

Accelerometers are devices that measure the vibration, or acceleration of motion of a structure. They have a transducer that converts mechanical force caused by vibration or a change in motion, into an electrical current using the piezoelectric effect. For monitoring and predictive maintenance applications, it is required a good frequency response, a long-term stability with minimum drift and a wide operating temperature range. These systems are already used to control rotating machines in many refineries.

3.2. Ultrasound Thickness Measurements

Techniques based on the ultrasonic (UT) method can be used to monitor the wall thickness at certain critical points of an equipment. The monitoring systems are essentially composed of high frequency ultrasound emitter (generally $1 \div 10$ MHz), a localization device and a wireless communication system. The performance of monitoring systems based on UT technologies surpasses those of traditional systems. Monitoring always requires a number of sensors in the network in all critical units, so redundancy helps to increase the overall reliability of the solution. Sensors are installed on critical pipeline or vessels in a permanent or semi-permanent way and can be accessed remotely. A few commercial systems for UT monitoring are already available for industrial applications.

3.3. Acoustic Emission Monitoring

Acoustic Emission (AE) refers to the generation of transient elastic waves (generally 20 KHz – 1 MHz) produced by a sudden redistribution of the stress state in a material. When a structure is subjected to an external stimulus (change in pressure, load or temperature), the localized sources trigger the release of energy, in the form of tension waves, which propagate to the surface and are recorded by the piezoelectric sensors array. The AE examination is a non-destructive method used for several decades to identify defects (e.g. cracks and micro cracks) in structures and components, both in civil and industrial engineering. The technology is particularly suitable to build a network of sensors across large structures, such as atmospheric storage tanks or pressure vessels. The system consists of a digital signal processor, standardized data transfer ports, reconfigurable logic and specific software. Even though AE monitoring is not yet popular in process industry, it has been demonstrated feasible by a few studies.

4. Dynamic approach to RBI, through innovative sensors

The Risk-Based Inspection approach is based on the concept that high-risk equipment is a limited number of critical items of the establishment (API, 2016a; API, 2016b). Accordingly, priorities and additional investments must be oriented to the maintenance of them. The approach includes the following steps: i) defining and measuring risk; ii) creating a risk-based ranking of critical equipment, and iii) optimizing inspections based on the probability of failure. All these steps require the management of numerous information, therefore, the execution of an RBI analysis is a highly time-consuming process. To support the manager in easily performing it, a number of applications has been developed. There are many software implementing the RBI approach. First of all, the API RBI software, which is based on the RBI quantitative approach as detailed in API RP 581, it was developed by subject matter experts from top multinational refiners and supported by the American Petroleum Institute. A RBI software popular in oil industry is *Credo*, which is an application, developed for the inspection management. A further product, worthwhile to be referred is Inspection Manager developed by *Antea*, an Italian firm and popular in Italian Process industry. It is a management software integrated with the RBI approach as detailed in API RP 581 (Vianello et al., 2016).

The revision of the RBI model identifies, besides various benefits, some limits that should be studied for a better optimization of inspection and maintenance activities. The adoption of the classical approach implies that the equipment prognosis is based on a number of a priori hypotheses (e.g. failure rates, factors associated with the damage mechanisms and complexity of the system under analysis and managerial factors, etc.), which are updated by inspection results. These hypotheses could lead to a false sense of safety and, thus, to unpredictable failures. For this reason, some international guidelines require the risk recalculation to achieve an effective management of changes inside the establishment (API, 2014). The RBI analysis could be imagined as a "frame" of the establishment, taken at time t, which guarantee, by accounting for the established level of reliability, the integrity of the system up to the time $t + \Delta t$ (where Δt is a number of years). This is obviously carried out, on the basis of consolidated knowledge, measurements, historical data of the equipment and a priori assumptions. This model followed by the API 581 is also valid for EEMUA159 and EN16991. The standard API 584 is more dynamic, because it also takes into account changes in operating parameters affecting the probability of failure and, thus, modifies the operating time before the intervention. The monitoring of the actual equipment conditions would be the solution to avoid incidents related to equipment deterioration, as indicated Bathia et al. (2019). In this context, the monitoring of online conditions clearly offers, as main advantage, the opportunity for a more detailed and reliable prognosis, through the processing of the measurement of the variables performed in real time. Unfortunately, the tools that are currently available for the execution of RBI analyses do not integrate the dynamic concept introduced by API 584. However, the use of the innovative sensors, described in Section 3, could provide information related to time interval Δt, i.e. it would provide a lot of new data about the equipment integrity, which would update the forecasts, without having to wait for the next stop, in such a way that prognostics can be updated in real time.

5. A software framework for integrating innovative sensors

In order to develop a software to manage the data provided in a continuous way by the sensors distributed throughout the plant, it is essential to have a shared platform, able to handle different communication protocols and different format types of data and information. The platform should also manage other important aspects, such as the user interface and database access.

5.1. "Smartbench" platform

"Smartbench" platform was selected, as meeting the essential requirements. It was developed in the Smartbench research project (2017-2019) co-funded by INAIL, the Italian Workers Compensation Authority and a few major Italian universities, with the aim to promote the use of smart safety system in the process industries. The platform provides a distributed infrastructure where, equipment, machines, environment, and workers are connected each other in order to retrieve relevant data from the field and provide early warnings. Different types of sensors may be handled, including environmental, wearable and integrity sensors, installed on the equipment . The platform provides a high-level communication protocol, layered on the usual industrial protocols, such as BLE and NFC. It enables to access into the cloud, where a database deals with different information, including equipment identification, inspections' results, and workers' position. The platform includes an ontology-based knowledge management system to make it able to handle different deterioration mechanisms, depending on materials, operating parameters, environmental conditions and in service age. The platform provides also a user-interface and supports vertical application targeted to workers, supervisors, auditors and external inspectors. It is suitable for both smartphone and control-room applications.

5.2. The modules

The application layered on the "Smartbench" platform aims at demonstrating the feasibility of a "dynamic" assessment of the integrity condition of the whole plant and of any item of equipment. Minimal requirements are the evaluation of the equipment ageing condition and the forecast of remaining useful life. This forecast is used to support the decision making about the safe life extension and stops' planning. RUL is the length of time an equipment is likely to operate before it requires repair or replacement, with a reasonable safety margin. The evaluation of equipment ageing can be carried out by using a sort of virtual sensor, which exploits the results of equipment inspections and elaborates appropriate simplified ageing-related metrics (Milazzo et al., 2019). These make use of accelerating and slowing down factors, as defined in the *Ageing FishBone model* (Milazzo and Bragatto, 2019). By means of a simple prognostic model ageing factors may be exploited to provide an estimation of the failure frequency and the remaining useful lifetime for each equipment. Input parameters are updated when an inspection is carried out by the competent authority or during a self-assessment by the operator. Taking advantage of the "SmartBench" platform, it is, however, possible to feed the virtual sensor with data from the online monitoring and, therefore, to obtain real-time updates of ageing metrics and, consequently, of RUL estimation. The overall framework is shown in fig. 1. The "Smartbench" platform provides already a few services for presenting the two-dimensional layout of the plant, highlighting equipment with relevant information and sensors. It may be used for presenting on mobile device (smartphone or tablet) the RUL associated with pipes or vessels. Augmented reality has been implemented as ageing indexes and related RUL may be displayed in a small sized screen (1.5 inch) embedded in a home-made smart helmet, interfaced with the platform. The helmet may be worn by the supervisor walking through the plant, in order to have an immediate feeling of the equipment integrity condition. There is, furthermore, a desktop application that shows the plant layout with the items characterized by different symbols and colours, to give a complete picture of the ageing indices. In order to evaluate the effects of different choices and support the decisions, future conditions are simulated and represented over the plant layout.

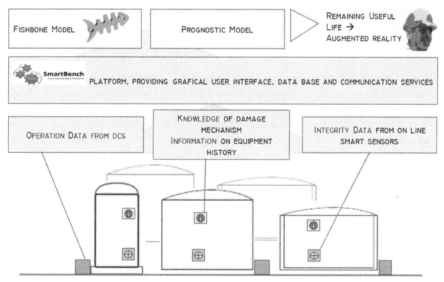

Figure 1 The software framework for the Dynamic Lifetime Extension of Ageing Equipment

6. First Results

As use case, a storage tank has been examined, whose prevalent damage mechanism is soil corrosion. To control the phenomenon, the tank is regularly inspected according to the standard EEMUA 159. In order to improve the control, the tank has been equipped with an AE monitoring system. The system is a network of connected sensors placed along the gunwale at a distance of some 1.5 meters. The system provides a signal for any minimal advance of cracking or thinning. It is robust enough to support outages that are frequent, due to external causes, including meteorological conditions. The ageing index is determined over the years by the *Ageing Fishbone model*. This index has the trend shown in Figure 1(a). Figure 1(b) gives the residual useful lifetime, calculated according to the assumed corrosion rate (i.e. on the conditions detected at the last inspection by using EEMUA 159). As the tank is equipped with the continuous EA monitoring system, the prognosis may be more accurate and updated. The zero signal from the monitoring system assures, with adequate certainty, that there are no cracks and corrosion in progress and RUL, consequently, would be further extended. If, instead, a positive signal is detected by AE monitoring, automatically RUL would be reduced.

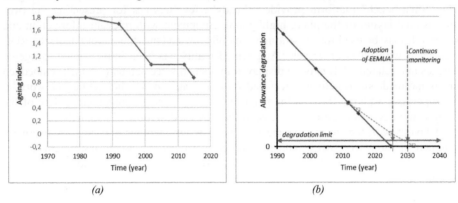

Figure 2 (a) Ageing Index calculated by the Ageing FishBone model; (b) Residual Useful Lifetime

7. Conclusions

The software architecture discussed in the paper is suitable to exploit the mass of measurement data coming continuously from the integrity sensors distributed in the plant in order to have trustable and updated evaluation of the equipment RUL, adequate to make reasonable decisions on the safe extension of equipment lifetime as well as on inspection scheduling and stop planning. A clear limit of the application is the naivety of the prognostic module. It will be replaced, in the continuation of the research by algorithms much more sophisticated, keeping anyway the other modules. Even the home made smart helmet will be replaced by commercial smart glasses, as soon as they will become reliable and cheap enough.

Acknowledgement

Funded by INAIL in the framework of the call BRIC/2018/ID=11 *(project MAC4PRO)*

References

API, 2014 Integrity Operating Windows RP 584,Washington, US

API, 2019 Risk-based Inspection Methodology RP 581,Washington, US

API, 2016 Risk-based Inspection RP 580, Washington, US

Bhatia, K., Khan, F. Patel, H., Abbassi, R., 2019. Dynamic risk-based inspection methodology. Journal of Loss Prevention in the Process Industries, 62, 1-12.

Bragatto, P., Ansaldi, S.M., Mennuti, C., 2018, Improving safety of process plants, through smart systems for critical equipment monitoring Chemical Engineering Transactions, 67, 49-54.

Milazzo, M.F, Bragatto, P., 2019. A framework addressing a safe ageing management in complex industrial sites: The Italian experience in «Seveso» establishments. Journal of Loss Prevention in the Process Industries, 58, 70-81.

Milazzo, M.F., Scionti, G., Bragatto, P., 2019. Estimation of the Equipment Residual Lifetime in Major Hazard Industries by Using a Virtual Sensor. Proceeding of 29th ESREL, 1764-1771.

Wood, M.H., Arellano, A.V., Van Wijk, L., 2013 Corrosion Related Accidents in Petroleum Refineries. European Commission Joint Research Centre Report EUR 26331 EN

Sauro Pierucci, Flavio Manenti, Giulia Bozzano, Davide Manca (Eds.)
Proceedings of the 30th European Symposium on Computer Aided Process Engineering
(ESCAPE30), May 24-27, 2020, Milano, Italy. © 2020 Elsevier B.V. All rights reserved.
http://dx.doi.org/10.1016/B978-0-12-823377-1.50294-9

A Computational Workflow to Study Particle Transport in Porous Media: Coupling CFD and Deep Learning

Agnese Marcato, Gianluca Boccardo, Daniele L. Marchisio

Department of Applied Science and Technology - Politecnico di Torino, Corso Duca degli Abruzzi 24, 10129 Torino, Italy

gianluca.boccardo@polito.it

Abstract

In this work, we studied the coupling of CFD simulation with machine learning models, by using a large set of computational result as the training dataset of a simple fully-connected neural network. The focus of the CFD investigation is the flow and colloid transport in porous media models, both simple and complex, with the end result of obtaining a computationally inexpensive data-driven surrogate model able to replace the CFD simulation, while keeping the same accuracy. While considerable success was obtained in the case of simpler geometries, more sophisticated deep learning models are needed to treat cases characterized by non-trivial fluid dynamic structures.

Keywords: CFD, porous media, machine learning, packed bed reactors, filtration, deep learning

1. Introduction

The study of particle transport in porous media is of the utmost importance as it touches a wide variety of different fields: from the study of contaminant transport in aquifers to the design of effective packed bed reactors in chemical engineering. One very difficult problem in this context is the distinction between Fickian and anomalous transport, with important implications: be it on the estimation of the travel length of a toxic contaminant plume in an aquifer, or in the estimation of the residence time in a packed bed reactor. One of the difficulties lies in the many parameters characterizing the porous media (which are generally geometric), and whose impact and synergy of action can be impossible to analytically predict.

These particularities, which render the problem of particle transport in random media difficult to treat, at the same time make it a prime candidate for machine learning (ML) and specifically deep-learning (DL) approaches, which are particularly suited to extract essential features hidden in data. ML and DL have been notably extensively used in computer science, and some examples of applications of these techniques are making their way in from chemical engineering, from molecular classification (Chang et al. 2019) to pharmaceutical processes (Rolandi, 2019). In this work we couple our recent CFD work laying the groundwork of computational analysis for parameter identification of anomalous transport in porous media, explored by Crevacore et al. (2016), with a variety of different classes of deep neural networks (DNNs).

2. Methods and numerical details

As explored in the Introduction, the objective of this work is to investigate the problem of fluid flow and particle transport (and filtration) in porous media from a first-principle perspective in order to gain a deep insight on the fluid dynamic and transport structure in different models of porous media. The results of these simulations (each characterized by its distinctive features) are then fed to a simple, fully-connected, neural network in order to build a fast surrogate model of the fully-resolved CFD simulation.

2.1. Computational Fluid Dynamics simulations

The first step in this framework is to build the computational models. We explored several different geometrical models of porous media, increasing in complexity, starting from a simple channel with two identical spherical obstacles, to random arrangements of mono-disperse and finally polydisperse spherical objects (these can be seen in Figure 1). Then, two sets of CFD simulations are performed, using the open-source code OpenFOAM. First, the fluid flow is explored by solving the Navier-Stokes equation in the limit of very small Reynolds numbers: from each simulation conducted, the porous model permeability was extracted by way of the well-known Darcy's law. Then, considering the (steady-state) flow field, the transport of dilute colloid particles (characterized by a certain molecular diffusivity) is studied by solving the advection-diffusion equation. In order to study the filtration of this colloid by the solid grains of the porous media (on which the colloid may deposit), a sink boundary condition for the transported scalar is set on the solid surface, and a filtration efficiency extracted following our work by Boccardo et al. (2014).

2.2. Neural network and construction of the surrogate data-driven model

For each of these geometries, a large number (from 1000 to 7000) of CFD simulations are run, each differing randomly in their geometrical or physical conditions: width of the channel, porosity, spheres polydispersity, Reynolds number, and colloid diffusivity. The aggregate set of numerical input features coupled with simulation results are then fed to a fully-connected feedforward neural network, built with MATLAB, initially constituted by one hidden layer with ten neurons, which later evolved to different architectures, as specified in Table 1 in the Results section.

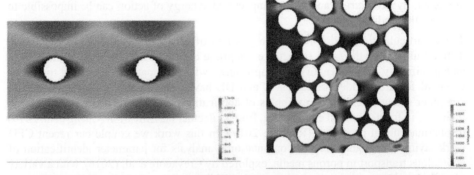

Figure 1. Geometrical model of a channel with two spherical obstacles (left), and of polydisperse periodic randomly arranged spheres (right). Shades of grey representing the fluid velocity contour plot.

3. Results and accuracy of the data-driven surrogate model

As it has been mentioned, the CFD results were analysed and post-processed with the purpose of obtaining, for each geometry considered, a set connecting the input features of the simulation with the result(s) obtained. The numerosity of this set is equal to the number of simulations performed to build the training set for the neural network (which, as mentioned, is numbering in the thousands).

In practical terms, this means that in the case of the polydisperse randomly placed media, each of the 1000 simulations performed was expressed (and fed to the network) as an array of chosen *input features*, namely mean sphere diameter, polydispersity index and porosity for the fluid flow simulations, to which pressure drop and colloid diffusivity are added in the case of colloid transport simulations. To these *input features* the corresponding *output values*, in the form of the Darcyan permeability and filtration efficiency, are then linked.

The full numerical details of computational results and the ranges of operating conditions explored can be found in the recent work from Marcato (2019).

After the neural network *training process*, the end result is a surrogate black-box model capable of predicting the output values when given a new set of input features, with varying accuracy depending on the geometric model considered and on the distance of the new input feature from the original set of features used in the training process. This accuracy is tested by choosing a set of input parameters, performing CFD simulations and obtaining their results, which are then compared to the predictions of the neural network for that same set of input parameters.

In the case of the channel with obstacles, the network performance was tested both on predictions of Darcyan permeability and of deposition efficiency: its performance is very good, as it can be seen from the parity diagram presented in Figure 2, corresponding to prediction errors lower than 1% (in both cases); for brevity, the figure only shows deposition efficiency results, with an identical diagram in the case of permeability. Given these very good performance, we extended the range of operation of the neural network by testing its prediction accuracy outside of its training range, i.e., the range of operating conditions of the CFD simulations used in the network training.

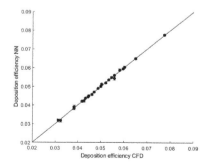 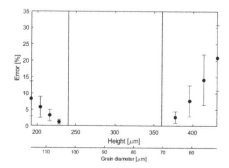

Figure 2. Channel with obstacles results: parity diagram between CFD results and surrogate model predictions (left) and prediction error for input features outside of the training range.

In the case of permeability prediction, the height of the channel and obstacles diameter were both varied, first in the same direction (increasing or decreasing both at the same time) and then one opposite to the other (increasing channel height while decreasing grain diameter), as Figure 2 shows. While the errors are still below 1% inside of the training range, they increase moderately the further the parameters move from the training range limits, reaching values between 10% and 20% for the cases considered; in the case of deposition efficiency prediction they reach larger values at the outer limits (between 20% and 60%). This exercise, which has a parallel in the practice of carefully extrapolating data trends outside of a range of experimental values, was done to better inform the trade-off between the cost of re-training a new network with a wider range of data (and thus, new CFD simulations to further populate the set), and the error of using an already trained network outside of its training range. In order to give an order of magnitude of these different simulation and training times, it is useful to note that (in our simple test cases) while the computational cost of a CFD simulation is of a few minutes, the equivalent network prediction is done in under one second, while the training of the full network takes under one minute.

Another thing to note is that, since the training of a neural network is not a deterministic process, different training runs result in slightly different parameterizations of the surrogate model, leading to a variation in the error prediction. This is expressed graphically in Figure 2 (and slightly less visibly in Figure 3) by means of error bars on the prediction errors, which were obtained by performing ten different network training runs on the same training set and calculating the average and the standard deviation of the ten resulting errors.

Then, a similar analysis was conducted for the case of the random media, whose results are shown in the parity diagram in Figure 3 (for the polydisperse case). As it can be seen, the prediction error is now noticeable, and is slightly higher in the case of the polydisperse media, most likely due to the additional input feature with respect to the monodisperse case (i.e.: the spheres polydispersity). In order to try to decrease this error (of the order of 29% and 17% for permeability and deposition efficiency respectively), two actions were taken.

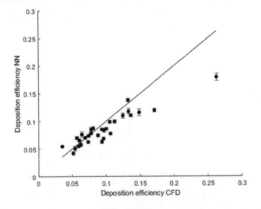

Figure 3. Polydisperse random spheres results: parity diagram between CFD results and surrogate model predictions.

First, the size of the training set (i.e. number of CFD simulations) was increased gradually from 1000 to 7000, in order to present a more feature-rich dataset to the training network.

As it is shown in Figure 4, the errors in both output values decrease appreciably but not in a significant way, with errors still higher than 20% and 10% respectively. Then, a few tentative steps in adjusting the network architecture were taken, specifically by changing the number of the hidden layers and the number of neurons in each one. The tested architectures are detailed in Table 1 along with the corresponding prediction errors for each of the networks: even with this technique some error reduction can be obtained (while noting that very deep networks, i.e. with more than 50 neurons per layer, suffer from higher overfitting errors), but it is clearly not possible to reach a confidence level equivalent to the data-driven surrogate model built on the simpler case, leading to the necessity of exploring more sophisticated techniques.

Table 1: surrogate model errors, in the case of the polydisperse porous media, for different neural network architectures. The number of components in each vector is the number of hidden layers, and their value the number of neurons; e.g. [5 5] means two layers constituted by five neurons each.

Architecture	Error on permeability prediction [%]	Error on deposition efficiency prediction [%]
[5]	24.9	15.9
[10]	28.8	17.1
[5 5]	28.3	15.3
[20]	26.8	16.2
[10 10]	27.2	16.4
[15 10 5]	31.4	17.4
[50]	28.9	18.4
[100]	34.5	21.1
[50 50]	35.6	23.1

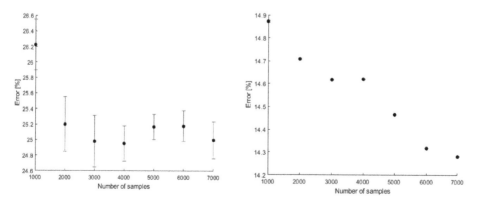

Figure 4. Trends of average prediction error on polydisperse random media by increasing number of training samples (permeability on the left and deposition efficiency on the right).

Conclusions and current work

In this work we have studied the coupling of CFD with machine learning models on different porous media models. In the first case, representing fluid moving in a channel past spherical objects, the performance of the data-driven model is very good, with errors below 1% between the surrogate model and CFD results: the network can also be used for extrapolation in ranges of operating conditions slightly outside the training range. On the other side, when considering more complex porous media, the surrogate model returns accuracies lower than 10% or 20% even by adjusting the network architecture.

The time required for the resolution of the advection diffusion equation (CFD simulation) is approximately 20 minutes, instead the training process of the neural network lasts less than 2 minutes and the response of the data-driven model to a new input is instantaneous. This simple data-driven models can then be reliably used in place of expensive CFD simulations (or in general, all "first principles" methods), as one single call of the neural network has a computational cost which is orders of magnitude lower than the full CFD simulation: in our test problems, under a second versus several minutes – with a total neural network training time of around one minute. This makes them attractive for all cases in which a quick (i.e. *real-time*) computation of the process impact of a change in operating conditions is desired or needed: examples are in-line industrial process control, or that of coupled multi-scale simulations, where lower-scale expensive models should be run many times in a single larger scale model (e.g.: a single process-scale CFD simulation instantiating several runs of a coupled mesoscopic simulation).

Instead, one promising avenue of research for more complex cases, which are now showing in lower accuracy, lies in turning to a "parameter-agnostic" approach, where instead of trying to calculate a set of relevant input parameters, the full geometry and CFD vector/scalar fields are used as training data. This is the approach taken with convolutive neural networks, which enjoyed particular success in the field of image recognition/classification/segmentation, and is the focus of our current research.

References

Chang, J.J., Kang, J.L., Wong, D.S.H., Chou, C.H., Hsu, H.H., Huang, C.H. and Lin, S.T., 2019. Machine Learning of Molecular Classification and Quantum Mechanical Calculations. In *Computer Aided Chemical Engineering* (Vol. 46, pp. 787-792).

Rolandi, P.A., 2019. The Unreasonable Effectiveness of Equations: Advanced Modeling For Biopharmaceutical Process Development. In *Computer Aided Chemical Engineering* (Vol. 47, pp. 137-150).

Crevacore, E., Tosco, T., Sethi, R., Boccardo, G. and Marchisio, D.L., 2016. Recirculation zones induce non-Fickian transport in three-dimensional periodic porous media. *Physical Review E, 94*(5), pp. 053118.

Boccardo, Gianluca, Daniele L. Marchisio, and Rajandrea Sethi, 2014. "Microscale simulation of particle deposition in porous media." *Journal of colloid and interface science* 417 – pp. 227-237.

Marcato, A., 2019, "Coupling CFD and Machine Learning: two case studies in process engineering" [Original title: "Accoppiamento di CFD e Machine Learning: due casi nell'ingegneria di processo"], *M.Sc. Thesis, Politecnico di Torino, Italy.*

Sauro Pierucci, Flavio Manenti, Giulia Bozzano, Davide Manca (Eds.)
Proceedings of the 30th European Symposium on Computer Aided Process Engineering
(ESCAPE30), May 24-27, 2020, Milano, Italy. © 2020 Elsevier B.V. All rights reserved.
http://dx.doi.org/10.1016/B978-0-12-823377-1.50295-0

Hybrid Mechanistic Data-Driven Modeling for the Deterministic Global Optimization of a Transcritical Organic Rankine Cycle

Wolfgang R. Huster[a] , Artur M. Schweidtmann[a] and Alexander Mitsos[b,a,c*]

[a]*Process Systems Engineering (AVT.SVT), RWTH Aachen University, 52074 Aachen, Germany*
[b]*JARA - ENERGY, 52056 Aachen, Germany*
[c]*Institute of Energy and Climate Research: Energy Systems Engineering (IEK-10), Forschungszentrum Jülich GmbH, Wilhelm-Johnen-Straße, 52425 Jülich, Germany*
amitsos@alum.mit.edu

Abstract

Global optimization is desirable for the design of chemical and energy processes as design decisions have a significant influence on the economics. A relevant challenge for global flowsheet optimization is the incorporation of accurate thermodynamic models. A promising alternative to conventional thermodynamic property models is the integration of data-driven surrogate models into mechanistic process models and deterministic global optimization in a reduced space. In our previous works, we trained artificial neural networks (ANNs) on thermodynamic data and included the surrogate models in the global flowsheet optimization of subcritical organic Rankine cycles (ORC). In this work, we extend the framework to the optimization of transcritical ORCs operating at a supercritical high pressure level and subcritical low pressure level. We train separate ANNs for supercritical and subcritical thermodynamic properties. ANNs with a small number of neurons can learn the thermodynamic properties to sufficient accuracy. We identify the optimal working fluid among 122 available fluids in the thermodynamic library CoolProp via a deterministic global optimization of the hybrid process model using the solver MAiNGO. The results show that the process can be optimized efficiently and that transcritical operation can enable high power generation.

Keywords: Surrogate model, Artificial neural networks, MAiNGO, Geothermal power, Supercritical properties

1. Introduction

Numerical optimization of the design and operation of energy processes using renewable energy resources is a key element for the transition to a carbon neutral economy. Making use of low-temperature power resources, such as geothermal brine, will become a relevant part of future power generation. However, the most relevant processes for this energy transformation, organic Rankine cycles (ORCs), often suffer from low thermal efficiencies. This is, among other effects, caused by the isothermal evaporation of the working fluid (WF), which results in high exergy destruction. One way to circumvent is the evaporation at supercritical pressure, i.e., at a pressure level higher than the critical pressure of the working fluid p_c. Fluids at supercritical pressure levels exhibit different thermodynamic properties than at subcritical pressure.
Supercritical pressure levels in ORCs have been investigated in many studies (Chen et al., 2006; Schuster et al., 2010; Gao et al., 2012). Most authors perform a variation of

process parameters to improve the performance (Shengjun et al., 2011; Yağlı et al., 2016; Xu et al., 2016) or apply a local optimization solver (Le et al., 2014; Maraver et al., 2014). Although rare, experimental investigations validated the potential advantages of operating ORCs at supercritical pressure (Kosmadakis et al., 2016). A review on transcritical ORC studies, experimental data, and existing plants is given by Lecompte et al. (2019).

In our previous works (Schweidtmann et al., 2018; Huster et al., 2019a,b), we investigated the deterministic global optimization of ORCs employing pure fluids at subcritical pressure levels. Solving the optimization problem in a reduced-space using our in-house solver MAiNGO (Bongartz et al., 2018), we were able to illustrate the benefit of using surrogate models for the calculation of accurate thermodynamic properties. For this, we train artificial neural networks (ANNs) on subcritical thermodynamic data, which allow for an explicit model formulation. Together with tighter relaxations compared to the original thermodynamic equations, this drastically reduces CPU times (Schweidtmann and Mitsos, 2019; Schweidtmann et al., 2018).

Surrogate models and ANNs have been discussed in engineering literature for decades (Wang, 2006; Himmelblau, 2000). Furthermore, ANNs have been employed for the prediction of supercritical fluid properties by several authors (Mehdizadeh and Movagharnejad, 2011; Eslamimanesh et al., 2011). Arslan and Yetik (2011) and Rashidi et al. (2011) used ANNs to learn ORC process models in a black-box approach and optimized these. The novelty of this work compared to earlier works is that ANNs have not been used for learning supercritical fluid properties and subsequently used in a hybrid model that is to be optimized to guaranteed global optimality. In this work, we apply ANNs for the prediction of supercritical fluid properties within an ORC process optimization. Further, we select the most promising fluid candidates among a wide range of fluids available in the thermodynamic library CoolProp (Bell et al., 2014).

2. ORC process model

We adopt the geothermal set up presented in (Huster et al., 2019a) and adjust the model to transcritical operation. Figure 1 shows the ORC flowsheet, indicating the super- and subcritical pressure levels. The models of the pump, expander and condenser are identical to (Huster et al., 2019a). We model the evaporator as a single process unit due to the continuous phase change and assume a constant heat transfer coefficient. The supercritical phase change requires constraining the minimum temperature difference along the heat transfer, similar to the use of WF mixtures (Huster et al., 2020). For this, the evaporator is discretized along its length. In each discretization cell, we introduce an inequality on the minimum temperature difference to avoid unphysical temperature crossover. When choosing ten cells or less in the process optimization, temperature crossovers occurred at the optimal solution point, resulting in a relaxed solution. To ensure sufficient temperature difference for all WF candidates, we choose 50 cells in all further optimizations. We found that the influence of cell number on the CPU time of the process optimization is almost linear between 10 and 100 cells, ranging from 95 to 632 s. This is summed over six cores that are used for the parallelized branch-and-bound algorithm. Further, we ensure that the expansion process does not cross the two-phase region by setting a lower bound for the specific entropy at the outlet of the evaporator, as illustrated in Figure 2. For the lower bound of the high pressure level p_{HP}, we select $1.1 \cdot p_c$. This avoids pressure levels close to or below the critical point, which requires different models to account for the two-phase region.

Hybrid Mechanistic Data-Driven Modeling for the Deterministic Global Optimization of a Transcritical Organic Rankine Cycle

1767

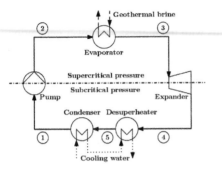

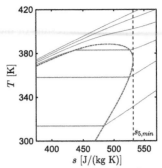

Figure 1: Flowsheet of the transcritical ORC. The circled numbers indicate fluid states. Above the dashed line, the process operates at supercritical pressure, below at subcritical pressure.

Figure 2: Lower bound for the minimum specific entropy of RC-318 (purple dashed line) for the superheated state at the expander inlet. Orange lines indicate isobars, the blue dash-dotted line indicates the two-phase region.

3. Method

CoolProp (Bell et al., 2014) provides accurate thermodynamic equations of state for 122 fluids. Many of these fluids are not suitable for the presented case study due to their thermodynamic properties. Thus, we only consider WF candidates that can be evaporated at supercritical pressure and condensed at the present conditions. We apply the following rigorous feasibility preselection criteria to all 122 fluids in CoolProp: critical temperature $T_c < 400$ K, saturation temperature at a pressure of 10 bar $T|^{sat}_{10\ bar} > 260$ K. For the preselected fluids, we perform an automated data generation using CoolProp, which we extend to transcritical properties. The procedure for subcritical properties is described in more detail in (Huster et al., 2019b). For supercritical properties, we generate 10^5 data points. We perform the ANN training in Matlab R2018b using the Bayesian backpropagation algorithm, 700 training epochs, and randomly split the data into 40% training data, 30% validation data, and 30% test data. In the training procedure, we minimize the mean-squared error (MSE) on the training data. We optimize the resulting hybrid model using our open-source deterministic global optimization solver MAiNGO (Bongartz et al., 2018).

4. Results

4.1. Artificial neural network accuracy

Table 1 shows that ANNs can learn temperature T as a function of pressure p and mass-specific enthalpy h in the supercritical region with high accuracy. Based on these results and desirable accuracy (Huster et al., 2019a), we select six neurons for both hidden layers for supercritical properties. For subcritical properties, we also select two hidden layers with six neurons each (Huster et al., 2019a,b).

Table 1: Mean-squared errors of the ANNs on the training data for the supercritical region, in dependence of the number of neurons in both hidden layers (input variables: p, h; output variable: T; fluid: RC318).

Number of neurons	5	6	7	8	9	10
MSE [K²]	$5.3 \cdot 10^{-8}$	$6.0 \cdot 10^{-9}$	$6.1 \cdot 10^{-9}$	$1.1 \cdot 10^{-10}$	$4.7 \cdot 10^{-10}$	$1.4 \cdot 10^{-10}$

4.2. Process optimization results

The process optimization results of the five fluids with the highest net power generation P_{net} (Table 2) show that transcritical operation allows for much higher net power generation than using isobutane at subcritical conditions ($P_{net,max}$ = 16.5 MW, (Huster et al., 2019a)). However, no general claim can be made as we have not performed the WF selection procedure for subcritical operation for this case study. We give p^* as the ratio of high pressure level and critical pressure ($p^* = p_{HP}/p_c$), and the thermal efficiency η_{th}. Aside from high power generation in the turbine P_{turb}, high values of p_{HP} also strongly increase power consumption in the pump P_{pump} and investment costs Inv respectively levelized cost of electricity $LCOE$. The CPU times are between $2\cdot10^2$ and $2\cdot10^4$ s. Using six CPU cores, this corresponds to less than one hour of wall time. Five of the 21 preselected fluid candidates are infeasible.

Table 2: Results of the thermodynamic optimization for the five WF candidates with the highest P_{net}, sorted by decreasing P_{net}.

Fluid	$\dot{m}_{WF}$ [kg/s]	p_{HP} [bar]	p_{LP} [bar]	P_{net} [MW]	P_{pump} [MW]	η_{th} [%]	Inv [m US-$]	$LCOE$ [US-$/MWh]	p^* [-]
R507A	17.2	65.2	15.8	25.5	10.3	9.1	51.4	57.3	1.8
R125	20.7	71.8	16.9	25.5	12.2	8.8	53.3	59.5	2.0
R143a	14.5	62.2	15.5	25.4	9.3	9.3	50.1	56.3	1.7
R404A	16.7	64.1	15.5	25.4	9.9	9.1	50.9	57.1	1.7
R227EA	20.9	31.9	5.8	25.3	5.0	9.2	46.0	52.1	1.1

The thermoeconomic optimization, i.e., minimization of $LCOE$, takes the investment cost of the process units into account. The results reflect the increased cost of operating at high pressure levels (Table 3). For four of the five given WF candidates, operating the ORC at $p^* = 1.1$ is economically favorable. As this is the lower bound for p_{HP} of each respective WF, the results suggest that subcritical operation could be the most economic option. The CPU times for the thermoeconomic optimizations are between $3\cdot10^2$ and $4\cdot10^4$ s, summed over all cores. Although the CPU times are higher compared to the thermodynamic optimization, they are still viable for process design.

Table 3: Results of the thermoeconomic optimization for the five WF candidates with the lowest $LCOE$, sorted by increasing $LCOE$.

Fluid	$\dot{m}_{WF}$ [kg/s]	p_{HP} [bar]	p_{LP} [bar]	P_{net} [MW]	P_{pump} [MW]	η_{th} [%]	Inv [m US-$]	$LCOE$ [US-$/MWh]	p^* [-]
R227EA	19.9	31.9	6.2	24.6	4.7	9.4	44.2	51.5	1.1
R1234yf	14.1	36.8	9.0	23.4	4.6	9.5	43.0	52.6	1.1
Propylene	5.7	49.6	14.8	22.5	5.0	10.1	42.8	54.4	1.1
R143a	13.5	55.6	16.1	25.0	7.4	9.3	47.8	54.8	1.5
n-Propane	5.4	46.3	12.3	21.7	4.8	10.3	41.6	54.8	1.1

The T-Q-plots for the best-performing WFs of the thermodynamic and thermoeconomic optimization are given in Figure 3. For $P_{net,max}$, the temperature curve is almost parallel along the evaporator, which comes close to minimum exergy destruction. This is not the case for $LCOE_{min}$, and higher temperature differences between heat source and WF occur. Like this, the HX investment cost is reduced due to the decreased area and a smaller pressure factor.

*Hybrid Mechanistic Data-Driven Modeling for the Deterministic Global
Optimization of a Transcritical Organic Rankine Cycle*

1769

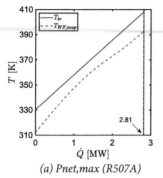

(a) Pnet,max (R507A)

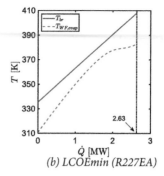

(b) LCOEmin (R227EA)

*Figure 3: T-Q-plots for the WFs with the highest net power (R507A) and lowest LCOE (R227EA),
illustrating the temperatures of the geothermal brine Tbr and WF in the evaporation TWF,evap.*

5. Conclusion and outlook

We propose an approach for globally optimal WF selection and process design for transcritical ORCs. For this, we train ANNs on accurate supercritical thermodynamic data and subsequently integrate them into a mechanistic process model. We solve the resulting hybrid model using the deterministic global solver MAiNGO. We identify the optimal WF among 122 fluids that are available in CoolProp.

We show that ANNs with a small number of neurons (two hidden layers with six neurons each) can learn supercritical data with high accuracy, which is comparable to subcritical data. The thermodynamic optimization reveals the potential of operating ORC at supercritical pressure levels. The nonisothermal evaporation allows to adjust the slope of the evaporation curve towards the heat source, approaching minimal exergy destruction in the evaporation. In contrast, the thermoeconomic optimization can lower investment costs significantly for similar net power generation. All optimizations can be solved to global optimality within less than two hours of wall time using six CPU cores. This demonstrates the viability of the proposed approach.

Future work includes the optimization of more detailed models with heat transfer correlations embedded. It would further be relevant to take the influence of fluid stability at high pressure levels and environmental fluid properties into account.

Acknowledgments: The authors gratefully acknowledge the financial support of the Kopernikus project SynErgie by the Federal Ministry of Education and Research (BMBF) and the project supervision by the project management organization Projektträger Jülich (PtJ).

References

Arslan, O., Yetik, O., 2011. ANN based optimization of supercritical ORC-binary geothermal power plant: Simav case study. Applied Thermal Engineering 31 (17-18), 3922-3928.

Bell, I. H., Wronski, J., Quoilin, S., Lemort, V., 2014. Pure and pseudo-pure fluid thermophysical property evaluation and the open-source thermophysical property library CoolProp. Industrial & Engineering Chemistry Research 53 (6), 2498-2508.

Bongartz, D., Najman, J., Sass, S., Mitsos, A., 2018. MAiNGO - McCormick-based Algorithm for mixed-integer Nonlinear Global Optimization. Tech. rep., Process Systems Engineering (AVT.SVT), RWTH Aachen University.

Chen, Y., Lundqvist, P., Johansson, A., Platell, P., 2006. A comparative study of the carbon dioxide transcritical power cycle compared with an organic Rankine cycle with R123 as working fluid in waste heat recovery. Applied Thermal Engineering 26 (17-18), 2142-2147.

Eslamimanesh, A., Gharagheizi, F., Mohammadi, A. H., Richon, D., 2011. Artificial neural network modeling of solubility of supercritical carbon dioxide in 24 commonly used ionic liquids. Chemical Engineering Science 66 (13), 3039-3044.

Gao, H., Liu, C., He, C., Xu, X., Wu, S., Li, Y., 2012. Performance analysis and working fluid selection of a supercritical organic Rankine cycle for low grade waste heat recovery. Energies 5 (9), 3233-3247.

Himmelblau, D. M., 2000. Applications of artificial neural networks in chemical engineering. Korean journal of chemical engineering, *17*(4), 373-392.

Huster, W. R., Schweidtmann, A. M., Mitsos, A., 2019a. Impact of accurate working fluid properties on the globally optimal design of an organic Rankine cycle. Computer Aided Chemical Engineering 47, 427-432.

Huster, W. R., Schweidtmann, A. M., Mitsos, A., 2019b. Working fluid selection for organic Rankine cycles via deterministic global optimization of design and operation. Optimization and Engineering, in press.

Huster, W. R., Schweidtmann, A. M., Mitsos, A., 2020. Globally optimal working fluid mixture composition for geothermal power cycles, submitted September 6th, 2019.

Kosmadakis, G., Manolakos, D., Papadakis, G., 2016. Experimental investigation of a low-temperature organic Rankine cycle (ORC) engine under variable heat input operating at both subcritical and supercritical conditions. Applied Thermal Engineering 92, 1-7.

Le, V. L., Feidt, M., Kheiri, A., Pelloux-Prayer, S., 2014. Performance optimization of low-temperature power generation by supercritical ORCs (organic Rankine cycles) using low GWP (global warming potential) working fluids. Energy 67, 513-526.

Lecompte, S., Ntavou, E., Tchanche, B., Kosmadakis, G., Pillai, A., Manolakos, D., Paepe, M. D., 2019. Review of experimental research on supercritical and transcritical thermodynamic cycles designed for heat recovery application. Applied Sciences 9 (12), 2571.

Maraver, D., Royo, J., Lemort, V., Quoilin, S., 2014. Systematic optimization of subcritical and transcritical organic Rankine cycles (ORCs) constrained by technical parameters in multiple applications. Applied Energy 117, 11-29.

Mehdizadeh, B., Movagharnejad, K., 2011. A comparison between neural network method and semi empirical equations to predict the solubility of different compounds in supercritical carbon dioxide. Fluid Phase Equilibria 303 (1),40-44.

Rashidi, M. M., Bég, O. A., Parsa, A. B., Nazari, F., 2011. Analysis and optimization of a transcritical power cycle with regenerator using artificial neural networks and genetic algorithms. Proceedings of the Institution of Mechanical Engineers, Part A: Journal of Power and Energy 225 (6), 701-717.

Schuster, A., Karellas, S., Aumann, R., 2010. Efficiency optimization potential in supercritical organic Rankine cycles. Energy 35 (2), 1033-1039.

Schweidtmann, A. M., Huster, W. R., Lüthje, J. T., Mitsos, A., 2018. Deterministic global process optimization: Accurate (single-species) properties via artificial neural networks. Computers & Chemical Engineering 121, 67-74.

Schweidtmann, A. M., Mitsos, A., 2019. Deterministic global optimization with artificial neural networks embedded. Journal of Optimization Theory and Applications 180 (3), 925-948.

Shengjun, Z., Huaixin, W., Tao, G., 2011. Performance comparison and parametric optimization of subcritical organic Rankine cycle (ORC) and transcritical power cycle system for low-temperature geothermal power generation. Applied Energy 88 (8), 2740-2754.

Wang, G. G., Shan, S., 2006. Review of metamodeling techniques in support of engineering design optimization. Journal of Mechanical Design 129, 370-380.

Xu, H., Gao, N., Zhu, T., 2016. Investigation on the fluid selection and evaporation parametric optimization for sub- and supercritical organic Rankine cycle. Energy 96, 59-68.

Yağlı, H., Koç, Y., Koç, A., Görgülü, A., Tandiroğlu, A., 2016. Parametric optimization and exergetic analysis comparison of subcritical and supercritical organic Rankine cycle (ORC) for biogas fuelled combined heat and power (CHP) engine exhaust gas waste heat. Energy 111, 923-932.

Sauro Pierucci, Flavio Manenti, Giulia Bozzano, Davide Manca (Eds.)
Proceedings of the 30th European Symposium on Computer Aided Process Engineering
(ESCAPE30), May 24-27, 2020, Milano, Italy. © 2020 Elsevier B.V. All rights reserved.
http://dx.doi.org/10.1016/B978-0-12-823377-1.50296-2

A Discrete Multiple Shooting Formulation for Efficient Dynamic Optimization

Morgan T. Kelley[a], Ross Baldick[b], Michael Baldea[a],*

[a]*McKetta Department of Chemical Engineering, The University of Texas at Austin (200 E Dean Keeton St. C0400, Austin, TX 78712)*

[b]*Electrical and Computer Engineering, The University of Texas at Austin (2501 Speedway C0803, Austin, TX 78712)*
mbaldea@che.utexas.edu

Abstract

The growing need for fast and efficient solution techniques for solving dynamic optimization problems is driven by a broad spectrum of applications in scheduling and control. We propose a novel framework for dynamic optimization that utilizes a multiple shooting "backbone" with discrete rather than continuous subproblems, thereby eliminating need for repeated time-integration. A Lagrangian relaxation (LR)-based decomposition scheme then dualizes the state continuity requirements between subproblems and enables parallel solution of the problem.

Keywords: dynamic optimization, multiple shooting, batch process control.

1. Introduction

Economic trends such as fast-changing electricity markets require that process operations increasingly rely on real-time decision-making based on dynamic models, motivating research in methods and tools for fast solution of dynamic optimization problems.

Existing methods fall into two broad categories. *Direct methods* utilize nonlinear programming (NLP) solvers for optimization of systems of equations via stepwise integration (Hargraves & Paris, 1987). In *single shooting,* the model equations are integrated over the entire time horizon, and only the decision variables are discretized in time (Vassiliadis et al., 1994). These methods enable the use of efficient solvers for differential algebraic equations (DAEs), but require repeated solution and integration over the time horizon. Furthermore, they cannot deal with open-loop unstable systems and path constraints are difficult to enforce. Conversely, *simultaneous methods* generate large nonlinear programs by discretizing the entire problem space (both state and decision variables). The accuracy of simultaneous methods increases with added discretization points, as does computational cost. However, simultaneous approaches are appealing due to their ability to deal with open-loop unstable systems. *Multiple shooting (MS)* can be regarded as a hybrid between single shooting and sequential methods, wherein the time horizon is divided into smaller intervals where the control vector is represented by simple functions; the solution of the differential constraints is sought for each interval and equality constraints enforce state continuity between time blocks (Bock et al. 1984). In this paper, we propose a new approach for dynamic optimization. Specifically, we further expand the symbiosis of MS and simultaneous methods by exploiting the parallelization capabilities offered by MS while considering a full discretization of the state variables in each block.

2. Problem Description

The (continuous-time) general dynamic optimization problem to be solved (**PI**) and its discretized version (**PII**) are given below:

$$\max_{u} J = f(x, y, u, t_f) \qquad\qquad \max_{u_i} J = f\left(x_{N_i,N_j}, y_{N_i,N_j}, u_{N_i}\right) \tag{1a}$$

$$\text{s.t. } \frac{dx}{dt} = g(x, y, u) \qquad\qquad \text{s.t. } x_{i,j+1} = g\left(x_{i,j+1}, y_{i,j+1}, u_i\right)\Delta j + x_{i,j} \tag{1b}$$

$$y(t) = h(u) \qquad\qquad\qquad y_{i,j} = h(u_{i,j}) \tag{1c}$$

$$x(t_o) = x_o \qquad\qquad\qquad x(t_o) = x_o \tag{1d}$$

$$x^L \leq x \leq x^U \qquad\qquad\qquad x^L \leq x_{i,j} \leq x^U \tag{1e}$$

$$y^L \leq y \leq y^U \qquad\qquad\qquad y^L \leq y_{i,j} \leq y^U \tag{1f}$$

$$u^L \leq u \leq u^U \qquad\qquad\qquad u^L \leq u_{i,j} \leq u^U \tag{1g}$$

$$\qquad\qquad\qquad\qquad\qquad\qquad x_{i-1,N_j} = x_{i,1} \;\forall\, i > 1 \tag{1h}$$

x represents the differential variables with initial conditions x_o, y are algebraic variables, and u the control/input variables. The objective, J, is a function of these variables evaluated at the final time point, t_f. In our new approach, problem (1) is discretized using two time grids: one for the controls/inputs (set i of length N_i), and another to represent state variable dynamics (set j of length N_j), where $N_i N_j = t_f$. We impose continuity conditions Eq. (1h) and utilize the implicit (backward) Euler method for discretization, with time step length Δj. The structure of the resulting system is block-angular (Figure 1). **PII** can be solved directly using NLP solvers. We observe that the state continuity conditions are complicating constraints. Thus, the solution of the problem can be parallelized using a Lagrangian Relaxation (LR) strategy (Kelley et al., 2018a). In our recent work (Kelley et al., 2018b), we demonstrated that LR was able to significantly reduce the computation time of a dynamically-constrained scheduling problem with linear constraints. In this work, we extend our previous findings to nonlinear problems.

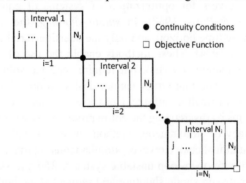

Figure 1: Block angular problem structure with an end-point objective, where control intervals are divided into dynamic time slots with state continuity conditions.

We propose a decomposition scheme based on Lagrangian relaxation (LR) (Fisher, 1981) that enables the solution of **PII** in parallel by decoupling the control intervals and creating N_i independent subproblems by dualizing the continuity conditions. We identify the continuity constraint violation with the variable γ_i:

$$\gamma_i = \left| x_{i-1,N_j} - x_{i,1} \right| \ \forall i > 1 \tag{3}$$

We represent the above absolute value calculation with Eq. (4), where ε is a sufficiently small number added to preserve the derivative continuity of **PII**.

$$\gamma_i = \sqrt{\left(x_{i-1,N_j} - x_{i,1} \right)^2 + \epsilon} \ \forall i > 1 \tag{4}$$

The constraint violations, γ_i, are then penalized in the objective function for **PII**, scaled by a fixed penalty variable, $\lambda_i > 0$:

$$L = J - \sum_i \lambda_i \gamma_i \tag{5}$$

The objective of the reformulated problem (**PIII**) becomes:

$$\max_{u_i} L = J - \sum_i \lambda_i \gamma_i \tag{6}$$

where all constraints besides the continuity constraints from **PII** are included Eq. (1b-g).

When $\gamma_i = 0$, **PII** and **PIII** are equivalent but are solved using different strategies which may result in different local solutions. If using fixed penalty multipliers (as in this work), the solution of **PIII** is relatively straightforward:

1. Initialize: Solve the process model in **PIII** Eq. (6, 1b-g) with bounds on continuity constraint violations, i.e. $\gamma_i \leq \theta$ with fixed control inputs, $\bar{u}_i$. The variable levels become initial guesses in the optimization step.

2. Optimize: Solve **PIII**, optimizing the controls/inputs to maximize objective L.

In the case of a linear program or a convex nonlinear program with equality constraints dualized, the optimality of **PIII** is guaranteed as long as **PII** is feasible and the continuity constraint violations are equal to zero (Guignard, 2003). However, for a nonconvex nonlinear problem, the equivalence of the optimal solution to **PII** and **PIII** cannot be proved. Nevertheless, the solution of **PIII** provides an upper bound on the optimal solution of **PII**, which in some cases is close to the optimal solution of **PII** (Fisher, 1981).

3. Case Study

The previously derived methods are applied to a batch reactor, whose model is an example supplied by Process Systems Enterprise with gPROMS Process Builder v1.3.1.

3.1. Process Description

Two exothermic reactions Eq. (7), with four total components, $\ell = \{A, B, C, D\}$, take place in the batch reactor over a time horizon of $t_f = 1000$ units, with desired product being C.

$$\begin{aligned} A + B &\to C \\ B + C &\to D \end{aligned} \tag{7}$$

The model equations for the batch reactor are given in Eq. (8), with the control input as the flow rate of the cooling water, F_{cw}. N_ℓ, C_ℓ, and h_ℓ are the number of moles, concentration, and enthalpy of each component, respectively. The volumetric holdup of the reactor is represented by V, the rate of reaction, r, is based on the temperature-dependent (T) rate constant, k, and C_A and C_B. Q_c is the rate of cooling, U is the cumulative amount of cooling water used in the process, and H is the total enthalpy of the process.

$$\frac{dN_\ell}{dt} = Vrv_\ell \qquad\qquad N_{\ell,i,j+1} = (V_{i,j+1}r_{i,j+1}v_\ell)\Delta j + N_{\ell,i,j} \tag{8a}$$

$$r = kC_A C_B \qquad\qquad r_{i,j} = k_{i,j}C_{A,i,j}C_{B,i,j} \tag{8b}$$

$$k = Le^{-\frac{E}{RT}} \qquad\qquad k_{i,j} = L * \exp\left(-\frac{E}{RT_{i,j}}\right) \tag{8c}$$

$$\frac{dH}{dt} = -Vr\Delta H - Q_{cR} \qquad\qquad H_{i,j+1} = (-V_{i,j+1}r_{i,j+1}\Delta H - Q_{cR_i})\Delta j + H_{i,j} \tag{8d}$$

$$Q_{cR} = MF_{cw} \qquad\qquad Q_{cR_i} = MF_{cw_i} \tag{8e}$$

$$\frac{dU}{dt} = F_{cw} \qquad\qquad U_{i,j+1} = (F_{cw_i})\Delta j + U_{i,j} \tag{8f}$$

$$H = \sum_\ell N_\ell h_\ell \qquad\qquad H_{i,j} = \sum_\ell N_{\ell,i,j}h_{\ell,i,j} \tag{8g}$$

$$h_\ell = a_\ell(T - \bar{T}) + \frac{b_\ell T^2 - \bar{T}^2}{2} \qquad\qquad h_{\ell,i,j} = a\_\ell(T_{i,j} - \bar{T}) + \frac{b_\ell(T_{i,j}^2 - \bar{T}^2)}{2} \tag{8h}$$

$$VC_\ell = N_\ell \qquad\qquad V_{i,j}C_{\ell,i,j} = N_{\ell,i,j} \tag{8i}$$

$$V = \sum_\ell \frac{N_\ell}{\rho_\ell} \qquad\qquad V_{i,j} = \sum_\ell \frac{N_{\ell,i,j}}{\rho_\ell} \tag{8j}$$

The discretized model has additional constraints in the form of state continuity conditions:

$$N_{\ell,i-1,N_j} = N_{\ell,i,1} \tag{9a}$$

$$H_{i-1,N_j} = H_{i,1} \tag{9b}$$

$$U_{i-1,N_j} = U_{i,1} \tag{9c}$$

Table 1: Model parameters for the batch reactor case study.

Parameter	Value
a	{150,175,200,175}
b	{0,0,0,0}
ρ	{10000,8000,11000,11000}
v	$-1,-1,1,1$
ΔH	-60000
E	19000
R	8.314
L	$7.5 * 10^{-4}$
$\bar{T}$	296
M	168000

Initial conditions are imposed on all differential state variables:

$$N(\ell,0) = N_{\ell,0} \qquad\qquad N_{\ell,1,1} = N_{\ell,o} \tag{10a}$$

$$H(0) = H_o \qquad\qquad H_{1,1} = H_o \tag{10b}$$

$$U(0) = U_o \qquad\qquad U_{1,1} = U_o \tag{10c}$$

The cooling water flowrate, F_{cw} is bounded according to:

$$0.1 \le F_{cw} \le 3 \qquad\qquad 0.1 \le F_{cw_i} \le 3 \tag{11}$$

and the reactor temperature, T, is bounded by a path Eq. (12) and an end-point Eq. (13) constraint.

$$T(t) \le 400 \qquad\qquad T_{i,j} \le 400 \tag{12}$$

$$310 \leq T(t_f) \leq 321 \qquad \Big| \quad 310 \leq T_{N_i, N_j} \leq 321 \tag{13}$$

The sequential optimization problem (referred to as **P1**) utilizes Eq. (8), (10)-(13), and the simultaneous optimization problem (referred to as **P2**) uses Eq. (8)-(13). The objectives, which seek to maximize the moles of the desired product, N_C while reducing the cumulative moles of cooling water used, U are given in Eq. (14).

P1	**P2**	
$\max\limits_{F_{cw_i}} J = 2N_{C,t_f} - U_{t_f}$	$\max\limits_{F_{cw_i}} J = 2N_{C,N_i,N_j} - U_{N_i,N_j}$	(14)

In order to apply LR to **P2**, continuity constraints Eq. (9) were removed and used to calculate the constraint violation, $\gamma_i = \{\gamma_N, \gamma_U, \gamma_H\}$, (following Eq. (4) with $\varepsilon = 10^{-8}$). Applying the LR scheme to Eq. (14) yields **P3**, which follows the format of **PIII** with Eq. (3), (8), and (10-13) and objective function:

$$\max\limits_{F_{cw_i}} L = J - \sum_i \left(\gamma_i^U \lambda_i^U + \gamma_i^H \lambda_i^H + \sum_\ell \gamma_{\ell,i}^N \lambda_{\ell,i} \right) \tag{15}$$

3.2. Results and Discussion

P1-P3 were solved on a 64 bit PC running Windows 10® with a 3.6 GHz Intel Core i7 processor with 32 GB of RAM and 8 threads available. **P1** was solved using gPROMS Process Builder v1.3.1 and **P2-P3** were solved using CONOPT3 version 3.17I in GAMS 25.0.3. In all cases, wall clock time is reported rather than CPU time since multiple threads were used to solve the decomposed problem, **P3**.

Figure 2 presents the solution times for **P2** and **P3** for N_j varied from 150 to 500 and $N_i = 4$ control intervals. The solution times of **P2** and **P3** are nearly equal for small subproblem sizes, demonstrating that the LR-based decomposition strategy in **P3** does not lead to added overhead solution time in the generation of independent subproblems. Furthermore, the solution time plot of **P3** stays relatively flat until the number of subproblem discretization points reaches 500. Conversely, solution time for **P2** increases almost exponentially with the number of discretization points used in each control interval. Figure 2 also demonstrates that the LR decomposition-based problem, **P3**, reaches nearly the same optimal solution as the non-decomposed problem, **P2**.

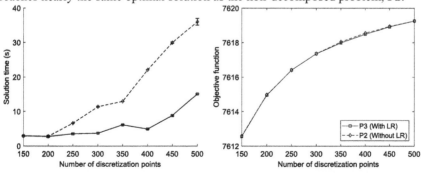

Figure 2: Solution time and optimal objective value versus problem size for **P2** and **P3**.

The optimization problems **P1-P3** were also solved considering different control intervals, $N_i = [2,10]$ with the total number of time points kept constant ($N_i N_j = 1000$). Figure 3 demonstrates that the solution of the sequential optimization problem (**P1**) is consistently slower than simultaneous methods, **P2** and **P3**. The simultaneous method using LR (**P3**) consistently solves fastest up until 10 intervals are used. This is expected with a constant number of time points, given that the size of the subproblems decreases as the number of intervals, N_i, grows, thereby increasing the number of penalty terms in the objective and the number of γ_i variables to calculate for each state variable. The sequential problem **P1** achieves a higher objective function value than the two simultaneous problems (**P2** and **P3**). This can possibly be attributed to the variable time step utilized by the single-shooting solver for **P1**, whereas the discretization of the time variable in **P2** and **P3** is based on a constant time step. However, the original problem (**P2**) and the relaxed problem (**P3**) achieve nearly the same result, demonstrating that it is possible to significantly reduce the computation time required to get the same solution by employing a LR-based decomposition strategy.

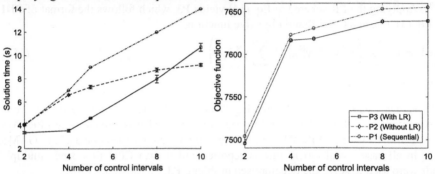

Figure 3: Solution time and optimal objective function value versus problem structure for **P1-P3**.

4. Conclusions and future work

We have supplied a general framework for dynamic optimization of nonlinear problems utilizing the structure of multiple shooting, but replacing the continuous subproblems with discrete subproblems, negating the need for repeated time-integration. We have applied an LR-based decomposition scheme which enables parallel solution of the problem, resulting in a solution time that remains low despite increasing problem size and is relatively resilient to increases in problem complexity (i.e. the addition of control intervals)

References

H.G. Bock, & K.J. Plitt, 1984, A Multiple Shooting Algorithm for Direct Solution of Optimal Control Problems. IFAC Proceedings, Vol. 17, 1603–1608.

M.L. Fisher, 1981, The Lagrangian Relaxation Method for Solving Integer Programming Problems. Management Science, 27, 1–18.

M. Guignard, 2003. Lagrangean relaxation. Top, 11(2), 151–200.

C.R. Hargraves, & S.W. Paris, 1987, Direct trajectory optimization using nonlinear programming and collocation. Journal of Guidance, Control, and Dynamics, 10, 338–342.

M.T. Kelley, R.C. Pattison, R. Baldick, & M. Baldea, 2018a, An efficient MILP framework for integrating nonlinear process dynamics and control in optimal production scheduling calculations. Computers & Chemical Engineering, 110, 35–52.

M.T. Kelley, R.C. Pattison, R. Baldick, & M. Baldea, 2018b, An MILP framework for optimizing demand response operation of air separation units. Applied Energy, 222, 951–966.

V.S. Vassiliadis, R.W.H. Sargent, & C.C Pantelides, 1994, Solution of a Class of Multistage Dynamic Optimization Problems. 1. Problems with Path Constraints. Industrial and Engineering Chemistry Research, 33(9), 2123–2133.

Sauro Pierucci, Flavio Manenti, Giulia Bozzano, Davide Manca (Eds.)
Proceedings of the 30th European Symposium on Computer Aided Process Engineering
(ESCAPE30), May 24-27, 2020, Milano, Italy. © 2020 Elsevier B.V. All rights reserved.
http://dx.doi.org/10.1016/B978-0-12-823377-1.50297-4

Backoff-Based Model-Based Design of Experiments Under Model Mismatch

Panagiotis Petsagkourakis , Federico Galvanin[*]

Department of Chemical Engineering, University College London (UCL), Torrington Place,

WC1E 7JE London, United Kingdom

f.galvanin@ucl.ac.uk

Abstract

Kinetic modelling has become an indispensable tool in industry for a quantitative understanding of reaction systems. In the presence of parametric and structural mismatch, the constraints that maintain safe experiments, e.g. solubility of a chemical may well turn out to be violated when that optimally designed experiment is performed, leading in the best case to less informative data sets or worse to an unsafe experiment. In this work, a Gaussian process is utilised to quantify the uncertainty realisation of the physical system to calculate the explicit back-offs through Monte Carlo stochastic simulations. The method provides a theoretical guarantee for the robust satisfaction of the constraints. The proposed method can be used for the design of optimal experiments starting from limited preliminary knowledge of the parameter set, leading to a safe exploration of the parameter space. The performance of this method is demonstrated through an illustrative case study regarding the parameter identification of the transient behaviour a nucleophilic aromatic substitution (SNAr).

Keywords: Gaussian Process, Uncertainty Propagation, Safe Design.

1. Introduction

A wide range of reaction systems are too complex for allowing the identification of exact mathematical laws governing the phenomena. The identification of model structures is affected by limitations related to the observability of the natural phenomena or/and systematic errors affecting the system. A trustworthy kinetic model can potentially be used to predict the behaviour of the system outside of the experimental conditions used in the model validation and then be utilized for design, optimisation and control in process systems engineering applications. Model-based design of experiments (MBDoE) has been widely used for the purposes of improving parameter precision in highly nonlinear dynamic systems (Franceschini & Macchietto, 2008). Several methods have been proposed in the literature for maximizing the collection of information for a limited amount of resources available for conducting the experiments (Galvanin et al., 2009; Telen et al., 2018). However, the robust satisfaction of potential constraints on the system (for example restrictions on the solubility of chemicals or on the reaction temperature in exothermic transformations) can still be challenging, since the model realisation of the physical system is uncertain at the stage of the experimental design. Various methods have been proposed for the probabilistic satisfaction of constraints, in the presence of parametric uncertainty (Galvanin et al. 2010; Mesbah & Streif, 2015; Telen et al., 2018), however constraint satisfaction that are based on the uncertainty set of the parameters may cause very conservative designs. The structural mismatch may cause large confidence ellipsoids, that subsequently may over-constrain or falsely constrain the feasibility set of the design. To accommodate this issue, a nonparametric probabilistic model, specifically Gaussian Process (GP), is proposed in this paper to approximate the physical system and propagate the uncertainty to future time instances. GP has been proven to accurately approximate the probability density function of a system and propagate the uncertainties effectively (Deisenroth & Rasmussen, 2011). GP allows us to run Monte Carlo simulation to compute the tightened constraints that will result in a probabilistic satisfaction of the constraints under the uncertainty scenario. The performance of this method is demonstrated through an illustrative case study, in which the optimal experimental design approach is tested on a flow reactor system, where transient experiments are designed and executed (Hone et al., 2017).

2. Problem Statement

We assume that a process model is described by a set of differential and algebraic equations (DAEs) in the form

$$\dot{\mathbf{x}} = \mathbf{f}(\mathbf{x}, \mathbf{u}, \boldsymbol{\theta}, t)$$
$$\mathbf{y} = \mathbf{h}(\mathbf{x}, \mathbf{u}, \boldsymbol{\theta}, t), \tag{1}$$

where $\mathbf{x} \in \mathbb{R}^{n_x}$ is the time dependent vector of state variables, $\mathbf{u} \in \mathbb{R}^{n_u}$ is the vector of the manipulated variables, $\boldsymbol{\theta} \in \mathbb{R}^{n_\theta}$ is the set of unknown model parameters to be estimated within a continuous realizable set Θ which is unknown and to be identified in the present problem, $\mathbf{y} \in \mathbb{R}^{n_y}$ are the responses measured in the process, $t \in \mathbb{R}_+$ is the time and $\hat{}$ represents the variables that are predicted by the model. In this work, we assume that there is plant-model mismatch, where the physical system is represented by $\mathbf{f}_{\text{real}}$ and $\mathbf{h}_{\text{real}}$ in (1), and the process model by $\mathbf{f}$ and $\mathbf{h}$. Given this mismatch, this work focuses on the safe exploration of the design space with a probabilistic guarantee of constraint satisfaction $\mathbb{P}(g_i(\mathbf{x}, \mathbf{u}) \leq 0) \geq 1 - \alpha$, where g_i is i-th constraint and $1 - \alpha$ is the probability for the constraint satisfaction. The MBDoE optimisation problem can then be defined in terms of maximizing a metric of the Fisher information matrix (FIM), $\sum_{t=1}^{N} \mathbf{y}_\theta^T \boldsymbol{\Sigma}^{-1} \mathbf{y}_\theta + \mathbf{M}_0$, or the variance-covariance matrix FIM^{-1}, where $\mathbf{y}_\theta$ is the sensitivity of the measured responses, $\boldsymbol{\Sigma}$ is the variance-covariance matrix of the measurement error, $\mathbf{M}_0$ is the FIM of the previous experiments and N the total number of measured instances. The MBDoE problem can be formulated as

$$\mathbf{u}^* = arg \max_{\mathbf{u}} \psi \left(\sum_{t=1}^{N} \hat{\mathbf{y}}_\theta^T \boldsymbol{\Sigma}^{-1} \hat{\mathbf{y}}_\theta + \mathbf{M}_0 \right)$$

$$s.t.$$
$$\hat{\mathbf{x}}(t = 0) = \mathbf{x}(t = 0)$$
$$\dot{\hat{\mathbf{x}}} = \mathbf{f}(\hat{\mathbf{x}}, \mathbf{u}, \boldsymbol{\theta})$$
$$\hat{\mathbf{y}} = \mathbf{h}(\hat{\mathbf{x}}, \mathbf{u}, \boldsymbol{\theta})$$
$$\dot{\hat{\mathbf{x}}}_\theta = \frac{\partial \mathbf{f}}{\partial \mathbf{x}} \hat{\mathbf{x}}_\theta + \frac{\partial \mathbf{f}}{\partial \boldsymbol{\theta}}$$
$$\hat{\mathbf{y}}_\theta = \frac{\partial \mathbf{h}}{\partial \mathbf{x}} \hat{\mathbf{x}}_\theta$$
$$\mathbb{P}(g_i(\hat{\mathbf{x}}, \mathbf{u}) \leq 0) \geq 1 - \alpha \ \forall i \in \{1, \dots, n_g\}. \tag{2}$$

However, the probabilistic constraints in (2) are subject to the presence of structural uncertainty. This is a two-sided intractable problem, since the probabilities are infinite dimensional and the uncertainty due to mismatch is not defined. To accommodate these issues, first a probabilistic model (GP) is proposed to approximate the physical system such that the uncertainty propagation can be performed efficiently. Subsequently, the tightening of the g_i constraints is performed to satisfy the probabilistic guarantee.

3. Gaussian Process Regression and Uncertainty Propagation

In this section, we briefly introduce the fundamentals of GPs (Rasmussen & Williams, 2006). GPs generalize multivariate Gaussian distribution to a distribution over infinite dimensional vector of functions. A GP is a collection of random variables of which any finite subset follows a Gaussian distribution. GP regression aims to model an unknown function $\mathbf{f}: \mathbb{R}^{n_x} \rightarrow \mathbb{R}^{n_y}$ given some noisy observations. For $\mathbf{f} = [f_1, \dots, f_{n_y}]$, this could be expressed as:

$$f_i(\cdot) \sim \mathcal{GP}(m_i(\cdot), k_i(\cdot, \cdot)), \tag{3}$$

with m and k are the prior mean and covariance functions. The mean and covariance function define the prior GP and, in this work, we choose zero mean function and squared exponential covariance function:

$$k_i(\mathbf{x}, \mathbf{x}') = \sigma_{f_i}^2 \exp(-\frac{1}{2}(\mathbf{x} - \mathbf{x}')^T \Lambda_i (\mathbf{x} - \mathbf{x}')), \tag{4}$$

where $\sigma_{f_i}^2$ is the covariance magnitude and $\Lambda_i = \frac{1}{\lambda_i^2}\mathbf{I}$ is a scaling matrix. Given the acquired n data points $\mathcal{D}: \{\mathbf{X}, \mathbf{y}\}$, with $\mathbf{X} = [\mathbf{x_1}, \dots, \mathbf{x_n}]$ and $\mathbf{y} = [\mathbf{y_1}, \dots, \mathbf{y_n}]$, the mean and variance of the posterior $p(f_i(\mathbf{x}^*)|\mathbf{x}^*)$ can be computed for a deterministic test data point $\mathbf{x}^*$,

$$\mu_i(\mathbf{x}^*) = \mathbb{E}[f_i(\mathbf{x}^*)] = \mathbf{k}_*^T(\mathbf{K} + \sigma_\epsilon^2 \mathbf{I})^{-1}\mathbf{y} = \mathbf{k}_*^T \beta$$
$$\sigma_i(\mathbf{x_*}) = \mathbb{V}(f_i(\mathbf{x}^*)) = k_{**} - \mathbf{k}_*^T(\mathbf{K} + \sigma_\epsilon^2 \mathbf{I})^{-1}\mathbf{k_*}, \tag{5}$$

where $\mathbf{k_*} = k_i(\mathbf{X}, \mathbf{x}^*)$, $k_{**} = k_i(\mathbf{x}^*, \mathbf{x}^*)$ and $K_{m,j} = k(\mathbf{x_m}, \mathbf{x_j})$. In the case of uncertain $\mathbf{x_*}$ that follows a distribution, then (5) is not suitable. This is observed when predictions are conducted for time series and the previous output is the input of the next time instant, since the output of the GP follows a normal distribution. Now if $\mathbf{x}^* \sim \mathcal{N}(\boldsymbol{\mu}^*, \boldsymbol{\Sigma}^*)$ then the posterior $p(f_i(\mathbf{x}^*)|\boldsymbol{\mu}^*, \boldsymbol{\Sigma}^*) = \int p(f_i(\mathbf{x}^*)|\boldsymbol{\mu}^*, \boldsymbol{\Sigma}^*)p(\mathbf{x}^*)d\mathbf{x}^*$ needs to be computed. As this is an analytically intractable problem, a numerical approach based on MC simulations is used where approximation methods are applied. An analytical Gaussian approximation can be conducted using moment matching, the law of iterated expectations and conditional variance, then the mean and variance of the predictions can be approximated using detailed expressions as in (Deisenroth & Rasmussen, 2011).

4. Proposed Methodology

In this section, the proposed methodology is described where the physical system is approximated using a GP and then MC are used to approximate the tightened constraints. First the probabilistic constraints are substituted by a deterministic one in the form of $\tilde{g}_i = g_i + b_i \leq 0$ and b_i is selected such that condition (7) is satisfied:

$$g_i(\hat{\mathbf{x}}, \mathbf{u}) + b_i = 0 \rightarrow \mathbb{P}(g_i(\mathbf{x}, \mathbf{u}) \leq 0) = 1 - \alpha. \tag{7}$$

When a constraint is active, the corresponding probabilistic constraint is also active. To compute b_i the inverse cumulative density function (CDF) is used and the exact expression can be derived

$$b_i = F_{g_i}^{-1}(1 - \alpha) - g_i(\hat{\mathbf{x}}, \mathbf{u}) \tag{8}$$

where F_{g_i} is the CDF of g_i. The estimation of F_{g_i} is not trivial, since the distribution of the close loop does not have a known special structure. The CDF is defined as

$$F_{g_i}(0) = \mathbb{P}(g_i \leq 0) = \mathbb{E}(\mathbf{1}_{g_i \leq 0}), \tag{9}$$

where $\mathbf{1}_{g_i \leq 0} = \begin{cases} 1, \text{if } g_i \leq 0 \\ 0, \text{otherwise} \end{cases}$ is the indicator of $g_i \leq 0$. A nonparametric inference method was proposed in (Bradford et al., 2019; Paulson & Mesbah, 2018) to avoid any assumption regarding the distribution. An empirical CDF (ECDF) can be computed using MC simulations,

$$\hat{F}_{g_i}(0) = \frac{1}{N_{MC}} \sum_{k=1}^{N_{MC}} \mathbf{1}_{g_i^k}, \tag{10}$$

with N_{MC} being a sample size of independent and identically distributed samples. The inverse ECDF can subsequently be computed using the quantile of the N_{MC} samples. Now that (8) can be approximated, the computation of the tightened constraints can follow. A GP is trained to describe the dynamic behaviour of the physical system, and an initial value for the backoffs is given (b_i^0) The optimal experimental design is computed using (2) and predictions for the time horizon are conducted using the GP, where the mean and variance are propagated through time using moment matching (Deisenroth & Rasmussen, 2011); constraints are evaluated using N_{MC} MC simulations. Subsequently, the inverse CDF is computed using the predictions from the GP, and the $g_i(\hat{x}, \mathbf{u})$ using the nominal model. Then, the backoffs are computed (8) and this process is repeated (see Algorithm 1). It should be noted that the GP is trained with scarce data which may result in conservative constraints, however as new data are becoming available the GP can be updated increasing the accuracy.

Algorithm 1: Backoff Computation

Input	$\mathcal{GP}$, N_{iter} , Optimisation Problem (2), b_i^0	Output:	b_i
1.	for $m = \{1, \dots, N_{iter}\}$ do		
	a. for $k = \{1, \dots, N_{MC}\}$ and each sampling time do		
	solve (2) using (7) with b_i^m $\forall i$ and get u^*.		
	Simulate $\mathcal{GP}$ using u^*		
2.	b. $b_i^m = F_{g_i}^{-1} - g_i(\hat{x}, \mathbf{u})$ $\forall i$		

5. Case study

The proposed methodology is tested on an online (re)-design of transient experiments case study involving nucleophilic aromatic substitution (SNAr) of 2, 4- difluoro nitrobenzene {1} with pyrrolidine {2} in ethanol (EtOH) to give a mixture of the desired product ortho-substituted {3}, para-substituted {4} and bis-adduct {5} as side products. This case study has been adopted from Hone et al. (2007) and the schematic of the reaction is depicted in Fig 1. A model mismatch is assumed to present and the experimental design was carried out by comparing *1*) a standard MBDoE approach (Galvanin et al., 2010) (SD); *2*) the proposed methodology (GP-BACKOFF). In this case study in-silico experiments were conducted, where {1}, {2} and EtOH have a decreasing flowrate given by a ramp. This allows us to use the residence time instead of time and length of reactor, namely if the flowrates are given as $v = \beta(v_0 - at)$ then the residence time τ for given length of reactor L and time t is $\tau(t, L) = \frac{-(v_0 - at) + \sqrt{(v_0 - at)^2 + 2aL/\beta}}{a}$.

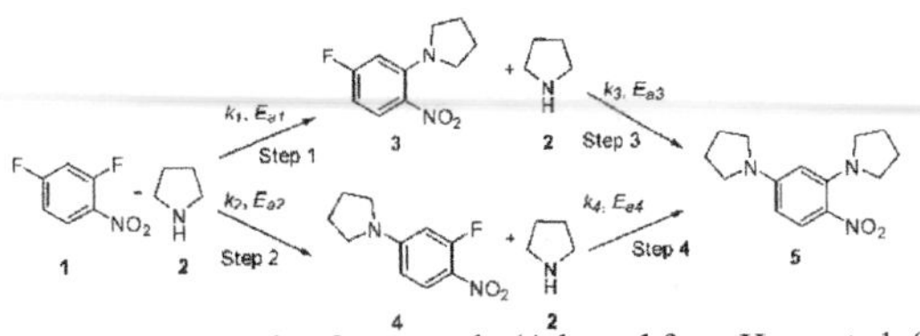

Figure 1: Reaction schematic of case study (Adopted from Hone et al. (2007))

As a result, the molar balance of the reactor can be written as:

$$\frac{dc_1}{d\tau} = -r_1 - r_2, \frac{dc_2}{d\tau} = -r_1 - r_2 - r_3 - r_4, \frac{dc_3}{d\tau} = r_1 - r_3,$$
$$\frac{dc_4}{d\tau} = r_2 - r_4, \frac{dc_5}{d\tau} = r_3 + r_4, \tag{11}$$

where the $i-th$ reaction rate for the real experiment is:

$$r_i = k_i \exp(-\frac{E_i}{R}(\frac{1}{T} - \frac{1}{T_{ref}}))c_i c_2 \text{ and } r_4 = k_4 \exp(-\frac{E_4}{R}(\frac{1}{T} - \frac{1}{T_{ref}}))\frac{c_4 c_2}{1+c_4}, i = \{1,2,3\} \tag{12}$$

with E_i, k_i are the kinetic parameters to be identified, $T_{ref} = 90^\circ C$. The design variables are the initial conditions for the {1}, {2}, and the temperature of the reactor. The assumed *true* kinetic parameters of (11) & (12) have the same values as in Hone et al. (2007). Additionally, a model mismatch is introduced, where the modeller constructed r_4 to be

$$r_4 = k_4 \exp(-\frac{E_4}{R}(\frac{1}{T} - \frac{1}{T_{ref}}))c_4 c_2.$$ Since {5} is soluble only when $c_5 \leq 0.01M$, a chance

constraint is applied to force the satisfaction of this constraint with probability 99% under the presence of the structural mismatch and 5% Gaussian noise of all the measurements. After the computation of the backoffs (offline), an online re-design is performed where the parameter estimation is conducted every time an additional measurement becomes available and the experiment is re-designed (Galvanin et al. 2009) maximizing the determinant of FIM. Six initial experiments were conducted using latin hypercube sampling where the design variables (temperature, and initial concentration of {1} and {2}) are assumed to be bounded with $30 (^\circ C) \leq T \leq 150(^\circ C)$, $0.2(M) \leq c_1^0 \leq 0.3(M)$ and $0.3(M) \leq c_2^0 \leq 2. (M)$. After the first measurements, a maximum likelihood estimation (MLE) is performed together with GP regression. Predictions for one set of experiments are shown in Fig 2. After 5 iterations of 1000 MC simulations the backoffs converged to produce 99% constraint satisfaction. Then, 3000 MC simulations were performed and the results are shown in Fig. 3 (a) and compared with the ones obtained from the SD case. The value of the tightened constraints that are needed in order to satisfy the chance constraints are also illustrated, where the shaded areas correspond to the 99.9% and 0.1 % quantiles. Subsequently, 8 loops of redesign and MLE have been performed, where after each experiment the parameters are estimated using MLE and then MBDoE is computed to result in a new set of experimental conditions. In Fig 3 (b) all 8 profiles of concentrations of {5} are depicted, where is clear that none of them violates the respective constraint.

6. Conclusions

In this work, a new backoff-based model-based design of experiments strategy is presented where the chance constraints are effectively satisfied under the presence of structural model mismatch. GP regression is utilized to accommodate the issue of the structural uncertainty and guarantee the feasibility of optimal experiments. The tools described in this work focus on the safe exploration of the design space, where new acquired experimental points can help to identify the "true" structure of the model. Results clearly show that the computed experimental conditions allow a safe conduction of experiments. Future work will concentrate on improving the accuracy of parameter estimation.

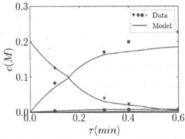

Figure 2: Predictions of experimental conditions for $T = 30.^o C$, $c_1 = 0.2 M$ and $c_2^0 = 1.4 M$

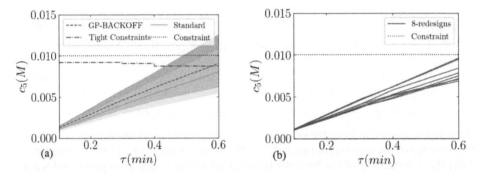

(a)　　　　　　　　　　　　　　　　　　　　(b)

Figure 3:(a) Probabilistic satisfaction of constrain of the proposed method and comparison with nominal satisfaction of constraints (b) Constraint satisfaction after 8 additional redesigns and parameter estimations in a closed loop operation. Each line corresponds to a different redesign.

References

E. Bradford, L. Imsland, D. Zhang, & E.A. del Rio Chanona, 2019, Stochastic data-driven model predictive control using Gaussian processes, http://arxiv.org/abs/1908.01786

M.P. Deisenroth, & C.E. Rasmussen, 2011, PILCO: A Model-Based and Data-Efficient Approach to Policy Search, in Proceedings of the 28th International Conference on Machine Learning.

G. Franceschini, & S. Macchietto, 2008. Model-based design of experiments for parameter precision: State of the art, Chemical Engineering Science, 63(19), 4846–4872.

F. Galvanin, M. Barolo & F. Bezzo, 2009, Online model-based redesign of experiments for parameter estimation in dynamic systems, Industrial & Engineering Chemistry Research, 48, 9, 4415-4427.

F. Galvanin, M. Barolo, F. Bezzo, & S. Macchietto, 2010, A backoff strategy for model-based experiment design under parametric uncertainty, AICHE, 56, 8, 2088-2102.

C.A. Hone, N. Holmes, G.R. Akien, R.A. Bourne, & F.L. Muller, 2017. Rapid multistep kinetic model generation from transient flow data, Reaction Chemistry and Engineering, 2, 103–108.

A. Mesbah, & S. Streif, 2015. Probabilistic approach to robust optimal experiment design with chance constraints, IFAC-PapersOnLine, 28, 8, 100–105.

J.A Paulson, & A. Mesbah, 2018, Nonlinear Model Predictive Control with Explicit Backoffs for Stochastic Systems under Arbitrary Uncertainty. IFAC-PapersOnLine, 51, 20, 523–534

C.E. Rasmussen, & C.K.I Williams, 2006, Gaussian Processes for Machine Learning.

D. Telen, Nimmegeers, Philippe, & J. Van Impe, 2018, Uncertainty in optimal experiment design: comparing an online versus offline approaches, IFAC-PapersOnLine, 51, 2, 771–776.

Sauro Pierucci, Flavio Manenti, Giulia Bozzano, Davide Manca (Eds.)
Proceedings of the 30th European Symposium on Computer Aided Process Engineering
(ESCAPE30), May 24-27, 2020, Milano, Italy. © 2020 Elsevier B.V. All rights reserved.
http://dx.doi.org/10.1016/B978-0-12-823377-1.50298-6

Computer-Aided Hazop: Ontologies and Ai for Hazard Identification and Propagation

Johannes I. Single, Jürgen Schmidt, Jens Denecke

CSE Center of Safety Excellence (CSE Institut), Joseph-von-Fraunhofer-Str.9, 76327 Pfinztal, Germany
Johannes.single@cse-institut.de

Abstract

The Hazard and Operability (HAZOP) study is an accepted hazard identification technique in the chemical process industry. It is a time and labor-intensive process and it can be prone to human error. Computer-aided HAZOP systems can be used to support human experts. In this research approach a semantically connected knowledge structure in the form of an ontology was developed that stores process safety engineering knowledge. Based on ontologies artificial intelligence methods and semantic reasoners are used to analyze the knowledge structure. Preliminary results show that an ontology-based reasoning algorithm in combination with case-based reasoning or a support vector machine algorithm is well-suited to infer hazards including their propagation.

Keywords: Computer-aided HAZOP studies, safety engineering ontologies, inference-based hazard identification, case-based reasoning, support vector machine

1. Introduction

During the entire life cycle of a chemical process plant, safety assessments are conducted during the process and plant design phase, plant revisions or in order to comply with amended legal regulations. Hazard and Operability (HAZOP) studies are conducted to identify and assess hazards and malfunctions that arise from processes and process plants. The HAZOP methodology is a human-centered and moderated technique and it is conducted by an interdisciplinary team of experts. The capabilities of the HAZOP practitioners can be reduced by repetitive tasks, stressful conditions and large amounts of data. Also, it is time and labor-intensive while the results of the study depend on the personal experience, level of training, moderation of the study, communication and safety culture. Computer-aided systems allow an experience-independent, completely systematic and uniform approach. They can assist HAZOP practitioners and serve as a decision support system. For over 30 years, different research groups proposed rule-based expert systems or graph-based approaches in order to automate HAZOP studies, see (Single et al., 2019). Some approaches make use of promising technologies, such as ontologies (Rodríguez and Laguía, 2019), case-based reasoning (Zhao et al., 2009), and model-based reasoning, but in many cases requirements from a process safety engineer's point of view are not considered. Thus, none of these approaches have been used in the process safety engineering community so far. In this paper an ontology-based computer-aided HAZOP systems (CAHS) approach to automatically identify hazards is proposed. The focus of this paper is on the ontology and the usage of artificial intelligence methods to detect the propagation of potential hazards.

2. Method

The proposed research approach consists of the following components: an ontology framework to store knowledge, process safety engineering knowledge that is fed into the framework, algorithms that use the knowledge to infer hazards.

2.1. Knowledge models

The hazard identification process is knowledge intensive where knowledge domains, such as substances, processes including chemical reactions, process plants, equipment, hazards and malfunctions, causes and consequences must be covered. In this research approach knowledge models in the form of ontologies are used due to their expressiveness, domain rules and the possibility to model knowledge unambiguously. The developed concepts (upper classes), such as HAZOP deviations, causes, hazardous events and consequences and their relations are shown in Figure 1. They are based on the following guiding principles that are developed to ensure a careful definition of the semantic context:

- Deviation + Context ⇒ Cause,
- Cause + Context ⇒ SuperCause,
- Deviation + Context ⇒ Effect,
- Effect + Context ⇒ Consequence.

For example, the deviation "LowFlow" and the equipment "Pump" could have the cause "IncreasedDifferentialPressure", while it could have the super-cause "IncreasedBackpressurePressureSide". The same applies to effects and consequences. The designed ontologies were formalized using the Web Ontology Language (OWL) that was recommended by the World Wide Web Consortium (W3C) in 2004, see (Hitzler et al., 2010). This means, it is specified using a set of classes, properties, individuals, property values and axioms. Therefore, the Python module Owlready2 by (Lamy, 2019). Owlready2 is also used to infer logical consequences based on the asserted facts and axioms that are defined through the formal specification of the ontology. This is done using semantic reasoners, such as HermiT (Glimm et al., 2014). Thus, ontologies can be queried to receive query answers and thereby make use of the modeled knowledge.

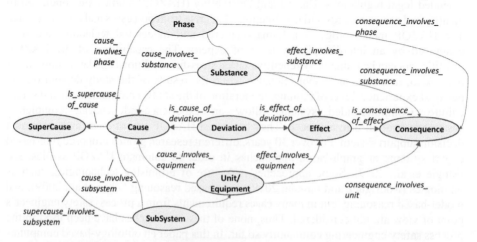

Figure 1 Semantic relationships between concepts

2.2. Hazard identification

The ontology is the foundation for an algorithmic hazard identification. It is queried to infer equipment-specific hazards and malfunctions using a reasoner, such as HermiT, as mentioned above. The influence of the equipment-specific conclusions on adjacent equipment of the process plant is analyzed using case-based reasoning (CBR) and support vector machine (SVM) algorithms. CBR is an established paradigm of Artificial Intelligence, see (Richter and Weber, 2013). It is a pattern-based problem-solving method where knowledge from past situations (cases) are reused in new situations (cases). This means the cases are compared while their similarity is measured using a similarity measure. For instance, for the cases A and B it is calculated from:

$$sim(A, B) = \sum_{i=0}^{n} sim(attr_{Ai}, attr_{Bi}) \cdot w_i \qquad (1)$$

A similarity measure of 1 would mean a perfect match between cases. In this work the case with the highest similarity measure is accepted. A case consists of various attributes and associated weights. Some exemplary cases of the case base are shown in Figure. 2 (a). For instance, case 1 is relatively simple and states that a "NoFlow" deviation is directly propagated downstream to the downstream equipment if there is one inlet and outlet. Case 2 describes a case where a "MoreFlow" deviation in a pump leads to an increased filling level in a downstream container. Case 3 describes a case where a "LowLevel" in a deviation leads to a "NoFlow" deviation in a downstream equipment. This means, the case-base serves as a memory.

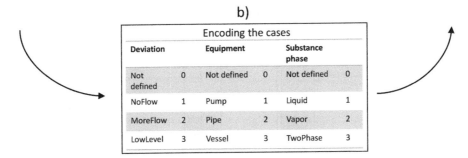

a)

Cases for case-based reasoning				
Case attributes	weight	Case 1	Case 2	Case 3
Current deviation	10	NoFlow	More Flow	Low Level
Current equipment/ subsystem	10	-	Pump	Vessel
Equipment (up/downstream)	10	-	Vessel (down)	-
Number of inlets/outlets	1	1/1	1/1	-
Substance property/phase	5	-	Phase: liquid	Phase: liquid
Propagated deviation	-	NoFlow (down)	HighLevel (down)	NoFlow (down)

c)

Training data for vector support machine			
Features	Case 1	Case 2	Case 3
Current deviation	1	2	3
Current equipment	0	1	3
Equipment (up)	0	0	0
Equipment (down)	0	3	0
Number of inlets	1	1	0
Number of outlets	1	1	0
Substance phase	0	1	1

b)

Encoding the cases					
Deviation		Equipment		Substance phase	
Not defined	0	Not defined	0	Not defined	0
NoFlow	1	Pump	1	Liquid	1
MoreFlow	2	Pipe	2	Vapor	2
LowLevel	3	Vessel	3	TwoPhase	3

Figure 2 Cases and encoding of the cases

As an alternative to CBR a support vector machine (SVM) algorithm was also used. The machine learning algorithm SVM is used here for the classification and therefore identification of propagations. It can be used for linear and non-linear classification problems and is applied in this work using the Scikit-learn library for Python, see (Pedregosa et al., 2011).

For this purpose, the categorical features (case attributes) from Figure 2 (a) were encoded (using Figure 2 (b)) into a numeric matrix that serves as training data, see Figure 2 (c). In this example only three cases are shown for illustration purposes. The SVM is trained using the training data that is represented by the encoded cases. Afterwards, the SVM classifier is used to make a prediction regarding a potential propagation. For the training data (cases) in this research, the application of CBR and SVM provided equivalent results, i.e. the same propagations were identified. Using the CBR approach the determination of the similarity measure requires the tuning of the attribute weights to uniquely identify cases. This carries the risk that several identical similarity measures may occur. On the contrary SVM is particularly suitable for finding unique solutions.

2.3. Handling propagations using the propagation stack method

In order to identify propagating deviations, the so-called Propagation Stack Method is developed in this work. This means, propagating deviations are detected using CBR or SVM, see Figure 2. Afterwards, the detected deviation is pushed into an equipment specific stack, see Figure 3. There can be several propagating deviations per equipment. From the stack, where the deviation was detected, every deviation is propagated downstream until the last equipment/unit of the system. For instance, in case the deviation "NoFlow" is detected in the pump it is propagated through the pipe into the vessel, see Figure 3. Thus, the effects of this deviation are evaluated in the equipment: pipe and vessel.

A flow chart of the overall method is shown in Figure 4. First, the process plant is analyzed equipment-wise (beginning to end) in order to detect equipment specific hazards and to fill the propagation stacks with the propagating deviations (equipment-specific inference using a semantic reasoner). Afterwards, the deviations within the propagation stacks are consecutively propagated downstream through the system (see propagation stack-based inference in Figure 3). Based on the propagated deviations super-causes, causes, effects and consequences are inferred. This is repeated until all deviations in the propagation stacks are considered. The proposed propagation stack method solves the problem that some hazards cannot be inferred solely based on equipment-specific relationships but only with consideration of adjacent equipment and units.

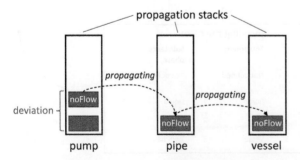

Figure 3 Hazard propagation using the propagation stack method

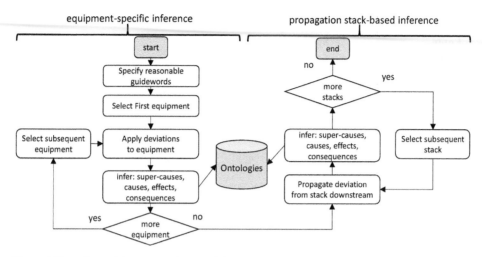

Figure 4 Flow chart of the proposed methodology

3. Case-study

The proposed methodology is applied to an exemplary process plant consisting of two pumps, an open vessel containing the solvent methanol in liquid phase and a downstream scrubber, see Figure 5. The first pump (P1) supplies the vessel (V) with the liquid solvent (methanol), while the second pump (P2) transports methanol from the vessel (V) and supplies the scrubber (S) which cleans the unspecified process gas. In this case-study the focus is on the capabilities of the propagation stack method. Thus, only propagating hazards are considered in the following and equipment specific deviations, effects or consequences are not considered here. By applying the proposed methodology various propagating deviations were identified and are shown in Table 1. The detected causal relationships of propagating deviations can be described as follows:

- No flow in pump (2) ⇒ no flow in scrubber (solvent feed),
- Low flow in vessel (V) ⇒ no flow in scrubber (solvent feed),
- More flow in pump (1) ⇒ high level in vessel (overflow),
- No flow in pipe after pump (2) ⇒ high pressure in pipe after pump 2.

This case-study demonstrates, that causes that lie upstream in the system can be detected using the propagation stack method.

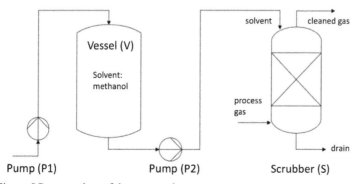

Figure 5 Process plant of the case study

Table 1 Exemplary HAZOP results of the case study considering only propagated circumstances

Equipment	Deviation	Super-Cause	Cause	Effect	Consequence
Scrubber (solvent feed)	NoFlow	propagated	propagated (P2 not working)	no solvent; no cleaning effect	release of untreated process gas
Scrubber (solvent feed)	NoFlow	propagated	propagated (V empty)	no solvent; no cleaning	release of untreated process gas
Vessel	HighLevel	propagated	propagated (P1 high flow)	overflow vessel	loss of containment, fire, explosion
Pipe after P2	HighPressure	propagated	propagated (Pipe blocked)	leakage, pipe bursting	loss of containment, fire, explosion

4. Conclusions

In this research approach ontologies are used to model process and plant safety knowledge. Based on that, different reasoning techniques are used to identify hazards in a HAZOP like manner. For the identification of hazards that propagate across equipment case-based reasoning or support vector machine algorithms were used. Therefore, the propagation stack method is developed and applied in a case-study. The first results show, that the proposed method is well-suited to identify propagating hazards. More research is needed regarding the backpropagation of deviations and effects, propagation effect on non-neighborly equipment and multi-failure propagation effects. The application limits of machine learning, such as support vector machine must be further explored. Finally, this research approach contributes to establish computer systems for HAZOP studies in the chemical process industry.

References

B. Glimm, I. Horrocks, B. Motik, G. Stoilos, Z. Wang, 2014, HermiT: An OWL 2 Reasoner, Journal of Automated Reasoning, 53, 3, pp. 245-269

P. Hitzler, M. Kroetzsch, S. Rudolph, 2010, Foundations of Semantic Web Technologies, CRC Press, New York

J. B. Lamy, 2017, Owlready: Ontology-oriented programming in Python with automatic classification and high level constructs for biomedical ontologies, Artificial Intelligence In Medicine, 80, pp. 11-28

F. Pedregosa, G. Varoquaux, A. Gramfort, V. Michel, B. Thirion, O. Grisel, M. Blondel, and P. Prettenhofer, R. Weiss, V. Dubourg, J. Vanderplas, A. Passos, D. Cournapeau, M. Brucher, M. Perrot, E. Duchesnay, 2011, Scikit-learn: Machine Learning in Python. Journal of Machine Learning Research, 12, pp. 2825-2830

R. R. Richter, R. O. Weber, 2013, Case-Based Reasoning: A Textbook, Springer Publishing Company, Incorporated

M. Rodríguez, J. Laguía, 2019, An Ontology for Process Safety, Chemical Engineering Transactions, 77, pp. 67-72

J. I. Single, J. Schmidt, J. Denecke, 2019, State of research on the automation of HAZOP studies, Journal of Loss Prevention in the Process Industries, https://doi.org/10.1016/j.jlp.2019.103952

J. Zhao, L. Cui, L. Zhao, T. Qiu, B. Chen, 2009, Learning HAZOP expert system by case-based reasoning and ontology, Computers & Chemical Engineering, 33, 1, pp. 371-378

Sauro Pierucci, Flavio Manenti, Giulia Bozzano, Davide Manca (Eds.)
Proceedings of the 30th European Symposium on Computer Aided Process Engineering
(ESCAPE30), May 24-27, 2020, Milano, Italy. © 2020 Elsevier B.V. All rights reserved.
http://dx.doi.org/10.1016/B978-0-12-823377-1.50299-8

Machine Learning-aided Process Design for Formulated Products

Liwei Cao[a,b], Danilo Russo[a], Werner Mauer[c], Huan Huan Gao[d], Alexei A. Lapkin[a,b] *

[a]*Department of Chemical Engineering and Biotechnology, University of Cambridge, Cambridge CB3 0AS, UK*
[b]*Cambridge Centre for Advanced Research and Education in Singapore, CARES Ltd. 1 CREATE Way, CREATE Tower #05-05, 138602, Singapore*
[c]*BASF Personal Care and Nutrition GmbH, 40589 Duesseldorf-Holthausen, Germany.*
[d]*BASF Advanced Chemical Co., Ltd., No. 300 Jiangxinsha Road, 200137 Shangai, China.*
aal35@cam.ac.uk

Abstract

Robotic experiments were coupled with the previously published Thompson Sampling Efficient Multiobjective Optimization (TS-EMO) algorithm, using a batch sequential design approach, in order to optimize the composition and the process conditions of a commercial formulated product. The algorithm was trained with a previously collected data set used to optimize the formulation without taking into account the influence of the process conditions. The target was to obtain a clear homogeneous formulation within a certain viscosity range, minimizing the cost of the adopted ingredients. The GP surrogate models used in the algorithm were found suitable to model the complex unknown relationship between the input space and the outputs of interest, identifying suitable samples with a general decrease in the formulation price, needed mixing power, and process time. The proposed methodology can lead to quicker product design and therefore can generate considerable profit increase with an early product release time.
Keywords: robotic experiments, closed loop optimization, multiobjective optimization, formulated product, process design.

1. Introduction

Formulated products are ubiquitous in the chemical industry, ranging from household detergent to synthetic fuels. They are obtained by mixing selected ingredients in order to get the desired product functions. The design of formulated products is a complex multidisciplinary process, especially when specific product microstructural attributes strongly depend on the selected manufacturing technologies and operating conditions. The integration of product and process design is crucial (Martin and Martinez, 2013; Bernardo, 2016). Grossmann (2004) introduced product-process design as one of the future challenges of chemical engineering. Since then, various attempts have been made to develop systematic methodologies. There are mainly three approaches to the design of formulated products (Ng et al., 2006). Many formulated products are developed through trial-and-error experiments by specialists with extensive experience in producing the specific product under consideration. Cussler and Moggridge (2011) proposed a four-step generic framework to guide such an integrated problem from needs, ideas and selection to manufacture. Although heuristics and experiments often lead to the successful development of the, it is practically impossible to screen a large number of product prototypes experimentally when there are few alternative ingredients to choose. Moreover, this approach is not suitable for engineers with limited experience in formulating a new type of product.

The orthogonal approach is design by simulations. For relatively simple molecules and homogenous mixtures with well-defined target properties, design methods are available, known as computer-aided product design, which is a combination of computer-aided molecular design and computer aided mixture/blend design techniques (Gani and Ng, 2015). These tools consist of mathematical programming and hybrid methods and provide a promising framework for the development of new chemicals, formulations and methods to estimate different target properties. A large number of computer-aided methods were developed and successfully applied to solvent design (Gani et al., 1991; Macchietto et al., 1990; Pretel et al., 1994; Gani et al., 2005), mixture design (Eden et al., 2004), refrigerant design (Joback and Stephanopolous, 1989; Churi and Achenie, 1996), chemical (Kalakul et al., 2016, Gani et al., 2014) and formulated products (Martin and Martinez, 2013, Arrieta-Escobar et al., 2017, Martin and Martinez, 2016, Arrieta-Escobar et al., 2019). However, this approach is highly depended on validated mathematical models for the estimation of all desired properties. For the cases where no suitable physical model is available the role of model-based design is limited.

A hybrid experiment- and model-based techniques was proposed when mathematical models are not available for all desired properties and/or product-process performance evaluations (Conte et al., 2012). According to this approach, physical models can be used to generate and test alternatives in order to identify a small number of candidates, which may be further investigated through the experiment-based trial and error approach. However, a physical model is still needed in the integrated approach, which can be a limitation to some extent. Here we ask a question, *is it possible to train a surrogate statistical model to describe the desired product properties in the absence of a physical model, and use it to optimize the product and process design in an automated fashion?*

With the increase in computational power, machine learning methods become available to many new application areas and present a transformative approach to optimization. The application of machine learning in chemical engineering is a rapidly developing field (Venkatasubramanian, 2019). Important advances were made within the area of catalyst design (Goldsmith et al., 2018; Medford et al., 2018), chemical synthesis (Amar et al., 2019), process optimization (Lee et al., 2018) and so on. In this work, we present an integrated approach, which is a combination of a machine learning algorithm and a robotic experimental platform for the optimization of a formulated product. To achieve the optimal design of a product and a process, a Bayesian multi-objective optimization algorithm was adopted, specifically. Thompson Sampling Efficient Multi-Objective (TS-EMO) (Bradford et al., 2018). The algorithm trains Gaussian processes (GPs) as the surrogate models on the experimental dataset and then identifies new samples based on the predictions and uncertainty of the surrogates. The TS-EMO algorithm was incorporated in the robotic experimental platform to guide the next-run experiments.

The experimental results were then used as inputs for the TS-EMO algorithm for the next iteration of optimization till the set criterion of the formulated product is met.

2. Materials and Methods

The formulated product under consideration is a real industrial case study. The formulation consists of a mixture of three surfactants (S1 = Texapon SB3, S2 = Dehyton AB30, S3 = Plantacare 818), a polymer (P1 = Dehyquart CC7), a thickener (T1 = Arlyon TT), and water at a specific pH.

A scheme of the experimental system is shown in Fig. 1. The robotic system was developed at University of Glasgow, in the group of Prof. Leroy Cronin. At each iteration of the optimization procedure, 8 new formulation recipes and process conditions are suggested by the algorithm. These conditions are summarized in a .csv file, triggering the Robotic Platform no. 1 for the samples preparation. Automated syringe pumps (Tricontinent, Gardner Denver, C-Series) dispense the proper amount of each ingredient in 20 mL vials placed on a rotating wheel. At each iteration a batch of 8 samples is prepared. They are then moved into an incubator, where they are shaken at a fixed temperature, mixing power, and time. Process conditions were also suggested by the algorithm. The processed samples are then cooled to room temperature and analyzed using the robotic platform no. 2. In this platform turbidity of each sample is measured and pH is tested to ensure it is constant. No pH variations were observed after processing in any of the samples. Sample viscosity at a shear rate of 10 s^{-1} is finally measured off-line with a rotational viscometer (controlled strain rheometer, ARES Rheometric Scientific, couette configuration) and the results exported to a new .csv file for the next iteration of the TS-EMO algorithm. A batch-sequential design was used to suggest the next 8 experiments (Bradford et al., 2018). The three target functions to minimize were chosen as turbidity value, the squared distance of the measured viscosity from the target viscosity (3,000 mPa·s), and price, calculated as the sum of the unit price of each ingredient multiplied by the dispensed amount. The variables of interest were concentrations of the 5 ingredients S1, S2, S3, T1, P1, and three process variables (temperature T, mixing power MP, and time t). Constraints suggested by process knowledge were: S1+S2+S3 = 15 g/L; T1 < 2 g/L; P1 < 2 g/L; 30 < T < 60 °C; 30 < MP < 300 rpm; 10 < t < 120 min. Surrogate GPs model were used to model the unknown outputs, i.e. viscosity and turbidity.

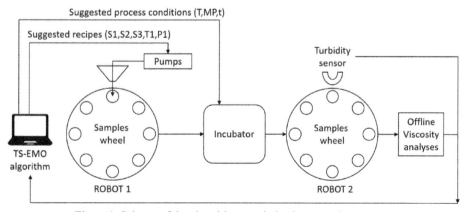

Figure 1. Scheme of the closed-loop optimization operations.

3. Results and Discussion

A batch of 224 experimental data at fixed process conditions (T = 50 °C; MP = 300 rpm; t = 2 h) was used to train the algorithm and start the iterative process. This data set was already available from a previous explorative experimental campaign devoted to optimise the formulation at fixed process conditions. The choice of using these previously collected data is justified to mimic a common situation in products development, in which a preliminary investigation provides an initial data set. Other 12 training data were collected at a fixed recipe (S1 = 5.62; S2 = 2.50; S3 = 6.88; P1 = 0.90; T = 2.00 g/L) at different process conditions. Hence, the overall training dataset consisted of 236 data points. 15 iterations of the closed-loop optimization (120 samples) were carried out in order to assess predictive performance of the obtained surrogate models and to evaluate the results of the optimization. Among the conditions suggested by the algorithm, 7 non-dominated solutions were found (Table 1) in the experimental Pareto front of the data set.

Table 1. Non-dominated solutions suggested by the TS-EMO algorithm.

S1 (g/L)	S2 (g/L)	S3 (g/L)	P1 (g/L)	T1 (g/L)	T (°C)	MP (rpm)	t (min)	Turbidity (NTU)	Viscosity (mPa·s)	Price ($/L)
2.80	3.20	9.00	0.40	1.46	35	137	77	152	2,409	1.81
1.09	2.45	11.45	1.20	1.92	54	211	118	157	3,424	1.79
0.00	0.52	14.48	0.40	1.33	30	220	42	28	197	1.51
0.00	2.01	12.99	0.01	1.24	51	180	73	31	409	1.45
5.10	5.89	4.01	0.00	1.97	49	230	70	24	3,681	2.05
5.10	5.65	4.25	0.76	1.91	49	230	83	25	3,071	2.14
0.93	5.63	8.44	0.94	1.94	52	206	115	30	2,337	1.74

All of the obtained formulations were clear, homogeneous samples, with no phase separation. 5 out of 7 non-dominated solutions satisfy the viscosity requirement to be in the range 2,000 – 4,000 mPa·s. The presence of two samples with a viscosity lower than 1,000 mPa·s is due to their relatively low price and turbidity, which is in agreement with the interpretation of the Pareto front as a trade-off between different conflicting objectives. Further criteria can be used to discriminate between the obtained best solutions. It is also worth noticing that all proposed solutions were obtained with a significant reduction of the required time and mixing power. The non-dominated solutions that passed the viscosity and turbidity criteria in the training set are reported in Table 2.

Table 2. Non-dominated experimental data in the training set.

S1 (g/L)	S2 (g/L)	S3 (g/L)	P1 (g/L)	T1 (g/L)	T (°C)	MP (rpm)	t (min)	Turbidity (NTU)	Viscosity (mPa·s)	Price ($/L)
3.97	3.16	7.87	0.84	1.60	50	300	120	11	2,678	2.00
4.61	2.62	7.76	1.24	1.04	50	300	120	28	3,574	2.06
8.40	3.18	3.43	0.48	1.80	50	300	120	18	2,948	2.43
2.79	2.93	9.28	1.72	0.88	50	300	120	26	2,632	1.92
10.94	3.94	0.12	1.8	1.36	50	300	120	28	2,992	2.80
4.02	3.09	7.89	0.99	1.34	50	300	120	15	2,824	2.00
3.01	0.64	11.35	0.53	1.75	50	300	120	50	2,789	1.87
3.06	1.96	9.95	0.31	1.42	50	300	120	23	3302	1.82

As one can see by comparing Tables 1 and 2, among the solutions that passed both criteria, those suggested during the optimization procedure have a lower average price of the ingredients, which together with the advantages in terms of low mixing power and processing time, might have a significant effect on the overall economics and productivity. The predictive performances of the adopted models were evaluated comparing the predicted Pareto front of the GPs with the experimental non-dominated solutions, Figure 2.

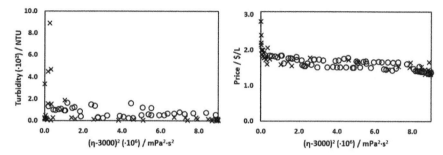

Figure 2. Two projections of the experimental (X) and predicted (O) Pareto front.

The satisfactory predictive performances can enable further improvements in formulations design, based on different *a posteriori* criteria that may be selected by human intuition and/or expertise.

4. Conclusions

In this paper, robotic experiments were used in combination with a machine learning algorithm to optimize both the recipe and the process conditions of a formulated product. The proposed methodology enabled to identify new formulations meeting the discriminating criteria. Moreover, the suggested sample were generally cheaper and required less mixing power and process time, which can generate considerable profits on scale. The overall optimization procedure was completed within 2 weeks, avoiding human bias and using automated operations, exploring a complex, multidimensional chemical space. As a result, the developed methodology can lay the groundwork for a faster and more efficient process development and a consequent early product release time, without requiring any extensive expertise of the human operators. GPs were confirmed to be suitable surrogate model to predict the complex relationships between the input variables and the target properties when no physical models are available.

Acknowledgements

LC is grateful to BASF for co-funding her PhD. This project was co-funded by the UKRI project "Combining Chemical Robotics and Statistical Methods to Discover Complex Functional Products" (EP/R009902/1), and National Research Foundation (NRF), Prime Minister's Office, Singapore under its Campus for Research Excellence and Technological Enterprise (CREATE) program as a part of the Cambridge Centre for Advanced Research and Education in Singapore Ltd (CARES). The Authors are grateful to Prof. Lee Cronin, Dr. Abhishek Sharma, Mr. Daniel Salley, and Mr. Graham Keenan for providing designs, software and practical help in the assembly of the robotic platform.

References

Y. Amar, A.M. Schweidtmann, P. Deutsch, L. Cao, A. Lapkin, 2019, Machine learning and molecular descriptors enable rational solvent selection in asymmetric catalysis, Chem. Sci., 10, 27, 6697-6706.

J.A. Arrieta-Escobar, F.P. Bernardo, A. Orjuela, M. Camargo, L. Morel, 2017, An integrated methodology for emulsified cosmetic product formulation using integer programming with logical constraints, Comput. Aided Chem. En., 40, 985-990.

J.A. Arrieta-Escobar, F.P. Bernardo, A. Orjuela, M. Camargo, L. Morel, L. Wendling, 2019, Integration of consumer preferences and heuristic knowledge in the design of formulated products: application to a cosmetic emulsion, Comput. Aided Chem. En., 46, 433-438.

F.P. Bernardo, 2016, Chapter 12 – Integrated process and product design optimization, Comput. Aided Chem. En., 39, 347-372.

E. Bradford, A.M. Schweidtmann, A. Lapkin, 2018, Efficient multiobjective optimization employing Gaussian processes, spectral sampling and a genetic algorithm, J. Global Optim., 71, 2, 407-438.

N. Churi, L.E.K. Achenie, 1996, Novel mathematical programming model for computer aided molecular design, Ind. Eng. Chem. Res., 35, 10, 3788-3794.

E. Conte, R. Gani, Y.S. Cheng, K.M. Ng, 2012, Design of formulated products: experimental component, AIChE J., 58, 1, 173-189.

E.L. Cussler, G.D. Moggridge, 2011, Chemical product design, Cambridge University Press.

M.R. Eden, S.B. Jorgensen, R. Gani, M.M. El-Halwagi, 2004, Chem. Eng. Process.: Process Intensification, 43, 5, 595-608.

R. Gani, B. Nielsen, A. Fredenslund, 1991, A group contribution approach to computer-aided molecular design, AIChE J., 37, 9, 1318-1332.

R. Gani, C. Jimenez-Gonzalez, D.J.C. Constable, 2005, Method for selection of solvents for promotion of organic reactions, Comput. Chem. Eng., 29, 1661-1676

R. Gani, K.M. Ng, 2014, Product design – from molecules to formulations to devices, Comput. Aided Chem. En., 34, 108-123.

R. Gani, K.M. Ng, 2015, Product design – molecules, devices, functional products, and formulated products, Comput. Chem. Eng., 81, 70-79.

B.R. Goldsmith, J. Esterhuizen, J.X. Liu, C.J. Bartel, C. Sutton, 2018, Machine learning for heterogeneous catalyst design and discovery, AIChE J., 64, 7, 2311-2323.

I.E. Grossmann, 2004, Challenges in the new millenium: product discovery and design, enterprise and supply chain optimization, global life cycle assessment, Comput. Chem. Eng., 29, 29-39.

K.G. Joback, G. Stephanopoulos, 1989, Designing molecules possessing desider physical property values, Proceedings FOCAPD, 89, 363-387.

S. Kalakul, S. Cignitti, L. Zhang, R. Gani, 2016, Integrated computer-aided framework for sustainable chemical product design and evaluation, Comput. Aided Chem. En., 38, 2343-2348.

J.H. Lee, J. Shin, M.J. Realff, 2018, Machine learning: overview of the recent progresses and implications for the process systems engineering field, Compu. Chem. Eng., 114, 111-121.

M. Martin, A. Martinez, 2013, A methodology for simultaneous product and process design in the customer products industry: the case study of the laundry business, Comput. Aided Chem. En., 32, 715-720.

M. Martin, A. Martinez, 2016, Chapter 13 – Tools for formulated product design, Comput. Aided Chem. En., 39, 373-392.

A.J. Medford, M.R. Kunz, S.M. Ewing, T. Borders, R. Fushimi, 2018, Extracting knowledge from data through catalysis informatics, ACS Catal., 8, 8, 7403-7429.

K.M. Ng, R. Gani, K. Dam-Johansen, 2006, Chemical product design: towards a perspective through case studies, 23, Elsevier.

S. Macchietto, O. Odele, O. Omatsone, 1990, Design of optimal solvents for liwuid-liwuid extraction and gas absorption processes, Chem. Eng. Res. Des., 68, 429-433.

E.J. Pretel, P.A. Lopez, S.B. Bottini, E.A. Brignole, 1994, Computer-aided molecular design of solvents for separation processes, AIChE J., 40, 8, 1349-1360.

V. Venkatasubramanian, 2019, The promise of artifical intelligence in chemical engineering: is it here, finally?, AIChE J., 65, 2, 466-478.

Sauro Pierucci, Flavio Manenti, Giulia Bozzano, Davide Manca (Eds.)
Proceedings of the 30th European Symposium on Computer Aided Process Engineering
(ESCAPE30), May 24-27, 2020, Milano, Italy. © 2020 Elsevier B.V. All rights reserved.
http://dx.doi.org/10.1016/B978-0-12-823377-1.50300-1

A Novel Multi-stage Stochastic Formulation with Decision-dependent Probabilities for Condition-based Maintenance Optimization

Egidio Leo[*] , Sebastian Engell

Process Dynamics and Operations Group, Department of Biochemical and Chemical Engineering, Technische Universität Dortmund, EmilFigge-Str.70, 44221 Dortmund, Germany.

egidio.leo@tu-dortmund.de

Abstract

The challenge addressed in this work is the integrated production planning and condition-based maintenance optimization for a process plant. We take into account uncertain information of the predicted equipment degradation adopting a stochastic programming formulation. To adjust the likelihood of the failure scenarios, we embed a prognosis model, the Cox model, into the optimization problem. We propose here a novel endogenous uncertainty formulation where the decisions at one point in time have an impact on the probability of the uncertainty. We provide computational results implementing a custom branching within the global solver BARON and decomposing the problem via the Benders algorithm.

Keywords: Condition-based maintenance, Prognosis, Stochastic programming, Endogenous uncertainty, Cox model

1. Introduction

Condition-based maintenance (CBM) is a paradigm that is based on the idea of integrating production planning and maintenance scheduling via a degradation model that describes the health of the equipment. The goal of a CBM optimization is to find the best compromise between operating costs and maintenance costs. In fact, a high production rate might result into high production volumes but also high maintenance costs due to frequent maintenance activities because of high degradation rates. Most of the work in this direction assumes a perfectly known degradation model that is able to predict the degradation trajectory and the Remaining Useful Life (RUL) of the equipment according to the operating conditions (Leo and Engell, 2017). To the best of our knowledge, only two works perform a CBM optimization under uncertainty. In (Basciftci et al., 2018) the authors used a degradation model to create failure scenarios, which then were included into a chance-constraint programming approach. Since the degradation model is only used for the generation of the scenarios, the optimization does not take into account the effects of the selected operating strategy on the status of the equipment. This is taken into account in (Wiebe et al., 2018), where parametric uncertainty of the degradation model is considered by solving an adjustable robust optimization problem. To avoid uncertain time-varying parameters, which result in a very conservative solution, the authors assume a complete realization of the future degradation parameters after the first collection of measurements. In this work we propose a novel formulation that integrates CBM, prognosis and production planning, adopting the multi-stage stochastic programming framework with decision-dependent uncertainty (Hellemo et al.,2018).

2. Problem statement

We consider a continuous production plant with fixed and known product demand over the planning horizon. The goal is to minimize the difference between the plant costs, consisting of the feed purchasing cost, the resource consumption cost and the product purchasing cost, and the plant income, due to the produced products. The decisions variables are:

- the feeds to be purchased;
- the operating conditions of the plant and the resulting degradation trajectory;
- the amount of product to be purchased from other sources;
- the timing of the maintenance activities.

3. The proposed endogenous uncertainty MINLP formulation

3.1. Uncertainty modelling

The standard stochastic programming formulation models the uncertainty by discrete scenarios with fixed and known scenario probabilities and the decisions are made at different stages, which are defined by the realization of the uncertainty. In this work, the discrete scenarios represent possible realizations of the uncertain RUL of the equipment. The proposed endogenous uncertainty formulation computes the probabilities of the uncertain RULs according to the degradation trajectory that is defined by the plant operating conditions (e.g., a higher degradation, due to harder operating conditions, increases the failure probabilities by shorter RULs). The relation between the probabilities of the scenarios and the degradation trajectory is identified via the survival analysis equations and the Cox Model (Cox, 1972). The Cox model is a prognosis technique that is able to adjust the hazard function (and therefore the probability of an event) according to the influencing variables, in this work the degradation level and, therefore, the operating strategy. It is worth to highlight that even though the Cox model is a well-known standard prognosis model, in this work for the first time it is embedded into a stochastic programming optimization. Figure 1 shows the scenario tree of the proposed formulation. The first-stage decisions are the feed purchasing decisions, the maintenance timing decisions and the plant operating conditions before any RUL realizations. The recourse decisions are the plant operating conditions. We consider a time horizon of 40 days and the uncertain RULs belong to the set $F_s = \{30, \dots, 40\}$.

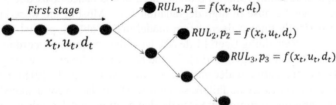

Figure 1 Scenario tree of the proposed formulation.

Indices *t: time, f: feed, i: input, p: product, j: state, s: scenario.*
Continuous variables: $y_{p,t,s}$: plant output, $x_{j,t,s}$: plant operating conditions, S_s: survival function, p_s: scenario probability, $purchase_{p,s}$: purchased product, $d_{t,c,s}$: degradation trajectory, $Pr_{p,t,s}$: cumulative production, h_s: hazard function, $u_{i,t,s}$: plant inputs. **Binary variables** $x_{maintenance_t}$: 1 if maintenance is active in t, x_{feed_f}: 1 if feed f is purchased, $y_{feed_{f,t}}$: 1 if feed f is used at time t, $start_{feed_{f,t}}$: 1 if the utilization of feed f starts at time t.

A novel multi-stage stochastic formulation with decision-dependent probabilities for condition-based maintenance optimization

1797

3.2. Process constraints

Eqs. (1)-(2) represent the process constraints where $u_{i,t,s}$ indicates the resource consumption, $x_{j,t,s}$ the plant operating conditions and $y_{p,t,s}$ the plant production. The degradation level $d_{t,s}$ affects the plant production. Eqs. (3) - (4) set the upper and lower bounds of the plant inputs $u_{i,t,s}$. If the maintenance is active ($x_{maintenance_t} = 1$) the resource consumption is forced to be zero. Eq. (5) computes the cumulative production of product p at each time step t. The maximum production capacity is defined in Eq. (6). A demand satisfaction constraint (Eq. (7)) enforces that the product demand is covered by the production or by purchasing the product from external sources. The matrices $A_{j,i}, B_{p,j}$ represent process parameters linking inputs, outputs and states of the plant.

$$x_{j,t,s} = \Sigma_i A_{j,i} * u_{i,t,s} \qquad\qquad \forall j \in J, s \in S, t \in T \quad (1)$$

$$y_{p,t,s} = \Sigma_j B_{p,j} * x_{j,t,s} - d_{t,s} * red_p \qquad\qquad \forall p \in P, s \in S, t \in T \quad (2)$$

$$u_{i,t,s} \leq UB_{i,s} * (1 - x_{maintenance_t}) \qquad\qquad \forall i \in I, s \in S, t \in T \quad (3)$$

$$u_{i,t,s} \geq LB_{i,s} * (1 - x_{maintenance_t}) \qquad\qquad \forall i \in I, s \in S, t \in T \quad (4)$$

$$Pr_{p,t,s} = \Sigma_{t' \leq t} y_{p,t',s} \qquad\qquad \forall p \in P, s \in S, t \in T \quad (5)$$

$$y_{p,t,s} \leq yUB_{p,s} * (1 - x_{maintenance_t}) \qquad\qquad \forall p \in P, s \in S, t \in T \quad (6)$$

$$Pr_{p,|T|,s} + purchase_{p,s} \geq D_p \qquad\qquad \forall p \in P, s \in S \quad (7)$$

3.3. Feed purchasing constraints

The following constraints define the feed purchasing strategy of the plant and the allocation of the feeds over the time horizon. The quality of the feed (indicated by the parameter IC_f) influences the degradation trajectory (see Eqs. (15) - (16)). Eq. (8) - (9) impose a minimum and maximum allocation of the purchased feeds. Eq. (10) ensures that no feed is used if the maintenance activities are performed. Eqs. (11) - (13) define the starting time of the feed utilization for each purchased feed.

$$\Sigma_t y_{feed_{f,t}} \geq Feed_{day_{min}} * x_{feed_f} \qquad\qquad \forall f \in F \quad (8)$$

$$\Sigma_t y_{feed_{f,t}} \leq Feed_{day_{max}} * x_{feed_f} \qquad\qquad \forall f \in F \quad (9)$$

$$\Sigma_f y_{feed_{f,t}} = 1 - x_{maintenance_t} \qquad\qquad \forall t \in T \quad (10)$$

$$start_{feed_{f,t}} \geq y_{feed_{f,t}} - y_{feed_{f,t-1}} \qquad\qquad \forall f \in F, t \in \{2, ..., |T|\} \quad (11)$$

$$start_{feed_{f,t}} \leq x_{feed_f} \qquad\qquad \forall f \in F, t \in T \quad (12)$$

$$\Sigma_t start_{feed_{f,t}} \leq x_{feed_f} \qquad\qquad \forall f \in F \quad (13)$$

3.4. Degradation model

The following constraints compute the degradation trajectory. Eqs. (15) - (16) define the degradation model that depends on the feed quality IC_f, the operating conditions of the plant and the history of the degradation. Eq. (14) sets the threshold for the degradation.

$$d_{t,s} \leq d_{thresholds_{s,t}} * (1 - x_{maintenance_t}) \qquad\qquad \forall t \in T, s \in S \quad (14)$$

$$d_{t,s} \geq d_{init} * (1 - x_{maintenance_t}) + \Sigma_f IC_f * y_{feed_{f,t}} + \qquad\qquad \forall t \in T, \quad (15)$$
$$\Sigma_{t' \leq t,i} a_{1,i} * u_{i,t',s} + \Sigma_{t' \leq t,j} a_{2,j} * x_{j,t',s} - M * x_{maintenance_t} \qquad s \in S$$

$$d_{t,s} \leq d_{init} * (1 - x_{maintenance_t}) + \Sigma_f IC_f * y_{feed_{f,t}} + \qquad\qquad \forall t \in T, \quad (16)$$
$$\Sigma_{t' \leq t,i} a_{1,i} * u_{i,t',s} + \Sigma_{t' \leq t,j} a_{2,j} * x_{j,t',s} + M * x_{maintenance_t} \qquad s \in S$$

3.5. Maintenance constraints

The maintenance constraints implement the maintenance policy. Eq. (17) ensures that the maintenance activities are started only once over the considered time horizon. Eqs. (18) - (19) forces the maintenance to be performed in a specific time window (between day 30 and 40). Eq. (20) defines the duration of the maintenance.

$$x_{maintenance_t} \geq x_{maintenance_{t-1}} \qquad\qquad \forall t \in T, t \neq 1 \quad (17)$$
$$\Sigma_{t \in window}\, x_{maintenance\_t} \geq 1 \qquad\qquad\qquad\qquad\qquad (18)$$
$$\Sigma_{t \notin window}\, x_{maintenance\_t} = 0 \qquad\qquad\qquad\qquad\qquad (19)$$
$$\Sigma_t\, x_{maintenance\_t} \geq dur \qquad\qquad\qquad\qquad\qquad\qquad (20)$$

3.6. Prognosis constraints

These constraints embed the prognosis model within the production planning optimization. This is achieved introducing as variables the probabilities of the scenarios (namely of the RUL estimations), the hazard function and the survival function (Eq. (21)) according to the Cox model. Eqs. (22) - (24) implement the relations among these variables. Eq. (25) sets to zero the probabilities of those scenarios with RULs that realize after the maintenance activities start. In other words, those scenarios do not realize. Eqs. (26) - (27) implement a linearized version of the Cox model ($h_s = h_s^0 * e^{\mu * d_{t,s}} \approx h_s^0 * \mu * d_{t,s}$). Eq. (26) determines the hazard function of the earliest uncertain RUL according to the degradation trajectory. The hazard functions of the remaining scenarios are adjusted linearly (Eq. (27)). The nominal hazard function (h_s^0) and the parameter μ must be estimated from plant data.

$$0 \leq h_s \leq 1, 0 \leq p_s \leq 1, 0 \leq S_s \leq 1 \qquad\qquad \forall s \in S \quad (21)$$
$$p_s = h_s * S_s \qquad\qquad\qquad\qquad\qquad\qquad \forall s \in S \quad (22)$$
$$S_s = \Sigma_{s'>s}\, p_{s'} \qquad\qquad\qquad\qquad\qquad\qquad \forall s \in S \quad (23)$$
$$S_s - S_{s+1} = p_s \qquad\qquad\qquad\qquad\qquad\qquad \forall s \in S \quad (24)$$
$$p_s \leq 1 - x_{maintenance_{F_S[s]-1}} \qquad\qquad\qquad \forall s \in S \quad (25)$$
$$h_s = h_s^0 * \mu * d_{t,s} \qquad\qquad\qquad\qquad\qquad\qquad s = 1 \quad (26)$$
$$h_s = h_{s1} + (1 - h_s)/(|S| - 1) * s \qquad\qquad s \in S, s \neq 1 \quad (27)$$

3.7. Objective function

The following constraints compute the plant cost and the objective function Eq. (28). The plant cost (Eq. (29)) is the sum of the feed cost (Eq. (30)), the product purchasing cost (Eq. (31)), the resource consumption cost (Eq. (32)) minus the income of selling the products (Eq. (33)).

$$\min end o_{cost} = \Sigma_s\, p_s * cost_s \qquad\qquad\qquad\qquad\qquad (28)$$
$$cost_s = feed_{cost} + purchasing_{cost_s} + R_{cost_s} + shutdown_{cost} - selling_s \quad (29)$$
$$feed_{cost} = \Sigma_f\, feed_{price_f} * x_{feed_f} \qquad\qquad\qquad\qquad (30)$$
$$purchasing_{cost_s} = \Sigma_p\, price_p * purchase_{p,s} \qquad\qquad (31)$$
$$R_{cost_s} = \Sigma_i \Sigma_t\, u_{i,t,s} * price_i \qquad\qquad\qquad\qquad (32)$$
$$selling_s = \Sigma_{t,p}\, prices_{p,t} * y_{p,t,s} \qquad\qquad\qquad\qquad (33)$$

4. The solution strategy

The proposed endogenous uncertainty formulation gives rise to a non-convex MINLP due to the bilinear terms in the survival equations and in the objective function (Eqs. (22) - (28)). We solved the deterministic equivalent with the global solver BARON (Kilinc and Sahinidis, 2018) implementing a custom branching strategy. We prioritize the variable influencing the probabilities of the scenarios (degradation variable) along the spatial branch-and-bound algorithm. Additionally, we implemented the Benders algorithm:

- the master problem corresponds to the first stage (all equations except of Eq.(7) for $t \in \{1, ..., 29\}$
- the sub-problem is the aggregation of the scenarios (equations (1) - (8), (17) - (19), (24) - (31) for $t \in \{30, ..., 40\}$).

A novel multi-stage stochastic formulation with decision-dependent probabilities for condition-based maintenance optimization

1799

After the solution of the master problem is passed to the sub-problem, the probabilities of the scenarios are fixed and therefore the sub-problem is a linear program whose solution provides also the dual variables to compute the optimality cuts in the Benders decomposition. However, in the case of bilinear terms, the Benders decomposition is not guaranteed to converge to the global optimum.

5. Results

5.1. Computational results

Table 1 presents the computational results obtained solving the deterministic equivalent problem with a custom branching and the Benders decomposition. The results show that the Benders decomposition clearly outperforms the global solver. The influence of the custom branching is very limited (the same results were obtained solving the deterministic equivalent without the custom branching). The reason might be the fact that even when the probabilities of the scenarios are branched, the problem remains an MINLP due to the nonlinear survival constraints (Eq. (22)).

Table 1 Computational results (time limit 3600 [s]) - UB is the best feasible solution found

	z^*	CPU [s]
DE with custom branching (BARON)	22423.2 (UB = 22423.2, LB = -4917.89)	3600
Benders Decomposition	17669.16 (UB=17669.16, LB= 17669.16)	383.6

5.2. Discussion

We compare the results obtained solving the proposed formulation with the Benders algorithm (upper and lower bounds shown in Figure 3) and the solution of the deterministic optimization problem where the degradation model is assumed to be perfectly known. The Value of the Stochastic Solution is equal 3031.43 (16.6%) (the objective value of the stochastic program is equal to 17669.16 and the objective value of the recourse problem is equal to 20700.6). The resulting cost items for the stochastic program and the recourse program (where the first stage variables are fixed to the solution of the deterministic problem) are shown in Figure 2. Figures 4 - 6 show the degradation trajectories, the timing of the maintenance activities, the feed purchasing strategies and the production levels. The stochastic approach proposes a different operating strategy compared to the deterministic optimization: the stochastic optimization anticipates the maintenance activities, increasing the production rates to reduce the product purchasing in all the scenarios. It is worth to highlight that the SP identifies also a different optimal feed purchasing strategy thereby reducing the feed cost. Figure 7 shows how the optimization shapes the probabilities of the scenarios via the prognosis variables (the survival and hazard functions).

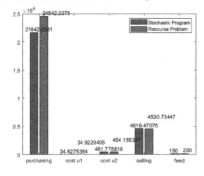

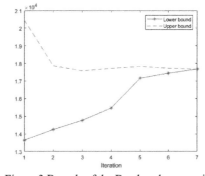

Figure 2 Cost items   Figure 3 Bounds of the Benders decomposition

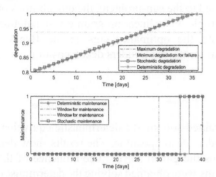

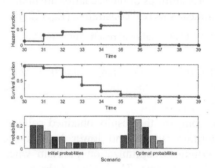

Figure 4 Degradation and maintenance profiles

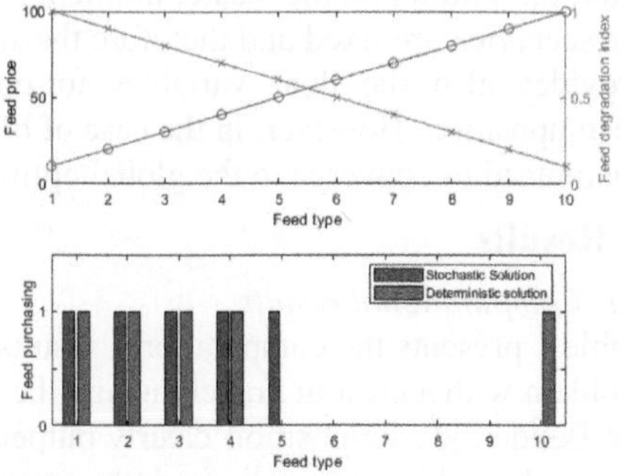

Figure 5 Feed purchasing strategy

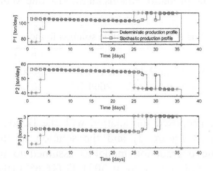

Figure 6 Production profiles

Figure 7 Prognosis variables

6. Conclusion

An endogenous uncertainty stochastic programming formulation is proposed to integrate condition-based maintenance, production planning and prognosis. The advantages of the proposed formulation and the benefit of the Benders decomposition are shown on a continuous plant. There are several open questions for this class of optimization problems from the algorithm design to find the global optimum to the integration of a risk measure.

Acknowledgements: Financial support is gratefully acknowledged from the EID-ITN project "PRONTO", Grant agreement No 675215.

References

E. Leo and S. Engell, Condition-based operational optimization of industrial combined heat and power plants under time-sensitive electricity prices. Proceedings of ESCAPE 27

B Basciftci, S Ahmed, N Gebraeel, M Yildirim, Stochastic Optimization of Maintenance and Operations Schedules under Unexpected Failures. IEEE Transactions on Power Systems, 2018

J. Wiebe, I. Cecílio and R. Misener, Data-Driven Optimization of Processes with Degrading Equipment, Ind. Eng. Chem. Res. 2018

L. Hellemo, P.I. Barton and A. Tomasgard, Decision-dependent probabilities in stochastic programs with recourse, Computational Management Scienc, 2018

Cox, David R (1972). Regression Models and Life-Tables. Journal of the Royal Statistical Society, Series B. 34 (2): 187–220. JSTOR 2985181

Kilinc, M. and N. V. Sahinidis, Exploiting integrality in the global optimization of mixed-integer nonlinear programming problems in BARON, Optimization Methods and Software, 540-62.

Sauro Pierucci, Flavio Manenti, Giulia Bozzano, Davide Manca (Eds.)
Proceedings of the 30th European Symposium on Computer Aided Process Engineering
(ESCAPE30), May 24-27, 2020, Milano, Italy. © 2020 Elsevier B.V. All rights reserved.
http://dx.doi.org/10.1016/B978-0-12-823377-1.50301-3

Efficient Evaluation of Vacuum Pressure-swing Cycle Performance using Surrogate-based, Multi-objective Optimization Algorithm

Héctor Octavio Rubiera Landa,[a] Yoshiaki Kawajiri,[b,a] Matthew J. Realff[a,*]

[a]*School of Chemical & Biomolecular Engineering, Georgia Institute of Technology, 311 Ferst Drive N. W., Atlanta, GA 30332-0100, U.S.A.*
[b]*Department of Materials Process Engineering, Nagoya University, Furo-cho 1, Engineering Building 1, Nagoya, 464-8603, Japan*
matthew.realff@chbe.gatech.edu

Abstract

The performance evaluation of vacuum pressure-swing adsorption (VPSA) cycles with detailed, full-order models (FOMs) is typically a time-consuming and resource-intensive task. Popular state-of-the-art approaches include e.g., dynamic optimization approaches—see e.g., Swartz and Kawajiri (2019); and application of evolutionary algorithms, i.e., genetic algorithms, see e.g., Fiandaca et al. (2009). In this work, we present a strategy that combines two techniques in order to improve the computational efficiency of VPSA process modeling. Firstly, we improve the convergence in the calculation of cyclic steady state (CSS), using the FOM, by treating the calculation task as a fixed-point iteration (FPI) problem. We apply the FPI acceleration method by Anderson (1965) to improve FPI computations. Secondly, we embed the accelerated CSS computation into algorithm 'Surrogate Optimization of Computationally Expensive Multiobjective Problems' (SOCEMO) created by Müller (2017), which specifically addresses multi-objective optimization of expensive-to-evaluate black-box functions. This combination of approaches improves computational performance for Pareto frontier estimation that requires evaluation of process metrics at CSS, without sacrificing high-fidelity of the full-order VPSA model, and thus constitutes an attractive alternative to evaluate cyclic adsorption processes.

Keywords: surrogate-based multi-objective optimization, periodic processes

1. Introduction

The dynamic character of periodic adsorption operations, as well as their required spatiotemporal description, continues to represent a challenge from the computational point of view. The lack of closed-form solutions to the mathematical models applied to represent these processes is traditionally addressed by numerical approximations, which oftentimes can become challenging to solve. Moreover, if the end goal is to conduct parametric investigations or optimization for conceptual process design using these models, we are confronted with a computationally-intensive task. The process optimization of periodic adsorption processes may become even more expensive if we include competitive adsorption equilibria principles with non-trivial adsorption isotherm courses, see e.g., Rubiera Landa et al. (2013), or more-detailed mass-transfer mechanisms meant to describe particle-level adsorption phenomena dynamically. Another potential source of complexity—not addressed herein—is related to multi-column processes with column-interacting steps, e.g., pressure equalization. Therefore, there is an inherent need to develop computational tools & strategies to surmount these challenges.

Investigated vacuum pressure-swing adsorption cycle: The process that we consider in this work is a 4-step VPSA cycle with light-product pressurization (LPP) that targets heavy-product recovery at high purity. Figure 1 illustrates graphically this cycle and its operational steps. We have developed a full-order model (FOM) to describe the dynamic operation of this process applying a thermally-modulated structured fiber contactor in Rubiera Landa et al. (2020b). Interest in these types of adsorbents has grown in the last years driven by process intensification, as well as addressing difficult gas separations such as CO_2 capture by economically-viable routes—see e.g., Bui et al. (2018) and references therein. The applied mathematical model

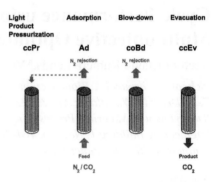

Figure 1: Illustration of investigated 4-step VPSA cycle with light-product pressurization (LPP), applying thermally-modulated fiber composite adsorbent—see DeWitt et al. (2019) & Rubiera Landa et al. (2020b).

consists of a set of one-dimensional, time-dependent PDEs that represent the coupled, nonisothermal, non-isobaric, mass, energy & momentum balances, characterizing the dynamic behavior of a packed-bed adsorber. These equations describe the periodic features of the 4-step VPSA cycle by adscribing appropriate BCs and ICs. The model implementation includes competitive adsorption equilibria as expressed by the Ideal Adsorbed Solution Theory (IAST) developed by Myers and Prausnitz (1965), as well as other well-known explicit competitive equilibria equations. In order to represent thermal modulation, we consider microencapsulated PCM embedded in the fibers as demonstrated by DeWitt et al. (2019). A smooth-interface model, see e.g., Surana et al. (2015), is included in the energy balance equation to account for the phase-transition enthalpy and temperature-dependent physical properties of the PCM. Model details may be consulted in Rubiera Landa et al. (2020b).

2. Methods & algorithms

Numerical solution of model equations: We transform the PDEs that describe adsorber dynamics into a time-dependent ODE system by applying the method of lines with a cell-centered finite-volume spatial discretization (FVM). Cell averages of the

$$state\ variables,\ x = \left[\bar{y}_{1_j}, \bar{q}_{1_j}, \bar{y}_{2_j}, \bar{q}_{2_j}, \bar{p}_j, \bar{T}_j \right]^{\mathrm{T}},\ j = 1, \ldots, J,\ are\ integrated\ in\ time$$

by adaptive step, multi-stepping, backward differentiation formulæ (BDF). This discretization warrants the necessary robustness to treat the adsorber model as a black-box function as required by the applied MOO algorithms.

Genetic algorithms for MOO of VPSA cycle: Several approaches exist to perform MOO of cyclic adsorption processes. If the process simulation is sufficiently robust,

Efficient evaluation of vacuum pressure-swing cycle performance using surrogate-based, multi-objective optimization algorithm

1803

then we can apply evolutionary optimization techniques—e.g., a genetic algorithm (GA). The FOM is hereby treated as a black-box function, without requiring its gradient information, which in turn may be difficult to generate for some adsorption process models. On the other hand, this aspect of evolutionary algorithms can be a drawback, because identifying non-dominated points that constitute the sought-after Pareto frontiers usually requires many function evaluations. Clearly, if these functions are expensive to evaluate, this becomes a computationally-intensive procedure. For the purpose of benchmarking our results, we applied a variant of the well-established NSGA-II algorithm by Deb et al. (2002) to our FOM.

Applied black-box function formulation: The function calls executed by the optimization algorithms entail the CSS simulation of the 4-step VPSA cycle for given values of the design variables and evaluating subsequently process performance metrics that define the objective space of the MOO tasks to solve. The selected design variables, u, include process conditions of the cycle or design parameters of the FOM; these are: 1.) high-pressure level, p_{high} ; 2.) feed gas velocity, v_{feed} ; 3.) adsorption step time, t_{Ad} ; 4.) evacuation pressure level, p_{Ev} ; & 5.) weight fraction of adsorbent in fiber composites, ω_{MOF}. The objective variables considered for the VPSA cycle are: 1.) product purity, $\Phi_{Pu,i}(u)$; 2.) product recovery, $\Phi_{Re,i}(u)$; 3.) productivity, $\Phi_{Prod,i}(u)$; & 4.) specific energy consumption, $\Phi_{En,i}(u)$.

Fixed-point iteration formulation of CSS calculation: Traditionally, calculation of CSS entails the dynamic simulation that the process would follow during transient operation, e.g., start-up. In essence, we simulate for a cycle ℓ , store the vector of state variables, x_ℓ , at a specified time of the cycle, e.g., at the end of the evacuation step, $t = t_{Ev,end}$, and then apply it as IC to obtain the next iterate, $x_{\ell+1}$. This is equivalent to the procedure expressed by Picard Iteration (PI)

$$x_{\ell+1} = g(x_\ell), \quad \ell = 0,1,2,\cdots, \textit{(until convergence)}, \tag{1}$$

where we simply substitute successively x_ℓ in map g to obtain $x_{\ell+1}$. In practice, we verify if CSS is attained by applying e.g., the ℓ_2 -norm, $\| e \|_2 \leq \delta_{tol.}$, with $e := g(x_\ell) - x_{\ell+1}$, for a small, specified threshold, $\delta_{tol.}$. The simulation of the process is therefore formulated as a fixed-point iteration (FPI) task, which can be solved efficiently by applying methods for the acceleration of sequences, such as the vector extrapolation methods published by Sidi (2017).

Anderson Acceleration (AA): An interesting alternative that we investigate in Rubiera Landa et al. (2020a) consists of applying the algorithm developed by Anderson (1965) to accelerate the FPI calculation, Eq. (1), therefore reducing its computational cost. We implement AA as described by Walker and Ni (2011), employing their code. Application of this FPI acceleration technique helps to reduce the cost in terms of number of iterations required to fulfill the CSS condition by factors ranging from 1.3x to **2x** w.r.t. PI, with superlinear convergence rate, as documented in Rubiera Landa et al. (2020a).

Initialization of the fixed-point iteration: The CSS calculation may be initialized in two ways, depending on the IC applied at the start of the dynamic simulations: a) cold-start mode: the adsorber is either free of the more-adsorbed component or has been fully-regenerated; & b) warm-start mode: the adsorber has been partially loaded with adsorbates. Typically, a stored vector of state variables, $x = x(t, z)$, from a previous CSS calculation may be applied to perform warm-start initialization with the purpose of attaining CSS with a smaller number of iterations—this is the mode applied below.

Surrogate-based multi-objective optimization using accelerated black-box function evaluation: We apply the SOCEMO algorithm, a bound-constraint surrogate-based multi-objective optimization strategy created by Müller (2017) that has been designed to address expensive black-box problems with relatively large numbers of decision variables and objectives. In brief, this optimizer generates a radial-basis function (RBF) approximation for each objective constituting the specified multi-objective problem. A careful, well-thought-out algorithm that applies a GA plus adaptive sampling using the RBF surrogates' information aims at reducing the expensive black-box function evaluations—i.e., the accelerated FPI calculations—to a minimum, whilst simultaneously refining the quality of the RBF surrogates as the algorithm continues to identify the Pareto frontiers. This yields a powerful general-purpose MOO solver that can be applied easily to the periodic adsorption process at hand. We denominate the proposed combined solution strategy as 'SOCEMO+AA'.

Investigated MOO task: In order to assess the computational performance of this combination of techniques, we formulate a two-objective (bi-objective, BOO) task and solve it first with NSGA-II, applying the conventional PI and name this strategy 'NSGA-II+PI'. Afterwards, we solve identical tasks applying the 'SOCEMO+AA' strategy.

Table 1: Applied bounds for design variables of BOO Task.

The optimization tasks explore the process performance of the aforementioned 4-step VPSA cycle w/ LPP for a

Variable	p_{high}	v_{feed}	t_{Ad}	p_{Ev}	ω_{MOF}
Units	atm	m / s	s	atm	-
Lower bound	3.0	0.1	15	0.10	0.15
Upper bound	7.5	1.0	120	0.35	0.35

typical dry flue gas stream, employing a thermally modulated fiber composite loaded with a metal-organic framework (MOF) and decision variables' bounds listed in Table 1:

- **BOO Task.** *Identify the Pareto frontier for recovery vs. purity* formulated as:

$$\text{maximize} \quad \{\Phi_{Pu,CO_2}(u), \Phi_{Re,CO_2}(u)\}, \text{s.t.} -\infty \leq u^{lb} \leq u \leq u^{ub} \leq \infty.$$

For 'NSGA-II+PI' we allow a maximum of 30 generations with a population size of 80 function evaluations. In the case of 'SOCEMO+AA' we set a total budget of 150 function evaluations.

Efficient evaluation of vacuum pressure-swing cycle performance using surrogate-based, multi-objective optimization algorithm

1805

3. Results & discussion

Figure 2 illustrates the Pareto frontiers obtained by applying 'NSGA-II+PI' as well as 'SOCEMO+AA' for cold-start and warm-start initialization modes. Table 2 summarizes the computational performance results of all runs. Both strategies allow us to identify non-dominated points accurately at the prescribed tolerances. A slightly worse result was obtained for the particular 'NSGA-II+PI' run executed with cold-start initialization mode. The two runs performed with 'SOCEMO+AA' yielded almost identical Pareto frontiers with good spread, while outperforming slightly the warm-start 'NSGA-II+PI' run in terms of the identified non-dominated points.

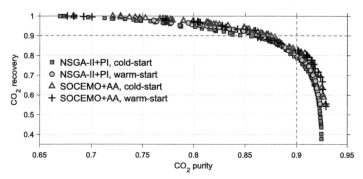

Figure 2: Computed Pareto frontiers for 4-step VPSA cycle w/ LPP applying a thermally-modulated contactor loaded with MOF UTSA-16 as reported by Xiang et al. (2012) and operating at 298 K. Design variables & bounds applied are listed in Table 1. AA parameters $(m = 4, \beta = 1)$ set in 'SOCEMO+AA' runs.

The two results obtained with 'NSGA-II+PI' would likely improve with tighter tolerances and increased function evaluations' budget, at the expense of an even higher computational cost, in order to match the obtained 'SOCEMO+AA' Pareto frontiers. The 'SOCEMO+AA' strategy applying warm-start initialization mode gave the most efficient result, requiring approximately 6 % of the time needed by 'NSGA-II+PI' with cold-start initialization mode. In other words, for this particular example, we achieved roughly a 17-fold reduction in computational cost. The effect of the initialization mode can be observed from the mean times required for computing a single CSS. Both warm-start runs required less time than their cold-start counterparts.

Table 2: Computational costs for solving BOO Task with 'NSGA-II+PI' & 'SOCEMO+AA'. Calculations were performed in MATLAB™ on a PC with i7-3770 CPU at 3.40 GHz & 8 GB RAM.

	NSGA-II+PI cold-start	NSGA-II+PI warm-start	SOCEMO+AA cold-start	SOCEMO+AA warm-start
No. generations (max. 30)	25	30	n/a	n/a
No. function evaluations	2000	2400	160	152
No. non-dominated points	80	80	47	47
Mean calculation time per CSS, s	46	37	84	36
Total calculation time, s	92815	88326	13440	5467

4. Conclusion

We have introduced a powerful and easy-to-implement strategy to perform multi-objective optimization of cyclic adsorption processes, exemplified by a 4-step VPSA cycle designed for CO_2 capture. The strategy consists of applying AA to improve the convergence efficiency to CSS when evaluating expensive black-box function evaluations of FOMs for periodic adsorption processes. In combination with the MOO solver SOCEMO, we estimated the Pareto frontier of a typical VPSA process optimization task in a computationally efficient manner. An important feature of the proposed 'SOCEMO+AA' strategy is that no offline or *a priori* sampling phase needs to be carried out, as it is often required by other meta-modeling techniques, since SOCEMO constructs surrogates of objective functions and identifies non-dominated points *'on the fly'*, i.e., their calculation is embedded in the execution of the algorithm. We demonstrated that a reduction in computational cost of one order of magnitude, with only a fraction of the number of black-box function evaluations needed by a GA, can be achieved with the proposed strategy, preserving high-fidelity of the optimization results.

Acknowledgement: We thank the U.S. Department of Energy for support through grant DE-FE0026433. Any opinions, findings, conclusions or recommendations expressed herein are those of the authors and do not necessarily reflect the views of the DOE.

References

D. G. M. Anderson, 1965. Iterative Procedures for Nonlinear Integral Equations. Journal of the Association for Computing Machinery 12 (4), 547-560.

M. Bui, C. S. Adjiman, A. Bardow, E. J. Anthony, A. Boston, S. Brown, P. S. Fennell, S. Fuss, A. Galindo, L. A. Hackett, J. P. Hallett, H. J. Herzog, G. Jackson, J. Kemper, S. Krevor, G. C. Maitland, M. Matuszewski, I. S. Metcalfe, C. Petit, G. Puxty, J. Reimer, D. M. Reiner, E. S. Rubin, S. A. Scott, N. Shah, B. Smit, J. P. M. Trusler, P. Webley, J. Wilcox, N. M. Dowell, 2018. Carbon capture and storage (CCS): the way forward. Energy & Environmental Science 11 (5), 1062-1176.

K. Deb, A. Pratap, S. Agarwal, T. Meyarivan, 2002. A Fast and Elitist Multiobjective Genetic Algorithm: NSGA-II. IEEE Transactions on Evolutionary Computation 6 (2), 182-197.

S. J. A. DeWitt, H. O. Rubiera Landa, Y. Kawajiri, M. J. Realff, R. P. Lively, 2019. Development of Phase-Change-Based Thermally Modulated Fiber Sorbents. Industrial & Engineering Chemistry Research 58 (15), 5768-5776.

G. Fiandaca, E. S. Fraga, S. Brandani, 2009. A multi-objective genetic algorithm for the design of pressure swing adsorption. Engineering Optimization 41 (9), 833-854.

J. Müller, 2017. SOCEMO: Surrogate Optimization of Computationally Expensive Multiobjective Problems. INFORMS Journal on Computing 29 (4), 581-596.

A. L. Myers, J. M. Prausnitz, 1965. Thermodynamics of Mixed-Gas Adsorption. AIChE Journal 11 (1), 121-127.

H. O. Rubiera Landa, D. Flockerzi, A. Seidel-Morgenstern, 2013. A Method for Efficiently Solving the IAST Equations with an Application to Adsorber Dynamics. AIChE Journal 59 (4), 1263-1277.

H. O. Rubiera Landa, R. P. Lively, Y. Kawajiri, M. J. Realff, 2020a. Applying Anderson Acceleration to improve the simulation efficiency of periodic adsorption processes. (in preparation).

H. O. Rubiera Landa, R. P. Lively, Y. Kawajiri, M. J. Realff, 2020b. Theoretical investigation of vacuum pressure-swing adsorption process using thermally-modulated fiber composite adsorbents. (in preparation).

A. Sidi, 2017. Vector Extrapolation Methods with Applications. SIAM Series on Computational Science & Engineering. Society for Industrial and Applied Mathematics, ISBN 978-1-61197-495-9.

K. S. Surana, A. D. Joy, L. A. Quiros Fonseca, J. N. Reddy, 2015. Mathematical Models and Numerical Solutions of Liquid-Solid and Solid-Liquid Phase Change. Journal of Thermal Engineering 1 (2), 61-98.

C. L. E. Swartz, Y. Kawajiri, 2019. Design for dynamic operation – A review and new perspectives for an increasingly dynamic plant operating environment. Computers & Chemical Engineering 128, 329-339.

H. F. Walker, P. Ni, 2011. Anderson Acceleration for Fixed-Point Iterations. SIAM Journal on Numerical Analysis 49 (4), 1715-1735.

S. Xiang, Y. He, Z. Zhang, H.Wu,W. Zhou, R. Krishna, B. Chen, 2012. Microporous metal-organic framework with potential for carbon dioxide capture at ambient conditions. Nature Communications 3 (954), 1-9.

Sauro Pierucci, Flavio Manenti, Giulia Bozzano, Davide Manca (Eds.)
Proceedings of the 30th European Symposium on Computer Aided Process Engineering
(ESCAPE30), May 24-27, 2020, Milano, Italy. © 2020 Elsevier B.V. All rights reserved.
http://dx.doi.org/10.1016/B978-0-12-823377-1.50302-5

QMaC: A Quantum Mechanics/Machine Learning-based Computational Tool for Chemical Product Design

Qilei Liu, Kun Tang, Jinyuan Zhang, Yixuan Feng, Chenyang Xu, Linlin Liu, Jian Du, Lei Zhang*

Institute of Chemical Process Systems Engineering, School of Chemical Engineering, Dalian University of Technology, Dalian 116024, China
keleiz@dlut.edu.cn

Abstract

Chemical industry is focusing more on higher value-added materials compared to commodity chemicals. Chemical-based product design has now become a key topic in chemical engineering. A few computer-aided chemical product design platforms/tools have been developed to help design various chemical products. In this work, a Quantum mechanics/Machine learning-based Computational property prediction tool (QMaC) is developed for chemical product design, aiming to employ the Quantum Mechanics (QM) and Machine Learning (ML) techniques to better design organic solvents, inorganic materials, fertilizers and pesticides, polymers, catalysts and other chemical products for human needs. A case study is given to demonstrate the validity of the developed product design tool.

Keywords: product design, computer-aided molecular design, quantum mechanics, machine learning, surrogate model.

1. Introduction

Chemical-based product design is rapidly becoming a key topic in chemical engineering (Zhang et al., 2017). However, most of products are still designed based on trial-and-error methods, which need much manpower, material and financial resources. Therefore, it is desirable to develop a systematic method to design promising alternatives to satisfy sets of product attributes to serve as candidates for final experimental verification. Computer-Aided Molecular Design (CAMD) technique is a kind of such method (Zhang et al., 2016). It provides a systematic methodology where numerous molecules are assembled and evaluated through a set of predefined descriptors.

Up to now, many computer-aided chemical product design tools have been developed to assist in the chemical product design problems. Gani et al. (1997) developed the ICAS-Integrated Computer Aided System (www.pseforspeed.com/icas/), which combines computer-aided tools for property prediction, simulation, modelling, synthesis/design, analysis and control into a single integrated system. ProCAMD is a molecular product design toolbox based on a multi-level CAMD technique (Harper and Gani, 2000). Samudra and Sahinidis (2013) developed an Automated MOlecular DEsign using Optimization (AMODEO) toolbox to solve the CAMD problem in a non-gradient way. More recently, the VPPD-Lab has developed the chemical product simulator ProCAPD (Kalakul et al., 2017), which offers the options of single species product design, product evaluation, database search, modelling toolbox, multi-species product design templates, and new product template design. Liu et al. (2019) developed an optimization-based framework for molecular and mixture product design, where associated models, solution algorithms and databases are implemented in a toolbox called "OptCAMD". However, even with these recently developed computer-aided tools, chemical product design is still problem specific due to the lack of product property parameters (e.g., binary interaction parameters in UNIFAC model) that obtained from experiments for modeling, and the difficulties in modeling some complex chemical products (e.g., catalysts). Therefore, a computer-aided tool based on quantum mechanics and machine learning techniques has been receiving increasing interest within the PSE community.

In this paper, a Quantum mechanics/Machine learning-based Computational property prediction tool (QMaC) for chemical product design is presented. In Section 2, the QMaC framework that consists of the QM-derived mechanism models and QM-based machine learning models is discussed in detail. In Section 3, a case study is given for highlighting the applications of QMaC tool in chemical product design.

2. QMaC framework

The QMaC framework and its relationships with the database and OptCAMD are shown in Figure 1.

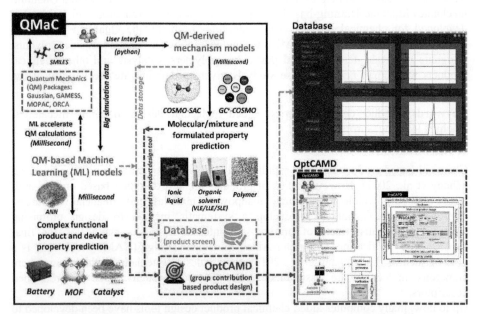

Figure 1. QMaC framework and its relationships with the database and OptCAMD. The input data of QMaC is a set of molecules represented with SMILES (Simplified Molecular Input Line Entry Specification), CAS number or CID number (in PubChem database). QM calculation packages, e.g., Gaussian (Ochterski, 2000), MOPAC (Stewart, 2016), GAMESS (Schmidt et al., 1993), etc., are incorporated into QMaC as the execution module for molecular simulations. The functions of the execution module include molecular structure optimization, single point energy calculation, Gibbs free energy calculation, HOMO-LUMO calculation and all other functions that QM packages provide. Users can select QM packages, execution module functions and functional method/basis set parameters in QMaC interface.

2.1. QM-derived mechanism models

The QM-derived mechanism models, e.g., the COSMO-SAC (COnduct-like Screening Model for Segment Activity Coefficient) model (Hsieh et al., 2010), have been developed using C++ and embedded in the QMaC tool. These models are able to predict molecular/mixture and formulated properties (e.g., activity coefficient, VLE/LLE/SLE) for organic solvents, ionic liquids, etc. Considering the computational cost, some shortcut methods are developed to make fast predictions (in milliseconds) for product properties, for example, the GC$^+$-COSMO method using group contribution-based methods to predict the σ-profiles. In the following we will take the COSMO-SAC model and GC$^+$-COSMO method as the examples for introduction.

2.1.1. COSMO-SAC model

In this paper, the state-of-the-art revised COSMO-SAC model (Hsieh et al., 2010) with its corresponding adjusted model parameters (Chen et al., 2016) is employed in our work. The procedure of the COSMO-SAC model can be divided into three steps.

Step (a). The COSMO calculation procedure starts from the Density Functional Theory (DFT) calculations (a variety of first principles methods in QM calculation), through which the structure of the molecule of interest is optimized and surrounded with a virtual conductor, inducing the screening charge density σ on the conductor surface. In this paper, a database of 1432 molecules (from Virginia Tech database (Mullins et al., 2006)) was established, and DFT calculations were performed by Gaussian 09W software (http://www.gaussian.com/) (Ochterski, 2000) using B3LYP/6-31g(d,p). The COSMO-SAC model parameters are adopted from Chen et al. (2016)'s work, which have been specially reparametrized for B3LYP/6-31g(d,p) functional method/basis set, since these parameters have great impacts on σ-profiles, activity coefficients γ and other activity coefficient related properties.

Step (b). With the screening charges obtained in Step (a), the surface of a molecule is dissected to segments. The segment σ distribution is projected into a two-dimensional discrete profile known as σ-profile.

Step (c). As σ-profiles provide qualitative information to identify isomers, complex molecular interactions, as well as quantitative information on both pure and solvent mixture properties, they are employed for the thermodynamic property calculations. More detailed information of the state-of-the-art revised COSMO-SAC model can be found in the literature (Hsieh et al., 2010; Chen et al., 2016).

2.1.2. GC$^+$-COSMO method

The time-consuming DFT calculations in the COSMO-SAC model have hindered the development of the COSMO-CAMD methodology for molecular design. A shortcut method should be developed to achieve the well-balanced compromise between accuracy and computation efficiency. Up to now, most COSMO-CAMD methodologies employed first-order group based GC-COSMO method to correlate σ-profile with functional groups (Mu et al., 2007). However, the GC-COSMO method has poor predictive powers in some cases when polarity effects exist among highly polar molecules and also has difficulties in identifying the isomers.

In this work, a GC$^+$-COSMO method is developed to solve the above problems, where a strategy of multi-order groups is adopted to introduce new group descriptors for the interactions between polar functional groups and allow the identification for the isomers. The multi-order groups consist of zero, first, second and third-order groups. The zero-order groups are defined as single molecules with small molecular weights (e.g., H_2O). Since the number of single molecules is limited and the GC methods have difficulties in describing small molecules, it is reasonable to define zero-order groups to describe these molecules. The first-order and second-order (super-groups contain several first-order groups) groups are defined as MG (Marrero and Gani (2001)) groups in python scripts. As for the third-order groups, they are obtained from the Bemis/Murcko (BM)-type decomposition (Bemis and Murcko, 1996) method using the RDKit library (Landrum, 2006), which is able to transform the molecules to side chains and core circular skeletons. It should be noted that the QMaC tool has a set of options for GC-COSMO and GC$^+$-COSMO methods.

2.2. QM-based machine learning models

Besides, QMaC also provides abundant simulation data as the inputs or outputs for QM-based Machine Learning (ML) model constructions, which can further be used to predict complex functional product and device properties (e.g., cycling lifespan, selectivity) for battery, MOF, catalyst, etc. Machine learning has strong abilities in autonomously learning data characteristics and fitting nonlinear relationships between chemical product structures and properties, which is an opportunity to design complex chemical products since that the inherent mechanisms of these products are usually unclear and the traditional linear/nonlinear fitting methods often fail to capture the structure-property relationships. What's more, ML is also an efficient surrogate model with high-throughput calculation speed. When the simulation data are worked as the outputs for ML models, i.e., the simulation data are target properties to evaluate the product performances, easily accessible descriptors (e.g., a set of groups) need to be prepared as model inputs for QM-based ML model constructions (Zhang et al., 2018). If the simulation data are worked as the inputs for ML models (e.g., using σ-profiles to predict product properties), it suggested that some surrogate models (e.g., ML models) should be employed to correlate the molecular descriptors (e.g., molecular fingerprints) with the simulation data to ensure the inputs of QM-based ML model can be fast obtained, otherwise the product design efficiency will be limited to the bottleneck of DFT calculations.

2.3. The connection of QMaC to database and OptCAMD

All computation results will be stored in the database and users can make a fast product property screening through it. For example, users can choose 1432 commonly used solvents for COSMO-SAC model predictions. Experimental data can also be identified in this database for model (COSMO-SAC, ML, etc.) parameters fit or model prediction comparison. Besides, both QM-derived mechanism and QM-based ML models can be integrated to the OptCAMD tool to extrapolate their property prediction abilities for high-throughput chemical product design. Once the Quantitative Structure-Property Relationship (QSPR) models and their corresponding shortcut methods are given, the OptCAMD tool is able to design molecular structures within the constraints of molecular structure and product property to maximize/minimize objective functions based on the mathematical optimization-based approaches.

3. Case study

A case study of designing solvents for extracting phenol from wastewater (Liu et al., 2018) is performed through QMaC and OptCAMD tools using the COSMO-SAC model. The objective function is to design a solvent with a large distribution coefficient for phenol. The following groups are selected: CH$_3$, CH$_2$, CH, C, CH$_2$(cyc), CH(cyc), C=C, C=C(cyc), aCH, aC-CH$_3$, OH, CH$_3$CO, CH$_2$CO, CH$_3$COO, CH$_3$O, CH$_2$O, CH-O, COOH, COO, aC-OH. The lower and upper bonds for structure and property constraints and the best designed solvent are shown in Table 1.

A decomposition-based strategy (Karunanithi et al., 2006) was employed to solve the
CAMD problem. 89 molecules were firstly obtained within the constraints of molecular
structure and solvent properties (molecular weight Mw, melting point T_m, boiling point
T_b, solubility parameter $Solp$, density ρ, viscosity η and toxicity LC_{50}), among which 3
molecules were further designed within the constraints of solvent loss Sl, solvent power
Sp and selectivity β. Finally, the best designed solvent is listed in Table 1 for further
experimental verification.

Table 1. The lower and upper bonds for structure and property constraints and the best designed
solvent.

Properties	Lower bound	Upper bound	Properties	Prediction results	Experimental values
N_G	4	8	Molecule	$C_6H_{12}O$	-
N_S	-	7	Molecular structure		-
N_F	1	7			
Mw (g/mol)	74	170	Mw (g/mol)	100.2	100.2
T_m (K)	-	298	T_m (K)	219.6	189.2
T_b (K)	335	468	T_b (K)	377.1	389.6
$Solp$ (MPa$^{1/2}$)	16	22	$Solp$ (MPa$^{1/2}$)	16.1	-
ρ (g/cm^3)	-	0.95	ρ (g/cm^3)	0.763	0.800
η (cP)	-	10	η (cP)	0.494	-
$-\log(LC_{50})$ ($-\log$(mol/L))	-	5	$-\log(LC_{50})$ ($-\log$(mol/L))	2.098	-
Sl	-	0.005	Sl	0.0016	-
Sp	0.5	-	Sp	7.23	-
β	13	-	β	604	-

4. Conclusions

In this paper, a computer-aided property prediction tool (QMaC) for chemical product
design is developed, where quantum mechanics and machine learning techniques are
used. Database and OptCAMD tool are integrated with the QMaC tool for chemical
product screen and design procedure. A case study of designing extraction solvents is
performed, which demonstrates the effectiveness of the QMaC framework.

Acknowledgement

Thanks for the financial support of NSFC [21808025]; National College Students
Innovation and Entrepreneurship Training Program [2019101410101010186].

References

Zhang, L., Mao, H., Liu, L., Du, J., & Gani, R. (2018). A machine learning based computer-aided
molecular design/screening methodology for fragrance molecules. Computers & Chemical
Engineering, 115, 295-308.

Zhang, L., Fung, K. Y., Zhang, X., Fung, H. K., & Ng, K. M. (2017). An integrated framework
for designing formulated products. Computers & Chemical Engineering, 107, 61-76.

Zhang, L., Babi, D. K., & Gani, R. (2016). New vistas in chemical product and process design.
Annual review of chemical and biomolecular engineering, 7, 557-582.

Schmidt, M. W., Baldridge, K. K., Boatz, J. A., Elbert, S. T., Gordon, M. S., Jensen, J. H., ... &
Windus, T. L. (1993). General atomic and molecular electronic structure system. Journal of
computational chemistry, 14(11), 1347-1363.

Samudra, A. P., & Sahinidis, N. V. (2013). Optimization - based framework for computer - aided
molecular design. AIChE Journal, 59(10), 3686-3701.

Ochterski, J.W., 2000. Thermochemistry in gaussian. Gaussian Inc.

Mullins, E., Oldland, R., Liu, Y. A., Wang, S., Sandler, S. I., Chen, C. C., ... & Seavey, K. C. (2006). Sigma-profile database for using COSMO-based thermodynamic methods. Industrial & engineering chemistry research, 45(12), 4389-4415.

Mu, T., Rarey, J., & Gmehling, J. (2007). Group contribution prediction of surface charge density profiles for COSMO‐RS (Ol). AIChE journal, 53(12), 3231-3240.

MOPAC2016, James J. P. Stewart, Stewart Computational Chemistry, Colorado Springs, CO, USA, HTTP://OpenMOPAC.net (2016).

Marrero, J., & Gani, R. (2001). Group-contribution based estimation of pure component properties. Fluid Phase Equilibria, 183, 183-208.

Liu, X., Zhao, Y., Ning, P., Cao, H., & Wen, H. (2018). Modified structural constraints for candidate molecule generation in computer-aided molecular design. Industrial & Engineering Chemistry Research, 57(20), 6937-6946.

Liu, Q., Zhang, L., Liu, L., Du, J., Tula, A. K., Eden, M., & Gani, R. (2019). OptCAMD: An optimization-based framework and tool for molecular and mixture product design. Computers & Chemical Engineering, 124, 285-301.

Landrum, G. (2006). RDKit: Open-source cheminformatics.

Karunanithi, A. T., Achenie, L. E., & Gani, R. (2006). A computer-aided molecular design framework for crystallization solvent design. Chemical Engineering Science, 61(4), 1247-1260.

Kalakul, S., Eden, M. R., & Gani, R. (2017). The chemical product simulator–ProCAPD. In Computer Aided Chemical Engineering (Vol. 40, pp. 979-984). Elsevier.

Hsieh, C. M., Sandler, S. I., & Lin, S. T. (2010). Improvements of COSMO-SAC for vapor–liquid and liquid–liquid equilibrium predictions. Fluid Phase Equilibria, 297(1), 90-97.

Harper, P. M., & Gani, R. (2000). A multi-step and multi-level approach for computer aided molecular design. Computers & Chemical Engineering, 24(2-7), 677-683.

Gani, R., Hytoft, G., Jaksland, C., & Jensen, A. K. (1997). An integrated computer aided system for integrated design of chemical processes. Computers & Chemical Engineering, 21(10), 1135-1146.

Chen, W. L., Hsieh, C. M., Yang, L., Hsu, C. C., & Lin, S. T. (2016). A critical evaluation on the performance of COSMO-SAC models for vapor–liquid and liquid–liquid equilibrium predictions based on different quantum chemical calculations. Industrial & Engineering Chemistry Research, 55(34), 9312-9322.

Bemis, G. W., & Murcko, M. A. (1996). The properties of known drugs. 1. Molecular frameworks. Journal of medicinal chemistry, 39(15), 2887-2893.

Sauro Pierucci, Flavio Manenti, Giulia Bozzano, Davide Manca (Eds.)
Proceedings of the 30th European Symposium on Computer Aided Process Engineering
(ESCAPE30), May 24-27, 2020, Milano, Italy. © 2020 Elsevier B.V. All rights reserved.
http://dx.doi.org/10.1016/B978-0-12-823377-1.50303-7

The Value of Direct Programming the PID Control Law in MATLAB®

Bartolomeo Cosenza, Michele Miccio

Dipartimento di Ingegneria Industriale, Università degli Studi di Salerno,
Via Giovanni Paolo II 132, 84084 Fisciano SA, Italy
mmiccio@unisa.it bartolomeocosenza@hotmail.it

Abstract

This work deals with Matlab® and the PID controller. Frequently, codes implementing PID-controlled case studies as tutorial sessions or examples for undergraduate students are available as programmed in Simulink®, the companion toolbox for block modeling, simulation and analysis of dynamic systems. Vice versa, the student, who has access to the source code and directly operates on it in Matlab®, better masters the underlying theoretical background, develops a greater skill related to coding and understands the computational results in a clearer way. This skill can be useful in any work context, especially where Simulink cannot be used.

In this article a particular didactic approach is suggested for "hands on" the PID controller and the feedback control system, a simple case study based on the classical continuous bioreactor is built together with and for the class students, both set-point tracking and disturbance rejection at closed loop are covered, the most important outcomes are discussed from a didactical viewpoint. The adopted teaching strategy and the various phases necessary to its effective implementation in Matlab® have been subjected to an assessment procedure during the class of "Modeling and control of process systems", with encouraging results.

Keywords: PID controller, Matlab®, bioreactor, feedback, set point tracking, disturbance rejection

1. Introduction

The PID control is known from about 1 century: huge numbers of scientific papers, textbooks and software (either commercial or open source) implementations cope with PID. It continues to be widely and successfully used even for complex and nonlinear processes, alone or integrated with other control strategies. As far as recent applications, a double Q-PID algorithm for mobile robot control was developed by Calucho et al. [2]; Urooj and Singh [3] developed a fractional-order PID control strategy for blood pressure control using sodium nitroprusside during surgical operation; Zhao et al. [4] proposed an adaptive PID control to improve the power tracking performance of solar photovoltaic air-conditioning systems, Miccio and Cosenza [5] developed the control of a distillation column by type-2 and type-1 fuzzy logic PID controllers and a graphical user interface for dynamics and feedback PID control of chemical reactors [6]; the control of a PWR nuclear reactor core power was realized by Mousakazemi [7] using scheduled PID with GA. In all these examples, ranging in all fields of control application, beyond the strategies used, the PID control action remains a simple and effective core of the control system. Matlab® is a well-known programming platform for engineers and scientists, with a lot of free, user-developed codes in the File Exchange repository [1]. Its matrix-based language allows the most natural expression of computational mathematics [8]. To further simplify the study of dynamic systems, Matlab provides the Simulink® toolbox as an interactive, graphical environment for modeling, simulating, and analyzing dynamic systems. The great advantage of Simulink is a graphical user interface (GUI) for building models as block diagrams [9]. Predefined blocks, including the PID controller, are included in a library and can be easily used (drag-and-drop mouse operations) to construct graphical models of systems.

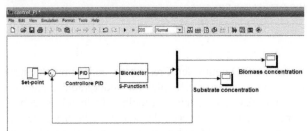

Figure 1. Feedback PID-based control scheme of the continuous bioreactor in a Simulink® worksheet

If it is true that a graphical block programming language in the school makes easy and immediate the student's job on the application of the PID control, it is also true that its excessive use promotes mechanical actions that lead to misunderstanding or even obscuring the content of each block. The greatest difficulty arises when switching from an easy and intuitive pre-packaged simulation environment to a real system whose automatic control, for example, requires non-block programming languages. For this reason it is important that students understand how to implement a PID control system from scratch, without needing pre-packaged blocks. Students must be aware of what they are doing, step by step, to develop computational thinking. This latter is essential not only in engineering, e.g., in computer programs (coding) for practical applications, but also in non-scientific disciplines, e.g., economics, social science, humanities, etc., to develop problem solving skills and tools [10].

In this work a teaching strategy is proposed and discussed to ensure that students implement, in a Matlab® code, the classical PID control algorithm applied to a continuous bioreactor.

2. A case study: bioreactor model and control

Biochemical reactors are usually produce a large number of intermediate and final products, including pharmaceuticals, food and beverages. The simplest bioreactor model needs only two "reacting" components: biomass and substrate. The biomass consists of cells that consume the substrate. The isothermal continuous bioreactor considered in this paper has constant volume V and constant physical-chemical properties. Its state-space dynamical model is given by the following mass balance eqs. [11]:

$$\frac{dX_b}{dt} = \mu(S)X_b - \frac{X_b F}{V} \tag{1}$$

$$\frac{dS}{dt} = -\frac{\mu(S)X_b}{Y} + \frac{(S_F - S)F}{V} \tag{2}$$

$$\mu(S) = \frac{\mu_{max}S}{K_m + S}$$

The considered model is a perfectly stirred continuous bioreactor; it is widely and successfully used for a large number of simplified nonlinear processes. The eqs.1 and 2 originate from the biomass, X_b, and the substrate, S, balance, respectively. Both are coupled through the nonlinear growth rate coefficient $\mu(S)$, in the form proposed by Monod, which is the main source of nonlinearity in the model. The model variables and parameters, together with their values, are reported in [11].

In a process control strategy of the bioreactor, the variation of the substrate feed concentration, S_F, represents a disturbance to the system. The variable to be controlled is the substrate concentration S. The dilution rate, F/V, represents the manipulation variable.

3. Implementation plan

3.1 Teaching strategy

It is well known that learning is effective when starts from a practical and problematic situation. The teacher's purpose is to show how programming skills can be used in many contexts. Some interface devices (for example Arduino® or National Instruments DAQ®) for the control of many real systems do not include the use of block language typical of Simulink®; vice versa, they lend themselves to be programmed by means of Matlab®, i.e., one of the most used programming environments in the educational field. There are many control methodologies of different type and complexity (e.g., Fuzzy, MPC, Feed-Forward, Neural Networks, etc.), but the PID controller, besides being widespread and widely used (as specified in the introduction), represents an excellent test bench for the development of programming skills. To carry out the control, for example that of a bioreactor, it is necessary for the student to acquire the skills to program (coding) a PID controller, ready to be applied to the control of a process variable (such as a tank temperature or, in the case of the bioreactor, the concentration of the substrate).

The present implementation plan is subdivided in sequential phases for the case study of closed loop control of a simple non-linear bioreactor. When possible, the direct Matlab coding is compared to its equivalent in the Simulink® environment.

To motivate the use of PID control, the teacher can focus on some of the recent and novel applications, as those listed in the Introduction. This is the first phase and is very important from a didactical viewpoint, because motivation and interest are the fuel of every learning process.

The following phases deal with actual programming.

3.2 Implementation of discrete time

The teacher must dwell on the fact that a simulation allows to see the behavior of a system (and therefore the trend of the state variables) over time. In Simulink® time is running in background and it is possible to change the start time and stop time for the simulation by entering new values in the "Start time" and "Stop time" fields. The same must be done in a corresponding Matlab® code. The teacher can then suggest the realization of a time interval (*deltat*) between a control action and the next one in a discrete time framework, the initial and final simulation time (*t0* and *tf*, respectively), a vector integration *time* and a count parameter *nstep* as follows:

```
deltat =1;              % interval between a control action and the next
                        % (since the PID always operates on a discrete system);
t0 = 0;                 % initial simulation time;
tf = 200;               % final simulation time (200 hours);
time = [t0:deltat:tf];  % vector of integration times;
nstep = length(time);   % number of steps to consider;
```

3.3 PID controller guided implementation

In the phase 3, the teacher has to recall the PID control law, involving a proportional, integral and derivative action.

the teacher has first to declare the parameters of the controller (with their units) and its *bias*, and, second, to assign them a value:

Kc = 0.5;   *% controller gain;*
tauI =5;   *% integral time constant;*
tauD =0.5;   *% derivative time constant;*
ic0 = 0.3;   *% bias, i.e., value of the control action at time t=0;*

The simply proportional action is

ic = ic0 + Kc*(yysp-y(end,2));   *% proportional controller;*

where *ic* stands for the manipulation variable (the dilution rate, F/V, in the present case study); *y(end,2)* is the state variable to be controlled (the substrate concentration in the bioreactor) and *yysp* is the set-point.

Then, the teacher recalls that a proportional action only is not enough to guarantee the achievement of the set-point: integral action is necessary to avoid offset. At this point, the teacher has to points out that it is necessary to use a numerical method to implement an integral action in a simulation environment. Numerical integration methods can generally be described as combining algebraic evaluations of the integrand to get an approximation to the integral. The simplest numerical integration method is the "rectangle method", assuming that the function has a constant value within each little interval. Students are then invited to implement the integration algorithm in Matlab language as follows:

integral = integral + deltat*(yysp-y(end,2));

Then, the teacher recalls that reaching the set-point is sometimes not enough, but the derivative action is required to speed up or improve the quality of the control action.
Again, in a numerical simulation environment, the true derivative must be approximated by a numerical formula:

$$\frac{dy}{dx} \approx \frac{\Delta y}{\Delta x} = \frac{y_2 - y_1}{x_2 - x_1} \tag{3}$$

Here, the students are invited to adopt the simplest one by considering a unit time step (the true derivative is the limit to zero of the value of the difference quotient Δx). This becomes in Matlab:

derivative=(y(end,2)-y(end-1,2))/(t(end)-t(end-1));

Finally, the students add the above integral and derivative actions to the proportional action as follows:

ic = ic + (Kc/tauI)*integral + tauD*derivative;   *% PID control action*

Taking advantage of the previous code (the one concerning time and the simulation step) the teacher invites the students to write the code of the control system for the set point tracking problem as follows:

```
ysp = 0.18*diag(eye(nstep-1));   % declaration of a row vector with nstep components
                                 % all  equal to 0.18 (initial set-point value);
for i = 60:100
ysp(i) = 0.20;                   %  starting at 60 (time, h) the set-point value
end                              %  is stepped from 0.18 to 0.20;
```

In a similar way (not addressed here for lack of space) the students can implement the control system for the disturbance rejection problem. With appropriate modifications, different time-variation laws of set-points and disturbances can be embodied within the Matlab simulation environment. Further, the effects of changing the PID parameters (tuning) can be investigated.

3.4 Implementation of the bioreactor model

This is perhaps the simplest phase of the whole work, because it is quite easy to write, in Matlab language, the mathematical model of the bioreactor. The teacher may advise to write the code in a different file, paying attention to the use of parentheses (a simple out-of-place parenthesis can compromise the whole simulation) as follows:
M.file (Bioreactor)

```
function yp = Bioreactor (t,y)    % y(1) and y(2) are state variables, respectively biomass
                                  % and substrate concentration. y(2) is the controlled
                                  % variable;
global Y km k1 mumax              % System parameters;
global ic yysp  ssf               % ic is the manipulation variable; yysp is the set-point
                                  % variable (included in ic) and ssf the disturbance;
yp = zeros(2,1);
yp(1) = y(1)*((mumax*y(2)/(km+y(2)))-ic);
yp(2) = ic*(ssf-y(2))-y(1)*(mumax*y(2)/(km+y(2)))/Y;
```

The teacher focuses on the mathematical model and on what it represents. It is therefore appropriate to briefly describe the characteristics of the bioreactor in question, focusing on the aspects related to the control (as highlighted in the section on bioreactor model and control). It is important for the students, before control the system, to know what the system is for, what its practical purpose is, what it produces, and what the reaction products are for. It would not make sense to ask for the control of something to be an end in itself, a mere speculative exercise without practical implications.

3.5 Simulation at closed loop

The next phase gets into the heart of the simulation. Within this 4th phase, the teacher introduces the students to a Matlab built-in ode system solver, for example ODE 45, and to a plotting command (not addressed here for lack of space).
Finally, the students get the plot of their simulated results. Just as a proving example, Fig. 2 reports the graph obtained from a simulation of the bioreactor control system that provides for set-point tracking and disturbance rejection.

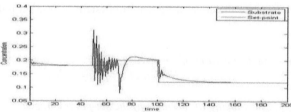

Figure 2. Time evolution of the substrate concentration after two step changes in the set-point: from 0.18 to 0.2 at time 60 h and from 0.20 to 0.12 at time 100 h; step disturbance in feed concentration from 4 to 5 at time 50 h and from 5 to 3 at time 70 h.

4. Evaluation results and conclusions

The simulation task on the control of a bioreactor was carried with 21 students in the class, who were asked to undergo an assessment test. Fig. 3 shows the marks obtained by the students (evaluation) and the grade that each student has attributed to the proposed teaching activity (auto-evaluation).

Both of the scores represent promising results. It is therefore concluded that the activity improved the sense of self-efficacy in each student and helped develop digital skills.

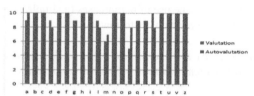

Figure 3. Evaluation and auto-evaluation for each student in the class.

References

[1] https://it.mathworks.com/matlabcentral/fileexchange, last visited on October 11, 2019
[2] I. Carlucho, M. De Paula, G. G. Acosta, 2019, Double Q-PID algorithm for mobile robot control Expert Systems with Applications, Vol. 137, Pages 292-307.
[3] S. Urooj, B. Singh, 2019, Fractional-order PID control for postoperative mean arterial blood pressure control scheme, Procedia Computer Science, Vol. 152, Pages 380-389.
[4] B.Y. Zhao, Z. G. Zhao, Y. Li, R. Z. Wang, R. A. Taylor, 2019, An adaptive PID control method to improve the power tracking performance of solar photovoltaic air-conditioning systems, Renewable and Sustainable Energy Reviews, Vol. 113.
[5] M. Miccio, B. Cosenza, 2014, Control of a distillation column by type-2 and type-1 fuzzy logic PID controllers, Journal of process control, Vol. 24, Pages 475–484.
[6] Cosenza B., Miccio M., 2017, A graphical user interface for dynamics and Feedback Control Studies: Focus On Chemical Reactors Proc. of the 5th Int. Conference on Advances In Civil, Structural and Environmental Engineering – ACSEE'17, Roma. Best paper certificate 5th ACSEE.
[7] S. Mohammad, H. Mousakazemi, 2019, Control of a PWR nuclear reactor core power using scheduled PID controller with GA, based on two-point kinetics model and adaptive disturbance rejection system, Annals of Nuclear Energy, Vol. 129, Pages 487-502.
[8] A. Stormy, Matlab – 5th Edition, 2018, A practical introduction to programming and problem solving, Butterworth-Heinemann.
[9] S.T. Karris, 2011, Introduction to Simulink: with engineering applications (third edition), Orchard Pubns.
[10] J. Krauss, K. Prottsman 2016, Computational Thinking {and Coding} for Every Student, Corwin.
[11] B.W. Bequette, 1998, Process dynamics: modeling, analysis and simulation. New Jersey: Prentice Hall, p. 534.

Sauro Pierucci, Flavio Manenti, Giulia Bozzano, Davide Manca (Eds.)
Proceedings of the 30th European Symposium on Computer Aided Process Engineering
(ESCAPE30), May 24-27, 2020, Milano, Italy. © 2020 Elsevier B.V. All rights reserved.
http://dx.doi.org/10.1016/B978-0-12-823377-1.50304-9

Treated Industrial Wastewater as a Water and Nutrients Source for Tomatoes Cultivation: an Optimisation Approach

Fatima-zahra Lahlou,[a] Sarah Namany,[a] Hamish R. Mackey,[a] Tareq Al-Ansari[a,b]

[a]*Division of Sustainable Development, College of Science and Engineering, Hamad Bin Khalifa University, Qatar Foundation, Qatar*
[b]*Division of Engineering Management and Decision Sciences, Hamad Bin Khalifa University, Qatar Foundation, Qatar*
talansari@hbku.edu.qa

Abstract

The need to meet growing demands for food products is heavily associated with intensive exploitation of energy and water resources to drive the operations for irrigation, production of fertilisers, transportation and machinery amongst other key operations, which result in the emissions of greenhouse gases (GHG). The reuse of treated industrial wastewater (TIW) represents a promising alternative for growing food products in water scarce regions, as it reduces the reliance on renewable water sources whilst remaining an important source of nutrients. In this work, the potential for using TIW to cultivate tomato is investigated through a mixed-integer linear program aimed at minimising the environmental impact represented by the global warming potential (GWP). The optimisation model developed determines the optimal configuration of industries generating TIW that satisfy the crop water requirement and nutrients intake. Transportation emission along with the offset of GHG generated from fertilisers production are used as criterions impacting the selection of the optimal sources of TIW generating industries. Outcomes suggest that for the practise to be carbon neutral, tomato water requirements should be obtained from various sources to meet water and nutrients whilst minimising the GWP emissions. To satisfy the potassium requirements, fruit and vegetable processing plants along with cement industries represent the most optimal TIW sources. As for the nitrogen intake, it should be fulfilled from TIW originating from meat and poultry slaughterhouses.

Keywords: industrial treated wastewater, nutrient recovery, fertigation, optimization, tomato.

1. Introduction

With the significant rise in the global population, the demand for food products is expecting a large increase that requires agricultural intensification and heavy cultivation activities. Irrigation is one of the major inputs for food production, which frequently is sourced from unsustainable sources, such as energy-intensive desalination processes or over-abstraction of groundwater. Both means contribute to resources depletion along with environmental emissions. Deploying sustainable water resources were proven efficient in reducing the environmental impact associated with conventional water systems such as groundwater (Namany et al., 2019). Treated industrial wastewater (TIW) represents a promising water substitute for crops irrigation. Agricultural irrigation requires high levels of nutrients for optimal growth of crops. The use of TIW in agriculture can alleviate the burden resulting from the significant use of chemical fertilizers. In 2016, carbon emissions associated with agriculture were estimated at 49 Mt CO_2eq.year^{-1} (USEPA, 2019). One of the main contributors to these emissions is the use of commercial fertilisers, especially ammonia, which is produced through the natural gas intensive Haber-Bosch process. The main benefit of using TIW instead of raw wastewater (RW) resides in their diminished number of harmful contaminants whilst maintaining a large proportion of the original nutrients content. In contrast to RW, use of TIW for irrigation purposes does not; deteriorate soil characteristics, induce plant root diseases, and alter plant features such as height, length and leaf area (Neto et al., 2012). Rather, it was observed to have positive impacts on the soil fertility and plant growth. Foglia et al. (2019) examined the produced water from an anaerobic membrane bioreactor treatment process that requires low energy. The effluent constitutes high nitrogen (N) and phosphorus (P) levels, with 60 mg.L^{-1} and 6 mg.L^{-1} concentrations respectively, thus reducing the reliance on commercial fertilisers. Another study found that only 50% of gerberas flowers' water requirement need to come from nutrient solution, while the rest can be sourced from treated wastewater (Damasceno et al., 2010). Urbano et al. (2017) found that *Escherichia coli* levels were either undetectable or below the national threshold values established by the Spanish royal decree when irrigating lettuce with TIW. The same was observed with bacteria levels in pepper cultivation, which was not hindered during the legume's growth stages (Dagianta et al., 2014). In addition, wastewater produced from different industries contains diverse levels of contaminants, especially nutrients, due to the difference in the industrial processes for which the water is exposed to prior to treatment. For instance, wastewater produced from dairy processing industries contains high levels of phosphorus with values that can reach up to 700 mg.L^{-1} (Gil-Pulido et al., 2018). Alternatively, meat and poultry industries, contain phosphorus levels that do not exceed 300 mg.L^{-1}, although nitrogen concentrations can reach 6000 mg.L^{-1} (Martí-Herrero et al., 2018; Muhmood et al., 2019). For this reason, each industry uses different wastewater treatment processes to reach acceptable levels of discharge. In the light of the multiple advantages associated with the usage of TIW for irrigation systems, this paper investigates the benefits of using TIW as an alternative water and nutrients source for tomato crop cultivation, which represent an important segment in the agricultural sector, with the highest share in the area dedicated for vegetables cultivation (MDPS, 2017). It suggests an optimisation framework aiming to identify the set of TIW generating industries that minimise GWP emissions while satisfying the needs of the crop from nutrients and water.

2. Methods and methodology

2.1. Cultivation Area and Irrigation Standards

The farm chosen for this study is Wadi Al Araig. Situated in the south west of the State of Qatar, it is characterized with an area of 70 ha, and has a high average yield of tomato with 47.7 ton.ha^{-1} (Hashim, 2009). For this study, the contaminants considered in the irrigation water standards are the chemical oxygen demand (COD), biological oxygen demand (BOD), and total suspended solids (TSS), which need to be maintained at levels lower than 150, 30 and 50 mg.L^{-1} (Ras Laffan City, 2005).

2.2. Water and Nutrients Requirements

The potential evapotranspiration rates of tomato are computed using the Penman Monteith Equation (1) and the adjusted crop coefficient ($k_{c,adj}$) (Allen et al., 1998) for the

210 day cultivation period which is chosen to start in September to be able to have minimal crop water requirements.

$$ET_0 = \frac{0.408\,\Delta\,(R_n-G)+\gamma\,\frac{900}{T+273}u_2\,(e_s-e_a)}{\Delta+\gamma(1+0.34\,u_2)} \tag{1}$$

With Δ being the slope of the vapour pressure curve, $(R_n - G)$ is the difference between the net radiation measured at the crop surface and the heat flux density of the soil, γ is the psychometric constant, T is the temperature of the air, u_2 is the speed of the wind, $(e_s - e_a)$ is the deficit of the saturation vapour pressure.

The weather characteristics are retrieved from the closest meteorological station to the farm and from the literature. The irrigation technique used in Wadi Al Araig farm is the furrow method, which is found to have an irrigation efficiency of 60% (η) (Brouwer et al., 1989). The nutrients required for optimum growth of tomato are found from the literature. It is reported that for a yield approaching 50 ton.ha^{-1}, 290, 34 and 383 kg.ha^{-1} of N, P and K are required, respectively.

2.3. TIW source and quality

The industries chosen for this study are the ones that are important in the industrial sector, meaning that they generate significant amounts of wastewater (Sawe, 2018). The iron and steel, cement, meat and poultry, dairy processing and fruits and vegetables canning industries are the ones considered in this study. Table 1 shows the industries from the different sectors, their distances from the farm, and their N, P, K and contaminants concentrations. Due to lack of data regarding the effluent's nutrient and contaminant concentrations, the ones used in this study are retrieved from U.S.A based industries which adhere to the USEPA discharge guidelines. The industry retained from each sector is the closest one to the farm, in order to reduce the energy associated with water transportation.

Table 1: Distances from industries from six different sectors to Wadi Al Araig farm, and their nutrients and contaminants concentrations.

Name of the Industry	Distance (km)	Contaminants' concentration (mg.L^{-1})					
		N	P	K	TSS	COD	BOD
1- Iron and steel industry							
-Etihad Steel Factory	82	12	1.3	13	53	26	8.6
-Panorama Steel Aljaber Group	82						
-Qatar Steel	83						
2- Cement manufacturing							
-Qatar National Cement Co	68	3.9	0.6	235	77	41	6.7
-United Golf Cement Company	105						
-Al Jabor Cement Industries Company	105						
- Al Khalij Cement Company	84						
3- Meat and poultry production							
-Arab Qatari Company for Poultry Production	125	172	64	209	90	585	268
4- Petroleum refining							
Qatar Petroleum Oil Refinery	116	4.3	1.1	21	30	64	8.2
5- Canned fruits and vegetables processing							
Al Manal Food Factory	81	2.3	1.8	242	26	32	70
Gulf Food Production Factory	81						
Tasco Factory for Food Production	-						
6- Dairy processing							
Baladna	136	4.4	4.4	3.3	39	35	101

2.4. Optimization Model

A mixed integer linear optimization model was developed in Matlab®. The objective of the optimization was to minimize the carbon footprint (CF) associated with the fertigation using the TIW, as described in Equation (2), while meeting the water and ±5% of the nutrients demands of tomato, and while respecting the irrigation water standards.

$$CF = \sum_{i=1}^{6} 2.7 \frac{0.041 \, x_i \, k_{c,adj} \, ET_0}{37.5 \, \eta} \, d_i - \sum_{i=1}^{6}(19.13 \, n_i +$$

$$4.28 \, p_i + 3.37 \, k_i) \, x_i \frac{k_{c,adj} \, ET_0}{1000 \, \eta} \tag{2}$$

Where x_i is the decision variable and it designates the percentage of total water required that will come from industry i (%), d_i is the distance between the farm and industry i (km), n_i, p_i, and k_i are the N, P and K concentration in the TIW originating from industry i (mg.L^{-1}). The reference evapotranspiration ET_0 (m^3.ha^{-1}) is multiplied by the crop coefficient of tomato ($k_{c,adj}$) to take into consideration the crop characteristics at the different growth stages.

The CF computation takes into consideration the energy required to transport in truck tankers the total water required for optimum tomato growth as well as the CF offset from relying on the TIW as a source of nutrients instead of energy intensive chemical fertilizers. The energy required for the TIW treatment is not considered as, in all cases, it needs to be treated to meet discharge quality. Truck tankers use 0.041 L of diesel per km, and have an average capacity of 37.5 m^3 (International Council on Clean Transportation, 2017). Each litre of diesel consumed is found to emit 2.7 kg-$CO_{2,eq}$ into the air (Australian Bureau of Statistics, 2007). The CF associated with the use of 1 kg of N, P and K when produced using natural gas is found to be equal to 10.9, 2.4, 1.9 kg-$CO_{2,eq}$, respectively (Gellings and Parmenter, 2004).

Equalities associated with the optimisation are:

$$\sum_{i=1}^{6} x_i = 1 \tag{3}$$

Inequalities associated with the optimisation are:

$$\forall \, x_i \, s.t. \, i \in (1-6), x_i \geq 0 \qquad ; \qquad 0.95 \, N_R \leq \sum_{i=1}^{6} n_i \frac{x_i \, ET_c}{1000 \, \eta} \leq 1.05 \, N_R$$

$$0.95 \, P_R \leq \sum_{i=1}^{6} p_i \frac{x_i \, ET_c}{1000 \, \eta} \leq 1.05 \, P_R \qquad ; \qquad 0.95 \, K_R \leq \sum_{i=1}^{6} k_i \frac{x_i \, ET_c}{1000 \, \eta} \leq 1.05 \, K_R$$

$$\sum_{i=1}^{6} TSS_i \, x_i < 50 \qquad ; \qquad \sum_{i=1}^{6} COD_i \, x_i < 150 \qquad ; \qquad \sum_{i=1}^{6} BOD_i \, x_i < 30$$

3. Results and discussion

3.1. Tomato Water Requirements

The water requirements of tomato are found to be equal to 6580 m^3, with a maximum daily evapotranspiration rate equalling 6.7 mm. This rate was observed on the 12th of March and is mainly due to the high temperature and wind speed on that day which averaged 29 °C and 8.1 m.s^{-1} and reached 38 °C and 13.1 m.s^{-1}. The lowest rate recorded was witnessed on the 27th of December which was characterized with relatively low temperatures and wind speeds.

3.2. Optimization Model Results

No solution was found which meets the objective while satisfying all the constraints. In fact, the N requirement of tomato cannot be met with fertigation using TIW only. Therefore the model was changed into a multi-objective optimization one where the constraint related to N was omitted, and where a new objective was added which is to maximize NT, the total N provided to the crop (Equation (3)).

$$NT = \sum_{i=1}^{6} n_i \frac{x_i\, k_{c,adj}\, ET_0}{1000\, \eta} \qquad (4)$$

The function used is "gamultiobj". The optimal pareto front of the multi-objective optimization is shown in Figure 1. All of the solutions result in more or less the same output. The average optimal solution supplies tomato with 125.7 kg-N.ha^{-1}, and offset as much as 2,116 kg-CO$_{2\text{-eq}}$. Table 2 shows the corresponding water allocation from the six industries. Most of the N and P will be supplied from the meat and poultry production industry's effluents, with almost 54% and 79% of the total requirements supplied from these two industries, respectively. 41.6% of total K required for tomato cultivation will come from canned fruits and vegetables processing industries. The BOD and TSS values happen to be equal to the irrigation limits, while the COD level supplied to the crop is lower than the maximum level allowed. This practise is environmentally friendly as it offsets the CF resulting from the transportation of the TIW. In addition, it can also offset the energy required for the remaining N needed. Even if the remaining 164.32 kg-N.ha^{-1} is provided through chemical fertilizers, for which carbon the footprint is computed to be equivalent to 1,775.28 kg-CO$_{2\text{-eq}}$, the practise will remain carbon neutral. Thereafter, each ton produced will offset more than 8 kg-CO$_{2\text{-eq}}$. Fertigation using TIW in the whole farm will result in a yearly CF offset of 27 ton-CO$_{2,eq}$.

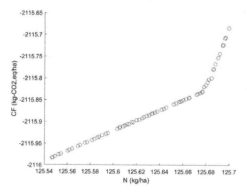

Figure 1: Optimal pareto front for the optimization model.

Table 2: Allocation of the water from the various industries, and the final contaminants concentration and nutrients supply. 1 – Iron and steel industry, 2 – Cement manufacturing, 3 – Meat and poultry, 4 – Petroleum refining, 5 – Canned fruit and vegetables processing, 6 – Dairy products processing.

Industry	%total water	TSS	COD	BOD	N	P	K
		(mg.L^{-1})				(kg)	
1	65.36%	34.80	17.32	5.61	50.92	5.55	57.76
2	3.27%	2.53	1.33	0.22	0.83	0.13	50.55
3	6.01%	5.41	35.20	16.14	67.96	25.30	82.99
4	15.82%	4.78	10.20	1.29	4.52	1.21	21.86
5	9.54%	2.48	3.03	6.73	1.44	1.13	151.86
6	0%	0	0	0	0	0	0
	Total	50.00	67.09	30.00	125.68	33.31	365.02

4. Conclusion

A water planning framework for tomato cultivation in a farm in the State of Qatar was developed. It was found that the TIW cannot supply all of the N demand of tomato which happens to be very high. Alternately, P and K demand were successfully satisfied, mainly from the meat and poultry industry and from the canned fruits and vegetables industry. This practice was found to be carbon neutral, which emphasizes on the sustainability of this fertigation technique. In future work, the study does not necessarily have to be limited to the biggest industries in Qatar. A better estimation of the fertilizers' embodied energy can be calculated depending on the country from which they are imported. Environmental burden can be evaluated using other parameters such as the water footprint.

References

R.G. Allen, L.S.Pereira, D. Raes, M. Smith, 1998, Guidelines for computing crop water requeriments, FAO Irrigation and drainage paper, https://doi.org/10.1016/j.eja.2010.12.001

Arabian Business, 2014, Qatar's top 30 companies [WWW Document]. URL:https://www.arabianbusiness.com/

Australian Bureau of Statistics, 2007, Survey of Motor Vehicle Use.

C. Brouwer, K. Prins, M. Heibloem, 1989, Irrigation Water Management: Irrigation Scheduling Training, Food and Agriculture Organization of the United Nations.

E. Dagianta, D. Goumas, T. Manios, N. Tzortzakis, 2014, The use of treated wastewater and fertigation in greenhouse pepper crop as affecting growth and fruit quality. Journal of Water Reuse and Desalination, 4(2), 92–99. https://doi.org/10.2166/wrd.2014.048

L. M. O. Damasceno, A. S. de Andrade Júnior, H. R. Gheyi, 2010, Cultivation of gerbera irrigated with treated domestic effluents. Revista Brasileira de Engenharia Agrícola e Ambiental, 14(6), 582–588. https://doi.org/10.1590/s1415-43662010000600003

G. Foglia, G. Cipolletta, N. Frison, S. Sabbatini, S. Gorbi, A. L. Eusebi, F. Fatone, 2019, Anaerobic membrane bioreactor for urban wastewater valorisation: Operative strategies and fertigation reuse. Chemical Engineering Transactions, 74(November 2018), 247–252. https://doi.org/10.3303/CET1974042

C. Gellings, K. Parmenter, 2004, Production and use, In Knowledge for Sustainable Development—An Insight into the Encyclopedia of Life Support Systems II, 419–450.

B. Gil-Pulido, E. Tarpey, E. L. Almeida. , W. Finnegan, X. Zhan, A.D.W. Dobson, N.O'Leary, 2018, Evaluation of dairy processing wastewater biotreatment in an IASBR system: Aeration rate impacts on performance and microbial ecology, Biotechnol, Reports 19, e00263.

M. A. Hashim, 2009,Water, Agriculture and Environment in Arid Lands: Water and Agricultural Vision by 2020 ,Friends of Environment Center.

International Council on Clean Transportation, 2017, Fuel Consumption Standards for Heavy - Duty Vehicles in India 1–9.

Ministry of Development Planning and Statistics, 2017, Agricultural Statistics.

S. Namany, R. Govindan, T. Al-Ansari, 2019, Optimisation of the energy, water, and food nexus for food security scenarios, Computers & Chemical Engineering, 129, 106513.

O. N. S. Neto, J. A. Filho, N. da S. Dias, J. R. L. Rebouças, F. R. A. de Oliveira, A. A. Diniz, 2012, Fertigação do algodoeiro utilizando efluente doméstico tratado. Revista Brasileira de Engenharia Agricola e Ambiental, 16(2), 200–208. https://doi.org/10.1590/S1415-43662012000200011

Ras Laffan City, 2005, Environmental Regulations for Ras Laffan Industrial City 30.

B.E. Sawe, 2018, What Are The Biggest Industries In Qatar? [WWW Document]. WorldAtlas. URL https://www.worldatlas.com

V. R. Urbano, T. G. Mendonça, R. G. Bastos, C. F. Souza, 2017, Effects of treated wastewater irrigation on soil properties and lettuce yield. Agricultural Water Management, 181, 108–115. https://doi.org/https://doi.org/10.1016/j.agwat.2016.12.001

USEPA, 2019, Inventory of U.S Greenhouse Gas Emissions and Sinks. 53(9), 1689–1699.

Sauro Pierucci, Flavio Manenti, Giulia Bozzano, Davide Manca (Eds.)
Proceedings of the 30th European Symposium on Computer Aided Process Engineering
(ESCAPE30), May 24-27, 2020, Milano, Italy. © 2020 Elsevier B.V. All rights reserved.
http://dx.doi.org/10.1016/B978-0-12-823377-1.50305-0

Uncovering the True Cost of Ionic Liquids using Monetization

Husain Baaqel,[a] Victor Tulus,[b,c] Benoit Chachuat,[a] Gonzalo Guillén-Gosálbez[b,*] Jason Hallett[a]

[a]*Department of Chemical Engineering, Centre for Process Systems Engineering, Imperial College London, London, United Kingdom*
[b]*Institute for Chemical and Bioengineering, Department of Chemistry and Applied Biosciences, ETH Zürich, Vladimir-Prelog-Weg 1, Zürich, Switzerland*
[c]*Departament d'Enginyeria Química, Universitat Rovira i Virgili, Av. Països Catalans 26, 43007 Tarragona, Spain*
gonzalo.guillen.gosalbez@chem.ethz.ch

Abstract

Due to their attractive properties, ionic liquids have found their way into many applications where they show high potential to replace existing chemicals. However, rising concerns over their ecological impacts, e.g., toxicity and biodegradability, and high cost have limited their use. Techno-economic and life cycle assessment studies were carried out to compare ionic liquids with existing solvents, yet the outcome of these analyses is often hard to interpret, as multiple metrics need to be considered simultaneously between which trade-offs exist. Here, for the first time the concept of monetization is coupled with process simulation and life cycle assessment to estimate the true cost of four lignocellulosic biomass pretreament solvents: triethylammonium hydrogen sulfate [TEA][HSO$_4$], 1-methylimidazolium hydrogen sulfate [HMIM][HSO$_4$], acetone from fossil sources and glycerol from renewable sources. The results show that monetized cost can be higher than or as high as the production cost. The real cost of production accounting for externalities can be more than 100% of direct costs estimated using conventional economic assessment methods. Our results show that [TEA][HSO$_4$] has the lowest cost, while glycerol has the highest cost. We expect this to be a starting point for future studies targeting the design of more sustainable ionic liquids.

Keywords: ionic liquids, techno-economic analysis, life cycle assessment, monetization.

1. Introduction

Some ionic liquids, such as protic ionic liquids, have shown high potential for commercialization due to their low production cost. Chen et al. (2014) conducted a technoeconomic assessment on the bulk production of protic ionic liquids, namely triethylammonium hydrogen sulfate [TEA][HSO$_4$] and 1-methylimidazolium hydrogen sulfate [HMIM][HSO$_4$]. Their results showed that the cost of ionic liquids could be as low as \$1.24/kg, a value below the cost of some organic solvents such as acetone and ethyl acetate, which cost between \$1.3-1.4/kg (Chen et al., 2014).

Conventional economic assessments of ionic liquids often disregard indirect costs due to environmental externalities, that is, impacts that occur along the product's life cycle and need to be mitigated *via* tailored actions that incur an additional cost, e.g., extra expenditures in health care due to respiratory effects in humans. Hence, in order to calculate the "true" cost of a product, one needs to account for these "hidden" costs often omitted in any standard economic assessment.

Monetization or monetary valuation converts social and environmental impacts into monetary units. It has been used to determine the cost of non-market goods in a wide range of areas, e.g., in energy systems modeling to estimate the environmental cost of a specific energy mix, health care to quantify the value of informal care, and catastrophe insurance to predict the demand by homeowners, among others. It has also been used in the weighting phase of LCA to evaluate trade-offs (Fougerit et al., 2012; Lim et al., 2013; Nguyen et al., 2016).

Here we apply for the first time life cycle assessment and monetization to quantify the "true" cost of ionic liquids. To this end, we focus on two ionic liquids widely used for biomass treatment due to their lignin solvating power (Brandt et al., 2013), which were compared against acetone and glycerol regarded as the conventional business as usual alternatives (Huijgen et al., 2010; Liu et al., 2010). An environmental assessment of [TEA][HSO$_4$] and [HMIM][HSO$_4$] using LCA was first conducted to evaluate their environmental impact. The results, expressed in LCA units such as DALY and species.yr, were then converted into a single monetary unit via monetization, which was combined with the direct costs (CAPEX and OPEX calculations) to estimate the total economic cost. Finally, the results generated are analysed and conclusions are drawn.

2. Synthesis

In this study, we evaluate four different solvents, two produced at present industrially, i.e., acetone and glycerol, and two ionic liquids, i.e., [TEA][HSO$_4$] and [HMIM][HSO$_4$]. For the two ionic liquids we developed process models to scale-up experimental synthesis procedures. The synthesis of the two ionic liquids is described in the following subsections.

2.1. Ionic liquids

The ionic liquids in this work are synthesized through the transfer of a proton from a Brønsted acid to a Brønsted base (Greaves and Drummond, 2008). Since the reaction is highly exothermic, water is added to dilute the mixture and cool it down to avoid unwanted phase transition, thermal decomposition or undesired products. The product is then easily separated through a simple distillation, where the water can be recycled back to the process. The acid used is sulfuric acid, while the bases are triethylamine and 1-methylimidazole for [TEA][HSO4] and [HMIM][HSO4], respectively.

2.1.1. 1-methylimidazole

Imidazoles are prepared using the Debus-Radziszewski reaction (Ebel et al., 2012). This is a one pot synthesis, where glyoxal, formaldehyde, methylamine and ammonia react in equimolar molar ratios and condense to form water and 1-methylimidazole. The reaction takes place at 50-100°C in water with a yield between 60-85%.

3. Tools and Methods

Several tools and approaches were used to carry out the assessment. In essence, we combined process simulation models in Aspen-HYSYS with LCA, costing and monetization.

3.1. Process modeling and simulation

Aspen-HYSYS version 9 was used to model the production processes of the ionic liquids and their precursors for which no LCA or price data were available. Here, the synthesis of ionic liquids and 1-methylimidazole were modeled using a combination of experimental data, group contribution methods, literature data and heuristics.

3.1.1. Properties modeling

Data for some properties like density were obtained from experiments or from the literature ("Ionic Liquids Database - ILThermo," n.d.). Some unknown properties for the ionic liquids like critical properties, and normal boiling points were estimated using the group contribution method developed by Valderrama (2009). The missing properties for 1-methylimidazole were estimated from the molecular structure using the Property Constant Estimation System (PCES) built in Aspen-HYSYS V9.

3.2. Economic assessment

In order to estimate the cost of ionic liquids, both capital expenses (CAPEX) and operating expenses (OPEX) are calculated assuming a standard chemical plant that operates 330 days (equivalent to 7,920 hours) a year for 10 years with a production rate equivalent to 144,000 tons per year (Chen et al., 2014). The economic assessment methodology proposed by Towler and Sinnott (2012) is followed in this work. The prices of raw materials and utilities are obtained from ecoinvent 3.5, which reflect current market prices (Wernet et al., 2016). Size of equipment is determined from process simulation results using sizing guidelines by Towler and Sinnott.

3.3. Environmental assessment

A life cycle assessment following ISO 14040 principles was applied. The LCA modeling was performed using SimaPro® 9.0 software interfacing with ecoinvent 3.5.

3.3.1. Goal and scope

A cradle-to-gate scope is adopted that considers the impacts of extracting the raw materials up to the synthesis of the final product. In terms of geographic limits, it is assumed that the production takes place in Europe. The ionic liquids considered in this work are mainly used for biomass pre-treatment, where the efficiency of the ionic liquid is measured in terms of biomass loading defined as the weight ratio of biomass to ionic liquid. We neglect the use phase and set up one kilogram of IL/solvent as functional unit.

3.3.2. Inventory analysis

Data for the background processes were retrieved from ecoinvent 3.5 database (Wernet et al., 2016), which was combined with information of the foreground system, mainly mass and energy flows, obtained from the process simulation.

However, data like emissions and waste treatment are estimated using proxy data where data for similar processes or those with similar characteristics are adapted and used to bridge the gap.

3.3.3. Impact assessment

In this phase, the LCI entries are converted into impact using the ReCiPe 2016 method (Huijbregts et al., 2016), where the inventory entries are characterized and categorized into 17 midpoints that are further aggregated into three endpoints or damage categories: resources, human health and ecosystems.

3.4. Monetization

There are several monetary valuation methods proposed in the literature (Pizzol et al., 2015). These methods usually measure individual's Willingness-to-Pay (WTP) to avoid the environmental impacts brought by the activity of concern. In this work, two methods are used for converting human health damage and ecosystem quality damage, respectively, into money (Weidema, 2009): (i) budget constraint and (ii) choice modelling. Budget constraint is a monetary valuation method where the value of one quality adjusted life year (QALY), a year-based biophysical unit for describing the human health quality, is derived from the potential economic production of the individual per year. Unlike other monetary valuation methods, budget constraint lowers the uncertainty by valuing directly the economic production, although it assumes that what is earned must be spent.

Choice modelling assigns a value to ecosystems based on the economic penalty that an individual is willing to accept for protecting certain areas such as the environment. Choice modeling is widely used in health state evaluations to monetize human well-being, and it can be applied on ecosystem quality.

Here the monetary values of 74k EUR2003/DALY (125.3k USD2019/DALY) and 9.5M EUR2003/species.yr (16M USD2019/species.yr) proposed by Weidema (Weidema, 2009) using the methods mentioned above are used to monetize human health and ecosystem quality, respectively, as illustrated in Equation 1.

$$Cost_{Monetized} = \sum_{i=1}^{e} MF_i EP_i \qquad (1)$$

Where *e* refers to the end points to be monetized based on the characterization method used, MF_i is the monetization factor for endpoint i and EP_i is the damage in that endpoint.

4. Results and discussion

Figure 1 shows the total cost of production after combining the direct costs from the economic assessment and indirect costs from the monetization of environmental impacts. In terms of the direct costs, The results show that [HMIM][HSO₄] has the highest cost ($1.46/kg) while [TEA][HSO₄] shows the lowest ($0.78/kg). This is largely due to the relatively large number of processes involved in the production of [HMIM][HSO₄], i.e., around 11 steps, compared to the other solvents. Another factor that plays a key role is the raw materials cost. For example, [TEA][HSO₄] is produced from triethylamine with a cost of $1.4/kg, while [HMIM][HSO₄] is produced from 1-methylimidazole, with an estimated cost of $4.4/kg. The low cost of sulfuric acid ($0.05/kg) helps to reduce the overall cost of [TEA][HSO₄] below that of glycerol and acetone. The cost of glycerol is relatively higher than [TEA][HSO₄], since the former is produced from relatively more expensive starting materials like rapeseed and soybean oils (Quispe et al., 2013).

In terms of the indirect costs, glycerol has the highest monetized cost ($2.07/kg) while [TEA][HSO₄] shows the lowest ($1.09/kg). The low cost of [TEA][HSO₄] is mainly attributed to the fact that it is relatively simple to synthesize compared to other solvents and uses less fossil sources for processing. In contrast, glycerol's high monetized cost is due to the significant impact on ecosystem quality, with land use being the major contributor. The latter is due to the large areas needed for planting and growing the necessary feedstock, mainly soybean and rapeseeds. The monetized cost of [HMIM][HSO₄] remains relatively high due to its complex synthesis and raw materials required, which affect both direct and indirect costs. Overall, the monetized costs are higher than the direct costs for all solvents. This finding shows that indirect costs, often omitted in conventional economic assessments, can be significant and thus need to be accounted for in the assessment.

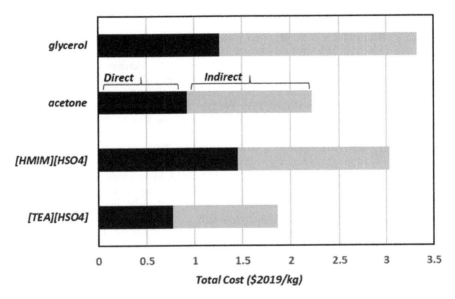

Figure 1. Total cost of production combining both direct and monetized costs.

5. Conclusion

A framework was developed to the assessment of ionic liquids combining process simulation, LCA and monetization to account for externalities. Monetized costs were added to direct costs to compare the total cost of two ionic liquids: [HMIM][HSO₄] and [TEA][HSO₄], a fossil-derived acetone and a bio-based glycerol. The results show that [HMIM][HSO₄] has the highest direct cost among all solvents due to the lengthy 1-methylimidazole production process. When externalities are considered, glycerol has the highest indirect cost, which is mainly due to its high impact on ecosystem quality linked to land use. The results also show that [TEA][HSO₄] is the cheapest option in both direct and indirect cost, since it is produced from relatively inexpensive materials and using simple synthesis procedure. When both costs, direct and indirect, are combined, glycerol's total cost is the highest followed by [HMIM][HSO₄], acetone and [TEA][HSO₄], respectively.

This shows that renewable solvents are not necessarily environmentally better than other solvents, including ionic liquids. Our results, therefore, challenge conventional wisdom that ionic liquids are costly and damaging to the environment. They also highlight the need to account for negative externalities in the comparison of solvents.

References

Brandt, A., Gräsvik, J., P. Hallett, J., Welton, T., 2013. Deconstruction of lignocellulosic biomass with ionic liquids. Green Chemistry 15, 550–583. https://doi.org/10.1039/C2GC36364J

Chen, L., Sharifzadeh, M., Mac Dowell, N., Welton, T., Shah, N., Hallett, J.P., 2014. Inexpensive ionic liquids: [HSO4]--based solvent production at bulk scale. Green Chemistry 16, 3098–3106. https://doi.org/10.1039/c4gc00016a

Ebel, K., Koehler, H., Gamer, A.O., Jäckh, R., 2012. Imidazole and Derivatives. Ullmann's Encyclopedia of Industrial Chemistry 610. https://doi.org/10.1002/14356007.a13_661

Fougerit, V., Auclair, P., Bonhoure, S., 2012. Monetary weighting of LCA results to integrate a two-stage management system in the decision process, in: Proceedings 2nd LCA Conference. p. 7.

Greaves, T.L., Drummond, C.J., 2008. Protic ionic liquids: properties and applications. Chem. Rev. 108, 206–237. https://doi.org/10.1021/cr068040u

Huijbregts, M.A.J., Steinmann, Z.J.N., Elshout, P.M.F., Stam, G., Verones, F., Vieira, M.D.M., Hollander, A., Zijp, M., Van Zelm, R., 2016. ReCiPe 2016: A harmonized life cycle impact assessment method at midpoint and endpoint level Report I: Characterization.

Huijgen, W.J.J., Reith, J.H., den Uil, H., 2010. Pretreatment and fractionation of wheat straw by an acetone-based organosolv process. Ind. Eng. Chem. Res. 49, 10132–10140. https://doi.org/10.1021/ie101247w

Ionic Liquids Database - ILThermo [WWW Document], n.d. URL https://ilthermo.boulder.nist.gov/ (accessed 5.28.19).

Lim, S.-R., Kim, Y.R., Woo, S.H., Park, D., Park, J.M., 2013. System optimization for eco-design by using monetization of environmental impacts: a strategy to convert bi-objective to single-objective problems. Journal of Cleaner Production 39, 303–311. https://doi.org/10.1016/j.jclepro.2012.07.040

Liu, J., Takada, R., Karita, S., Watanabe, Takahito, Honda, Y., Watanabe, Takashi, 2010. Microwave-assisted pretreatment of recalcitrant softwood in aqueous glycerol. Bioresource Technology 101, 9355–9360. https://doi.org/10.1016/j.biortech.2010.07.023

Nguyen, T.L.T., Laratte, B., Guillaume, B., Hua, A., 2016. Quantifying environmental externalities with a view to internalizing them in the price of products, using different monetization models. Resources, Conservation and Recycling 109, 13–23. https://doi.org/10.1016/j.resconrec.2016.01.018

Pizzol, M., Weidema, B., Brandão, M., Osset, P., 2015. Monetary valuation in life cycle assessment: a review. Journal of Cleaner Production 86, 170–179. https://doi.org/10.1016/j.jclepro.2014.08.007

Quispe, C.A.G., Coronado, C.J.R., Carvalho Jr., J.A., 2013. Glycerol: Production, consumption, prices, characterization and new trends in combustion. Renewable and Sustainable Energy Reviews 27, 475–493. https://doi.org/10.1016/j.rser.2013.06.017

Towler, G., Sinnott, R., 2012. Chemical Engineering Design: Principles, Practice and Economics of Plant and Process Design. Elsevier.

Valderrama, J.O., Rojas, R.E., 2009. Critical properties of ionic liquids. Revisited. Ind Eng Chem Res 48, 6890–6900.

Weidema, B.P., 2009. Using the budget constraint to monetarise impact assessment results. Ecological economics 68, 1591–1598.

Wernet, G., Bauer, C., Steubing, B., Reinhard, J., Moreno-Ruiz, E., Weidema, B., 2016. The ecoinvent database version 3 (part I): overview and methodology. Int J Life Cycle Assess 21, 1218–1230. https://doi.org/10.1007/s11367-016-1087-8

Sauro Pierucci, Flavio Manenti, Giulia Bozzano, Davide Manca (Eds.)
Proceedings of the 30th European Symposium on Computer Aided Process Engineering
(ESCAPE30), May 24-27, 2020, Milano, Italy. © 2020 Elsevier B.V. All rights reserved.
http://dx.doi.org/10.1016/B978-0-12-823377-1.50306-2

Multi-Objective Optimization of a Bioethanol Distillation considering Heat Exchanger Fouling and Sustainability Indicators

Fabian Zapf, Thomas Wallek

Graz University of Technology, Inffeldgasse 25C, 8010 Graz, Austria
fabian.zapf@tugraz.at

Abstract

A bio-ethanol column as part of an ETBE (ethyl-tert-butylether) plant is optimized in view of OPEX costs, CO_2 emissions as a sustainability indicator and the columns ethanol product stream. Therefore, three scalarization methods, i.e. the weighting approach, the ε-constraint method and a modified normal boundary intersection method, and a genetic algorithm (NSGA-II) are implemented and applied to two optimization cases. Additionally, a heat exchanger fouling model is incorporated to account for highly nonlinear maintenance interval effects in the reboiler of the column.

Keywords: Multi-objective optimization, Heat exchanger fouling, OPEX costs

1. Introduction

The use of a variety of commercial process simulators is state of the art, offering the possibility of calculating mass transfer phenomena, thermodynamics and reaction kinetics of single processes, individual production plants and entire production sites.

The final step in process simulation is the optimization of the design and/or operating parameters of the plant in view of economy, operational safety, environmental impacts and social aspects. As these aspects are often conflicting each other, this frequently implies a multi-objective optimization (MOO) problem, also called Pareto optimization, like optimizing investment costs vs. operational costs.

Beside these optimization issues, the aspect of process flexibility, such as load-shift and product-shift capability, is of increasing interest. Using MOO gives the possibility to investigate and optimize plants in view of varying production requirements.

Popular process simulators, like Aspen Plus®, Aspen HYSYS®, CHEMCAD® and gProms®, include optimization modules, which are capable of performing only single objective optimization (SOO). To overcome this drawback, introducing MOO in process simulators is commonly realized by coupling the process simulator with an external application which runs a stochastic optimization algorithm (Lopez et al., 2018). Stochastic optimization algorithms require only information about the dependent variables (objectives or output of the system) and the independent variables (process parameters to be optimized). Thus, they are suitable for optimizing black-box functions, such as process simulators running in sequential modular mode. Their main limitation is the relatively slow convergence, due to many evaluations of the objective functions in the course of evaluation runs of the process simulator (Rangajah, 2016).

In this work, several approaches for applying MOO in process simulation are compared among their effort for realization and their suitability for optimization in process engineering. They are implemented in the framework of Wolfram Mathematica®, which is coupled with KBC PetroSIM® as a process simulator via a COM Interface.

2. Methods

Multi-objective optimization can be divided in several classes. The top level divides them into generating methods, which do not require any preferences from the user, while preference-based methods do so and only generate one Pareto solution (Rangaiah, 2016). Thus, we are interested in generating methods, which provide sets of Pareto solutions, so called Pareto fronts. This class of methods can be split up into the class of scalarization methods and population-based methods.

Scalarization methods reduce the multi-objective optimization problem into several single-objective optimization problems, which then can be solved by one of the many available algorithms for single-objective optimization.

Population based methods, on the other hand, tackle the multi-objective optimization problem directly by storing the entire actual Pareto front and evolving the population in each iteration step.

2.1. Scalarization Methods

In this paper three different scalarization methods, which show a very different effort for implementation, are implemented, applied and compared. The single-objective optimization of the scalarized objectives is carried out with a simulated annealing algorithm, capable of finding global minima, which is essential when dealing with process simulators.

2.1.1. Weighting Approach

The weighting approach can be seen as the most primitive scalarization method. It bases on multiplying each objective function f_j with a weight w_j and optimizing the sum of them. Often the objective functions are of different orders of magnitude, thus it is necessary to rescale them, e.g. by linear transformation:

$$\bar{f}_j(x_i) = \frac{f_j(x_i) - f_j^{min}}{f_j^{max} - f_j^{min}} \tag{1}$$

Therefore, it is necessary to perform a single-objective optimization of each single objective function, thus the end points of the Pareto front (and by that, f_i^{min} and f_i^{max}) for rescaling can be obtained. The resulting objective function $u(x_i)$

$$u(x_i) = \sum_j w_j \cdot \bar{f}_j(x_i) \tag{2}$$

is the linear combination of the objective functions. By varying the weights whose sum has to be unity, several single objective optimization problems are generated which then can be minimized with the simulated annealing algorithm.

2.1.2. ε-constraint Method

The ε-constraint method is a very popular method, due to the fact that it is very simple to implement, while offering the possibility of producing very homogenously distributed Pareto points. This is done by setting only one of the objectives as the target function, e.g. the first objective $j=1$:

$$u(x_i) = f_1(x_i) \tag{3}$$

and converting all other objective function into inequality constraints, in the 2-dimensional case:

$$f_2(x_i) \le \varepsilon \tag{4}$$

Multi-Objective Optimization of a Bioethanol Distillation considering Heat Exchanger Fouling and Sustainability Indicators

1833

By optimizing the target function with a range of ε values a set of Pareto points can be obtained.

In this method, the realization of holding the constraint is an issue. Depending on which single-objective optimization algorithm is used, there are many methods available in literature. Due to the deterministic nature of the simulated annealing algorithm, which does not involve gradient information, a simple penalty function can be used (Yeniay, 2005). Incorporating this penalty function, the target function for the optimizer changes to:

$$u(x_i) = f_1(x_i) + p * Max(0, f_2(x_i) - \varepsilon) \tag{5}$$

where p denotes a factor for penalizing the violation of the constraint. It was found, that a value of 1000 works well for most applications.

2.1.3. Modified Normal Boundary Intersection Method

The modified normal boundary intersection from Lim et al. (2001) represents the most advanced scalarization method in this work. In general, this method obtains the end points of the Pareto front and normalizes the objective functions. By obtaining the middle point of the Pareto front, it gets possible to obtain an even more homogenous distribution of the Pareto points. This advantage is bought by using equality constraints, which are computationally expensive when using stochastic algorithms. These equality constraints are also enforced by using the penalty method.

2.2. Genetic Algorithm

The Nondominated Sorting Genetic Algorithm II (NSGA-II) from Deb et al. (2002) is part of the population based evolutionary genetic algorithms, which are known to be very robust and popular (Ramteke and Gupta, 2016). Especially in process simulation robustness of the algorithms plays a critical role, due to the fact that the results of process simulators are typically fluctuating because of numerical inaccuracy.

Genetic algorithms base on the decoding of the variables into genes (e.g. a bit), chromosomes (all bits of a variable) and chains of chromosomes (representing one individual with all its variables), e.g., binary coding, opening the possibility to perform simple and nature inspired operations on them. There are two main operators: the recombination operation between two chromosomes, which further improves the population, and the mutation operation, responsible for exploration of new areas of possible solutions.

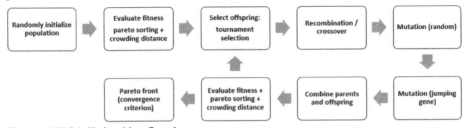

Figure 1: NSGA-II algorithm flowchart

A special aspect of the NSGA-II algorithm is its elitism preservation mechanism (prevents good solutions from random death), ensuring a fast convergence, and the crowding distance as a measure in selection, to ensure a broad Pareto front. This working principle of the algorithm is depicted in Figure 1.

In process simulation optima often lie directly on the bounds of the input variables, which can be hardly reached randomly by gene mutation or crossover. Thus, jumping gene (JG) operators are introduced as a second type of mutation, facing these issues. These operators replace randomly larger parts of chromosomes, leading to larger fluctuations. There exist several types of JG operators in literature, in this work the five types from Ramteke and Gupta (2016) are implemented and tested.

All operators are always applied with a certain probability to each chromosome (crossover and JG) or gene (mutation). The parameters for the optimization are listed in Table 1.

Table 1: Genetic algorithm parameters

Population size	Generations	Chromosome length	Crossover probability	Mutation probability	Jumping gene probability
20	500	16	0.95	0.05	0.5

3. Example – Distillation Column

For demonstration, a distillation column for recycling bio-ethanol in an ETBE (ethyl-tert-butylether) process is selected. The reboiler is heated with an oil stream from a refinery, causing fouling inside the reboiler, which shows a highly nonlinear relationship to several parameters.

In general, the operation mode of the column can be widely varied, e.g., by changing reflux ratio and reboiler duty, and by that, product quantities and qualities are influenced. In daily business, columns are always operated at minimal energy costs and maximum product recovery. In this work, also economical aspects arising from maintenance caused by fouling in the reboiler are considered, which may lead to other optima.

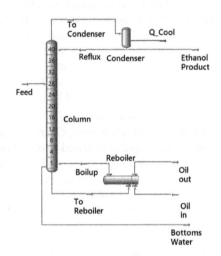

Figure 2: Column flowsheet

3.1. Column Model

The distillation column, which splits up ethanol and water, is simulated in KBC PetroSIM® as a process simulator, using NRTL with Poynting correction as a thermodynamic calculation method. This gives the capability of obtaining all stream data for further calculations, the column parameters are summarized in Table 2.

Table 2: Column parameters

Parameter	Value
Total Stages	40
Feed Stage	28
Condenser Pressure	1.7 bar abs.
Reboiler Pressure	2.1 bar abs.
Ethanol in Feed Stream	13 mol-%

Table 3: Fouling parameters (Costa et al., 2013)

Parameter	Value
α	277.8 m²K/J
γ	$4.17*10^{-13}$ m²K/J
E_a	48 kJ/mol
Pr (assumed)	25

Multi-Objective Optimization of a Bioethanol Distillation considering Heat Exchanger Fouling and Sustainability Indicators

1835

3.2. Fouling Model

Heat exchanger fouling is commonly modeled as the change of fouling resistance R_f over time. The model used from Polley et al. (2002)

$$\frac{dR_f}{dt} = \alpha * Re^{-0.8} * Pr^{-0.33} * Exp\left(\frac{-E_a}{RT_f}\right) - \gamma * Re^{0.8} \tag{6}$$

depends on the Reynolds (Re) and Prandtl (Pr) number, the wall temperature T_f and the model parameters α, γ and E_a from Costa et al. (2013), which are listed in Table 3.

3.3. Economics

The operational expenditures (OPEX) in this work consider heat exchanger cleaning costs by relating the actual fouling rate to a base case (50,000 €/a), the make-up costs of the lost ethanol through the bottoms product (400 €/t) as well as energy costs of the reboiler (17.24 €/MWh).

3.4. Sustainability indicator

In this particular case, the energy taken from the oil stream for reboiling reduces the downstream district heat production, what is compensated by methane burners in the worst case. Thus, the reboiler duty can be expressed by a CO_2 emission per year. Assuming a boiler efficiency of 90%, this results in 1921 kg CO_2/a per kW reboiler duty.

4. Application and Results

The three scalarization methods and the NSGA-II algorithm are applied to two optimization cases: (i) optimization of CO_2 emissions vs. OPEX costs (both minimized), where the reflux ratio and ethanol recovery of the column are varied, and (ii) optimization of the ethanol product flow (maximized) vs. OPEX costs (minimized), by varying the feed stream, reflux ratio and ethanol recovery of the column. The number of calculated Pareto points is in each case 20.

Figure 3 shows the results for the first case. The dependency of both objectives shows a very linear relationship, even though highly nonlinear effects like heat exchanger fouling are incorporated. It gets clear, that the weighting approach fails to generate points between the ends points, while the NSGA-II algorithm generates a quite homogenous front, without travelling too much in the suboptimal region.

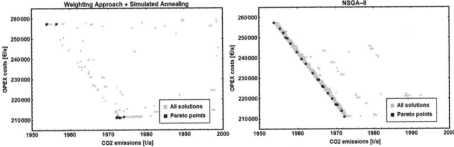

Figure 3: Results for the optimization of CO_2 emissions vs. OPEX costs

In Figure 4 the results for the second case are shown. Also in this case both objectives show a nearly linear relationship, the slope of the curve increases only slightly with increasing ethanol production. The ε-constraint method is capable of providing a very homogenously distributed Pareto front, while the modified boundary intersection method randomly produces wrong points. This arises from the computationally expensive equality constraints, which need to be fulfilled and are obviously not met when running the single points with maximum 3000 iterations.

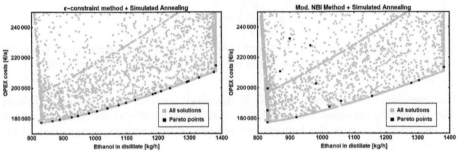

Figure 4: Results for the optimization of ethanol in distillate vs. OPEX costs

5. Conclusions

In process simulation multi-objective optimization can be a powerful tool for optimizing plants and processes in view of economic aspects as well as for evaluating them in view of process flexibility. Because multi-objective optimization is not part of commercial process simulators yet, scalarization methods provide an economic possibility to realize that. In this work it turns out, that the ε-constraint method is the fastest and most reliable beside the weighting approach and modified normal boundary intersection method. By implementing the NSGA-II algorithm with jumping gene adaptions, the convergence speed and stability of the optimization can be further improved significantly. The investigated bio-ethanol column was optimized in view of OPEX costs, CO_2 emissions as a sustainability indicator and the ethanol product, which showed linear relationship.

References

A.L.H. Costa, V.B.G. Tavares, J.L. Borges, E.M. Queiroz, F.L.P. Pessoa, F.d.S. Liporace, S.G.d. Oliveira, 2013, Parameter Estimation of Fouling Models in Crude Preheat Trains,: Heat Transfer Engineering, Vol. 34, No. 8-9, pp. 683-691

K. Deb, A. Pratap, S. Agrawal, T. Meyarivan, 2002, A fast and elitist multiobjective genetic algorithm: NSGA-II, IEEE Trans. Evol. Computat., Vol. 6 No. 2, pp. 182-197

Y.I. Lim, P. Floquet, Xavier Joulia, 2001, Efficient Implementation of the Normal Boundary Intersection (NBI) Method on Multiobjective Optimization Problems, Ind. Eng. Chem. Res., Vol. 40, pp. 648-655

C.A.M. Lopez, D. Telen, P. Nimmegeers, L. Cabianca, F. Logist, J. V. Impe, 2018, A process simulator interface for multiobjective optimization of chemical processes, Computers and Chemical Engineering, Vol. 109, pp. 119-137

R.T. Marler, J.S. Arora, 2004, Survey of multi-objective optimization methods for engineering, Structural and Multidisciplinary Optimization, Vol. 26, pp 369-395

G.T. Polley, D.I. Wilson, B.L. Yeap, S.J. Pugh, 2002, Evaluation of laboratory crude oil threshold fouling data for application to refinery pre-heat trains, Applied Thermal Engineering, Vol. 7, No. 22, pp. 777-788

M. Ramteke, S. K. Gupta, 2016, Multi-Objective Genetic Algorithm annd Simulated aAnnealing with the Jumping Gene Adaptions, Multi-Objective Optimization, Advances in process systems engineering, Vol. 5, pp 1-27

G.P. Rangajah, 2016, Introduction, Multi-Objective Optimization, Advances in process systems engineering, Vol. 5, pp 1-27

Ö. Yeniay, 2005, Penalty Function Methods for Constrainted Opimization with Genetic Algorithms, Mathematical and Computational Applications, Vol. 10., No. 1, pp. 45-56

Sauro Pierucci, Flavio Manenti, Giulia Bozzano, Davide Manca (Eds.)
Proceedings of the 30th European Symposium on Computer Aided Process Engineering
(ESCAPE30), May 24-27, 2020, Milano, Italy. © 2020 Elsevier B.V. All rights reserved.
http://dx.doi.org/10.1016/B978-0-12-823377-1.50307-4

Maximising Food Security through a Macronutrient Optimisation Approach Considering Energy and Water Constraints

Nayla Al-Thani[a], Tareq Al-Ansari[a,b*], Rajesh Govindan[b]

[a] *Division of Sustainable Development, College of Science and Engineering, Hamad Bin Khalifa University, Qatar Foundation. Doha, Qatar*
[b] *Division of Engineering Management and Decision Sciences, College of Science and Engineering, Hamad Bin Khalifa University, Qatar Foundation. Doha, Qatar*
talansari@hbku.edu.qa

Abstract

Considering the relationship between food security and malnutrition, a 'Decade of Action' was certified by the UN in 2016 promoting the need to end all types of malnutrition. In the context of nutrition, this study evaluates the possibility to maximise nutritional benefits through the optimal allocation of water and energy resources using a hypothetical case study in Qatar. Two complementary models were developed using goal programming and linear programming formulations, both of which were utilised to solve various scenarios. The multi-objective function of goal programming minimises the weighted negative deviation from the targeted food groups and nutrients. Meanwhile, the linear programming model was implemented to increase the self-sufficiency percentage of food groups and nutrients. For the case study analysed, the model results demonstrate clearly that the quantity of natural fresh water and energy utilisation is not sufficient to meet the targeted 40% self-sufficiency levels of either food groups or nutrients. In addition, the results indicate the dependency between increasing the self-sufficiency of different nutrients with the increased production of dates group, implying that dates can be considered a strategic crop for Qatar in terms of food security. Moreover, the results suggest an alternative production mix that will provide approximately 38% carbohydrates, 9% protein, and improves the fibres to about 3.5% from 0.5%, which offers more diversity in the diet and reduces the fat to about 8.5% from about 150% compared to the current production.

Keywords: Agriculture, Nutrients, Food Security, Optimisation, EWF Nexus.

1. Introduction

Agriculture is the main primary activity related to enhancing global food production, and thus it is fundamental for food security. As such, it involves the provision of nutrients required by mankind to lead a healthy and nutritious life (UNSDSN, 2013). According to the Food and Agriculture Organisation of the United Nations (FAO), since the 1960s, aggregate global food production has increased by 145%, resulting in a 5% more food per capita (Pretty, 2013). However, the effort was narrowly focused mass extensification of land to produce staples rich in calories, of which 12 species contributed to 80% of global dietary intake. Furthermore, intensification of agriculture production has demonstrated compounded effects on the environment, such as greenhouse gas (GHG) emissions contributing to climate change, resource depletion, and other environmental impacts. It consumes 70% of global fresh water reserves, the single largest consumer (FAO, 2015), and contributes 17-32 % of global GHG emissions (Berntrup and Pallière, 2008). Thus, agriculture production requires a mobilisation of energy and water resources, and it is therefore considered important to derive maximum nutritional benefit within a sustainable development framework which promotes optimum resource consumption, minimal environmental impact, and maximum benefit to society. However, research into resource management and optimisation in the context of nutritional requirements is limited, and there is currently no appropriate methodology that exists linking the two.

The objective of this study is to develop such a framework that allows the optimisation of resources-use efficiency whilst maximising the nutritional benefit from agricultural output. The study adopts the energy, water and food (EWF) nexus approach which emphasises the interlinkages between EWF resource sectors (Hoff, 2011). The analysis of EWF Nexus systems forms an important aspect of modelling related to achieving food security targets (Al-Ansari *et al.*, 2015), forming the basis of integrated nutrition and resource modelling. The tool presented in this study informs decisions pertaining to agriculture production and the optimum composition of production quantities that maximises the self-sufficiency ratio of food groups and nutrients. Essentially, the tool improves resources allocation whilst maximising the production of food groups. Furthermore, the study investigates the status of the water and energy allocation for agriculture in Qatar under macro nutrients constraints. As such, the contribution in this paper is two-fold: firstly, the introduction of two novel mathematical model formulations that aim to optimise agricultural benefits represented as the macro nutrients within food groups under different water and energy constraints; and secondly, the representation of food security in terms of the macro nutrients needs of a population.

2. Available Data

2.1. Nutrient guidelines

The report of the dietary guidelines for Qatar by the Ministry of Public Health listed six food groups that are recommended to be consumed for a healthy population (SCH, 2015). The food groups in the guideline are vegetables, fruit, cereals and starchy vegetables, legumes, milk and dairy products, and fish, poultry and meat. According to the MDPS (2016) legumes are not grown locally thus it is excluded from the analysis. In order to extract the nutrients content of each food group, an averaging approach is utilised by Gephart *et al.* (2016). The first step is to list all the crops produced locally along with their respective nutrient density (*i.e.* nutrient content per 100g) for each food group which is obtained from USDA (2018). Finally, the values are averaged to determine the nutritional content for each food group which are listed in Table 1.

Table 1. Quantity of nutrients n in different food groups per 100g.

Food Group	Energy (kcal)	Carbohydrate (g)	Protein (g)	Fibre (g)	Fatty acids*** (g)
Vegetables	23.5	5.4	1.3	1.9	0.1
Fruits	49.6	12.4	1.0	2.2	0.0
Dates	279.5	75.0	2.1	7.4	0.0
Cereals & Starchy Vegetables	213.0	44.9	7.3	6.2	0.2
Milk, Dairy Products	269.4	5.4	13.3	0.0	6.7
Fish, Poultry, Meat	280.2	0.2	17.3	0.0	10.1
Total amount required for the population per year (tonne)**	152869.8	143315.5	28663.09	6191.2	6191.2

2.2. Water and Energy resources

As for the life cycle energy and water requirements to produce different food groups, the data is estimated from Webber (2012) and is illustrated in Table 2.

Table 2. Unit amount of energy and water required to grow different food groups.

Food Group	The amount of energy required kWh/tonne	The amount of water utilised (m³/tonne)
Vegetables (tonne)	7494.9	497.0
Fruits (tonne)	8657.9***	945.1
Dates (tonne)	8657.9***	866.7
Cereals & Starchy Vegetables (tonne)	3715.1	1934.0
Milk, Dairy Products (tonne)	10563.9	3920.8**
Fish, Poultry, Meat (tonne)	14537.5	10333.3**

*Average water requirement for combined fruits and dates.
**(FAO, 2003).
*** It is assumed that the energy required to grow one tonne of fruits and dates are identical.

3. Methodology

The methodology utilised to fulfil the stated objectives of this study includes the development of complementary goal programming (GP) and linear programming (LP) model formulations. Table 3 lists the notations used in the mathematical formulations that follow.

Table 3. Nomenclature used in the formulations.

Notation	Description	Unit
	Sets	
G	Set of food groups	
N	Set of nutrients	
g^*	number of food groups	
n^*	number of nutrients	
	Parameters	**Unit**
W_g	Unit amount of water needed by food group g, g=1,..., g^*	m³/tonne
E_g	Unit amount of energy needed by food group g, g=1,..., g^*	kWh/tonne
E_w	Total amount of energy required for groundwater abstraction for agriculture	kWh
W_{max}	Maximum amount of water that is available for the agricultural sector	m³
E_{max}	Maximum amount of energy that is available for the agricultural sector	kWh
N_{ng}	Fractional amount of nutrient n that is available in food group g, n=1,..., n^*, g=1,..., g^*	-
F_g	Target amount to be produced for food group g, g=1,..., g^*	Tonne
L_n	Target amount to be produced from nutrient n, n=1,..., n^*	Tonne
U_n	weight of nutrient n, n=1,..., n^*	Tonne
U_g	weight of food group g, g=1,..., g^*	Tonne

The GP model minimises the negative deviation (*i.e.* shortage) from the set target for the different food groups and selected macro nutrients, whereas the LP model maximises the self-sufficiency ratio of the food groups and nutrients. In effect, the models optimise the allocation of water and energy resources in order to increase the self-sufficiency of the agriculture sector. The results of the two models were integrated, relating the model outputs through a self-sufficiency relationship. It is important to note that although both the production targets and food demand requirements are related, they are not necessarily satisfied simultaneously, and thus the need to have separate models to optimise and assess the solutions obtained therein.

3.1. GP model formulation

Minimise $\sum_{n \in N} U_n \frac{d_n^-}{L_n} + \sum_{g \in G} U_g \frac{t_g^-}{F_g}$

s.t. $\quad \sum_{g=1}^{g} w_g x_g \leq W_{max} \qquad\qquad \forall\, g \in G$

$\quad\quad \sum_{g=1}^{g} (E_g x_g + E_w W_{max}) \leq E_{max} \qquad g \in G$

$\quad\quad \sum_{g=1}^{g} N_{ng} x_g = L_n - d_n^- + d_n^+ \qquad \forall\, n \in N$

$\quad\quad \sum_{g=1}^{g} x_g = F_g - t_g^- + t_g^+ \qquad\quad \forall\, g \in G$

$\quad\quad x_g \geq 0 \qquad \forall\, g \in G$

x_g: The amount to be produced locally from each food group that will optimally allocate the available water and energy for the agriculture sector.
t_g^-: The negative deviation from the set target of each food group g, g=1,...,g*
t_g^+: The positive deviation from the set target of each food group g, g=1,...,g*
d_n^-: The negative deviation from the set target of each nutrient n, n=1,...,n*
d_n^+: The positive deviation from the set target of each nutrient n, n=1,...,n*

3.2. LP model formulation

Maximise $\sum_{n \in N} U_n z_n + \sum_{g \in G} U_g y_g$

s.t. $\quad \sum_{g=1}^{g} w_g x_g \leq W_{max} \qquad\qquad \forall\, g \in G$

$\quad\quad \sum_{g=1}^{g} (E_g x_g + E_w W_{max}) \leq E_{max} \qquad \forall\, g \in G$

$\quad\quad \sum_{g=1}^{g} N_{ng} x_g = z_n T_n \qquad\quad \forall\, n \in N$

$\quad\quad \sum_{g=1}^{g} x_g = y_g F_g \qquad\qquad \forall\, g \in G$

$\quad\quad 0 \leq x_g, y_g \leq 1 \quad \forall\, g \in G$
$\quad\quad 0 \leq z_n \leq 1 \qquad \forall\, n \in N$

F_g = Annual consumption of food group g, g=1,..., g*
T_n = Annual population requirements for nutrient n, n=1,..., n*
x_g = amount to be produced locally from food group g, g=1,..., g*
y_g = self-sufficiency ratio of food group g, g=1,..., g*
z_n = self-sufficiency ratio of nutrient n, n=1,..., n*,

4. Results and discussion

Both the GP and LP models are solved for multiple scenarios that are selected based on mainly two aspects: (a) it reflects the preferences of the policy makers; and (b) it is related to the water requirement for each food group. As such, weights are assigned that essentially reflect the dietary guidelines recommended for the state of Qatar that was developed by the Supreme Council of Health and the Nutrition Department in the WHO (SCH, 2015), according to which: (a) scenario 1 gives equal weightage to all food groups and nutrients which represents the baseline scenario; (b) scenario 2 gives higher weightage to the vegetables, fruits and dates groups to reflect the recommendation developed by the Supreme Council of Health, in addition to the fact that it requires the least amount of water to be produced; (c) scenario 3 increases the weightage of some nutrients to study the impact on the optimal solution compared to scenario 2, and to test the sensitivity of the models; and (d) scenario 4 gives higher weightage to all nutrients to investigate which of the food groups will present a higher impact in satisfying the nutritional need.

Figures 1(a) and 1(b) illustrate the self-sufficiency levels achieved in different food groups when the desired target is set 40% of the total annual population requirements using the GP model, and for maximum achievable self-sufficiency level using the LP model, respectively. These results generally demonstrate that the production of fish, poultry, meat groups are not favourable in all the scenarios. This can be attributed to the large quantities of water required to produce one tonne in this food group. Meanwhile, the dates group satisfied with positive deviation implying that it exceeds target in all scenarios. This is due to the high nutritional content of the dates and the low water requirements. The respective self-sufficiency levels achieved for different nutritional requirements are illustrated in Figures 2(a) and 2(b).

Figure 1. Self-sufficiency levels achieved for different food groups using: (a) goal programming; (b) linear programming

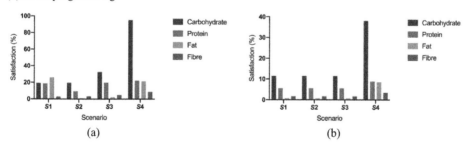

Figure 2. Self-sufficiency levels achieved for different nutritional requirements using: (a) goal programming; (b) linear programming

5. Conclusions

This study introduces a tool that can inform decision making with regards to maximising national food self-sufficiency. The methodology presented consists of two complementary mathematical formulation that optimises the status of the self-sufficiency ratios under given water and energy constraints for different cases and scenarios. The LP model aims to maximise the production of different food groups and nutritional content through examining different production quantities within pre-specified water and energy resources. While the objective in the GP model is to minimise the undesired deviation from the set goals, *i.e.* the targets of different food groups and nutrients, which is essentially a sub-goal of the LP model. For the Qatar case study considered, the results demonstrate that the current quantity of utilised water and energy will not be sufficient to meet the target of the 40% self-sufficiency for all food groups or nutrients. Therefore, further investment in water and energy resources is required. The results demonstrate that dates are the most favourable group specific to Qatar, owing to the fact that it requires the least quantity of water and energy resources for production. The models developed as part of this study have not considered costs of production, land, environment and the climate condition of the area, which is considered a limitation, thus forming the basis of future work.

References

T. Al-Ansari, A. Korre, Z. Nie, N. Shah, 2015, Development of a life cycle assessment tool for the assessment of food production systems within the energy, water and food nexus, Sustainable Production and Consumption, 2, 52-66.

F. Berntrup, C. Pallière, 2008, GHG emissions and energy efficiency in European nitrogen fertilizer production and use, International Fertiliser Society Conference. UK.

FAO, 2003. Agriculture, Food and Water. Rome, Italy.

FAO, 2015, Towards A Water and Food Secure Future: Critical Perspectives for Policy-makers. Marseille.

J.A. Gephart, K.F. Davis, K.A. Emery, A.M. Leach, J.N. Galloway, M.L. Pace, 2016, The environmental cost of subsistence: Optimizing diets to minimize footprints, Science of The Total Environment, 553, 120-127.

J.A. Gephart, K.F. Davis, K.A. Emery, A.M. Leach, J.N. Galloway, M.L. Pace, 2016, The environmental cost of subsistence: Optimizing diets to minimize footprints, Science of The Total Environment, 553, 120-127.

J. Hoff, 2011, Understanding the nexus. In: Background Paper for the Bonn 2011 Conference: The Water, Energy and Food Security Nexus, Bonn, Germany. Stockholm Environment Institute, Stockholm, Sweden.

J. Pretty, 2013, The Consumption of a Finite Planet: Well-Being, Convergence, Divergence and the Nascent Green Economy, Environmental and Resource Economics, 55, 475-499.

MDPS, 2016, Economic Statistics : Agriculture Statistics. Ministry of Development Planning and Statistics, Qatar.

SCH, 2015, Qatar Dietary Guidelines, The Supreme Council of Health, Doha, Qatar.

UNSDSN, 2013, Solutions for Sustainable Agriculture and Food Systems- Technical Report for the Post-2015 Development Agenda. Sustainable Development Solutions Network: A Global Initiative for the United Nations.

USDA, 2018, USDA Food Composition Databases.

M.E. Webber, 2012, More Food, Less Energy: Changes in agriculture, policy and personal behaviors can reduce the energy a nation uses to feed itself and the greenhouse gases it emits, Scientific American, pp. 74-79.

Sauro Pierucci, Flavio Manenti, Giulia Bozzano, Davide Manca (Eds.)
Proceedings of the 30th European Symposium on Computer Aided Process Engineering
(ESCAPE30), May 24-27, 2020, Milano, Italy. © 2020 Elsevier B.V. All rights reserved.
http://dx.doi.org/10.1016/B978-0-12-823377-1.50308-6

Modelling Circular Structures in Reaction Networks: Petri Nets and Reaction Network Flux Analysis

Jana M. Weber,[a] Artur M. Schweidtmann,[b] Eduardo Nolasco,[a]
Alexei A. Lapkin [a,c*]

[a]*Department of Chemical Engineering and Biotechnology, University of Cambridge, West Cambridge Site, Philippa Fawcett Drive, Cambridge CB3 0AS, U.K.*
[b]*Process Systems Engineering (AVT.SVT), RWTH Aachen University, Aachen 52074, Germany*
[c]*Cambridge Centre for Advanced Research and Education in Singapore, CARES Ltd. 1 CREATE Way, CREATE Tower #05-05, 138602 Singapore*
aal35@cam.ac.uk

Abstract

Optimal reaction pathways for the conversion of renewable feedstocks are often examined by reaction network flux analysis. An alternative modelling approach for reaction networks is a Petri net. These explicitly take the reaction sequence into account. In the optimisation of a network, this can allow the implementation of constraints on circular reaction structures, which are common substructures in chemical reaction networks. In this study, we compare the performance of the models in an illustrative minimal working example of a circular reaction substructure. The reaction network flux analysis is shown to be a relaxation of the Petri net formulation. Most notable, this work contributes to well-reasoned model choices for reaction networks.

Keywords: Reaction network, Petri nets, Reaction network flux analysis

1. Introduction

By the year 2030, it is estimated that the chemical production will become the main driver of global oil consumption (Kätelhön et al., 2019), hence the transition towards sustainable chemistry (Jenck et al., 2004) and more explicitly the development of novel processes based on renewable feedstocks has gained major importance (Sheldon, 2014). However, identification of efficient process routes based on biological feedstocks remains a challenge, and suitable models for rapid evaluations of processes are highly desirable. Methods, such as reaction network flux analysis (RNFA), have recently received much attention, as they enable a system-wide study on the utilisation of feedstock components. Stochastic semantics, i.e. how many molecules go through each reaction, are used to describe such systems quantitatively (Bartocci and Lió, 2016). First introduced by Voll and Marquardt (2012b), the RNFA finds optimal reaction fluxes in a given set of reactions. The approach was applied for investigation of possible routes to biofuels (Ulonska et al., 2018, 2016; Voll and Marquardt, 2012a) and for biomass-derived polymer production (Zhang et al., 2017). It was shown that the RNFA is well-suited for optimal pathway identification within a set of alternative routes in networks of sizes of the order of 116 reactions and 80 substances (Voll and Marquardt, 2012b). Besides the size of a chemical reaction network, also its structure plays an important role. Networks of chemical reactions naturally exhibit special architectures (Fialkowski et al., 2005; Grzybowski et al., 2009) and nodes with extreme connectivity patterns (Szymkuć et al., 2016; Weber et al., 2019). Furthermore, they include a multitude of local substructures (Feinberg and Horn, 1974; Van Der Schaft et al., 2016), such as bidirectionalities due to reversible reactions and circular structures due to e.g. chemical looping or molecules functioning as catalysts or protecting groups. In the manually assembled reaction networks, circular structures are seldom encountered. However, with the increasing availability of reaction data, there is a rapid advance in algorithmic assembling of reaction networks, which frequently contain circular substructures. In light of this, we present this work as a part of a much larger study. We investigate the influence of circular substructures on the RNFA and on an alternative approach, a Petri net optimisation (PNO) formalism. Petri nets have been used to model chemical and biological reaction networks (Chaouiya, 2007; Koch, 2010; Petri, 1962; Peterson, 1977), while the use of PNO in chemical engineering has to date mostly focused on batch scheduling (Gu et al., 2003; Yamalidou and Kantor, 1991).

In this work, we introduce PNO for chemical reaction sequences and show both models' behaviour regarding circular substructures. The remainder of this article is organised as follows. Section 2 describes the RNFA and PNO formalisms, Section 3 introduces an illustrative case study, and results are presented and discussed in Section 4. Lastly, Section 5 concludes the article and shows future perspectives.

2. Methods

The RNFA is formulated as a linear programming problem (LP) and the PNO as a mixed-integer linear programming problem (MILP). Both were implemented and solved using Python 3.6 with Pyomo modelling language and CPLEX 12.9 as a solver. (Implementation: https://github.com/Jana-Marie-Weber/Reaction_net_opt)

2.1. Reaction network flux analysis (RNFA) formalism

The RNFA originated from flux balance analysis of metabolic networks, where the overall metabolic supply chain is assumed to be at equilibrium (Orth et al., 2010). For this assumption to hold, the RNFA introduces both supply and removal pseudo-reactions. Due to the scope of this work, we do not show the formalism of RNFA, which we have adapted from Voll and Marquardt (2012b) and refer the reader to that reference.

2.2. Petri net optimisation (PNO) formalism

Petri nets, first introduced by Carl Adam Petri (Petri, 1962), are directed bipartite networks, where the two node types are *places*, represented by circles, and *transitions*, represented by bars (see Figure 1).

Reaction 1 (R1): A + B → C
Reaction 2 (R2): C + E → B + D

(a)   (b)

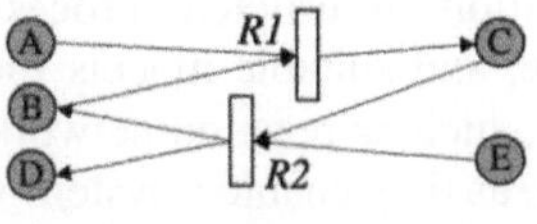

Figure 1. Sample reactions. (a) A reaction set with a circular substructure. (b) A graph representation of reactions in (a). Circles are *places* and bars *transitions* in Petri net notation.

The input and output relations between places and transitions are shown by connecting links, called *arcs* and an incidence matrix. The *state* of a Petri net is given by a marking of places with *tokens*. Tokens change from one place to another through firing of transitions. A transition is enabled, that is, it is able to fire and thus to move tokens, when its input places meet the incidence matrix' token demands (Ghaeli et al., 2005; Peterson,

1977). Firing a transition thereby leads to a change of state, introducing the order of events, a linear temporal logic (LTL) (Bartocci and Lió, 2016). The optimisation problem determines an optimal sequence of firing certain transitions. Extending the work of Yamalidou and Kantor (1991) we formulate the PNO as follows:

$$\min_{\substack{m_{p,k=K}\\ q_{t,k}\\ y_{t,k}}} J = -\sum_{p=1}^{P} c_p \cdot m_{p,k=K} + \sum_{t=1}^{T} \left(s_t \cdot \sum_{k=1}^{K} q_{t,k} \right) + \sum_{t=1}^{T} \left(b_t \cdot \sum_{k=1}^{K} y_{t,k} \right) \tag{1}$$

s.t.

$$m_{p,k=1} = a_p \qquad\qquad \forall p \in \{1,..,P\} \tag{2}$$

$$m_{p,k} \geq 0 \qquad\qquad \forall p \in \{1,..,P\}, \forall\, k \in \{2,..,K\} \tag{3}$$

$$m_{p,k+1} = m_{p,k} + \sum_{t=1}^{T} d_{p,t} \cdot q_{t,k} \qquad\qquad \forall p \in \{1,..,P\}, \forall k \in \{1,..,K-1\} \tag{4}$$

$$\sum_{t=1}^{T} y_{t,k} \leq 1 \qquad\qquad \forall k \in \{1,..,K-1\} \tag{5}$$

$$\sum_{t=1}^{T} y_{t,k+1} \leq \sum_{t=1}^{T} y_{t,k} \qquad\qquad \forall k \in \{1,..,K-2\} \tag{6}$$

$$y_{t,k}/M \leq q_{t,k} \leq y_{t,k} \cdot M \qquad\qquad \forall t \in \{1,..,T\}, \forall k \in \{1,..,K-1\} \tag{7}$$

where P is the number of places (molecules), K is the number of states (molar distributions after each reaction step), and T is the number of transitions (reactions) in the system. The elements $m_{p,k}$ represent the marking at molecule p, and reaction step k. Note that there are K mol distributions for $K-1$ reaction steps. The elements $q_{t,k}$ represent the amount of token (mol) passing reaction t, at reaction step k and the elements $y_{t,k}$ are binary variables with value one if the transition (reaction) is active and zero otherwise. We do not consider kinetics/reaction times; transitions fire without any associated time value. The binary variables offer the possibility to include throughput independent process costs, which is an important practical consideration in (bio-)chemical process development. The vector $c \in \mathbb{R}^P$ is the revenue for selling molecule p, $s \in \mathbb{R}^T$ is the cost associated with a reaction flux and $b \in \mathbb{R}^T$ is a constant cost associated with a reaction. The objective function (Eq. (1)) minimises the total cost consisting of product revenue, flux related and non-flux related reaction costs. The parameters $d_{p,t}$ are the elements of the incident matrix (stoichiometric matrix) of the reaction system, where consumption and production of molecule p in reaction t is specified. The vector $a \in \mathbb{R}^P$ represents the initial mol distribution. Similar to the RNFA (Voll and Marquardt, 2012b), the initial or the final state of the system need to be specified so that the MILP problem is bounded. We set the initial distribution in Eq. (2). The constraints in Eq. (4) describe the mol distribution over all molecules based on the previous distribution and the changes of the system due to a reaction step. In combination with Eq. (3), this guarantees that a reaction can only take place if the mol distribution of all incoming arcs is sufficient with regard to the stoichiometric matrix. Constraints in Eq. (5) allow only one reaction in every reaction step k, ensuring the LTL. The *big M* constraints in Eq. (7) couple the reaction fluxes $q_{t,k}$ to $y_{t,k}$, if and only if one is active the other can occur, and give a lower and upper bound for $q_{t,k}$. In case K is chosen too high, constraints in Eq. (6) guarantee that reaction steps at the beginning are active while inactive reaction steps are at the end. This breaks a symmetry in the optimisation.

In general, we find that a PNO solution will always be a feasible solution of the RNFA, while the RNFA solution might be infeasible for the PNO due to the event dependencies. Thus, RNFA can be understood as a relaxation of the PNO problem.

3. An illustrative case study

The example chosen is a simplified circular substructure shown in Figure 1. *R1* is an irreversible bimolecular reaction producing intermediate C, whereas *R2* is an irreversible bimolecular reaction leading to the formation of product D and regeneration of species B. The chemical meaning of substance B could be for instance a homogeneous catalyst or a protecting group (PG). A and E are reactants. We introduce two scenarios. In Scenario I, 100 mol of each A, B, and E are given as the input; R1 and R2 have a reaction cost of five and product D has a selling price of 50 per mol. In Scenario II, no B, i.e. a catalyst or a PG, is initially available. Further parameters remain unchanged. Both scenarios are solved with both methods, allowing up to two reaction steps; $K = 3$ states for the PNO.

4. Results and Discussion

Hereafter, we outline and discuss the behaviour of both models with regard to a circular substructure. We also qualitatively compare the scalability of the two models. Note, that there are further important factors for model selection, e.g. the desired problem scenario, the actual size of a real-world problem, or the incorporation of evaluation metrics.

Comparing both methodologies for Scenario I, we find that either lead to the same molar distributions over reactions and substances and an identical objective value of -4,000 (see Table 1). Key differences are that the proposed PNO formalism provides information on the sequence of reactions but requires/allows defining the utmost number of the allowed reaction steps. If more steps than necessary are given, the problem size is larger than necessary, but the solution stays the same; there will be inactive steps.

Comparing both methodologies for Scenario II, we encounter differences in the optimal solution. Specifying the input of B as zero leads to no performed reactions in the PNO formalism as event dependencies prevent any reaction. The RNFA approach performs the same reactions as previously (objective value of -4,000), as the material balance for B is intrinsically fulfilled within the circular structure. One can imagine this circular structure as follows: assuming B is present (could be borrowed), we perform reaction *R1*. Then, *R2* takes place and reproduces B (it can be returned). This leads to the desired product D and is, based on the objective function, more desirable than not performing any reaction. Still, for conducting the actual set of reactions, B is needed at the start of the first reaction.

Table 1. Obj. value and molar flux distribution over reactions and outputs in both scenarios (Sc.I and Sc. II) and both approaches. For the PNO, * represents the first and + the second reaction step.

		Obj. value	Reaction flux		Final mol distribution				
			R1	R2	A	B	C	D	E
Sc. I	RNFA	-4,000	100	100		100		100	
	PNO	-4,000	100*	100+		100		100	
Sc. II	RNFA	-4,000	100	100				100	
	PNO	0			100				100

Comparing the model size, the RNFA is smaller (see Table 2) and scales linearly with the network size, i.e. number of reactions (T) and number of molecules (P). The PNO method further scales with the number of desired steps (K-1). This is often a constant parameter, independent from the network size with K<<P and K<<T. Thus, the PNO also scales linearly with network size. According to the Leyffer-Linderoth-Luedtke measure of complexity, MILPs of approximately $2 \cdot 10^4$ variables (LPs of about $5 \cdot 10^7$) could be solved using state-of-the-art solvers in 2016. Thus, previous literature cases (Voll and Marquardt, 2012b) with about 116 reactions and 80 substances would also be solvable by the PNO. Regarding a network of all chemical knowledge contained in large databases, e.g. Reaxys® (>119M compounds and >46M reactions), problems most likely need to be broken down for both methods or heuristic solution strategies would be required.

Table 2. Model complexity of RNFA and PNO formalisms. * Variable bounds are not counted as constraints (PNO based on Eq. (4-7) and RNFA based on substance balances).

		RNFA	PNO
Problem size	No. of continuous variables	T+P	$(P+T) \cdot (K-1)$
	No. of binary variables	0	$T \cdot (K-1)$
	No. of constraints*	P	$((P+T+1) \cdot (K-1))+(K-2)$

This illustrative experiment indicates firstly that network substructures play an important role in modelling. Secondly, if the aim is to build reaction sequences only on the currently available substances, PNO seems the more appropriate choice. If, on the other hand, the circular structures should be incorporated in the reaction sequences, e.g. through recycle streams and separation units, RNFA exhibits advantages. Thirdly, the event dependencies in the PNO lead to higher model complexity. Finally, a possible limit on the allowed number of reaction steps may be advantageous. Both methods are promising choices.

5. Conclusions

We compare RNFA and PNO for optimal decision making in a circular reaction substructure. The PNO accurately captures the possible assumption that only given feedstocks are utilised but shows higher model complexity, indicating potential problems when large networks are to be investigated. The RNFA can take advantage of intrinsic circular structures. Both approaches are valuable for the optimisation of reaction networks. The key contribution of this work is a better model understanding which will guide future works towards appropriate model choices, or possibly a model combining both approaches, for larger scales and more complex network optimisation problems.

Acknowledgments: J. M. Weber thanks Dr. W. Kähm for his support during the modelling process, Prof. Pietro Liò for advising the project, and the Department of Chemical Engineering for funding her studentship. This work was funded, in part, by the National Research Foundation (NRF), Prime Minister's Office, Singapore under its Campus for Research Excellence and Technological Enterprise (CREATE) program as a part of the Cambridge Centre for Advanced Research and Education in Singapore Ltd (CARES).

References

E. Bartocci, P. Liò, 2016, Computational modeling, formal analysis, and tools for systems biology, PLoS Computational Biology, 12, 1, 1–22.

C. Chaouiya, 2007, Petri net modelling of biological networks, Briefings in Bioinformatics, 8, 4, 210–219.

M. Feinberg, F. J. M. Horn, 1974, Dynamics of open chemical systems and the algebraic structure of the underlying reaction network, Chemical Engineering Science, 29, 3, 775–787.

M. Fialkowski, K. J. M. Bishop, V. A. Chubukov, C. J. Campbell, B. A. Grzybowski, 2005, Architecture and evolution of organic chemistry, Angewandte Chemie - International Edition, 44, 44, 7263–7269.

M. Ghaeli, P. A. Bahri, P. Lee, T. Gu, 2005, Petri-net based formulation and algorithm for short-term scheduling of batch plants, Computers & Chemical Engineering, 29, 2, 249–259.

B. A. Grzybowski, K. J. M. Bishop, B. Kowalczyk, C. E. Wilmer, 2009, The "wired" universe of organic chemistry, Nature Chemistry, 1, 1, 31–36.

T. Gu, P. A. Bahri, G. Cai, 2003, Timed Petri-net based formulation and an algorithm for the optimal scheduling of batch plants, International Journal of Applied Mathematics and Computer Sciences, 13, 4, 527–536.

J. F. Jenck, F. Agterberg, M. J. Droescher, 2004, Products and processes for a sustainable chemical industry: A review of achievements and prospects, Green Chemistry, 6, 11, 544–556.

A. Kätelhön, R. Meys, S. Deutz, S. Suh, A. Bardow, 2019, Climate change mitigation potential of carbon capture and utilization in the chemical industry, Proceedings of the National Academy of Sciences, 166, 23, 11187–11194.

I. Koch, 2010, Petri nets - A mathematical formalism to analyze chemical reaction networks, Molecular Informatics, 29, 12, 838–843.

J. D. Orth, I. Thiele, B. O Palsson, 2010, What is flux balance analysis?, Nature Biotechnology, 28, 3, 245-248.

J. L. Peterson, 1977, Petri nets, ACM Computing Surveys, 9, 3, 223–252.

C. A. Petri, 1962, Kommunikation mit Automaten. Ph.D. Thesis, Technische Universität Darmstadt, Darmstadt, Germany.

A. J. Van Der Schaft, S. Rao, B. Jayawardhana, 2016, A network dynamics approach to chemical reaction networks, International Journal of Control, 89, 4, 731–745.

R. A. Sheldon, 2014, Green and sustainable manufacture of chemicals from biomass: State of the art, Green Chemistry, 16, 3, 950–963.

S. Szymkuć, E. P. Gajewska, T. Klucznik, K. Molga, P. Dittwald, M. Startek, M. Bajczyk, B. A. Grzybowski, 2016, Computer-assisted synthetic planning: The end of the beginning, Angewandte Chemie - International Edition, 55, 20, 5904–5937.

K. Ulonska, A. König, M. Klatt, A. Mitsos, J. Viell, 2018, Optimization of multiproduct biorefinery processes under consideration of biomass supply chain management and market developments, Industrial and Engineering Chemistry Research, 57, 20, 6980–6991.

K. Ulonska, A. Voll, W. Marquardt, 2016, Screening pathways for the production of next generation biofuels, Energy and Fuels, 30, 1, 445–56.

A. Voll, W. Marquardt, 2012a, Benchmarking of next- generation biofuels from a process perspective, Biofuels, Bioproducts and Biorefining, 6, 3, 292–301.

A. Voll, W. Marquardt, 2012b, Reaction network flux analysis: Optimization-based evaluation of reaction pathways for biorenewables processing, AIChE Journal, 58, 6, 1788–1801.

J. M. Weber, P. Lió, A. A. Lapkin, 2019, Identification of strategic molecules for future circular supply chains using large reaction networks, Reaction Chemistry and Engineering, 4, 1969-1981.

E. C. Yamalidou, J. C. Kantor, 1991, Modeling and optimal control of discrete-event chemical processes using Petri Nets, Computers & Chemical Engineering, 15, 7, 503–519.

D. Zhang, E. A. del Rio-Chanona, N. Shah, 2017, Screening synthesis pathways for biomass-derived sustainable polymer production, ACS Sustainable Chemistry & Engineering, 5, 5, 4388–4398.

Sauro Pierucci, Flavio Manenti, Giulia Bozzano, Davide Manca (Eds.)
Proceedings of the 30th European Symposium on Computer Aided Process Engineering
(ESCAPE30), May 24-27, 2020, Milano, Italy. © 2020 Elsevier B.V. All rights reserved.
http://dx.doi.org/10.1016/B978-0-12-823377-1.50309-8

An Agent-based Model for Sustainable Power Generation using Optimal Biomass Utilisation

Sarah Namany, Ahmed AlNouss, Rajesh Govindan, Gordon Mckay, Tareq Al-Ansari *

Divison of Sustainable Development, College of Science and Engineering, Hamad Bin Khalifa University, Qatar Foundation, Doha, Qatar.
talansari@hbku.edu.qa

Abstract

Exponential growth in the global population induces larger dependencies on natural resources to meet the demands for products causing resource depletion and environmental degradation. As such, there is an impetus to transform current industrial systems into systems that operate based on inherent sustainable values. While most of the current energy systems are based on polluting fossil fuels, alternative sources have exhibited high performances both economically and environmentally. Biomass for instance, represents a potential source for energy utilisation. Understanding the functioning of biomass gasification strategies as part of the biorefinery system's operations is fundamental, yet, not sufficient to grant sustainable energy provision. The deployment of biomass technologies should also be assessed whilst considering the interaction with other energy sources. The purpose of this work is to design a dynamic and sustainable decision-making scheme that predicts the performance of the power generation system. The framework is developed as an agent-based model illustrating the several entities contributing to the shift towards a biomass-fuelled energy system. The power generation system and biomass feedstock producers are the main categories of agents interacting with one another following a set of rules restricting their behaviors with an ultimate aim to determine the optimal energy portfolio to meet energy demands whilst considering the contribution of existing natural-gas power plants and biomass blending. Rules of interactions impacting strategies adopted are imposed through two different scenarios representing the environmental and economic performances. Findings of this research demonstrate that under environmental restrictions, a diversified energy mix supporting the contribution of biomass is environmentally viable, as it contributes to a 34% reduction in emissions. However, it entails an economic expenditure amounting to 64% increase owing to the deployment of biomass technologies. The optimal biomass blending indicates the domination of manure feedstock over date pits, sludge and food waste in both scenarios, being the lowest in both economic and environmental costs.

Keywords: Power, Biomass, Agent-based Modelling, Sustainable decision-making

1. Introduction

In the light of the ever-increasing technological advancements, energy resources are experiencing significant pressures owing to the need to satisfy the growing demand. This upsurge will result in a major environmental degradation, especially with the contribution of fossil-fuel based power plants as a major supplier of energy, and which is the central cause of global CO_2 emissions. To offset the environmental burden engendered by conventional power sources, there is an incumbent need to invest in sustainable energy technologies. Biomass is considered a promising renewable energy source with a CO_2 neutrality that has the potential to support the worldwide energy demand with sustainable power and fuels while contributing to an approximately 20% reduction in CO_2 emissions. The recent advancements in thermochemical conversion technologies of biomass demonstrates the excellence of the gasification technique in delivering a high-energy combustible gas. The biomass gasification process can positively result in a larger calorific value content through lowering the ratio of carbon to hydrogen in the effluent syngas. This high-energy syngas serves as an intermediate for the generation of clean fuels and power (AlNouss et al., 2020).

In a country like Qatar, where natural gas-based power plants are well established and are the largest suppliers of energy, deploying a new technology is challenging and requires a thorough decision-making process that considers the economic and environmental implications of each decision undertaken. In a gradually fluctuating environment, decision-making is a multifaceted process necessitating dynamic models. Agent-based modelling (ABM) is a powerful tool that enables the flexible and holistic representation of real-life problems through its modular characteristic allowing the dissection of complex problems into smaller sub-problems, which are analysed independently then aggregated to generate an integrated solution (Barbati et al., 2012). ABM is heavily used in problems involving several actors competing to either achieve conflicting or aligned goals. Marvuglia et al. (2017) assessed the economic and environmental performance of an agricultural system involving the simulation of crops' behaviour as a response to the farmers' decisions. Bieber et al. (2018) adopted an ABM approach to analyse the relationship between humans' socio-economic behaviours and the trend of water and energy demands. Generally, ABM has proven efficient in solving resources-related problems, especially, when it is combined with optimization, as both tools reveal a complimentary connection, such that optimisation models are embedded into an ABM scenarios to generate optimal results (Namany, 2019a). In this paper, ABM is used to forecast the future decisions of the power sector that is striving to satisfy monthly demands over a three-year time period using two sources of energy: natural gas and biomass. The model determines, in the form of an ABM behavioral rule, the optimal biomass feedstock blend that generates the maximum energy while minimising economic costs. This optimal feedstock blend is identified based on the results of economic and environmental performance according to Qatar's biomass feedstock availability and characteristics. Results of the model generate the percentage of contribution of each energy source in the satisfaction of the demand under cost and environmental constraints.

2. Model Development

The model developed as part of this study involves an ABM to perform sustainable planning within the energy sector in Qatar. The designed framework serves as a decision-making tool that enables the prediction of portfolio decisions for the power generation system, as a means to satisfy the local demand from energy. Benefits from deploying biomass energy systems as a sustainable alternative power source are also investigated through an economic and environmental scenario. The following section 2.1 describes the detailed formulation of the ABM along with the tool used to execute the simulation. Section 2.2 explains the proposed scenarios and the data sets available to run the model.

2.1. An ABM simulation for sustainable power generation

An agent is an independent unit characterized by a set of behaviors and attributes. It is governed by specific rules that regulate its interactions with other agents along with the environment where it exists (Lopez-Jimenez et al., 2018). In this study, two main categories of agents are interacting to satisfy the local demand from energy while abiding by economic and environmental constraints. The ABM model developed simulates the monthly decisions of the energy sector for a period of 3 years (n=36), where the main agent, represented by the power generation system P, interacts with B_i, $i \in B$ such that B is the set of biomass feedstock producers. Both agents interact in an environment representing the local economy. Figure 1 and table 1 describe the different elements of the ABM studied along with their features.

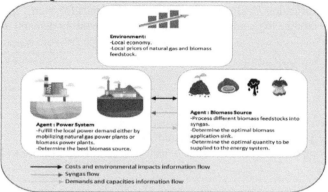

Figure 1: High-level illustration of the different elements of the ABM.

Table 1: Main characteristics of the participating agents.

Agent	Attributes	Behaviours
Power system (P)	- Total grid capacity C (kW) -Monthly demand for energy d_n (kWh) -Monthly energy supplied from natural gas plants Q_{ng} (kWh) -Monthly energy supplied from biomass Q_{bm}(kWh) -Global Warming Potential from generating power from natural gas or biomass (kg CO_{2eq}).	- Supply power from natural-gas plants (NG). - Supply power from biorefineries (BM).
Biomass producers (B_i)	-Monthly feedstock production capacities P_i (kg) -Monthly energy production capacities X_i (kWh)	-Determine the optimal biomass application sinks (S).

2.1.1 Agents

Agent: Power System

The power system P is the core element in the model as it is the agent that guarantees the satisfaction of monthly demands for power d. In order to achieve this aim, P represented by the power grid receives power from two sources: natural gas-based plants and biorefineries, such that the total grid capacity C is not exceeded. The choice of the source is formulated using two different strategies that can be individually or jointly selected: 1) supply the power from natural gas-based sources (NG) or 2) supply the power from biomass sources (BM). Each decision depends on economic and environmental factors elaborated in section 3, along with the operations and attributes associated with the biomass producers' agents B_i. Figure 2 describes the logic adopted by P to satisfy the monthly demand d_n.

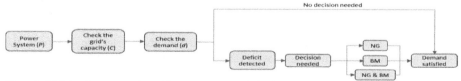

Figure 2. High-level representation of the power system's behaviors.

Agent: Biomass feedstock producers

In this study, four biomass feedstock producers are considered as agents B_i, counting producers of manure, date pits, sludge and food waste. These sources represent a promising sustainable and carbon neutral power supply when combusted. Gasification is the utilisation strategy adopted to generate energy in this case. As part of their behavior, B_i first identify the optimal biomass blend to produce the syngas, which is used in power generation as an application sink. The quantities supplied to the grid from biorefineries depend on the production capacity of each feedstock P_i, the capacity of generation of energy from gasification X_i, along with the monthly demands for energy in the country d_n. Figure 3 describes the logic adopted by B_i to satisfy the monthly demand d_n.

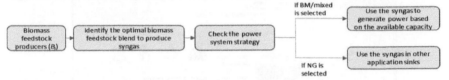

Figure 3. High-level representation of the biomass feedstock producers' behaviors.

To assess the performance of P, economic EC and environmental EI costs for each strategy are computed at each time step n using the following equations (1-4):

Strategy (NG):

$$EC = Q_{ng} \times p_{ng} \qquad\qquad\qquad\qquad\qquad\qquad\qquad\qquad\text{eq.(1)}$$
$$EI = Q_{ng} \times e_{ng} \qquad\qquad\qquad\qquad\qquad\qquad\qquad\qquad\text{eq.(2)}$$

such that Q_{ng} is the monthly amount of energy in kWh from natural gas-based plants represented by combined-cycle gas turbines (CCGT). p_{ng} is the unit cost of energy in \$/kWh estimated based on a previous study by Govindan et al. (2018). e_{ng} is the unit of environmental impact quantified as the global warming potential (GWP) associated with CCGT power generation calculated in previous study by Namany et al. (2019b).

Strategy (BM):

$$EC = Q_{bm} \times p_{bm} \qquad\qquad\qquad\qquad\qquad\qquad\qquad\qquad\text{eq.(3)}$$
$$EI = Q_{bm} \times e_{bm} \qquad\qquad\qquad\qquad\qquad\qquad\qquad\qquad\text{eq.(4)}$$

such that Q_{bm} is the monthly amount of energy supplied from biorefineries in kWh. p_{bm} is the total unit cost of producing energy from each biomass feedstock. It includes the cost of transforming it to syngas and the cost of transporting the syngas to the appropriate application sink, which is in this case power generation. e_{bm} is the GWP associated with the entire process of producing energy from biomass feedstock. Both p_{bm} and e_{bm} were estimated using Process Economic Analyzer and Energy Analyzer in Aspen Plus, as part of a previous study conducted by the authors (AlNouss, 2019).

3. Scenario formulation and results

Two scenarios were formulated to assess the viability of integrating biomass energy in Qatar's power production sector. The first scenario considers the economic costs associated with each energy technology as a decision-making criterion influencing the monthly strategies. The ABM model under this scenario allocates percentages of contribution for each technology to the energy mix giving the largest proportion to the cheapest one. The second scenario generates decisions based on the environmental performance of each energy source regardless of the cost of power generated. Although the economic and environmental components are the main selection criterion, the fluctuating monthly capacities along with varying demands have significant influence on the agents' behaviour.

To generate results, two softwares were used. First, Aspen Plus was applied to simulate the environmental and economic performances of biomass-based integrated oxygen gasification combined cycle (BIGCC) consisting of syngas production section from feedstock and power generation section from gas and steam turbines. This BIGCC model is simulated following the literature study in (AlNouss, 2019). Then, the results of this simulation were used as data sets for the ABM that was formulated in Python using the MESA library (MESA, 2016).

Scenario 1: Economic restrictions

Under the economic scenario, the power generation system advises the adoption of a mixed strategy involving natural gas (NG) and biomass energy (BM) in order to satisfy the local demands. Yet, natural gas is assigned the largest share with a full 100% participation in some months (figure 4-5). This distribution is due to the low cost associated with producing power from natural gas. As for biomass, the manure and sludge are the dominating feedstock thanks to their high energy generation flowrates and their relatively cheap cost.

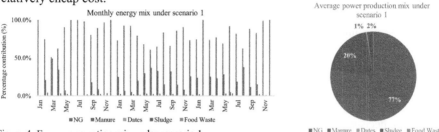

Figure 4. Energy generation mix under scenario 1.

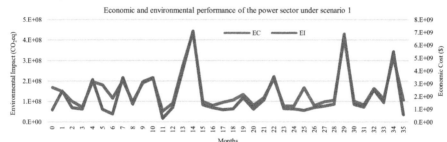

Figure 5. Scenario 1 economic and environmental costs.

Scenario 2: Environmental restrictions

Under environmental restrictions, the power generation system is still adopting a mixed strategy involving both natural gas and biomass with a major participation of natural gas (figure 6). However, the average share of fossil fuel is reduced by 12% in this scenario compared to the previous case (figure 7). This reduction is mainly associated with the high emissions it entails. Biomass share in this scenario is more diversified, allowing the date pits and food waste to contribute. However, manure and sludge are still dominating thanks to their cleaner thermal conversion to power. In comparison with the previous scenario, the environmental case proposes an interesting eco-friendly alternative that reduces the average GWP emissions by 34%. However, a 64% increase in costs is needed to deploy the cleaner biomass energy.

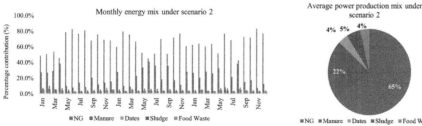

Figure 6. Energy generation mix under scenario 2.

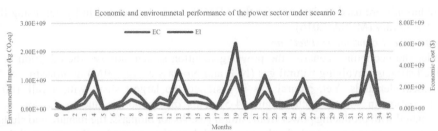

Figure 7. Scenario 2 economic and environmental costs.

4. Conclusion

In this work, an ABM was developed to predict the future behavior of the power generation sector under economic and environmental circumstances. The model also integrates the biomass energy as a sustainable alternative that reduces emissions while satisfying the local demand from power. Under the price-sensitive scenario, natural gas is dominant being the cheapest option, with a fewer contributions for biomass. Under the environmental-friendly case, the contribution of biomass energy, characterized by a large participation of manure and sludge as feedstock, is more significant. The results provide an insight to decision-makers in the power generation system about potential investment in the energy field.

References

A. AlNouss, G. McKay, and T. Al-Ansari, 2020, Production of syngas via gasification using optimum blends of biomass, Journal of Cleaner Production, 242, 118499.

A. AlNouss, G. McKay, T. Al-Ansari, 2019, A techno-economic-environmental study evaluating the potential of oxygen-steam biomass gasification for the generation of value-added products, Energy Conversion and Management, 196, 664–676.

M. Barbati, G. Bruno, A. Genovese, 2012, Applications of agent-based models for optimisation problems: A literature review, Expert Systems with Applications.

R. Govindan, T. Al-Ansari, A. Korre, N. Shah, 2018, Assessment of Technology Portfolios with Enhanced Economic and Environmental Performance for the Energy, Water and Food Nexus, Computer Aided Chemical Engineering, 43, 537-542.

J. Lopez-Jimenez, N. Quijano, A.V. Wouwer, 2018, On the Use of Agent-Based Modeling for Smart Farming, 22nd International Conference on System Theory, Control and Computing.

A. Marvuglia, S. Rege, T. Navarrete Gutiérrez, L. Vanni, D. Stilmant, E. Benetto, 2017, A return on experience from the application of agent-based simulations coupled with life cycle assessment to model agricultural processes, Journal of Cleaner Production, 142, 1539–1551.

Project Mesa Team, 2016, Mesa Overview.

S. Namany , T. Al-Ansari, R. Govindan, 2019a, Sustainable energy, water and food nexus systems: A focused review of decision-making tools for efficient resource management and governance, Journal of Cleaner Production, 225, 610-626.

S. Namany, R. Govindan, T. Al-Ansari, 2019b, Optimisation of the energy, water, and food nexus for food security scenarios, Computers & Chemical Engineering, 129, 106513

Sauro Pierucci, Flavio Manenti, Giulia Bozzano, Davide Manca (Eds.)
Proceedings of the 30th European Symposium on Computer Aided Process Engineering
(ESCAPE30), May 24-27, 2020, Milano, Italy. © 2020 Elsevier B.V. All rights reserved.
http://dx.doi.org/10.1016/B978-0-12-823377-1.50310-4

A New Lagrangian Relaxation Approach for Multistage Stochastic Programs under Endogenous Uncertainties

Zuo Zeng, Selen Cremaschi*

Department of Chemical Engineering, Auburn University, Auburn, AL 36849, USA
selen-cremaschi@auburn.edu

Abstract

Optimization problems with endogenous (decision-dependent) uncertainties are commonly observed in process industry. Most optimization problems with endogenous uncertainties, by nature, can be modelled as multi-period multi-stage stochastic programs (MSSPs), where possible future states of the system are modelled as scenarios by enumerating all possible outcomes of uncertain parameters. However, MSSPs rapidly grow and quickly become computationally intractable for real-world problems. This paper presents a new Lagrangian relaxation for obtaining valid dual bounds for MSSPs under endogenous uncertainties. By exploiting the structure of the MSSP, a tight dual problem is formulated, which reduces the total number of Lagrangian multipliers. The paper also introduces a modified multiplier-updating scheme. We applied the new Lagrangian relaxation to bound instances of artificial lift infrastructure planning (ALIP) problem under uncertain production rates and the clinical trial planning (CTP) problem under uncertain clinical trial outcomes. The computational results reveal that the proposed Lagrangian relaxation generates tight dual bounds compared to the original Lagrangian relaxation formulation and that the proposed multiplier-updating scheme reduces the zigzagging behavior of the Lagrangian dual solutions as iterations progress.

Keywords: multistage stochastic programming, Lagrangian relaxation, endogenous uncertainty, dual bound

1. Introduction

This paper considers multistage stochastic programs (MSSPs) under endogenous uncertainty, where the decisions determine the realization times of uncertain parameters e.g., R&D pipeline management (Colvin and Maravelias, 2008), synthesis of process networks with uncertain process yields (Apap and Grossmann, 2017), and artificial lift infrastructure planning (Zeng and Cremaschi, 2017). Uncertainty is incorporated using scenarios to MSSPs where scenarios represent the unique outcomes of uncertain parameters. Multistage stochastic programs have multiple stages where state decisions are made and recourse actions are taken. The decision variables are defined for each scenario and are constrained by non-anticipativity constraints (NAC) to avoid the state decisions from anticipating future realizations of uncertain parameters. The size of MSSPs, especially with endogenous uncertainty, grows exponentially with the increasing number of uncertain parameters and outcomes of uncertain parameters partially due to the increase in NACs. In general, the MSSPs are solved using heuristic or decomposition approaches, and it has been shown that moderate-size problems can be solved to optimality. Recent approaches include Lagrangian decomposition (Gupta and Grossmann, 2014), sequential scenario decomposition (Apap and Grossmann, 2017), a generalized knapsack decomposition (Zeng et al., 2018), and absolute expected value solution (Zeng and Cremaschi, 2019).

This paper presents a new Lagrangian relaxation formulation for bounding MSSPs under endogenous uncertainties. Similar to the existing Lagrangian relaxation schemes (Gupta and Grossmann, 2014), the new Lagrangian relaxation regards the NACs as the complicating constraints, however it utilizes the special structure of the NACs to formulate a tighter dual problem, which also eliminates half of the Lagrangian multipliers. To obtain tight dual bounds using Lagrangian relaxation, the multipliers should be updated appropriately. The most widely used technique to update the multipliers is sub-gradient optimization method (Ardalan et al., 2016). We introduce an algorithm to be used in the sub-gradient optimization method to update multipliers. The algorithm dynamically updates the multipliers based on the ratio of the value of the dualized constraints in the objective function to the original objective function value. We applied the new Lagrangian relaxation to bound instances of ALIP problem (Zeng and Cremaschi, 2017) under uncertain production rates and the CTP problem (Colvin and Maravelias, 2008) under uncertain clinical trial outcomes. We describe an example MSSP formulation under endogenous uncertainty in §2. The original and new Lagrangian relaxation formulations and the modified multiplier updating schemes are presented in §3. The problem instances and the dual bounds obtained by Lagrangian relaxations are given and discussed in §4. Finally, we present the concluding remarks.

2. The MSSP formulation under endogenous uncertainty

A simple deterministic equivalent formulation of a MSSP with complete recourse under endogenous uncertainties is derived from Zeng et al. (2018). The uncertain source $i \in I$ associated with its uncertain parameter (θ_i) has finite outcomes represented by a finite set $\{\theta_i^1, \theta_i^2, \ldots, \theta_i^{R_i}\}$. The scenario set (S) is constructed using the Cartesian product: $S := \{\times_{i \in I} \theta_i\}$. The planning horizon is discretized, $t \in T = \{1, 2, 3, \ldots, T\}$. The uncertain parameters are endogenous, and we define an endogenous scenario pair set $(s, s') \in S_E$ for scenarios s and s' that are indistinguishable in terms of the realization of the endogenous uncertain parameter i: $S_E := \{(i, s, s'): i \in I, \theta_i^s = \theta_i^{s'}\}$. The MSSP is defined by Eqns. (1)-(6):

$$OV = max \sum_s p_s \sum_i \sum_t G_{i,t,s}(\theta_i^s, b_{i,t}^s, \gamma_t^s) \tag{1}$$

$$h(b_{i,t}^s, \gamma_t^s, \theta_i^s) = 0 \quad \forall i \in I, t \in T, s \in S \tag{2}$$

$$g(b_{i,t}^s, \gamma_t^s, \theta_i^s) \leq 0 \quad \forall i \in I, t \in T, s \in S \tag{3}$$

$$b_{i,1}^s = b_{i,1}^{s'} \quad \forall i \in I, \forall(s, s') \in S \tag{4}$$

$$\begin{bmatrix} Z_t^{s,s'} \\ b_{i,t}^s = b_{i,t}^{s'} \end{bmatrix} \vee [\neg Z_t^{s,s'}] \quad \forall(i, s, s') \in S_E, \forall t \in T, t > 1 \tag{5}$$

$$b_{i,1}^s, Z_t^{s,s'} \in \{0,1\}, \gamma_t^s \in \mathbb{R} \quad \forall(i, s, s') \in S_E, \forall t \in T, \forall i \in I \tag{6}$$

Binary variables $b_{i,t}^s$ represent state decisions made at the beginning of each time period, and variables γ_t^s represent recourse-action decisions that follow the state decisions. The state decisions $b_{i,t}^s$ are enforced to be identical until the differentiating event occurs either by initial or conditional NACs. The recourse variables γ_t^s are determined by scenario specific constraints. The optimum objective function value is defined by variable OV.

The objective function (Eqn. (1)) maximizes the expected value of the total profit/gain associated with state variables $b_{i,t}^s$ and recourse-action decision variables γ_t^s, where p_s is the probability of scenario s and the function $G_{i,t,s}(V_{i,t}, \theta_i^s, b_{i,t}^s, y_{i,t}^s, \gamma_t^s)$ calculates the total profit/gain for specific scenario s. Scenario specific inequality and equality constraints are presented in Eqns. (2) and (3) that may or may not include the uncertain parameters (θ_i^s). Functions $G_{i,t,s}(\cdot)$, $h(\cdot)$, and $g(\cdot)$ in Eqns. (1), (2), and (3) can either be linear or nonlinear. Equation (4) is initial NACs, and Eqn. (5) is conditional NACs that are enforced depending on the value of the Boolean variable, $Z_t^{s,s'}$. This variable is equal to one if scenarios s and s' are indistinguishable at time period t, and zero otherwise.

3. A new Lagrangian relaxation formulation

3.1. Original Lagrangian relaxation problem (LR)

Lagrangian relaxation removes complicating constraints from the original problem and adds them to the objective function with a penalty term, which are called multipliers. The Lagrangian multipliers represent penalties for solutions not satisfying the particular constraints (Lin et al., 2011). In Lagrangian relaxation of a MSSP, the initial and conditional NACs are regarded as the complicating constraints. The conditional NACs in Eqn. (5) are reformulated as two inequalities, Eqns. (7) and (8):

$$b_{i,t}^s - b_{i,t}^{s'} \le 1 - Z_t^{s,s'} \quad \forall i \in I, t \in T, s, s' \in S \tag{7}$$

$$b_{i,t}^s - b_{i,t}^{s'} \ge Z_t^{s,s'} - 1 \quad \forall i \in I, t \in T, s, s' \in S \tag{8}$$

To construct Lagrangian relaxation of a MSSP, both initial (Eqn. 4) and reformulated conditional NACs (Eqns. (7) and (8)) are dualized in the objective function. The original Lagrangian relaxation of MSSP (LR) is given in Eqns. (9) – (12):

$$
\begin{aligned}
OV = \max \sum_s p_s \sum_i \sum_t & G_{i,t,s}(\theta_i^s, b_{i,t}^s, \gamma_t^s) \\
+ \sum_{i,t,s,s'} & \left(\lambda 0_{i,s,s'}(b_{i,1}^s - b_{i,1}^{s'}) + \lambda 1_{i,t,s,s'} \left(1 - Z_t^{s,s'} - b_{i,t}^s + b_{i,t}^{s'} \right) \right. \\
& \left. + \lambda 2_{i,t,s,s'} \left(1 - Z_t^{s,s'} + b_{i,t}^s - b_{i,t}^{s'} \right) \right)
\end{aligned}
\tag{9}
$$

$$h(b_{i,t}^s, \gamma_t^s, \theta_i^s) = 0 \quad \forall i \in I, t \in T, s \in S \tag{10}$$

$$g(b_{i,t}^s, \gamma_t^s, \theta_i^s) \le 0 \quad \forall i \in I, t \in T, s \in S \tag{11}$$

$$b_{i,1}^s, Z_t^{s,s'} \in \{0,1\}, \gamma_t^s \in \mathbb{R}, \lambda 0_{i,s,s'} \in \mathbb{R}, \lambda 1_{i,t,s,s'}, \lambda 2_{i,t,s,s'} \ge 0 \mathbb{R} \quad \forall(i,s,s') \in S_E, \forall t \in T, \forall i \in I \tag{12}$$

The multipliers $\lambda 0_{i,s,s'}$ for initial NACs can either be positive or negative. The multipliers of conditional NACs, $\lambda 1_{i,t,s,s'}$ and $\lambda 2_{i,t,s,s'}$, can only take non-negative values, which enforces the dualized constraints to be great than or equal to zero. The solution of the relaxed problem LR yields a valid dual bound for the original MSSP.

3.2. A modified Lagrangian relaxation formulation (mLR)

In the original relaxation, Lagrangian multipliers penalize the violation of the dualized constraints (Eq. (9)). All possible values of the conditional NACs (Eqns. (7) and (8) in Eq. (9)) are given in Table 1.

Table 1. All possible values of dualized constraints (Eqns. (7) and (8) in Eq. (9))

$Z_t^{s,s'}$	$b_{i,t}^s$	$b_{i,t}^{s'}$	$1 - Z_t^{s,s'} - b_{i,t}^s + b_{i,t}^{s'}$	$1 - Z_t^{s,s'} + b_{i,t}^s - b_{i,t}^{s'}$	$Z_t^{s,s'}$	$b_{i,t}^s$	$b_{i,t}^{s'}$	$1 - Z_t^{s,s'} - b_{i,t}^s + b_{i,t}^{s'}$	$1 - Z_t^{s,s'} + b_{i,t}^s - b_{i,t}^{s'}$
0	0	0	1	1	1	0	0	0	0
0	0	1	2	0	1	0	1	1	-1
0	1	0	0	2	1	1	0	-1	1
0	1	1	1	1	1	1	1	0	0

As can be seen from Table 1, the conditional NACs are always satisfied when indicator variables ($Z_t^{s,s'}$) are equal to zero and can only be violated for indicator variable values equal to one. To tighten the dual bound (Eqn. (9)), we propose a modified relaxation that is shown in Eqns. (13) and (14), where the constraints ($b_{i,t}^s - b_{i,t}^{s'}$) are dualized only when indicator variable ($Z_t^{s,s'}$) values are equal to one.

$$OV = max \sum_s p_s \sum_i \sum_t G_{i,t,s}(\theta_i^s, b_{i,t}^s, \gamma_t^s) + \sum_{i,t,s,s'} (\lambda 0_{i,s,s'}(b_{i,1}^s - b_{i,1}^{s'}) + u_{i,t,s,s'}) \tag{13}$$

$$\begin{bmatrix} Z_t^{s,s'} \\ u_{i,t,s,s'} = \lambda_{i,t,s,s'}(b_{i,t}^s - b_{i,t}^{s'}) \end{bmatrix} \vee \begin{bmatrix} \neg Z_t^{s,s'} \\ u_{i,t,s,s'} = 0 \end{bmatrix} \quad \forall (i, s, s') \in S_E, \forall t \in T, t > 1 \tag{14}$$

The disjunction in Eq. (14) ensures that a conditional NAC is only dualized and added to the objective function (Eq. (13)) with a Lagrangian multiplier $\lambda_{i,t,s,s'} \in \mathbb{R}$ if its associated indicator variable ($Z_t^{s,s'}$) value is equal to one. If the value of the indicator variable is equal to zero, the dualized constraint variable $u_{i,t,s,s'}$ is set to zero. In this modified relaxation, the dualized constraint is equivalent to an equality constraint for indistinguishable scenarios (i.e., for $Z_t^{s,s'} = 1$) with assigned Lagrangian multipliers. The modified Lagrangian relaxation formulation has half of the Lagrangian multipliers compared to the original one ($\lambda_{i,t,s,s'}$ vs. $\lambda 1_{i,t,s,s'}, \lambda 2_{i,t,s,s'}$). Eqns. (13) and (14) can be reformulated as Eq. (15).

$$OV = max \sum_s p_s \sum_i \sum_t G_{i,t,s}(\theta_i^s, b_{i,t}^s, \gamma_t^s) + \sum_{i,t,s,s'} \left(\lambda 0_{i,s,s'}(b_{i,1}^s - b_{i,1}^{s'}) + \lambda_{i,t,s,s'} Z_t^{s,s'}(b_{i,t}^s - b_{i,t}^{s'}) \right) \tag{15}$$

The modified Lagrangian relaxation formulation (mLR) is given by Eqns. (15), (10), (11), (12). Both LR and mLR have the same KKT conditions, and they are both dual bounds for the original MSSP.

3.3. A Lagrangian multiplier updating scheme for sub-gradient optimization method

To obtain tight dual bounds using Lagrangian relaxation, the multipliers should be updated appropriately. The most widely used technique to update the multipliers is sub-gradient optimization method (Gupta and Grossmann, 2014). Given an initial λ_n^0 ($n \in N$) (multipliers for a total of $|N|$ dualized constraints), the multipliers at the kth iteration, λ_n^k, are calculated using Equation (16) (Fisher, 1981),

$$\lambda_n^{k+1} = max\{0, \lambda_n^k - \gamma^k(Ax_n^k - b)\} \tag{16}$$

where x_n^k is the solution of Lagrangian relaxation at iteration k. $Ax_n^k - b$ represents the dualized constraints in the objective function where A and b are parameters. The variable γ^k is the positive step size at iteration k, which is calculated by Equation (17),

$$\gamma^k = scale \frac{Z(\lambda_n^k) - Z^*}{\sum_n (Ax_n^k - b)^2} \tag{17}$$

where $Z(\lambda_n^k)$ is the dual bound from Lagrangian relaxation at the kth iteration and Z^* is the best known primal bound. In Equation (17), the parameter $scale$ is a scalar satisfying $0 \leq scale \leq 2$. Often the value of $scale$ is set to two at the first iteration. If the dual bound fails to converge after a number of iterations, the value of $scale$ is decreased.

Here, we introduce an algorithm for dynamically updating the values of γ^k and *scale* in the sub-gradient optimization method. This algorithm is summarized in Figure 1. The iteration counter (k) and multipliers are initialized as zero, and the scale is set to two at initialization. The first dual bound is obtained by solving the Lagrangian relaxation. The algorithm then determines the number of dualized constraints that were violated. The primal bound in Equation (17) is obtained by the generalized knapsack decomposition algorithm GKDA, $GKDA^*$ in Figure 1 (Zeng et al., 2018). The difference between the dual and the primal bounds are divided by the total number of violated dualized constraints. The step size variable γ^k is updated using the difference of the dual and the primal bounds, multiplying this difference with *scale* and dividing it by the number of violated dualized constraints. From the second iteration, the algorithm dynamically updates the value of *scale* based on the ratio of the sum of the dualized constraint values to the original objective function value to reduce the zigzagging behavior of the Lagrangian dual solutions as iterations progress. The stopping criteria are either reaching a predetermined maximum number of iterations or satisfying all dualized constraints.

$k, \lambda_n^k \ (n \epsilon N) := 0, scale^k := 2$
FOR $k = 1$ to K_{max}
        $Z(\lambda_n^k) :=$ dual bound from Lagrangian relaxation with multipliers $\lambda_n^k \ (n \epsilon N)$
        $x^k :=$ solution of Lagrangian relaxation
        $N^v :=$ number of violated constraints of dualized constraints
        $GKDA^* :=$ primal bound from generalized knapsack decomposition algorithm
        IF $k \geq 2$ THEN
            IF $\dfrac{dualized \ constaints \ value}{Original \ objective \ function \ value} \geq 10\%$ THEN
                $scale^k = \dfrac{scale^{k-1}}{1.618}$
        $\gamma^k := scale^k \dfrac{Z(\lambda_n^k) - GKDA^*}{N^v}$
        FOR $n = 1$ to N
            Update λ_n^{k+1} with dualized constraints and γ^k
        IF no violated constraints THEN BREAK

Figure 1. Modified sub-gradient optimization method for updating Lagrangian multipliers

4. Case Study

We applied the original Lagrangian relaxation (RL) and modified Lagrangian relaxation (mLR) formulations to generate dual bounds for ALIP problem with a planning horizon of 12 months and CTP problem with three products and clinical trials, and a planning horizon of 12 periods. The complete parameters of the instances can be found in Zeng and Cremaschi (2017). The models and algorithms were implemented in Pyomo and solved using CPLEX 12.6.3 on a standard node of Auburn University Hopper Cluster. The maximum number of iterations was 100 for the sub-gradient optimization method.

The results are compiled in Figure 2, which plots how the relative gap (calculated using the optimum solution and the dual bound) changes with the number of iterations for standard (LR) and modified Lagrangian (mLR) dual problem formulations where the multipliers are updated using the standard and our proposed modified approaches. Figure 2 reveals that the modified algorithm, which dynamically updates the scale in the sub-gradient optimization method for estimating the multipliers, improves the quality of the dual bounds for both LR and mLR. It can also be seen that mLR yields tighter dual bounds compared to LR. The mLR obtains 0% percentage relative gap for ALIP instance. For the 3-product CTP problem, both LR and mLR cannot converge within 100 iterations, while LR (standard) and mLR (modified) yield 9.7% and 6.7% relative gaps, respectively.

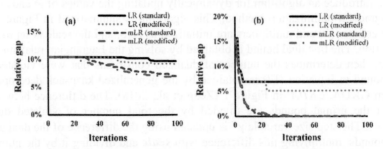

Figure 2. The change in relative gap with the number of iterations of multiplier updates using both LR and mLR dual problem formulations and standard (LR standard, mLR standard) and modified algorithms for sub-gradient optimization method (LR modified, mLR modified), (a) 3-product CTP problem; (b) 12-month planning horizon ALIP problem.

5. Conclusion

This paper contributes a new Lagrangian relaxation reformulation (mLR) and a modified scheme to dynamically update Lagrangian multipliers in sub-gradient optimization method for multistage stochastic programs under endogenous uncertainties. The modified Lagrangian relaxation utilizes a disjunctive structure to indicate which conditional NACs should be dualized to the objective function of the dual model. The mLR reduces the number of dualized constraints and of Lagrangian multipliers compared to the original Lagrangian relaxation formulation. We compare the bounds obtained by the original and the modified Lagrangian relaxation formulations for two planning problems. The results indicate that mLR generates tighter dual bounds in fewer iterations.

Acknowledgements

This work was financially supported RAPID Manufacturing Institute, the U.S.A and was completed in part with resources provided by the Auburn University Hopper Cluster.

References

Apap, R. M., & Grossmann, I. E. (2017). Models and computational strategies for multistage stochastic programming under endogenous and exogenous uncertainties. Comput. Chem. Eng, 103, 233-274.

Ardalan, Z., Karimi, S., Naderi, B., & Khamseh, A. A. (2016). Supply chain networks design with multi-mode demand satisfaction policy. Computers & Industrial Engineering, 96, 108-117.

Lin, Z., Liu, R., & Su, Z. (2011). Linearized alternating direction method with adaptive penalty for low-rank representation. In Advances in neural information processing systems (pp. 612-620).

Colvin, M., & Maravelias, C. T. (2008). A stochastic programming approach for clinical trial planning in new drug development. Comput. Chem. Eng, 32(11), 2626-2642.

Gupta, V., & Grossmann, I. E. (2014). A new decomposition algorithm for multistage stochastic programs with endogenous uncertainties. Comput. Chem. Eng, 62, 62-79.

Zeng, Z., & Cremaschi, S. (2017). Artificial lift infrastructure planning for shale gas producing horizontal wells. Proceedings of the FOCAPO/CPC, Tuscan, AZ, USA, 8-12.

Zeng, Z., Christian, B., & Cremaschi, S. (2018). A generalized knapsack-problem based decomposition heuristic for solving multistage stochastic programs with endogenous and/or exogenous uncertainties. Ind. Eng. Chem. Res., 2018, 57 (28), pp 9185–9199.

Zeng, Z., & Cremaschi, S. (2019). A general primal bounding framework for large-scale multistage stochastic programs under endogenous uncertainties. Chemical Engineering Research & Design, 141, 464-480.

Sauro Pierucci, Flavio Manenti, Giulia Bozzano, Davide Manca (Eds.)
Proceedings of the 30th European Symposium on Computer Aided Process Engineering
(ESCAPE30), May 24-27, 2020, Milano, Italy. © 2020 Elsevier B.V. All rights reserved.
http://dx.doi.org/10.1016/B978-0-12-823377-1.50311-6

A Hybrid Method for Integration of Heat Pump Assisted Distillation System with Intermediate Reboiler/condenser

Jiaxin Yang[a], Minbo Yang[a], Xiao Feng[a], Yufei Wang[b]

[a]*School of Chemical Engineering& Technology，Xi'an Jiaotong University，Xi'an 710049，China;*
[b]*State Key Laboratory of Heavy Oil Processing, China University of Petroleum, Beijing, 102249, China*
yangmb@xjtu.edu.cn.

Abstract

Setting an intermediate reboiler/condenser for heat transfer with the heat pump can reduce both requirements of hot and cold utilities and the temperature lift of the heat pump. This paper proposes a hybrid method that combines rigorous process simulation and mathematical programming for targeting the optimal heat pump placement in the presence of intermediate reboiler/condenser to minimize the overall energy consumption. First, the grand composite curve of distillation column is determined via rigorous process simulation. A simulation model for the vapor compression heat pump is also established. Next, the column grand composite curve is taken as constrains for formulating a simulation-based optimization model by data interaction between Aspen HYSYS and Matlab. The model is solved using the genetic algorithm toolbox to determine the optimal placement of the heat pump. A de-heavy fractionator in the isobutene unit is studied to illustrate the applicability of the proposed method.

Keywords: heat pump, distillation column, intermediate reboiler/condenser, minimum operating cost

1. Introduction

As well known, energy has become a hot issue around the world, and many countries are committed to developments of new energy and energy-saving technologies (Soave and Feliu, 2002). The chemical industry accounts for a large part of industrial energy consumption. As the most important and widely used separation operation, distillation is quite energy intensive and accounts for about 3% of the world energy consumption. Besides, it also suffers from very low thermodynamic efficiency of 5%-20% (Shahandeh et al., 2014). In order to improve energy efficiency and reduce operating costs, a large number of complex tower technologies, such as heat integration distillation columns, heat pump assisted distillation, and intermediate reboiler/condenser have been widely studied and applied.

In a conventional distillation column, heat is supplied at the bottom reboiler by a hot utility, while waste heat is discharged to a cold utility at the overhead condenser, thus causing a substantial energy degradation (Amiya K. Jana, 2014). An effective way to solve this problem is to couple the reboiler and condenser. The integration between a distillation column and a heat pump is well known as heat pump assisted distillation. Compared to conventional distillation, heat pump assisted distillation can separate the mixture with less energy consumption. The reasonable setting of a heat pump in a distillation system can not only improve the utilization of low-grade heat, but also simultaneously reduce heating and cooling demands, which could achieve the purpose of energy saving. Amiya K. Jana (2014) portrayed heat pump assisted distillation as an energy-efficient separation technology, particularly vapor recompression column (VRC) and its hybrid configurations. Patrascu et al. (2018) proposed a novel hybrid separation process based on a heat pump assisted azeotropic dividing-wall column (A-DWC), which makes the energy requirement for butanol separation using heat integration and vapor recompression assisted A-DWC reduce a lot.

Traditional heat pump assisted distillation integrates the reboiler and condenser of a distillation column. Thus, it is only applicable to cases where the temperature difference between the reboiler and condenser is small. In a distillation column, the temperature gradually rises from the top to bottom. An alternative is the use of an intermediate reboiler whose temperature level is lower than the bottom reboiler. Thus, a lower-temperature, less expensive heat source can be used. Similarly, an intermediate condenser is able to save expensive cold utility. Based on the second law of thermodynamics, the addition of intermediate heat exchangers does not reduce the total energy demand, but it can reduce the irreversible energy loss and improve the thermodynamic efficiency of a distillation column (Bandyopadhyay et al.,1999). On this basis, Lynd and Grethlein (1986) presented the technique of IHOSR (intermediate heat pumps and optimal side stream return) distillation. The IHOSR distillation allows heat to be moved between points in a distillation column with greater efficiency than several other methods of heat addition and removal by stream removal, phase change, or optimal side stream return in a distillation column for distillation. An et al. (2008) presented a simulated annealing-based approach for the optimal synthesis of distillation column considering intermediate heat exchangers arrangements. The synthesis problem is formulated as a mixed integer nonlinear programming (MINLP) problem, which can then be solved with an improved simulated annealing algorithm. However, research on how to target the optimal setting location for a heat pump that connects the intermediate reboiler and condenser of a distillation column has not been reported.

The main objective of this paper is to address the optimal design of heat pump assisted distillation with intermediate reboiler/condenser based on simulation-based optimization. First, we simulate a distillation column in Aspen PLUS to obtain data of each stage and calculate the Column Grand Composite Curve (CGCC). Next, Aspen HYSYS is employed for rigorous process and thermodynamic modelling of the heat pump system. With help of the CGCC, the simulation-based optimization model is formulated and solved in the Matlab platform to minimize the operating cost, identifying the optimal setting position of the heat pump.

2. Model formulation

In this paper, a simulated-based optimization is established for heat pump assisted distillation with intermediate reboiler and condenser with the help of CGCC, which is a *T–H* curve at the practical near-minimum thermodynamic condition. The energy-saving potential for different column modifications like reflux reduction, feed conditioning, and scope for side reboiler/condenser can be addressed on such a *T–H* diagram (Bandyopadhyay et al., 1999). Therefore, the model includes the generation of CGCC, simulation of heat pump system, and the objective function.

2.1. The generation of CGCC

For a distillation column, Bandyopadhyay et al., (1999) put forward a method to obtain the CGCC through the Invariant Rectifying and Stripping (IRS) curve without extra enthalpy calculation as below.

For the rectifying section, the overall mass balance and component balance yield the minimum flows of liquid (L_{min}) and vapor (V_{min}), as Eqs. (1) and (2), respectively.

$$L_{min} = D(x_D - y^*)/(y^* - x^*) \tag{1}$$

$$V_{min} = D(x_D - x^*)/(y^* - x^*) \tag{2}$$

where D is the flow rate of top product, x_D is the mole fraction of the key component in the top product, y^* and x^* represent the gas and liquid molar fractions of the key component on the corresponding stage while gas-liquid equilibrium is reached.

The enthalpy balance for the envelope is used to evaluate the enthalpy surplus (H_R) as Eq. (3).

$$V_{min}H_V = L_{min}H_L + DH_D + H_R \tag{3}$$

where H_V, H_L, H_D indicate the enthalpy of gas, liquid, and top product on the corresponding stage, respectively.

For the stripping section, similarly, the overall mass balance and component balance yield the minimum flows for L_{min} and V_{min} as Eqs. (4) and (5), respectively.

$$L_{min} = B(y^* - x_B)/(y^* - x^*) \tag{4}$$

$$V_{min} = B(x^* - x_B)/(y^* - x^*) \tag{5}$$

where B signifies the flow rate of bottom product, x_B signifies the mole fraction of the key component in the bottom product.

The enthalpy balance for the envelope is used to evaluate the enthalpy deficit (H_s) as Eq. (6), where H_B indicates the enthalpy of the bottom product.

$$L_{min}H_L + H_S = V_{min}H_V + BH_B \tag{6}$$

The relationship between duties of condenser and reboiler (Q_c and Q_r) and H_{CGCC} is expressed as Eq. (7).

$$\begin{aligned} H_{CGCC} &= Q_c + H_{def} \\ \text{Rectifying section}: H_{def} &= -H_R \\ \text{Stripping section}: H_{def} &= -H_S + Q_r - Q_c \end{aligned} \tag{7}$$

2.2. Simulation of heat pump system

The vapor compression heat pump system consists of four major devices: evaporator, condenser, compressor, and throttle valve. The heat pump system connects the intermediate reboiler and condenser as shown in Figure 1(a). The working fluid is vaporized in the intermediate condenser of the distillation column and enters the compressor to be pressurized. It then releases heat and condenses in the intermediate reboiler. Afterwards, the working fluid passes through the throttle valve to reduce the pressure.

The heat transferred by a heat pump is constrained by the CGCC of a distillation column as shown in Figure 1(b). In the stripping section, the heat delivered to any stage should not exceed the corresponding heat deficit, namely $Q_1 \leqslant H_1$. Similarly, in the rectifying section, the heat taken from any stage cannot be greater than the heat surplus, namely $Q_2 \leqslant H_2$. In addition, the energy balance of a heat pump can be expressed as $Q_1 = Q_2 + W$.

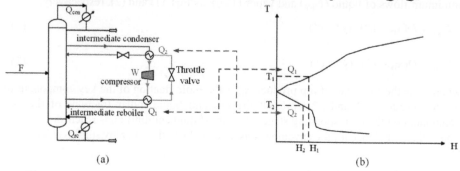

Figure 1 Integration of heat pump assisted distillation system with intermediate reboiler/condenser: (a) illustrative process scheme; (b) analysis based on CGCC.

2.3. Objective function

The main purpose of setting heat pump is to minimize the operating cost of distillation. The total operating cost is composed of hot utility, cold utility, and power. The objective function is given as Eq. (8).

$$Obj = a \cdot Q_{hot} + b \cdot Q_{cold} + c \cdot W \tag{8}$$

where Q_{hot} and Q_{cold} represent the consumption of hot and cold utilities after setting the heat pump. a, b and c are prices of hot utility, cold utility, and power. $a = ¥0.29$ $(kW·h)^{-1}$, $b = ¥0.04$ $(kW·h)^{-1}$, and $c = ¥0.75$ $(kW·h)^{-1}$.

A simulation-optimization model for a distillation column with intermediate condenser and reboiler is established by coupling the heat pump simulation model in Aspen HYSYS with the mathematical model of CGCC in Matlab. The use of CGCC can effectively avoid the convergence failure of column simulation that always stops the optimization. It also means that parameters except hot and cold duties are independent of the setting position of the heat pump. This model can be solved by genetic algorithm based on the data interaction between Aspen HYSYS and Matlab. It is a simulation-based mixed integer linear programming (MILP) problem, since the delivered and received temperature of the heat pump at every stage are discrete variables.

3. Case study

A methanol distillation column in an isobutylene production unit in a petrochemical plant is modelled using Aspen Plus V10. It has 20 stages (including condenser and reboiler) and the feed is introduced above the 10th stage. RadFrac is chosen for the distillation model with the SRK package. The simulation results are given in Table 1. The hot utility consumption is 580.56 kW, and the cold utility consumption is 308.33 kW. Taking methanol as the heavy key component, the temperature, molar flow rates and enthalpy of gas and liquid at each stage are extracted in order to calculate the H_R, H_S, and H_{CGCC}, according to Eqs. (1)-(7). The IRS curves and CGCC are illustrated in Figure 2.

Table 1. Feed and product specifications

	Feed	Top product	Bottom product
Molar flow (kmol·h⁻¹)	181.53	19.68	161.85
Pressure (MpaG)	0.70	0.55	0.60
Temperature (℃)	63.10	52.40	119.61
More fractions			
MTBE	0.0068	5.08×10^{-7}	0.0076
i-butene	0.1144	0.9994	0.0068
Methanol	0.8768	0.0006	0.9833
Tert butyl alcohol	0.0020	3.62×10^{-11}	0.0022

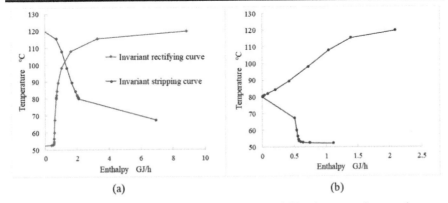

(a) (b)

Figure 2 (a) Invariant rectifying-stripping (IRS) curves and (b) column grand composite curve

Table 2 The comparison of three conditions

Items	Distillation column	Traditional heat pump assisted distillation	The proposed model
Heat taken temperature (°C)	53.40	42.40	57.24
Heat delivery temperature (°C)	119.61	129.61	108.10
Temperature lift (°C)	-	86.21	50.86
Flow rate (kg·h⁻¹)	-	531.0	229.0
Cold utilities (kW)	308.05	0	166.95
Hot utilities (kW)	580.53	116.23	404.53
Heat delivery (kW)	-	464.30	176.0
Heat taken (kW)	-	308.05	141.10
Power (kW)	-	156.25	34.85
COP	-	2.972	5.050
Operating cost (¥·yr⁻¹)	1.426×10^{6}	1.205×10^{6}	1.189×10^{6}

A heat pump system is modelled in Aspen HYSYS V10. According to the temperature profile of the distillation column, R718 is chosen as the working fluid, because it can work at high temperature (Arpagaus et al., 2018). The Peng-Robinson package is selected for the heat pump system. The minimum temperature difference for heat exchange (ΔT_{min}) is taken as 10°C. By solving the model in Matlab R2018b, the optimal setting parameters of the heat pump is obtained as given in Table 2. The heat pump takes heat from the 9th stage and delivers heat to the 18th stage. For comprehensive comparison, traditional heat pump assisted distillation is modelled and results are presented as well. Compared with the distillation column without heat pump, the heat pump assisted distillation with intermediate reboiler/condenser can save 35.7% of energy and reduce operating costs by 16.6%. Although traditional heat pump assisted distillation results in the most savings of hot and cold utilities, it leads to a notable higher temperature lift and a much lower COP than heat pump assisted distillation with intermediate reboiler/condenser. As a result, traditional heat pump assisted distillation shows a slightly higher operating cost by 1.3%. Such results indicate that heat pump assisted distillation with intermediate reboiler/condenser can increase the energy efficiency of the distillation column and improve the utilization of the heat pump.

4. Conclusions

In this paper, a simulated-based optimization method was presented to target the optimal placement of heat pump to assist distillation with intermediate reboiler/condenser, in order to minimize the operating cost. This model was formulated and solved by coupling the simulation model of heat pump in Aspen HYSYS with the mathematical model of CGCC in Matlab. The case study showed that the proposed method could reduce the annual operating cost by 16.6% compared with conventional distillation and by 1.3% compared with traditional heat pump assisted distillation. Besides, heat pump assisted distillation with intermediate reboiler/condenser resulted in a higher COP by 69.9% compared with heat pump assisted distillation. Therefore, the proposed method could extend the application of heat pumps. Furture work may take the investment of heat pump system into account.

Acknowledgments

This work was supported by the National Natural Science Foundation of China (No. 21736008) and the Fundamental Research Funds for the Central Universities (No. xzy012019031).

References

W. An, F. Yu, F. Dong, Y. Hu, 2008. Simulated annealing approach to the optimal synthesis of distillation column with intermediate heat exchangers. Chinese Journal of Chemical Engineering 16, 30-35.

C. Arpagaus, F. Bless, M. Uhlmann, J. Schiffmann, S.S. Bertsch, 2018. High temperature heat pumps: Market overview, state of the art, research status, refrigerants, and application potentials. Energy 152, 985-1010.

S. Bandyopadhyay, R.K. Malik, U.V. Shenoy, 1999. Invariant rectifying-stripping curves for targeting minimum energy and feed location in distillation. Computers & Chemical Engineering 23, 1109-1124.

A.K. Jana, 2014. Advances in heat pump assisted distillation column: A review. Energy Conversion and Management 77, 287-297.

L.R. Lynd, H.E. Grethlein, 1986. Distillation with intermediate heat-pumps and optimal sidestream return. AIChE Journal 32, 1347-1359.

I. Patrascu, C.S. Bildea, A.A. Kiss, 2018. Heat pump assisted azeotropic DWC for enhanced biobutanol separation, 28th European Symposium on Computer Aided Process Engineering. Elsevier Science Bv, Amsterdam, 791-796.

H. Shahandeh, J. Ivakpour, N. Kasiri, 2014. Internal and external HIDiCs (heat-integrated distillation columns) optimization by genetic algorithm. Energy 64, 875-886.

G. Soave, J.A. Feliu, 2002. Saving energy in distillation towers by feed splitting. Applied Thermal Engineering 22, 889-896.

Sauro Pierucci, Flavio Manenti, Giulia Bozzano, Davide Manca (Eds.)
Proceedings of the 30th European Symposium on Computer Aided Process Engineering
(ESCAPE30), May 24-27, 2020, Milano, Italy. © 2020 Elsevier B.V. All rights reserved.
http://dx.doi.org/10.1016/B978-0-12-823377-1.50312-8

Optimal Evacuation Route Prediction in Fpso Based on Deep Q-Network

Seokyoung Hong,[a] Kyojin Jang,[a] Jiheon Lee,[a] Hyungjoon Yoon,[a] Hyungtae
Cho,[b] Il Moon[a*]

[a]*Department of Chemical and Biomolecular Engineering, Yonsei University, 50 Yonsei-ro, Seodaemun-gu, Seoul, 03722, Republic of Korea*
[b]*Green Materials & Processes Group, Korea Institute of Industrial Technology, 55 Jongga-ro, Jung-gu, Ulsan, 44413, Republic of Korea*
pselab@yonsei.ac.kr

Abstract

As a major production facility for oil and gas exploration, a dangerous working environment can cause serious accidents in FPSOs. The hull of the FPSO can be severely damaged or flooded, and in such cases, it is very difficult for workers to escape due to the large and complex structure of the FPSO. Even in an emergency situation, In an emergency situation, rational reasoning is blurred, and objective and prompt judgment cannot be made. It is necessary to provide quick and efficient evacuation guidance in case of emergency in order to prevent casualties. In this study, deep Q-network, a method of reinforcement learning, was applied to the optimal path prediction model to calculate the optimal evacuation route for workers in case of an accident. Deep Q-network can be applied to models with large and complex structure, and the environment of the model consists of 4 parts: deck, accommodation, backward, and frontward. The agent receives penalties for every move and is rewarded when it arrives at one of the four exits on the deck. As a result, the average number of movements is less than 30 when escaping from all locations in the environment consisting of 621 grids. This study contributes to provide an optimal escape route that is fast and safe in a changing environment. Through the analysis of the results of this study, it is expected that the safety inspection on the FPSO can be carried out and it will help the safe FPSO design.

Keywords: Deep Q-Network, Optimal Route Prediction, 3D Environment.

1. Introduction

Floating Production, Storage and Off-loading(FPSO) is a primary method of oil and gas processing and storage for deep-water fields. The number of FPSOs in operation or available for deployment has grown by 33% over the past 10 years. However, the FPSOs are still prone to accidents with a high probability of harsh working. Once serious accident occurs, FPSO may be seriously destroyed and even flooded. In these instances, it is very difficult for workers to evacuate out of the FPSO due to the large scale and complex structure of the FPSO. To avoid causalities, offering workers the effective escape route is essential.

Evacuation route analysis methods can be roughly divided into simulation and optimization. Optimization approaches in evacuation planning are adopted by numerous previous researches. In mathematical modeling, linear programming and dynamic programming models are widely used. Network flow algorithm is utilized to model crowd movement with blocking effect(Luh et al., 2012). As a meta-heuristic approach, ant colony optimization algorithm is implemented to solve multi-objective evacuation routing problem(Fang et al., 2011) and has evolved into quantum ant colony algorithm(Liu et al., 2016). Genetic algorithm (GA) is also a popular heuristic solution method. Multi-criteria problem(Goerigk et al., 2014) and level of service design(Li et al., 2019) for efficient evacuation planning are solved by GA. Compared to mathematical modeling, using heuristic based algorithm reduces the computational cost but does not guarantee exact solution.

To solve this, Q-learning algorithm has been attempted to find a safe and short path(Su et al., 2011). Q-learning is very suitable for solving discrete motion sequence decision problem like path planning, but it is no longer able to approximate the value function as the number of states and actions increases. Most of maritime evacuation researches have been focused on passenger ship and little attention has been paid to the FPSO evacuation. In case of FPSO, different from ships or buildings, the structure of workspace is complex, passages are narrow, and the operating equipment are concentrated. There is a still lack of model to solve such a large-scale problem.

Thus, in this paper, we introduced deep Q-network(DQN)(Mnih et al., 2015) algorithm that combines deep learning with reinforcement learning to optimize the evacuation route in FPSO. We modeled the environment referring to the actual FPSO design (Figure 1). The agent is trained to find the shortest path without stepping back or passing the dangerous area. We compare the results of 2 scenarios and have a discussion about the evacuation system.

2. Problem statement and objective

Spill/release of chemicals occurs most frequently in the types of FPSO accidents. Since the accident may lead to the massive fire, operators who are working on the FPSO have to evacuate safely and quickly. When an accident happens, the operators are evacuated to the lifeboats which are located on both sides of the ship following the exit signs. Therefore, objective is to find an evacuation plan to get to the nearest destination of the four points from current position.

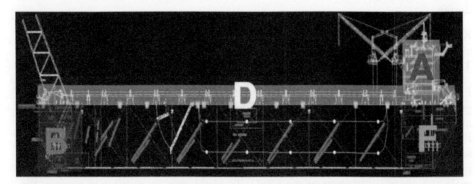

Figure 1. Structure of FPSO: 'A' for accommodation, 'B' for backward, 'F' for forward, 'D' for deck

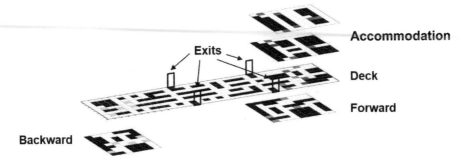

Figure 2. 3-D structure of FPSO environment.

However, as the accident progressed, the optimal route to the exits can be changed. Thus, we considered 2 possible evacuation scenarios under this situation. In the first scenario, an agent finds the nearest exit and chooses the shortest route in no accident, which is called 'normal situation'. The second scenario considered the case that one of the lifeboats reached the maximum capacity, which is called 'accident situation'. In this case, the exit is not available and a sign has to guide the route to another lifeboats before the agent goes in vain. The agent learns the optimal evacuation route and the evacuation time is calculated for each case.

The actual scheme is simplified and expressed as three-dimensional grids. It used to be multi-story structure, but each section is reduced into one or two floors. Therefore, the environment considered in this paper assumes 4 sections, total 621 states. The cells represent different area as the following:

1) Work space, room, or passage (white areas in Figure 2). Agent can move freely and safely.

2) Stair (pink, orange, yellow areas in Figure 2). Pink, orange, yellow respectively means that stairs link the deck to the accommodation, forward and backward section.

3) Blocked area (black areas in Figure 2). Agent cannot move to this kind of areas.

With this environment, the model should satisfy two requirements: 1) It should solve large size problem considering the scale and complexity of FPSO. 2) It should be fast in order to be used in real-time evacuation.

3. Reinforcement learning: Deep Q-Network

Reinforcement learning (RL) is one category of machine learning but it is different from supervised or unsupervised learning. It consists of an agent, an environment, states, actions, rewards and policies. The agent chooses a proper action at each state by trial-and-error and an optimal policy (or a series of actions) maximizing the reward back from the environment can be found. From the point of policy control method, the way to find the optimal policy, on-policy and off-policy learning are considered. A typical off-policy algorithm is Q-learning. In Q learning, a function $Q(s, a)$ is defined representing the expected discounted reward for action a at state s. Q-learning algorithm produces and updates a Q table to find the best action at a given state. However, this method is

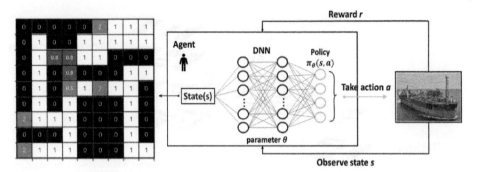

Figure 3. Training algorithm of DQN.

ineffective in large space environment since there are countless number of cases. To overcome the limit of Q-learning, deep Q network (DQN) algorithm was proposed. DQN algorithm uses neural network to approximate Q values instead of Q table. A neural network with weights θ is referred to as Q network. Q-network learns a state-action value function Q by minimizing loss function $L_i(\theta_i)$ Eq. (1):

$$L_i(\theta_i) = \frac{1}{2}[r + \gamma \max_{a'} Q(s', a'; \theta_{i-1}) - Q(s, a; \theta_i)]^2 \qquad (1)$$

Also, the network is trained with a mini-batch from a replay memory which stores experience data collected during learning. This technique called experience replay makes the network more stable. (Target network) Therefore, the algorithm achieves stability by breaking temporal dependency and can obtain an optimal strategy.

In this paper the agent is assumed to be a worker on the FPSO. At each cell, according to the result of the neural network the agent decides an action between 4 directions - up, down, left and right. Also, agent can move up or down to the other floor by the stairs. The problem is how the agent finds the safe and fast route to the lifeboats. The agent gains the reward r_t for the selected action. The agent makes a decision sequentially to maximize the reward. Therefore, the reward represents the learning tendency and it also means objectives and constraints of the action. There are five different rewards according to the area types.

$$r_t = \begin{cases} r^{ga}, & \text{if the agent reaches the goal} \\ r^{ba}, & \text{if the agent moves to the blocked cell} \\ r^{va}, & \text{if the agent moves to the visited cell} \\ r^{sa}, & \text{if the agent moves to the stair cell} \\ r^{na}, & \text{if the agent moves to the normal cell} \end{cases}$$

and the reward value always satisfies $r^{ga} \gg r^{na} > r^{sa} > r^{va} > r^{ba}$. r^{ga} has a positive value to encourage the agent to find the goal and the others have negative values to find the optimal routes. Additionally, we restricted the minimum value of reward to prevent the agent wander endless.

At first, agent wanders the whole map without any information. Then sometimes the agent may reach the minimum reward we constrained and sometimes arrive at the destination by chance. Whether the agent succeed or not, the chosen action and reward the agent got at every discrete state he visited are used to update the neural network.

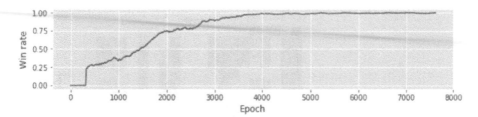

Figure 4. Result of win rate during the training

4. Result and discussion

The proposed DQN is trained with 20000 epochs. The policies and networks have been mentioned in previous section. To evaluate the performance of the model, success rate is recorded. Success rate is defined as the ratio of the number of episodes that successfully find the goal to the recent 300 episodes. Also, average number of moves is calculated in both normal and accident situation. The results are compared to verify whether the agent can find an alternative route properly.

In normal situation, all exits are available then the agent finds the nearest exit from the current position. When starting at 2nd floor of accommodation, the agent finds the shortest route to the exit via the 1st floor and deck and Figure 5 shows the result. The average moves of all starting points in each section are shown in Figure 6 and verify that the agent can evacuate safely regardless of where it starts.

In accident situation, one of four exits is not available due to the capacity of boats and the agent must detour by alternative route. Figure 6 shows how the agent bypasses when exit 3, which is available under normal situation, is closed. Seeing Figure 5, the closure of exit 3 affects escape from all sections except the backward. The reason the backward is not affected is that all escape routes in the backward are not involving exit 3. Although the agent bypasses the route by the effect of exit 3 closure, it finds an alternative route quickly and accurately.

5. Conclusion

A success rate at evacuation from FPSO consistently rises to 100% as training as the training progresses. Although it takes a lot of time to train the model at first, the model makes a quick caculation for every starting point once the train is completed.

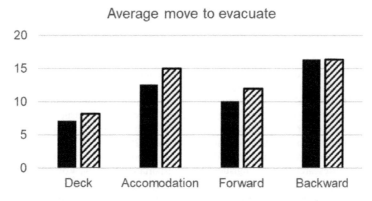

Figure 5. Result comparison of the number of moves between normal and accident situation.

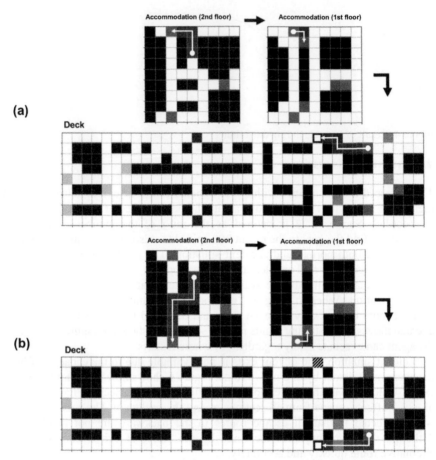

Figure 6. Evacuation test under normal situation (a) and accident situation (b)

Deep Q-Network model can find the shortest evacuation route in complex structure of FPSO. In addition, the route decision is flexible according to accidents and environmental changes. Used in actual marine rescue, it would be helpful to find the optimal evacuation route quickly and rationally in an emergency.

References

P. Luh, 2012, Modeling and Optimization of Building Emergency Evacuation Considering Blocking Effects on Crowd Movement, IEEE Transactions on Automation Science and Engineering, Volume 9, Issue 4, Pages 687-700.

Z. Fang, 2011, Hierarchical multi-objective evacuation routing in stadium using ant colony optimization approach, Journal of Transport Geography, Volume 19, Issue 3, Pages 443-451.

M. Liu, 2016, Evacuation path optimization based on quantum ant colony algorithm, Advanced Engineering Informatics, Volume 30, Issue 3, Pages 259-267.

M. Goerigk, 2014, A comprehensive evacuation planning model and genetic solution algorithm, Transportation Research Part E: Logistics and Transportation Review, Volume 71, Pages 82-97.

Z. Su, 2011, Path selection in disaster response management based on Q-learning, International Journal of Automation and Computing, Volume 8, Issue 1, pp 100–10.

Sauro Pierucci, Flavio Manenti, Giulia Bozzano, Davide Manca (Eds.)
Proceedings of the 30th European Symposium on Computer Aided Process Engineering
(ESCAPE30), May 24-27, 2020, Milano, Italy. © 2020 Elsevier B.V. All rights reserved.
http://dx.doi.org/10.1016/B978-0-12-823377-1.50313-X

A Methodology for Data Based Root-cause Analysis for Process Performance Deviations in Continuous Processes

Patrick D. Schiermoch,[a] Benedikt Beisheim,[a,b] Keivan Rahimi-Adli,[a,b] Sebastian Engell[b]

[a]INEOS Manufacturing Deutschland GmbH, Alte Straße 201, 50739 Köln, Germany
[b]Technische Universität Dortmund, Department of Biochemical and Chemical Engineering, Process Dynamics and Operations Group, Emil-Figge-Str. 70, 44221 Dortmund, Germany
patrick.schiermoch@ineos.com

Abstract

The surge of computational power and the increasing availability of data in the process industry result in a growing interest in data based methods for process modelling and control. In this contribution a concept is described that uses statistical methods to analyse the root-causes for deviations from baselines that are used for the monitoring of the resource efficiency of the production in dashboards. This is done by comparing historical data during resource efficient operation under similar process conditions with data during inefficient operation. Statistically significant deviations are identified, sorted by the likelihood of causing the performance deviation. The concept is applied to a reference model called Best Demonstrated Practice which is in use at INEOS in Cologne. It represents the most resource efficient process performance under given conditions. Deviations from efficient plant performance are analysed using the described concept and the results are given to the operators as a decision support tool, including reference values for the degrees of freedom under the control of the operators. This concept is already used in a root-cause analysis tool at INEOS in Cologne and detected energy savings of over 20% for specific cases.

Keywords: Data analysis, operator advisory, root-cause analysis, anomaly detection

1. Introduction

The European industrial landscape is faced with challenging changes in legal requirements and ambitious goals regarding emissions and the consumption of resources. Furthermore, the European market is driven by high pressure induced by the strong competition due to the imports from the Middle East and North America and a soft demand. To survive in a competitive market the industry is constantly developing methods to uncover improvement potentials and increase the cost and resource efficiency. However, due to high costs that are bound to retrofitting of mature processes or investments into new processes, the industry in Europe pursues alternative methods of process improvements.. One commonly used tool to improve the performance of processes is advanced process control (APC). However, APC solutions are usually bound to high investments. Another approach that is commonly found to improve processes is the development of first principle models. The development of these requires expert knowledge of the processes and is time intensive. A less cost intensive approach is the use of resource monitoring and energy dashboards which have been reported by Sučić et al. (2015) for building complexes and by Rahimi-Adli et al. (2019) for chemical processes. They use historical data that is prevalent in the process industry to develop baseline models for resource efficient plant operation under the given circumstances. These models are incorporated into dashboards that indicate target values for the resource efficiency to the plant operators. However, the reasons for deviations of the current plant operation from these baseline values are not always straight-forward and the performance improvement depends on the experience and the training of the operators. In this paper a concept is developed that uses historical data and statistical methods to gain insight into the process and reasons for deviations from the baseline to facilitate the transition to more resource efficient process operation.

This concept is applied to an industrial case at INEOS in Cologne, where dashboards are used to monitor the resource efficiency of the production plants of the site. The approach is used as a decision support tool to return reference values for the degrees of freedom of a process that can be used by plant operators to increase the resource efficiency significantly.

2. Methodology

The models that are developed to predict the resource efficiency for the dashboards are data based. They have been developed using neural networks and adaptive neuro-fuzzy inference systems for buildings by Li et al. (2011) and by a set of predefined basis functions for chemical processes by Beisheim et al. (2019). The data based models according to Beisheim et al. (2019) can be described as input-output models shown in equation 1.

$$F(t) = I(t) \cdot M + C, \tag{1}$$

where $F(t)$ describes the predicted value and $I(t)$ is the input vector at specific time t, M and C are model parameter vectors and a constant term, both determined during the model development. For a time series $I(t)$ takes the form described in equation 2.

$$I(t) = \begin{pmatrix} I_{1,t_1} & \cdots & I_{n,t_1} \\ \vdots & \ddots & \vdots \\ I_{1,t_m} & \cdots & I_{n,t_m} \end{pmatrix}, n, m \in \mathbb{N}. \tag{2}$$

The index t indicates the time step that the input variables belong to, n describes the number of different input variables and m describes the number of time steps in the time series. Each value I can be a direct measurement or transformed into the form needed for the model by mathematical equations (e.g. squaring, exponential, etc.).

In this paper models that are used to calculate the energy or resource efficiency are called baseline models. In the remaining paper all sorts of energy or resources will be simply called resource.

This difference between the model prediction for the baseline and the actual current consumption is called ΔF and is calculated as:

$$\Delta F(t) = \hat{F}(t) - F(t), \tag{3}$$

where $\hat{F}(t)$ describes the measured resource efficiency at t. As previously discussed, reasons for deviations of measured resource efficiencies from the predicted values are usually not easily identified as the modelled system can be very complex. Expert knowledge is helpful to identify potential reasons for deviations, however, trial and error as well as intensive data analysis is usually required to be successful.

In order classify the resource efficiency into values that are within an acceptable range to the predicted baseline values and when the resource efficiency is not a maximal allowed deviation ΔF_{max} is introduced:.

$$\Delta F_{max}(t) = F(t) \cdot p_{allowed}. \tag{4}$$

$p_{allowed}$ describes a percentage of relative deviation from the model prediction that is considered to be acceptable and should be used as tuning factor. By introducing this classification a subspace of allowed data points can be defined that only contains data of efficient process operation. This concept is shown in **Errore. L'origine riferimento non è stata trovata.** for a model that is depending on the load of a plant.

However, comparing the measurement of an inefficient operation point $\hat{F}(t_{ineff})$ to the whole data set of efficient process data that is indicated as squares and circles in Figure 1 will most likely not result in insights into the root-causes for the deviation $\Delta F(t_{ineff})$. This is caused by data that is spread over the whole operational space of the process where it is assumed to contain multiple different operational states. Therefore, the data space that should be used for a comparison has to be further limited to only contain data that uses inputs that are similar to the inefficient operation point that is analyzed. In order to do that a neighborhood is defined that relies on the distance metric d_{I,t_j} defined in equation 5. This metric calculates the distance of the inputs $I(t)$ of each operating point to the inputs $I(t_{ineff})$ of the inefficient operation point. This value can be used to estimate the similarity of operating points in the efficient data set to the analyzed operation point.

$$d_{I,t_j} = \sqrt{\Sigma_i(I_{i,t_j} - I_{i,t_{ineff}})^2} \, , \forall j = 1,2,...m. \tag{5}$$

The index j describes the time step that is evaluated. It is assumed that operating points that result in a smaller value for d_{I,t_j} use similar inputs $I(t)$ to the inefficient operation point and are more suitable for a comparison. Due to the fact that the I_{i,t_j} for a model can vary greatly in size and range, a simple distance metric as used in equation 5 will strongly favor values with little variance to them. Therefore, it is necessary to standardize the size of the input space and equalize it. Mean centering and UV-scaling is used for data standardization as described in equation 6.

$$I_{i,t_j,\sigma} = \frac{I_{i,t_j} - \mu_{I_i}}{\sigma_{I_i}}, \tag{6}$$

where μ_{I_i} describes the mean and σ_{I_i} describes the standard deviation of the model input parameter i. After the standardization of the input space the distance metric described in equation 5 can be used in combination with $I_{i,t_j,\sigma}$ from equation 6 to obtain a standardized distance metric for the input space in equation 7.

$$d_{I,t_j,\sigma} = \sqrt{\Sigma_i(I_{i,t_j,\sigma} - I_{i,t_{ineff},\sigma})^2} \, , \forall j = 1,2,...m. \tag{7}$$

Due to the assumption that the operating points that result in small values for $d_{I,t_j,\sigma}$ are using similar input data for the models these should be used for a comparison.

Therefore, a neighborhood is defined that uses that metric. Due to the fact that the similarity of the data points is decreasing with increasing $d_{I,t_j,\sigma}$ the neighborhood has to be limited. In order to do guarantee enough data points to ensure a statistical sound comparison of the efficient data points the neighborhood should be defined large enough to hold a minimal amount of operating points. This has to be chosen based on the data density. If the data points are sparse in the input space of the inefficient operation point the neighborhood could become too big and the similarity of the data base will be lost. Therefore, a distance

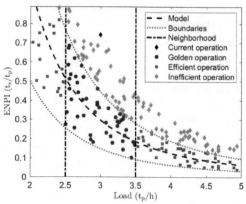

Figure 1: Schematic representation of the baseline model, allowed deviations (Boundaries), the neighborhood and the classification of the operating points

metric $d_{I,t_j,\sigma,max}$ is defined that is exactly the distance that includes the minimal number of operating points that was previously defined. All operating points that follow the inequalities in equation 9 and 10 are assumed to be efficient operating points in the neighborhood of the inefficient operation point that is analyzed and denoted here as "golden operating points" in the rest of this paper.

$$d_{I,t_j,\sigma} \leq d_{I,t_j,\sigma,max}, \tag{9}$$

$$F(t) - \Delta F_{max}(t) \leq \hat{F}(t) \leq F(t) + \Delta F_{max}(t) \tag{10}$$

This results in a clearly defined set of operating points as indicated in Figure 1, where the boundaries of the neighborhood are shown as vertical lines.

After the definition of the golden operating points these can be compared to the operation point that results in resource inefficiency. In order to do that all data that is suspected to have an influence on the resource efficiency (e.g. ambient temperature, pressure, etc) is collected for the same time as the golden operating points in the matrix D_{gol} which is described in equation 11, where k denotes the number of influences that is analyzed and s describes the number of golden operating points. The same data is collected for the current operation point in the vector D_{ineff} in equation 11.

$$D_{gol} = \begin{pmatrix} J_{1,t_{gol},1} & \cdots & J_{k,t_{gol},1} \\ \vdots & \ddots & \vdots \\ J_{1,t_{gol},s} & \cdots & J_{k,t_{gol},s} \end{pmatrix}, D_{ineff} = \begin{pmatrix} J_{1,t_{ineff}} & \cdots & J_{k,t_{ineff}} \end{pmatrix}, k, s \in \mathbb{N}. \tag{11}$$

As the data in D_{gol} is also subject to different variance, the data space has to be standardized. The mean value and standard deviation for D_{gol} is calculated resulting in the vectors μ_{gol} and σ_{gol}. These values are used in equation 12 to compute the standardized deviation $\Delta\sigma_{ineff}$ of each data point that was collected in D_{ineff}.

$$\Delta\sigma_{ineff} = \frac{D_{ineff} - \mu_{gol}}{\sigma_{gol}}, \tag{12}$$

which is a measure for the difference of that specific data to the golden operating points. It is assumed that a higher value of $\Delta\sigma_{ineff}$ for data makes it more likely to be the reason for the deviations $\Delta F(t_{ineff})$. Therefore, $\Delta\sigma_{ineff}$ is sorted in a last step and shown to the operator in the order of magnitude as the potential reason for the inefficiency. To ensure that data is statistically considered anomalous when compared to the golden operating points, it is suggested to only consider values for $\Delta\sigma_{ineff}$ that surpass values of 2 because a standard deviation of 2 is considered to indicate a probability of 95% that the difference is significant as described by Czitrom et al. (1997).

3. Root-cause analysis at INEOS in Cologne

At INEOS in Cologne dashboards are used that indicate which resource consumption is efficient under the given operation conditions. Therefore baselines models are used that indicate how much resources were used in the same plant section when it was operated efficiently, given the specific operation mode. However, reaching the predicted resource efficiency is difficult and strongly depends on the experience and motivation of the plant operators to make the right adjustments to the process while maintaining a safe production.

The results of the root-cause analysis will be presented for a single plant section that was able to save significant amounts of energy using this concept. The investigated unit operation is an evaporator that is schematically shown in Figure 2. The analyzed operation point was prominent due to a highly inefficient operation that caused a resource consumption that was 25% higher than the baseline value. The unit operation consists of a feed stream that enters the evaporator on the side. Water is evaporated and leaves at the top where it is condensed using cooling water. The water is split into a part that leaves the evaporator and a part that is used as reflux flow into the evaporator to increase the purity of the water that leaves the unit operation on the top. The product stream leaves the evaporator at the bottom free of water. A reboiler is installed at the bottom of the evaporator to introduce heat into the system. $I(t)$ only contains the load of the evaporator which is defined as the process water stream leaving the unit operation on the top. The threshold of data that should be included in the golden operating points was set to 100 data points to ensure a sufficient data base for a comparison while maintaining a small neighborhood. All set-points for the controllers of the evaporator has been included in D_{gol} because they are the degrees of freedom a plant operator has. The calculation of $\Delta\sigma_{ineff}$ for the selected data resulted in high values for the set-points of the bottom temperature ($\Delta\sigma_{ineff,T_{bot}} \approx 3$) and for the reflux flow ($\sigma_{Reflux} \approx 2.5$). These results were discussed with plant personnel and it was determined that the deviation of these two set-points causes a high value of $\Delta F(t)$. The problem initially arose during the testing of a new operation mode. The reboiler temperature has been increased due to internal reasons. After a while the water contained increased amounts of organic compounds close to the product specifications. Instead of decreasing the bottom temperature the reflux stream has been increased resulting in a higher purity of the head product while also increasing the overall energy

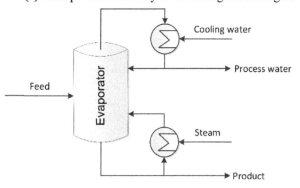

Figure 2: Schematic representation of the evaporator that is analyzed by the root cause analysis

consumption. The values for the controller set-points were adjusted to the mean value of the golden operating points μ_{gol}, resulting in a rapid decrease of the resource consumption by over 20%, resulting in an resource consumption approximately 5% above the baseline value. The root-cause analysis was used again after the adjustment and no other anomalies were detected.

4. Conclusions

In this paper a methodology has been presented that can be used to identify the root-causes for deviations of real process data from baseline values using statistical methods. This concept was implemented in resource efficiency dashboards at INEOS in Cologne that describe reference values for highly resource efficient process operation under similar operating conditions. The implementation of the root-cause analysis helps with the analysis of deviations in the dashboard and facilitates a more resource efficient operation of processes. The concept has been used on an evaporator and it is shown that the energy consumption for one process unit was reduced by over 20% by giving the plant operators set-points for controllers of process parameters. The use of the root-cause analysis facilitated the analysis of deviations from baseline values and gave the plant operators hints to increase the resource efficiency of the current production. This concept is expected to be universally applicable for dashboards that use baseline models for the process monitoring. This can have a contribution to increase the resource efficiency of different processes in the European industry which can lead to an improved position in the difficult market of the process industry.

Acknowledgment

The project leading to this publication has received funding from the European Union's Horizon 2020 research and innovation program under grant agreement No 723575 (CoPro) in the framework of the SPIRE PPP.

References

B. Beisheim, K. Rahimi-Adli, S. Krämer, & S. Engell, (2019). Energy performance analysis of continuous processes using surrogate models. Energy.

V.Czitrom, & P. D. Spagon, (1997). Statistical case studies for industrial process improvement, Siam, Vol. 1, p.486

K. Li, H. Su, & J. Chu, (2011). Forecasting building energy consumption using neural networks and hybrid neuro-fuzzy system: A comparative study. Energy and Buildings, Vol. 43(10), pp. 2893-2899.

K. Rahimi-Adli, P. D. Schiermoch, B. Beisheim, S. Wenzel, & S. Engell, (2019). A model identification approach for the evaluation of plant efficiency. In Computer Aided Chemical Engineering, Vol. 46, pp. 913-918

B. Sučić, A. S. Anđelković, & Z. Tomšić, (2015). The concept of an integrated performance monitoring system for promotion of energy awareness in buildings. Energy and Buildings, Vol. 98, pp. 82-91.

Sauro Pierucci, Flavio Manenti, Giulia Bozzano, Davide Manca (Eds.)
Proceedings of the 30th European Symposium on Computer Aided Process Engineering
(ESCAPE30), May 24-27, 2020, Milano, Italy. © 2020 Elsevier B.V. All rights reserved.
http://dx.doi.org/10.1016/B978-0-12-823377-1.50314-1

Reduced-order Modelling (ROM) Approach for Optimal Microclimate Control in Agricultural Greenhouses

Farhat Mahmood[a], Ikhlas Ghiat[a], Rajesh Govindan[b], Tareq Al-Ansari[a,b*]

[a]*Division of Sustainable Development, College of Science and Engineering, Hamad Bin Khalifa University, Qatar Foundation. Doha, Qatar*
[b]*Division of Engineering Management and Decision Sciences, College of Science and Engineering, Hamad Bin Khalifa University, Qatar Foundation. Doha, Qatar*
talansari@hbku.edu.qa

Abstract

Recent efforts to boost self-sufficiency for food through the intensification of domestic production has been considered imperative to insulate from the vagaries of the global food markets. The State of Qatar is an example where more local fresh food production is being promoted, including the current expansion of agricultural greenhouse facilities for domestic vegetables production across the country. However, the hyperarid regional climatic conditions and extreme weather volatilities locally has a direct impact on the greenhouse microclimate owing to the physical processes of energy transfer (radiation and heat) and mass balance (wind and humidity). This consequently results in unpredictability of requirements for: (a) energy for cooling and ventilation; and (b) water for irrigation. In view of these challenges, the objective of the research presented in this paper is to develop a simulation-based methodology for greenhouse microclimate control. A 2D computational fluid dynamics (CFD) model for indoor temperature distribution was used to implement low-dimensional reduced order models (ROM) based on the Proper Orthogonal Decomposition (POD) and Galerkin projection techniques. The results obtained demonstrate that ROM representations are computationally efficient for predictive greenhouse microclimate control systems, providing novel opportunities for timely mitigation of high temperature risks, thereby enhancing the resilience of greenhouses productivity.

Keywords: Food Security, Greenhouse Microclimate, Reduced Order Models.

1. Introduction

The global population is increasing exponentially and expected to grow up to 9.7 billion in 2050 (UN DESA, 2019). To meet the proportional increase in demand for food production, it is required to develop self-sustaining environment friendly solutions in terms of energy and water consumption. Agricultural greenhouses present a feasible solution as the yield production increases up to 10-20%, with a reduction in fuel consumption by 25-35% yearly (De Gelder *et al.*, 2012). Greenhouses provide a closed and controlled environment for the plants to grow, thus optimising the yield conditions. As such, the greenhouse microclimate of a greenhouse can be controlled based on the region and type of crop being grown.

The greenhouse microclimate is constituted by a combination of variables, including temperature, humidity, wind and radiation to which the vegetation is directly exposed.

Besides external macroclimate conditions, the influence of factors inside the greenhouse, including vegetation type, soil conditions and irrigation, also play a major role in impacting its microclimate. As such, the temperature and photosynthetic day light integral (DLI) radiation are the main environmental factors that affect the growth and development of crops (Moccaldi and Runkle, 2007), whilst humidity can modify the final yield and quality of crops in varied ways.

The air temperature evolution inside the greenhouse is directly related to the heat flux from the radiation, conduction and convection with the air on the outside. Thus, greenhouses can be used to provide artificial cooling, especially during the summer season, providing optimally controlled temperature to ensure productivity throughout the year (Montero, 2006), particularly in the harsh climate of arid regions, such as that of the State of Qatar. Hemming et al. (2019) recently demonstrated that autonomous greenhouses equipped with sensor monitoring; actuators for screening, lighting, ventilation, fogging, CO_2 enrichment, irrigation and fertilisation; and predictive control using artificial intelligence performed better than manually controlled systems in terms of enhanced productivity, optimal land and water resource usage, and the overall efficient food production economics. Among various approaches, model predictive control (MPC) is an effective strategy that utilises prediction of disturbances to optimise future system behavior under certain constraints (Govindan and Al-Ansari, 2019).

Whilst data-driven algorithms have become indispensable for modern intelligent control problems, physical system models based on them are essentially "black boxes" that do not provide insights into the complex behavior of nonlinear dynamical systems, such as greenhouse microclimate, to better understand the potential development of emerging risks within them. Thus, the objective of the research presented in this paper is to develop physics-based models for greenhouse microclimate simulation and optimisation. Low-order representation, namely reduced order modelling (ROM), was used in this study to transform the complexities of the developed computational fluid dynamics (CFD) model of greenhouse microclimate, particularly for indoor temperatures, into computationally efficient surrogate models for predictive control and risk mitigation.

2. Data and model specifications

The model domain was setup using the COMSOL Multiphysics software. A 2D pitch roof greenhouse model was considered with silica glass as the covering material (Shklyar and Arbel, 2004; Al-Mahdouri et al., 2013). The properties of various materials considered were assumed from the built-in material library in the software, as indicated in Table 1.

Table 1. Physical and chemical properties of the materials used for the greenhouse model

Material	Thermal conductivity [W/(m*K)]	Density [kg/m^3]	Heat capacity at constant pressure[J/(kg*K)]
Silica glass	1.38	2203	703
Air	0.026	1.225	1420
Water	0.5918	1000	4185.5

The assumed model spans 6m in width and 5m in height (see Figure 1). The use of this model is justified due to the expectation of a high level of symmetry in the heat transfer within the greenhouse (Carlini *et al.*, 2019), which further allows simplification for demonstrating the concept of model order reduction proposed in this study. The model domain is meshed using finite element method which allows flexibility for various boundary conditions whilst considering the governing the greenhouse microclimate. External factors, particularly impacting the temperature, namely the solar radiation and ambient air were applied at the model boundary in the form of a heat flux. The heat flux values were varied to determine the temperature distribution inside the greenhouse under different conditions throughout the year (Caponetto *et al.*, 2000). Furthermore, the cooling control is incorporated, in this case using five pipelines circulating cold water at the bottom of the greenhouse, as illustrated in Figure 1. Table 2 indicates other specifications assumed for the model.

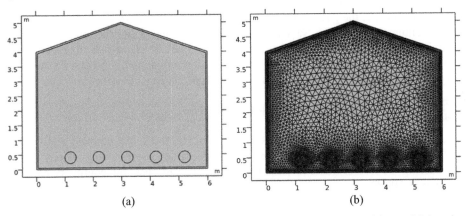

(a)   (b)

Figure 1. (a) 2D domain setup of greenhouse model; (b) Triangular meshing of the model domain

Table 2. Specifications of the greenhouse model setup

Parameter	Value	Definition
T_c	18°C	Temperature of the cold water in the pipelines
R_p	100 cm	Radius of the pipeline carrying the cold water
L_{gh}	6 m	Length of the greenhouse
H_v	4 m	Height of the side wall
L_R	3.16m	Length of the inclined roof

Optimal control for temperature at various points inside the greenhouse is based on the data available for specific crops, namely tomato and lettuce (Table 3). As such, uneven temperature distribution inside the greenhouse poses a risk for these crops in terms of their development.

Table 3. Optimum temperature ranges for specific crop growth

Plant	Optimum Temperature[°C]
Tomato	18 - 30
Lettuce	17 - 23

3. Methodology

3.1. Governing equations in the greenhouse model

The governing equation for convective heat transfer is a second order partial differential equation representing the energy conservation principle, which states that rate of change of total thermal energy equals the sum of: (a) the rate of exchange of heat flux (conduction); (b) the rate of change of energy due to convection and pressure variations (compression and expansion); and (c) the rate of change of energy due to viscous dissipation, expressed in terms of the variable temperature (T), as (Bird *et al.*, 1966):

$$\rho C \left(\frac{\partial T}{\partial t} + \vec{v} \nabla T \right) - \kappa \nabla^2 T + T \alpha \nabla . \vec{v} + \boldsymbol{\tau} . \nabla \vec{v} = 0 \tag{1}$$

where, ρ is the air density; C is the specific heat; $\vec{v}$ is the 2D velocity vector; κ is the thermal conductivity; α is the coefficient of thermal expansion; and $\boldsymbol{\tau}$ is viscous stress tensor. Meanwhile, the governing equation for fluid flow, representing the conservation of momentum, based on the Naviér-Stokes equation, which states the rate of change of total linear momentum equals the sum of: (a) rate of change of momentum by convection; (b) pressure force and rate of change of momentum by viscous transfer; and (c) gravitational force, expressed as (Bird *et al.*, 1966; White, 1999):

$$\rho \frac{\partial \vec{v}}{\partial t} + \rho \vec{v} (\nabla . \vec{v}) + \vec{v} (\nabla . \rho \vec{v}) + \nabla p + \nabla . \boldsymbol{\tau} - \rho \vec{g} = 0 \tag{2}$$

where, p is the pressure force; and $\vec{g}$ is the gravitational force. The coupled heat transfer and fluid flow model aims to jointly solve for temperature, pressure and velocity vector, considering the conservation of mass principle, given by the flow continuity equation (Bird *et al.*, 1966):

$$\frac{d\rho}{dt} + \nabla . \rho \vec{v} = 0 \tag{3}$$

3.2. Reduction via Proper Orthogonal Decomposition (POD) and Galerkin projection

In the POD formulation, a new set of basis functions are constructed from the snapshots obtained from the solutions of equations (1), (2) and (3) that evolve through time. In this study, the snapshots of solutions obtained for the temperature variable is recorded for the simulation period of seven hours, with an interval of 30 minutes. A snapshots matrix $\mathcal{T} = [\mathcal{T}_1 \, \mathcal{T}_2 \, ... \, \mathcal{T}_{S-1} \, \mathcal{T}_S]$ is generated of size $N \times S$, where N denotes the number of mesh elements, and S denotes the number of snapshots. Taking the deviation from the mean $(\bar{\mathcal{T}})$ forms a modified snapshots matrix $\tilde{\mathcal{T}}$, given by:

$$\tilde{\mathcal{T}}_S = \mathcal{T}_S - \bar{\mathcal{T}} \tag{4}$$

where, $\bar{\mathcal{T}} = \frac{1}{S} \sum_{S=1}^{S} \mathcal{T}_S$ \hfill (5)

Subsequently, the goal of POD is to find a set of orthogonal basis functions $\{\Phi_S\}$, s $\in$ $\{1, 2, ..., S\}$. This was achieved by implementing Singular Value Decomposition (SVD) of the modified snapshots matrix $\tilde{\mathcal{T}}$, given by:

$$\tilde{\mathcal{T}} = \mathcal{T}_1 \, \Sigma \, \mathcal{T}_2{}^T \tag{6}$$

leading to the orthogonal basis functions $\{\Phi_S\}$, such that:

$$\Phi_s = \frac{\widetilde{\mathcal{T}}.\mathcal{T}_{2(:,s)}}{\sqrt{\lambda_s}}, \text{for } s \in \{1, 2, ..., \} \tag{7}$$

where, λ_s are the eigenvalues in the diagonal matrix Σ. Thus, in POD, the temperature variable for each snapshot was predicted using a subset of basis functions corresponding to the largest P eigenvetors (*i.e.* the first P columns of $\mathcal{T}$, and $P \ll S$), expressed as:

$$\mathcal{T}_S' = \bar{\mathcal{T}} + \sum_{j=1}^{P} \alpha_j \Phi_j \tag{8}$$

Finally, the POD coefficients α_j is solved in the ROM using the Galerkin projection in the model domain Ω, given by:

$$\frac{\alpha_k^t - \alpha_k^{t-1}}{\Delta t} = \langle F(\bar{\mathcal{T}} + \sum_{j=1}^{P} \alpha_j \Phi_j), \ \Phi_k \rangle_\Omega \tag{9}$$

such that, $F(\psi) = \frac{d\psi}{dt}$ \hfill (10)

4. Results and Discussion

The results of ROM prediction for the temperature distribution inside the greenhouse provides a high-fidelity representation comparable to the full CFD model simulation. Thus, the ROM model provides valuable predictive control information for the cooling system - the five pipelines circulating cold water - with enough load to maintain the desired temperature in the cultivation area of the greenhouse, and potentially mitigate the risk of increasing temperatures. Figure 2 illustrates example snapshots of temperature distribution during the simulation period, where the core temperature is roughly maintained in the optimal range of 17 - 27°C (see Table 3).

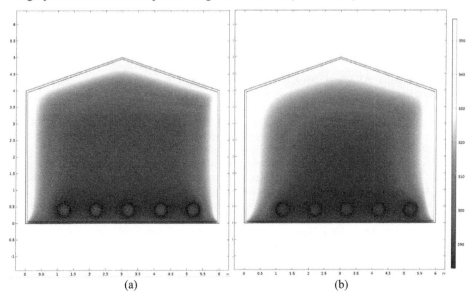

(a) \hspace{5cm} (b)

Figure 2. ROM predictive control for temperature in the greenhouse after: (a) 3.5 hours; (b) 7 hours.

5. Conclusions

The study presented in this paper describes a computational physics-based approach for the development of prediction and optimal control of greenhouse microclimate parameters, particularly that of the evolution of indoor temperatures owing to impact of external climate conditions, including solar temperature, temperature and humidity. It is envisaged that the reduced order model (ROM) application for greenhouses provides the flexibility for rapid integration with "black box" data-driven approaches and artificial intelligence algorithms, so as to better understand the risks with low occurrence probability that can potentially arise within a greenhouse, and are not necessarily captured by historical data. One of the major limitations of the current study is, however, the lack of simultaneous prediction of multiple and non-linearly correlated microclimate variables, and coupling those with cooling and irrigation requirements, which is a subject of ongoing studies. Nevertheless, the model reduction approach presented in this paper is computationally efficient and expected to readily scale to larger number of predictors and model domains, that will also be considered in future investigations.

References

A. Al-Mahdouri, M. Baneshi, H. Gonome, J. Okajima, and S. Maruyama, 2013, Evaluation of optical properties and thermal performances of different greenhouse covering materials, Solar Energy, 96, 21–32.

R.B. Bird, W.E. Stewart and E.N. Lightfoot, Transport Phenomena, John Wiley & Sons, Inc., New York, 1966.

R. Caponetto, L. Fortuna, G. Nunnari, L. Occhipinti and M.G. Xibilia, 2000, Soft computing for greenhouse climate control, IEEE Transactions on Fuzzy Systems, 8, 6, 753–760.

M. Carlini, S. Castellucci, A. Mennuni, and S. Morelli, 2019, Numerical modeling and simulation of pitched and curved-roof solar greenhouses provided with internal heating systems for different ambient conditions, Energy Reports.

A. De Gelder, J.A. Dieleman, G.P.A Bot and L.F.M. Marcelis, 2012, An overview of climate and crop yield in closed greenhouses. Journal of Horticultural Science and Biotechnology, 87, 3, 193–202.

R. Govindan and T. Al-Ansari, 2019, Computational decision framework for enhancing resilience of the energy, water and food nexus in risky environments, Renewable and Sustainable Energy Reviews, 112, 653-668.

S. Hemming, F. de Zwart, A. Elings, I. Righini and A. Petropoulou, 2019, Remote Control of Greenhouse Vegetable Production with Artificial Intelligence - Greenhouse Climate, Irrigation, and Crop Production, Sensors, 19, 8, p.1807.

L.A. Moccaldi and E.S. Runkle, 2007, Modeling the effects of temperature and photosynthetic daily light integral on growth and flowering of Salvia splendens and Tagetes patula, Journal of the American Society for Horticultural Science, 132, 3, pp.283-288.

J.I. Montero, 2006, Evaporative cooling in greenhouses: Effect on microclimate, water use efficiency and plant respons, Acta Horticulturae, 719, 373–383.

A. Shklyar and A. Arbel, 2004, Numerical model of the three-dimensional isothermal flow patterns and mass fluxes in a pitched-roof greenhouse, Journal of Wind Engineering and Industrial Aerodynamics, 92, 12, 1039–1059.

UN DESA, 2019, World population prospects 2019. In United Nations, Department of Economic and Social Affairs, World Population Prospects 2019, Retrieved from http://www.ncbi.nlm.nih.gov/pubmed/12283219

F. M. White, Fluid Mechanics, McGraw-Hill, 1999

Sauro Pierucci, Flavio Manenti, Giulia Bozzano, Davide Manca (Eds.)
Proceedings of the 30th European Symposium on Computer Aided Process Engineering
(ESCAPE30), May 24-27, 2020, Milano, Italy. © 2020 Elsevier B.V. All rights reserved.
http://dx.doi.org/10.1016/B978-0-12-823377-1.50315-3

Network Optimization Model for a Sustainable Supply Network for Greenhouses

Ikhlas Ghiat,[a] Rajesh Govindan,[b] Sarah Namany,[a] Tareq Al-Ansari [a,b*]

[a]*Divison of Sustainable Development, College of Science and Engineering, Hamad Bin Khalifa University, Qatar Foundation, Doha, Qatar.*
[b]*Division of Engineering Management and Decision Sciences, College of Science and Engineering, Hamad Bin Khalifa University, Doha, Qatar.*
talansari@hbku.edu.qa

Abstract

Meeting the demand for food in arid and water-scarce regions can be economically and environmentally challenging. Uncertainties related to climate change and global warming exacerbates technical challenges for efficient food production. Protected agriculture in the form of greenhouses grow different types of crops in a controlled microclimate offering better conditions for healthy and profitable production. Moreover, CO_2 enrichment has also been proven to increase crop yields at low costs, and can be supplied from burning carbon-based resources and transferring the carbon recovered through pipeline networks or tanks. However, the sustenance of CO_2 supply to greenhouses requires compliance with the global sustainability standards, and as such there is a need for economically viable and environmentally-friendly networks for the supply of CO_2 required by the greenhouses. The objective of this study is to design an optimum supply chain network for a sustainable supply of CO_2 to greenhouses. The framework developed is based on an optimisation model solved using integer linear programing (ILP) aiming to minimise the economic cost associated with the operations of the entire supply chain network serving greenhouses. An environmental assessment is also conducted in quantifying the CO_2 offset related to the CO_2 utilisation in agricultural greenhouse applications. The proposed model was implemented for a case study based in Qatar, comprising of a set of hypothetical greenhouses placed at various locations; a source of CO_2 from a biomass based power plant, a distribution centre, and existing pipeline and roadway networks. GIS optimisation models previously developed for the Qatar case study provide locations for greenhouses, pipeline and road transportation routes for CO_2 fertilisation as inputs for the proposed supply chain model. The demand for resources, CO_2 transport networks, and the distances between the source and greenhouses were assumed to be the constraints impacting the design of the supply chain network. The results obtained indicate the optimal CO_2 supply quantities to the greenhouses following a proposed network of pipelines and road routes, with a minimum associated cost of transportation of approximately 0,09$/kg of CO_2.

Keywords: Sustainability, Agricultural, Greenhouse, Supply Chains, Network Optimisation.

1. Introduction

In view of the significant shift in the global world population, the food production is expecting an ever-increasing intensification to accommodate the growing demands. This enlarged production entails the deployment of sophisticated agricultural technologies involving advanced machinery and developed processes (Al-Ansari et al., 2016). However, this change in the food system induces severe environmental degradation associated with energy-intensive water and fertilizers' production systems required for enhanced food production levels, such as high global warming potential (GWP) and water depletion (Namany et al., 2019). To offset the environmental impact caused by the food sector, novel techniques are implemented such that yields are enhanced while emissions are reduced. CO_2 fertilisation is a sustainable process that was proven effective in mitigating climate change by reducing CO_2 concentration in the atmosphere through using it in plants' cultivation (Islam, 2012). In fact, CO_2 enrichment improves the photosynthesis of crops leading to higher yields. It also reduces water consumption resulting in optimal water utilization for irrigation (Dion et al., 2011). Adopting CO_2 fertilisation as part of agricultural activities is a very promising approach to enhance crops behavior and increase productivity; applying this method is a challenging task that requires founded planning and significant investments. Current sources of CO_2 are still difficult to implement due to their relatively expensive costs including expenses associated with ways of processing and transportation from the source to greenhouses (Chau et al., 2009). Many efforts are conducted in literature to identify frameworks which might reduce economic and logistical complexities associated with using CO_2 enrichment in food production. Govindan and Al-Ansari (2019) proposed a novel model that analyses the potential of deploying CO_2 fertilisation in greenhouses with an aim to improve food security through increasing crops productivity. The framework determines, based on GIS, the optimal CO_2 fertilisation network comprised of power plants coupled with carbon capture technology, greenhouses and transportation means counting roadways and pipelines, that can satisfy the fulfillment rates. Similarly, this paper contributes to the efforts carried out to solve the supply chain issue associated with the implementation of this sustainable technique.

The objective of this study is to develop an optimisation model for a sustainable supply of CO_2 to agricultural greenhouses to enhance the productivity and reduce water usage. The model can be applied to a multi-echelon network with various complexities and interdependencies as shown in Figure 1. The study uses a hypothetical scenario of potential greenhouses for the supply of CO_2 captured from a potential biomass based power plant, and a potential distribution center all located in the State of Qatar. The aim is to supply the greenhouses with the required CO_2 concentrations to reduce the water use from the evapotranspiration of the plants by 25%. For this, an optimisation model is presented to sustainably supply CO_2 at a minimum cost and evaluate the overall CO_2 reduction in the atmosphere associated with CO_2 capture and utilisation.

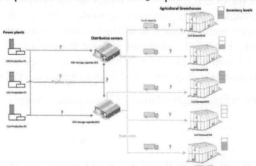

Figure 1: Multi-echelon network problem of CO_2 supply to greenhouses.

2. Available data and assumptions

Multimodal datasets specific to the State of Qatar are used to derive the information needed for this study based on spatially distributed data, mainly farming lands, weather data, and possible routes for CO_2 transport via pipeline and road. A previous study presented viable potential agricultural greenhouse locations in the State of Qatar based on balancing the energy used for CO_2 transport and the energy saved from water reduction by means of CO_2 enrichment (Al-Ansari et al., 2018). These locations were taken in this study for setting the greenhouse network model, along with a possible biomass based power plant, and a distribution center based on the available pipeline and road routes.

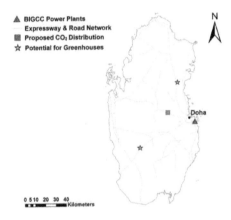

Figure 2: Potential locations for greenhouses, BIGCC plant, and a distribution center in the State of Qatar (Modified after Al-Ansari et al. (2018)).

Two greenhouses were selected, one located in Al-Khor area in the northern part, and one in Al-Kiranah area in the southern part of Qatar. Compressed CO_2 gas (~80 MPa) is assumed to be transported from the BIGCC to the distribution center via a 60 km pipeline following an existing pipeline road currently used for another application in Qatar. Once at the distribution center, the CO_2 follows further processing to get a low pressure liquid at a temperature below ambient, and is stored in 9kg capacity cylinders. This step is necessary for the next transportation of CO_2 from the distribution center to the two greenhouses via road by means of trucks. One truck is assumed to load a maximum number of 50 cylinders of CO_2. The distance between the distribution center and the greenhouses is 53 km for Al-khor and 69 km for Al-Kiranah.

The two greenhouses were assumed to have different crop profiles of producing tomatoes and cucumbers with a harvesting period of two months. Different crop profiles are studied particularly to showcase the importance of optimising a dynamic model that can depend on the owners' choice, or the market demand. Other assumptions are taken into consideration in this study related to source and sinks capacities, safety stocks, and distances between the different network nodes. In this study, a small scale BIGCC capturing 1 kt/year of CO_2 is considered. The storage capacities at each node are assumed; 84 tonnes/month for the distribution center, 180 kg/month for Al-Khorr greenhouse, 224 kg/month for Al-Kiranah greenhouse.

3. Methodology

3.1. CO₂ demand

The CO₂ demand corresponding to the crop profile of the two greenhouses was calculated to achieve a 25% reduction in water loss from the plants' evapotranspiration. The evapotranspiration equation takes into consideration monthly weather data of the particular greenhouse location, in addition to a CO₂ conductance factor as shown in equation (1) (Islam, 2012).

$$ET = k_c \cdot \frac{0.408\,\Delta(R_n - G) + \gamma \frac{900}{T+273} u_2 (e_s - e_a)}{\Delta + \gamma(1 + \frac{0.34 u_2}{CO_2 factor})} \tag{1}$$

The $CO_2 factor$ represents the stomatal conductance g_{CO2} at the unknown CO₂ level over the stomatal conductance a baseline CO2 level of 330 ppm as shown in equation (2) and (3).

$$CO_2 factor = \frac{g_{CO2=x}}{g_{CO2=330}} \tag{2}$$

$$g_{CO2} = 0.0485 - 7e^{-5}(CO_2) + 3.4e^{-8}(CO_2)^2 \tag{3}$$

where Δ represents the slope of the vapor pressure-temperature curve, R_n is the average solar radiation, G is the solar heat flux density, γ is the psychrometric constant, T is the average temperature, u_2 is the average wind speed, $(e_s - e_a)$ represents the vapor pressure deficit, and k_c is the crop coefficient.

An optimisation is conducted to find the optimal CO₂ levels needed to achieve 25% reduction in evapotranspiration for both tomatoes and cucumbers in both greenhouses and for every month. The CO₂ levels in ppm were then converted to a corresponding value in kg per month by multiplying the ppm levels with the volume of the greenhouses and an assumed CO₂ injection rate.

3.2. Network optimisation model

An integer linear programing model was developed for the optimisation of CO₂ supply network to greenhouses taking into consideration the varying evapotranspiration reduction levels between crop profiles and greenhouse locations. The objective of this optimisation is to minimize the operational cost associated with CO₂ transport, and storage at the level of the distribution center and greenhouses. The formulation of this optimisation problem is showcased below.

Variables:
- $C_{T,j}$: cost of transportation by truck to greenhouse j ($/cylinder)
- H_j: CO₂ holding cost in greenhouse j ($/kg of CO₂/month)
- H_{DC}: CO₂ holding cost in distribution center ($/kg of CO₂/month)
- cap_c: capacity of one cylinder (kg of CO₂/cylinder)
- S_j: safety stock needed for greenhouse j (kg of CO₂/month)
- $I_{i,j}$: initial CO₂ inventory in month i for greenhouse j (kg of CO₂/month)
- $D_{i,j}$: CO₂ demand in month i for greenhouse j (kg of CO₂/month)
- cap_j: CO₂ storage capacity in greenhouse j (kg of CO₂/month)
- cap_T: CO₂ capacity of a transport truck (cylinders)

Decision variables:
$Q_{i,j}$: number of CO₂ cylinders transported in month i to greenhouse j (cylinders)

Objective function:
Minimise:

$$\sum_{i=1}^{12} \sum_{j=1}^{2} Q_{i,j} C_{T,j} + cap_c \sum_{i=1}^{12} \sum_{j=1}^{2} H_j Q_{i,j} - cap_c H_{DC} \sum_{i=1}^{12} \sum_{j=1}^{2} Q_{i,j} \qquad (4)$$

Constraints:
$$S_j \le I_{i,j} + Q_{i,j}. cap_c - D_{i,j} \le cap_j$$
$$Q_{i,j} \le cap_T$$
$$Q_{i,j} \ge 0; \ integer$$
where: $I_{i,j} = Q_{i-1,j} cap_c - D_{i-1,j} + I_{i-1,j}$; for $i = 1, 2, 3, \ldots, 12$ and $j = 1,2$.

4. Results and discussion

The integer linear programing model was solved and the resulted minimised overall cost was retrieved to be around 0.09\$/kg of CO_2. Figure 3) andFigure 4) represent the variation of the CO_2 transported with the changing demand and inventory levels. For example, for Al-Kiranah greenhouse in month 6, there is no demand for CO_2 because the crop profile for that greenhouse indicates that no production will take place in that month. Although, there will be no production, CO_2 is still being sent for that month to account for a safety stock. It is important to track the inventory levels at all echelons of the supply chain in order to minimise the holding and transportation costs while meeting the demand.

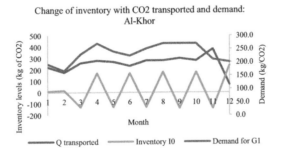

Figure 3: Change of CO_2 inventory levels with supply and demand: Al-Khor

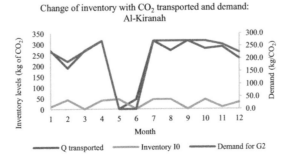

Figure 4: Change of CO_2 inventory levels with supply and demand: Al-Kiranah

The CO_2 offsetted by the two greenhouses during a year reaches 5,27 tonnes CO_2/year from direct CO_2 utilisation only, representing a small amount of CO_2 being produced from the BIGCC. Hence, more greenhouses can be added to this network to effectively use the CO_2 captured from the BIGCC, and efficiently use the pipeline and road transportation capacities suggested in this network model. Moreover, both greenhouses have been set to reduce their crop evapotranspiration by 25%, which represents an additional CO_2 reduction related to water production. Assuming the water source comes from reverse osmosis desalination, this model will reduce CO_2 emissions from virtual water by 1,2 tonnes CO_2/year as compared to the baseline case operating without CO_2 enrichment. Thus, the total abated CO_2 from this application adds to an amount of 6.47 tonnes CO_2/ year.

5. Conclusions

CO_2 enrichment in greenhouses has become a viable and proven solution to enhance crop productivity and reduce the water loss due to evapotranspiration of the plants. However, the CO_2 supply chain for agricultural greenhouse applications lacks research and more optimisation is needed to sustainably utilise this source. Thus, in this study an economic optimisation network model for CO_2 supply to greenhouses is presented. The model can be scaled up to include multiple CO_2 sources, distributions centres, and agricultural greenhouses having different crop profiles and CO_2 demands. For the hypothetical scenario chosen in this study, CO_2 supply to greenhouses can be possible at a cost of 0.09\$/kg of CO_2, and a total amount of 6.47 tonnes of CO_2/year is offsetted from both CO_2 consumption and virtual water loss due to evapotranspiration.

References

T. Al-Ansari, A. Korre, Z. Nie, & N. Shah, 2016, Integration of Biomass Gasification and CO_2 Capture in the LCA Model for the Energy, Water and Food Nexus. 26th European Symposium on Computer Aided Process Engineering, 2085–2090.

S. Namany, R. Govindan, T. Al-Ansari, 2019, Optimisation of the energy, water, and food nexus for food security scenarios, Computers & Chemical Engineering, 129, 106513.

A. Islam, L. R. Ahuja, L. A. Garcia, L. Ma, A. S. Saseendran, 2012, Modeling the Effect of Elevated CO_2 and Climate Change on Reference Evapotranspiration in The Semi-Arid Central Great Plains, American Society of Agricultural and Biological Engineers ISSN 2151-0032.

L.-M. Dion, M. Lefsrud, & V. Orsat, 2011, Review of CO_2 recovery methods from the exhaust gas of biomass heating systems for safe enrichment in greenhouses, Biomass and Bioenergy, 35(8), 3422–3432.

J. Chau, J. Sowlati, S. Sokhansanj, F. Preto, S. Melin, X. Bi, 2009, Techno-economic analysis of wood biomass boilers for the greenhouse industry, Appl Energ, 86:364.

R. Govindan, & T. Al-Ansari, 2019, Simulation-based reinforcement learning for delivery fleet optimisation in CO_2 fertilisation networks to enhance food production systems. Computer Aided Chemical Engineering 29th European Symposium on Computer Aided Process Engineering, 1507–1512.

T. Al-Ansari, R. Govindan, A. Korre, Z. Nie, & N. Shah, 2018, An energy, water and food nexus approach aiming to enhance food production systems through CO_2 fertilization. 28th European Symposium on Computer Aided Process Engineering, 1487-1492.

Sauro Pierucci, Flavio Manenti, Giulia Bozzano, Davide Manca (Eds.)
Proceedings of the 30th European Symposium on Computer Aided Process Engineering
(ESCAPE30), May 24-27, 2020, Milano, Italy. © 2020 Elsevier B.V. All rights reserved.
http://dx.doi.org/10.1016/B978-0-12-823377-1.50316-5

Integration of Chemical Process Simulators with Algebraic Modeling Languages

R. Ruiz-Femenia[a], J. Javaloyes-Antón [a], R. Salcedo-Díaz [a], M. A. S. S. Ravagnani [b], J. A. Caballero[a]

[a]Institute of Chemical Process Engineering, University of Alicante, Alicante, Spain.
[b]Chemical Engineering Department, State University of Maringá, Brazil
ruben.ruiz@ua.es

Abstract

In this work, we use the external equations facility available in GAMS to incorporate in the optimization model the library packages of a commercial process simulator such as Aspen-Hysys, which provides an extensive component database and reliable physical property methods. To this end, we write a source code in the C programming language that connects with Matlab, which in turn uses the Microsoft Component Object Model (COM) interface to communicate with Aspen-Hysys. The methodology is illustrated with a case study of the reaction section of a methanol plant. The results show that a thermodynamic rigorous optimization can be performed without losing the high index capabilities, few verbose and simple syntax that an AML offers.

Keywords: GAMS, external equations, Aspen-Hysys, optimization.

1. Introduction

The relevant value of Algebraic Modeling Languages (AMLs) is widely accepted by their capability for solving real-world optimization problems. AMLs allow to define variables and write constraints with a concise mathematical representation, which is essential for large-scale problems that involve thousands or millions of variables and constraints. One of the main contributions for the development of AMLs came for the discipline of chemical engineering, under which is natural to view an understand the world and its behavior as a mathematical program (Kallrath, 2004). The General Algebraic Modeling System (GAMS) is one of the most widely used AMLs in universities and in the energy and chemical industries. One of its strengths is that provided access to more than 25 solvers, including the state-of-the-art commercial solvers. As other AMLs, GAMS distinguishes between abstract model and concrete problem instances, and also offers a file format (GDX) that allows to send data for a GAMS model and store the results from the same model to be post-processed in external software. An alternative strategy to AMLs for solving optimization problems is to use a high-level programming language to formulate optimization models, which are then solved with an optimizer written in low-level languages. This approach combines the flexibility of a high-level language to build the model with the efficiency of a low-level language for numerical computation. The most mature software that uses this approach is TOMLAB (Navarro-Amorós et al., 2014), which provides access to the commercial optimization solvers inside the Matlab environment. Like any other commercial AML, GAMS does not use this two-language approach, but GAMS does offer a customizable modeling component by the usage of the external equations facility, which permits to emulate the above-mentioned flexibility of a high-level programming language such as Matlab.

In this work, we use the external equations facility available in GAMS to incorporate in the optimization model the library packages of a commercial process simulator such as Aspen-Hysys, which provides an extensive component database and reliable physical property methods.

2. Methodology

2.1. Optimization with an embedded process simulator

When sequential modular process simulators are used as calculation engines in mixed-integer nonlinear programming (MINLP) optimization problems, it is convenient to define a partition of the vector of continuous variables x, into dependent and independent (or design) variables. The values of the dependent variables, x^{Sim}, are provided by the external equation. On the other hand, the design variables x^I, are the set of optimization variables and its dimension is equal to the degrees of freedom of the problem when the set of binary variables are fixed. By this partition, the resulting representation of the optimization problem, using the generalized disjunctive programming (GDP) formulation (Balas, 1979; Raman & Grossmann, 1994), is shown in Figure 1 (left problem). The common equality constraints $h(\cdot)$ can be solved for a given vector of independent variables. Then, the dependent variables are expressed as a function of decision variables $x^{Sim} = h^{Ext}(x^I)$. (see right problem in Figure 1). Similarly, in the disjunctions, for each equipment i assigned to a task k, the dependent variables associated with it can be expressed as functions of the decision variables $x^{Sim} = s_{ik}^{Ext}(x^I)$. In this work, dependent variables x^{Sim}, are not explicitly written in terms of decision variables, but they are externally calculated at the level of the process simulator, and then used at the optimization level to evaluate the objective function and the common and disjunctive constraints.

Note that in the reformulation of the GDP, as we introduce dependent variables in explicit equations (for example in $h(x^{Sim}, x^I) = 0$ or in $g(x^{Sim}, x^I) \leq 0$, a sequential function evaluation is required). First, the implicit constraints are solved within the process simulator, and then, the explicit constraints written in GAMS are evaluated.

$$\min_{x, Y_{ik}} \quad z = f(x) \longrightarrow \min_{x^{Sim}, x^I, Y_{ik}} \quad z = f(x^{Sim}, x^I)$$

$$s.t. \quad h(x) = 0 \longrightarrow x^{Sim} = h^{Ext}(x^I)$$
$$h(x^{Sim}, x^I) = 0$$

$$g(x) \leq 0 \longrightarrow g(x^{Sim}, x^I) \leq 0$$

$$\bigvee_{i \in D_k} \begin{bmatrix} Y_{ik} \\ r_{ik}(x) \leq 0 \\ s_{ik}(x) = 0 \end{bmatrix} k \in K \longrightarrow \bigvee_{i \in D_k} \begin{bmatrix} Y_{ik} \\ r_{ik}(x^{Sim}, x^I) \leq 0 \\ x^{Sim} = s_{ik}^{Ext}(x^I) \\ s_{ik}(x^{Sim}, x^I) = 0 \end{bmatrix} k \in K$$

$$\Omega(Y) = True$$

$$\Omega(Y) = True \qquad\qquad x^{I, lo} \leq x^I \leq x^{I, up}, x^I \in \mathbb{R}^{n_I}$$
$$x^{lo} \leq x \leq x^{up}, x \in \mathbb{R}^n \longrightarrow x^{Sim, lo} \leq x^{Sim} \leq x^{Sim, up}, x^{Sim} \in \mathbb{R}^{n-n_I}$$
$$Y_{ik} \in \{True, False\} \qquad\qquad Y_{ik} \in \{True, False\}$$

Figure 1. Transformation of a general GDP formulation to embed a process simulator in the optimization model.

2.2. Connection between GAMS and process simulator

Figure 2 illustrates the main parts to establish a connection between the AML (GAMS) and the Hysys-Aspen simulator. The required inputs are the GAMS modeling file and the Aspen-Hysys flowsheet. Aside from the common GAMS declarations and definitions included in a GAMS file, it must be also defined each external equation by mapping its

$$f_1^{Ext}\left(x_1,\dots,x_n,x^{Sim}\right)=0$$

```
Ext_Eq1.. sum(i,ord(i)*x(i)) + (card(i)+1)*xSim=X=1;
```

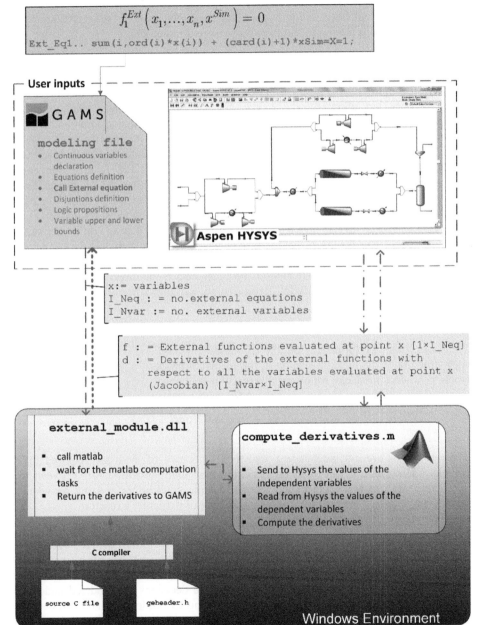

Figure 2. Scheme of the connection between GAMS and Aspen-Hysys through the external equations GAMS Facility.

variable names and its corresponding variables indices. The key component of this connection system is the external module, which is the responsible for the evaluation of the external equation and its Jacobian at a given point (these evaluations are not performed by the GAMS run-time system). The source code for this module is written in C, and as our methodology is developed under Windows environment, is built as a dynamically linked library (.dll). The final connection with Aspen-Hysys is performed through Matlab, which uses the Microsoft Component Object Model (COM) interface to send and receive information to and from the process simulator.

2.3. Solution strategy for a GDP model

The ongoing optimization problem is special since the evaluation of the black-box functions does not allow relaxed values for the binary variables. Such features automatically exclude some mixed-integer algorithms, such as, nonlinear branch and bound. To overcome this difficulty, we use the Logic-based Outer Approximation (OA) (Ruben Ruiz-Femenia et al., 2014; Türkay & Grossmann, 1996). The Logic-based OA shares the main idea of the traditional OA for MINLP (Mixed Integer NonLinear Programming), which is to solve iteratively a MILP master problem, which gives a lower bound of the solution, and an NLP subproblem, which provides an upper bound. The NLP subproblem is derived from the GDP representation of the problem by fixing the values of the Boolean variables (i.e., given a flowsheet configuration). The key difference of the logic approach versus the OA is that in the logic based OA algorithm only the constraints that belong to the selected equipment or stream are imposed. This leads to a substantial reduction in the size of the NLP subproblem compared to the direct application of the traditional OA method over the MINLP reformulation of the GDP problem.

2.4. Case study

We assess the performance of the proposed methodology using a simplified superstructure of the reaction section of the methanol process, where the synthesis gas reacts to produce methanol following this reaction system:

$$CO + 2H_2 \rightarrow CH_3OH$$
$$CO_2 + 3H_2 \rightarrow CH_3OH + H_2O$$
$$CO + H_2O \leftrightarrow CO_2 + H_2$$

These reactions are not independent, and then, only two of them are required for a complete description of the reaction system, which exhibits a trade-off between the conversion reached according to the thermodynamic equilibrium and the conversion governed by reaction kinetics and the residence time of particular a reactor.

The different flowsheet alternatives considered for this process are shown in Figure 3. A total of 64 feasible flowsheets topologies arise from the two types of the feed stream, the compression systems (located at the feed and recycle stream) that have one or two compressors and can operate at low and high pressure, and the two alternative rectors for the low and high operating pressure. These discrete decisions are modeled under the generalized disjunctive programming framework using 12 Boolean variables. A detailed description of this case study can be found in (Navarro-Amorós et al., 2014; Rubén Ruiz-Femenia et al., 2017).

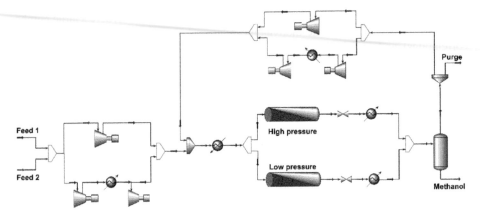

Figure 3. Superstructure for the reaction section of the methanol synthesis process.

The modelling framework above described provides the solution shown in Figure 4. Both, discrete (i.e. one stage compression and low pressure) and continuous decisions match the results obtained in the previous works (Navarro-Amorós et al., 2014; Rubén Ruiz-Femenia et al., 2017). This fact strengths the validation of our methodology.

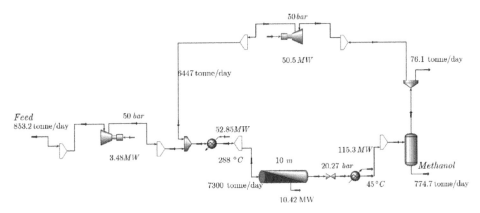

Figure 4. Optimal flowsheet for the reaction section of the methanol process.

3. Conclusions

The performance of the methodology to integrate process simulators with AMLs has been tested with a simplified case study of the reaction section of the methanol process. The results show that a thermodynamic rigorous optimization can be performed without losing the high index capabilities, few verbose and simple syntax that an AML offers.

An advantage of our approach, compared to similar ones, such as the optimization interface (OPTI) toolbox under Matlab environment, is that GAMS offers more NLP solvers, in particular the efficient and reliable solver CONOPT for the large-scale nonlinear optimization. Furthermore, the proposed approach allows to compute the submatrix of the total Jacobian only with respect the independent variables required to cover the degrees of freedom in the process simulator. An addition strength of the proposed methodology is that the external equations, which could involve a large number of equations (e.g. rigorous thermodynamic relationships or detailed equipment design correlations) and variables, are solved at the level of the process simulator, taking advantage of reliable tailored methods implemented in the flowsheeting programs. Remark that these equations and variables do not contribute to enlarge the size of the optimization problem defined in the AML used, since they are hidden from the optimization solver.

A limitation of our approach is that solvers that need to analyze the algebraic structure of the model instance, such as global solver BARON (Tawarmalani & Sahinidis, 2005), cannot be used with external equations.

Further work involves extending this optimization tool to larger industrial case studies, and developing an approach to restore the optimization procedure from process simulator convergence failures.

Acknowledgements

The authors gratefully acknowledge financial support to the Spanish «Ministerio de Economía, Industria y Competitividad» under project CTQ2016-77968-C3-2-P (AEI/FEDER, UE).

References

Balas, E. (1979). Disjunctive Programming. Annals of Discrete Mathematics, 5, 3-51.

Kallrath, J. (2004). Modeling languages in mathematical optimization. Boston: Kluwer Academic Publishers.

Navarro-Amorós, M. A., Ruiz-Femenia, R., & Caballero, J. A. (2014). Integration of modular process simulators under the Generalized Disjunctive Programming framework for the structural flowsheet optimization. Computers and Chemical Engineering, 67, 13-25.

Raman, R., & Grossmann, I. E. (1994). Modelling and computational techniques for logic based integer programming. Computers and Chemical Engineering, 18, 563-578.

Ruiz-Femenia, R., Fernández-Torres, M. J., Salcedo-Díaz, R., Gómez-Rico, M. F., & Caballero, J. A. (2017). Systematic Tools for the Conceptual Design of Inherently Safer Chemical Processes. Industrial & Engineering Chemistry Research, 56, 7301-7313.

Ruiz-Femenia, R., Flores-Tlacuahuac, A., & Grossmann, I. E. (2014). Logic-Based Outer-Approximation Algorithm for Solving Discrete-Continuous Dynamic Optimization Problems. Industrial & Engineering Chemistry Research, 53, 5067-5080.

Tawarmalani, M., & Sahinidis, N. V. (2005). A polyhedral branch-and-cut approach to global optimization. Mathematical Programming, 103, 225-249.

Türkay, M., & Grossmann, I. E. (1996). Logic-based MINLP algorithms for the optimal synthesis of process networks. Computers and Chemical Engineering, 20, 959-978.

Sauro Pierucci, Flavio Manenti, Giulia Bozzano, Davide Manca (Eds.)
Proceedings of the 30th European Symposium on Computer Aided Process Engineering
(ESCAPE30), May 24-27, 2020, Milano, Italy. © 2020 Elsevier B.V. All rights reserved.
http://dx.doi.org/10.1016/B978-0-12-823377-1.50317-7

Prediction of Sustainability Related Properties: Data Science Methods with Incorporated Prior Knowledge

Gulnara Shavalieva[a], Pietro Postacchini[b,a], Stavros Papadokonstantakis[a]

[a]Energy Technology, Chalmers University of Technology, Horsalsvagen 7B, Gothenburg 41296, Sweden
[b]AVT – Aachener Verfahrenstechnik, Process Systems Engineering, RWTH Aachen University, Aachen 52074, Germany
gulnara.shavalieva@chalmers.se

Abstract

Many of the registered chemicals, newly synthesized or long existing, lack information on their hazard for the environment and human health. To perform the holistic safety assessment of chemicals, data on molecular properties, mostly obtained by test on living organisms, are collected. However, extensive experimentation is neither economically feasible nor ethical, and thus development of accurate prediction models is required. The recent advances in the area are associated with data science methods; however, there are certain limitations of these models with respect to their transparency, interpretability or even availability of well distributed training data to ensure robust generalization. Hybrid models combining machine learning with prior knowledge of the research field can potentially provide the solution to these limitations. The current study presents the first step of creating hybrid models, namely extraction of knowledge that can be utilized to create prior knowledge for future incorporation into hybrid models.

Keywords: prior knowledge, text mining, hybrid model

1. Introduction

There are currently over 157 million unique chemical substances registered with a Chemical Abstract Service (CAS) identifier and this number is constantly growing. Some of these chemicals enter our everyday life as food additives, ingredients of cosmetics, personal care products, cleaning agents, toys, clothes, electronics, pharmaceuticals, etc. (World Health Organization, 2016). Others are associated with industrial applications, such as solvents and separation agents for chemical and pharmaceutical industry, refrigerants, catalysts, ionic liquids, etc. The chemicals are constantly released to the environment as emissions during production and use. Despite the regular exposure of humans and environment to such chemicals, many of them lack information on their impact on human health and environment (ECHA,2019). Experimental hazard assessment of chemicals with respect to their impact on environment and human health is traditionally performed on living organisms, what is not feasible neither from economical nor ethical point of view. In fact, EU legislation promotes the use of alternative *in vitro* or *in silico* approaches to replace the cruel animal testing (European Commission, 2017). Furthermore, plethora of novel molecular structures need to be tested *in silico* during computer-aided molecular design approaches for innovative applications. Obviously, experimental testing is not a feasible option during thousands of iterations of the respective optimization approaches.

Various *in silico* approaches, including for instance structural alerts (Limban et al., 2018), read-across (Stanton and Kruszewski, 2016), and group contribution methods (Hukkerikar et al., 2012) have been developed over the years with the aim to predict molecular properties of chemicals required for safety assessment. Even though the approaches are widely used, recent models utilizing advanced methods of data science, mostly machine learning, reported to show improved accuracy of prediction (Zhang et al., 2018, Hartung, 2019). Despite the improvement of the prediction, the models obtained by means of machine learning are difficult to interpret (Zhang et al., 2018). Furthermore, it is challenging to create prediction models for some of molecular properties (e.g., permissible exposure levels, acute toxicity dermal, persistency, acidification potential, global warming) due to limited amount of experimental data. One of the ways to address these limitations is to incorporate to the model knowledge existing in the field (i.e., herein called prior knowledge). The prior knowledge can refer to data labelling, generic conclusions, functional trends between target and predictor variables, simplified input/output models for specific classes of chemicals, etc. The approach has been successfully applied in various fields, e.g., medicine (Craft et al., 2017), drug safety (Lysenko et al., 2018), materials (Chakraborty et al., 2017), image recognition (Bougie et al., 2018). However, to the best of our knowledge, the approach has not been systematically used for prediction of properties (e.g., acute aquatic toxicity, bioconcentration, persistency) required to perform holistic sustainability assessment of chemicals. One of the main reasons is that prior knowledge is not systematically extracted, classified and formulated in a way that can be effectively used for hybrid modelling.

The current work describes an approach for this first step of knowledge extraction for development of hybrid prediction models. The knowledge is extracted from research publications by means of natural language processing.

2. Method

The current method used for knowledge extraction is presented in Figure 1. It consists of two main steps: data collection and knowledge extraction. Each step is subdivided into procedures which can be either automated by machine learning approaches or require some form of human intervention.

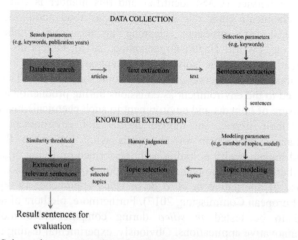

Figure 1. Schematic representation of method used for knowledge extraction

Aquatic toxicity molecular property is used for this study. The objective is, with the help of published work over the last 20 years research, to extract information that can be potentially used as prior knowledge in hybrid prediction model.

2.1. Data collection

Data collection involved the search of potentially relevant peer-reviewed research articles or review papers using a database of bibliographic information. Web of Science (WoS) was used as the main database for this study. The relevant papers were identified based on the following keywords search: "aquatic toxicity", which was selected to be as generic as possible for the investigated field. The timespan for publications was set to years from 1998 to 2018. The search resulted in 1780 papers. The distribution of the publications over the years is presented in Figure 2 together with the line showing the increase of the research works related to articles resulting from a search based on a the more generic keyword "environment". Both lines show the same trend and as expected the sources related to the more generic topic (i.e., environment) are more smoothly increasing over the years. The outcome of the analysis of bibliometric information is presented in Figures 3a -3b. The results show that except three first articles and three authors, the results are very evenly distributed.

From the found works, 66 published in Elsevier were selected to perform text mining and illustrate the proposed approach. The current method seemed to perform better text extraction from the articles of the Elsevier format, however, the method is to be refined in the future to overcome this limitation.

Text extraction have been performed on the 66 selected papers with the help of Python packages PDFMiner (Shinyama, 2013) and Spacy (SpaCy, 2019). The collected text has been further processed to extract sentences that comply with selection criteria, which for this study comprised the words "toxicity, 'LC50' and 'EC50'. LC50 and EC50 is the concentration of a chemical in water causing death or certain effect (e.g., growth reduction), respectively, in 50% of population of specific living organisms (e.g, daphnia magna, fish). The acute toxicity is a common parameter of various hazard assessment frameworks. Different selection criteria, e.g., certain structure of the sentence, indication to table, figure or equation can be added, depending on the scope of knowledge extraction and also considering the intended machine learning model hybridization approach.

At the end of this step, a significant text reduction is performed (i.e., 2-3 order of magnitudes in terms of counted words) and the available text is grouped into sentences or small paragraphs relevant to the selected keywords.

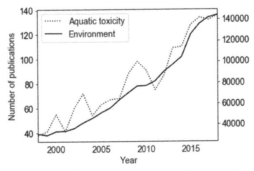

Figure 2. Number of articles published under two topics from year 1998 to 2018.

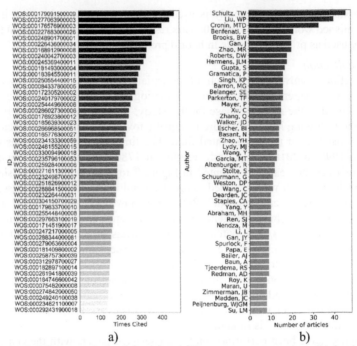

a)   b)

Figure 3. Fifty most cited articles (a) and fifty most common authors (b) for the found papers on WoS.

2.2. Knowledge extraction

The knowledge extraction starts with the topic modeling step that utilizes the sentences extracted from the articles during the data collection (See Figure 4). First, sentences go through a preprocessing step, consisting of the removal of stop words (e.g. articles), and lemmatization, which returns the base form of the words. The unique words found in the sentences are then numbered and collected to a list, called dictionary. The sentences are transformed into vectors containing the frequency of appearance of the unique words in the corresponding sentence. This results in a matrix (corpus) combining the corresponding of all the sentences. The corpus serves as basis for the actual topic modeling. Two different techniques have been tested for the topic modeling: Latent Semantic Indexing (LSI) and Latent Dirichlet Allocation (LDA). The techniques differ by the way they perform identification of topics. LSI performs truncated singular value decomposition to achieve dimensionality reduction based on the number of underlying topics and returns topics in form of vectors of words co-occurring together. LDA assumes that sentences, extracted from the articles, are set up by a probabilistic distribution of topics. Each topic, in turn, is probabilistic distribution of words. These distributions are obtained from the corpus matrix through variational Bayes approximations and Gibbs sampling (Williams and Betak, 2018).

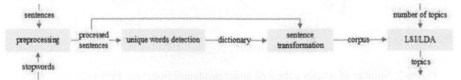

Figure 4. Topic modeling steps.

The optimal number of topics for LDA is taken based on a maximum value for a coherence score giving a measure of how good the topics generated by the model are. The maximum coherence score was obtained for a maximum number of topics equal to 50 for both models. From these 50 topics, five were selected as potentially relevant, based on human expertise. The selected five topics were used as a query to rank all the sentences extracted from the articles. The ranking used a cosine similarity score, which evaluates the similarity between the query and each of the sentence vectors. The closer the cosine similarity to one, the greater the match between the vectors. Thus, topic selection and threshold value for the cosine similarity score were used for information reduction to get a reasonable number of sentences. This kind of cut-off criteria are necessary to reduce the amount of information required to be processed by human.

3. Results

The results of two topic modelling models and various similarity scores are presented in Table 1. As can be seen, the LSI results are more sensitive to the similarity score threshold value than the LDA results both for the number of resulting sentences and for the number of potentially relevant sentences.

Table 1. Results for LSI and LDA models.

Similarity score	Number of resulting sentences		Number of potentially relevant sentences	
	LSI	LDA	LSI	LDA
0.3	1020	478	34	24
0.4	483	400	21	22
0.5	171	344	9	21

The potentially relevant sentences contain rules, correlations, indications to QSARs or read-across predictions of aquatic toxicity. For example, sentences like "Longer chain alcohols display a very strong structure-activity relationship to acute fish toxicity as a function of hydrophobicity", "There is a linear relationship between both acute and chronic toxicities and $LogK_{ow}$, suggesting that with the increase of hydrophobicity the aquatic toxicity increases" might be obtained.

Additionally, the main parameters affecting the results of the study have been identified and considered for further improvement. More general keywords combination used for search of the articles (e.g. "aquatic toxicity" instead of "aquatic LC50") result in more relevant sentences. More specific search ("aquatic LC50") leads to identification of numerous sentences devoted to various experimental studies limited to certain test conditions difficult to be generalized as prior knowledge.

The identification of the potentially relevant topics generated by the models is not straightforward, is heavily based on human expertise and may have a significant impact on the results. The evaluation of the resulting sentences, in turn, revealed the necessity to back track the documents containing potentially useful information (e.g., extracting more context by the surrounding text of the identified sentences). Thus, the approach can serve as additional indication to promising articles to retrieve more data for generation of prior knowledge. However, it should be noted that this will require an additional step of human intervention in the overall prior knowledge extraction procedure.

4. Conclusions

The presented procedure showed potential in extraction of relevant information to generate prior knowledge for hybrid data driven models. More general keyword combination for initial search of research papers and certain modelling parameters as topic selection criteria and cut-off score are the main factors affecting the results of the procedure. Including the various forms of extracted knowledge in machine learning approaches will further highlight which of these forms can be better utilised to develop hybrid models with advanced generalisation capabilities.

References

Bougie, N., Cheng, L.K., Ichise, R., 2018. Combining deep reinforcement learning with prior knowledge and reasoning. ACM SIGAPP Applied Computing Review 18, 33–45.

Chakraborty, S., Chattopadhyay, P.P., Ghosh, S.K., Datta, S., 2017. Incorporation of prior knowledge in neural network model for continuous cooling of steel using genetic algorithm. Applied Soft Computing Journal 58, 297–306.

Craft, D., Ferranti, D., Krane, D., 2017. The value of prior knowledge in machine learning of complex network systems. Bioinformatics 33, 3610–3618.

ECHA, 2019. REACH compliance - an Agency priority for 2019. Available at: https://newsletter.echa.europa.eu/home/-/newsletter/entry/reach-compliance-an-agency-priority-for-2019 (Accessed: 28 November 2019).

European Commission, 2017. Alternatives to animal testing and safety assessment of chemicals. Available at: https://ec.europa.eu/jrc/en/research-topic/alternatives-animal-testing-and-safety-assessment-chemicals (Accessed: 28 November 2019).

Hartung, T., 2019. Predicting toxicity of chemicals: software beats animal testing. EFSA Journal.

Hukkerikar, A.S., Kalakul, S., Sarup, B., Young, D.M., Sin, G., Gani, R., 2012. Estimation of environment-related properties of chemicals for design of sustainable processes: Development of group-contribution+ (GC +) property models and uncertainty analysis. Journal of Chemical Information and Modeling 52, 2823–2839.

Limban, C., Nuță, D.C., Chiriță, C., Negreș, S., Arsene, A.L., Goumenou, M., Karakitsios, S.P., Tsatsakis, A.M., Sarigiannis, D.A., 2018. The use of structural alerts to avoid the toxicity of pharmaceuticals. Toxicology Reports 5, 943–953.

Lysenko, A., Sharma, A., Boroevich, K.A., Tsunoda, T., 2018. An integrative machine learning approach for prediction of toxicity-related drug safety. Life Science Alliance 1, 1–14.

Shinyama,Y., 2013. PDFMiner. Available at: https://pdfminer-docs.readthedocs.io/pdfminer_index.html (Accessed: 28 November 2019).

SpaCy, 2019. Industrial - Strength Natural Language Processing. Available at: https://spacy.io/. (Accessed: 28 November 2019)

Stanton, K., Kruszewski, F.H., 2016. Quantifying the benefits of using read-across and in silico techniques to fulfill hazard data requirements for chemical categories. Regulatory Toxicology and Pharmacology 81, 250–259.

Williams, T., Betak, J., 2018. A Comparison of LSA and LDA for the Analysis of Railroad Accident Text. Procedia Computer Science 130, 98–102.

World Health Organization, 2016. Chemical safety and protection of human health: the Slovenian experience (2016) Available at: http://www.euro.who.int/en/countries/slovenia/publications/chemical-safety-and-protection-of-human-health-the-slovenian-experience-2016 (Accessed: 28 November 2019).

Zhang, L., Zhang, H., Ai, H., Hu, H., Li, S., Zhao, J., Liu, H., 2018. Applications of Machine Learning Methods in Drug Toxicity Prediction. Current Topics in Medicinal Chemistry 18, 987–997.

Sauro Pierucci, Flavio Manenti, Giulia Bozzano, Davide Manca (Eds.)
Proceedings of the 30th European Symposium on Computer Aided Process Engineering
(ESCAPE30), May 24-27, 2020, Milano, Italy. © 2020 Elsevier B.V. All rights reserved.
http://dx.doi.org/10.1016/B978-0-12-823377-1.50318-9

A Framework for Stochastic and Surrogate-Assisted Optimization using Sequential Modular Process Simulators

Alberto T. Penteado, Erik Esche, Joris Weigert, Jens-Uwe Repke

Group of Process Dynamics and Operations, Technische Universität Berlin, Sekretariat KWT 9, Straße des 17. Juni 135, 10623 Berlin, Germany
alberto.penteado@tu-berlin.de

Abstract

A Python framework is introduced enabling automated simulation and stochastic and surrogate-assisted optimization (SAO) using Aspen Plus flowsheets. A new modification to the Probability of Improvement method for SAO is proposed to handle non-converged simulations. Two chemical engineering optimization problems are solved using gradient-based, stochastic, and the new SAO algorithms.

Keywords: sequential optimization, black-box optimization, stochastic optimization, surrogate-assisted optimization, probability of improvement

1. Introduction

Process design and operation in both industry and academia rely heavily on simulation and optimization with Sequential Modular (SM) flowsheets. Gradient-based optimization with SM flowsheets is challenging because objective and constraints are only evaluated once and if flowsheet convergence is achieved and, most often, only numerical derivatives are available. Since the model structure and derivatives are unknown to the optimizer, this is often called a black-box problem. Further difficulties are imposed because objective and constraints may be numerically noisy, discontinuous, non-differentiable, and undefined at some points, which led the research community towards direct search (DS) methods (Martelli and Amaldi 2014). Surrogate-Assisted Optimization (SAO) has also been applied (Carpio et al. 2018). These normally require more simulations to converge, but additionally present important global search characteristics. This work presents a framework (Section 2) using Python and Aspen Plus for automated simulation and process optimization using DS methods and a new modified SAO algorithm (Section 3) to handle failed or non-converged simulations. Two chemical engineering problems are solved using different methods (Section 4).

2. The Framework

Most process simulators have built-in SQP algorithms. However, DS and SAO require connection to external software such as Matlab or Python. Several frameworks are reported in literature using Aspen Plus/HYSYS, ChemCad, Pro II, EMSO, among others, but programming code is seldom provided. Furthermore, this is often not supported by software developers. Aspen Tech only officially supports connection to Excel / VBA, so that essentially no documentation on other programming languages is available. This makes the development of such frameworks a tedious trial-and-error process and led to the idea of implementing and publishing the source code for the present framework.

$$PI(u,x) = \Phi\left(\frac{T - \hat{f}(u,x)}{s(u,x)}\right) \qquad (1)$$

$$PC_c(u,x) = \Phi\left(\frac{0 - \hat{g}_c(u,x)}{s_c(u,x)}\right) \qquad (2)$$

$$PI_c(u,x) =$$

$$P_{conv} \cdot PI \cdot \prod_{c=1}^{constraints} PC_c \qquad (3)$$

The framework for Black-Box Optimization of sequential modular flowsheets (Bbop) automates the connectivity and wraps the available functions/methods of the COM (Component Object Model) object exposed by Aspen Plus and is implemented in Python 2.7. The commented source code is provided in gitlab.tubit.tu-berlin.de/dbta/bbop.git along with an example containing the Aspen Plus model of example 4.1 and a Python script using Bbop to automate simulations and perform optimizations.

For the examples in Section 4, several optimization algorithms have been tested in an attempt to reach better results and to provide a comparison basis for the newly developed SAO algorithm. These are the built-in SQP algorithm from Aspen Plus, the gradient-based Sequential Least Squares Programming (SLSQP) algorithm by Kraft (1988), the stochastic Differential Evolution (DE) algorithm by Storn and Price (1997), and the Lipschitz optimization algorithm Simplicial Homology Global Optimization (SHGO) by Endres et al. (2018). DE and SHGO are chosen as readily available and robust global optimization methods and SLSQP is used to refine their solutions. The three methods are available in the SciPy optimization library (Jones et al. 2001).

3. The Enhanced Probability of Improvement Algorithm

The original Probability of Improvement (PI) method (Jones 2001) has recently been extended for constrained problems and applied to chemical engineering examples (Carpio et al. 2018). It attempts to use surrogate models in order to reduce the number of rigorous function evaluations, thus being suited for simulation-based optimization with expensive functions like SM process flowsheet.

To initialize the algorithm, a Design of Simulations (DoS) covering the entire design space is required. The PI method searches for the global minimum of an objective function $f(u,x)$ by repeatedly solving an auxiliary optimization problem as given in Figure 1. This consists in fitting a surrogate mode $\hat{f}(u,x)$ to the objective function using Gaussian Process Regression (GPR) and then maximizing the probability of achieving a target improvement T in the objective function as given by Eq. 1. PI is a multi-modal function with high values in points where the predicted objective function value is low and / or the predicted standard error s is high. In each iteration, the rigorous model (in this case the Aspen Plus simulation) is only sampled at the local maxima of the PI auxiliary function, thus very likely leading to improvements in the objective function value and / or in the surrogate model's prediction quality.

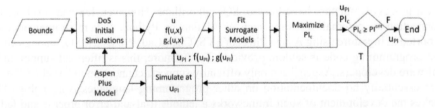

Figure 1 – Algorithm Flowchart for the enhanced PI method

For inequality constraints of the type $g(u,x) \leq 0$ an analogous approach has been proposed (Carpio et al. 2018). Surrogate models $\hat{g}(u,x)$ are fitted to each constraint c and the probability of fulfilling a constraint is then given by Eq. 2. The probability of improvement for a constrained problem is given by multiplying PI to the product of all PC_c leading to the two last product terms of Eq. 3. The toolbox scikit-learn has been used to fit all surrogate models using a squared-exponential kernel (Pedregosa et al. 2011).

In Eq. 1 and 2, PI is the probability of improvement for an unconstrained problem; u is the set of decision/control/optimization variables; x are the state-variables; Φ is the normal cumulative distribution function; T is the target improvement (e.g., a percentual improvement over the current best-known objective function value); $\hat{f}$ is the GPR surrogate model for the objective function; s is the standard error of the objective function predictions; PC_c is the probability of fulfilling constraint c; $\hat{g}_c$ is the GPR surrogate model for constraint c; s_c is the standard error of the constraint predictions.

One question that often arises when performing black-box optimization is what to do if a simulation fails. This issue is mentioned by Carpio et al. (2018), but no further discussion or solution is proposed. According to the authors, a large objective function value is returned to the optimizer if a simulation fails, creating an artificial peak in this area. This is a common and simple solution but has disadvantages. First, this has detrimental effects to the GPR surrogate model, which will incorporate the arbitrarily high value and falsely reduce standard error around it. Secondly, SM simulators often rely on previous solutions for initialization and, thus non-convergent areas may become convergent once more solutions become available in its neighbourhood. By completely avoiding non-convergent areas, the algorithm may oversee interesting points near them. This is critical if the simulation is difficult to converge near the optimum solution.

To overcome this issue, a k-Nearest Neighbour (kNN) binary classification method is applied using the algorithm available from scikit-learn (Pedregosa et al. 2011). In each iteration, all known simulation points are classified into non-converged (class=0) and converged (class=1). The probability of a new trial point belonging to the converged class (P_{conv}) is given by the distance-weighted average of the class values from its k known nearest neighbours. The failed simulations are left out of the construction of the surrogate models, so there is no need to assign arbitrarily high objective values to them. The term P_{conv} is introduced into the objective function of the auxiliary PI maximization problem, leading to Eq. 3. It acts as a dampener and reduces the probability of improvement (PI_c) near known failed simulations, thus reducing the chance of the optimizer moving in that direction on a probabilistic basis instead of an arbitrary basis. If later more simulations converge around the failed simulation, P_{conv} is increased and, if PI and PC_c are also high enough, this area may be revisited. This modified version of the algorithm has been implemented in Python 2.7 and applied for both optimization problems.

Table 1 - Optimization Results for the HDA Process

Method	Benzene Cost [$\$\cdot t^{-1}$]	Number of Simulations	Decision Variables	
			Purge Ratio	H$_2$: Toluene Ratio
DE	86.3	831	0.049	0.913
PI	86.7	149	0.060	0.896
SHGO Sobol	86.8	1091	0.064	0.899

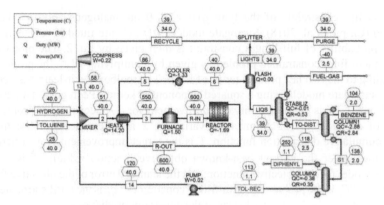

Figure 2 - Simulation Flowsheet of the HDA Process

4. Examples

4.1. Hydrodealkylation (HDA) Process

The HDA process for producing benzene from toluene and hydrogen has been implemented in Aspen Plus using property package PENG-ROB. The flowsheet containing two recycle streams is shown in Figure 2. The objective is minimizing the cost of benzene production given by the hydrogen (H_2) educt cost rate plus the total utility cost rate (electricity, gas-fired heat, steam, cooling water, and refrigeration) divided by the mass flow rate of produced benzene. The decision variables are (1) the hydrogen to toluene feed ratio (toluene feed is kept constant) and (2) the light gases purge ratio, which is set at the block SPLITTER.

This problem has been solved using PI, DE, and SHGO with Sobol sampling with the solutions being further polished by the SLSQP algorithm. Objective values, number of simulations, and decision variables are reported in Table 1. A high cost is assigned to the H_2 educt, so that the solution lies at very low H_2:Toluene and purge ratios, rendering simulation convergence challenging near the optimum. The SQP algorithm from Aspen Plus failed to converge, highlighting the importance of having other methods available.

The solution of this problem by the PI algorithm is shown in Figure 3. The initial design of simulations has been carried out using a low-discrepancy Hammersley set with 10 samples per input variable and the auxiliary PI maximization sub-problem is solved in every single iteration with the global SHGO algorithm. As it can be seen in the left-hand

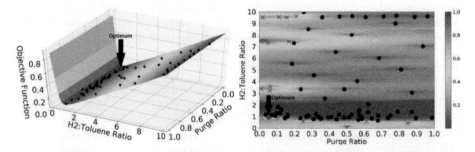

Figure 3 - HDA Process Optimization by the modified PI algorithm. Left: surrogate model predictions (surface) and rigorous model evaluations (dots). Right: Probability of convergence (colourmap), converged simulations (dots), failed simulations (crosses).

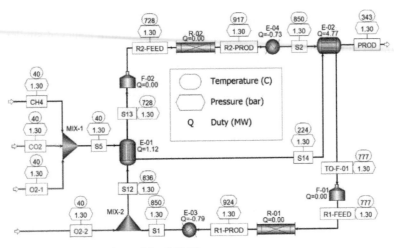

Figure 4 - Simulation Flowsheet of the OCM Process

plot of Figure 3, the convergence basin is quickly identified, and most new samples are placed therein. Yet, the global character of the PI method is also highlighted by the samples placed near the upper bounds of the decision variables, where objective value predictions were not particularly low, but the error was still high.

The right-hand plot in Figure 3 shows the probability of convergence (P_{conv}) for the HDA flowsheet computed by the kNN classifier with $k=3$ as a colour plot. This probability is high (darker colour) around converged simulations (dots) and lower (lighter colour) around failed ones (crosses). Simulations tend to diverge for hydrogen to toluene ratios below 1 and purge ratios lower than 0.1. Nevertheless, the solver is still able to move into this area, since the predicted objective values are low, and find the local optimum. In fact, the optimum lies very close to two failed simulations.

4.2. Oxidative Coupling of Methane (OCM) Process

The OCM reaction is the catalytic oxidation of methane into ethane and ethylene. The reaction section is modelled in Aspen Plus using two kinetic adiabatic Plug Flow Reactors (RPlug) (Penteado et al. 2018) as shown in Fig. 4. Biogas containing CH_4 and CO_2 can be used as renewable feedstock for this process. To model different types of biogas, CH_4 is mixed with a pure CO_2 stream, which serves as a diluent gas and helps to contain the reactions' exothermicity. The objective is to maximize the combined ethane and ethylene (C_2) yield, which is reported to be around 15% for industrial implementation (Siluria Technologies 2015). Methane feed is constant, and the seven decision variables are the feed temperatures, amounts of catalyst, and O_2 flowrates (limiting reactant) in each reactor, and the CO_2 flowrate. This is a very challenging problem because the objective function is incredibly stiff near the intended operating area of complete O_2 conversion.

Table 2 - Optimization Results for the OCM Process

Solver	C_2 Yield %	No. of Sim.	°C		kmol·h⁻¹			kg	
			T_{feed}^{R-01}	T_{feed}^{R-02}	$\dot{F}^{CO2}$	$\dot{F}^{O2-1}$	$\dot{F}^{O2-2}$	W_{cat}^{R-01}	W_{cat}^{R-02}
DE	16.12	38,582	742	747	399	48	40	389	402
PI	15.96	4,869	760	776	402	46	38	134	196
SQP	15.12	1,457	755	756	392	36	39	337	246

The solution for the OCM process optimization is listed in Table 2. The highest yield is achieved with DE after 38,582 simulations. The PI algorithm achieved similar results with significantly fewer simulations. Nevertheless, optimization time is similar because (1) DE can be efficiently parallelized; (2) as the number of samples grow in the PI method, the surrogate model becomes more expensive to fit; and (3) for for higher dimensional problems, the PI maximization sub-problem becomes expensive and challenging to solve globally. Hence, the PI algorithm is better suited for time-consuming flowsheets with few decision variables. Both algorithms outperformed Aspen Plus' built-in SQP.

Higher CO_2 dilution (upper bound) is favourable to reaction performance. Optimal O_2 flow rates render CH_4:O_2 ratios of 8 and 10 for R-01 and R-02 respectively (stoichiometric is 2). Trade-offs are observed between feed temperature and amount of catalyst.

5. Conclusion

A framework for automated simulation, stochastic, and surrogate-assisted optimization of SM Aspen Plus flowsheets is implemented in Python and published as an open-source project. A new SAO algorithm is developed by modifying the PI method making it more suitable to handle failed simulations. The framework is successfully applied to solve two practical chemical engineering examples. Future work aims at minimizing the total annualized cost for the biogas-based OCM process, including the downstream CO_2 removal and distillation sections which have not been included herein.

Acknowledgements

Financial support from German Federal Ministry of Education and Research (BMBF 01DN1703/031B0608A) and CAPES/Brazil (11946/13-0) are gratefully acknowledged

References

R. R. Carpio, R. C.Giordano, A. R. Secchi, 2018, Enhanced surrogate assisted framework for constrained global optimization of expensive black-box functions, Computers & Chemical Engineering 118, 91–102

S. C. Endres, C. Sandrock,; W. W. Focke, 2018, A simplicial homology algorithm for Lipschitz optimisation, Journal of Global Optimization 72(2), 181–217

D. R. Jones, 2001, A Taxonomy of Global Optimization Methods Based on Response Surfaces, Journal of Global Optimization 21, 345–383

E. Jones, T. Oliphant, P. Peterson, others, 2001, SciPy: Open source scientific tools for Python. Available online at http://www.scipy.org/

D. A. Kraft, 1988, A software package for sequential quadratic programming, Collogne, Germany: DLR German Aerospace Center. Available online at Tech. Rep. DFVLR-FB 88-28.

E. Martelli, E. Amaldi, 2014, PGS-COM: A hybrid method for constrained non-smooth black-box optimization problems, Computers & Chemical Engineering 63, 108–139

F. Pedregosa, G. Varoquaux, A. Gramfort, V. Michel, B. Thirion, O. Grisel, M. Blondel, P. Prettenhofer, R. Weiss, V. Dubourg, J. Vanderplas, A. Passos, D. Cournapeau, M. Brucher, M. Perrot, E. Duchesnay, 2011, Scikit-learn: Machine Learning in Python, Journal of Machine Learning Research 12, 2825-2830

A. T. Penteado, M. Kim, H. R. Godini, E. Esche, J.-U. Repke, 2018, Techno-economic evaluation of a biogas-based oxidative coupling of methane process for ethylene production, Frontiers of Chemical Science and Engineering, 12(4), 598–618

Siluria Technologies, 2015, Oxidative Coupling of Methane Implementations for Olefin Production, Patent no. US 2015/0210610 A1

R. Storn, K. Price, 1997, Differential Evolution - A Simple and Efficient Heuristic for global Optimization over Continuous Spaces, Journal of Global Optimization, 11, 341–359.

Sauro Pierucci, Flavio Manenti, Giulia Bozzano, Davide Manca (Eds.)
Proceedings of the 30th European Symposium on Computer Aided Process Engineering
(ESCAPE30), May 24-27, 2020, Milano, Italy. © 2020 Elsevier B.V. All rights reserved.
http://dx.doi.org/10.1016/B978-0-12-823377-1.50319-0

Quantitative Risk Assessment and Management for CO_2 Utilisation Industrial Network

Ali Attiq Al-Yaeeshi[a], Rajesh Govindan[b], Tareq Al-Ansari[a,b]*

*a*Divison of Sustainable Development, College of Science and Engineering, Hamad Bin Khalifa University, Qatar Foundation, Doha, Qatar
*b*Divison of Engineering Management and Decision Sciences, College of Science and Engineering, Hamad Bin Khalifa University, Qatar Foundation, Doha, Qatar
talansari@hbku.edu.qa

Abstract

As a means to control CO_2 emissions, various technologies and processes related to carbon capture and utilisation have been studied with a view of creating large-scale industrial symbiosis for CO_2 recycling and re-use. Such industrial networks consequently provide new economic opportunities as value-added products can be produced from waste CO_2. However, investments in such networks at national or transnational scales entail technical, social and environmental risks that in turn affect the expected economic returns, with a further potential in devaluation of such investments. This study presents a hazard identification (HAZID) and quantitative risk assessment (QRA) methodology for large-scale carbon capture and utilisation networks based on existing sources and sinks in the State of Qatar, capturing technical viabilities at the process and systems levels, and compliance with local and international environment regulations. The QRA integrates hydrocarbon leakage and dispersion modelling simulation using data obtained from existing GIS databases into a single model. In assessing network failure scenarios, the model considers (a) CO_2 sources, such as from LNG plant and chemical process industries, such as Methanol, Urea and Gas-to-Liquid (GTL) fuels; (b) CO_2 transportation (pipeline) service corridors; and (c) CO_2 sinks that manufacture value added products. Stochastic variables used to assess network robustness are represented by pipeline layouts, material and composition, diameter, pressure, temperature, heat and mass balance, other equipment items, *e.g.* compression station, turbine and reactors. The results demonstrate that the CO_2 network should be located outside high population density area. The approach demonstrates CO_2 release from 20" pipeline rupture to nearby residential area is relatively very low 19.07 $\mu g/m^3$ (0.0191 ppm) that would no impact the population while the CO_2 concentration at 1,000 meter wide from the centerline, 4 $\mu g/m^3$.

Key words: CO_2 utilisation, Methanol, Urea, GTL, Quantitative Risk Assessment

Introduction

Carbon Capture and Storage (CCS) and Carbon Capture and Utilisation (CCU) technologies are considered effective methods to mitigate CO_2 emissions. Contrary to CCS, which depends on the storage of CO_2 in underground storage sites after capture, compression and transportation, CCU seeks to convert CO_2 into value-added products.

The Global CCS institute (2010) reported that there are 275 CCS projects globally, of which 213 were active, or still in the planning phase representing a growth in the industry. Transportation of CO_2 is a key component of the CCU network which largely depends on pipelines that can pass through densely populated areas resulting in costly routing challenges. The USA is the leading transporter of CO_2 pipeline worldwide with over 6000 km mainly dedicated to EOR projects, and a combined capacity from Australia, Europe, and Africa amounting to 500 km (Koornneef *et al.*, 2010; Vianello *et al.*, 2016). In anticipation of the growth of CO_2 pipeline capacity, it is important to devise safety and quantitative risk assessment (QRA) procedures that can inform routing challenges. In this regard, Nyborg *et al.* (2011) evaluated through the occurrence probabilities of pipeline leakages for different routes. The methodology combines the GIS-based risk analysis and social risk assessment to determine route selections in order to reduce costs and risks. Koornneef *et al.* (2010) presented a systematic assessment based on gaps and uncertainties of QRA results applied in different literature studies which include failure rate, pipeline pressure, temperature and the direction of release. The study demonstrated a significant difference in the risk results after applying dispersion and impact models that conclude the risk levels varies between 0 to 204 meter contours, extending to 7.2 kilometres. Woolley *et al.* (2014) demonstrated that to overcome the challenges to predict the equilibrium phase, thermodynamic and transport properties of the CO_2, the adequacy of control measures for CO_2 pipelines, along with practical guidelines and validated experiments shall be developed. Knoope *et al.* (2014) assessed the locational and societal risks of CO_2 transportation in dense area is cost effective attributed that to the additional risk mitigation measures. The study model used EFFECTS and RISKCURVES to estimate the dispersion and risk contour. The case study applied to meet regulations in the Netherlands, and conclude that the dense phase CO_2 transport can be routed in safe operation if system is well controlled. Vianello *et al.* (2016) elaborate some concerns in CO_2 release consequence as demonstrated in the QRA in CO_2 pipeline network in UK as one of the major consequences is the CO_2 phase when it releases from the pipeline where it will form gaseous, liquid and solid.

The objective of the study is to present a QRA for a CCU network in Qatar in order to assess the societal impact risk of pipeline rupture. This has an implication for making decisions on selecting the optimal route. The QRA considers failure risk type identification and quantification inventories for multiple stages of the network that are based on major hazards to the public and environment, such as pipeline layouts, and product properties. The QRA methodology is based on hydrocarbon leakage and dispersion modelling simulation, integrated with GIS mapping-based on the pipeline layout design and product properties.

Network data analysis for CCU system

The CO_2 pipeline network considered comprises of a single CO_2 source, namely Qatar Gas (QG), and five potential sinks that have been identified for the economic utilisation of CO_2, namely: Qatar Fertilizer Company (QAFCO); two plants in Qatar Fuel Additives Company (QAFAC), one utilising natural gas, whilst the other utilising hydrogen; Oryx GTL; and Pearl GTL, all located in the Mesaieed and Ras Laffan industrial zones. It is envisaged that the pipeline construction would be placed in accordance with a comprehensive risk analysis which includes the hazard scenarios and their impact on people, assets, environment and economics. Thus, the best practice model would be applied to ensure the high level of safety for pipeline transmission and distribution along with risk mitigation measures by attempting to reduce the failure frequency and controlling the event consequences. The compression station is considered to be located at source section to meet the sinks pressure requirements. The pipeline length between Messaid and Ras Laffan industrial zones is 100 km, including the distribution network inside the industrial cities. The design is according to the API 5L X60 and diameter 20". The operating parameters are listed in Table 2. Locally, fuel and feed gas through a service corridor designed to comply with safety regulations and risk reduction by applying 120 km length and 800 m width (Al-Rasheed, 2014).

Methodology

The methodology developed in this study is an extension of previous studies by Al-Yaeeshi *et al.* (2018;2019) which set the basis of optimised allocation of CO_2 to sinks. The models considered a CO_2 pipelines from QG to QAFCO, QAFAC with NG, QAFAC with H_2, Oryx GTL and Pearl GTL. The objective of the research presented in this paper is to mitigate the risk of pipeline rupture potentially releasing CO_2 that can affect humans and the environment. Failure scenarios and their probability are varied from place to another due to the topographical features, construction guidelines, material selection and product properties. Based on the historical failure frequency per 1000 km /year of the pipelines, including different products based on the data from USA, UK and EU, are attributed to corrosion and weld defects.

3.1. Dispersion Model and consequences of a CO_2 release

In the assessment of CO_2 dispersion, an empirical Gaussian method is used to estimate the vertical and horizontal concentration of CO_2 that will reach the nearest residential area upon leakage (Sutton, 1932; Abdel-Rahman, 2008). The Gaussian dispersion model is applied to quantify CO_2 emissions and concentration levels in the atmosphere along with consequences scenario to measure the risk and to simulate hazard scenarios.

$$C(x, y, z; H) = A1 * A2(A3 + A4)$$
$$= \frac{Q}{2\pi u \ \sigma_y \sigma_z} \left[Exp \left(- \frac{y^2}{2\sigma_y{}^2} \right) \right] \left[Exp \left(- \frac{(z - H)^2}{2\sigma_z{}^2} \right) \right.$$
$$\left. + Exp \left(- \frac{(z + H)^2}{2\sigma_z{}^2} \right) \right]$$

C= Steady -state concentration at a point (x,y,z), $\mu g/m^3$
Q= mass emission rate, $\mu g/m^3$
X= downwind distance, m
y= horizontal distance from plume centerline, m
z= vertical distance from ground level, m
σ_y= Lateral dispersion coefficient function (m)
σ_z= vertical dispersion coefficient function (m)
u_s= average wind speed at stack height, m/s
H= stack height (H= h+Δh, where h= physical stack height and Δh= plume rise, m).

Coefficient function or Diffusion parameters are defined as the standard deviation and they are important to demonstrate the results. In this study, the McElroy-Pooler formula (for urban conditions) is used to estimate the coefficient functions σ_y and σ_z as indicated in Table 1. Here, X is the downwind distance (X, m), and stability A is the worst case condition, classified as unstable scenario.

Table 1: Formulae McElroy-Pooler (Urban Condition).

Stability	σ_y	σ_z
A	0.32X (1.0+0.0004 X)$^{-1/2}$	0.24X (1.0+0.001 X)$^{1/2}$
B	0.32X (1.0+0.0004 X)$^{-1/2}$	0.24X (1.0+0.001 X)$^{1/2}$
C	0.22X (1.0+0.0004 X)$^{-1/2}$	0.20 X
D	0.16X (1.0+0.0004 X)$^{-1/2}$	0.14X (1.0+0.003 X)$^{-1/2}$
E	0.11X (1.0+0.0004 X)$^{-1/2}$	0.08X (1.0+0.015 X)$^{-1/2}$
F	0.11X (1.0+0.0004 X)$^{-1/2}$	0.08X (1.0+0.015 X)$^{-1/2}$

Discussion and Results

The CO_2 20" pipeline being proposed to lay above the ground on existing pipeline corridor from Ras Laffan to Mesaieed (north to south of State of Qatar), approximately 100 km length . The risk of pipeline rupture will release large volume of CO_2 gas in which it will affect to the human that living nearby the pipeline. The nearest populated area is at middle of the country, approximately 2.5 km away from the CO_2 pipeline. The empirical Gaussian method was thus used to estimate the vertical and horizontal concentration of CO_2 that will reach the nearest residential area. The following incident scenario, depicted in table 2, was considered in developing the CO_2 gas dispersion using Gaussian model:

Table 2: Data Input Gaussian model.

CO_2 Transmission Ton per year	6000000
CO_2 Transmission Ton per day	16438.3562
CO_2 Transmission kg/hr	684.931507
CO_2 Transmission g/s	190.26
CO_2 density at 30 deg c,kg/m^3	1.777
CO_2 flow rate, m^3/hr	385.442604
Operating Temperature, C	45
Operating Temperature, Kelvin	318.15
Ambient Temperature, C (Winter)	15
Ambient Temperature, K	288.15
Operating Pressure, barg	20
Pipe size, in	20
Pipe size, m	0.508
Velocity, m/s	1

The pipeline is considered to be on full transfer mode to customers in Mesaieed. It is assumed that the pipeline rupture occurs during night time, when most of the population are resting 2.5 km away from the pipeline. The wind speed is 5 m/s in the direction of the residential area. The residential area size is 1,000 m x 1,000 m and it is assumed the tallest building does not exceed 10 m. The weather condition is winter season, where the expected dispersion is generally low level. With the above scenario, outcomes of the Gaussian method calculated from the spread sheet are as follows:

- CO_2 concentration is high at the ground level, about 19.07 µg/m^3, refer figure 1.
- CO_2 concentration at 1,000 meter wide from the center line, 4 µg/m^3, refer figure 2.

Based on the HAZID Analysis and Risk Assessment, it can be suggested that:

1- CO_2 release from 20" pipeline rupture to nearby residential area about 2.5 km distance is relatively very low 19.07 $\mu g/m^3$ (0.0191 ppm) resulting in no impact to the population.

2- It is recommended to bury the CO_2 in a shared corridor with other gas pipelines, which will reduce the dispersion to the populated area in case of rupture. It should also consider future expansion of the residential area.

3- It is recommended for the asset holder to develop a pipeline inspection and maintenance program. A pigging facility should also be installed at Ras Laffan and Mesaieed to ensure the pipeline integrity and increase its lifecycle in addition mitigate the risk.

4- Leak detection system and emergency shut down valve system should be installed.

5- Proper access to the CO_2 pipeline should be provided for Maintenance.

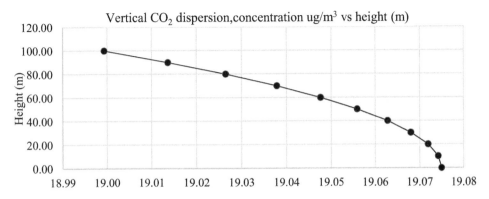

Figure 1: Vertical distribution of CO2 gas from source of leak, 2. 5 km away.

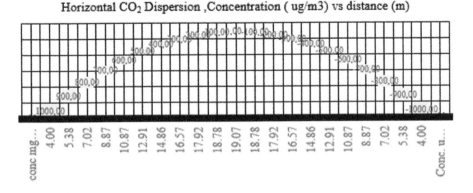

Figure 2: Horizontal distribution of CO2 gas from source of leak, 2.5 km away.

Conclusion

This study introduces a quantitative risk assessment (QRA) methodology for large-scale carbon capture and utilisation networks based on existing sources and sinks in the State of Qatar as a case study. The approach demonstrates CO_2 release from 20" pipeline rupture to nearby residential area is very low 19.07 $\mu g/m^3$ (0.0191 ppm), and as a result there would be no impact on the population as the CO_2 concentration at a point 1,000 meter wide from the centerline is 4 $\mu g/m^3$. It is recommended to bury the CO_2 pipeline in a service corridor which includes many hydrocarbon pipelines and utilities in order to mitigate the risk of dispersion in the case of rupture. There should also be a consideration for urban development and expansion and how that may impact pipeline routing.

References

Abdel-Rahman, A.A., 2008, October. On the atmospheric dispersion and Gaussian plume model. In *Wwai'08: Proceedings of the 2nd International Conference on Waste Management, Water Pollution, Air Pollution, Indoor Climate* (pp. 31-39).

Al-Yaeeshi, A.A., Al-Ansari, T. and Govindan, R., 2018. The potential for carbon dioxide capture and utilisation within the State of Qatar. In Computer Aided Chemical Engineering (Vol. 43, pp. 1499-1504). Elsevier.

Al-Yaeeshi, A.A., Al-Ansari, T. and Govindan, R., 2019. A network model-based optimisation analysis for the utilisation of CO2 in Qatar's chemical industries. In Computer Aided Chemical Engineering (Vol. 46, pp. 295-300). Elsevier.

Al-Rasheed, A.E., 2014, January. The Hydrocarbon Pipeline Network and Development in Qatar. In IPTC 2014: International Petroleum Technology Conference.

GLOBAL CCS INSTITUTE, 2010, Strategic analysis of the global status of carbon capture and storage. Report 1: status of carbon capture and storage projects globally.   Available   from: https://hub.globalccsinstitute.com/publications/strategic-analysis-global-status-carbon-capture-storage-report-1/11-purpose [Accessed 7 December 2017].

Knoope, M.M.J., Raben, I.M.E., Ramírez, A., Spruijt, M.P.N. and Faaij, A.P.C., 2014. The influence of risk mitigation measures on the risks, costs and routing of CO2 pipelines. *International Journal of Greenhouse Gas Control*, *29*, pp.104-124.

Koornneef, J., Spruijt, M., Molag, M., Ramírez, A., Turkenburg, W. and Faaij, A., 2010. Quantitative risk assessment of CO_2 transport by pipelines, a review of uncertainties and their impacts. *Journal of hazardous materials*, *177*(1-3), pp.12-27.

Nyborg, M., Arvidsson, K., Johansson, J., Liljemark, S. and Olsson, L., 2011. Risk analysis methodology for CO2 transport including quantified risk calculation. *Energy Procedia*, *4*, pp.2816-2823.

Sutton, O.G., 1932. A theory of eddy diffusion in the atmosphere. Proceedings of the Royal Society of London. Series A, Containing Papers of a Mathematical and Physical Character, 135(826), pp.143-165.

Vianello, C., Mocellin, P., Macchietto, S. and Maschio, G., 2016. Risk assessment in a hypothetical network pipeline in UK transporting carbon dioxide. *Journal of Loss Prevention in the Process Industries*, *44*, pp.515-527.

Woolley, R.M., Fairweather, M., Wareing, C.J., Falle, S.A., Mahgerefteh, H., Martynov, S., Brown, S., Narasimhamurthy, V.D., Storvik, I.E., Sælen, L. and Skjold, T., 2014. CO2PipeHaz: quantitative hazard assessment for next generation CO2 pipelines. *Energy Procedia*, *63*, pp.2510-2529.

Sauro Pierucci, Flavio Manenti, Giulia Bozzano, Davide Manca (Eds.)
Proceedings of the 30ᵗʰ European Symposium on Computer Aided Process Engineering
(ESCAPE30), May 24-27, 2020, Milano, Italy. © 2020 Elsevier B.V. All rights reserved.
http://dx.doi.org/10.1016/B978-0-12-823377-1.50320-7

Assessing Thermodynamic Flexibility Boundaries via Residue Curve Maps

Alessandro Di Pretoro[a,b], Ludovic Montastruc[a]*, Flavio Manenti[b], Xavier Joulia[a]

[a]*Laboratoire de Génie Chimique, Université de Toulouse, CNRS/INP/UPS, Toulouse, France*
[b]*Politecnico di Milano, Dipartimento di Chimica, Materiali e Ingegneria Chimica "Giulio Natta", Piazza Leonardo da Vinci 32, 20133 Milano, Italia*
ludovic.montastruc@ensiacet.fr

Abstract

Residue curve maps (RCMs) are a widely exploited tool to assess whether a multicomponent mixture separation by distillation results to be feasible or not. They usually refer to a given feed composition and to the products purities as specifications; sometimes the whole distillation regions can be discussed in order to evaluate all the mixture possible splits (Petlyuk & Danilov (2001), Petlyuk (2004)).

All these considerations are nevertheless related to nominal operating conditions, that is for a given and constant feed composition. If feed perturbations are likely to occur (e.g. separation downstream a fermentation process) a flexibility analysis is required to assess the operation feasibility boundaries under uncertain conditions (Swaney & Grossmann (1985)). Moreover, product recovery is often a more appealing specification from an industrial point of view since it is directly related to the process productivity.

For all these reasons, this study deals with the use of RCMs to assess the thermodynamic flexibility limits of a simple distillation case study for a given bottom product recovery and purity under uncertain operating conditions. The starting binary mixture is water and n-butanol, a common and well-known mixture whose separation by simple distillation shows an heterogeneous azeotrope. One component at a time is then added up to obtain an ABE/W (acetone, butanol, ethanol and water) mixture.

Due to the high nonideality of the mixture, the addition of an organic component substantially affects the equilibria. A thermodynamic flexibility analysis methodology was outlined for both the binary and ternary cases as well as for the quaternary one. After that, the separation feasibility of the binary mixture was compared to the others (Di Pretoro et al. (2019)). Beside illustrating the procedure for thermodynamic flexibility assessment via RCMs, this analysis aims to show how to enhance the separation from a flexibility point of view taking advantage of the mixture nonideality.

Keywords: flexibility, residue curve maps, thermodynamics, distillation

1. Introduction

Residue Curve Maps (RCM) were first introduced by Ostwald in 1900 [1] to analyze phase equilibrium for three component azeotropic mixtures. They received poor attention until the second half of the 20ᵗʰ century thanks to Zharov and Serafimov (1967, 1968a, 1968b, 1969, 1975) who developed a generalized theory about these topological objects aimed to classify multicomponent mixtures behaviors. However, it is only thanks to Petlyuk et al. (2001, 2004) that the scientific knowledge about residue curve maps was spread outside Russia. In particular he showed their useful application to the optimal design of distillation columns.

On the one hand then, this useful tool has a long history, on the other hand distillation column design under uncertain conditions is a younger research field. Thus this paper will couple them by mean of the procedure explained in the following chapter in order to provide the design engineer the physical feasibility boundaries of the process under perturbated operating conditions.

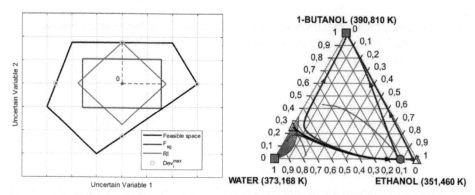

Figure 1 – Resilience Index Example (left); Residue Curve Maps Example (right)

2. Methodologies

2.1. A Measure for Flexibility

In order to quantify flexibility a corresponding flexibility index is required. Several flexibility indexes, both deterministic and stochastic, aimed to this purpose were proposed in literature.

In this paper the so called Resilience Index (Saboo et al. (1985)) is used since it is the most suitable for an easy understanding of the methodology. However, the outcome of the analysis does not qualitatively depend on the flexibility index that is used.

The Resilience Index (hereafter RI) is defined as the largest total disturbance load, independent of the direction of the disturbance, a system is able to withstand without becoming unfeasible. From a mathematical point of view it stands as:

$$RI = \min_{i}\{|l_i|\} \tag{1}$$

$$s.t.\{\max_{j} f_j(\theta) \le 0, \forall l: \sum_{i} |l_i| \le RI\} \tag{2}$$

From an operational point of view it corresponds to evaluating the largest possible polytope inscribed inside the feasible region defined by the inequalities here above. The RI is then equal to the distance between a vertex of the polytope and the nominal operating point 0 as shown in Figure 1 .

2.2. Residue Curve Maps

A Residue Curve (RC) is defined as the locus of compositions satisfying the equation:

$$\frac{dx_i}{d\xi} = x_i - y_i \tag{3}$$

The equation comes from the mass balance on the residue in an open distillation process where ξ indicates a temporal variable. The Residue Curve obtained by its integration describes the time evolution of the residue composition. The same expression can be found if the mass balances are performed on an infinite distillation column at infinite reflux; in that case the RC outlines the composition profile along the column equilibrium stages.

3. Case studies

Three distillation case studies about the ABE/W mixture are discussed. All of them aim to recover 96 % of the butanol present in the feed with 0.99 w/w purity by means of atmospheric distillation. Starting from the water-butanol binary mixture the ternary and quaternary case studies are built by adding namely Ethanol and Acetone one at a time. At the end a typical value of an ABE/W mixture feed composition upstream a separation section is obtained as shown in Table 1.

Table 1 - Feed components partial flowrates

Component	Partial flowrate (mol/s)
n-Butanol	61.328
Water	9.583
Ethanol	3.839
Acetone	12.030

The butanol recovery feasibility analysis is equivalent to the flexibility assessment of the first distillation column in the indirect configuration of a distillation train aimed to separate this multicomponent mixture.

The uncertain variables taken into account during the flexibility analysis are butanol and water partial flowrates since they are both the most critical parameters and the ones most likely to vary because of the floating nature of the feedstock and because of a possible underperformance of the upstream dewatering section.

4. Results

4.1. Binary Mixture

The first case study concerns the Water-Butanol binary distillation without decantation. This mixture was deeply studied in literature since it is the typical case of aqueous-organic mixture with liquid phase demixing and that shows an heterogeneous azeotrope (x_{water}=0.747 mol/mol). Given the feed composition and the distillation specifications discussed in the previous chapter, the corresponding equilibrium phase diagram is plotted in Figure 2.

As it can be noticed, in the binary case, the residue curve corresponds to the diagonal of the phase diagram. If the feed is located on the left of the azeotrope the stable and unstable nodes are namely pure butanol and the azeotrope. If the feed is located on the right of the azeotrope the stable and unstable node shifts to pure water and pure butanol cannot be obtained anymore by simple distillation.

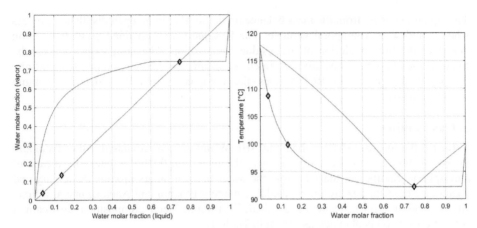

Figure 2 – Binary mixture phase diagram and characteristic points (y vs x and T vs xy)

Given the process specifications, the characteristic points related to the bottom product, feed and distillate respectively (from the left to the right) are represented in the phase diagram. Excepted particular cases, the necessary and sufficient condition to separate a multicomponent mixture by distillation is that the Residue Curve of the feed and the products lie in the same distillation region. As it can be noticed, under nominal operating conditions, the distillate characteristic point is close to the boundary defined by the azeotrope. This means that the operation is feasible under nominal operating conditions but as soon as an increase of the water content occurs the system is not able to obtain the desired products anymore, i.e. its flexibility index RI is equal to zero.

4.2. Ternary Mixture
Ethanol was then added to the previous components with the consequent introduction of the corresponding water-ethanol homogeneous azeotrope in the phase equilibrium diagram.

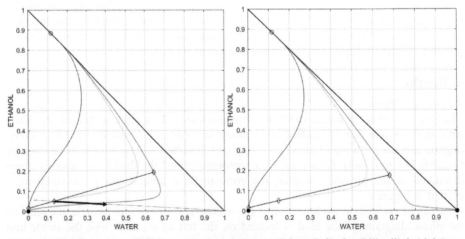

Figure 3 – Ternary mixture RCMs: nominal operating conditions (left); feasibility limit (right)

A new stable node is present in the phase diagram (i.e. the homogeneous azeotrope) while pure ethanol is a saddle point. Under nominal operating conditions separation by distillation results feasible (see Figure 3 left) since RCs corresponding to feed, bottom and distillate fall into the same distillation region. The flexibility assessment can be then performed by perturbing butanol and water molar flowrates. The most constraining limit for each of them is 41.7 mol/s (-32%) and 10.55 mol/s (+10.1%) respectively. The Resilience Index for the ternary mixture is the most constraining among each single variable maximum load, i.e. RI=10.1 %. The RCMs for a water partial flowrate crossing the feasibility boundary is shown in Figure 3 (right).

4.3. Quaternary Mixture

Acetone is finally included in the analysis obtaining a feed composition equal to the feed stream composition of an ABE/W plant separation section after dewatering.

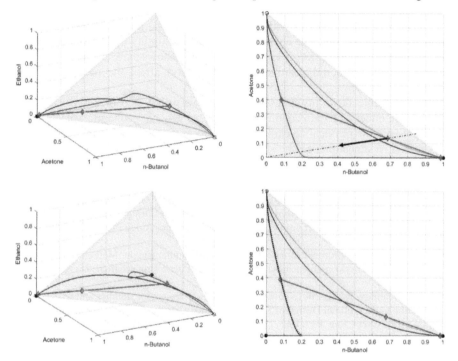

Figure 4 – RCM under nominal operating conditions (top); RCM out of the feasibility boundary (bottom) – Red: distillate, Green: feed, Blue: bottom.

While for binary and ternary mixtures process simulators are already able to provide 2D phase diagrams and RCMs, for the quaternary mixtures an interface between Matlab® and Simulis Thermodynamics® was coded in order to perform 3D Residue Curve Mapping. Results for nominal operating conditions are shown in Figure 4 (top).

Butanol and water partial flowrates are disturbed until unfeasible conditions are achieved. Water results once again the most constraining variable with a maximum flowrate in the feed equal to 13.3 mol/s. The RI for the quaternary mixture is then higher than the ternary one and equal to RI=39.1%. Due to the convexity of the distillation boundary (cf Figure 3 bottom) acetone addition enhances the separation showing an "entrainer-like" behavior.

On the other hand, if the separation process aims to recover water, i.e. a distillation column operating in the other distillation region, the feasibility boundary would show its concave side towards the operating line, that means the acetone addition would have a negative impact on the separation.

5. Conclusions

The thermodynamic flexibility assessment of a distillation process has been successfully performed by means of Residue Curve Mapping for binary, ternary and quaternary mixtures. The binary case study is barely feasible under nominal operating conditions, thus no flexibility could be detected.

The addition of ethanol, although introducing an additional azeotrope in the thermodynamic system, had a positive impact on the process shifting the maximum withstood water perturbation up to 10.1%. Finally, the presence of acetone strongly improves the separation performance under uncertain conditions with a corresponding RI value equal to 39.1 %.

Coupling the flexibility analysis with RCMs resulted to be an useful methodology to provide an "a priori" knowledge about the maximum flexibility of a distillation system likely to undergo disturbances. Moreover this paper shows how the presence of an additional component could positively (or negatively) affect the operation from a flexibility point of view.

The thermodynamic flexibility assessment is the very first step of a further detailed process design under uncertain conditions taking into account economic aspects as well and it represents the physical constraint of the design problem that cannot be violated whatever the investment that can be afforded.

References

Di Pretoro, A., Montastruc, L., Manenti, F., Joulia, X., 2019. Flexibility Assessment of a Distillation Train: Nominal vs Perturbated Conditions Optimal Design, Computer Aided Chemical Engineering, 29 European Symposium on Computer Aided Process Engineering, 46, pp. 667–672.

Ostwald, W. (1900). Dampfdrucke ternarer Gemische, Abhandlungen der Mathematisch-Physischen Classe derKonige Sachsischen. Gesellschaft derWissenschaften, 25, 413–53 (Germ.).

Petlyuk, F.B., Danilov, R.Yu., 2001. Theory of Distillation Trajectory Bundles and its Application to the Optimal Design of Separation Units: Distillation Trajectory Bundles at Finite Reflux. Chem. Eng. Res. Des., Distillation and Absorption 79, 733–746.

Petlyuk, F.B., 2004. Distillation Theory and its Application to Optimal Design of Separation Units. Cambridge University Press.

Saboo, A.K., Morari, M., Woodcock, D., 1985. Design of Resilient Processing Plants .8. a Resilience Index for Heat-Exchanger Networks. Chem. Eng. Sci. 40, 15531565. https://doi.org/10.1016/0009-2509(85)80097-X

Serafimov, L. A., 1969. The Azeotropic Rule and the Classification of Multicomponent Mixtures. 4. N-Component Mixtures. J. Phys. Chem., 43, 981–3 (Rus.).

Swaney, R.E., Grossmann, I.E., 1985. An index for operational flexibility in chemical process design. Part I: Formulation and theory. AIChE J. 31, 621–630.

Zharov, V. T., 1967. Free Evaporation of Homogeneous Multicomponent Solutions. J. Phys. Chem., 41, 1539–55 (Rus.).

Zharov, V. T., 1968a. Free Evaporation of Homogeneous Multicomponent. Solutions. 2. Four Component Systems. J. Phys. Chem., 42, 58–70 (Rus.).

Zharov, V. T., 1968b. Free Evaporation of Homogeneous Multicomponent Solutions. 3. Behavior of Distillation Lines Near Singular Points. J. Phys. Chem., 42, 195–211 (Rus.).

Zharov, V. T., & Serafimov, L. A., 1975. Physico-Chemical Foundations of Bath Open Distillation and Distillation. Leningrad: Khimiya (Rus.).K. M. Guthrie, 1969, 'Capital Cost Estimating', Chemical Engineering, 76.3, 114-142.

Sauro Pierucci, Flavio Manenti, Giulia Bozzano, Davide Manca (Eds.)
Proceedings of the 30th European Symposium on Computer Aided Process Engineering
(ESCAPE30), May 24-27, 2020, Milano, Italy. © 2020 Elsevier B.V. All rights reserved.
http://dx.doi.org/10.1016/B978-0-12-823377-1.50321-9

A Straightforward Optimization Approach for a Baseload Propane-Mixed Refrigerant Process

Mary Katebah, Mohamed Hussein, Easa I. Al-musleh[*]

Department of Chemical Engineering, Qatar University, P.O.Box 2713, Doha, Qatar
e.almusleh@qu.edu.qa

Abstract

As the energy markets adjust to the increasing demand on liquefied natural gas (LNG) and growing global warming concerns, a compelling need arises to operate existing LNG plants as efficiently as possible. Cryogenic systems, such as those used for natural gas (NG) liquefaction, are very complex. This makes optimizing their performance a frustrating task. In this paper, we propose a simple and systematic optimization approach for cryogenic processes characterized by large numbers of independent variables and sophisticated heat integration schemes. The method is composed of successive optimization levels that rely on shortcut thermodynamic techniques and sequential quadratic programming (SQP). In this paper, we are reporting the results of the proposed approach for optimizing an actual baseload propane mixed refrigerant (C3MR) process. Results showed a 6 % compression power reduction compared to the plant's current consumed power. The method is currently being tested for a more sophisticated LNG system employing C3MR cycles integrated with natural gas liquids (NGL) recovery, helium extraction, and nitrogen rejection processes.

Keywords: Natural gas liquefaction, C3MR LNG plant, Optimization, Aspen Plus™, Simulation

1. Introduction

Liquefied natural gas (LNG) plants are associated with large energy penalties, mainly compression power, that are costly and result in significant amounts of greenhouse gas emissions (Almeida-Trasvina and Smith, 2019). However, compared to other fossil fuels, LNG has gained popularity due to its abundance and high energy content per mole carbon (Bittante et al., 2015). As of November 2019, global nominal and proposed liquefaction capacity reached 393 and 843 million tonnes per year (tpy), respectively (IGU, 2019). A significant portion of the forecasted capacity is expected to be from Qatar's North Field Expansion (Energy Insights by McKinsey, 2019). Qatar's plans of increasing its production by 64 % in the 2020s solidifies its position as the global leader in terms of capacity and exports (John, 2019). Increased LNG demand and stringent environmental regulations place utmost importance on energy efficiency optimization. In addition to potentially higher production volumes and profit, LNG process optimization can reduce CO_2 emissions, thereby assisting with the global dual challenge of producing more energy with less carbon (BP, 2019).

Figure 1 illustrates the block flow diagram of a typical LNG plant. After the removal of condensate, carbon dioxide, and sulfur-containing compounds (H_2S, mercaptans, etc.), the NG is routed to the dehydration unit prior to entering the cold section. First, heavier hydrocarbons (NGLs) are removed from the NG, after which the gas gets liquefied and sent to the helium extraction and nitrogen removal units to produce in-spec LNG ready to be stored and shipped to the consumers. Within the LNG processing plant, our LNG supply chain model showed that over 55 % of CO_2 emissions originate from the cold section (Katebah et al., 20XX). Furthermore, our chain exergy analysis indicated that within the cold section ~91 % of the losses occur in the propane pre-cooled mixed refrigerant (C3MR) liquefaction cycles and natural gas liquids (NGL) recovery unit (Bouabidi et al., 20XX). Therefore, this paper focuses on the energy efficiency optimization of an actual C3MR process in Qatar, the world's largest LNG capacity holder and exporter. While there are numerous studies in the literature on the optimization of LNG liquefaction cycles, most of them require linking standard simulators to sophisticated solvers and/or time intensive coding, resulting in complex and time-consuming calculations and convergence challenges (Austbø et al., 2014). For example, the work of Wang et al. focused on minimizing energy consumption of a C3MR plant by using LINDO Global solver in GAMS to solve the optimization problem. (Wang et al., 2012). Sun et al. utilized GA for the optimization of an AP-X process by reducing the process's power consumption (Sun et al., 2016). Aspelund et al. used a gradient free optimization-simulation method for a LNG process modeled using Aspen HYSYS®. Their approach was based on a Tabu Search and Nelder-Mead Downhill Simplex method (Aspelund et al., 2010). Almeida-Trasvina and Smith optimized a novel cascade refrigeration cycle and other commercial cycles by applying a stochastic search optimization (GA) routine and the best solution was used as an initial point for deterministic optimization (SQP) (Almeida-Trasvina and Smith, 2018) . In this work, we are proposing a simpler optimization approach that relies on system decomposition and thermodynamic considerations to simplify such optimization problems without compromising solution quality. In addition to reducing computational times and easing convergence, the simplicity of this approach caters to both experienced and inexperienced standard simulators users such as process engineers and students. Moreover, the methodology can result in meaningful process insights that are otherwise unseen in conventional approaches.

2. Methodology

Instead of optimizing the entire linked model at once, we suggest dividing the system into subcomponents for subsequent optimization in a step-wise approach, while using simplified black-box exergy models to predict the performance of the surrounding units. We also recommend shortlisting adjustable operating variables by conducting a degree of freedom (DOF) analysis. Furthermore, process constraints (such as design limits, products specification, etc.) need to be identified based on insights and discussions with plant operators. Variables and constraints that should be maintained at their limits (referred in this article as *active variables and constraints, respectively*) for enhanced performance should also be identified. In addition to prediction using exergy techniques, the method capitalizes on pairing designated variables with constraints that should be maintained active, thereby reducing the number of optimization variables and search space, and easing flowsheet convergence. We are currently validating methods, such as parametric analysis, that can be integrated with the proposed approach for validation and/or enhancing solution quality.

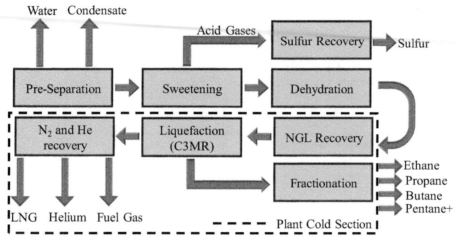

Figure 1: Block Flow Diagram of the LNG Plant

3. Process Description and Simulation

Figure 2 depicts a process flow diagram of the process at hand. We utilized actual plant data and AspenPlus™ software to build and validate a base-case model for the liquefaction section of a LNG plant with a 3.65 million tpy capacity. Sweet, dry, pre-treated NG enters the cold section of the LNG plant, where it gets pre-cooled by the C3 cycle from 21 to -27 °C. NG is then throttled to 54.9 bar before entering the NGL recovery unit. GERG-2008 equation of state was used to model the NGL recovery as it was best suited to match model results with plant data. The process is essentially a distillation column (C-1) that uses part of the main cryogenic heat exchanger (MCHE, E-1) as the condenser. The liquid portion leaving the condenser at, -54°C, re-enters the column as reflux, whereas the gas is routed to the MCHE for liquefaction and subcooling. This unit also produced approximately 9.9 KSbbl/day (at 15.6 °C and 1.01 bar) of extracted NGLs to be sent to the fractionation unit for further processing. The C3MR process comprises of two refrigeration cycles: a mixed refrigerant (MR) and C3 cycle. Peng-Robinson equation of state was used to simulate the cycles. C3 cycle pre-cools the NG and MR to about -31 °C with four C3 evaporation pressures: high high pressure (HHP) at 7.8 bar, high pressure (HP) at 5.1 bar, medium pressure (MP) at 2.9 bar, and low pressure (LP) at 1.6 bar. Other streams cooled in the cycle include streams in the fractionation unit such as de-ethanizer overhead and liquefied petroleum gas (LPG). The evaporated C3's enter a 3-stage compressor (K-1) and gets compressed to 16.7 bar for subsequent condensation using sea water available at 33°C. At base-case conditions, the C3 cycle required ~ 44.3 MW of compression power. MR comprising of 2.1 % nitrogen (N_2), 43.8 % methane (C1), 40 % ethane (C2), and 13.8 % C3 passes through another 3-stage compressor (K-2), sea water intercooler, and pre-cooling exchangers in sequence. After reducing its temperature and pressure to -154 °C and 3.1 bar, respectively, the MR, in addition to a cold fuel gas stream from the helium extraction and nitrogen removal units, provide the cooling duty of the MCHE. LNG leaving the MCHE was subcooled to -144 °C. The MR cycle required ~78.6 MW of compression energy. In total, the entire cycle necessitated 123 MW of compression power. When comparing simulation results with plant data, minimal discrepancy was observed.

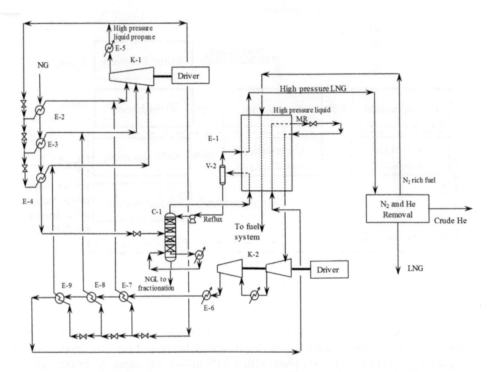

Figure 2: Process Flow Diagram of the integrated C3MR/ NGL recovery units. The de-ethanizer condenser and LPG cooling are not shown for clarity purposes

4. C3MR Optimization

For the C3MR process shown in Figure 1, the optimization approach consisted of two successive steps: first the MR cycle was rigorously optimized while predicting C3 cycle compression power. Next, the C3 cycle power was rigorously optimized at optimum MR cycle variables. DOF analysis showed that the process under consideration has 57 adjustable variables. After fixing active variables and devoting certain operating variables to maintain product specifications and active constraints (via for loop routines), variables available for optimization were reduced to 20. After further simplification, the adjustable variables decreased to 8.

4.1. MR Cycle

Optimization of the MR cycle was performed while modeling the C3 cycle as a black-box. The C3 cycle's power was predicted using exergy balances and C3 cycle base case efficiency, see Eq. (1) and Eq. (2). At base case conditions, the C3 cycle's efficiency was calculated to be 22%. The cycle's main constraints are the MCHE minimum temperature approach (MTA), NGL recovery/purities, and final LNG temperature. Pairing them with appropriate variables reduced the optimization variables from 57 to 13. Literature shows that the MR composition is one of the primary parameters in the cycle's optimization (Abdullah Alabdulkarema, Amir Mortazavi, 2011). Therefore, to simplify the problem, the effect of varying the composition (flowrates) was investigated while maintaining remaining adjustable variables at base values. Relative to the base-case, optimum MR composition was found to be 1.4, 39, 36.9 and 22.6 mol% N_2, C1, C2, and C3, respectively at a total MR and predicted C3 power of 105.5 MW (MR and C3 power of 87 and 18.5 MW, respectively). The system favored increasing the cooling load on the

MR, while decreasing the C3 load relative to the base case. This can be explained by the cycles' efficiencies, as the MR cycle (base-case efficiency of 37%) is almost twice as efficient as the C3 one. Since this method aims towards obtaining predictive independent variables values rather than actual power values, a final step of optimizing the C3 cycle at optimum MR was necessary to obtain actual powers that are operationally feasible.

$$W_{C3,\min} = Ex_{NG,in} + Ex_{MR,in} - Ex_{NG,out} - Ex_{MR,out} \tag{1}$$

$$W_{C3,predicted} = \frac{W_{C3,\min}}{\mu_{C3}} \tag{2}$$

Where:

- $W_{C3,\min}$ and $W_{C3,predicted}$ are the C3 cycle's minimum and predicted power, respectively.
- $Ex_{NG,in}$ and $Ex_{NG,out}$ are the exergy rates of the NG streams entering and leaving the C3 cycle, respectively.
- $Ex_{MR,in}$ and $Ex_{MR,out}$ are the exergy rates of the MR streams entering and leaving the C3 cycle, respectively.
- μ_{C3} is the C3 cycle efficiency at base-case conditions (22%).

4.2. C3 Cycle
In this final step, rigorous C3 cycle optimization was performed at optimum MR variables. C3 flowrates/ split fractions to evaporators and HHP/LP evaporation pressures were devoted towards maintaining base-case MTAs for all the chillers, in addition to propane degrees of superheat at the chillers' outlets. C3 was allowed to be slightly superheated to prevent the formation of liquid at the compressor suction. After variable pairing, the system was left with 2 adjustable variables available for optimization: HP and MP C3 evaporation pressures. Results showed that a C3 power of 28.5 MW was achievable at optimum operating variables. This gave a total actual C3MR power of 115.5 MW.

5. Conclusion

A simple and systematic method is proposed and tested for optimizing an actual C3MR liquefaction process. A base-case model was simulated using Aspen Plus™ software, and results were validated with plant data with minimal discrepancy. Detailed DOF analyses pinpointed the variables available and effective for optimization. Each unit was rigorously optimized while predicting the performance of its interlinked sections via an exergy model. Results showed that near 7 MW reduction of compression power can be achieved, which amounted to 6 % of current requirements. Advantages of this method compared to other approaches include its simplicity, lower computational time, and ability to produce trends/ insights. This approach is viable and can be extended to other highly integrated chemical processes. Currently we are testing the method for the rigorous optimization of a fully integrated system comprising of NGL recovery and helium/nitrogen extraction. Techniques to improve the quality of the solution are also under investigation and we expect to publish them soon.

Acknowledgements

This paper was made possible by NPRP grant No. NPRP8-964-2-408 from the Qatar National Research Fund (a member of Qatar Foundation). The authors would also like to acknowledge Dr. Hassan Alfadala for his contribution in this work. The statements made herein are solely the responsibility of the authors.

References

Abdullah Alabdulkarema, Amir Mortazavi, Y.H., 2011. Optimization of propane pre-cooled mixed refrigerant LNG plant. Appl. Therm. https://doi.org/10.1016/j.applthermaleng. 2010.12.003

Almeida-Trasvina, F., Smith, R., 2019. Novel refrigeration cycle configurations for performance improvements in LNG processes at small scale, in: Computer Aided Chemical Engineering. https://doi.org/10.1016/B978-0-12-818634-3.50071-0

Almeida-Trasvina, F., Smith, R., 2018. Design and Optimisation of Novel Cascade Refrigeration Cycles for LNG Production, in: Computer Aided Chemical Engineering. https://doi.org/10.1016/B978-0-444-64235-6.50111-X

Aspelund, A., Gundersen, T., Myklebust, J., Nowak, M.P., Tomasgard, A., 2010. An optimization-simulation model for a simple LNG process. Comput. Chem. Eng. 34, 1606–1617. https://doi.org/10.1016/j.compchemeng. 2009.10.018

Austbø, B., Løvseth, S.W., Gundersen, T., 2014. Annotated bibliography-Use of optimization in LNG process design and operation. Comput. Chem. Eng. 71, 391–414. https://doi.org/10.1016/j.compchemeng. 2014.09.010

Bittante, A., Jokinen, R., Pettersson, F., Saxén, H., 2015. Optimization of LNG Supply Chain, Computer Aided Chemical Engineering. Elsevier. https://doi.org/10.1016/B978-0-444-63578-5.50125-0

Bouabidi, Z., Katebah, M., Hussein, M., Shazed, A.R., Al-musleh, E.I., 20XX. Rigorous Thermodynamic Analysis for a Full-Scale Baseload LNG Supply Chain. In Preparation.

BP, 2019. BP Energy Outlook 2019 edition The Energy Outlook explores the forces shaping the global energy transition out to 2040 and the key uncertainties surrounding that. BP Energy Outlook 2019.

Energy Insights by McKinsey, 2019. Global gas & LNG outlook to 2035.

IGU, 2019. 2019 World LNG Report. World LNG Rep. 126.

John, P., 2019. LNG production increase a big boost for national economy: Al-Kaabi. Gulf Times.

Katebah, M., Hussein, M., Shazed, A.R., Bouabidi, Z., Al-musleh, E., 20XX. Simulation, Energy and Environmental Analysis of a baseload LNG Supply Chain. In Preparation.

Sun, H., He Ding, D., He, M., Shoujun Sun, S., 2016. Simulation and optimisation of AP-X process in a large-scale LNG plant. J. Nat. Gas Sci. Eng. 32, 380–389. https://doi.org/10.1016/j.jngse. 2016.04.039

Wang, M., Zhang, J., Xu, Q., 2012. Optimal design and operation of a C3MR refrigeration system for natural gas liquefaction. Comput. Chem. Eng. 39, 84–95. https://doi.org/10.1016/j.compchemeng. 2011.12.003

Sauro Pierucci, Flavio Manenti, Giulia Bozzano, Davide Manca (Eds.)
Proceedings of the 30th European Symposium on Computer Aided Process Engineering
(ESCAPE30), May 24-27, 2020, Milano, Italy. © 2020 Elsevier B.V. All rights reserved.
http://dx.doi.org/10.1016/B978-0-12-823377-1.50322-0

Market-like Distributed Coordination of Individually Constrained and Coupled Production Plants with Quadratic Approximation

Simon Wenzel*, Felix Riedl, Sebastian Engell

Process Dynamics and Operations Group, Department of Biochemical and Chemical Engineering, TU Dortmund, Emil-Figge Straße 70, 44227 Dortmund, Germany
simon.wenzel@tu-dortmund.de

Abstract

The optimal operation of large chemical or petrochemical production sites is challenging, because streams of shared resources such as steam or intermediates physically couple the individual production plants. For a feasible operation, it is essential to coordinate the production of the plants to balance the networks for the shared resources. Often, finding a central solution to this site-wide optimization problem is not possible due to various barriers such as the lack of models, too large complexity, or the management structure that hinders the exchange of relevant information. Market-like distributed optimization tackles some of these barriers, especially if only limited data exchange is possible between the constituent production plants. However, distributed optimization algorithms typically need many iterations, which hinders their practical application. In this contribution, we compare an algorithm for distributed market-like coordination that we formulated in previous work for individually constrained coupled systems with ADMM for a novel case study.

Keywords: Distributed optimization, Shared resource allocation, Quadratic approximation, Lagrangian relaxation, ADMM,

1. Introduction

In a more and more digitized, integrated, and connected production environment, the coordination of complex coupled systems of systems is essential to ensure a resource efficient and optimal operation. Large chemical or petrochemical production sites or industrial clusters are examples of such coupled systems of systems, where a large number of challenges exist in their coordination. One of the challenges is the physical coupling of the individual production plants via networks of shared resources. Figure 1 illustrates such a coupling of different production plants via three networks.

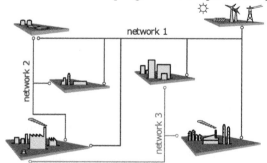

Figure 1 Visualization of shared resource networks at a production site.

Typical shared resources are steam on different pressure levels, intermediate products, waste treatment units or heating gas. Although the decision making on the operation of the individual production plants is usually done in a decentralized fashion, the overall balance of the shared resource networks has to be satisfied, which requires collaboration between the individual production plants either by communicating with the managers of the other production plants or with a central coordinator. If the individual production plants belong to different business units or to different companies in an industrial cluster, they can only share a restricted amount of data. In this situation, market-like distributed coordination methods can be used to establish an auction mechanism for shared resources within the system to coordinate the production and consumption of the subsystems and thus to balance the shared resource networks, i.e. to ensure that the consumed amount of shared resources meets the produced amount of shared resources. The limited data exchange in the auction mechanism ensures a high level of confidentiality between the subsystems. However, the drawback of these methods is that they typically require a large number of communication rounds between the production plants and the coordinator (auctioneer) to find the system-wide optimum. We recently proposed a hierarchical coordination algorithm that approximates the responses of the individual production plants by a quadratic function to find the optimal solution within fewer iterations. In this paper, we extend the evaluation of the performance of the algorithm from Wenzel et al. (2019) to a comparison with ADMM (Boyd 2010) for subsystems with individual constraints and coupling constraints.

The rest of the paper is structured as follows: First, the site-wide optimization problem is formulated as a general non-linear constrained mathematical optimization problem. Then market-like distributed coordination is introduced and ADMM as well as our novel algorithm are briefly introduced. Afterwards, the case study is explained, which is followed by the presentation of the computational results. Finally, we draw conclusions and indicate directions of future work.

2. Mathematical problem formulation

The coordination of the production of different production plants that are coupled by streams of material and energy can be formulated as a mathematical optimization problem:

$$
\begin{aligned}
\min_{u_i, \forall i} \ J(u) &= \sum_{i=1}^{N_S} J_i(u_i) \\
\text{s.t. } &\forall i \in C^{g_i} \colon g_i(u_i) \leq 0 \\
&\forall i \in C^{h_i} \colon h_i(u_i) = 0 \\
&C^r \colon \sum_{i=1}^{N_S} r_i(u_i) = b,
\end{aligned}
\tag{1}
$$

where $J \colon \mathbb{R}^{n_u} \to \mathbb{R}$ is the site-wide objective function, which can be split into N_S individual objective functions $J_i \colon \mathbb{R}^{n_{u_i}} \to \mathbb{R}$ of the subsystems i (plants). Every subsystem has to satisfy a set of inequality constraints C^{g_i} and a set of equality constraints C^{h_i}. The vector of manipulated variables of subsystem i is denoted by $u_i \in \mathbb{R}^{n_{u_i}}$. We assume that the only constraint that is not separable is the network balance of the shared resource networks C^r, which is also referred to as the complicating constraint. It is assumed that the individual resource utilization vectors $r_i \colon \mathbb{R}^{n_{u_i}} \to \mathbb{R}$ (i.e., the production or consumption of the resources) are affine in u_i and the cost functions J_i are convex (Boyd

2010). Streams that are fed into the networks are modelled as negative quantities; a positive sign denotes consumption. The right hand side of the complicating constraint **b** is a constant vector that, e.g., represents amounts of shared resources that enter or leave the balance space of the site. If it is zero, then all shared resource streams are consumed and produced at the site.

3. Market-like distributed coordination

The term market-like distributed coordination originates from the economic interpretation of distributed optimization algorithms based on Lagrangian relaxation of the complication constraint. At the optimal solution, the values of the Lagrange multipliers of the complicating constraint correspond to the equilibrium price in a Walrasian auction. At the equilibrium price, the demand and the supply of the traded goods match and thus the market clears. Applied to (1), this means that the amount of produced and consumed shared resources sums up to zero, i.e., the network is balanced. To find the equilibrium price, different strategies can be employed. These methods mainly differ in the way they find the equilibrium by iterating between a coordinator (auctioneers) and the subsystems. Depending on the method, more or less information on the individual optimization problems is communicated to the coordinator. We focus on methods that only exchange minimal information, i.e., the coordinator only receives information about the resource utilization of each subsystem, and the coordinator can only announce updated prices. In the case of ADMM, the coordinator in addition communicates reference values to the individual subsystems. In the following, we introduce the most intuitive and classic scheme of subgradient based price updates, ADMM (Boyd 2010), and our proposed algorithm QAC (Wenzel and Engell (2019), Wenzel et al. (2019)).

3.1. Subgradient updates

By relaxing the network constraint in (1), the Lagrangian of the optimization problem can be decomposed into N_s individual Lagrange functions

$$\mathcal{L}_i(\boldsymbol{u}_i, \boldsymbol{\lambda}) = J_i(\boldsymbol{u}_i) + \boldsymbol{\lambda}^T \boldsymbol{r}_i(\boldsymbol{u}_i), \tag{2}$$

where the vector of Lagrange multipliers $\boldsymbol{\lambda}$ represents the prices of the shared resources. Each individual subsystem solves the following optimization problem and computes its intended resource utilization $\boldsymbol{r}_i\left(\boldsymbol{u}_i^{k+1}\right)$ afterwards:

$$\forall i \; \boldsymbol{u}_i^{k+1} := \arg\min_{\boldsymbol{u}_i} \mathcal{L}_i(\boldsymbol{u}_i, \boldsymbol{\lambda}^k) \tag{3}$$
$$\text{s.t.} \quad \mathcal{C}^{g_i} : \boldsymbol{g}_i(\boldsymbol{u}_i) \leq \boldsymbol{0}$$
$$\mathcal{C}^{h_i} : \boldsymbol{h}_i(\boldsymbol{u}_i) = \boldsymbol{0}.$$

On the coordinator level, the resource utilization is aggregated and the following price update for the vector of Lagrange multipliers is performed:

$$\boldsymbol{\lambda}^{k+1} := \boldsymbol{\lambda}^k + \alpha^k \left(\sum_{i=1}^{N_s} \boldsymbol{r}_i\left(\boldsymbol{u}_i^{k+1}\right) - \boldsymbol{b} \right), \tag{4}$$

where index k denotes the iteration index. For a sufficiently small α^k, convergence to the optimal solution is ensured for strictly convex problems (Bertsekas 1999). Choosing a very small value for α^k however results in many iterations, which can be a barrier for the implementation in practice (Wenzel and Engell (2019), Wenzel et al. (2019)).

3.2. The alternating direction method of multipliers (ADMM)

The alternating direction method of multipliers (ADMM, Gabay and Mercier (1976)) converges under milder assumptions on the optimization problem and gained a lot of popularity recently (Boyd 2010). The augmented Lagrangian term in ADMM is made separable by introducing auxiliary reference variables z_i. Reformulating (1) results as

$$\min_{u_i, \forall i} \sum_{i=1}^{N_s} J_i(u_i)$$
$$\text{s.t. } C^{r_i}: r_i(u_i) - z_i = 0, \forall i,$$
$$C^z: \sum_{i=1}^{N_s} z_i = -b,$$
$$u_i \in C^{g_i} \cup C^{h_i}, \forall i,$$

(5)

which has a separable augmented Lagrangian

$$\mathcal{L}_{\rho,i}(u_i, \lambda) = J_i(u_i) + \lambda^T (r_i(u_i) - z_i) + \frac{\rho}{2} \|(r(u_i) - z_i)\|_2^2 \qquad (6)$$

with the penalty parameter ρ. The update steps can be written as

$$\forall i, u_i^{k+1} := \arg \min_{u_i \in C^{g_i} \cup C^{h_i}} J_i(u_i) + \lambda^T (r_i(u_i) - z_i^k) + \frac{\rho}{2} \|r(u_i) - z_i^k\|_2^2, \qquad (7)$$
$$\forall i, z_i^{k+1} := r_i(u_i^{k+1}) - \bar{r}(u^{k+1}), \qquad (8)$$
$$\lambda^{k+1} := \lambda^k + \rho \cdot \bar{r}(u^{k+1}), \qquad (9)$$

with $\bar{r}$ as the mean of the network residuals.

3.3. Quadratic approximation coordination (QAC)

The quadratic approximation coordination (QAC) algorithm approximates the squared 2-norm of the network residual to compute the optimal Lagrange multipliers using less iterations compared to subgradient based price updates (Wenzel and Engell (2019), Wenzel et al. (2019)). In each iteration, the algorithm computes an updated quadratic approximation based on a selection of past points and performs a price update that is limited by a step size constraint:

$$\lambda^{k+1} := \arg \min_{\lambda} \; \phi(\lambda, p_\phi^k)$$
$$\text{s.t.} \qquad \lambda \in \hat{\mathcal{E}}^k(\Lambda_\phi).$$

(10)

Here, p_ϕ^k are the model parameters of the quadratic model and $\hat{\mathcal{E}}^k$ is the covariance based step size constraint. The constraint hinders the algorithm to perform too aggressive price updates. The individual subsystems compute their updated resource utilization in the same way as in classical subgradient based price updates (3). For a detailed description of the algorithm, the reader is referred to (Wenzel and Engell (2019), Wenzel et al. (2019)).

4. Case study

In order to compare the performance of the different algorithms, 1400 constrained quadratic problems were randomly generated. The 1400 problems were taken from Wenzel et al. (2019). They are of the following form, which is a special case of (1):

Market-like distributed coordination of individually constrained and coupled production plants with quadratic a pproximation

1931

$$\min_{u_i, \forall i} \sum_{i=1}^{N_s} \frac{1}{2} u_i^T Q_i u_i + q_i^T u_i$$

$$\text{s.t.} \sum_{i=1}^{N_s} A_i u_i = 0 \tag{11}$$

$$\underline{u} \le u \le \bar{u}.$$

The optimization problems are strictly convex and the constraints are limited to the bounds on the decision variables with a lower bound $\underline{u} = -10$ and an upper bound $\bar{u} = 10$. We used a standard formulation of ADMM, where the penalty parameter ρ is updated dynamically as proposed by He et al. (2000). As convergence tolerance, we defined a threshold of $\varepsilon_p = 1 \times 10^{-2}$ for the primal residual, i.e., the 2-norm of the network balance $\|w_p\|_2 = \sum_{i=1}^{N_s} A_i u_i$, and a maximum number of iteration of $k_{max} = 500$.

5. Results

A graphical overview of the results for the constrained quadratic programs is shown in Figure 2, and Table 1 gives an overview about the mean of the 1400 test problems. In Figure 2 the results are illustrated as follows: On the horizontal axis the number of iterations upon convergence is shown and on the vertical axis the final primal residual is shown. With empty circles the results of the 1400 runs with subgradient based price updates upon termination of the coordination are shown, while the results for ADMM are shown with filled circles. The results of QAC are indicated with diamond symbols. The vertical black line marks the maximum number of iterations. Within the maximum number of iterations the subgradient based updates only solve overall 14% of the test problems, ADMM solves 89%, while QAC solves 76% (see Table 1). Many of the tested problems cannot be solved by subgradient based price updates at all within the maximum number of iterations, which is visible by the results on the black vertical bar. It can be seen that the average of the final primal residual of QAC is significantly smaller compared to subgradient based updates and to ADMM. For the converged instances, the subgradient based price updates require on average 370 iterations, ADMM requires on average 142 iterations, while QAC needs on average 129 iterations.

Table 1: Results for the coordination of constrained quadratic programs. The mean number of iterations including the runs that reached k_{max} is denoted as $\bar{k}$. The mean number of iteration of only the converged runs is denoted as $\bar{k}_c$. The percentage of the converged runs is listed under $\%_c$ and the mean final value of the primal residual of the converged runs is denoted with $\|w_p\|_2$.

Algorithm	$\bar{k}$	$\bar{k}_c$	$\|w_p\|_2$	$\%_c$
Subgradient based	479	370	9.87×10^{-3}	14
ADMM	161	142	6.74×10^{-3}	89
QAC	234	129	1.51×10^{-3}	76

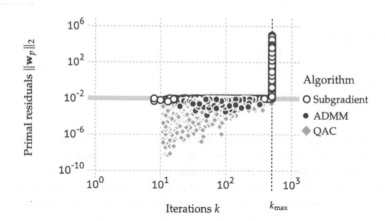

Figure 2: Results for the coordination of the constrained quadratic programs. The plots show the final values of the norm of the primal residual against the number of iterations. The vertical black line marks the maximum number of iterations; the horizontal gray bar marks the threshold for the primal residual ε_p.

6. Conclusions and future prospects

The number of iterations for QAC was reduced to approximately a third compared to subgradient based updates. QAC does not solve as many problems as ADMM. However, it has to be noticed that the exchanged data for QAC is more limited than for ADMM, which makes a fair comparison difficult. In addition, the mean final primal residual of QAC is far below the one of ADMM. Thus, for smaller thresholds of the primal residual, QAC is expected to also outperform ADMM w.r.t. the number of required iterations. Further research should be devoted to increasing the robustness of QAC and to a detailed investigation of the pitfalls that prohibit a convergence of the algorithm in certain cases.

Acknowledgement

The project leading to this publication has received funding from the European Union's Horizon 2020 research and innovation programme under grant agreement No 723575 (CoPro, spire2030.eu/copro) in the framework of the SPIRE PPP.

References

Bertsekas, D. P. Nonlinear Programming; Athena Scientific: Belmont, Massachusetts, 1999.

Boyd, S. Distributed Optimization and Statistical Learning via the Alternating Direction Method of Multipliers. *Found. Trends® Mach. Learn.* **2010**, *3* (1), 1–122. https://doi.org/10.1561/2200000016

Gabay, D.; Mercier, B. A Dual Algorithm for the Solution of Nonlinear Variational Problems via Finite Element Approximation. *Comput. Math. with Appl.* **1976**, *2* (1), 17–40. https://doi.org/10.1016/0898-1221(76)90003-1.

He, B. S.; Yang, H.; Wang, S. L. Alternating Direction Method with Self-Adaptive Penalty Parameters for Monotone Variational Inequalities. *J. Optim. Theory Appl.* **2000**, *106* (2), 337–356. https://doi.org/10.1023/A:1004603514434.

Wenzel, S.; Riedl, F.; Engell, S. An Efficient Hierarchical Market-like Coordination Algorithm for Coupled Production Systems Based on Quadratic Approximation. *Comput. Chem. Eng.* **2019**, *in rev.*

Wenzel, S.; Engell, S. Coordination of Coupled Systems of Systems with Quadratic Approximation. *IFAC-PapersOnLine* **2019**, *52* (3), 132–137. https://doi.org/10.1016/j.ifacol.2019.06.023

Sauro Pierucci, Flavio Manenti, Giulia Bozzano, Davide Manca (Eds.)
Proceedings of the 30th European Symposium on Computer Aided Process Engineering
(ESCAPE30), May 24-27, 2020, Milano, Italy. © 2020 Elsevier B.V. All rights reserved.
http://dx.doi.org/10.1016/B978-0-12-823377-1.50323-2

Synthesis and Assessment of Waste-to-resource Routes for Circular Economy

Adrián Pacheco-López[a], Ana Somoza-Tornos[a], Edrisi Muñoz[a], Elisabet Capón-García[b], Moisés Graells[a], Antonio Espuña[a]

[a]*Department of Chemical Engineering, Universitat Politècnica de Catalunya
Escola d'Enginyeria de Barcelona Est, C/ Eduard Maristany 16, 08019 Barcelona, Spain*
[b]*ABB Switzerland Ltd., Segelhofstrasse 1K, 5405 Baden-Dättwil, Switzerland*
antonio.espuna@upc.edu

Abstract

The benefits of the circular economy paradigm have been proven during the past two decades, but its application poses some challenges that still need to be tackled. This contribution presents a systematic way to generate a list of potential waste-to-resource technologies based on the use of a semi-automatic ontological frameworks. The ontology is instantiated, giving the possibility to generate and assess a list of transformation processes alternatives, according to the potentially available waste streams and resource requirements in a specific area and/or sector. The resulting list is then analyzed and classified according to pre-established parameters, thus presenting which are the potentially best alternatives to close the material loops and recover chemical resources from available waste. The capabilities of the method to identify promising transformation technologies are assessed through an illustrative case study: the evaluation of different routes for the treatment of plastic waste materials, with the focus on chemical recycling.

Keywords: circular economy, product transformation, waste-to-resource, ontology, chemical recycling

1. Introduction

In the last years, there has been an increasing concern about the degradation of the environment due to the large amount of waste generated by the constantly growing world population. In this line, plastic waste deserves special attention, since it is one of the most abundant and lasting types of waste. Its manufacture entails a significant consumption of energy and resources considering its short average lifespan. Hence, there is a rising awareness on the need of not only treat waste, but also convert it into valuable feedstock for other processes, thus eliminating the problem of waste disposal and reducing the consumption of fresh raw materials.

Promising processes for chemical recycling have been proposed in the direction of closing the loop of materials, but most of them are still in development at lab scale. Hence, they are often disregarded, due to the lack of information on their cost, profitability and performance at industrial plant scale level. Furthermore, and opposed to traditional product-based processes, it is not always clear which is the best way to convert a specific waste stream into which added-value product(s), or even which specific waste streams will offer better economic or environmental potential to be reused or recycled.

Thus, systematic tools should be developed to address the generation of process alternatives that enhance resource upcycling. The aim of this work is to develop a method to synthesize and assess routes for waste-to-resource transformations.

The approach presented in this contribution is based on ontologies and knowledge modelling. An ontology is a formal, explicit specification of shared conceptualization (Studer R. et al, 1998). The extended use of ontologies has allowed the development of ontology-based engineering systems, providing a semantical environment and a knowledge management tool. Previous research has demonstrated the applicability of ontologies to circular economy and industrial symbiosis problems (Zhou et al., 2018, Cecelja et al., 2015, Rafaat et al., 2013).

In this work, a formal ontology that models the enterprise process engineering domain, so called Enterprise Ontology Project (EOP), has been used (Munoz et al, 2013). EOP model sets well-defined domain concepts encompassed by a taxonomic arrange, terminology, definitions and relations. The domain of this ontology is process system engineering including areas such as batch processes, control and automation, planning and scheduling, supply chain management and life cycle assessment. Thus, this ontology provides to process functionalities a consistent structure for explicit, shareable and reusable formal knowledge representation.

2. Problem statement

The problem addressed in this contribution can be stated in the following terms: ranging from a pre-defined ontology for the classification of waste-to-resource processes along with their specifications, and scientific documentation related to the domain of study. A list of tentative processes suitable to treat the considered waste with their specifications, such as operating conditions as well as economic and environmental data, should be determined.

Subsequently, given the previously obtained list, a set of characterized available wastes, potential products demand with quality requirements to meet, and data assessment criteria to analyze the adequacy of the process to the given waste, the objective is to determine a list of relevant technologies sorted by the criteria defined above.

3. Methodology

The methodology used in this work is described in Figure 1 and is divided into two main tasks; the first one consists of ontology selection and instantiation with information retrieved from scientific documentation, obtaining then a set of processes suitable for the domain of study. The second task consists of a reasoner that, starting from the potential transformation processes, would be able to obtain a list of processes and weight the best ones based on the assessment criteria mentioned below in section 3.2.

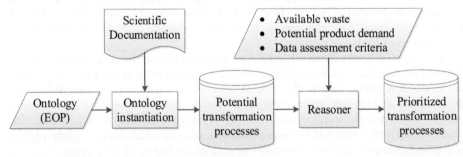

Figure 1. Methodology description

3.1. Ontological framework

An ontological framework is used to model resources, waste and potential transformation technologies considering their composition, characteristics and other specifications.

First, a set of transformation processes available in the domain of study are populated and implemented in the ontology framework mentioned above. These transformation processes have to be well defined and all the relevant parameters must be registered in the ontology.

In order to connect the available wastes with the final marketable products, an input-output matching method has to be applied, thus being able to generate different process paths (or routes) with their eventual outcomes and taking into consideration eventual intermediate products, which will enforce specific sequencing constraints.

Finally, end-of-life treatment processes for any non-marketable by-product, such as incineration for energy recovery or landfill, should be included in the proposed process network, if necessary.

3.2. Sorting and classification of instances (reasoner)

For each one of the transformation processes routes available in the ontology, a list is created and a ponderation is applied in order to sort them out, seeking the maximum economic and environmental profit, as well as promoting the use of simpler and more mature processes.

The process characteristics to be analyzed are sorted in three main categories: economical, environmental and matureness. Main economic aspects are: products selling price (including energy recovery benefits), waste purchase price, and processing cost. The environmental impacts of the feedstock, products and process are obtained (and eventually monetized) according to the life cycle impact model ReCiPe2016 (Huijbregts et al, 2016). And finally, the matureness of the technology is assessed with the Technology Readiness Level (TRL) as defined by the EU Horizon 2020 (European Commission, 2014).

Products prices are obtained from the Prodcom Annual Data 2018 (European Commision, 2018), waste prices and processes cost for the case study are taken from scientific literature review.

Then, the economic and environmental profits for every process path (the letter j is used to represent the set of processes to be studied) can be calculated as shown in Eq. (1) and Eq. (2).

$$P_{eco,j} = V_{products} - C_{waste} - C_{process} \tag{1}$$

$$P_{env,j} = EI_{products} - EI_{waste} - EI_{process} \tag{2}$$

Additionally, weighting factors are calculated in order to prioritize paths with higher economic and environmental profits against those with lower values, as shown in Eqs. (3, 4).

$$f_{eco,j} = \frac{P_{eco,j} - \min_j \left\{ P_{eco,j} \right\}}{\max_j \left\{ P_{eco,j} \right\} - \min_j \left\{ P_{eco,j} \right\}} \tag{3}$$

$$f_{env,j} = \frac{P_{env,j} - \min_{j}\{P_{env,j}\}}{\max_{j}\{P_{env,j}\} - \min_{j}\{P_{env,j}\}} \tag{4}$$

And another factor will be calculated from the TRL in order to promote the use of more mature technologies, as seen in Eq. (5):

$$f_{TRL,j} = \frac{TRL_{j}}{\max_{j}\{TRL_{j}\}} \tag{5}$$

Finally, an objective function can be calculated as shown in Eq. (6), which has to be maximized, that is to say, the routes with the greatest O.F. will be at the top of the list and the ones with lowest will be at the bottom.

$$OF_{j} = \left(P_{eco,j} + P_{env,j}\right) f_{eco,j} \cdot f_{env,j} \cdot f_{TRL,j} \tag{6}$$

4. Case study

With the purpose of illustrating the methodology, a case study has been proposed for the treatment of plastic waste, such as polyethylene waste (PEw). A list of tentative processes has been obtained from scientific literature and other public domain sources. Other alternatives have been added, such as, direct mechanical recycling, direct downcycling, landfilling and incineration for energy recovery. A list of processes suitable for PEw recycling has been obtained and schematized in Figure 2.

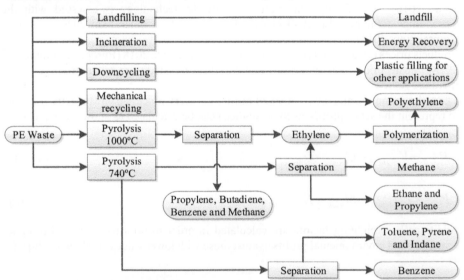

Figure 2. Possible alternatives for PE waste treatment.

According to the structure obtained in Figure 2, there are 7 different paths that can be followed for the conversion of waste into valuable products, each one of them leading to a different outcome. For simplicity purposes, the number of processes in the path generation has been limited to a maximum of 3. Tables 1 and 2 show the studied paths and their main specifications.

5. Results and discussion

Economic and environmental impacts of the processes are calculated in order to sort them out from the most profitable economically and environmentally to the less. The result is shown in Table 3, which is sorted by the objective function. Based on these results, the most profitable process would be PEw pyrolysis at 740°C, followed by pyrolysis at 1000°C, along with the separation of the resulting gas and oil fractions in each case; while landfilling is found to be the less profitable option.

Chemical recycling appears to be a very promising way of treating waste and closing the materials loop, thus obtaining raw materials that can potentially be used instead of fresh raw materials. Additionally, these processes are economically and environmentally far more profitable than the traditional way of treating this kind of waste, namely landfill or incineration.

Table 1. Economic specifications for the analyzed processes.

Process path	Total Cost (€/t)	Waste purchase price (€/t)	Products Value (€/t)	Economic Profit (€/t)
Pyrolysis 740°C + Separation	216.61	307.98	698.47	173.88
Pyrolysis 1000°C + Separation	215.15	307.98	695.63	172.50
Pyro. 1000°C + Sep. + Polymerization	320.60	307.98	709.93	81.35
Direct Downcycling PE	0.00	307.98	307.98	0.00
Direct Recycling PE	106.66	307.98	528.03	113.39
Incineration	128.20	307.98	493.12	56.95
Landfill	97.53	307.98	0.00	-405.51

Table 2. Environmental impact (E.I.) specifications and TRL of the analyzed processes.

Process path	E.I. Process (€/t)	E.I. Feed (€/t)	E.I. Products (€/t)	E.I. Profit (€/t)	TRL
Pyrolysis 740°C + Separation	79.27	13.23	292.13	199.63	7
Pyrolysis 1000°C + Separation	105.27	13.23	185.47	66.97	6
Pyro. 1000°C + Sep. + Poly.	141.37	13.23	221.57	66.97	7
Direct Downcycling PE	0.00	13.23	13.23	0.00	9
Direct Recycling PE	139.68	13.23	125.87	-27.04	8
Incineration	209.35	13.23	162.37	-60.21	9
Landfill	19.10	13.23	0.00	-32.33	9

Table 3. Results and weighting parameters for the different process paths

Process path	Economic factor	Environment. factor	TRL factor	O.F.	Global position
Pyrolysis 740°C + Separation	0.98	1.00	0.78	1041.90	1
Pyrolysis 1000°C + Separation	0.98	0.64	0.67	516.69	2
Pyro. 1000°C + Sep. + Poly.	0.89	0.64	0.78	510.35	3
Direct Downcycling PE	0.82	0.46	1.00	376.03	4
Direct Recycling PE	0.92	0.39	0.89	344.85	5
Incineration	0.87	0.30	1.00	258.48	6
Landfill	0.44	0.37	1.00	92.88	7

6. Conclusions

This work presents a methodology for the systematic generation of a list of potential waste-to-resource technologies based on the use of ontologies. Thanks to this method, new technologies can be identified and compared to others that are well-established, and a manageable list of technologies can be obtained for further optimization and superstructure analysis, as well as a more profound development.

The growing application of circular economy principles entails the emergence of new waste-to-resource technologies, such as chemical recycling. A fair evaluation of the potential technologies has to consider its TRL, as its application is riskier than the one of well-established alternatives. Thus, the proposed objective function includes a factor to assess the maturity of the technology.

The framework also allows the generation of routes based on linking consecutive processes in a building-blocks approach. This method leads to flexible product compositions, aiding decision-makers to identify the most economically and environmentally beneficial solutions.

With the aim of ensuring that the list of alternatives includes the most up-to-date transformation technologies, future work will address the development of a procedure for the systematic search of waste-to-resource processes.

Acknowledgements

Financial support received from the Spanish Competitiveness, Industry and Economy Ministry and the European Regional Development Fund, both funding the research Projects AIMS (DPI2017-87435-R) is fully acknowledged. Adrian Pacheco-Lopez thankfully acknowledges financial support received from the Spanish Ministry Science, Innovation and Universities (grant ref. PRE2018-087135) and Ana Somoza-Tornos thankfully acknowledges financial support received from the Spanish Ministry of Education, Culture and Sport (grant ref. FPU15/02932).

References

Raafat, T., Trokanas, N., Cecelja, F., Bimi, X., 2013, An ontological approach towards enabling processing technologies participation in industrial symbiosis, Computers & Chemical Engineering 59, 33-46

Cecelja, F., Trokanas, N., Raafat, T., Yu, M., 2015, Semantic algorithm for Industrial Symbiosis network synthesis, Computers & Chemical Engineering 83, 248-266

Zhou, L., Zhang, C., Karimi, I.A., Kraft, M., 2018, An ontology framework towards decentralized information management for eco-industrial parks, Computers & Chemical Engineering 118, 49-63

Studer, R., Benjamins, V. R., Fensel, D., 1998, Knowledge engineering: principles and methods, data Knowledge engineering 25, 161-197.

Munoz E., Capon-Garcia E., Espuna A., Puigjaner L., 2013, Considering environmental assessment in an ontological framework for enterprise sustainability. Journal of Cleaner Production. Vol. 47, Pp. 149-164.

Huijbregts MAJ, Steinmann ZJN, Elshout PMF, Stam G, Verones F, Vieira MDM, Hollander A, Van Zelm R, 2016, ReCiPe2016: A harmonized life cycle impact assessment method at midpoint and endpoint level. RIVM Report 2016-0104. Bilthoven, The Netherlands.

European Commission Decision C (2014)4995 of 22 July 2014. Horizon 2020 Framework Programme 2014-2015 part 19. General Annexes, section G.

European Commission Eurostat, 2018, Statistical Classification of Economy Activity in the European Union (NACE 2). 2018 Annual detailed data by PRODCOM list

Sauro Pierucci, Flavio Manenti, Giulia Bozzano, Davide Manca (Eds.)
Proceedings of the 30th European Symposium on Computer Aided Process Engineering
(ESCAPE30), May 24-27, 2020, Milano, Italy. © 2020 Elsevier B.V. All rights reserved.
http://dx.doi.org/10.1016/B978-0-12-823377-1.50324-4

Shape Optimization of a Fixed-bed Reactor using Additive Manufacturing

Alexis Courtais[a,*], François Lesage[a], Yannick Privat[b], Cyril Pelaingre[c],

Abderrazak M. Latifi[a]

[a]*Laboratoire Réactions et Génie des procédés, CNRS, Université de Lorraine, Nancy, France*
[b]*Institut de Recherche Mathématique Avancée, CNRS, Université de Strasbourg, France*
[c]*Centre Européen de Prototypage et Outillage Rapide, Saint-Dié des Vosges, France*
alexis.courtais@univ-lorraine.fr

Abstract

This paper deals with a geometric shape optimization of a fixed-bed reactor. The objective is to determine the shape of the packing that maximizes the reaction conversion rate subjected to the process model equations, operating constraints (iso-volume, energy dissipated by the fluid) and manufacturing constraints. The process model is described by the mass balance equations and Navier-Stokes equations. Incompressible fluid, a homogeneous first order reaction and steady-state conditions in the reactor are the main assumptions considered. The free software OpenFOAM is used as CFD solver. The optimization approach developed is based on the adjoint system method and the resulting algorithm is tested on a two-dimensional fixed-bed reactor in laminar flow regime. The results show a significant improvement of the conversion rate and the optimal shape obtained with the manufacturing constraints can be easily printed by means of an additive manufacturing technique.

Keywords: Shape optimization, CFD, Fixed-bed reactor, Additive manufacturing.

1. Introduction

The objective of shape optimization is to deform the outer boundary of an object in order to minimize or maximize a cost function, such as the performances of a process, while satisfying given constraints. Historically, the shape optimization methods have been used in cutting edge technologies mainly in advanced areas such as aerodynamics. However, they have recently been extended to other engineering areas where the shape greatly influences the performances. For example, in hydrodynamics, the shape of a pipe that minimizes the energy dissipated by the fluid due to viscous friction was analyzed (Henrot and Privat, 2010, Tonomura et al., 2010, Courtais et al., 2019).

In chemical engineering however where the shape of unit operations (e.g. reactors, tanks, stirrers, pipes…) is an important design parameter, the shape optimization has not been extensively investigated. This important issue deserves therefore to be addressed and will probably result in a paradigm shift in optimal design and operation of processes.

Basically, there are three types of shape optimization: parametric, geometric and topologic. In this paper, only geometric optimization is considered. The objective is to develop an optimization approach based on Hadamard method using the adjoint system equations. The case study is a 2D fixed-bed reactor with a laminar single phase liquid flow where a homogenous first order chemical reaction takes place. The objective is to determine the shape of the packing that maximizes the reactor conversion rate.

2. Fixed-bed reactor modelling

The optimization method developed in this work is based on the process model equations that describe the flow through the fixed-bed reactor. A two-dimensional model is therefore developed and involves mass and momentum balance equations. Figure 1 shows the schematic representation of the fixed-bed considered.

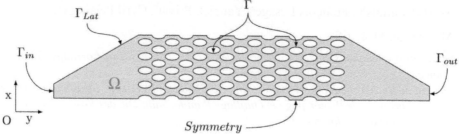

Figure 1: Schematic representation of the fixed-bed reactor

The studied domain consists of the free volume Ω and its boundaries given by the union of the inlet (Γ_{in}), outlet (Γ_{out}), lateral wall (Γ_{lat}) and free (Γ) limits.

The momentum transport is described by the following Navier-Stokes equations along with the associated boundary conditions:

$$\left|\begin{array}{ll} -\nu\,\Delta U + U\cdot\nabla U + \nabla p = 0 & \text{in }\Omega \\ \nabla\cdot U = 0 & \text{in }\Omega \\ U = U_{in} & \text{on }\Gamma_{in} \\ U = 0 & \text{on }\Gamma_{lat}\bigcup\Gamma \\ \sigma(U,p)\boldsymbol{n} = 0 & \text{on }\Gamma_{out} \end{array}\right. \qquad (1)$$

where ν is the kinematic viscosity of the fluid, $\sigma(U,p) = 2\nu\varepsilon(U) - p\boldsymbol{I}$ the viscous stress tensor, p the fluid absolute pressure, $\boldsymbol{I}$ the identity matrix and $\varepsilon(U)$ the strain tensor.

The mass balance equations and their associated boundary conditions are given by Eqs. (2). It is important to point out that the reaction takes place only in the bulk of the reactor, i.e. in Ω and not on the walls Γ and Γ_{lat}.

$$\left|\begin{array}{ll} -D\Delta C + U\cdot\nabla C + kC = 0 & \text{in }\Omega \\ C = C_{in} & \text{on }\Gamma_{in} \\ \dfrac{\partial C}{\partial n} = 0 & \text{on }\Gamma_{out}\bigcup\Gamma_{lat}\bigcup\Gamma \end{array}\right. \qquad (2)$$

where C is the reactant concentration and D the constant diffusion coefficient of the reactant.

3. Optimization problem formulation

The formulation of the shape optimization problem requires the definition of a performance index, decisions variables and constraints. These ingredients are detailed below.

3.1. Performance index

The aim of this work is to determine the packing shape (i.e. the position and the shape of the free boundary Γ) of the fixed-bed reactor that maximizes the reaction conversion rate or minimizes the average outlet concentration of the reactant. The performance index is therefore defined by Eq. (3) as:

$$J(\Omega) = \int_{\Gamma_{out}} C d\sigma \tag{3}$$

3.2. Decision variable

The decision variable is defined by the free boundary Γ that will evolve with the iterations of the optimization algorithm. The other boundaries are fixed.

3.3. Equality and inequality constraints

The optimization problem is subjected to different constraints. The most obvious ones are given by the process model equations (Eqs.(1-2)). The other constraints consist of :

- An iso-volume constraint introduced in order to guarantee the same residence time between initial and optimized shapes (Eq.(4)).

- An inequality constraint on the energy dissipation by the fluid due to viscous friction and is given by Eq. and *(5)*. Such a constraint is relevant since the energy dissipation and the pressure drops are directly correlated.

$$C_1 = V(\Omega) - V(\Omega_0) = 0 \quad \text{and} \quad C_2 = 2v\int_\Omega |\varepsilon(U)|^2 dx - 2v\int_{\Omega_0} |\varepsilon(U)|^2 dx < 0 \tag{4 and 5}$$

- Since the resulting optimal shape will be fabricated by means of a 3D printing technique, manufacturing constraints should be accounted for in the optimization problem. They are of inequality type and impose minimum values on the pores width (Ω domain) and on the packing thickness.

4. Optimization method

The shape optimization approach developed is a gradient-based method and uses the Hadamard's boundary variation method (Henrot and Pierre, 2006). The gradient, called shape gradient, is computed by means of adjoint system method. The shape gradient G is defined on the free boundary (Γ) and depends on the different state variables (U,p and C) and their associated adjoint states introduced by the method (U_a, p_a and C_a). The gradient will allow us to compute the mesh displacement vector V that decreases the Lagrangian of the constrained optimization problem given by (Eq.(6)).

$$L(\Omega) = \int_{\Gamma_{out}} C d\sigma + \lambda_V \left(V(\Omega) - V(\Omega_0)\right) + \lambda_E \left(2v\int_\Omega |\varepsilon(U)|^2 dx - 2v\int_{\Omega_0} |\varepsilon(U)|^2 dx\right) \tag{6}$$

The vector field V is the solution of Eqs. (7).

$$\begin{cases} -\Delta V + V = 0 & \text{in } \Omega \\ \quad V = 0 & \text{on } \Gamma_{in} \cup \Gamma_{out} \cup \Gamma_{lat} \\ \nabla V n = -G n & \text{on } \Gamma \end{cases} \tag{7}$$

Once the vector field V is computed, the next step in the method is to move all meshpoints according to the following relation:

$$\Omega_{i+1} = (X + tV)(\Omega_i) \tag{8}$$

where t is the method step and must be chosen small, X is the vector of each meshpoint coordinates. More details on the shape gradient calculations can be found in (Courtais et al., 2020).

5. Optimization algorithm

The optimization algorithm developed has been implemented using C++ language within the free and open source OpenFOAM software (Weller et al., 1998). The latter solves PDEs, i.e. Navier -Stokes, mass balance system and their adjoint system equations, using finite volume method. The python library "pyFoam" is used to link the iterations to each other using its utility *"pyFoamMeshUtilityRunner.py"*. The algorithm proceeds as follows:

1. Formulation of an initial shape and generation of the associated mesh using cfMesh and snappyHexMesh, two mesh utilities supplied by OpenFOAM.
2. Resolution of the four systems of PDEs. The pressure-velocity coupling equations are solved using SIMPLE (Semi-Implicit Method for Pressure-Linked Equations) algorithm.
3. Computation of the shape gradient G and the mesh displacement V. The manufacturing constraints are considered at this stage. The pore constraint is considered using the OpenFOAM function "wallDist". This function computes the distance between the cells and boundaries. The thickness constraint is taken into account by computing the local distance between the obstacle and its skeleton. The skeleton of an obstacle is the set of equidistant points from the obstacle on each side (see (Feppon et al., 2018) for more details).
4. The Lagrange multipliers associated to the volume and energy constraints are updated by means of the following relation :

$$\lambda_{i+1}^k = \lambda_i^k + \varepsilon\, C_i^k \tag{9}$$

where ε is a parameter with a small value, k and i refer to the constraint and iteration respectively.
5. At the end of iterations, a test on the mesh quality is carried out through three criteria:
    i.   the maximum value of the mesh aspect ratio which is defined as the ratio of the longer side to the shorter side of a mesh.
    ii. the mesh non-orthogonality defined by the angle between the vector linking two adjacent cell centers and the normal of the face connecting cells.
    iii. the face skewness defined by the distance between the face center and the intersection of the vector linking adjacent cells with their common face considered (see (Holzinger, 2015) for more details).

The upper bounds of these three criteria are 10, 65 and 3.8 respectively. If the mesh quality fails, remeshing process takes place.

6. A test on the convergence is done through the maximum displacement of the mesh. If the latter is higher than 10^{-5} m, then the algorithm goes back to step 2.

6. Results and discussion

Figure 2 presents the reactant concentration profiles in the initial configuration (a) of the fixed-bed reactor and in the optimized ones without (b) and with (c) the manufacturing constraints. It can be seen that in the initial configuration, a dead zone in the reactor inlet area (i.e. light zone on the figure) appears where the reaction conversion rate is very low, thus leading to lower reactor performances. In the optimized fixed-bed without manufacturing constraints, the dead zone has disappeared, but the reactor exhibits very narrow channels (pores) which are not easy to manufacture. In the optimized shape with constraints however, the dead zone is no longer there and all the channels can easily be printed. On the other hand, Figure 3 presents the residence time distribution (RTD) of initial and optimized (with manufacturing constraints) configurations and shows that the fluid flow is more homogeneous in the optimized configuration. Indeed, the standard deviation of the RTD is three times lower in the optimized reactor (i.e. 75 vs 25s). Finally, the disappearance of the dead zone and the better homogeneity of the flow the improvement of the conversion rate and therefore of the performance index by is about 10%.

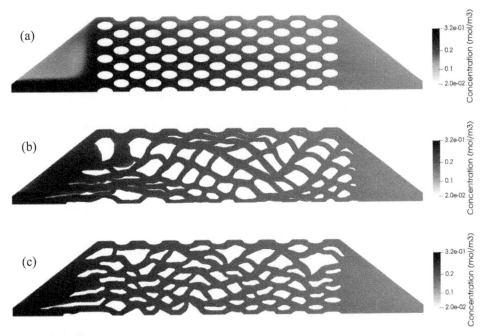

Figure 2: Initial configuration of the fixed-bed reactor (a), optimized shape without manufacturing constraint (b), optimized shape with manufacturing constraint (c)

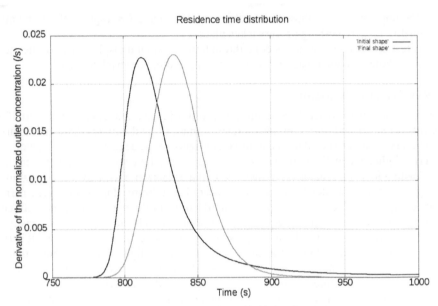

Figure 3: Residence time distribution of initial and optimized shapes

7. Conclusions

In this work, a geometrical shape optimization based on the adjoint system method has been developed, implemented within OpenFOAM and used in order to optimize the configuration of a fixed-bed reactor where a first order homogeneous reaction occurs. The objective was to determine the shape that minimizes the average concentration of the reactant at the reactor outlet. The optimization was subjected to volume, energy and manufacturing constraints and to momentum and mass balance equations. A significant decrease of the performance index is obtained which results in a substantial improvement of the reactor conversion rate.

References

C. Barlier , 1991, Procédé pour la création et la réalisation de pièces par CAO et pièces ainsi obtenues, Brevet français et brevet européen.

A. Courtais, F. Lesage, Y. Privat, P. Frey, A.M. Latifi , 2019, Adjoint system method in shape optimization of some typical fluid flow patterns. In Computer Aided Chemical Engineering, 46, 871-876. https://doi.org/10.1016/B978-0-12-818634-3.50146-6

A. Courtais, Y. Privat, F. Lesage, A.M. Latifi, 2020, Geometrical optimization of fixed-bed reactors in process engineering. *In preparation.*

F. Feppon, G. Allaire, C. Dapogny, 2018, A variational formulation for computing shape derivatives of geometric constraints along rays.

A. Henrot, M. Pierre, 2006, Variation et optimisation de formes: une analyse géométrique, 48, Springer Science & Business Media.

A. Henrot, Y. Privat, 2010. What is the optimal shape of a pipe?. Archive for rational mechanics and analysis, 196(1), 281-302. https://doi.org/10.1007/s00205-009-0243-8

G. Holzinger, 2015, Openfoam a little user-manual. CD-Laboratory-Particulate Flow Modelling Johannes Keplper University, Linz, Austria.

O. Tonomura, M. Kano, S. Hasebe, 2010, Shape optimization of microchannels using CFD and adjoint method. In Computer Aided Chemical Engineering, 28, 37-42.

H.G. Weller, G. Tabor, H. Jasak, C. Fureby, 1998. A tensorial approach to computational continuum mechanics using object-oriented techniques. Computers in physics, 12(6), 620-631.

Sauro Pierucci, Flavio Manenti, Giulia Bozzano, Davide Manca (Eds.)
Proceedings of the 30th European Symposium on Computer Aided Process Engineering
(ESCAPE30), May 24-27, 2020, Milano, Italy. © 2020 Elsevier B.V. All rights reserved.
http://dx.doi.org/10.1016/B978-0-12-823377-1.50325-6

Systematic Modelling of Flow and Pressure Distribution in a Complex Tank

Robert Pujan,[a,b] * Heinz A. Preisig[b]

[a]*DBFZ Deutsches Biomasseforschungszentrum gemeinnützige GmbH, Torgauer Straße
116, 04347 Leipzig, Germany*
[b]*NTNU Norwegian University of Science and Technology, Høgskoleringen 5, 7491
Trondheim, Norway*
robert.pujan@dbfz.de

Abstract

The presented study proposes a systematic modelling approach for both the flow and pressure distribution in dynamic plants. A generic example illustrates the method on a generic example, which describes the hydraulic behaviour of mixing and storage tanks as well as stirred tank reactors. First, the plant is abstracted as a topology, which in turn has a precise mathematical description. In order to depict the pressure distribution within a plant, the paper expands on the transformation of the dynamic topology into a pseudo-steady state one. The model is based on an ontology that includes the entirety of physical as well as geometrical concepts and definitions necessary for describing the plant's behaviour. The main advantage of this ontology-based approach is that most of common problems like typing errors are eliminated. Since the ontology is defined off-line, a centralisation of the crafted process models is feasible, thus allowing rapid assembly of new specific plant models.

Keywords: process modelling, ontology, topology, dynamics, model reduction

1. Motivation

The pressure distribution in a plant as well as this system's behaviour under dynamic conditions is essential information for process control, plant design and optimisation (Zhan et al., 2020), and hazard assessments (Labovská et al., 2014). Applying the modelling methods established by Preisig (2014b), this study proposes a systematic modelling approach for both the flow and pressure distribution in plants. The general workflow is 1) plant depiction in a network of directed graphs, 2) definition of the mathematical model ontology, 3) model reduction via time-scale assumptions, and 4) assembling of the reduced plant model. Step 1 specifies the model structure by subdividing the plant into a network of multiple, finite volumes (capacities) that are communicating with each other via fixed, directed arcs. This network is what we refer to as a topology. This abstraction as a graph enables the mathematical definition of complex processes within a plant. The mathematical characterisation is achieved in step 2 by an equation ontology. The term ontology encompasses the entirety of concepts, definitions, properties, and relations applied to the description of a plant's behaviour. Through step 3, the finite volumes captured in the graph are further detailed by defining their dynamic nature. For example, plug-flow reactors can be reduced to event-dynamic, distributed systems, whereas continuous stirred tank reactors can simplify to lumped volumes. Thanks to the ontology being centrally established, assembling the plant model in step 4 is easy. One merely combines the model assumptions and constraints with the respective model equations. Each equation, even if used in several model units, has thus to be implemented only once. Combination of the ontology and an automatic code generator like the software *ProMo* (Elve and Preisig, 2019) essentially eliminates typing errors and eliminates code debugging, thus increases productivity.

Using the example of a gas-liquid tank with extensive piping, this paper illustrates the general procedure of ontology-based topology modelling, on the example a fundamental model for fluid-containing tanks.

2. The example – a fluid-containing tank

Figure 1 illustrates the tank T with a liquid feed F and a breathing pipe B at the top, a liquid bottom-outlet O, and a liquid outlet W at the tank's wall. The scope of this analysis is the hydraulic behaviour without considering heat transfer, phase transitions, and chemical reactions. The plant's structure is similar to the one studied in (Preisig, 2014a) but extended by valves and level control.

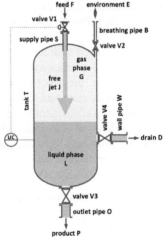

The liquid feed leaves its supply pipe S at the very top of the tank, thus forming a free jet J downwards to the surface of the tank's liquid phase L. In the beginning, the only liquid outflow occurs via the bottom outlet O, driven by the sum of hydrostatic pressure and the pressure of the gas phase G on top. As soon as the liquid is completely covering the opening of W, valve $V4$ is opened to release a drain D, preventing the tank from flooding. If the liquid level rises even further, the level controller LIC intervenes by adjusting the feed via valve $V1$. This feed-controlled system is therefore suited for applications in which the feed can be altered but a certain product flow P has to be met. If an outflow-regulated level control is required, LIC would correspondingly be coupled with valve $V3$.

Figure 1: Sketch of the plant

While liquid accumulates, gas is squeezed out via B, thus equalising the tank's pressure with the pressure of the environment E. However, if the liquid level changes fast, the tank pressure can increase above the environmental pressure due to flow resistance in B and $V2$. Like any plant, the tank's dynamics are driven by the conditions at its boundaries. The boundaries are the ports of the system to its environment, namely D, E, F, and P. The pressures at these boundaries drive the convective mass flows in the established system.

3. Translation of the plant into a topology

The process modelling procedure by abstracting the plant as a topology represented as a graph with the nodes representing capacities of conserved quantities, and the arcs the flows of extensive quantities. The latter are driven by gradients of the intensive properties. For more details, Preisig (2014a) and (2014b) recommended. A possible first topology for the plant is shown in Figure 2 on the left. Mass flows are drawn as black arrows, volume work as dashed, grey arrows, and dynamic, distributed capacities as ellipses. In contrast to lumped systems, where the intensive properties are not a function of the position, they are so for distributed systems. The tank is assumed to be rigid as indicated by the dashed outlines of tank-internal volumes. Compared to the considered dynamic system, the environment is modelled as infinitely large, a set of reservoirs that have constant properties. In the topology, reservoirs are represented as half circles. Black bars depict boundaries, which are event-dynamic surfaces that mark discrete changes between two coupled capacities.

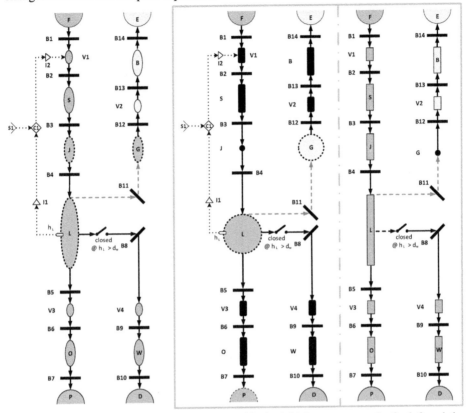

Figure 2: Topology representation of the plant with the initial structure on the far left and the time-scale model split in the box (left: dynamic, right: event-dynamic)

The described physical domain is augmented with a control domain, comprising the liquid level controller *C1* and a set-point *S1*, which defines the maximum liquid level. The controller collects information about the current liquid level in the tank and computes a control output $u(h_L)$, sent to valve *V1*. Dotted, black arrows represent information flow. The physical domain and the control domain are each self-contained networks. They communicate with each other through interfaces, which in the topology are represented as white triangles. The mathematical representation of these interfaces is outside the scope of this exposition and will be covered in another paper. The initial topology represents the choice of granularity. Therefore, it always contains maximum information. Model simplifications, which are fundamentally the neglect of structural parts of the model (Preisig, 2015), are possible in later stages but the addition of new structures is not. In order to represent the visible dynamics of mass distribution and the supposedly immediate pressure dissipation, the topology is split into two: One for the fast time scale, capturing the pressure distribution, and one for the slow time scale, representing the material and energy flow. The result is a dynamic domain for the mass and an event-dynamic one for the pressure. In the latter, the current state of the dynamic mass distribution, the slow part in this relation, appears in pseudo-steady state. Mathematically, the split is the inner and the outer solution of a singular perturbation. As shown in the box of Figure 2, all pipes and valves are now reduced to a plug-flow. In the dynamic domain, they are drawn as black rectangles, indicating event-dynamic capacities without distributional effects, whereas in the event-dynamic domain they are depicted as coloured rectangles due to the pressure change within them. The tank volumes of gas and liquid are depicted as lumped systems in the dynamic domain (circles). In the event-dynamic domain, the capacity L is distributed due to the hydrostatic pressure. G is considered to hold the same pressure at any point, thus being a point capacity - a lumped, event-dynamic node (black circle). Since J is represented by a point capacity in the dynamic domain, its relatively small capacity is neglected and the mass transport from S to L instantaneous. Both are assumed to be negligible and of no impact to the mass-flow investigations.

4. Assembling the ontology

Each component in the topology is linked to a set of state-dynamic equations in the mathematical ontology. Table 1 shows the relevant equation ontology for the physical domain of example model. The structure of the directed graph of the topology enters as the incidence matrix $\underline{F}$. Vectors are depicted as $\underline{x}$, where a dot decorator represents an accumulation and a hat a flow. In Eq. (12), $u(h_L)$ represents a controller output that adjusts the valve opening if required. Since flow through W is only enabled after reaching a specified h_L, Eq. (11) replaces Eq. (10) in W. The ontology is designed according to the assumptions that a) the tank is rotationally-symmetric with a rigid volume, b) all pipes and the free jet are cylindrical and straight with constant diameter, c) no reactions, heat exchange or thermal effects are considered, d) friction does not impact the internal energy U, e) liquid and gas phases are considered homogeneous, f) the liquid has constant density, and g) the friction factor of turbulent flows is taken from the Moody chart. Case-specific assumptions and constraints that are not universally valid are not part of the ontology but of the model reduction instead.

On closer inspection of Table 1, it becomes apparent that the vectors of velocity v and pressure p are not fully specified. In any mass transport, v and p are interdependent. Due to this correlation, the model's initiation has to provide appropriate initial values for at least one of these variables in every capacity to start the iterative process.

5. The reduced plant model

Assumptions reduce the initial model to a specific simulation case. Table 2 shows the assumptions and the resulting reduced model. The capacities' mass balances are either Eq. (3) with the accumulation term nullified (all pipes, valves, and J) or identical to Eq. (1) (L and G). Most of the assumptions eliminate particular terms. Implementing a constraint on the sum of the liquid and the gas volume to be constant, thus modelling a rigid tank, requires quite some effort. It leads to an overdetermined system, as the constraint introduces an algebraic link between the two accumulation terms. The constraint consequently replaces the volume workflow, thus Eq. (8) has to be eliminated from G to avoid over-determination.

All that is left at this point is the model initialisation with boundary conditions, parameters like density and molar mass, as well as basic geometrical dimensions of the plant.

Table 1: Equations ontology of the physical domain

Description	Equation	
Integrals		
Mass	$\underline{m} = \int_0^t \underline{\dot{m}}(\tau)d\tau + \underline{m}(0)$	(1)
Energy	$\underline{E} = \int_0^t \underline{\dot{E}}(\tau)d\tau + \underline{E}(0)$	(2)
Balances		
Mass conservation	$\underline{\dot{m}} = \underline{\underline{F}}\hat{m}$	(3)
Energy conservation	$\underline{\dot{E}} = \underline{\underline{F}}\hat{U} + \underline{\underline{F}}\hat{K} + \underline{\underline{F}}\hat{P} + \underline{\underline{F}}\hat{w}^y + \underline{\underline{F}}\hat{w}^f$	(4)
Flows		
Mass flow	$\hat{m} = \rho\hat{V}$	(5)
Kinetic energy flow	$\hat{K} = \frac{1}{2}\hat{m}v^2$	(6)
Potential energy flow	$\hat{P} = \hat{m}hg$	(7)
Volume work flow	$\underline{\hat{w}}^y = \underline{p}\hat{V}$	(8)
Friction work flow	$\hat{w}^f = \Delta\underline{p}^f\hat{V}$	(9)
Volume flow	$\hat{V} = \underline{v}A$	(10)
Volume flow (wall pipe)	$\hat{V} = \text{sgn}\left\lfloor 1 + \text{sgn}\left(\text{sgn}\{h_L - d_w\} - \frac{1}{2}\right)\right\rfloor \underline{v}A$	(11)
Material properties		
Cylindrical cross-section	$\underline{A} = \underline{u}(h_L)\pi\left[\underline{r}(l)\right]^2$	(12)
Liquid level	$h_L := root\left[\underline{\underline{F}}_L V = \pi\int_0^{h_L}\left\{\underline{\underline{F}}_L\underline{r}(l)\right\}^2 dl\right]$	(13)
Mass density ideal gas	$\rho = M\underline{p}(R\underline{T})^{-1}$	(14)
Voluminous property	$V = \underline{m}\rho^{-1}$	(15)
Darcy-Weisbach model	$\Delta\underline{p}^f = \frac{1}{2}f^i v^2 \rho l\left[2\underline{r}(l)\right]^{-1}$	(16)
Darcy friction factor	$f^i := f^{la}$ if $\text{Re} \le 2,100$; $f^i := f^t$ if $\text{Re} > 2,100$	(17)
Friction factor (laminar)	$f^{la} = 64\,\text{Re}^{-1}$	(18)
Friction factor (turbulent)	$f^t = f(\text{Re}, \in)$	(19)
Reynolds number	$\text{Re} = 2\rho vr(l)\eta^{-1}$	(20)

6. Conclusions

As this paper shows, topologies are a fast and very handy method to discuss and define the structure of any model, while the implementation of ontologies minimises errors and time effort. For this reason, the modelling suite *ProMo* is currently in development at the NTNU (Elve and Preisig, 2019). Based on the user-imposed topology, the software automatically selects the required ontology equations and generates executable program

Table 2: Reduced plant model

Pipes	$s := B, O, S$	Eq. (1-5, 7-10, 12, 16-20)
Assumptions	$\underline{\underline{F}}_s \hat{\underline{U}} = 0 ; \quad \underline{\underline{F}}_s \hat{\underline{K}} = 0$	
Pressure distribution	$0 = \underline{\underline{F}}_s \hat{\underline{P}} + \underline{\underline{F}}_s \hat{\underline{w}}^y + \underline{\underline{F}}_s \hat{\underline{w}}^f = \underline{\underline{F}}_s \left(\underline{\rho} \underline{h} g + \underline{p} + \Delta \underline{p}^f \right)$	
Wall pipe	$s := W$	Eq. (1-5, 7-9, 11, 12, 16-20)
Assumptions	$\underline{\underline{F}}_s \hat{\underline{U}} = 0 ; \quad \underline{\underline{F}}_s \hat{\underline{K}} = 0$	
Pressure distribution	$0 = \underline{\underline{F}}_s \hat{\underline{P}} + \underline{\underline{F}}_s \hat{\underline{w}}^y + \underline{\underline{F}}_s \hat{\underline{w}}^f = \underline{\underline{F}}_s \left[\underline{\rho} \underline{h} g + \underline{p} + \Delta \underline{p}^f \left(\hat{V}(h_L) \right) \right]$	
Valves	$s := V1, V2, V3, V4$	Eq. (1-8, 10, 12)
Assumptions	$\underline{\underline{F}}_s \hat{\underline{U}} = 0 ; \quad \underline{\underline{F}}_s \hat{\underline{w}}^f = 0$	
Pressure distribution	$0 = \underline{\underline{F}}_s \hat{\underline{K}} + \underline{\underline{F}}_s \hat{\underline{P}} + \underline{\underline{F}}_s \hat{\underline{w}}^y = \underline{\underline{F}}_s \left(\frac{1}{2} \underline{\rho} \underline{v}^2 + \underline{\rho} \underline{h} g + \underline{p} \right)$	
Free jet	$s := J$	Eq. (1-5, 8, 10, 12)
Assumptions	$\underline{\underline{F}}_s \hat{\underline{U}} = 0 ; \quad \underline{\underline{F}}_s \hat{\underline{K}} = 0 ; \quad \underline{\underline{F}}_s \hat{\underline{P}} = 0 ; \quad \underline{\underline{F}}_s \hat{\underline{w}}^f = 0$	
Pressure distribution	$0 = \underline{\underline{F}}_s \hat{\underline{w}}^y = \underline{\underline{F}}_s \underline{p} \hat{\underline{m}} \underline{\rho}^{-1}$	
Liquid phase	$s := L$	Eq. (1-5, 7, 8, 10, 12, 13, 15)
Assumptions	$\underline{\underline{F}}_s \hat{\underline{U}} = 0 ; \quad \underline{\underline{F}}_s \hat{\underline{K}} = 0 ; \quad \underline{\underline{F}}_s \hat{\underline{w}}^f = 0$	
Pressure distribution	$0 = \underline{\underline{F}}_s \hat{\underline{P}} + \underline{\underline{F}}_s \hat{\underline{w}}^y = \underline{\underline{F}}_s \left(\underline{\rho} \underline{h} g + \underline{p} \right)$	
Gas phase	$s := G$	Eq. (1-5, 10, 12, 14, 15)
Assumptions	$\underline{\underline{F}}_s \hat{\underline{U}} = 0 ; \quad \underline{\underline{F}}_s \hat{\underline{K}} = 0 ; \quad \underline{\underline{F}}_s \hat{\underline{P}} = 0 ; \quad \dot{V}_L + \dfrac{\partial}{\partial m_G} \dfrac{\partial}{\partial \rho_G} V_G = 0$	
Pressure distribution	$0 = \underline{\underline{F}}_s \hat{\underline{w}}^y = \underline{\underline{F}}_s \underline{p} + R \left(\underline{\underline{F}}_s \hat{\underline{m}} \underline{\rho} \right)^{-1} \underline{\underline{F}}_s \hat{\underline{m}} \underline{T} M^{-1}$	

code, thus enabling rapid design of plant models. Current work focuses on the automatic realisation of the pressure distribution by the software as well.

Acknowledgments

As part of the research centre Bio4Fuels, this study has received funding from the Research Council of Norway (RCN) under the support code 257622 and is hosted by the Norwegian Centre for Environment-friendly Energy Research (FME).

References

A.T. Elve, H.A. Preisig, 2019, From ontology to executable program code, Comput. Chem. Eng., 122, 383-394

Z. Labovská, J. Labovský, Ľ. Jelemenský, J. Dudáš, J. Markoš, 2014, Model-based hazard identification in multiphase chemical reactors, J. Loss Prevent. Proc., 29, 155-162

H.A. Preisig, 2014a, A Graph Approach to Representing the Pressure Distribution in Complex Plants, Comput. Aided Chem. Eng., 33, 865-870

H.A. Preisig, 2014b, Visual Modelling, Comput. Aided Chem. Eng., 34, 729-734

H.A. Preisig, 2015, Model Reduction in Visual Modelling, Comput.Aided Chem.Eng, 37,629-634

Y. Zhang, S. Li, Y. Zheng, Y. Zou, 2020, Multi-model based pressure optimization for large-scale water distribution networks, Control Eng. Pract., 95, doi:10.1016/j.conengprac.2019.104232

Sauro Pierucci, Flavio Manenti, Giulia Bozzano, Davide Manca (Eds.)
Proceedings of the 30th European Symposium on Computer Aided Process Engineering
(ESCAPE30), May 24-27, 2020, Milano, Italy. © 2020 Elsevier B.V. All rights reserved.
http://dx.doi.org/10.1016/B978-0-12-823377-1.50326-8

A New Methodology to Design Optimal Exchanges Network for Facing Concrete Industrial Problems

Florent Mousqué, Marianne Boix*, Stéphane Négny, Ludovic Montastruc, Serge Domenech

Laboratoire de Génie Chimique, Université de Toulouse, CNRS, INPT, UPS, Toulouse, France

marianne.boix@toulouse-inp.fr

Abstract

Nowadays, industries are facing significant environmental and competitive stakes. An efficient way for companies to overcome these difficulties is to gather and collaborate in Eco-Industrial Parks (EIP). Nevertheless, establish an optimal eco-industrial exchange is a task that requires the development of methods. This article therefore proposes a method for Multi-Objective (MO) optimal design of EIP exchange networks that deals with net present cost and complexity of the network. A new network complexity indicator is defined that represents the topological feasibility but also the management of the designed network. An iterative resolution procedure is developed to solve large MILP problems. This procedure sets the minimum flow capacity threshold throughout the iterations, whereas in previous papers it was set arbitrarily. The developed method is assessed on a large EIP energy network. Results show that network complexity is considerably reduced using this MO approach in comparison to economic mono-objective solution.

Keywords: Industrial Ecology, Eco-Industrial Parks, Design, Multi-Objective Optimization, Mathematical Programming, Network complexity

1. Introduction

An EIP is a cluster of industries that aims at optimizing their economic gains while reducing their environmental impact through the synergistic benefits of cooperation (Chertow, 2000). This is being possible by mutualizing and sharing materials, energy, water and by-products. To achieve these objectives, optimization methods are required to design optimal exchange networks between companies.

A major challenge in optimization methods development is to deal with the network complexity of the solutions (Kastner et al., 2015), especially when a lot of interconnections are considered, as it is the case in EIP. Indeed, the so-called network complexity, previously defined as the number of interconnections (Aviso et al., 2011) is directly linked to the topological feasibility of the network, but also to its management complexity. Furthermore, (Boix et al., 2012) have shown that the cost and the complexity of networks, such as minimizing the number of interconnections are interesting criteria to address in a MO optimization approach because of their antagonism. Indeed, without these interconnections, there are no more synergetic economic benefits.

Classically in the literature, network complexity is optimized by minimizing the number of interconnections or managed by setting a minimum flow threshold for interconnections with an arbitrary value. For the latter constraint, it limits the number of interconnections by avoiding designing a network whose interconnection makes no sense on an industrial scale because the flow is smaller than the fixed value (Boix et al., 2012). This arbitrarily fixed threshold constitutes a key parameter because it has a significant influence on the resulting network. Another issue in network design through mathematical programming is related to EIP large networks where many interconnected plants and processes must be involved. The developed optimization procedure has to be generic and able to handle these large complex problems.

The contribution of this paper is the development of a new methodology to perform MO optimization with concrete industrial challenges: the minimization of the net present cost, and the minimization of the network complexity. A new indicator is developed to assess the network complexity, based on two parameters: the number of interconnections to be minimized and the minimum flow capacity of interconnections to be maximized. The flow capacity represents the maximum flow rate of an interconnection over time. This method has been developed in an iterative way, in order to reduce computational difficulty and therefore to cope with the difficulty of solving such large mathematical problems. The main novelty of this work is the development of an iterative resolution procedure where the threshold of the flow capacity of interconnections evolves.

As a result, this method gives an optimal set of solutions, the final solution is determined with the TOPSIS Multi-Criteria Decision-Making (MCDM) tool. The procedure is assessed on a case study based on an EIP coupled energy network supplying heat and electricity that has been presented in a previous paper (Mousqué et al. 2019).

2. Methodology

This section discusses the methodology of resolution, the first part describes the new network complexity indicator, the issues and the principles of the method and then the last part details the general procedure.

2.1. Network Complexity Indicator definition

The defined network complexity indicator is based on the number of interconnections and the minimum flow capacity of interconnections in the network ($Min_{Capacity}^{Interc}$).

- The number of interconnections is a classical criterion to be used during the design step (Boix et al., 2015). Indeed, interconnections cause maintenance operations, so it is important to minimize this objective function.

- The novelty of this method is the integration of $Min_{Capacity}^{Interc}$ as a criterion: it measures the flow capacity of the smallest interconnection in the network. This criterion has to be maximized in order to foster larger flow interconnections rather than smaller ones that are not interesting at the industrial scale.

2.2. Computational challenges

As detailed hereafter, the two main challenges of the developed method are to solve large models as EIP exchanges network and to handle MO optimization with economic and network complexity criteria. With regard to the first issue, in models to design EIP networks, the number of binary variables used to select interconnections increases exponentially with the number of companies and processes. For this reason, these binaries classically become the super-variables, i.e. the bottleneck variables for the calculation time. The issue is that they are too many super-variables to be able to handle them separately. Hence, the principle of the procedure is to reduce the number of super-variables by designing with a limited number of interconnections. The selected interconnections are those of the mono-objective optimization with the economic criterion. This approach is intended to provide results close to the global optimum while ensuring shorter calculation time.

The second stake is to achieve a MO optimization having the value of the minimum flow capacity threshold of the interconnections ($Min_{Threshold}^{Interc}$) that is no longer arbitrarily settled. For this purpose, the resolution procedure developed uses $Min_{Threshold}^{Interc}$ as a parameter that varies throughout the iterative optimization procedure in order to select the optimal value for this threshold.

For the sake of clarification, $Min_{Threshold}^{Interc}$ is the minimum threshold fixed as a parameter, while $Min_{Capacity}^{Interc}$ is the minimum value measured on the solution obtained.

2.3. Resolution procedure

Resulting from these discussions, the complete resolution procedure shown in Figure 1 is described hereafter.

The first step consists of a mono-objective optimization to obtain the solution that minimizes the economic criterion. Then, from this initial solution, the limited list of interconnections used for the rest of the procedure is determined. This is done by setting the selection binary of the unused interconnection as a parameter that is equal to 0 (i.e. the interconnection is not selected). Afterwards, the procedure is iterative. At each iteration, the principle is to remove the minimum sized interconnection from the previous solution and to economically optimize the network with selected interconnections. Moreover, at each iteration, the minimum flow capacity threshold of interconnections in the network ($Min_{Threshold}^{Interc}$) is constrained to be equal or greater to the minimum size of interconnection present in the network of the previous iteration. This $Min_{Threshold}^{Interc}$ constraint, which increases throughout the resolution procedure, aims to avoid obtaining solutions with very low flow capacity interconnections ($Min_{Capacity}^{Interc}$).

At the end of the method, when there are no more interconnections, a set of solutions is provided. In order to rank all the solutions obtained and to determine the selected one, TOPSIS MCDM tool is used during the post-treatment phase. To go further, TOPSIS (Technique for Order Preference by Similarity to Ideal Solution) is a well-known technique that consists in comparing the distance of each solution between the ideal one (having the best reachable value for each criterion) and its opposite, the negative-ideal one.

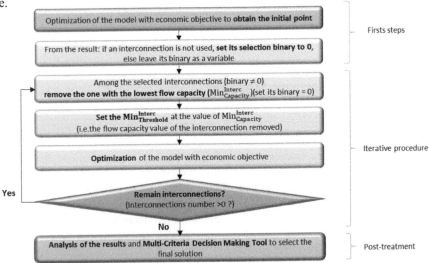

Figure 1: Iterative resolution procedure.

3. Case study

The developed method is then applied over the case study presented below. As mentioned before, the case study is based on a previous model developed by Mousqué et al. (2019). This case study is chosen for its specificity to represent a large EIP network because it couples heat and electricity energy networks with 15 industries and many interconnections possibilities.

The optimization model is formulated as a Mixed Integer Linear programming (MILP) to design an optimal energy network coupling the utility system supplying heat (i.e. steam) with the Hybrid Power System (HPS) producing electricity for an EIP.

The general superstructure of this model that represents design possibilities is presented in Figure 2. The utility system producing steam at four levels of pressures (j) works as a closed-loop in each industry, after production in the boilers (i), electricity production through the turbines (t) and process use, the condensed steam return to the water unit. The HPS can supply electricity thanks to solar panels, wind turbines or outsourced electricity purchased. The design is carried out using binary variables to select boiler and turbine technologies while the power for the HPS sources is sized thanks to continuous variables. Finally, the steam interconnections with other companies (e) are selected by means of binaries and sized thanks to a continuous variable, i.e. the flow-capacity of interconnections. Binaries are also used for the operating conditions of boilers, turbines and interconnections.

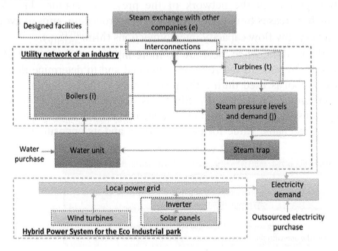

Figure 2: Superstructure of the coupled energy network of the EIP (from Mousqué et al., 2019).

4. Results and discussion

4.1. Resolution procedure assessment

A preliminary study was conducted to discuss the influence of the increase throughout the resolution process of the minimum flow capacity of interconnection threshold (i.e. $\text{Min}_{\text{Threshold}}^{\text{Interc}}$). The procedure is then compared to the same method without the constraint to limit the minimum flow capacity of interconnection. The set of solutions obtained according to cost, number of interconnections and minimum flow capacity of interconnections is provided in Figure 3 (a) for the method with the increasing threshold and (b) for the method without threshold. On Figure 3 (a), the TOPSIS solution to be detailed hereafter is also represented.

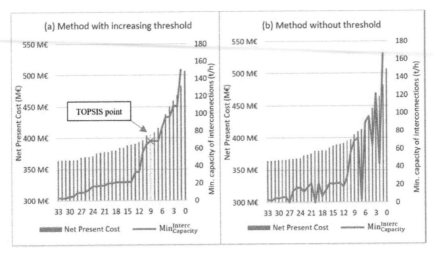

Figure 3: Results for the method with increasing threshold (a) and without threshold (b).

Thus, results are obtained starting from the mono-objective economic minimum (i.e 33 interconnections). The evolution profiles of the net present cost curves for both methods are similar, i.e. the cost increases with the decrease in the number of interconnections. Differences between both methods are observed at some points, interconnections number is similar while the cost is slightly different (+ or − 1.7 %). Then in relation to cost, results for both methods are close.

 The other criterion highlighted in these figures is the minimum flow capacity of interconnections in the network, $Min_{Capacity}^{Interc}$. Throughout the resolution process, when the number of interconnections decreases, the $Min_{Capacity}^{Interc}$ increases for the method with constraint while it evolves in an irregular way and reaches very low levels at some points, for the method without constraint. It is then shown that the increasing threshold avoids nonsensical interconnections to be selected.

Finally, it is to be noticed, that the developed iterative procedure provides results with a significantly reduced calculation time compared to a one-step method consisting of constraining the number of interconnections. Indeed, the addition of a constraint on these super-variable binaries considerably increases the computation time.

In conclusion of this part, the developed resolution method, as proven to be able to solve large MILP network design problems. The procedure to set the key-parameter of $Min_{Threshold}^{Interc}$ avoids interconnections with very low flow capacity without having a significant impact on the cost criterion. Then, in the following part, the final solution is selected, using MCDM tool.

4.2. TOPSIS optimal solution analysis
Henceforth, once the different solutions of the developed method have been obtained, these solutions are ranked using TOPSIS tool. The final solution selected by TOPSIS is indicated in Figure 3(a). For this case study, the same weight is assigned to economic and network complexity criteria.
The optimal solution selected using TOPSIS is the solution with a number of interconnections of 9 with a $Min_{Capacity}^{Interc}$ of 68.4 t/h and a global cost of 405 M€. In comparison to the mono-objective optimization, the cost is increased by 11 % while

network complexity is significantly decreased, i.e. number of interconnections is decreased from 33 to 9, and $Min^{Interc}_{Capacity}$ to be maximized goes from 3 t/h to 68.4 t/h.

Finally, these results lead to a conclusion on the general interest of the multi-objective method, namely that with complex systems such as EIP exchange networks, it is important and more realistic to consider several criteria.

5. Conclusions

In this paper, a method is provided for the optimal design of an EIP exchange network performing a MO optimization through economic (i.e. net present cost) and network complexity criteria. An iterative method for the optimization of the complexity and for solving large MILP problems has been developed. In previous industrial network design papers, the network complexity was managed with two criteria, the number of interconnections in the network and the threshold value for the minimum flow capacity of interconnections which was up to now set as an arbitrary value. Indeed, the minimum flow capacity threshold of interconnection is henceforth determined by the method as a threshold increasing during the procedure. As a result, the developed resolution procedure solves a large coupled energy network case study of 15 companies EIP. Results show that compared to mono-objective optimization on cost, a small cost increase allows getting a solution with significantly reduced complexity. Therefore, the selected interconnections are designed to be the most cost-effective, and their number is limited to reduce topological and management complexity of the network. Next improvements for this model are identified as integrating other criteria, particularly resilience and sustainability (i.e. environmental and social).

References

Aviso, Kathleen B., Raymond R. Tan, Alvin B. Culaba, and Jose B. Cruz. (2011). "Fuzzy Input-Output Model for Optimizing Eco-Industrial Supply Chains under Water Footprint Constraints." *Journal of Cleaner Production.* https://doi.org/10.1016/j.jclepro.2010.09.003.

Boix, Marianne, Ludovic Montastruc, Catherine Azzaro-Pantel, and Serge Domenech. (2015). "Optimization Methods Applied to the Design of Eco-Industrial Parks: A Literature Review." *Journal of Cleaner Production* 87 (1): 303–17. https://doi.org/10.1016/j.jclepro.2014.09.032.

Boix, Marianne, Ludovic Montastruc, Luc Pibouleau, Catherine Azzaro-Pantel, and Serge Domenech. (2012). "Industrial Water Management by Multiobjective Optimization: From Individual to Collective Solution through Eco-Industrial Parks." *Journal of Cleaner Production* 22 (1): 85–97. https://doi.org/10.1016/J.JCLEPRO.2011.09.011.

Chertow, Marian R. (2000). "Industrial Symbiosis: Literature and Taxonomy." *Annual Review of Energy and the Environment* 25: 313–37. https://doi.org/10.1146/annurev.energy.25.1.313.

Kastner, Catharine A., Raymond Lau, and Markus Kraft. (2015). "Quantitative Tools for Cultivating Symbiosis in Industrial Parks; a Literature Review." *Applied Energy.* Elsevier. https://doi.org/10.1016/j.apenergy.2015.05.037.

Mousqué, Florent, Marianne Boix, Stéphane Négny, Ludovic Montastruc, and Serge Domenech. (2019). "On-Grid Hybrid Power System and Utility Network Planning to Supply an Eco-Industrial Park with Dynamic Data." *Computer Aided Chemical Engineering,* 46:1717–22. https://doi.org/10.1016/B978-0-12-818634-3.50287-3.

Sauro Pierucci, Flavio Manenti, Giulia Bozzano, Davide Manca (Eds.)
Proceedings of the 30th European Symposium on Computer Aided Process Engineering
(ESCAPE30), May 24-27, 2020, Milano, Italy. © 2020 Elsevier B.V. All rights reserved.
http://dx.doi.org/10.1016/B978-0-12-823377-1.50327-X

Nested Sampling Strategy for Bayesian Design Space Characterization

Kennedy P. Kusumo[a], Lucian Gomoescu[a,b], Radoslav Paulen[c], Salvador García-Muñoz[d], Costas C. Pantelides[a,b], Nilay Shah[a], Benoit Chachuat[a,*]

[a] *Centre for Process Systems Engineering, Department of Chemical Engineering, Imperial College London, UK*
[b] *Process Systems Enterprise Ltd, London, UK*
[c] *Faculty of Chemical and Food Technology, Slovak University of Technology in Bratislava, Slovakia*
[d] *Small Molecule Design and Development, Eli Lilly & Company, Indianapolis, USA*
b. chachuat@imperial.ac.uk

Abstract

Design space is a key concept in pharmaceutical quality by design, providing better understanding of manufacturing processes and enhancing regulatory flexibility. It is of paramount importance to develop computational techniques for providing quantitative representations of a design space, in accordance with the ICH Q8 guideline. The focus is on Bayesian approaches to design space characterization, which rely on a process model to determine a feasibility probability that is used for measuring reliability and risk. The paper presents three improvements over an existing nested sampling method: two-phase strategy with the first phase using a cheap sorting function based on nominal model parameters; dynamic sampling strategy to refine the target design space; and vectorization to evaluate costly functions in parallel. These improvements are implemented as part of the python package DEUS and demonstrated on an industrial case study.

Keywords: pharmaceutical processes, quality-by-design, design space, nested sampling

1. Introduction

The quality-by-design (QbD) initiative, through the ICH Q8 guideline (Reklaitis et al., 2017), introduced the concept of design space (DS) to improve regulatory flexibility of processes in the pharmaceutical industry. Given a set of critical quality attributes (CQA), the DS represents a set of critical process parameters (CPP) that result in on-spec pharmaceutical production. Peterson (2008) defined the probabilistic DS in terms of feasibility probabilities, a concept akin to stochastic flexibility (Straub and Grossmann, 1990). As the use of mathematical models to support DS characterization is becoming more common in industrial practice (García-Muñoz et al., 2015), the uncertainty related to model parameters and structure needs to be considered and efficient computational tools are of great interest.

Existing computational approaches to probabilistic DS characterization differ in how they account for process model uncertainty and how they approximate the DS itself. Process model uncertainty may be represented as a sampled distribution (e.g. a joint posterior from Bayesian estimation) or a joint confidence region (e.g. a frequentist confidence ellipsoid). Sampling methods seek to produce a set of CPP values that belong to the DS at a desired reliability level, whereas optimization-based methods seek to inscribe a simple shape (e.g. box or ellipsoid) within the DS. For instance, Laky et al. (2019) proposed two optimization-based strategies akin to the classic feasibility test and index formulations that exploit confidence ellipsoids for the model parameters. Monte Carlo and Bayesian techniques have also been used to propagate the uncertainty to the CQAs and estimate a feasibility probability (Peterson et al., 2017; Bano et al., 2018). These techniques have proven effective in practice, but they are computationally expensive and mainly tractable for low-dimensional DS at present.

Recently, Kusumo et al. (2019) presented a sampling strategy based on an adaptation of the nested sampling (NS) algorithm (Skilling, 2004). The algorithm maintains a given set of live points through regions with increasing probability feasibility until reaching a desired reliability level. It leverages efficient strategies from Bayesian statistics for generating replacement proposals during the search and is applicable to problems with disjoint DS or black-box models. This paper presents three ideas to further improve the computational performance of nested sampling for DS characterization. These improvements are demonstrated on a comparative study of the Suzuki coupling reaction.

2. Background

Consider a manufacturing process for a pharmaceutical product that has its quality defined by some CQAs, denoted by $s \in \Box^{n_s}$. Assume that a mathematical model of the process (either knowledge- or data-driven) is available that predicts the CQAs corresponding to the CPPs, denoted by $d \in K$ within the knowledge space $K \subset \Box^{n_d}$:

$$s = f(d, \theta) \tag{1}$$

The model parameters, $\theta \in \Box^{n_\theta}$ represent uncertain quantities e.g., physical constants, coefficients in a regression model, or disturbances that affect the CQAs. Feasibility of the process is defined by the CQA limits alongside other process constraints:

$$G(d, \theta) := g(d, f(d, \theta)) \le 0 \tag{2}$$

The mappings f and G need not be given in closed-form but could be implicitly defined via a DAE model or a CFD simulation. Given a set of nominal model parameters θ_{nom}, the nominal DS is defined as:

$$D_{nom} := \{d \in K : G(d, \theta_{nom}) \le 0\}. \tag{3}$$

However, the value of θ is inherently uncertain by nature of the modelling exercise. A Bayesian framework considers θ as random variables with a joint distribution $p(\theta)$ that describes the belief on the value of θ. In this framework the model is used to predict the probability that the manufacturing process is feasible for a given $d \in K$:

$$P[G(d, \cdot) \le 0 \mid p(\theta)] := \int_{\{\theta : G(d, \cdot) \le 0\}} p(\theta) \, d\theta \tag{4}$$

This paper focuses on characterizing the probabilistic DS given by:

$$D_\alpha := \{d \in K : P[G(d, \cdot) \le 0 \mid p(\theta)] \ge \alpha\} \tag{5}$$

where $0 < \alpha \le 1$ is the reliability value.

3. Improved nested sampling for design space characterization

The NS algorithm for DS characterization (Algorithm 1) starts with N_L *live points* $d_i \in K$, sampled uniformly within the knowledge space. These live points are sorted according to their estimated feasibility probabilities, evaluated as:

$$\hat{P}\left[G(d_i, \theta_j) \leq 0 \mid S_\theta\right] := \sum_{(\theta_j, w_j) \in S_\theta} \mathbf{1}\left(G(d_i, \theta_j)\right) w_j, \quad \text{with } \mathbf{1}(\cdot) := \begin{cases} 1, & \text{if } g_k \leq 0, \ \forall k \\ 0, & \text{otherwise,} \end{cases} \tag{6}$$

where S_θ is a set of model parameter scenarios θ_j and its weight w_j, sampled from $p(\theta)$. The feasibility probability of a point $d_i \in K$ is denoted by P_i below for brevity. Each iteration generates N_P *proposal points* d_k, for instance by sampling within an enlarged ellipsoid enclosing the current live points (Mukherjee et al., 2006). Following the same order as per their generation, each proposal d_k will replace d_{min} – the live point with the lowest P – when $P_{min} < P_k$. The replaced point d_{min} – called a *dead point* – is recorded alongside its feasibility probability, while the point d_{min} and its feasibility probability P_{min} are updated. A stop criterion is checked after each iteration, for instance testing if all live points belong to design space with target reliability value α^*. Three improvement strategies over this basic algorithm are described next:

Strategy 1 – Two-phase nested sampling. A first phase, called *nominal*, is added to Algorithm 1 (lines 5-12), whereby the feasibility is only evaluated at θ_{nom} - a much cheaper test than evaluating N_θ scenarios to estimate P (Eq. 6). This phase continues until all live points are in D_{nom} (Eq. 3). Though it is possible that D_{nom} may exclude parts of D_{α^*}, we observe that $D_{\alpha^*} \subset D_{nom}$ when the target reliability α^* is close to unity and θ_{nom} is chosen as the maximum likelihood estimate or the mode or mean of the model parameter's posterior distribution. The second phase (lines 17-38), called *probabilistic*, is initialized with the live points from the first phase, after computing and sorting their feasibility probabilities (lines 13-16).

Strategy 2 – Dynamic live point population. The term *dynamic* is in reference to the strategy of increasing the number of live points N_L and proposals N_P over the course of the algorithm in order to generate a denser sample at the target reliability level (lines 27-34). N_L is increased every time the feasibility probability of the current nest, P_{min} gets larger than a predefined threshold, according to a user-specified top-up schedule S_T. The number of proposals N_P may also be adjusted when N_L is increased.

Strategy 3 – Vectorized function evaluations. Evaluations of the feasibility probability of the live points, replacement proposals, and top-up proposals are carried out in parallel using Python's multiprocessing to exploit multiple processors in modern computers.

An implementation of these algorithmic improvements is available in the Python package DEUS, which can be obtained from: https://github.com/omega-icl/deus. The input file for the case study below can also be retrieved from this link. In DEUS the candidate points are generated by sampling in a single ellipsoid enclosing the current live points (Mukherjee et al., 2006). In addition to setting the numbers of live points, replacement proposals, and the top-up schedule, other tuning parameters include the initial enlargement factor of the ellipsoid (default: 0.1), and the shrinking rate of that enlargement factor at each iteration (default: 0.3).

Algorithm 1 Nested sampling tailored to design space characterization

1: **Inputs**: $S_\theta = \left\{ \left(\theta_j, w_j \right) \sim p(\theta) : j = 1, \ldots, N_\theta \right\}$, $S_T = \left\{ \left(P_t^+, N_{L,t}^+, N_{P,t}^+ \right) : t = 1, \ldots, N_T \right\}$,

K, α^*, θ_{nom}, N_L, and N_P.

Initialization

2: $S_L \leftarrow \left\{ d_i \in K : i = 1, \ldots, N_L \right\}$

3: $DS \leftarrow \varnothing$

4: $t \leftarrow 0$

Phase I: Nominal

5: **while** $\exists d_i \in S_L : G(d_i, \theta_{nom}) > 0$ **do**

6: $\quad S_P \leftarrow \left\{ d_k^+ \in K : k = 1, \ldots, N_P \right\}$

7: $\quad$ **for all** $d_k^+ \in S_P$ **do**

8: $\quad\quad$ **if** $G\left(d_k^+, \theta_{nom} \right) \leq 0$ **then**

9: $\quad\quad\quad S_L \leftarrow S_L \cup \left\{ d_k^+ \right\} \setminus \left\{ d_i \right\}$

10: $\quad\quad$ **end if**

11: $\quad$ **end for**

12: **end while**

Reinitialization

13: **for all** $d_i \in S_L$ **do**

14: $\quad DS \leftarrow DS \cup \left\{ \left(d_i ; P\left[G(d_i, \cdot) \leq 0 \mid S_\theta \right] \right) \right\}$

15: **end for**

Phase II: Probabilistic

16: **while** $\exists d_i \in S_L : P\left\lfloor G(d_i, \cdot) \leq 0 \mid S_\theta \right\rfloor \leq \alpha^*$ **do**

17: $\quad S_P \leftarrow \left\{ d_k^+ \in K : k = 1, \ldots, N_P \right\}$ $\qquad\qquad$ ▷ propose replacements

18: $\quad$ **for all** $d_k^+ \in S_P$ **do** $\qquad\qquad\qquad$ ▷ decide accepted replacements

19: $\quad\quad P_{min} \leftarrow \min \left\{ P\left[G(d_i, \cdot) \leq 0 \mid S_\theta \right] : d_i \in S_L \right\}$

20: $\quad\quad d_{min} \leftarrow \arg\min \left\{ P\left[G(d_i, \cdot) \leq 0 \mid S_\theta \right] : d_i \in S_L \right\}$

21: $\quad\quad$ **if** $P\left\lfloor G\left(d_k^+, \cdot \right) \leq 0 \mid S_\theta \right\rfloor > P_{min}$ **then**

22: $\quad\quad\quad S_L \leftarrow S_L \cup \left\{ d_k^+ \right\} \setminus \left\{ d_{min} \right\}$

23: $\quad\quad\quad DS \leftarrow DS \cup \left\{ \left(d_{min}, P_{min} \right) \right\}$

24: $\quad\quad$ **end if**

25: $\quad$ **end for**

26: $\quad$ **if** $P_{min} \geq P_{t+1}^+$ **then** $\qquad\qquad\qquad\qquad$ ▷ top-up live points if needed

27: $\quad\quad t \leftarrow t + 1$

28: $\quad\quad$ **while** $N_L < N_{L,t}^+$ **do**

29: $\quad\quad\quad N_L \leftarrow N_L + 1$

30: $\quad\quad\quad S_L \leftarrow S_L \cup \left\{ d_{N_L} \in K : P\left[G\left(d_{N_L}, \cdot \right) \leq 0 \mid S_\theta \right] > P_{min} \right\}$ ▷ top-up proposal

31: $\quad\quad$ **end while**

32: $\quad\quad N_P \leftarrow N_{P,t}^+$

33: $\quad$ **end if**

34: **end while**

35: **for all** $d_i \in S_L$ **do** $\qquad\qquad\qquad\qquad\qquad$ ▷ add current live points

36: $\quad DS \leftarrow DS \cup \left\{ \left(d_i, P\left[G(d_i, \cdot) \leq 0 \mid S_\theta \right] \right) \right\}$

37: **end for**

38: **return** DS

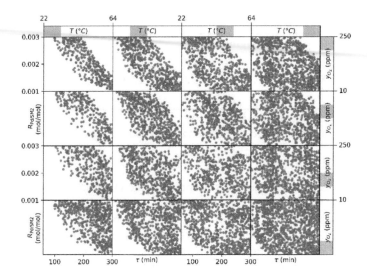

Figure 1: Probabilistic DS at a reliability $\alpha^* = 0.85$ for the Suzuki coupling reaction computed using Algorithm 1 with 1,000 uncertainty scenarios and 10,000 live points.

4. Case study: Suzuki coupling reaction

This case study investigates the Suzuki coupling reaction between a boronic ester (SM1) and an organohalide (SM2) to produce a desired pharmaceutical intermediate (P1) and a dimeric impurity (Imp1) related to SM1. The reaction is biphasic and conducted in batch mode. The gaseous phase is inert with traces of O_2 in vapor-liquid equilibrium with a liquid phase containing 17 chemical species dissolved in a mixture of water and THF. The active species participate in 12 reactions, 3 of which are reversible and 1 is considered instantaneous. The uncertain parameters are the 14 pre-exponential factors of the reactions. The DS is the set of (i) batch durations $\tau \in [75, 300]$ (min), (ii) catalyst equivalents $R_{Pd|SM2} \in [0.001, 0.003]$ (mol/mol), (iii) temperatures $T \in [22, 64]$ (°C), and (iv) O_2 molar fractions in the head space $y_{O_2} \in [10, 250]$ (ppm) such that the product has (i) unreacted SM2 less than 0.001 mol/mol, and (ii) Imp1 less than 0.0015 mol/mol. Full details about the case study can be found in Kusumo et al. (2019).

For comparison with Kusumo et al. (2019) we compute the probabilistic DS at a reliability $\alpha^* = 0.85$ using Algorithm 1 with and without parallelization, considering two cases: (i) $N_0 = 200$ and $N_L = 5,000$; (ii) $N_0 = 1,000$ and $N_L = 10,000$. Case (i) was initialized with $N_L = N_P = 100$ and schedule $S_T = \{(0.01, 1000, 200), (0.20, 2000, 200), (0.85, 5000, 500)\}$; case (ii) uses the same with double N_L and N_P. We opted for larger N_P to more efficiently parallelize proposal computations with Python's multiprocessing package. Computational statistics are presented in Table 1. Applying Strategies 1+2 decreases the number of evaluations by nearly 20% in both cases and saves 16 hours of computational time for case 2, but only minor savings for case 1. Parallelization results in approximately 4 to 5-fold reduction in CPU time. The returned 4-dimensional samples for case 2 are visualized with a trellis chart in Figure 1, where only the target DS at reliability $\alpha^* = 0.85$ is shown since the improvement strategies are designed to describe that set quicker. The comparison with Kusumo et al. (2019) confirms that no part of the target DS is missed.

Table 1: Computational statistics for Suzuki coupling reaction using Algorithm 1.

		Original		With strategies 1–2		
N_L	N_θ	# eval.[1]	Serial (hr.)[2]	# eval.[1]	Serial (hr.)	Parallel (hr.)[2]
5,000	200	1.45	9.6	1.18	9.3	2.3
10,000	1,000	14.54	112.4	11.80	96.5	21.8

[1] Number of model evaluations (in million).
[2] CPU times (in hours) obtained on AMD Ryzen 5 2600X processor with 6 cores.

5. Conclusions

To address the need for efficient tools for probabilistic DS characterization, Kusumo et al. (2019) proposed a tailored nested-sampling algorithm. We have presented three improvement strategies to the algorithm, namely a two-phase strategy to exploit information from nominal model parameters, a dynamic sampling strategy to delineate the target design space faster, and a vectorization strategy to evaluate costly functions in parallel. These improvements were demonstrated on an industrial case study, leading to a four-fold reduction in CPU time on a typical desktop computer.

Acknowledgements: This work is supported by Eli Lilly and Company through the Pharmaceutical Systems Engineering Lab (PharmaSEL) program. Radoslav Paulen gratefully acknowledges the contribution of the European Commission under grant 790017 (GuEst) and the contribution of the Slovak Research and Development Agency (project APVV 15-0007). The authors are grateful to Carla Vanesa Luciani for her assistance with the case study.

References

G. Bano, P. Facco, F. Bezzo, M. Barolo, 2018. Probabilistic design space determination in pharmaceutical product development: A Bayesian/latent variable approach. AIChE Journal 64 (7), 2438–2449.

S. García-Muñoz, C. V. Luciani, S. Vaidyaraman, K. D. Seibert, 2015. Definition of design spaces using mechanistic models and geometric projections of probability maps. Organic Process Research & Development 19 (8), 1012–1023.

K. P. Kusumo, L. Gomoescu, R. Paulen, S. García-Muñoz, C. C. Pantelides, N. Shah, B. Chachuat, 2019. Bayesian approach to probabilistic design space characterization: A nested sampling strategy. Industrial & Engineering Chemistry Research (in press, doi: 10.1021/acs.iecr.9b05006).

D. Laky, S. Xu, J. S. Rodriguez, S. Vaidyaraman, S. García Muñoz, C. Laird, 2019. An optimization-based framework to define the probabilistic design space of pharmaceutical processes with model uncertainty. Processes 7 (2), 96.

P. Mukherjee, D. Parkinson, A. R. Liddle, 2006. A nested sampling algorithm for cosmological model selection. The Astrophysical Journal Letters 638 (2), L51.

J. J. Peterson, 2008. A Bayesian approach to the ICH Q8 definition of design space. Journal of Biopharmaceutical Statistics 18 (5), 959–975.

J. J. Peterson, M. Yahyah, K. Lief, N. Hodnett, 2017. Predictive distributions for constructing the ICH Q8 design space. In: G. V. Reklaitis, C. Seymour, S. García-Muñoz (Eds.), Comprehensive Quality by Design for Pharmaceutical Product Development and Manufacture. Wiley & Sons, Ch. 4, pp. 55–70.

G. V. Reklaitis, C. Seymour, S. García-Muñoz (Eds.), 2017. Comprehensive Quality by Design for Pharmaceutical Product Development and Manufacture. Wiley & Sons.

J. Skilling, 2004. Nested sampling. AIP Conference Proceedings 735 (1), 395–405.

D. A. Straub, I. E. Grossmann, 1990. Integrated stochastic metric of flexibility for systems with discrete state and continuous parameter uncertainties. Computers & Chemical Engineering 14 (9), 967–985.

Sauro Pierucci, Flavio Manenti, Giulia Bozzano, Davide Manca (Eds.)
Proceedings of the 30th European Symposium on Computer Aided Process Engineering
(ESCAPE30), May 24-27, 2020, Milano, Italy. © 2020 Elsevier B.V. All rights reserved.
http://dx.doi.org/10.1016/B978-0-12-823377-1.50328-1

Neural Ordinary Differential Equations-based Explainable Deep Learning for Process Modeling

Michael R. Wartmann[a], B. Erik Ydstie[b]

[a]*Nouryon B.V., Digital Technology, Christian Neefestraat 2, 1077 WW Amsterdam, NL*
[b]*Carnegie Mellon University, 5000 Forbes Avenue, 15213 Pittsburgh, USA*
michael.wartmann@nouryon.com

Abstract

Most recent advances in the machine learning domain pose the challenge of how to naturally integrate new data-driven methods with classical process models and control. We propose a process modeling framework enabling integration of data-driven algorithms through consistent topological properties and conservation of extensive quantities. Interconnections among process network units are represented through connectivity matrices and network graphs. The basic requirement is that the flow conditions can be expressed in terms of conic sector (passivity) conditions. Our formalism allows integration of fundamental conservation properties from topology with learned dynamic relations from data through sparse deep neural networks.

We demonstrate in a practical example of a simple inventory control system how to integrate the basic topology of a process with a neural network ordinary differential equation model. The system specific constitutive equations are left undescribed and learned by the deep neural network using the adjoint method in combination with an adaptive ODE solver from synthetic time-series data. The resulting neural network forms a state space model for use in a model predictive control algorithm.

Keywords: neural ordinary differential equations, network theory, deep learning, process networks, process modelling

1. Introduction

Modeling process systems poses the challenge of deriving a meaningful mathematical representation capturing the fundamental laws of nature while representing the systems actual real-world behavior within its given system context. Intelligent use of data in the process of modeling complex systems provides the context while model structure and general behavior is derived from first principles knowledge of the system.

A typical challenge within the context of process systems is that available data of the process is limited for the particular case at hand (Venkatasubramanian 2018). Individual systems differ significantly from each other such that data of one system cannot be simply transferred or combined with data from similar other systems. As such, the need arises to model process systems in structurally consistent ways and take maximal advantage of the knowledge derived from first principles relationships (Ydstie 2002). While machine or deep learning algorithms are suitable to extract even very complex non-linear behavior, in the context of process systems, simple relationships such as fundamental mass, energy and component balances have to be learned ab initio, i.e., the data itself has to provide the context for those relationships. The available data should be used to provide information about the dynamics of the system beyond those fundamental relationships and be extracted through statistical methods or machine learning.

To provide the most optimal starting point for any machine learning based model in the context of process systems, the structure of the material and energy flow of the process system would need to be embedded in the model itself. In a deep learning context for example, the algorithm simply searches for the best possible fit of the given neural network structure to the input and output data provided. As a result, deep learning models have faced the challenge of explainability (Doran et al 2017), i.e., parameters and structure of the resulting neural network cannot be explained or related to the fundamental laws of nature.

A relevant component of using deep learning-based methods is therefore to understand how connections between the subunits of a process network lead to complex system behavior and how the connections can be built into a deep learning-based model, i.e., a neural network.

For the integration of data-driven methods, we provide an organizational framework for process systems using ideas from network theory in this paper.

2. Network theory and process systems

Process networks are written as a collection of interconnected sub-systems

$$\dot{x}_I = F(x_i) + \sum_{j=0, j \neq i}^{n} G(u_i, x_i, x_j), \qquad i = 0, \dots, n \tag{1}$$

$$y_i = H(x_i) \tag{2}$$

x_i is the state of subsystem i and $x_i(0)$ is the initial condition. The function F describes the unforced motion of the system, the function G describes how the system is connected with other sub-systems, and the output function H relates the state of the system to the measurement functions y_i. The functions u_i represent the manipulated variables. The functions F, G, H are all differentiable at least once. The state of the entire network is given by the vector $x = (x_0^T, x_1^T, \dots, x_n^T)^T$.

Subscript zero refers to the reference (exo-) system. Often, we are not interested in the dynamics of the exo-system, or more likely, it is too complex to model. The process system is modeled as the reduced system without the reference sub-system. Its state is given by the vector $x = (x_1^T, \dots, x_n^T)^T$. The interactions with the exo-system are then established through the boundary conditions.

The network form, as illustrated in Figure 1 is convenient when we model systems with a graph structure.

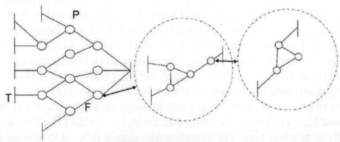

Figure 1: Graphical network representation: Topological structure of a network consisting of nodes, terminals, and flows. Nodes can contain subgraphs and give rise to a hierarchical multi-scale structure.

In such systems the interactions between the sub-systems depend on the state of the sub-system itself and the state of its immediate neighbors. Not all dynamical systems can be decomposed in this fashion. However, many large-scale systems have sparse interconnections and they can be modeled compactly as networks of sub-systems with interconnections. It is also easy to see that many physical systems, especially those that satisfy the principle of local action, can be decomposed in the manner shown in Eq. (1).

By a graph G we mean a finite set $v(G) = (v_1, ...l, v_{nP})$, whose elements are called **nodes**, together with the set $\varepsilon(G)$ whose elements are called **branches**. A branch is therefore an ordered pair of distinct nodes.

Definition 1. A network of nodes P_i, $i = 1,...,n_p, n_p + 1,...,n_v$ consisting of nodes and terminals interconnected through branches E_i, $i = 1,...,n_f$ with topology defined by the graph set $G = (E, P)$.

The system (1) is called a *process network* if its interconnection structure is described by a directed graph and we have

(1) **1st law:** There is an inventory E (the energy) satisfying the conservation property
(2) **2nd law:** There is an inventory S (the entropy) satisfying the Clausius-Planck property

Definition 2. The $n_t \times n_f$ matrix $\mathbf{A_a}$ is called incidence matrix for the matrix elements a_{ij} being

$$a_{ij} = \begin{cases} 1, \text{if flow } j \text{ leaves node } i \\ -1, \text{if flow } j \text{ enters node } i \\ 0, \text{if flow } j \text{ is not incident with node } i \end{cases}$$

One node of the network is set as reference or datum node P_0 representing the exo-system. The $(n_t - 1) \times n_f$ matrix $\mathbf{A}$, where the row that contains the elements a_{0j} of the reference node P_0 is eliminated, is called reduced incidence matrix.

The connections between nodes through branches can be uniquely defined using the incident matrix $\mathbf{A}$. The conservation laws of Eq. 1 can now be written

$$\mathbf{AF} = 0 \tag{3}$$

for the node-to-branch incident matrix $\mathbf{A}$, where $\mathbf{F}^T = (\frac{dz_1}{dt}, \frac{dz_2}{dt}, ..., \frac{dz_t}{dt}, f_{12}, f_{13}, ..., f_{n_{t-1}, n_t}, p_1, ..., p_t)$. The flows f_{ij} represent connections between two nodes i.e. f_{ij} connects node i to node j, p_i denotes sources or sinks. The direction of the flows is defined according to the directionality established in the graph. We now define a vector $\mathbf{W}$ so that

$$\mathbf{W} = \mathbf{A}^T \mathbf{w} \tag{4}$$

where $W_{ij} = w_i - w_j$ are the potential differences across flow connections. The variables $\mathbf{w}$ are conjugate to $\mathbf{Z}$ if they are related via the Legendre transform of a convex potential like the entropy.

Eqs. 3 and 4 only reflect the topological properties of the process system. To complete a full dynamic model, we require functions relating the flow of extensive quantities $\mathbf{F}$ to the potential differences $\mathbf{W}$ and a relationship between the inventories $\mathbf{Z}$ and the potentials $\mathbf{w}$. These relationships often contain non-linearities in classical process models, e.g.

kinetic relationships, pressure drop relations, thermodynamic models and chemicals potentials etc. (Wartmann and Ydstie 2009).

3. Neural Ordinary Differential Equations for Process Networks

A new family of deep neural network models have been introduced by Chen et al (2018). Instead of specifying a discrete sequence of hidden layers, in Chen et al. (2018) the derivative is parameterized using a neural network. The deep neural network models allow discretization of a dynamic system in time, in which each hidden layer of the neural network represents a particular state in time. These models are especially powerful, when used in the context of time-series correlated data and allow learning differential equations from data. For process systems, dynamic models for control can be derived by applying a deep neural network if trained from e.g. operational step testing data.

Chen et al. show that for training of continuous-depth neural networks, reverse mode differentiation or backpropagation can best be carried out through an ODE solver method. The well-known adjoint method is suitable to calculate the gradients of a scalar-valued loss function L for neural network weight training when combined with a gradient decent method for backpropagation. From a process network perspective, learning the dynamic behavior of a set of time-series data is essentially equivalent to modeling the right-hand side of a differential equation system as in Eq. 1 through a neural network representation. For a template of a neural network model with trainable weights, it would be ideal to have the process system's topology already represented in the neural networks layers such that the (non-linear) relations between flows $\mathbf{F}$ and inventories $\mathbf{Z}$ and the potentials $\mathbf{w}$ are learned from data while inventory balances and their structure are pre-imposed. As shown in Fig. 3, if potentials $\mathbf{w}$ of a network are measurable inputs, then continuity of the potentials allows relating them to differentials $\mathbf{W}$ and flow variables $\mathbf{F}$ through these relations (e.g. pressure differential drives convective flow). Further, flow variables $\mathbf{F}$ in the hidden layer relate to the inventory balance and allow calculation of the inventory differences $\Delta \mathbf{Z}$.

To represent the topology of a process network in a neural network model, some of the weights in the incident matrix $\mathbf{A}$ have to be set to zero resulting in a sparsely connected neural network where no physical connection is present. In the process of training the weights, these zero weights have to be pruned in training reducing the computational effort, preserving the process topology, and resulting in potentially explainable parameters for the remaining weights.

4. An inventory system modeled by a neural ODE

A small dynamic flow and storage example shows how process networks can be modelled using neural ODE's. The network consists of two connected pipelines where each pipeline flows through a cylindrical storage tank with volume open to the atmosphere, see Fig. 2. The resulting linear classical ODE can be derived from the balances around the nodes P_1 and P_2 for Z_1 and Z_2 i.e., $dZ_{1,2}/dt = F_{1,3}-F_{2,4}$, constant terminal potentials w_{T1} and w_{T2}, the flow constitutive equations $F_i = K_i W_i$ with $i=1,..,4$, the potential differences $W = w1 - w2$ as in Eq. (4), and $w_i = C_i Z_i$

$$
\begin{aligned}
C_1^{-1} \frac{dw_1}{dt} &= -(K_1 - K_3)w_1 + K_1 w_{T1} + K_3 w_{T2} \\
C_2^{-1} \frac{dw_1}{dt} &= -(K_2 - K_4)w_2 + K_2 w_{T1} + K_4 w_{T2}
\end{aligned}
\tag{5}
$$

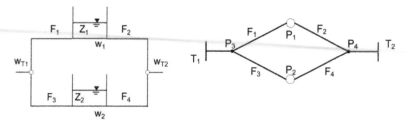

Figure 2: Graphical network representations: Problem specific representation on the left, a generalized graph representation on the right.

Discretization using the explicit Euler method for demonstration purposes and using ReLU's as activation functions leads to Eq. 6.

$$w^{t+1T} = w^{tT} + \Delta t \, \text{ReLU}(\text{ReLU}(w^{tT}A_K)A_C{}^T) \tag{6}$$

where the connectivity matrices A_K and A_C are given as in Fig 3.

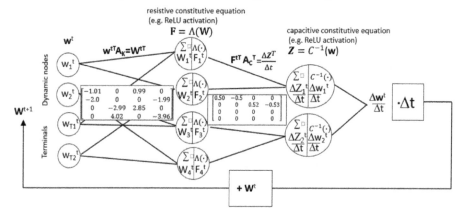

Figure 3: Neural network representation of the process network example, with potentials w in the input layer, flows F at the hidden layer, and potential differences per time step at the output layer. Final weights after training as given in the connectivity matrices are equivalent to the differential equation system from which synthetic data was derived.

The Neural ODE system was trained in Google Co-Lab using cloud GPU's based on synthetic dynamic data with added Gaussian noise (5%) from the corresponding ODE of Eqs. 5 with parameters $K_1=1$, $K_2=2$, $K_3=3$, $K_4=4$, $C_1=C_2=2$, and $w_{T1}=4$, $w_{T2}=0$. A Pytorch Python-based implementation was chosen with a time discretization using the explicit Euler method and time steps of $\Delta t = 0.02$ s. The process topology of the neural ODE was generated by pruning weights of non-incident edges, i.e., setting the corresponding weights to zero in every forward pass iteration during training. An adaptive deep learning stochastic gradient descent algorithm was applied for backpropagation to train the non-zero weights of the neural network. Training batches were selected through randomly choosing time periods within the synthetic data and 1000 training iterations carried out. The training run took T=17 sec and the neural network model matched the original data of the synthetic model where weights match with the original ODE (see Fig. 4) for the final w_1-w_2 time trajectory versus training data.

The resulting neural network simulates the dynamic system even if initial conditions are chosen differently from the original training data, i.e., extrapolates versus the dynamic trajectory of the original data.

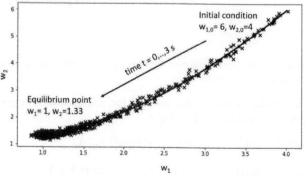

Figure 4: Time trajectory of dynamic potentials w1-w2 of inventory system after training the neural network. Synthetic time series data (marks) vs. neural network model (solid line).

5. Conclusions and Outlook

Using a graph theory based neural network representation for a process network allows using the topology of the system to be incorporated into the neural network through the incident matrices between edges and nodes. A sparsely connected neural network with meaningful topology allows preservation of e.g. inventory balances and a consistent potential field. Relationships between extensive quantities such as flows and inventories to intensive quantities, i.e., potentials are learned from data through training the remaining non-zero weights in the neural network through pruning. By applying classical ODE solvers and discretizing in time via e.g. the explicit Euler method in combination with adjoint equations allows determining gradients through backpropagation with a deep learning stochastic gradient descent method. Neural ODE models for process systems and networks have the potential to be used for model predictive control for which weight parameters are explainable and can be understood and updated when new data becomes available or the fundamental process structure is changed.

References

R.T.Q. Chen,Y. Rubanova, J. Bettencourt, and D. Duvenaud, 2018, Neural ordinary differential equations. *ArXiv 1806.07366.*

D. Doran, S. Schulz, and T. R. Besold. 2017, What does explainable AI really mean? a new conceptualization of perspectives. *ArXiv 1710.00794.*

M. R. Wartmann and B.E. Ydstie, 2009, Network-based analysis of stability, optimality of process networks. *Proceedings of ADCHEM*, 197–202.

B.E. Ydstie, 2002, New vistas for process control: Integrating physics and communication networks. *AICHE*, 48, 422–426.

V. Venkatasubramanian, 2019, The Promise of Artificial Intelligence in Chemical Engineering: Is It Here, Finally? *AICHE*, 65, 466-478.

Sauro Pierucci, Flavio Manenti, Giulia Bozzano, Davide Manca (Eds.)
Proceedings of the 30th European Symposium on Computer Aided Process Engineering
(ESCAPE30), May 24-27, 2020, Milano, Italy. © 2020 Elsevier B.V. All rights reserved.
http://dx.doi.org/10.1016/B978-0-12-823377-1.50329-3

Global Optimization of Bilinear Programs by Elementary Functions Substitutions

Miloš Bogataj*, Zdravko Kravanja

Faculty of Chemistry and Chemical Engineering, University of Maribor, Smetanova ulica 17, SI-2000 Maribor, Slovenia
milos.bogataj@um.si

Abstract

In this paper, we present an approach to global optimization of bilinear programs based on a transformation of bilinear terms to elementary functions of single variables. The substitutions relocate bilinear terms to additional equality constraints. The complicating variables in these constraints are separated by logarithm operations. Finally, the log-linear constraints are relaxed by piecewise linear approximations and/or linearizations. The transformation produces a lower-bounding mixed-integer linear program, which is used in conjunction with the original bilinear program in a global optimization algorithm. The approach was tested by pooling problems from the literature. The global optimum was obtained in all the test problems; however, more elaborate algorithmic schemes would be needed to make the proposed approach computationally efficient.

Keywords: global optimization, bilinear programming, algorithm, elementary function, mixed-integer programming.

1. Introduction

Global optimization of bilinear programs is an ongoing endeavour in optimization. Its role is prominent in applications involving water networks and optimization of petroleum blending operations (Ahmetovic and Grossmann, 2010; Misener and Floudas 2009, Faria and Bagajewicz, 2012). The common approach to global optimization of bilinear problems is based on using convex envelopes (McCormick, 1976), coupled with spatial branch and bound search procedures. More efficient algorithms, which provide tighter convex relaxations, incorporate piecewise linear relaxation of bilinear terms (Karupiah and Grossmann 2006, Myer and Floudas 2006). Kolodziej et al. (2013) presented a derivation of the multiparametric disaggregation technique by Teles et al. (2001) for solving nonconvex bilinear programs. The relaxation derived by the authors scales more favourably than the relaxation that relies on piecewise McCormick envelopes. Finally, Misener et al. (2011) proposed a relaxation for modelling bilinear terms with piecewise McCormick envelopes, which ensures that the number of binary variables needed for the piecewise formulation scales logarithmically with the number of segments in the piecewise relaxation.

In this work, we focus on global optimization of bilinear problems in which the bilinear terms are the only source of nonlinearities and nonconvexities. As the main novelty, we present the formulation of a lower-bounding problem by convex envelopes of logarithmic functions of single variables. We propose a simple algorithm by which the gap is closed between the original nonconvex formulation, serving as an upper-bounding problem, and its lower-bounding counterpart. Finally, we present and discuss the results of numerical studies.

2. Bilinear problem

The bilinear problem considered in this work can be written as the nonconvex nonlinear programming problem (P). In (P), $a_{i,j}$, $b_{i,j,k}$, $b_{i,j,l}$ are scalars and $f_0(x)$, $f_l(x)$, $f_k(x)$ linear functions. The bilinear terms $x_i x_j$ represent the nonlinear parts of the objective function and the constraints. We assume that the lower bounds on continuous variables x are zero and the upper bounds nonzero positive values x^{UP}. In addition, we assume that no quadratic terms (i.e. $i = j$) are present in (P), although the proposed approach is equally valid for those cases as well.

$$\min Z = \sum_{i,j(i\neq j)} a_{i,j} x_i x_j + f_0(x)$$
$$s.t.$$
$$h_k(x) = \sum_{i,j(i\neq j)} b_{i,j,k} x_i x_j + f_k(x) = 0 \qquad\qquad (P)$$
$$g_l(x) = \sum_{i,j(i\neq j)} b_{i,j,l} x_i x_j + f_l(x) \leq 0$$
$$0 \leq x \leq x^{UP}, \; i \in I, \; j \in J, \; k \in K, \; l \in L$$

3. Reformulation and relaxation of the bilinear problem

We reformulate (P) by substituting the bilinear terms $x_i x_j$ with variables $w_{i,j}$ and introducing additional constraints $w_{i,j} = x_i x_j$. The variables in these constraints are separated by logarithm operation and the resulting logarithmic terms substituted by slack variables ($W_{i,j}$, X_i and X_j). The reformulation can be represented as a linear generalized disjunctive program (PL-GDP).

$$\min Z = \sum_{i,j} a_{i,j} w_{i,j} + f_0(x)$$
$$s.t.$$
$$h_k(x) = \sum_{i,j(i\neq j)} b_{i,j,k} w_{i,j} + f_k(x) = 0$$
$$g_l(x) = \sum_{i,j(i\neq j)} b_{i,j,l} w_{i,j} + f_l(x) \leq 0$$
$$W_{i,j} = X_i + X_j$$

$$\begin{bmatrix} Y_{W_{i,j}} \\ W_{i,j} \leq f^O\left(\log(w_{i,j})\right) \\ W_{i,j} \geq f^U\left(\log(w_{i,j})\right) \\ \varepsilon_{x_i}\varepsilon_{x_j} \leq w_{i,j} \leq x_i^{UP} x_j^{UP} \end{bmatrix} \vee \begin{bmatrix} \neg Y_{W_{i,j}} \\ w_{i,j} = 0 \end{bmatrix}, \qquad\qquad \text{(PL--GDP)}$$

$$\begin{bmatrix} Y_{X_i} \\ X_i \leq f^O\left(\log(x_i)\right) \\ X_i \geq f^U\left(\log(x_i)\right) \\ \varepsilon_{x_i} \leq x_i \leq x_i^{UP} \end{bmatrix} \vee \begin{bmatrix} \neg Y_{X_i} \\ 0 \leq x_i \leq x_i^{UP} \end{bmatrix}, \quad \begin{bmatrix} Y_{X_j} \\ X_j \leq f^O\left(\log(x_j)\right) \\ X_j \geq f^U\left(\log(x_j)\right) \\ \varepsilon_{x_j} \leq x_j \leq x_j^{UP} \end{bmatrix} \vee \begin{bmatrix} \neg Y_{X_j} \\ 0 \leq x_j \leq x_j^{UP} \end{bmatrix}$$

$$Y_{W_{ij}} \Rightarrow Y_{X_i} \wedge Y_{X_i}$$
$$0 < \varepsilon_{x_i}, \varepsilon_j \leq 1$$
$$i \in I, \; j \in J, \; k \in K, \; l \in L$$

The disjunctions and the logical proposition encapsulate the generation of convex envelopes of the logarithmic terms. If all the Boolean variables in the disjunctions are *True*, the slack variables become bounded by linear over- and underestimators of logarithmic functions (f^O, f^U). Otherwise, the convex envelopes become redundant.

An important observation is that, if the Boolean variables are *True*, the continuous variables $w_{i,j}$, x_i and x_j become bounded by nonzero lower bounds. This is necessary because the logarithmic function is undefined at 0. In addition, to keep the feasible region of the original problem intact to the greatest extent, we set the lower bounds on variables $w_{i,j}$ to the product of the nonzero lower bounds on x_i and x_j (i.e. $w_{i,j} \geq \varepsilon_i \varepsilon_j$). Similarly, we set the upper bounds on $w_{i,j}$ to the product of the upper bounds on the x_i and x_j variables.

3.1. Lower bounding mixed-integer linear problem

We reformulate the (PL-GDP) to a mixed-integer linear program (PL) using the mixed-integer (MI) translation of variables. For comprehensive insight into the reformulation, the reader is referred to the works by Ropotar and Kravanja (2010) and Bogataj and Kravanja (2018, 2019). Here we offer a brief explanation for the two extreme cases.

In (PL), $w^T_{i,j}, x^T_i, x^T_j$ and $w^F_{i,j}, x^F_i, x^F_j$ are the disaggregated variables and $y_{i,j}, y_i, y_j$ binary variables. First, we consider the case when $y_{i,j} = y_i = y_j = 1$. In this case, variables $w_{i,j}, x_i$ and x_j become equal to $w^T_{i,j}, x^T_i$ and x^T_j, which are bounded by nonzero lower bounds. $W_{i,j}$, X_i and X_j become bounded by the corresponding convex envelopes defined over the domains of $w^T_{i,j}, x^T_i$ and x^T_j. In the case when $y_{i,j} = y_i = y_j = 0$, variables $w^T_{i,j}, x^T_i$ and x^T_j are forced to their nonzero lower bounds ($\varepsilon_i \varepsilon_j, \varepsilon_i, \varepsilon_j$). Consequently, the variables $W_{i,j}$, X_i and X_j become fixed at their lower bounds ($\log(\varepsilon_i \varepsilon_j), \log(\varepsilon_i), \log(\varepsilon_j)$) too. The feasible region bounded by over- and underestimators thus becomes reduced to points ([$\varepsilon_i \varepsilon_j, \log(\varepsilon_i \varepsilon_j)$], [$\varepsilon_i, \log(\varepsilon_i)$] and [$\varepsilon_j, \log(\varepsilon_j)$]). On the other hand, variables $w_{i,j}, x_i$ and x_j become equal to variables $w^F_{i,j}, x^F_i, x^F_j$, which are defined over the complete domain of variables $w_{i,j}, x_i$ and x_j.

$$\min Z = \sum_{i,j} a_{i,j} w_{i,j} + f_0(x)$$

$$s.t.$$

$$h_k(x) = \sum_{i,j(i \neq j)} b_{i,j,k} w_{i,j} + f_k(x) = 0$$

$$g_l(x) = \sum_{i,j(i \neq j)} b_{i,j,l} w_{i,j} + f_l(x) \leq 0$$

$$W_{i,j} = X_i + X_j$$

$$w_{i,j} = w^T_{i,j} - (1 - y_{i,j})\varepsilon_i \varepsilon_j \qquad x_i = x^T_i - (1 - y_i)\varepsilon_i + x^F_i \qquad x_j = x^T_j - (1 - y_j)\varepsilon_j + x^F_j$$

$$w^T_{i,j} \leq x^{UP}_i x^{UP}_j y_{i,j} + (1 - y_{i,j})\varepsilon_i \varepsilon_j \qquad x^T_i \leq x^{UP}_i y_i + (1 - y_i)\varepsilon_i \qquad x^T_j \leq x^{UP}_j y_j + (1 - y_j)\varepsilon_j$$

$$w^T_{i,j} \geq \varepsilon_i \varepsilon_j \qquad\qquad x^T_i \geq \varepsilon_i \qquad\qquad x^T_j \geq \varepsilon_j$$

$$\qquad\qquad x^F_i \leq x^{UP}_i (1 - y_i) \qquad x^F_j \leq x^{UP}_j (1 - y_j)$$

$$\qquad\qquad x^F_i \geq 0 \qquad\qquad x^F_j \geq 0 \qquad\qquad \text{(PL)}$$

$$y_{i,j} \leq y_i$$

$$y_i \leq y_j$$

$$y_{i,j} \geq y_i + y_j - 1$$

$$f^{\mathrm{U}}\left(\log\left(w_{i,j}^{\mathrm{T}}\right)\right) \le W_{i,j} \le f^{\,\mathrm{O}}\left(\log\left(w_{i,j}^{\mathrm{T}}\right)\right)$$

$$f^{\mathrm{U}}\left(\log\left(x_i^{\mathrm{T}}\right)\right) \le X_i \le f^{\,\mathrm{O}}\left(\log\left(x_i^{\mathrm{T}}\right)\right)$$

$$f^{\mathrm{U}}\left(\log\left(x_j^{\mathrm{T}}\right)\right) \le X_j \le f^{\,\mathrm{O}}\left(\log\left(x_j^{\mathrm{T}}\right)\right)$$

The (PL) formulation encompasses two important facts. First, the linear over- and underestimators of logarithmic functions are defined over the domain of variables in interest even if the corresponding binary variables are set to 0. Second, the equivalency between the value of the bilinear terms when one or both of the variables x_i, x_j become 0 and the sum of slack variables is preserved (1).

$$x_i x_j \overset{\substack{x_i=0 \\ \vee \\ x_j=0}}{=} 0 \Leftrightarrow W_{i,j} - \left(X_i + X_j\right) \overset{\substack{x_i=0 \\ \vee \\ x_j=0}}{=} 0 \tag{1}$$

The relationship given by equation (1) is clearly true when both binaries (y_i, y_j) are 0 or 1. However, we should note that when only one of the two binaries becomes 1 (e.g. $y_i=1$, $y_j = 0$), the corresponding constraints bounding the disaggregated variables ($\varepsilon_i \le x^{\mathrm{T}}_i \le x^{\mathrm{UP}}_i$) do not impose hard bounds on the original variables (x_i). If preferred by the direction of optimization, the binary variable y_i can become 0, thus keeping the domain of the original variable (x_i) intact and the equality constraint correlating the slack variables valid. The same is true in the opposite case.

3.2. Global optimization algorithm

The optimization algorithm used in this study is based on iterations between the upper-bounding problem (P) and the lower-bounding problem (PL). The relaxation gap is tightened by restricting the feasible region of (PL) through the addition of generated under- and overestimators. The algorithm is summarized as follows:

Step 1: Solve (P):
    i.   Set $Z = Z^{\mathrm{UP}}$,
    ii.   Generate a set of over- and underestimators (OUP) in the unique solutions of (P)
    iii.   Add set (OUP) to (PL)

Step 2: Solve (PL):
    i.   Set $Z = Z^{\mathrm{LO}}$
    ii.   If: abs(Z^{UP}-Z^{LO}) $\le \varepsilon$ →STOP
    iii.   Else: Generate a set of over- and underestimators (OUPL) in the unique solutions of (PL)
    iv.   Add set (OUPL) to (PL)
    v.   Return to step 1.

It should be noted that solving the upper bounding problem (P) in each iteration is not necessary. However, if the upper bound changes (improves) during the computation, it might help to tighten the relaxation gap.

4. Numerical studies

To demonstrate the proposed approach, we present the results of 5 numerical studies. The test problems were the following pooling problems in pq-formulation (Tawarmalani and

Sahinidis, 2002): Haverly1, Bental4, Foulds4 and Foulds5 and RT2. The results of the numerical experiments are summarized in Table 1.

The models were coded in GAMS. CONOPT was used as an NLP solver and CPLEX as the MILP solver. The overestimators in (PL) were modelled as tangents of logarithmic functions, while the underestimators were modelled as their piecewise linear approximations, using SOS2 variables. The lower bound on variables corresponding to x^T_i and x^T_j in (PL) was set to 0.0001. The convergence criterion (i.e. absolute tolerance) was set to 0.

Table 1: Results of numerical experiments.

Model	Haverly1	Bental4	Foulds4	Foulds5	RT2
			NLP		
No. of variables	11	14	673	673	35
No. of equations	24	29	767	767	69
Global optimum	−400.00	−450.00	−8.00	−8.00	−4,391.82
			MILP		
Initial lower bound[a]	−496.97	−549.23	−8.00	−8.00	−6,034.87
No. of iterations	31	33	1	1	25
No. of all variables[b]	253	336	4,468	4,468	803
No. of binary variables	8	11	672	672	30
No. of equations	215	294	7,031	7,031	981
t_{CPU}/s	5.6	9.6	0.8	1.2	>3,600
Final lower bound[b]	−400.00	−450.00	−8.00	−8.00	−4,391.82

[a]solution of first MILP
[b]total number of continuous variables incl. SOS2 variables
[c]solution of last MILP

The results presented in Table 1 indicate that the proposed approach identifies globally optimal solutions in all the cases studied. While the computational time is relatively short in the Haverly1 and Bental4 instances of the pooling problem, it is considerably longer in the RT2 instance, although the NLP sizes and the number of iterations to obtain the global optimum are within the same order of magnitude. On the other hand, the Foulds4 and Foulds5 instances, although the largest instances in terms of the problem size, are solved in a single iteration.

5. Conclusions

In this work, we presented an approach to the global optimization of bilinear problems that relies on transformation of bilinear terms to functions of single variables. A logarithm operation is used to separate the variables participating in bilinear terms. The reformulation to a lower-bounding MILP is then performed, using the mixed-integer translation of variables.

Although the proposed approach is presented as a method to solve bilinear problems to global optimality, it is apparent that its potential scope is greater. The approach can be applied in principle to any nonlinear problem whose nonlinearities can be transformed into elementary functions of single variables. The results presented in this study indicate that the proposed approach is feasible. However, to make it computationally more efficient, more elaborate algorithmic procedures should be adapted.

References

E. Ahmetović, I. E. Grossmann, 2010, Strategies for the Global Optimization of Integrated Process Water Networks. Computers and Chemical Engineering. 28, 901–906.

M. Bogataj, Z. Kravanja, 2018, Alternative Mixed-integer Reformulation of Generalized Disjunctive Programs, Computer Aided Chemical Engineering, 43, 549–554.

M. Bogataj, Z. Kravanja, 2019, On Robustness of Mixed-Integer Reformulations of Generalized Disjunctive Programs, Computer Aided Chemical Engineering, 46, 1117–1122.

D. Faria, M. Bagajewicz, 2012, A new approach for global optimization of a class of MINLP problems with applications to water management and pooling problems, AIChE Journal, 58, 2320–2335.

R. Karuppiah, I. E. Grossmann, 2006, Global optimization for the synthesis of integrated water systems in chemical processes, Computers and Chemical Engineering, 30, 650–673.

S. Kolodziej, P. M. Castro, I. E. Grossmann, 2013, Global optimization of bilinear programs with a multiparametric disaggregation technique, Journal of Global Optimization, 57: 1039, DOI 10.1007/s10898-012-0022-1.

G. P. McCormick, 1976, Computability of global solutions to factorable nonconvex programs: Part 1-convex underestimating problems. Mathematical Programming, 10, 147–175.

C. A. Meyer , C. A. Floudas, 2006, Global optimization of a combinatorially complex generalized pooling problem, AIChE Journal, 52, 1027–1037.

R. Misener, C. A. Floudas, 2009, Advances for the pooling problem: Modeling, global optimization, and computational studies Survey, Applied and Computational Mathematics, 8 (1), 3–22.

R. Misener , J. P. Thompson, C. A. Floudas, 2011, APOGEE: Global optimization of standard, generalized, and extended pooling problems via linear and logarithmic partitioning schemes, Computers and Chemical Engineering, 35, 876–892.

M. Ropotar, Z. Kravanja, 2009, Translation of Variables and Implementation of Efficient Logic-Based Techniques in the MINLP Process Synthesizer MIPSYN, AIChE Journal, 55 (11), 2896– 2913.

M. Tawarmalani, N. Sahinidis, 2002, Convexification and Global Optimization in Continuous and Mixed-Integer Nonlinear Programming - Theory, Algorithms, Software, and Applications, Springer Science+Business Media Dordrecht.

J. P. Teles, P. M. Castro, H. A. Matos, 2012, Global Optimization of Water Networks Design using Multiparametric Disaggregation, Computers and Chemical Engineering 40, 132–147.

Sauro Pierucci, Flavio Manenti, Giulia Bozzano, Davide Manca (Eds.)
Proceedings of the 30ᵗʰ European Symposium on Computer Aided Process Engineering
(ESCAPE30), May 24-27, 2020, Milano, Italy. © 2020 Elsevier B.V. All rights reserved.
http://dx.doi.org/10.1016/B978-0-12-823377-1.50330-X

Uncertainty Analysis and Model Reduction Based Global Optimisation of Distributed Large-scale Systems

Min Tao, Constantinos Theodoropoulos

Department of Chemical Engineering and Analytical Science, University of Manchester, Manchester M13 9PL, UK
k.theodoropoulos@manchester.ac.uk

Abstract

Uncertainty arises in many large-scale distributed industrial systems, needing efficient computational tools. Uncertainty propagation techniques have been developed and applied including power series expansions (PSE) and polynomial chaos expansions (PCE). However, such fast low-order approximate models generate errors and, in general, require prior knowledge about uncertainty distribution. In this work, the recursive projection method (RPM) was adopted to accelerate the computation of steady state solutions of complex large-scale dynamic systems. These accelerated models including uncertainty were subsequently utilised in an efficient Bayesian global optimisation framework. The performance of the proposed robust optimisation framework was demonstrated through an illustrative example: a tubular reactor where an exothermic reaction takes place.

Keywords: Uncertainty analysis, Distributed parameter systems, Recursive projection method, Bayesian global optimisation

1. Introduction

Complex distributed-parameter systems are common in industrial practice. Due to the inherent stochasticity and/or insufficient knowledge about processes, uncertainty arises (Eldred, 2009). In particular, parametric uncertainty in system models can greatly impact output performance. To robustly account for the impact of parametric uncertainties, uncertainty propagation techniques have been developed. Power series and polynomial chaos expansions methods have been used to address uncertainty through the application of low-order models, which worked efficiently for robust control (Nagy and Braatz, 2007). However, low-order approximate models may require prior knowledge about the distributions of parametric uncertainty (Kimaev and Richardez-Sandoval, 2018). For example, polynomial chaos expansion is implemented through "suitable" orthogonal polynomials corresponding to the uncertainty distribution (Xiu, 2010), which significantly affects computational accuracy. From the view of computational accuracy and generalised ability to handle uncertainty, directly using the original system model could be a better choice. To deal with intensive computational requirements of dynamic system models, the recursive projection method (Shroff and Keller, 1993) is used here. RPM has been multiply implemented as an effective model reduction technique for input/output systems for optimization and control purposes (Luna-Ortiz and Theodoropoulos, 2005; Bonis et al, 2013). RPM requires only a few utilisations of the (black-box) time integrator, to accelerate the computation of steady states through the calculation of low-order system Jacobians. Nevertheless, the computation of low-order derivatives including uncertainty is costly. Kriging surrogate model and Bayesian optimisation strategies are efficient for the expensive black-box systems (Jones et al, 1998). In this work, uncertainty analysis and robust optimisation framework have been constructed for large-scale input/output systems. Firstly, a RPM-based methodology was proposed to propagate parametric uncertainty in an accelerated way. Subsequently, the accelerated model with uncertainty was used by kriging models and a Bayesian global optimisation procedure to produce a robust optimal solution.

2. Uncertainty Analysis

2.1. Large-scale distributed system with parametric uncertainty

This work deals with the optimization of large-scale spatially distributed processes, described by a set of nonlinear dissipative PDEs with uncertainty:

$$\frac{\partial X}{\partial t} = D\left\{\frac{\partial X}{\partial y}, \frac{\partial^2 X}{\partial y^2}, ..., \frac{\partial^n X}{\partial y^n}\right\} + E(X, P_1, P_2) \tag{1}$$

Where D is the dissipative spatial differential operator, $E(X, P_1, P_2)$ is the nonlinear function, X is the set of state variables, $P_1 \in R^{n1}$ are the design variables and $P_2 \in R^{n2}$ are the uncertain parameters.

2.2. Recursive projection method (RPM)

The dynamic systems in Eq. (1) are discretised and solved by a fixed-point procedure:

$$U^{n+1} = F(U^n, P_1, P_2; \tau) \tag{2}$$

Where $U \in R^N$ is the discretised unknown variable, n is the number of iteration steps, $F : R^N \times R^{n1} \times R^{n2} \to R^N$, τ is the reporting horizon of the black-box simulator.

The steady state solutions of the above fixed-point procedure are also the steady state solutions of the dynamic system:

$$X = f(X, P_1, P_2) \tag{3}$$

The recursive fixed-point procedure is time-consuming. To accelerate the computation, RPM is employed to decompose the solution space R^N into two subspaces: the low-dimensional P and its orthogonal complement Q:

$$R^N = P \oplus Q \tag{4}$$

The orthonormal basis Z of the slow subspace P can be efficiently computed by matrix-free algorithms, such as the Arnoldi method. Then:

$$I = Z^T Z, \quad P = ZZ^T \tag{5}$$

Where I is the identity matrix, $Z \in R^{N \times m}$ with m being the dimension of P.

The low dimensional Jacobians of subspace P can then be approximated by directional perturbations:

$$F_U Z = \frac{1}{2\varepsilon}(F(U + \varepsilon Z) - F(U - \varepsilon Z)) \tag{6}$$

Where ε is a small perturbation on the direction of Z.

Then the low-order Jacobian is given by:

$$H = Z^T F_U Z \tag{7}$$

Assuming the numerically stable time integration, the main RPM steps included the solution space decomposition (Eq. (8)), repeating Newton-Picard iterations (Eq. (9-10)) on the two subspaces and Picard iteration on the final sum to check the convergence $\|U(P_1,P_2) - F(U,P_1,P_2)\|$.

$$p^{(0)} = PU^{(0)}(P_1,P_2), \quad q^{(0)} = QU^{(0)}(P_1,P_2) \tag{8}$$

$$p^{(u+1)} = p^{(u)} + (I - ZHZ^T)^{-1} \times (PF(U^{(u)},P_1,P_2) - p^{(u)}) \tag{9}$$

$$q^{(u+1)} = QF(U^{(u)},P_1,P_2) \tag{10}$$

$$U^{(u+1)}(P_1,P_2) = p^{(u+1)} + q^{(u+1)} \tag{11}$$

Where u is the number of Newton-Picard iterations.

Here, the Monte Carlo (MC) sampling method was used to approximate the parametric uncertainty. Therefore, RPM coupled with MC sampling method together accelerate the computation of the parametric uncertainty at steady state. The computationally-accelerated model was subsequently applied in a Bayesian optimisation framework.

3. Bayesian optimisation

With the acceleration technique RPM, optimising the system model with uncertainty is still costly. In this work, Bayesian optimisation strategy was adopted through kriging model and expected improvement function, originating from efficient global optimisation (Jones et al, 1998).

3.1. Kriging model

Kriging model, a popular surrogate models, assumes that the random output variable $f(y)$ at any location point y with mean value μ and variance σ^2, and prior joint Gaussian distribution for the finite random variables:

$$f(Y) \sim N(\mu(Y), K(Y,Y)) \tag{12}$$

Where $f(Y) = (f(y_1), f(y_2) \dots f(y_N))$, $\mu(Y) = (\mu(y_1), \mu(y_2) \dots \mu(y_N))$ and $K_{ij} = k(y_i, y_j)$, $k(y_i, y_j)$ is the kernel function.

Here, Gaussian kernels are used:

$$k(y_i, y_j) = \sigma_f^2 \exp(-\frac{1}{2l^2}(y_i - y_j)^T (y_i - y_j)) \tag{13}$$

Where kernel parameters σ_f^2 and l are computed by a few initial observed samples.

The observed variables $f(Y)$ and unknown variables $f_*(Y_*)$ given new points Y_* satisfy a joint Gaussian distribution:

$$\begin{pmatrix} f(Y) \\ f_*(Y_*) \end{pmatrix} \sim N(\begin{pmatrix} \mu(Y) \\ \mu(Y_*) \end{pmatrix}, \begin{pmatrix} K & k(Y,Y_*) \\ k(Y_*,Y) & k(Y_*,Y_*) \end{pmatrix})$$

$$\tag{14}$$

The posterior predictive $f_*(Y_*)$ is still a Gaussian process:

$$f_* | (f(Y), Y, Y_*) \sim N(\mu_*, \sigma_*^2) \tag{15}$$

Where $\mu_* = \mu(Y_*) + k(Y_*, Y)K^{-1}(f(Y) - m(Y))$, $\sigma_*^2 = k(Y_*, Y_*) - k(Y_*, Y)K^{-1}k(Y, Y_*)$

3.2. Expected improvement (EI) function

In Bayesian global optimisation, acquisition functions decide the next sampling point. Here, EI function under kriging model is used to balance exploitation with exploration:

$$EI(y) = \begin{cases} (\mu(y) - f(y^+) - \varphi)\Phi(g) + \sigma(y)\phi(g) & \sigma(y) > 0 \\ 0 & \sigma(y) = 0 \end{cases} \tag{16}$$

Where

$$g = \begin{cases} \dfrac{\mu(y) - f(y^+) - \varphi}{\sigma(y)} & \sigma(y) > 0 \\ 0 & \sigma(y) = 0 \end{cases}$$

Here $\mu(y)$ and $\sigma(y)$ are the mean and the standard deviation of the kriging model, respectively. Φ and ϕ are the CDF and PDF of the standard normal distribution, respectively. y^+ is the location of current best sample and φ is a parameter that determines the amount of exploration.

4. Application

The effectiveness of the proposed optimisation framework is illustrated using an exothermic tubular reactor (Tao et al, 2019). The mathematical formulation is as follows:

$$\max_{Twi} \ a\mu(C_{exit}) - (1-a)\sigma(C_{exit})$$

$$s.t. \ \frac{\partial C}{\partial t} = \frac{1}{Pe_1}\frac{\partial^2 C}{\partial y^2} - \frac{\partial C}{\partial y} + Da(1-C)\exp(T/(1+T/\gamma))$$

$$\frac{\partial T}{\partial t} = \frac{1}{Pe_2}\frac{\partial^2 T}{\partial y^2} - \frac{\partial T}{\partial y} - \beta T + BDa(1-C)\exp(T/(1+T/\gamma)) + \beta T_w$$

$$T_w(y) = \sum_{i=1}^{3}(H(y - y_{i-1}) - H(y) - y_i)T_{wi}$$

$$Da \sim N(0.1, 0.01) \tag{17}$$

Here C and T are the dimensionless concentration and temperature respectively, C_{exit} the dimensionless output concentration, $\mu(C_{exit})$ is the mean value of the uncertain output C_{exit}. $\sigma(C_{exit})$ is the standard variance value of C_{exit}. T_w is the adiabatic wall temperature at the three cooling zones. H is the Heaviside step function. The system parameters are $Pe_1 = 5, Pe_2 = 5, \beta = 1.5, \gamma = 10, B = 12$. Da is the Damkohler number.

In this optimisation problem, the objective is to maximize the average value and minimize the variance of the output dimensionless product concentration, with uncertainty parameter Da and design variables T_w. a is the weight between the two terms, here set to be 0.6. The system model is given by a dynamic black-box simulator with inputs the design variables and the uncertain parameter and outputs the dimensionless concentration and temperature. The RPM algorithm was implemented in MATLAB R2019a and Bayesian optimisation in Python 3.7.3/PyCharm 2018.3.5 on a Desktop ((Intel Core(TM) i7-8700 CPU 3.2 GHz, 16 GB memory, 64-bit operating system, Windows 10).

4.1. Uncertainty analysis

To investigate the effect of parametric uncertainty on the output concentration, the uncertainty propagation was constructed. Firstly, the number of MC samples was decided to be 3000 by an independent numerical experiment. Then 3000 MC samples were generated to approximate the parameter distribution. To compare results of different uncertainty propagation methods, the same 3000 MC samples were utilized with the original dynamic solver, RPM using the dynamic solver, second-order PSE and second-order PCE. The report horizon was 0.01seconds the dimension of the dominant subspace was fixed to 10 for the RPM case. The perturbation, ε, was chosen to be 0.01 for PSE after numerical experiments with different perturbation sizes. 9 points of the original system were used for PCE. Table 1 shows that direct propagation uncertainty through the original dynamic solver is the most time-consuming. RPM significantly accelerated the computations with more than 87% saving and almost the same accuracy (also displayed in Figure 1). Although PSE took the least computational time, choosing the perturbation size increased the actual total cost to be 14.48 minutes. Compared with PSE, PCE produced more accurate mean value, low and upper bounds.Table 1 also shows the large variance of PSE and PCE because of missing a small spatial distribution as displayed in Figure 1.

Table 1. Uncertainty analysis (5% confidence level)

Models	Low bound C_{exit}	Up bound C_{exit}	Mean C_{exit}	Standard variance C_{exit}	Computational time (minutes)
Dynamic solver	0.1204	0.3136	0.1963	0.0999	319.24
RPM plus Dynamic solver	0.1204	0.3136	0.1963	0.0999	40.49
	Error : 0 %	Error : 0 %	Error : 0 %	Error : 0 %	
PSE	0.1266	0.2856	0.1869	0.0418	4.29
	Error: 5.15 %	Error : -8.93 %	Error : -4.79 %	Error : -58.16 %	
PCE	0.1215	0.3018	0.1876	0.0478	8.71
	Error: -0.91 %	Error: -3.76 %	Error: -4.43 %	Error: -52.15 %	

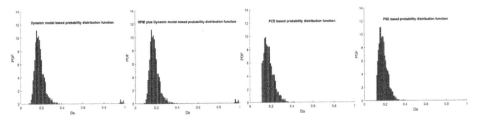

Figure 1. Probability density functions of the steady state output concentration

4.2. Bayesian optimisation

Using RPM with the black-box dynamic solver, Bayesian optimisation was constructed for the problem (Eq. (17)). Latin hypercube sampling method was utilised, taking 9.75

hours for the 8 initial samples. The optimisation process, as showed in Figure 2, converged to the optimum solution within 33 iterations and 30.91 hours.

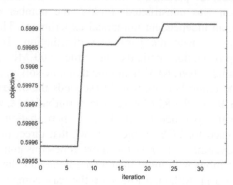

Figure 2. Bayesian optimisation of cooling process with parametric uncertainty

5. Conclusions

This paper presents a robust steady-state optimisation framework for large-scale dynamic systems with parametric uncertainty. RPM is employed to accelerate the dynamic systems to be steady state, resulting in significant cost reduction of uncertainty propagation. Furthermore, Bayesian optimisation with kriging model is utilised to find the optimum of the costly system within an acceptable number of iteration steps. The tubular reactor case study verifies the efficiency of our framework. In the future, the optimisation framework will be applied to scenarios of multivariate uncertainty and large-scale distributed stochastic systems.

References

M. Eldred, 2009, Recent advances in non-intrusive polynomial chaos and stochastic collocation methods for uncertainty analysis and design, In 50th AIAA/ASME/ASCE/AHS/ASC Structures, Structural Dynamics, and Materials Conference 17th AIAA/ASME/AHS Adaptive Structures Conference 11th AIAA No (p. 2274).

Z.K. Nagy, R.D. Braatz, 2007, Distributional uncertainty analysis using power series andlynomial chaos expansions, Journal of Process Control, 17(3), pp.229-240.

G. Kimaev, L.A. Ricardez-Sandoval, 2018, Multilevel Monte Carlo applied to chemical engineering systems subject to uncertainty. AIChE Journal, 64(5), pp.1651-1661.

G.M. Shroff, and H.B. Keller, 1993, Stabilization of unstable procedures: the recursive projection method, SIAM Journal on numerical analysis, 30(4), pp.1099-1120.

E. Luna-Ortiz, C. Theodoropoulos, 2005, An input/output model reduction-based optimization scheme for large-scale systems, Multiscale Modeling & Simulation, 4(2) pp. 691-708.

I. Bonis, W. Xie, C. Theodoropoulos, 2013, Multiple model predictive control of dissipative PDE systems, IEEE Transactions on Control Systems Technology, 22(3) pp. 1206-1214.

D.R. Jones , M. Schonlau, W.J. Welch, 1998, Efficient global optimization of expensive black-box functions, Journal of Global optimization, 13(4), pp.455-492.

M. Tao, J. Li, C. Theodoropoulos, 2019, Reduced model-based global optimisation of large-scale steady state nonlinear systems, In Computer Aided Chemical Engineering (Vol. 46, pp. 1039-1044). Elsevier.

Sauro Pierucci, Flavio Manenti, Giulia Bozzano, Davide Manca (Eds.)
Proceedings of the 30th European Symposium on Computer Aided Process Engineering
(ESCAPE30), May 24-27, 2020, Milano, Italy. © 2020 Elsevier B.V. All rights reserved.
http://dx.doi.org/10.1016/B978-0-12-823377-1.50331-1

Global Optimization with Ensemble Machine Learning Models

Alexander Thebelt[a], Jan Kronqvist[a], Robert M. Lee[b], Nathan Sudermann-Merx[b]
Ruth Misener[a]

[a]*Imperial College London, Exhibition Road, London SW7 2AZ, United Kingdom*
[b]*BASF SE, Carl-Bosch-Straße 38, 67063 Ludwigshafen am Rhein, Germany*
alexander.thebelt18@imperial.ac.uk

Abstract

Gradient boosted trees and other regression tree models are known to perform well in a
wide range of real-world, industrial applications. These tree models (i) offer insight into
important prediction features, (ii) effectively manage sparse data, and (iii) have excellent
prediction capabilities. We consider holistic decision-making problems where pre-trained
tree models are part of larger optimization tasks. Our contributions include: (i) explicitly
integrating model uncertainty considerations, (ii) solving the larger optimization problems that incorporate these uncertain tree models, (iii) proving that the resulting solutions
are globally optimal, i.e., no better solution exists.

Keywords: Gradient Boosted Trees, Global Optimization, Machine Learning, Optimization under Uncertainty

1. Introduction

While machine learning and deep learning have become invaluable in fields like image
recognition and automatic machine translation, the majority of traditional engineering
disciplines, are still seeking to integrate these powerful tools into their routines. Such
industrial applications are often subject to complex systems with high dimensional input
feature spaces. Sophisticated data-driven frameworks offer an attractive solution, especially when complete models are too complex or unknown. While advances in sensor
technology allow the collection of vast amounts of data, resulting datasets are subject to
low variability as industrial processes are often kept close to a few well-defined operating
states. On the other hand, experimental studies explore large regions of the input features
but are often limited due to high expenses. These two settings result in either large datasets with low variability or small datasets with high variability, respectively. However,
accurate data-driven models require large datasets with high variability, making model
uncertainty considerations inevitable. Gradient Boosted Tree (GBT) models have been
shown heuristically to work well in real-world industrial settings (Friedman, 2001).
Moreover, GBT models can be easily embedded into decision-making problems by encoding them as a Mixed Integer Linear Program (MILP) (Mišic, 2017).
The algorithm presented here is partially based on the work of Mistry et al. (2018) and
Mišic (2017), who investigate a similar optimization task. Generally, incorporating data-
driven models as surrogate models into optimization problems is enjoying growing popular ity (Bhosekar and Ierapetritou, 2018), e.g., algebraic equations (Boukouvala and
Floudas, 2017; Wilson and Sahinidis, 2017), artificial neural networks (Henao and Mar-
avelias, 2011; Schweidtmann and Mitsos, 2019) and Gaussian processes (Palmer and
Realff, 2002). We propose an algorithm that efficiently optimizes over pre-trained large-

scale tree models and that considers model uncertainty for arbitrarily distributed datasets. The algorithm derives mathematically proven global optimal solutions which is crucial in many industrial applications, e.g., production plants with high production margins, and safety critical settings.

2. Optimization over Ensemble Tree Models

Mistry et al. (2018) introduced the underlying Mixed Integer Nonlinear Program (MINLP) formulation:

$$\min_{v^L \leq x \leq v^U} \quad GBT(x) + \lambda\, \alpha_{Pen}(x), \tag{1}$$

$$s.t. \quad \text{[GBT MILP constraints]},$$

$$\text{[Variable linking constraints]},$$

$$\text{[Instance specific constraints]}.$$

We seek to minimize the objective function (1) which consists of $GBT(x)$, referring to the GBT model prediction, and $\alpha_{Pen}(x)$, defining a penalty function that handles model uncertainty. Additional *GBT MILP* constraints ensure the correct model evaluation, i.e., all necessary splits per tree leading to a leaf value occur in the correct order and only one leaf per tree is included in the prediction value. The *Variable Linking* constraints relate the continuous variable $x \in [v^L, v^U]$ to the intervals that are defined by the tree splits of the GBT model. Both, *GBT MILP* and *Variable linking* constraints, are discussed in detail in Mistry et al. (2018). The penalty $\alpha_{Pen}(x)$ is weighted by a positive parameter λ, such that larger values move the optimal solution x^* closer into regions of high data density.

2.1. Cluster Distance as a Penalty Measure

According to Mistry et al. (2018), their convex quadratic penalty function $\alpha_{Pen(x)}$ can only be expected to work for data that is uniformly distributed in a reduced subspace that covers most of its variability. In order to handle arbitrarily distributed datasets, we present a novel approach that prioritizes optimal solutions close to the training data. Initially, the dataset is pre-processed by utilizing a clustering method of choice, e.g. k-means (Lloyd, 1982), to derive cluster center coordinates $x_k \forall k \in \mathcal{K}$, with defining the set of clusters. These cluster centers indicate distinct areas where training data is located and where the model prediction error is expected to be small. The new penalty includes the following equations to the problem defined in (1):

$$\|diag(\sigma)^{-1}(x - \mu) - x_k\|_2^2 \leq \alpha_{Pen} + M(1 - b_k) \qquad \forall k \in \mathcal{K}, \tag{2a}$$

$$\sum_{k \in \mathcal{K}} b_k = 1, \tag{2b}$$

$$\alpha_{Pen} \geq 0, \tag{2c}$$

$$b_k \in \{0,1\} \qquad\qquad \forall k \in \mathcal{K}. \qquad (2d)$$

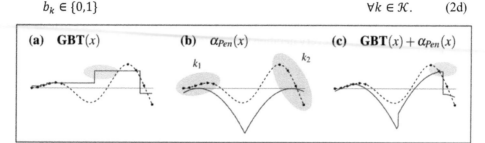

Figure 1: (a) Prediction of $f(x) = x\sin(x)$ by GBT model; (b) Cluster distance penalty measure; (c) Summation of GBT model prediction and cluster distance penalty measure.

Equations (2) define α_{Pen} as the squared Euclidean distance of the optimal solution to the closest cluster center by introducing "Big-M" constraints. Applying k-means to the standardized dataset requires the standardization of x by using sample mean μ and sample standard deviation σ. The coefficient M can efficiently be calculated as the sum of the maximum Euclidean distance between two cluster centers and the maximum radius of all clusters. The variables $b_k \in \{0,1\}$ function as a binary switch: when $b_k = 0$, the constraint is inactivated as the large value of M makes them redundant and when $b_k = 1$, the large M coefficient is multiplied by 0 and effectively disappears. To ensure that the distance to only one cluster center is active, (2b) is included. The full optimization model given by (1) and (2) is then characterized as a convex MINLP (Kronqvist et al., 2019).

Example: We define the ground truth of a system of interest as $f(x) = x\sin(x)$ and sample the function to create a dataset. Training a simple GBT model and maximizing it suggests a highly non-optimal point with respect to the ground truth due to large model prediction errors near a sample void in the middle of the function interval as shown in Figure 1 (a). Using the penalty definition introduced in Section 2.1 gives a function depicted in Figure 1 (b). Considering the sum of GBT model prediction and the penalty function as shown in Figure 1 (c) shifts the maximum to a more accurate solution with respect to the ground truth.

2.2. Main Algorithmic Elements

The main algorithm utilizes a deterministic branch-and-bound (B&B) approach that branches over the domain $[v^L, v^U]$, i.e., splits the domain into subdomains. Every domain is characterized by a lower bound on the best possible solution in the domain. B&B rejects individual domains in case of infeasible subproblems or when their lower bound exceeds the current best feasible solution, i.e., the upper bound. This way, the search space is constantly reduced, and B&B avoids the explicit enumeration of all possible solutions (Morrison et al., 2016). Mistry et al. (2018) propose strong branching to efficiently reduced the search domain. The new lower bound of objective function (1) is decomposed according to: $\hat{R}^S = b^{GBT,S} + b^{\alpha_{Pen},S}$, where $b^{GBT,S}$ and $b^{\alpha_{Pen},S}$ define lower bounds of GBT(x) and $\alpha_{Pen}(x)$ in domain S, respectively. Computing the tightest lower bound for GBT(x) in domain S is difficult to provide for large instances as it is NP-hard (Mišic (2017)). Therefore, an easier to compute weaker lower bound $b^{GBT,S}$ is derived by so-called partition refinement (Mistry et al., 2018). Due to the rapid growth of $\alpha_{Pen}(x)$ for regions distant from training data, deriving a weak bound for GBT(x) is often sufficient to reject domains as the "weak" lower bound already surpasses the current best feasible solution. This is especially appealing if $b^{\alpha_{Pen},S}$ can be computed easily. For all domains that cannot immediately be rejected, $b^{GBT,S}$ is recomputed to derive tighter bounds for $GBT(x)$ in domain S. After every iteration the best feasible solution and the lowest lower bound move closer together and ultimately prove global optimality which in practice is subject to a pre-defined optimality gap.

2.3. Computational Enhancements

The convex MINLP penalty constraints in (2) are in general more difficult to solve than the convex quadratic constraints introduced by Mistry et al. (2018) and require advanced algorithmic enhancements to achieve faster convergence. Firstly, instead of calling an external solver to derive the lower bound $b^{\alpha_{Pen},S}$, enforced by Eq. (2), we project the cluster centers onto the box defined by S, to determine all cluster center distances explicitly. The smallest distance defines the lower bound $b^{\alpha_{Pen},S}$ and thereby avoids the time-consuming computational overhead of an external solver. Secondly, good feasible solutions are derived to warm-start the algorithm. This allows faster convergence, as the search space is constantly reduced by rejecting regions S for which $\hat{R}^S$ exceeds the current best feasible solution. Pre-defined cluster centers by definition have $\alpha_{Pen}=0$ and a good initial feasible solution x_{feas} can therefore be derived by picking the coordinates x_k of the cluster center $k \in \mathcal{K}$ with the lowest value for $GBT(x_k)$.

3. Numerical Experiments

Here, we evaluate two case studies to show that the algorithm (i) derives optimal solutions with less model uncertainty for higher penalty parameter values and (ii) outperforms off-the-shelf global solvers for large instances. All numerical experiments are run on an Ubuntu 18.04.2 LTS system with 16GB RAM and an Intel Core i7-7700K @ 4.20Ghz CPU. For the modeling of the MINLP and interfacing with solvers we used Python 3.7.3 in combination with Pyomo 5.5.1 by Hart et al. (2017).

3.1. Penalty Parameter Study

A mechanistic model consisting of four differential and one algebraic equation Elqotbi et al. (2013) describes the product concentration C_P (output) of a fermentation process based on an oxygen mass transfer coefficient $k_L a$ (inputs) which is a control vector that determines how much oxygen is fed into the process at different time steps. The optimal control problem determines $k_L a$ to maximize C_P. The evaluation of the mechanistic model involves an integration procedure that is treated as a black-box. The mapping of input vector $k_L a$ onto the output C_P is given by: $C_P = Mech(k_L a)$. To imitate an industrial sample selection process, the input data is generated as blobs by using the scikit-learn library Pedregosa et al. (2011) and evaluated with the mechanistic model to create the dataset. The R package gbm Ridgeway (2007) is used to train a GBT model $GBT(x)$ which is then optimized for different penalty parameter values. The average relative model error $\bar{\epsilon}_{GBT}$ with respect to $Mech(k_L a)$ is computed based on 10 independent runs that each consider 10 different values for the penalty parameter. Directly optimizing the formulation with Gurobi 8.1.1. gives the results depicted in Figure 2. The results suggest that the penalty measure used can efficiently handle uncertainty in GBT models. A large penalty parameter value ($\lambda > 1$) resulted in average model errors $\bar{\epsilon}_{GBT} < 1$ %. On the other hand, low penalty parameter values identify regions where the average model error $\bar{\epsilon}_{GBT}$ is high but where good solutions with regard to optimality are predicted by the GBT model. Gathering more data in these regions could create an overall better performing GBT model and help to identify better solutions.

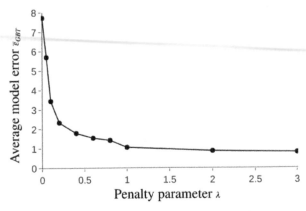

Figure 2: Average model error $\bar{\epsilon}_{GBT}$ for different penalty parameters λ.

3.2. Large-Scale Instance

Table 1: Results of the proposed algorithm and Gurobi 8.1.1 for a GBT model trained on the concrete mixture design dataset. Blank entries indicate premature solver termination.

[h]	Proposed Algorithm			Gurobi 8.1.1		
	ub	lb	gap	ub	lb	gap
2	-71.6	-105.7	48 %	-88.7	-138.8	56 %
4	-71.6	-103.0	44 %	-90.4	-127.5	41 %
6	-78.9	-102.0	29 %	-90.4	-116.9	29 %
8	-78.9	-100.8	28 %	-	-	-
40	-83.6	-94.7	13 %	-	-	-

To compare the overall performance of the proposed algorithm to the state-of-the-art solver Gurobi 8.1.1 we use the concrete strength dataset (Yeh (1998)) from the UCI machine learning repository (Dua and Graff (2017)). The dataset reports the compressive strength for different ingredient proportions. A GBT model is trained inside a caret framework Kuhn (2008) using cross-validation. The trained GBT model has 8 continuous variables describing different ingredient proportions of the concrete and maps onto its compressive strength. The resulting MINLP maximizes the compressive strength given a predefined time limit and has 8,481 binary variables $y_{i,j}$ and 280,107 constraints. With a penalty parameter $\lambda = 1$ and a solver time limit of 40 h, the results are summarized in Table 1. As shown in Table 1, the proposed algorithm reaches the same relative optimality gap as Gurobi 8.1.1 after 6 h of runtime, after which Gurobi 8.1.1 terminates prematurely due to memory exhaustion. While Gurobi 8.1.1 generates better upper bounds, the proposed algorithm derives stronger lower bounds which are needed to proof optimality and terminates due to the time limit of 40 h, reaching a significantly lower optimality gap of 13 %. Hence, the proposed algorithm outperforms off-the-shelf solvers, e.g. Gurobi, for large problem instances. Moreover, despite its more difficult to solve penalty function, the results compare well to Mistry et al. (2018), highlighting the efficiency of the proposed algorithm.

4. Conclusion

The proposed algorithm efficiently optimizes data-driven tree-based ensemble models to global optimality and outperforms state-of-the-art global solvers. Moreover, we introduce a novel penalty measure that allows model uncertainty consideration while optimizing and show its high effectiveness in numerical studies. Further improvements will focus on algorithmic, modeling and application related aspects. The results suggest that the proposed algorithm can also be useful in Design of Experiment applications and future research will include comparisons to other approaches in this field, e.g., Bayesian Optimization.

References

A. Bhosekar, M. Ierapetritou, 2018. Advances in surrogate based modeling, feasibility analysis, and optimization: A review. Computers & Chemical Engineering 108, 250 – 267.

F. Boukouvala, C. A. Floudas, Jun 2017. Argonaut: Algorithms for global optimization of constrained grey-box computational problems. Optimization Letters 11 (5), 895–913.

D. Dua, C. Graff, 2017. UCI Machine Learning Repository. M. Elqotbi, S. D. Vlaev, L. Montastruc, I. Nikov, 1 2013. CFD modelling of two-phase stirred bioreaction systems by segregated solution of the Euler-Euler model. Computers and Chemical Engineering 48, 113–120.

J. H. Friedman, 2001. Greedy function approximation: A gradient boosting machine. Annals of Statistics.

W. E. Hart, C. D. Laird, J.-P. Watson, D. L. Woodruff, G. A. Hackebeil, B. L. Nicholson, J. D. Siirola, 2017. Pyomo - Optimization Modeling in Python. Vol. 67 of Springer Optimization and Its Applications. Springer International Publishing.

C. A. Henao, C. T. Maravelias, 2011. Surrogate-based superstructure optimization framework. AIChE Journal 57 (5), 1216–1232.

J. Kronqvist, D. E. Bernal, A. Lundell, I. E. Grossmann, 6 2019. A review and comparison of solvers for convex MINLP. Optimization and Engineering 20 (2), 397–455.

M. Kuhn, 2008. Building Predictive Models in R Using the caret Package. Journal of Statistical Software 28 (5).

S. P. Lloyd, 1982. Least Squares Quantization in PCM. IEEE Transactions on Information Theory 28 (2), 129–137.

M. Mistry, D. Letsios, G. Krennrich, R. M. Lee, R. Misener, 2018. Mixed-integer convex nonlinear optimization with gradient-boosted trees embedded. arXiv 1803.00952.

V. V. Mišic, 2017. Optimization of tree ensembles. arXiv 1705.10883.

D. R. Morrison, S. H. Jacobson, J. J. Sauppe, E. C. Sewell, 2 2016. Branch-and-bound algorithms: A survey of recent advances in searching, branching, and pruning. Discrete Optimization 19, 79–102.

K. Palmer, M. Realff, 2002. Optimization and validation of steady-state flowsheet simulation metamodels. Chemical Engineering Research and Design 80 (7), 773 – 782.

F. Pedregosa, G. Varoquaux, A. Gramfort, V. Michel, B. Thirion, O. Grisel, M. Blondel, P. Prettenhofer, R. Weiss, V. Dubourg, J. Vanderplas, A. Passos, D. Cournapeau, M. Brucher, M. Perrot, E. Duchesnay, 10 2011. Scikit-learn: Machine learning in Python. Journal of Machine Learning Research 12, 2825–2830.

G. Ridgeway, 2007. Generalized Boosted Models: A guide to the gbm package. Compute 1 (4), 1–12.

A. M. Schweidtmann, A. Mitsos, 2019. Deterministic Global Optimization with Artificial Neural Networks Embedded. Journal of Optimization Theory and Applications 180 (3), 925–948.

Z. T. Wilson, N. V. Sahinidis, 2017. The ALAMO approach to machine learning. Computers & Chemical Engineering 106, 785–795.

I. C. Yeh, 1998. Modeling of strength of high-performance concrete using artificial neural networks. Cement and Concrete Research 28 (12), 1797–1808.

Sauro Pierucci, Flavio Manenti, Giulia Bozzano, Davide Manca (Eds.)
Proceedings of the 30th European Symposium on Computer Aided Process Engineering
(ESCAPE30), May 24-27, 2020, Milano, Italy. © 2020 Elsevier B.V. All rights reserved.
http://dx.doi.org/10.1016/B978-0-12-823377-1.50332-3

ECO2DES: Python Framework for the Eco-Design of Industrial Processes

Miguel García Casas,[a,b] Javier Dufour Andía,[a,c] Jose Luis Galvez Martos[c]

[a]*Chemical and Environmental Engineering Group, Rey Juan Carlos University, Móstoles, 28933, Spain*
[b]*Contactica S.L., Madrid, 28021, Spain*
[c]*Systems Analysis Unit, IMDEA Energy, Móstoles, 28935, Spain*
m.garciacasa.2018@alumnos.urjc.es / miguel.garcia@contactica.es

Abstract

More than 80% of the costs and environmental impacts of a new process are defined in the design phase, often without being properly assessed. *ECO2DES* is a new methodological approach for the eco-design of industrial processes (chemical, petro-chemical, energetic, bio-based…), integrated in a Python framework. *ECO2DES* allows for maximising economic parameters such, as the net present value, and minimising environmental impacts by the integration and automation of modelling, process simulation, life cycle assessment (LCA), life cycle costing assessment (LCC) and multi-objective optimisation algorithms (MOOA). This new methodology does not only design the optimal process from and sustainable point of view, but also reduces the workload accelerating the time-to-market of research and innovative projects in the process industry. In order to illustrate the potential of the framework, the methanation process for energy storage will be evaluated. The outputs of the *ECO2DES* framework clearly mark the way for the detailed engineering in the development of this process.

Keywords: Eco-design, process simulation, life cycle assessment, life cycle costing, optimisation.

1. Introduction

During the development of new innovative processes, there are no industrial data that can support any life cycle assessment, LCA, or life cycle cost, LCC, study, which gives rise to numerous trial-and-error phases during technology upscaling, exorbitantly increasing time-to-market and costs. Predictive models and process simulations, however, are able to compute, through physicochemical relationships, the behaviour of that technology under development at industrial scale and formulate scenarios for environmental or cost optimisation. However, process simulation, LCA and LCC methodologies are well structured and there are many options of commercial software specialised in these areas. Nowadays, at the best of our knowledge, there is no current research combining them in a holistic way for their application in the economic and environmental optimisation of any industrial design of process under research and/or development. With this premise, the *ECO2DES* framework was born. It is an object-oriented Python framework for sustainability-oriented optimisation of industrial processes. The tool takes advantage of the full feature set of Python, such as its facilities for fast prototyping and the several available libraries for data processing, data analysis, scientific computing and data visualisation. *ECO2DES* is a descriptive tool, which documents life cycle inventories and characterises them through their environmental impact and associated costs. It is a predictive tool, since it uses as inputs physicochemical models for process simulation in the research phase; and adaptive, since it automates process design selections based on multi-objective optimisation algorithms.

2. ECO2DES architecture

The architecture scheme of ***ECO2DES*** is illustrated in Fig. 1. It has an object-oriented design to make it flexible and expandable.

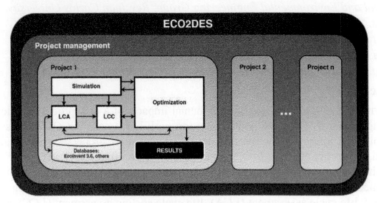

Figure 1. *ECO2DES* architecture scheme.

The core classes of ***ECO2DES*** are *projects, simulation, lca, lcc* and *optimization*. Class *projects* encapsulates the management tools, it offers several methods to create, delete, copy and assign projects. The initialisation of ***ECO2DES*** framework creates a folder inside the home directory in which all the projects are stored. Every project is linked to its own Ecoinvent 3.6 databases (Wernet et al., 2016), in order not to interfere with the changes made in another project. Class *simulation* allows to link with a model or simulation developed in Python, Excel or Aspen Plus, as well as defining the inputs and outputs of the simulation. Class *lca* inherits the most of its methods from *Brightway2*, (Mutel, 2017) an open-source framework for life cycle assessment. Some improvements regarding speedup calculation inside an optimisation loop, as well as several data visualisation tools were aggregated. Furthermore, this class allows the user to link the inputs and outputs defined in the class simulation with exchanges of an existing activity inside the database or a new one previously created. Class *lcc* was developed from scratch. It solves a financial life cycle costing of the product or products (from cradle to customer), but further implementations will be made to include a whole life cycle evaluation (from cradle to gate) and compute externalities costs derived from the environmental impacts assessed in the class *lca*. Finally, class *optimization* has methods to define the problem with variables from the classes *simulation, lca* and/or *lcc*; their boundaries, the problem constrains and the objectives from the three abovementioned classes. Class *optimization* has several algorithms for heuristic global optimisation and local optimisation, with a single or multiple objectives. These algorithms are inherited from *pygmo* (Biscani et al., 2010) and *scipy* (Virtanen et al., 2019), other libraries are under study to include their features, as well as own-developed implementations.

3. Case study: Sabatier for renewable energy storage in the natural gas grid

3.1. Background

Currently, conventional energy sources such as nuclear power or fossil fuels are being replaced by renewable ones such as wind or solar energy. However, most of the renewable sources cannot provide a base load electric power. To overcome this problem, storage systems have to be integrated in the power grid. For seasonal storage of the energy (charge / discharge period from 1 day to 1 year) in huge capacities, electrical energy can be converted into chemical energy by transferring it into fuels. The logical pathway is the conversion of electrical energy into hydrogen by water electrolysis, but nowadays there is no a hydrogen grid or a large enough storage system developed in any country. Until this requirement is satisfied, the highly developed natural gas grids can be used for the transport of excess energy (Bassano et al., 2019), using electrolysis to produce hydrogen to react with carbon dioxide in a methanation synthesis. So in addition to providing an energy carrier, the process consumes carbon dioxide, contributing to the reduction of GHGE. The methanation reactions of carbon monoxide and carbon dioxide were discovered at the beginning of the 20th century by Sabatier et al. (1902). The methanation of carbon dioxide is an exothermic catalytic reaction and is typically operated at temperatures between 200°C and 550°C depending on the used catalyst.

3.2. Sabatier process simulation

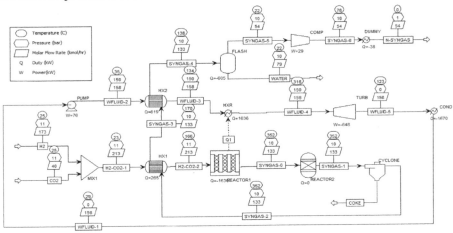

Figure 2. Aspen plus flowsheet of the Sabatier process simulation.

For the determination of the optimal reactor concept, the kinetic model 12 of Kopyscinski (2010) was used. The model parameters were implemented within a *RPLUG* reactor of Aspen Plus. Furthermore, the resulted gases are connected to a *RGIBSS* reactor to minimise the free energy of Gibbs following the Boudouard reaction (Gao et al., 2012). This way the potential formation of coke will be measured and taken into account for the deposition of solid over the catalysts, and, therefore, the economic model would take into account the regeneration and replacement cycles of the catalyst. The heat of the gas stream is recovered in the inlet current of the reactor as well as in the hybridisation with a Rankine cycle to generate electricity, which operates with water or cyclopentane as working fluid. Finally, the gas is dried and compressed to be injected into the grid. Then, if the hydrogen molar composition is higher than a 5 % a pressure swing adsorption, PSA, unit is needed, recovering 90 % of the hydrogen which is recirculated. Moreover, if carbon dioxide molar composition is higher than a 2 % a monoethanolamine (MEA)-based capture is needed, recovering 97% of the dioxide of carbon which is then recirculated. Both of them modelled as black boxes. Fig. 2 illustrates the layout of the Aspen Plus simulation.

3.3. ECO2DES implementation

3.3.1. Project creation and simulation linking

After importing **ECO2DES** framework, the first step is setting a project by name (if the project does not exist, this method creates it) and link it to the Aspen Plus simulation:

```
import eco2des as e2d

e2d.projects.set_current('Sabatier_case_study')
e2d.simulation.link('Sabatier_k.bkp')
aspen = e2d.simulation.com
```

Once the *link* method of the class *simulation* is run, the com object of the Aspen Plus simulation is created as an attribute of the class (see line 6 of the above code). This com object could be used to get access to the whole simulation data (for further understanding, please visit the Aspen Plus user guide, ActiveX section (AspenTech, 2010)), and with the *define_input* and *define_output* methods the variables of interest could be built.

3.3.2. Life cycle assessment

When the simulation is linked and the inputs and outputs defined, the life cycle assessment of the process could be modelled. The following code illustrates as an example how a database is picked, how a new activity is created and how a technosphere exchange is added to it:

```
ei36 = e2d.lca.database('Ecoinvent 3.6 cutoff')
sabatier = ei36.create_activity(name = 'Sabatier for storage of renewable energy in the gas grid',
            location = 'ES', unit = 'cubic meter', ref_product = 'SNG', production_amount = 1.0)
wastewater = [act for act in ei36 if act['name'] == 'market for wastewater, from residence'
                and act['location'] == 'RoW'][0]
sabatier.new_exchange(amount= -1*e2d.outputs['waste water'] / e2d.outputs['SNG'],
                input=wastewater, type="technosphere").save()
```

3.3.3. Life cycle costing assessment

When the simulation is linked and the inputs and outputs defined, the life cycle costing assessment of the process could be modelled. The following code illustrates as an example how the LCC object is instanced, how the reactor vessel is assigned to an **ECO2DES** correlation which calculates the cost based on the material needed computed based on the ASME BPVC, section VIII, division 1 (ASME, 1986). Finally, it shows how a William's correlation is used to compute the PSA cost.

```
lcc = e2d.lcc(local_factor = 0.89)
lcc.vessel(Q = e2d.outputs['Flow in'], rt = e2d.outputs['Residence time'], p=1e6,
        LD = e2d.inputs['LD ratio'], T = e2d.inputs['Reactor temperature'], phase = 'Fluids',
        kind = 'horizontal', material = 'Stainless 304', name = 'Sabatier reactor vessel')
lcc.william_equipment(name = 'PSA', cap = e2d.outputs['H2 recover']*0.09/1000*24, n = 0.7,
                ref_cap = 155.24, ref_cost = 7.32e6, ref_CEPCI = 444.2, phase = 'Fluids')
```

3.3.4. Multi-objective optimisation

Finally, the following code shows how a multi-objective optimisation problem is defined in **ECO2DES** (line 2), the optimisation algorithm is picked in line 1, in this case the multi-objective evolutionary algorithm with decomposition (MOEA/D) is used. An initial population is randomly constructed in line 12 and evolved in line 13. The problem has some constrains marked, based on the regulations for the natural gas grid: hydrogen composition lower than a molar 5 %, monoxide of carbon and dioxide of carbon composition lower than a molar 2 %. In this case, the constrains are treated as penalties during the simulation outputs definition.

```
algorithm = e2d.optimization.moead(gen = 20)
problem = e2d.optimization.problem(
            variables =(e2d.inputs['H2/CO2'], e2d.inputs['Reactor temperature'],
                        e2d.inputs['Reactor length'], e2d.inputs['Reactor LD'],
                        e2d.inputs['Working fluid']),
            bounds = ([4, 250, 1, 1, 0], [5, 400, 20, 10, 1]),
            objectives = (-1*e2d.outputs['Storage efficiency'], e2d.outputs['Climate change'],
                        e2d.outputs['Levelized cost']))
population = e2d.optimization.population(problem, 190)
evolved_pop = algorithm.evolve(population)
```

3.4. Results

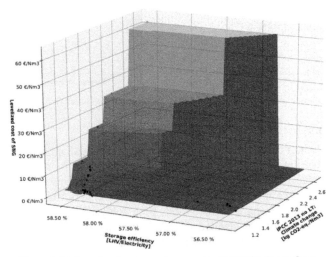

Figure 3. Methanation for energy storage using MOEA/D: Pareto front.

The storage efficiency is measured as the lower heating value (LHV) of the SNG divided by the electricity used (wind power for electrolysis minus the generated power). For LCA, the functional unit is 1 Nm^3 of SNG without considering the combustion and the limits of the system consider CO2 as free of environmental burdens, since it is a waste from the capture process. In this example, the climate change is assessed following the IPCC 2013 method without long term emissions for the characterization of the global warming potential. The levelised cost is calculated taking into account the capital expenditure (CAPEX) and operational expenditure (OPEX) assuming a loan of 60 % of CAPEX with a period for payment of 10 years and an interest of 4 %. A discount rate of 10 % is used during the 30 years of lifetime and a construction time of 1.5 years is assumed. The Pareto front for the three objectives optimisation problem is shown in Fig. 3. Moreover, two additional optimisation problems were solved using the non-dominated sorting genetic algorithm (NSGA-II): a two objectives problem with the storage efficiency and the levelised cost of SNG (see Fig. 4) and other with the climate change and the levelised cost of SNG which showed that these objectives are non-conflicting. The optimal solution of the methanation process, from the environmental and economic points of view, corresponds to the following conditions: hydrogen to carbon dioxide mole ratio of 4.44, a reactor temperature of 396 °C, a reactor length of 2.64 m, a reactor length to diameter ratio of 5.72 and using water as working fluid in the Rankine cycle. The calculated levelized cost of SNG is 1.481 €/Nm3, the climate change impact is 1.088 kg CO2-eq./Nm3 and the storage efficiency is 57.95 %. With this configuration a hydrogen recovery system is required, but carbon dioxide conversion is 98.63 % which allows injection SNG to the grid without recovering it.

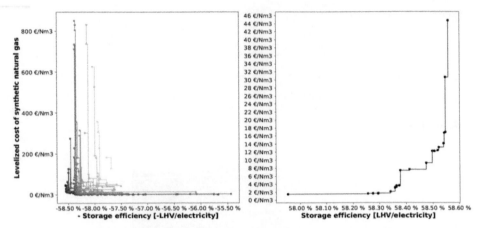

Figure 4. Methanation for energy storage using NSGA-II: Population evolution (left) and Pareto front (right).

4. Conclusions

ECO2DES, a Python-based framework for sustainability-based optimisation of industrial processes, has been presented in this paper. It provides support for accelerating the time-to-market of novel processes in different industries: automating the LCA and LCC, solving multi-objective and single-objective problems and performing upscaling studies. As an example, the methanation process has been analysed inside the framework. The results mark the way for the detailed engineering in the development of this process, showing that, on the one hand, environmental and economic objectives are non-conflicting. On the other hand, to improve storage efficiency will always compromise the environmental and economic performance of the process.

References

American Society of Mechanical Engineers (ASME), 1986. ASME Boiler and Pressure Vessel Code, Section VIII: Rules for Construction of Pressure Vessels, Division 1, pp. 382-383

AspenTech, 2010, Aspen Plus User Guide.

Bassano, C., Deiana, P., Lietti, L., Visconti, C. G., 2019. P2G movable modular plan operation on synthetic methane production from CO2 and hydrogen from renewables sources, Fuel, 253, pp.1071-1079.

Biscani, F., Izzo, D., Yam, C.H., 2010. A global optimisation toolbox for massively parallel engineering optimisation, preprint arXiv:1004.3824.

Gao, J., Wang, Y., Ping, Y., Hu, D., Xu, G., Gu, F., Su, F., 2012. A thermodynamic analysis of methanation reactions of carbon oxides for the production of synthetic natural gas, RSC Adv., 2(6), pp.2358-2368.

Kopyscinski, J., 2010. Production of synthetic natural gas in a fluidized bed reactor understanding the hydrodynamic, mass transfer, and kinetic effects, Doctoral Thesis.

Mutel, C. 2017. Brightway: An open source framework for Life Cycle Assessment. Journal of Open Source Software, , 2(12), pp.236.

Sabatier P., Senderens J.B., 1902. Direct hydrogenation of Oxides of Carbon in presence of various finely divided metals [in French]. C R Acad Sci, 134, pp.689–691.

Virtanen, P., Gommers, R., Oliphant, T., Haberland, M., Reddy, T., Cournapeau, D., et al., and SciPy 1.0 Contributors, 2019. SciPy 1.0–Fundamental Algorithms for Scientific Computing in Python, preprint arXiv:1907-10121.

Wernet, G., Bauer, C., Steubing, B., Reinhard, J., Moreno-Ruiz, E., and Weidema, B., 2016. The ecoinvent database version 3 (part I): overview and methodology. The International Journal of Life Cycle Assessment, 21(9), pp.1218–1230.

Sauro Pierucci, Flavio Manenti, Giulia Bozzano, Davide Manca (Eds.)
Proceedings of the 30th European Symposium on Computer Aided Process Engineering
(ESCAPE30), May 24-27, 2020, Milano, Italy. © 2020 Elsevier B.V. All rights reserved.
http://dx.doi.org/10.1016/B978-0-12-823377-1.50333-5

Operator Training for Non-Technical Skills in Process Industry

Hasan Mahbub Tusher[a], Steven Mallam[a], Gesa Praetorius[a,b], Zaili Yang[c], Salman Nazir[a*], Wilhelm Stock[d]

[a]*Training and Assessment Research Group (TARG), Department of Maritime Operations. Faculty of Technology, Natural Sciences & Maritime Sciences, University of South-Eastern Norway, Horten, 3184, Norway.*
[b]*Kalmar Maritime Academy, Linnaeus University, Sweden.*
[c]*Liverpool Logistics, Offshore and Marine Research Institute, Faculty of Engineering and Technology, Liverpool John Moores University, UK.*
[d]*RWE Power AG, Cologne, Germany.*

Salman.Nazir@usn.no

Abstract

The increasing levels of automation have redefined the nature of human-machine interactions in the process industry. The changing nature of work demands that Control-Room Operators and Field Operators are competent with the use of new and emerging methods and technologies in order to perform their tasks safely and effectively. A critical aspect of complex socio-technical systems is the requirement for humans to successfully interact with, and manage, both technical systems and team dynamics of human-to-human operations. Non-technical skills, such as communication, leadership, decision making, and teamwork are considered vital for safety in high-risk domains. Training has traditionally played a crucial role to instill the required technical and non-technical skills to the operators. Recurring training is also necessary for maintaining the knowledge and competencies required to face challenging operational environments. In this paper, four examples of non-technical skills training approaches used by an electric utility company for their operators are presented. This article reveals differing aspects of design and implementation of non-technical skills training in the process industry. It also demonstrates the necessity for research into the analysis of future training needs and assessment methods.

Keywords: process industry, training, safety, simulator, virtual reality

1. Introduction

Operators in the process industry are required to perform complex and safety-critical tasks with optimum efficiency. The complex nature of these tasks necessitates that operators manage adaptive automation, multilevel communication, and decision-making in dynamic work contexts. It is stated that approximately 90% of accidents in safety-critical industries are caused by human error (Leva, 2005). However, a wide range of issues from the organization, policies, equipment design, psychology, judgment and lack of competency are believed to contribute to underlying causes of what is eventually labelled "human error" (Whittingham, 2004; Manca et al., 2013). Both technical and non-technical competencies are required by operators to ensure safe and efficient operation of a plant and its processes. Non-technical skills (NTS) are defined as "*the cognitive, social and personal resource skills and complement technical skills, and contribute to safe and efficient task performance*" (Flin and O'Connor, 2017).

The connection between human error and NTS first originated in the aviation domain. Outcomes stemming from different aviation accidents revealed that lack of pilot NTS contributed more to the accidents than a lack of technical knowledge or aircraft malfunctioning (Flin and Maran, 2004). Considering the complexity of modern workplaces and the safety-critical nature of operations, NTS training elements were originally developed in the late 1980s for aviation pilots through Crew Resource Management (CRM) courses. CRM courses and their learning objectives have since been adopted in many high-risk domains including the nuclear, maritime and healthcare industries (Kanki et al., 2019; Flin et al., 2015). Ironically, nuclear power plant operators and healthcare personnel follow similar CRM training methods as in aviation, even whilst the workplace dynamics and goals differ greatly. Thus, there is a need for improved precision and more standardization of training for specialized domains (O'Connor et al., 2008; O'Dea et al., 2014).

NTS training often comprises a mixture of classroom-based lectures and practical simulation-based exercises (Hayward, Lowe & Thomas, 2018). However, there is typically little guidance to know when, what and how to train operators in different domains on NTS, as technical skills are often the focus. This paper specifically focuses on how *communication,* as a NTS, is trained within the process industry. Since communication is identified as an important aspect of safety across different safety-critical domains, including transport (Huang et al., 2018), healthcare (Lyndon, 2019), maritime (Sætrevik et al., 2018) and aviation (Ford et al., 2018), we present an overview of NTS training methods utilized by an electric utility company. Additionally, we address how the adopted NTS training methods bears significance in terms of long-term training assessment and inter-domain transferability through improved applications.

2. Case Study: Communication Skills Training in an Electric Utilities Company

Although there is no universally adopted method for training operators in the process industry, they all undergo various forms of education and training programs. The contents of these programs are structured and governed by the companies themselves, the relevant regulatory authorities or a combination of the two. Most training frameworks focus on technical knowledge relating to different processes, control loops, operation and troubleshooting (Nazir et al., 2015). Process industries typically involve some level of task-engagement between CROPs and FOPs working in teams. An independent individual task can become an interdependent team task for normal operations in unexpected situations, and thus communication becomes an important factor for task efficiency among team members.

The rapid changes in the workplace environment have necessitated that the process industry diversifies its training tools and methods. For example, the shift in communication techniques due to the inception of automated processes have altered non-verbal communication, as it can now be performed electronically (Kaber et al., 2001). An electric utility company is used as a reference to better understand how they train their

CROPs and FOPs in accordance with the current workplace requirements. The company employs diverse team-training and communication exercises within the NTS skills training framework of CROPs and FOPs, as described in Figure 1.

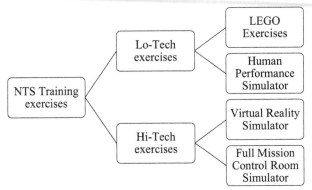

Figure 1: Differing methods of communication skill training.

2.1.1. Lo-Tech: LEGO Exercises

A lo-tech communication training exercise used in CROP training courses involves CROPs to interact with each other through the building of a LEGO toy (see Figure 2). For example, in one exercise, the pieces from a LEGO set (e.g., a 3-in-1 LEGO set which can form an aircraft, boat or car with the same combination of pieces) are presented to only one person without the build instructions, box or any reference to what the LEGO structure is. The step-by-step instructions for the LEGO sets are presented to another member of the team sitting across the room with their back to the person with the pieces. The individual with the instructions is tasked with describing the step-by-step procedures of building the desired structure (e.g. individual pieces to choose, sequence of construction, etc.) whilst under time pressure.

Figure 2: Examples of differing tools for NTS training (Lo-Tech)

Another example of a LEGO-based communication training exercise involves non-verbal communication. Members of a team are required to build a specific structure using LEGO pieces in the same configuration (one person with pieces, one person with instructions) but now physically facing each other. However, in this exercise, they are not allowed to communicate verbally.

In both exercises, the goal is to practice *communication skills* as a part of greater NTS training. The purpose of using LEGO as a medium to train is that it forces operators to use language and tasks that are not associated with their profession. These seemingly irrelevant tasks of LEGO building require operators to think, be creative, and communicate with their peers without falling into typical habits, shortcuts and nomenclature for which they are comfortable with and associated with their technical work and expertise. The second exercise has also been found to be useful for leadership training, as instructors' report that natural leaders emerge during these exercises. The subsequent debriefing sessions help establish "closed-loop communication" that construct a joint picture and language for the task that was performed, providing a platform for self-assessment and reflection.

2.1.2. Lo-Tech: Human Performance Simulator

A portable system consisting of a combination of small valves on a simulated piping network in a simple vertically mounted structure is used to train NTS and communication skills amongst teams. A correct sequential action is required to be performed in operating the valves to start an intended process and requires inputs from multiple team members to be successful. The valves are positioned far from each other and the team members need to share a common mental model in order to perform the task successfully. The trainees don't need to be an expert of the system, but they are required to be efficient with communication and work as a team. The inherent characteristics of these types of exercises make the background of participants irrelevant, and thus people with expertise from different domains can be trained together.

2.1.3. Hi-Tech: Online and Virtual Reality Training Platforms

This company also utilizes e-learning and online knowledge-sharing platforms as part of their operator (and general employee) education and training. The online learning

platform *Moodle* supports the company's social learning through virtual classrooms enabling synchronous online communication, media servers and plant simulators. For example, trainees can engage in virtual environments and scenarios to troubleshoot automated process control systems in power plants or open cast mining operations. 360-degree videos on VR headsets (see Figure 3) allow virtual tours of industrial environments and equipment in classroom training sessions or through the online learning portal. For operator training on bucket wheel excavators, Augmented Reality (AR) is deployed through Microsoft's HoloLens, providing training from complete virtual situations to on-site hybrid online support in the real working environment.

Figure 3: Virtual Reality Headset system used to train NTS in control room operations.

2.1.4. Hi-Tech: Full Mission Control Room Simulations

Within control room operator simulator courses, NTS training is typically embedded within the technical training content. Control room operators working for the company take periodic short-duration training courses (typically five days in duration) regularly throughout their career. Within one particular five-day course, two days are dedicated to communication and decision-making. During this time, short lectures on communication and decision-making are mixed with exercises and event-based simulation training (see Figure 4). The participants are exposed to differing process scenarios while being required to execute certain tasks. NTS performance indicators, including quality of communication, time to complete tasks, decision making and problem-solving, amongst other operational aspects are typically

Figure 4: Team discussion in a full-mission central-control room simulator

highlighted and discussed in the debriefing sessions. Furthermore, the training also contains leadership training, as participants are assigned different roles during the exercises, taking on the role of an assigned control room operator position (which may not be their current professional position in real-world plant operations). Simulation scenarios can vary from emergency operations (e.g., plant blackout) to normal and planned operations (e.g., startup from a cold or warm plant, planned shutdown of a particular block). NTS skills are not assessed with objective, quantifiable metrics, but rather analyzed and discussed subjectively in post-simulation debriefing sessions. The assessment is based on peer-to-peer feedback and instructor-to-operator feedback. The instructors reported that they act more as facilitators to the discussion, rather than assessors of "good" and "bad" performance during a debriefing at the end of each exercise.

3. Discussion

The four examples of NTS training practices in the above-mentioned electric utility company includes both *lo-tech* and *hi-tech* methods. Traditionally, such training is limited and typically implemented in conjunction with technical training exercises. NTS can be viewed as a resource-intensive aspect of training. Thus, lo-tech options can be used to implement NTS training, which are considered to be an effective and practical solution for operator NTS competency development.

Differing industries choose NTS training methods in accordance with their operational requirements, both in the control room and in the field. Future research should focus on testing and validation of more streamlined training methods for specific operations. Furthermore, team dynamics in different levels of communication between the novice and experienced workers operating automated systems should also be addressed. Addressing the non-technical aspects of equipment and system operations along with appropriate training can help better prepare current and future operators for managing their work in a complex and highly automated work environment. The extended evaluation of the discussed training methods in the process domain could provide insight into the transferability of these methods in other safety-critical domains as well. It could also add new dimensions in training and assessment methods through extended NTS training needs analysis, identifying training postulates and training possibilities across emerging new systems.

4. Conclusion

It is crucial to understand and develop differing methods and tools to effectively and efficiently deliver NTS training for process operators. CROPs and FOPs working in teams within the process industry require NTS and NTS training in order to hold the competencies required for managing the complexity of safety-critical social-technical systems. Different types of lo-tech and hi-tech training tools, ranging from simple puzzle exercises to e-Learning platforms and immersive simulation technologies are effective in training current and future operators. Further study is required to map out NTS training methods and tools in order to establish a wider understanding of requirements for current and future systems.

Acknowledgements

This project has received funding from the European Union's Horizon 2020 research and innovation programme under the Marie Skłodowska-Curie grant agreement No 823904. The corresponding author also acknowledges the support of the project "Innovating Maritime Training Simulators using Virtual and Augmented Reality (InnoTraining)" funded by the Research Council of Norway, project number 269424.

References

Flin, R., & Martin, L. (2001). Behavioral markers for crew resource management: A review of current practice. *The International Journal of Aviation Psychology, 11*(1), 95-118.

Flin, R., & Maran, N. (2004). Identifying and training non-technical skills for teams in acute medicine. *BMJ Quality & Safety, 13*(suppl 1), i80-i84.

Flin, R., & O'Connor, P. (2017). Safety at the sharp end: a guide to non-technical skills. CRC Press.

Flin, R., Youngson, G. G., & Yule, S. (Eds.). (2015). Enhancing surgical performance: A primer in non-technical skills. CRC press.

Ford, J., Henderson, R., & O'Hare, D. (2013). Barriers to intra-aircraft communication and safety: The perspective of the flight attendants. *The International Journal of Aviation Psychology, 23*(4), 368-387.

Hayward, B. J., Lowe, A. R., & Thomas, M. J. (2019). The migration of crew resource management training. In Crew resource management (pp. 421-447). Academic Press.

Huang, Y. H., Sinclair, R. R., Lee, J., McFadden, A. C., Cheung, J. H., & Murphy, L. A. (2018). Does talking the talk matter? Effects of supervisor safety communication and safety climate on long-haul truckers' safety performance. *Accident Analysis & Prevention, 117*, 357-367.

Kaber, D. B., Riley, J. M., Tan, K. W., & Endsley, M. R. (2001). On the design of adaptive automation for complex systems. *International Journal of Cognitive Ergonomics, 5*(1), 37-57.

Kanki, B. G., Anca, J., & Chidester, T. R. (Eds.). (2019). Crew resource management. Academic Press.

Leva, M. C. (2005). Human Errors Analysis and Safety Management Systems in Hazardous Activities.

Lyndon, A. U. D. R. E. Y. (2019). Failure to Rescue, Communication, and Safety Culture. *Clinical obstetrics and gynecology.*

Manca, D., Brambilla, S., & Colombo, S. (2013). Bridging between virtual reality and accident simulation for training of process-industry operators. *Advances in Engineering Software, 55*, 1-9.

Mathieu, J. E., Heffner, T. S., Goodwin, G. F., Salas, E., & Cannon-Bowers, J. A. (2000). The influence of shared mental models on team process and performance. *Journal of applied psychology, 85*(2), 273.

Nazir, S., Øvergård, K. I., & Yang, Z. (2015). Towards effective training for process and maritime industries. *Procedia Manufacturing, 3*, 1519-1526.

O'Connor, P., O'Dea, A., Flin, R., & Belton, S. (2008). Identifying the team skills required by nuclear power plant operations personnel. *International Journal of Industrial Ergonomics, 38*(11-12), 1028-1037.

O'Dea, A., O'Connor, P., & Keogh, I. (2014). A meta-analysis of the effectiveness of crew resource management training in acute care domains. *Postgraduate medical journal, 90*(1070), 699-708.

Parasuraman, R. E., & Mouloua, M. E. (1996). *Automation and human performance: Theory and applications.* Lawrence Erlbaum Associates, Inc.

Sætrevik, B., Ghanonisaber, S., & Lunde, G. E. (2018). Power imbalance between supply vessels and offshore installations may impede the communication of safety issues. *Safety science, 101*, 268-281.

Whittingham, R. (2004). *The blame machine: Why human error causes accidents.* Routledge.

Wiener, E. L., Chidester, T. R., Kanki, B. G., Palmer, E. A., Curry, R. E., & Gregorich, S. E. (1991). The impact of cockpit automation on crew coordination and communication. Volume 1: Overview, LOFT evaluations, error severity, and questionnaire data.

Sauro Pierucci, Flavio Manenti, Giulia Bozzano, Davide Manca (Eds.)
Proceedings of the 30th European Symposium on Computer Aided Process Engineering
(ESCAPE30), May 24-27, 2020, Milano, Italy. © 2020 Elsevier B.V. All rights reserved.
http://dx.doi.org/10.1016/B978-0-12-823377-1.50334-7

A Deterministic Global Optimization Method Based on Legendre-Fenchel Transform

Karim Alloula[a*], Jean-Pierre Belaud[b]

[a] *Université de Toulouse, Toulouse INP-ENSIACET*
4, allée Emile Monso, CS 44362, 31030 Toulouse Cedex 4, France
[b] *CNRS, Laboratoire de Génie Chimique (UMR 5503)*
4, allée Emile Monso, CS 44362, 31030 Toulouse Cedex 4, France
Karim.Alloula@toulouse-inp.fr

Abstract

This paper introduces a deterministic global continuous optimization method. Given some properties of the criterion function –the first and second order derivatives satisfy Lipschitz conditions or the criterion function is analytic-, it takes full advantage of some theoretical results related to the local convergence analysis of the Gauss-Newton method to calculate points, which may be global minima. This method is original in two ways. First, using the Gauss-Newton method, we try to find least squares solutions to an overdetermined system of global optimality conditions. Second, instead of solving the initial formulation, we apply a uniform scaling to the criterion function and obtain an equivalent problem, where the local convergence of the Gauss-Newton method is improved. The modified overdetermined system is solved from several initial points belonging to a simplicial research domain. This simplicial domain is subdivided recursively into smaller simplices until each of the covering simplices either contains no global minimum (exclusion), or contains one and only one global minimum (inclusion)
Keywords: process simulation, symbolic numeric calculations, deterministic global optimization, Legendre-Fenchel transform.

1. Introduction

The process system engineering activity mainly consists in modeling, and then optimizing, process units or whole plants. For optimizing continuous models, the CAPE community usually tries to find the global minimum of a continuous criterion under a set of linear or non-linear constraints. When the global optimization problem is not convex, it may be hard to solve because the number of local minima may increase exponentially with the number of variables. Any method, either deterministic or heuristic, may stop its iterations nearby one local minima or the calculation complexity of the global optimization algorithms may lead to huge delays for producing some optimum.

This paper exhibits the main principles of a new global continuous optimization method, which tries to overcome, at least partially, some of the drawbacks of the other deterministic global continuous methods in the unconstrained case.

2. Main principles of the global continuous optimization method

(Stork et al., 2018) classify the today algorithms for continuous global optimization. As presented in (Ryoo and Sahinidis, 1995) the "deterministic approaches include branch-and-bound, cutting plane algorithms and decomposition schemes". During the two last decades, when talking about the CAPE community only, the global continuous optimization research has mainly adopted branch-and-bound approaches. The original paper by (Androulakis et al., 1995) introduced the αBB method which the main principle is to "underestimate nonconvex terms of generic structure" both in the objective function and in the constraints. This method has been refined but some drawbacks remain: the underestimation efficiency greatly depends on the type of the nonconvex terms; the upper bound calculations can drastically increase the complexity of the partitioning process. Consequently, we choose to base our deterministic optimization strategy, no longer on the objective function expression as in the αBB-like methods, but on a condition of global optimality, first presented by Jean-Pierre Dedieu, and then cited in (Hiriart-Urruty, 1986):

$$(x \text{ is a minimum of } f) \Leftrightarrow (Df(x) = 0 \text{ and } f^{**}(x) = f(x)) \tag{1}$$

where f^{**} is the Legendre-Fenchel bi-conjugate of f. A first paper by (Alloula et al., 2011) summarized the application of the discrete Legendre-Fenchel bi-conjugate of f as a means for estimating the global minimum value. The new algorithm takes full advantage of the condition of global optimality by calculating only points x for which $f^{**}(x) = f(x)$, that is to say points where the tangent plane to the representative surface of f is also a supporting hyperplane, and where $\nabla f(x) = \vec{\eta}$ with $\|\vec{\eta}\| \ll 1$. The smaller the value of $\|\vec{\eta}\|$, the closer to the condition of global optimality. In this paper, we try to solve the global optimality conditions for a fixed value of $\|\vec{\eta}\|$, where $0 < \|\vec{\eta}\| \ll 1$.

This paper is organized according to the following sequence. First, we translate the global optimality conditions into an overdetermined system of nonlinear equations. Then, we build an equivalent system, for which the local convergence properties of the Gauss-Newton method are better. Third, we illustrate the combination of Gauss-Newton sequences starting from different initial points with a subdivision strategy of the research domain. A conclusion summarizes the main benefits and drawbacks of this approach.

3. Global optimality conditions

Let us consider a twice differentiable function $f: \mathbb{R}^n \mapsto \mathbb{R}$ and a compact set Σ of $\mathbb{R}^n$ such that $f_{|\Sigma}$ is bounded below. $f_{|\Sigma}$ has one or more global minima. Assuming that those global minima are interior points of Σ, we can prove the following:

$$\exists M_{\Sigma,f} \in \mathbb{R}^{++}; \forall \vec{\eta} \in \mathbb{R}^n; \|\vec{\eta}\| \leq M_{\Sigma,f} \Rightarrow \exists x \in \Sigma; Df(x) = \vec{\eta} \tag{2}$$

Assertion (1) says that, provided that we choose a vector $\vec{\eta}$ in $\mathbb{R}^n$ which norm is small enough, we can find at least one point x in Σ for which $Df(x) = \vec{\eta}$.

Under the same assumptions, we have the following result:

$$\exists N_{\Sigma,f} \in \mathbb{R}^{++}; \forall \vec{\eta} \in \mathbb{R}^n; \|\vec{\eta}\| \leq N_{\Sigma,f} \Rightarrow \exists x \in \Sigma; (Df(x) = \vec{\eta}) \text{ and } (f^{**}(x) = f(x)) \tag{3}$$

Eq. (3) means that, provided that we choose a vector $\vec{\eta}$ in $\mathbb{R}^n$ which norm is small enough, we can find at least one point x in Σ for which $Df(x) = \vec{\eta}$ and $(x, f(x))$ belongs to the representative surface of $f_{|\Sigma}^{**}$, the convex envelope of $f_{|\Sigma}$.

For any given vector $\vec{\eta}$ for which $\|\vec{\eta}\| \leq N_{\Sigma,f}$, we assume that we know $B = (b_1, b_2, \ldots, b_{n+1}) \in \mathbb{R}^{n+1}$ such that $\mathcal{H}(B, \vec{\eta})$, hyperplane defined by B and one normal vector $(\vec{\eta}, -1)$, is a hyperplane with no intersection with the hypograph of $f_{|\Sigma}$.

Let us consider now the function $F_{f,\vec{\eta},B}$ defined from $\Sigma \subset \mathbb{R}^n$ to $\mathbb{R}^{n+1}$ by:

$$F_{f,\vec{\eta},B}(x) = \begin{pmatrix} D_1 f(x) - \eta_1 \\ \vdots \\ D_n f(x) - \eta_n \\ \frac{[\sum_{i=1}^n (x_i - b_i)\eta_i] - (f(x) - b_{n+1})}{\|(\vec{\eta}, -1)\|} \end{pmatrix} \tag{4}$$

$\|\vec{\eta}\| \leq N_{\Sigma,f}$ so, from Eq. (3), there exists at least one point x_* where the first n coordinate functions of $F_{f,\vec{\eta},B}$ are zero. For such a point, it is easy to show that we have:

$$DF_{f,\vec{\eta},B}(x_*)^t . F_{f,\vec{\eta},B}(x_*) = 0 \tag{5}$$

In other words, provided that $\|\vec{\eta}\| \leq N_{\Sigma,f}$, there exists at least one stationary point $x_* \in \Sigma$ of $F_{f,\vec{\eta},B}(x)^t . F_{f,\vec{\eta},B}(x) = \left\|F_{f,\vec{\eta},B}(x)\right\|^2$ for which the first n coordinate functions of $F_{f,\vec{\eta},B}$ are zero. Among all the stationary points x_* in Σ, for which the first n coordinate functions of $F_{f,\vec{\eta},B}$ are zero, at least one minimizes the last coordinate of $F_{f,\vec{\eta},B}(x)$, which is a strictly positive quantity: the distance between $(x, f(x))$ and $\mathcal{H}(B, \vec{\eta})$. Such a point is a solution of the nonlinear least squares problem:

$$\min_{x \in \Sigma}\left\|F_{f,\vec{\eta},B}(x)\right\|^2 \tag{6}$$

The global optimization problem $\min_{x \in \Sigma}\left\|F_{f,\vec{0},B}(x)\right\|^2$ is an alternate formulation of the global optimality conditions (1). We choose to solve the minimization problem (6) for $\vec{\eta}$ such that $\|\vec{\eta}\| \leq N_{\Sigma,f}$ in order to guarantee the existence of a solution. Assuming the minimum value $\min_{x \in \Sigma}\left\|F_{f,\vec{\eta},B}(x)\right\|^2$ is a continuous function of $\vec{\eta}$, the smaller the value of $\|\vec{\eta}\|$, the closer the solution of $\min_{x \in \Sigma}\left\|F_{f,\vec{\eta},B}(x)\right\|^2$ to the solution of $\min_{x \in \Sigma}\left\|F_{f,\vec{0},B}(x)\right\|^2$.

So, let us consider now that we try to solve $\min_{x \in \Sigma}\left\|F_{f,\vec{\eta},B}(x)\right\|^2$ with:

$$0 < \|\vec{\eta}\| \ll 1 \tag{7}$$

The choice $0 < \|\vec{\eta}\|$ is justified later.

Figure 1 illustrates the geometrical meaning of Eq. (6). For a given function f, bounded below on a convex domain Σ, $\mathcal{H}(B, \vec{\eta})$ is a minorant hyperplane of the representative surface of $f_{|\Sigma}$. A solution of this optimization problem is a point x_* where the tangent hyperplane to the representative surface is normal to $(\vec{\eta}, -1)$ and for which the distance to $\mathcal{H}(B, \vec{\eta})$ is minimal. Provided that $\mathcal{H}(B, \vec{\eta})$ is horizontal enough, a solution exists.

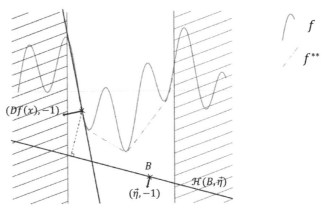

Figure 1: Trying to find a supporting hyperplane parallel to $\mathcal{H}(B, \vec{\eta})$.

As stated in (Ferreira et al., 2011), when the derivative of $\left\|F_{f,\vec{\eta},B}(x)\right\|^2$ is injective, finding stationary points of $\left\|F_{f,\vec{\eta},B}(x)\right\|^2$ "is equivalent to finding a least squares solution of the overdetermined nonlinear equation":

$$F_{f,\vec{\eta},B}(x) = 0 \qquad (8)$$

The Gauss-Newton method can be applied to Eq. (8). If it converges to $x_* \in \Sigma$, x_* is a stationary point of $\|F_{f,\vec{\eta},B}(x)\|^2$, "but we cannot conclude that x_* is a solution of Eq. (6) or $F_{f,\vec{\eta},B}(x_*) = 0$". This paper takes full advantage of the local convergence analysis of the Gauss-Newton method detailed in (Ferreira et al., 2011) for identifying unicity balls around some stationary points x_* of $\|F_{f,\vec{\eta},B}(x)\|^2$ where $Df(x_*) = \vec{\eta}$. When the Gauss-Newton method, starting from an initial point, reaches such a stationary point x_*, we can quantify the radius r of a ball $B(x_*, r)$ containing only one stationary point of $\|F_{f,\vec{\eta},B}(x)\|^2$. Combining this inclusion approach with an exclusion approach –exclusion theorems, like in (Dedieu et al., 1996), state that within a given ball there is no candidate for solving some problem- one can build a subdivision method to minimize $f_{|\Sigma}$.

Theorem 18 from (Ferreira et al., 2011) gives quantitative values for the radii of the convergence balls and of the unicity balls including stationary points. More precisely:

Let $\Omega \subseteq \mathbb{X}$ be an open set, and let $F: \Omega \to \mathbb{Y}$ be a continuously differentiable function. Let $x_* \in \Omega$ and $c := \|F(x_*)\|$, $\beta := \|F'(x_*)^\dagger\|$, $\kappa := sup\{t \in [0, R): B(x_*, t) \subset \Omega\}$.
Suppose that $F'(x_*)^* F(x_*) = 0$, $F'(x_*)$ is injective, and that there exists a $K > 0$ such that $\sqrt{2}c\beta^2 K < 1$, $\|F'(x) - F'(y)\| \leq K\|x - y\|$, $\forall x, y \in B(x_*, \kappa)$.
Let $r := min\{\kappa, (2 - 2\sqrt{2}K\beta^2 c)/(3K\beta)\}$. Then, the Gauss–Newton method for solving (6), with initial point $x_0 \in B(x_*, r)/\{x_*\}$, $x_{k+1} = x_k - F'(x_k)^\dagger F(x_k)/k = 0,1, ... /$ is well defined, the sequence generated $\{x_k\}$ is contained in $B(x_*, r)$, converges to x_*, and

$$\|x_{k+1} - x_*\| \leq \frac{\beta K}{2(1 - \beta K\|x_0 - x_*\|)}\|x_k - x_*\|^2 + \frac{\sqrt{2}c\beta^2 K}{1 - \beta K\|x_0 - x_*\|}\|x_k - x_*\|/k = 0,1, ... 1$$

Moreover, if $(2 - 2\sqrt{2}K\beta^2 c)/(3K\beta) < \kappa$, then $r = (2 - 2\sqrt{2}K\beta^2 c)/(3K\beta)$ is the best possible convergence radius.
If, additionally, $2c\beta_0 K < 1$, then x_* is the unique stationary point of $F(x)^* F(x)$ in $B(x_*, (2 - 2c\beta_0 K)/(\beta K))$, where $\beta_0 := \|[F'(x_*)^* F'(x_*)]^{-1}\|$.

When this theorem is applied to the overdetermined system Eq. 8, and when only stationary points x_* such that $Df(x_*) = \vec{\eta}$ are considered, the quantities appearing in the radii expressions become:

$$c = \frac{\|[\sum_{i=1}^{n}(x_i - b_i)\eta_i] - (f(x) - b_{n+1})\|}{\|(\vec{\eta}, -1)\|}, \beta = \|D^2 f(x_*)^{-1}\|, \beta_0 = \|[D^2 f(x_*)^2]^{-1}\| \qquad (9)$$

4. An overdetermined system suited for Gauss-Newton method

Assuming that a least squares solution is found to Eq. (8), Figure 1 can be updated to display the corresponding optimal point $(x_*, f(x_*))$ and the tangent hyperplane at this point. This updated figure can be scaled along the y axis by a scaling factor $\theta > 0$. The resulting figure represents a least squares solution x_* to Eq. (10):

$$F_{\theta f, \overline{\theta\eta}, (b_1, b_2, ..., \theta b_{n+1})}(x) = \begin{pmatrix} \theta. D_1 f(x) - \theta. \eta_1 \\ \vdots \\ \theta. D_n f(x) - \theta. \eta_n \\ \frac{[\sum_{i=1}^{n}(x_i - b_i)\theta. \eta_i] - (\theta. f(x) - \theta. b_{n+1})}{\|(\theta. \vec{\eta}, -1)\|} \end{pmatrix} = 0 \qquad (10)$$

For any $\theta > 0$, the least squares solutions of Eq. (8) and Eq. (10) are identical. However, when θ very large, solving Eq. (10) may be easier than solving Eq. (8). The quantities appearing in the radii expressions become:

$$\begin{cases} c_\theta = \frac{[\sum_{i=1}^n (x_i - b_i)\theta.\eta_i] - (\theta.f(x) - \theta.b_{n+1})}{\|(\theta.\vec{\eta}, -1)\|} = \frac{\theta.\|(\vec{\eta}, -1)\|}{\|(\theta.\vec{\eta}, -1)\|} \cdot c \\ \beta_\theta = \|D^2\theta.f(x_*)^{-1}\| = \frac{\beta}{\theta} \ and \ \beta_{0\theta} = \|[D^2\theta.f(x_*)^2]^{-1}\| = \frac{\beta_0}{\theta} \end{cases} \quad (11)$$

Assuming that both Df and D^2f are Lipschitzian over Σ and that $\theta \geq 1$, $F_{f,\vec{\eta},B}$ is K-Lipschitzian over Σ, $F_{\theta f,\overrightarrow{\theta\eta},(b_1,b_2,\dots,\theta b_{n+1})}$ is K_θ-Lipschitzian over Σ and:

$$K_\theta \leq \theta.K \quad (12)$$

Consequently,

$$c_\theta.\beta_\theta^2.K_\theta \leq c.\beta^2.K.\frac{\|(\vec{\eta}, -1)\|}{\|(\theta.\vec{\eta}, -1)\|} \quad (13)$$

When $\vec{\eta} \neq \vec{0}$ and $\theta \gg 1$, Theorem 18 is modified in a nice manner:

$$\begin{cases} c_\theta.\beta_\theta^2.K_\theta \approx 0 \ and \ c_\theta.\beta_{0\theta}.K_\theta \approx 0 \\ r_\theta \approx \frac{2}{3K_\theta\beta_\theta} \ and \ R_{\theta,unicity} \approx \frac{2}{K_\theta\beta_\theta} \approx 3.r_\theta \end{cases} \quad (14)$$

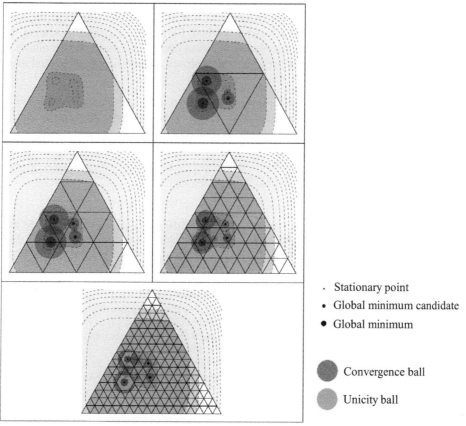

· Stationary point

• Global minimum candidate

● Global minimum

Convergence ball

Unicity ball

Figure 2: Locating the global minima of the Himmelblau function ($\|\vec{\eta}\| = 10^{-20}, \theta.\|\vec{\eta}\| = 10^{20}$)

From Eq. (14) we build a solving algorithm without information about the Lipschitz constants. We solve Eq. (10) by applying the Gauss-Newton method to a distributed set of initial points in Σ (Tóth et al., 2016). Whenever the sequence converges to a stationary point x_*, such that $Df(x_*) = \vec{\eta}$, we estimate numerically the convergence radius r_θ because it is also the quadratic convergence radius in this case. We get a ball centered on x_*, with radius $R_{\theta,unicity} \approx 3.r_\theta$, containing only one stationary point: x_*. When several unicity balls are computed, the values of f at the stationary points are compared.

This global continuous optimization method is applied to the Himmelblau function $f(x) = (x^2 + y - 11)^2 + (x + y^2 - 7)^2$, which admits 4 global minima. In the top left image of Figure 2 we represent the level sets of the function and Σ, the research domain, a regular simplex containing the global minima. Step 1 (top right image), finds three global minima (not guaranteed at this time) and a local minimum. After step 2, the four global minima are located. Step three detects an inconsistency: K value estimated from the Gauss-Newton iterates is too small, so several unicity balls cover two stationary points. K value is increased according to the distances between the stationary points and the radii are reduced proportionally. At the end of step four, some singular simplices, covered by unicity balls, are removed from the research domain.

5. Conclusions

A global continuous optimization method has been introduced here. This deterministic approach is not certified, but is consistent with theoretical results related to the local convergence analysis of the Gauss-Newton method. By means of a criterion scaling, the radii of the unicity balls containing only one stationary point are enlarged. This allows us to build an inclusion-exclusion algorithm, which proved to be efficient on several usual test functions for optimization.

For the time being, this work suffers from two weak points. First, the radii of the unicity balls have been estimated under a Lipschitz condition. (Ferreira et al., 2011) gives another convergence result where the criterion is an analytical function. Its integration in our method is under progress. Second, usual exclusion theorems still have to be implemented in order to remove additional simplices, containing no global minima, from the research domain.

References

Androulakis I.P., Maranas C.D. and Floudas C.A., 1995, αBB: A global optimization method for general constrained nonconvex problems, Journal of Global Optimization, 7, Issue 4, 337-363.

Alloula K., Belaud J.-P. and Le Lann J.-M., 2011, An homotopy method for global optimization of continuous models, Chemical Engineering Transactions, 24, 325-330.

Dedieu J.-P., Gourdon J., Yakoubsohn J.-C., 1996, Computing the distance from a point to an algebraic hypersurface, Lectures in Applied Mathematics, 32, 285–293.

Ferreira O. P., Gonçalves M.L.N., Oliveira P.R., 2011, Local convergence analysis of the Gauss-Newton method using a majorant condition, Journal of Complexity, 27, 111-125.

Hiriart-Urruty J.-B., 1986, When is a point x satisfying $\nabla f(x) = 0$ a global minimum of f?, The American Mathematical Monthly, 93, Issue 7, 556-558.

Ryoo H.S. and Sahinidis N.V., 1995, Global optimization of nonconvex NLPs and MINLPs applications in process design, Computers & Chemical Engineering, 19, Issue 5, 551-566.

Stork J., Eiben A.E. and Bartz-Beielstein T., 2018, A new taxonomy of continuous global optimization algorithms, 2018arXiv180808818

Tóth B.G., Hendrix E.M.T., Casado L.G., 2016, On refinement of the unit simplex using regular simplices, Journal of Global Optimization, 64, 305-323.

Sauro Pierucci, Flavio Manenti, Giulia Bozzano, Davide Manca (Eds.)
Proceedings of the 30th European Symposium on Computer Aided Process Engineering
(ESCAPE30), May 24-27, 2020, Milano, Italy. © 2020 Elsevier B.V. All rights reserved.
http://dx.doi.org/10.1016/B978-0-12-823377-1.50335-9

A New Method for Food Production Analysis and Optimization Applied to Citrus Industry

Martina Raymo[a], Maria C. Rulli[b], Laura Piazza[c], Flavio Manenti[a], Giulia Bozzano[a]

[a]*Politecnico di Milano, Dept. DCMC, P.zza L. Da Vinci, 32, Milan, 20133, Italy*
[b]*Politecnico di Milano, Dept. DICA, P.zza L. Da Vinci, 32, Milan, 20133, Italy*
[c]*Università degli Studi di Milano, Department of Environmental Science and Policy (ESP), Via Celoria 2, Milan, 20133, Italy*
giulia.bozzano@polimi.it

Abstract

This work is aimed to present a method for analyzing and optimizing food production processes from the primary production until the final residue. The aim is to have a global view on the entire production chain in order to put in light, through a deep analysis, the strength and the weaknesses of the process and to propose solutions for its improvement and optimization. The solutions, of course, depend on which is the main objective of the involved production realities and consider also the location of the production. Here is reported the first case study, the citrus industry, which products are citrus juices and essential oils. In this case the authors individuated some solutions and started to develop some of them. The results will be here presented.

Keywords: Food Value Chain, Optimization, SWOT Analysis, Circular Economy

1. Introduction

This paper refers to the first steps of a project aimed to develop a methodology to perform the analyses and the optimization of any food value chain. The procedure has been structured using as a first case study the citrus industry.

In the literature, there are few other studies on the topic here dealt, and it appeared that none of the existing works considers the citrus production, and, in general, any food production from the cradle to the grave. Articles on treatments of secondary products (exhausted peel) (Negro et al., 2017, Zema et al., 2018) have been found as well as some on the water optimization for the transformation step (Beccali et al., 2010, Thevendiraraj et al., 2003). There are some books dealing with the processing of citrus fruits, providing details on the main production techniques, even better explained by the equipment producers themselves. Beside this, none of the works address both the primary production and the transformation.

The novelty brought by this article lies precisely in addressing both aspects, the primary production and the transformation, leaving out of the analysis only the logistics part. The reason why the study shall address both the aforementioned parts is related to the accuracy and completeness that a 360-degree analysis can provide. Another reason is the strong and unbreakable link that exists between these two worlds and that holds all the phases of the value chain together. The final quality of a food process depends on the technology used, but nothing can be done if the raw materials aren't excellent from the point of view of quality and environmental aspects related to the production. The data obtained from the entire production process have been analyzed by using a SWOT analysis enriched by methods usually adopted by chemical engineering approach. This allowed to consider also the important aspects related to workers welfare and financial aspects related to the specific case study analyzed.

2. Objectives and Methodology

As aforementioned, the aim of the study is the definition of a method that thanks to a structured analysis allows to identify the existing gap of the value chain considered. The final goal of the citrus case is the presentation of innovative solutions to remove or reduce the detected issues. While structuring the study, defining each step and discovering the tools that best feted the needs, both the goals fixed for the "during construction" procedure and the citrus value chain have been accomplished.

The definition of all these needed steps has been done directly applying them to the case study. Some of the tools used are not typical of the engineering world (many of them are the results of talks with experts of other sectors: economics, design, mechanical and environmental engineering), giving to this work has an interdisciplinary face. Many of the information been collected during the visits to primary producers and the collaboration with the KOLs (Key Opinion Leaders) of both the sectors. The procedure adopted can be schematized as in Figure 1. It is a two-stage process, made of a theoretical and a practical part all of which is characterized by five sub-phases. To accomplish the theoretical stage the following tools have been adopted:

1. On site visits (three plantations and a plant), interview to the plantation holders, literature review. This helped in discovering what has been done in the field of multi-criteria optimization applied to food processes (Madoumier et al., 2019). Further, in the understanding of the value chain and in dividing it into macro-areas and sub-phases; it has further allowed to collect all the requested information to draw up the structured description.

2. SWOT (Strengths, Weaknesses, opportunities and Threats): it is a tool widely used in the world of strategic planning and is traditionally considered a form of brainstorming. It allows to investigate and at the same time identify and categorize in a 2x2 matrix the strengths and weaknesses (internal factors), opportunities and threats (external factors) typical of the area analyzed (Falcone et al., in press). The definition of the different points characterizing the matrix is often the result of qualitative considerations influenced by human subjectivity (Phadermrod et al., 2019). This make difficult to use the SWOT analysis as a single decision-making tool, since it is not only lacking in objectivity, but does not have an analytical method to prioritize the various activities identified for process optimization.

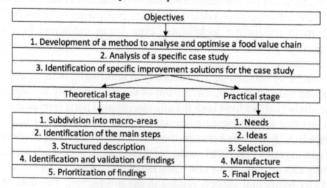

Figure 1- Objectives and Method

Here this technique is used to identify and validate the gap present in the citrus value chain and the critical issue aforementioned has been overcome using the tools and knowledge of the chemical engineering world.

3. **Impact-Feasibility Map.** It is a tool already seen and consolidated in areas such as Service Design, Enterprise Design Thinking and Project Management. It consists of a grid where the "impact" axis (y axis - on a low to high scale) expresses the importance and relevance that the proposal could have for users. The axis of "feasibility" (x-axis on a scale ranging from easy to difficult to realize) is instead connected to the feasibility of realization for the designer (information on how to realize it can be found in the IBM guide, "Design thinking field guide", (Johnson, 2016)). The aim of the amendments is to prioritize the result obtained from the SWOT analysis. This is the reason why the map just described has been modified, defining better the two parameters. The impact is quantified considering if the issues affect somehow the environment, the quality and yield, the selling price, the production speed and efficiency, the automation, the customer satisfaction and the worker safety. In the same time a note from high to low is given for the feasibility with respect to time, cost, resources needed to remove the gap.

4. For the realization of the practical phase the methodology used belongs to the Chemical Product Design (CPD) world. CPD is a branch of chemical engineering that deals with the development of new chemicals by acting as an interface between the world of consumers and industry, identifying customer needs and translating them into commercial products (Moggridge & Cussler, 2000). The typical steps of the CPD methodology are those shown here in bold and to apply them it appeared necessary to organize the analysis as follows:

Needs - Identification of the company's needs to answer the question: Which weak point characterizing the supply chain, the company must address? To answer the question the information used is the one collected during the field visits (farms and plantations), the writing of the structured description, the interviews with KOLs and the analysis of market trends.

Ideas - Presentation and characterization of improvement ideas. These possible solutions are for the sake of simplicity presented in a table in the form of a solution-criticality binomial.

Selections - Choosing the most appropriate solutions. This step can be made on the basis of the results obtained from the prioritization or following what has emerged from the needs identification steps. At this point, in order to support the decision making, heat and mass balances have been realized. This has made easier the decision-making procedure and has allowed to quantify the impact connected to the production (in terms of energy, water and wastes produced).

Manufacturing - Implementation of the selected solutions. To achieve these goals many tools have been used. For examples to quantify the amount of water needed for the plant (crop water requirement) a software called CROPWAT® has been used. It allows to quantify the amount of water needed for the cultivation of citrus fruits taking into account the climatic conditions and soil specific to the geographical area where the plantation is located. To accomplish the implementation of other solutions were helpful: Food Engineering-Unit Operations (Ibarz & Barbosa-Cánovas, 2002) and articles on filters, literature review (water legislation and filter technologies), interview and market analysis.

Figure 2- Relevant aspects of the analysis

Final project - Presentation of the results achieved. This might appear trivial, but due to the fact that the whole study has been structured on the idea of collaborating with the real world, it is also extremely relevant how the results are presented. This is the reason why for each solution implemented the results must refer to aspects reported in Figure 2.

3. Results and Discussion

The just introduced methodology has been followed to analyse the selected case study. The primary production of citrus value chain consists in the planting, cultivation and harvesting of lemons, oranges, tangerines, and bergamots from which during the transformation step the essential oil and the juice are obtained as main products and the exhausted peel as by-products. The production is characterised by both liquid and solid wastes that need to be treated and managed. While applying the first two steps of the method, it appeared that the production can be divided into four macro-areas each one characterised by its own subphases: 1)Primary production: planting, cultivation, harvesting; 2) Up-stream processes: unloading, visual inspection, washing; 3) Extraction: primary and secondary extraction; 4) Downstream processes: by-products, wastewater and solid wastes treatments, packaging and shipping.

The third step of the theoretical part allowed to acknowledge on the topic, collecting all the information needed for the next steps and understanding if there were any weak bond in the chain. The carried-out SWOT analysis putted on the light 18 findings and was used to both identify and validate them. Then a feasibility, impact map has been generated, (Table 1). Looking at Table 1 the number of crosses (from 1 to 8) gives the number related to process impact, the Low (L), Medium (M), High (H) have a corresponding number, respectively, 5,3 and 1 and are linearly organized in order to deduce the final feasibility. These critical issues have been so used, obtaining the map reported below (Figure 3). The findings present in the rectangle on the top right are the one that should be addressed immediately because with higher impact and feasibility: human error in visual inspection of fruits, visual inspection by a single operator, no recovery of washing and purified water, accumulation and dependence for fruits peelings treatment.

Once obtained the prioritised goals, the identification of the needs, ideas were sought to improve the chain, removing or reducing the weaknesses previously identified. Some of them were just mentioned and presented in the binomial form (criticality-ideas), others deeply investigated and presented in tables (here not reported for space reasons). Each table addressed the following points: hint, recourse needed, advantages, disadvantages, how to carry it out. The ideas were then selected according to the needs and prioritized following the impact-feasibility map. At the end of the third step, the solutions that appeared to have all the wanted characteristic were three, therefore three were the weaknesses faced.

Table 1 – process impact and feasibility map

Critical issues	Impact							Feasibility			Resulting impact	Average feasibility
	Environment	Quality Sell & Yield price	Production rate	Production Efficiency	Safety	Automation	Customer satisfaction	Time	Costs	Resources		
1.1 No recovery of irrigation water	X						X	H	M	L	2	3
1.2 Non efficient irrigation and fertilization	X	X	X				X	M	H	L	4	3
1.3 unquantified environmental impact	X		X				X	H	H	H	3	1
2.1 Manual handling of fruits and its consequences			X	X		X		M	H	L	3	3
2.2 use of trucks	X						X	H	M	L	3	3
2.3 randomly transport of fruits (no bins)		X				X		L	L	H	2	1
2.4 crushing of fruits in silos		X						M	H	M	1	2.5
2.5 human error in visual inspection of fruits	X	X		X		X		M	M	L	4	4
2.6 Visual inspection by a single operator	X	X	X	X	X			L	L	L	5	5
2.7 fruits with internal damages	X	X				X		L	H	L	3	3.5
2.8 No recovery of washing water	X		X				X	M	L	L	3	4.5
3.1 production standardisation		X	X	X	X		X	H	M	M	5	3
3.2 partial recovery of cooling water	X		X				X	H	H	M	3	1.5
3.3 energy from non-renewable resources	X		X				X	M	M	M	3	3
3.4 not optimized juice extractors		X	X				X	M	H	M	3	1.5
4.1 no recovery of purified water	X		X				X	L	M	L	3	4.5
4.2 waste water plant with no coverage	X				X			H	H	L	2	2
4.3 accumulation and dependence for fruits peelings (pastazzo) treatment	X		X	X			X	L	H	L	4	3.5

The implementation of the solutions allow the value chain to develop a sustainable agriculture, have a zero-wastewater production, move a first step in the direction of the circular economy. As a final result of the application of the method a ten years project has been obtained to improve the value chain. The goals to be achieved are fixed every two years and they regard different areas of the analyzed chain (water and energy optimization, anaerobic digestor, automatization of the lines). As an example (and for lacking of space) the two first years goal resulted in: cropwat analysis for all the company suppliers, water recycle system implemented into the fruit washing circuit, plantation irrigated with the purified water, two operators for the visual quality control of fruits, transportation of fruits by using bins.

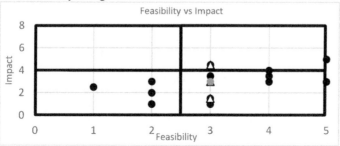

Figure 3- Feasibility vs Impact map

4. Conclusions

The method presented in this article appears to be a powerful tool to analyse and find solutions to optimise a food value chain. The first part of the theoretical stage allows to become experts of the sector investigated, while the second part, always of the theoretical stage, assures the identification of the strengths, the weaknesses, the opportunities and the threats of all the component areas of the chain. Besides, thanks to the prioritization process proposed the decision-making step is more objective and less dependent on whom is carrying out the analysis. Being interested in the optimization it is important to be able to easily select and define in which order addressing the critical issues.

The uniqueness of the approach is related to the possibility of finding solutions and therefore carry out projects to improve the chain having a global vision of the system.

It is the first time that the entire value chain has been studied within the same project allowing to find improvements for each of the two areas (primary production and transformation). The method gives the opportunity to work in line with the identified needs of the chain but at the same time it allows to detach from them by finding non inherent solutions. At the end of the analysis, together with the ten-years project also a has been obtained. The latest stress the importance of considering the workers, as a human being (soft skills) and as a member of a group (communication). A further results is the deduction of a way to improve the workspace, the security and safety of the workers, covering also the issue of plastic-free environment. Once again this underlines the ability of the method to take care of many different aspects. It comes up with a way to consider in the analysis also sustainability, that actually entails factoring in food production as well as processing.

References

Beccali M., M. Cellura, M. Ludicello, M. Mistretta, 2010, *Life cycle assement of Italian Citrus-based products. Sensitive Analysis and imporvememtns scenario*, Journal of Environmental Management, 91(7), 1415-1428

Falcone P.M., A.Tani, V.E. Tartiu, C. Imbriani, 2020, *Towards a sustainable forest-based bioeconomy in Italy: Findings from a SWOT analysis*, Forest Policy and Economics, 110, 101910

Ibarz A., G.V. Barbosa-Cánovas, 2002, *Unit operations in food engineering*, Taylor & Francis Group, editor G.V. Barbosa-Cánovas

Johnson S., 2016, *Design Thinking Field Guide*, IBM, 1–46

Madoumier M., G. Trystram, O. Sèbastian, A. Colligan, 2019, *Towards a holistic approach for multi-objective optimization of food processes. A critical review*, Trends in Food Science and Technology, 86(feb), 1-15

Moggridge G. D, E.L. Cussler, 2000, *An introduction to chemical product design, Chemical Engineering Research and Design*, 78(1), 5–11

Negro V., B. Ruggeri, D. Fino, D. Tonini, 2017, *Life Cycle Assement of orange peel waste management*, Resources, Conservation & Recycling. 127(September),148–158

Phadermrod B., R.M. Crowder, G.B. Wills, 2019, *Importance-Performance Analysis based SWOT analysis*, International Journal of Information Management, 44, 194–203

Thevendiraraj S., J. Klemeš, D. Paz, G. Aso, G.J. Cardenas, 2003, *Water and wastewater minimisation study of citrus plant*, Resource, Conservation and Recycling, 37(3), 227-250

Zema D. A., P.S. Calabrò, A. Folino, V. Tamburino, G. Zappia, S.M. Zimbone, 2018, *Valorisation of citrus processing waste: a review*, Waste Manag., 80, 252-273

Sauro Pierucci, Flavio Manenti, Giulia Bozzano, Davide Manca (Eds.)
Proceedings of the 30th European Symposium on Computer Aided Process Engineering
(ESCAPE30), May 24-27, 2020, Milano, Italy. © 2020 Elsevier B.V. All rights reserved.
http://dx.doi.org/10.1016/B978-0-12-823377-1.50336-0

Integration of Interactive CFD Simulations with AR and VR for Educational Use in CRE

Serkan Solmaz[*], Tom Van Gerven

Department of Chemical Engineering, KU Leuven, Leuven 3001, Belgium

serkan.solmaz@kuleuven.be

Abstract

Engineering simulations have since long been considered an imperative design and analysis tool for chemical reaction engineering (CRE). Notably, reactor and process design are domains in which multiphysics computational fluid dynamics (CFD) simulations are applied to understand phenomena that are difficult, time-consuming or expensive to be explored with experiments. On the other hand, advanced post-processing methods and virtual reality can enable high-quality educational content with engineering simulations. Nevertheless, the utilization of these tools in education is still underdeveloped. This study explores the potential of integration of multiphysics CFD simulations with AR/VR and its educational use. By iterating on this potential we present a generic system architecture with inter-disciplinary consideration of two building stones: (1) Recent advancements in CFD & multiphysics simulations, and (2) Emerging immersive technologies. A case study is demonstrated applying the generic methodology in order to illustrate the integration. The study promotes a rich and engaging environment with engineering simulations where interactivity can be empowered to entertain learners with AR/VR. This will primarily assist enthusiasts to develop feasible complementary environments with simulations.

Keywords: Chemical reaction engineering, Computational fluid dynamics, Augmented reality, System architecture, Learning environment.

1. Introduction

Multiphysics CFD simulations, one of the most applied computer-assisted process engineering (CAPE) tools, have been a maturing method increasing comprehension of engineering design and analysis. However, the educational implementation of this tool is still directly made with engineering software which has a primitive educational context, thereby preventing students to understand challenging concepts. Augmented reality (AR) and virtual reality (VR) have been getting prevalent in society today including research and education (Suh and Prophet, 2018). The integration of interactive CFD simulations in AR/VR reveals supportive features such as advanced visualizations, interactivity, attractiveness of digital media and so forth. In that sense, a virtual environment with CFD simulations could yield remedies for this primitive context.

The interest in CRE and CFD on multiple scales has recently convinced researchers to consider AR/VR by promoting virtual process engineering (Li, 2015; Ge et al., 2019). Despite this, several ambiguities are still present concerning the integration of CFD simulations with AR/VR in terms of system architecture. The term system architecture has come to be used as a portrayal of the system that consists of software and hardware including their functionalities and interactions (Blach et al., 1998). The present study develops a methodology for a sustainable system architecture to integrate the desired digital simulation contents into AR/VR.

1.1. Interactive Multiphysics CFD Simulations in AR/VR

Multiphysics CFD simulations for CRE have received much interest in the past decade. To date, several commercial and open-source software packages have been developed providing miscellaneous options to design and analyze reactive flow phenomena (Tian et al., 2018). These result in a broad database in the literature illustrating and solving multiple spatio-temporal cases. Integrating CFD simulations with AR/VR recently received scholarly attention due to technical complexities related to system architecture. Berger et al. was among the first ones to develop a plausible workflow for implementing CFD simulation results in AR/VR using the Unity3D game engine. However, these early studies exhibit a manual integration of CFD and AR/VR with dedicated instruments, with no consideration given to system architecture (Berger and Cristie, 2015). Various approaches have since then been reported to deal with the hurdles encountered. Kim et al. proposed a cloud computing network to entertain users' interaction in VR with CFD simulations (Kim et al., 2018). More recently, Fukuda et al. examined system design parameters and network connections for visualization of CFD simulations at indoor environment with AR and mapped simulation results (Fukuda et al., 2019). Concerning data processing, Lin et al. developed a data format to reduce the data size of CFD dataset in a mobile device-based AR (Lin et al., 2019). A recent review by Li et. al on engineering simulations in AR found that systems were mostly developed for very unique elements due to the use of dedicated software, hardware, and platform. This eventually resulted in several constraints in terms of data- and workflow, thus the system architecture. It was also highlighted that most of the studies dismissed two-way coupling between CFD simulation and user-interaction, and merely focused on the visualization of simulation results (Li et al., 2017). Moreover, low-accuracy real-time CFD simulations with the Lattice-Boltzmann method were highlighted as an alternative to traditional CFD simulations. Harwood et al. claimed that interaction of real-time CFD simulations in VR generated with Unreal Engine 4 is applicable and can present a vivid advancement to simplify the system architecture. It was also mentioned that the integration of real-time CFD simulation with VR/AR brings its own hurdles for post-processing of CFD simulations (Harwood et al., 2018). Real-time CFD simulations are currently merely viable for oversimplified models, for instance, laminar external fluid flow. This raises many questions about whether real-time simulations could be applicable in the near future. An important downside of the above-mentioned studies is that they neglect a two-way coupling between CFD simulator and the end-user environment. Another major criticism is the need for dedicated software, hardware, data format, data processing method and thereby system architecture (Li et al., 2017). Every change or replacement of a building block in the system may affect the whole system architecture due to changes in the data- and workflow.

1.2. Utilization of CFD Simulations in Education

In spite of the friendly user-interfaces (UI), engineering simulation software is still lacking an educational approach. This can hence prevent lecturers to use these tools directly in education. Alternatively, a fully-integrated CFD simulation in VR might present a remedy to prevail over this uneasiness. Few studies have been published to support traditional learning methods with CFD simulations. Chemical process (Li, 2015), internal combustion engine (Tian and Abraham, 2014), biomedicine (Quam et al., 2015), and food engineering (Wong et al., 2010) were the recent application fields where CFD was promoted as a complementary asset. Glessmer et al. assessed the efficacy of low-accuracy real-time CFD simulations to teach the basics of fluid mechanics. Results showed that both students' interest and comprehension on the topic were increased with using real-time CFD in an active learning environment (Glessmer and Janßen, 2017). The fundamental goal of the present research is to scrutinize the system design process of AV/VR with interactive multiphysics CFD simulations. Present study first proposes a methodology for a robust integration of CFD to AR/VR, then discusses a case study to illustrate the development of the digital environment, and finally dwells on the future direction of the proposed methodology.

2. Methodology

In our proposed methodology, integration of CFD simulations with AR/VR was demonstrated. To provide a sustainable integration, an approach was followed pinpointing each of the steps taken. This methodology presents a scaffold for a generic system architecture targeting two-way coupling.

2.1. Analysis of the system

To begin with, exploratory studies on integrating CFD simulation with AR/VR were performed using the methods available in the literature as reported in the introduction. CFD simulations from conventional to real-time and virtual environments from VR to AR were reviewed and evaluated in terms of the components of the system. Once a complete one-way integration was achieved, such as the visualization of streamlines in AR, steps taken throughout the integration were noted in the workflow and clustered with regards to the relevance of components. In this way, system components in the methodology were inclusively determined. This exploratory study indicated that software, hardware, bridging, add-in, networking and internet of things are the fundamentally required building blocks to develop a two-way coupled system architecture for interactive CFD simulations in AR/VR. In the second place, it was found that system architecture and end-user environment were also influenced by indirect components, namely academic content (Li et al., 2017) and learning analytics (Lai and Bower, 2019). Hamilton et al. reviewed an approach to design learning environments with relevant academic content and technological support. The study expressed the significant interference of indirect components to design a learning environment (Hamilton et al., 2016). In the present methodology only academic content was considered as an indirect component because of our focus on the system architecture.

2.2. Proposed methodology

A methodology was ultimately developed to establish a sustainable system architecture. A more generic, versatile integration was aimed at instead of using, for instance, a mere data format. The system architecture consists of components, requirements and indicators. Figure 1 outlines the proposed methodology integrating CFD simulation with AR/VR.

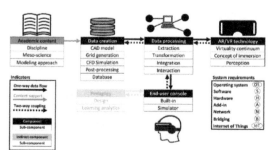

Figure 1. Proposed methodology for the system architecture to integrate process engineering simulation tools with AR/VR.

While components are the stages of workflow comprising dedicated tasks throughout the development of the end-user console, sub-components are the branches holding a responsibility to achieve devoted tasks. Indirect-components do not have any interference on the workflow, but may affect the requirements of components. System requirements are the specified platforms utilizing a variety of options to execute the tasks attained for each component. A sub-component must also be designed by selecting at least one of the requirements. Lastly, indicators are illustrated as binders of the components to outline the data flow. We believe this method represents a viable alternative to the literature.

3. Case study

A case study was carried out to evaluate the proposed system architecture. For simplicity, a benchmark CFD study was selected where we evaluated the run-time of calculations and validation. Being a mature application in CRE, the mixing process inside a stirred tank was simulated and results were visualized with mobile marker-based AR. Requirements used for each component were selected intuitively based on functionality, license, and customer support. All of the softwares used in the following sections were either open-source or accessible with a free personal-developer license. Neither commercial utilization or broadcasting was aimed at.

3.1. CFD Simulations

Initially, 3D geometry was designed with FreeCAD v0.18.4. Grid generation, pre-processing and calculations were performed through the use of pimpledymfoam in OpenFOAM v3.0.1. Extraction of the simulation dataset was done with ParaView v5.6.0. Once data processing was performed, the dataset was stored in the internal hard disk. The hardware employed was a Dell Precision 5530 Notebook (processor Intel(R) Core (TM) i7-8850H CPU @ 2.60GHz, 2592 MHz, 6 Cores, 12 Logical processors) with both Linux Ubuntu 16.04 and Microsoft Windows 10 as operating systems.

3.2. Development of AR application

Due to the customer support, Unity 3D 2019 game engine was chosen to develop the AR application. Although several AR software are available on the market, Vuforia was applied which provides a plug-in to enable its functionalities in Unity. Hence, by using Unity with the Vuforia plug-in, the required software for the development of AR was limited to one single platform. Interaction between the AR application and the real environment was realized with marker-based detection as an easy-to-adapt feature. Any kind of marker can be implemented depending on the developers' preferences. A procedure before final use should be set up online via the website of Vuforia to optimize detection and stability of the selected marker. In the present study human-computer interaction (HCI) was implemented by applying virtual buttons with Vuforia. This feature allowed to increase user-immersion further. The same laptop was used for the development of the application.

3.3. Integration

In Table 1 the workflow used in the case study is shown. Direct import of CFD data to Unity was the bottleneck because these software were using non-identical data formats. Therefore it was evident that an intermediate software must be considered to make processing possible. Blender v2.8 was chosen due to its versatile features for modeling 3D datasets. By comparing import and export data formats of ParaView, Blender and Unity, data processing without any data loss was only attainable with a single method. Once CFD simulation was completed and saved as raw C++ document, the data was then processed with ParaView and extracted to '.x3d' format. Afterwards Blender was used to transform '.x3d' to '.fbx', thereby making the dataset usable in Unity without any data loss. Not surprisingly, a major hindrance was found in the post-processing of the CFD results. Generating an iso-surface from the streamline visualized in Unity was impractical. Both iso-surfaces and streamlines should separately be post-processed in ParaView prior to data processing. Despite this handicap, ParaView and Blender are both environments that are based on Python programming language. A bridge can, therefore, be applicable between ParaView and Unity to solve this issue

Table 1. Workflow of the case study developed based on the proposed methodology.

Component	Data creation					Data processing	
Sub-component	CAD	Grid	Simulation	Post-processing	Database	Extraction	Transformation
OS	Windows	Ubuntu	Ubuntu	Ubuntu	Ubuntu	Windows	Windows
Software Hardware Add-in	FreeCAD laptop	OpenFOAM laptop	OpenFOAM laptop	ParaView laptop	File-based laptop	ParaView laptop	Blender laptop
Network Bridging IoT	Python	C++	C++	Python		Python	Python
Order of workflow	1	2	3	4	6	5	7

Table 1. Workflow of the case study developed based on the proposed methodology.

Data processing		AR/VR technology			End-user console	
Integration	Interaction	Virtuality continuum	Concept of immersion	Perception	Built-in	Simulator
Windows	Android	Windows	Android	Android	Windows	Android
Unity	Vuforia	Unity	Vuforia	Vuforia	Unity	Mobile application
laptop Vuforia LAN & WLAN	smartphone Marker	laptop Vuforia	smartphone Virtual button	smartphone Camera	laptop smartphone USB	smartphone Marker
C#	C#	C#	C#	C#	C#	C#
11	12	8	9	10	13	14

Applying system requirements for each sub-component gave a detailed workflow of the case study. It revealed that various softwares are available in the literature for tasks executed by each sub-component with different data formats. Nevertheless, direct integration was not possible without an intermediate data processing tool. A laptop and a smartphone were used to perform integration and to build the end-used application for mobile augmented reality, respectively. Interestingly, to give extra functions to both software and hardware, add-ins were found advantageous. This made workflow much more structured to express necessities clearly for each components. Another requirement that should not be dismissed was the network. It was experienced that the internet connection was needed to activate Vuforia plug-in inside Unity. The design of the marker for AR was also done through the website of Vuforia. To generate an AR application in a smartphone using Unity, a connection was realized between laptop and smartphone with a USB cable. The study also showed that communication between sub-components could be compatible with bridging different programming languages. Eventually, a two-way coupling might be developed between components. Further elaborations showed that the internet of things (IoT) could be an imperative asset to increase the level of communication and interaction among sub-components. The order of workflow presents a sequence for the particular case study. It can be readjusted in the other studies on purpose, for instance bridging.

3.4. End-user Console

A mobile application was generated with Unity 2019 to visualize the simulation results into mobile marker-based AR. Smartphone-based head-mounted display with Samsung A20e with Android Pie 9 was used to run the application for end-user interaction.

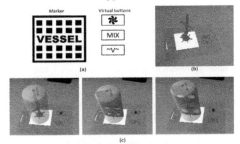

Figure 2. Mobile marker-based AR application; (a) marker and virtual buttons; (b) impeller; (c) visualization of transient CFD simulation.

Figure 2 illustrates the mobile AR application developed.

4. Conclusion

In this paper, we explored the integration of multiphysics CFD simulations with AR/VR. A methodology was presented to develop a sustainable system architecture. The results from this study indicate that the integration has significant potential to exploit multiphysics CFD simulation in AR/VR. This opens up new opportunities for developers dealing with engineering simulations to create desired digital content and integrate them with AR/VR. The research mainly stressed the importance of a sustainable system architecture by means of components, requirements, and indicators. A generic system architecture was proposed allowing alternative workflow and dataflow in the integration. Special attention should be paid by developers on dataflow to the integration of simulation data with AR/VR without the need of compromising on certain required datasets. This also underlines the importance of a database including a variety of complexities for CFD modeling from real-time to high accuracy. The present study only investigated a single way of dataflow. Therefore, future work will concentrate on accomplishing a two-way coupling. This will eventually deploy a sustainable integration.

Acknowledgements

This project has received funding from the European Union's EU Framework Programme for Research and Innovation Horizon 2020 under Grant Agreement 812716. This publication reflects only the author's view exempting the Community from any liability. Project website: https://charming-etn.eu/.

References

Berger, M., Cristie, V., 2015. CFD Post-processing in Unity3D. Procedia Computer Science 51, 2913–2922. https://doi.org/10.1016/j.procs.2015.05.476

Blach, R., Landauer, J., Rösch, A., Simon, A., 1998. A highly flexible virtual reality system. Future Generation Computer Systems 14, 167–178. https://doi.org/10.1016/S0167-739X(98)00019-3

Fukuda, T., Yokoi, K., Yabuki, N., Motamedi, A., 2019. An indoor thermal environment design system for renovation using augmented reality. Journal of Computational Design and Engineering 6, 179–188.

Ge, W., Guo, L., Liu, X., Meng, F., Xu, J., Huang, W.L., Li, J., 2019. Mesoscience-based virtual process engineering. Computers & Chemical Engineering 126, 68–82.

Glessmer, M., Janßen, C., 2017. Using an Interactive Lattice Boltzmann Solver in Fluid Mechanics Instruction. Computation 5, 35. https://doi.org/10.3390/computation5030035

Hamilton, E.R., Rosenberg, J.M., Akcaoglu, M., 2016. The Substitution Augmentation Modification Redefinition (SAMR) Model: a Critical Review and Suggestions for its Use. TechTrends 60, 433–441.

Harwood, A.R.G., Wenisch, P., Revell, A.J., 2018. A real-time modelling and simulation platform for virtual engineering design and analysis, in: Proceedings of 6th European Conference on Computational Mechanics (ECCM 6) and 7th European Conference on Computational FluidDynamics (ECFD 7). Glasgow, UK.

Kim, M., Yi, S., Jung, D., Park, S., Seo, D., 2018. Augmented-Reality Visualization of Aerodynamics Simulation in Sustainable Cloud Computing. Sustainability 10, 1362. https://doi.org/10.3390/su10051362

Lai, J.W.M., Bower, M., 2019. How is the use of technology in education evaluated? A systematic review. Computers & Education 133, 27–42. https://doi.org/10.1016/j.compedu.2019.01.010

Li, J., 2015. Approaching virtual process engineering with exploring mesoscience. Chemical Engineering Journal 278, 541–555. https://doi.org/10.1016/j.cej.2014.10.005

Li, W., Nee, A., Ong, S., 2017. A State-of-the-Art Review of Augmented Reality in Engineering Analysis and Simulation. Multimodal Technologies and Interaction 1, 17. https://doi.org/10.3390/mti1030017

Lin, J.-R., Cao, J., Zhang, J.-P., van Treeck, C., Frisch, J., 2019. Visualization of indoor thermal environment on mobile devices based on augmented reality and computational fluid dynamics. Automation in Construction 103, 26–40. https://doi.org/10.1016/j.autcon.2019.02.007

Quam, D.J., Gundert, T.J., Ellwein, L., Larkee, C.E., Hayden, P., Migrino, R.Q., Otake, H., LaDisa, J.F., 2015. Immersive Visualization for Enhanced Computational Fluid Dynamics Analysis. Journal of Biomechanical Engineering 137, 031004. https://doi.org/10.1115/1.4029017

Suh, A., Prophet, J., 2018. The state of immersive technology research: A literature analysis. Computers in Human Behavior 86, 77–90. https://doi.org/10.1016/j.chb.2018.04.019

Tian, Y., Demirel, S.E., Hasan, M.M.F., Pistikopoulos, E.N., 2018. An overview of process systems engineering approaches for process intensification: State of the art. Chemical Engineering and Processing - Process Intensification 133, 160–210. https://doi.org/10.1016/j.cep.2018.07.014

Tian, Z.F., Abraham, J., 2014. Application of Computational Fluid Dynamics (CFD) in Teaching Internal Combustion Engines. International Journal of Mechanical Engineering Education 42, 73–83.

Wong, S.Y., Connelly, R.K., Hartel, R.W., 2010. Enhancing Student Learning in Food Engineering Using Computational Fluid Dynamics Simulations. Journal of Food Science Education 9, 90–97.

Sauro Pierucci, Flavio Manenti, Giulia Bozzano, Davide Manca (Eds.)
Proceedings of the 30th European Symposium on Computer Aided Process Engineering
(ESCAPE30), May 24-27, 2020, Milano, Italy. © 2020 Elsevier B.V. All rights reserved.
http://dx.doi.org/10.1016/B978-0-12-823377-1.50337-2

Motivational Active Learning in Chemical Engineering

Manuel Rodríguez, Emilio J. González, María González-Miquel, Ismael Díaz

*Departamento de Ingeniería Industrial y del Medio Ambiente, ETSI Industriales,
Universidad Politécnica de Madrid, Calle de José Gutiérrez Abascal, 2, 28006 Madrid*

Manuel.rodriguezh@upm.es

Abstract

This paper presents how a new integrated innovative educational approach and shows how it helps students to improve their learning and understanding of the different concepts and thus to get better results in the subject and to achieve the desired outcomes. The approach is applied to core subjects taught in the Bachelor Degree in Chemical Engineering at the Technical University of Madrid. Different methodologies have been integrated and used as: flipped classroom, peer instruction, gamification, augmented reality, case-based learning, design thinking. In order to implement the mentioned methods, the following educational material has been developed: screencasts, concept tests, board games, augmented reality applications and simulations besides the traditional lecturing material (slides and text). Preliminary results show high student motivation, higher participation in class and better academic results.

Keywords: active learning, adaptive learning, flipped classroom, gamification, peer instruction

1. Introduction

Universities appeared more than 900 years ago, since the beginning lecturing has been, and still is in many places, the usual way of teaching. In the last 30 years new theories have appeared challenging the traditional approach. There is a change of paradigm as instruction now is seen as focused on learning and not on teaching and besides in this new paradigm an instructional method that engages students in the learning process seems fundamental. The importance of interest and motivation in education is not new, back in 1913 prof. John Dewey wrote an essay titled "Interest and effort in education" (Dewey,1913) where he indicated the influence of interest to achieve better results in education. The way our brain and cognitive processes work are still research subjects, everybody has experienced how differently we learn things depending on our interest in them (Renninger and Hidi, 2016, Harackiewicz et al., 2016, Shin et al., 2019). Active learning can be defined as "instructional activities involving students in doing things and thinking about what they are doing" (Bonwell,1991) or as "any instructional method that engages students in the learning process" (Prince, 2004). Previous approaches related to the implementation of active learning can be found in (Wilson and Jennings, 2000; Belcher, 2003; Beichner et al., 2007 or Nelson et al., 2019). The approach presented in this paper is closer to the format presented in Pirker et al. (2014).

2. Motivational Active Learning Integrated Approach

2.1. Motivation

Chemical Engineering is a Bachelor's Degree that includes the design of industrial processes that turn raw materials into valuable products. Moreover, many of the processes within chemical engineering involve complex operations, which should be considered in order to formulate more adequate designs. It needs a thorough understanding of how the different unit operations are included in a chemical plant and what are the implications of changing operation variables in a process. All these concepts are difficult to grasp for many students and they stay in a quite passive attitude, so a different innovative approach has been implemented in order to increase students' understanding, motivation and participation. The focus is on learning (instead of teaching) and motivating (or engaging) the students on the different subjects.

2.2. Objectives

The main objective is to foster a student-centred learning methodology. A motivating active learning integrated approach that allows a personalized evolution of the student. This objective is decomposed in the following subobjectives:

> Implement a new student-centred learning methodology
> Increase student motivation and participation in class
> Increase the understanding of the more complex concepts by the students
> Increase student results and the outcomes acquired
> Increase student acquisition of transversal competences
> Increase student awareness of the importance of sustainability
> Increase student soft skills capabilities: creativity, leadership, communication and teamwork
> Make the students aware of the importance of self-learning

The purpose of this work is to promote an active learning based on the joint use of several methodologies (flipped classroom, peer instruction, gamification, augmented reality, case-based learning, design thinking) in several subjects of the Chemical Engineering Degree at the Technical University of Madrid. Specifically, this approach has already been implemented in Process Control (4th course), Process and Product Design (4th course), Chemical Reactors (3rd course) and Chemical Engineering Lab III. Of course, not all the objectives are worked on with the same intensity in all the mentioned subjects.

2.3. Methodologies

Following the used methodologies are presented. Their use in the different subjects is commented on section 3.

2.3.1 Flipped Classroom

In this methodology educational material is provided to the students in advance of the lecture. The student has to learn by himself the contents of the topic that will be further discussed in class. The material developed has been mainly educational videos/screencasts. It has been complemented with traditional material such as slides or texts. One of the important benefits of this methodology is that it allows to spend more time in class for specific, more complex, parts of a topic. In order to decide what concepts are more difficult, flipped classroom must be combined with other methodologies like peer instruction. In this way, the students are the ones who establish what is being harder to understand instead of the teacher

2.3.2 Adaptive learning & Peer Instructions

Adaptive learning and peer instruction are implemented using concepts tests. These tests are presented at the beginning of the class. Individual comprehension can be evaluated in this way. After the test, the students gather in small groups and think about the more difficult topics, then the tests are run again and finally the teacher explains the topic in detail.

2.3.3 Gamification

The purpose of gamification is to improve the classroom experience, it helps to motivate the students and what they learn is fixed more deeply (and thus more easily recalled afterwards). This is a very valuable methodology, but it has to be used carefully, as there is a risk that the students focus more on the "game" than on to the learning process.

2.3.4 Team work & peer learning

In peer learning the students explain things to each other without the teacher being involved. Student learn from their peers. This is implemented mainly dividing the class into small groups and then an activity is presented to them. It can be a problem that solved by each group or a laboratory practice. In some cases, the solution of the problem (or the results of the practice) is handed to other group which corrects and evaluates it.

2.3.5 Learning by doing

When using learning by doing (meaning that the students not only listen and watch), the student effectively does something that allows him to understand the theory or validate it. This methodology is very efficient as the students retain more easily what they learn.

2.3.6 Traditional teaching

In this methodology the approach is lecturing using slides to explain, usually, theory. In order to promote class participation and involvement, some blanks are in the presentation and some quizzes are also inserted where the students see the results in real time.

2.3.7 Case-based reasoning. Design thinking.

Open problems are presented to the students (mainly in the process & product design subject). These problems are very focused on sustainability and on working the SDGs (Sustainable Development Goals)

2.3.8 Augmented reality

Finally, the last methodology used is augmented reality. Different videos and guides have been prepared for the equipment used in the Laboratories. The students know how they work and besides they have access to the description of the task they have to follow. Auresma software has been used for Augmented reality.

It is important to stress that the main idea is to use several methodologies in a subject, in this way the student is more alert, motivated and keen to learn and fix what they learn. In order to implement the mentioned methods, the following material has been developed: screencasts, concept tests, trivia contest, simulations, augmented reality material and case-based studies besides the traditional lecturing material (slides and text). Fig.1 shows the methodologies used to motivate and engage the students.

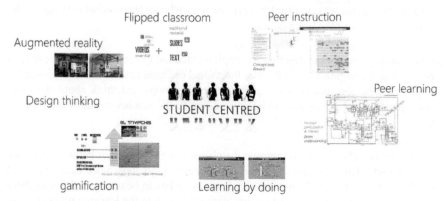

Figure 1. Integrated methodologies used to foster student motivation and learning.

3. Application to Chemical Engineering

3.1. Process Control

In this subject all the methodologies have been applied but case-based reasoning. This was the first subject where this integrated approach was implemented. The following material has been developed: more than 50 videos/screencasts (using ActivePresenter software), more than 300 questions for concept tests (using Classtime software), a board game (called Triviachis, a mix of a quiz game and a dice game) where the students divided in groups play between them in a tournament mode, augmented reality for use in the instrumentation lab and finally an Operator Training Simulator (implemented in Excel and using Aspen Dynamics) for learning by doing.

3.2. Process and Product Design

In this subject also many methodologies have been used and implemented. It is important to remark that this one has worked intensively the objective of sustainability. Fig. 2 shows how the different methodologies are related and have been approached in this subject. Educational material is comprised of more than 40 videos (mainly devoted to Aspen Plus), several Case-based reasoning scenarios focused more on creativity, communication and team work. The gamification has been implemented in a role-type game, where students play different roles (client, engineering company, contractors, etc).

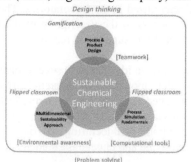

Figure 2. Methodologies and soft-skills applied in process and product design having sustainability as the leit motiv.

3.3. Chemical Reactors

This subject has also developed a lot of educational material related mainly to flipped classroom (using Active presenter), peer instruction with the creation of more than 150 tests (using Kahoot and Mentimeter software).

3.4. Chemical Engineering Lab III

Aurasma has been used to create real and virtual images and videos of the different equipment to be used in the Lab, like batch distillation, absorption or chemical reactors.

Table 1. Matrix showing the subjects and the methodologies applied.

Subject	flipped classroom	Adaptive learning & Peer Instructions	Gamification	Team work & peer learning	Learning by doing	Traditional teaching	Case-based reasoning. Design thinking	Augmented reality
Process control	X	X	X	X	X	X		X
Process & Product Design	X	X	X	X		X	X	
Chemical Reactors	X	X		X		X		
Chemical Eng. Lab				X	X	X		X

Table 1 summarizes the different techniques that have integrated in the subjects presented in this work.

4. Results

The implementation of this integrated approach in core subjects of Chemical Engineering is being very well accepted by the students. Although the application is very recent (3 years in process control, 2 years in the other subjects) there are some indicators to quantify in some manner the results achieved. Table 2 shows the academic results obtained in Process Control. The methodology was applied in 2017, the results (average and number of students that passed the subject) show a significant improvement, although more important than the marks are the students opinion about this new way of learning. In Chemical Reactors a survey was conducted (with Likert levels), the results obtained were:
Do you think that this methodology facilitates learning? 70% answered yes
Are you satisfied with this methodology? 75.1% are satisfied or very satisfied
Are you satisfied with the educational material (quality, contents, usefulness)? More than 90% said they were satisfied or very satisfied.

Table 2. Process control academic results since 2015

Year	Average grade (out of 10)	% Passed	# Students
2018	7.3	83	43
2017	7.4	91	54
2016	6.8	67	39
2015	5.6	72	43

The results are only of one-two years measurements so they have to be taken with caution but they seem quite promising and they show that this is the way to proceed.

5. Conclusions

New innovative education methodologies are not just a hype but a true improvement over traditional ones. Different methodologies have been presented in this work. All and every of them are valuable and can be used to improve the learning experience. But the main goal we seek is to engage our students in the learning process, to motivate them, and for that what best fits for a new way of teaching or more precisely a new way of learning is to integrate different methodologies (flipped classroom, peer instruction, gamification, augmented reality, case-based learning, design thinking). The main drawback is the amount of time and resources needed to develop all the material. Although this effort is compensated over time (as most of the material is reused) it would be more than desirable to have a shared platform in internet where teachers from over the world can share chunks of knowledge that others can reuse and take advantage of. To conclude, the use of motivational active learning will make the students more motivated, participative and more interested in what they are learning and thus enhancing their performance.

References

Beichner, R.J., Saul, J.M., Abbott, D.S., Morse, J.J., Deardorff, D., Allain, R.J., Bonham,S.W., Dancy, M.H., Risley, J.S., 2007. The student-centered activities for largeenrollment undergraduate programs (SCALE-UP) project. J. Res. Based Ref. Univ.Phys. 1 (1), 2–39.

Belcher, J.W., 2003. Improving Student Understandin with TEAL. MIT Fac. Newsl. 16(2), 7–11

Bonwell C.C, Eison J.A., 1991. Active Learning: Creating Excitemnet in the Classroom. ASHE-ERIC Higher Education Reports.

Dewey, J., 1913. Interest and Effort in Education. The Riverside Press, Cambridge.

Harackiewicz JM, Smith JL, Priniski SJ., 2016. Interest Matters: The Importance of Promoting Interest in Education. Policy Insights Behav Brain Sci.;3(2):220–227.

Nelson, Jill, et al., 2019. Improving STEM Teaching And Learning Through Active Learning. Innovations in Teaching & Learning Conference Proceedings. Vol. 11.

Pirker, Johanna, Riffnaller-Schiefer, Maria, Gütl, Christian, 2014. Motivational activelearning: engaging university students in computer science education. In: Pro-ceedings of the 2014 conference on Innovation & technology in computer scienceeducation (ITiCSE '14), ACM, New York, NY, USA, pp. 297–302,

Prince, M., 2004. Does Active Learning Work? A Review of the Research. Journal of Engineering Education, 93, 223-231.

Renninger, K.A., Hidi, S.E., 2016. The Power of Interest for Motivation and Engage-ment. Routledge, New York and London

Shin, D., Lee, H., Lee, G., & Kim, S., 2019. The Role of Curiosity and Interest in Learning and Motivation. In The Cambridge Handbook of Motivation and Learning (Cambridge Handbooks in Psychology, pp. 443-464). Cambridge: Cambridge University

Wilson, J.M., Jennings, W.C., 2000. Studio courses: How information technology ischanging the way we teach, on campus a and off. Proc. IEEE 88 (1), 72–80.

Sauro Pierucci, Flavio Manenti, Giulia Bozzano, Davide Manca (Eds.)
Proceedings of the 30th European Symposium on Computer Aided Process Engineering
(ESCAPE30), May 24-27, 2020, Milano, Italy. © 2020 Elsevier B.V. All rights reserved.
http://dx.doi.org/10.1016/B978-0-12-823377-1.50338-4

An E-learning Bot for Bioprocess Systems Engineering

Simoneta Caño de las Heras, Mark Nicholas Jones, Krist V. Gernaey, Ulrich Krühne, Seyed Soheil Mansouri

Process and Systems Eng.Centre (PROSYS), Dept. of Chemical and Biochemical Eng., Technical University of Denmark, Søltofts Plads, 2800 Kgs. Lyngby, Denmark
seso@kt.dtu.dk

Abstract

Receiving an engineering education is not a smooth path and in the last years, several digital platforms have been developed with the aim to help the students in the field. Nonetheless, the initial efforts to use digital platforms have not yet been successful, partly due to the lack of support to the teachers, the lack of motivation strategies inside the platforms or the loss of the social interaction, which is key in a collaborative learning process. Collaborative learning integrates the interaction between the students and the teacher, or in the case of digital learning, with an educational software. However, it is difficult to provide such a frame of interaction between learners inside an educational software. Therefore, a chatbot is proposed with its own design and architecture which behaves like a "friend" or colleague in the education, here applied to bioprocesses. Along with the chatbot architecture, it is explained how it is integrated in the learning design through its database. This tailored database contains training example dialogs through questions raised by students from a course on Bioprocess Technology, while it also collects their common mistakes, etc. Moreover, this database contains a novel system of twin databases; one with correct information and another with small errors. Using this system, the chatbot provides a more accurate representation of a learner's peer and triggers critical thinking. Finally, the chatbot architecture is embedded inside a prototype open-source Educational Virtual Bioprocess Plant developed by the Department of Chemical and Biochemical Engineering of the Technical University of Denmark, called *FermProc*. **Keywords:** Knowledge transfer, Bioprocess, Chatbot, Process System Education.

1. Introduction

During the past two decades, our world has drastically changed due to the use of internet in our daily life and the democratization of personal smartphones and computers. It has affected our means of communication and added new societal dimensions with economic implications. In the case of education, the creation of massive open on-line courses (MOOC) (Conole, 2016), educational computer games (Zendesk, n.d.), or educational simulators (Dyrberg, et al., 2017; Ebner & Holzinger, 2007) has demonstrated a clear interest in using digital platforms in teaching. Moreover, in the case of higher and tertiary education, there has been a growing need for flexible training towards continuing education and professional training, endorsing a learning outside the classroom supported by digital tools. However, the success in the integration of digital platforms as learning tools has not been as expected with a dropout rate of about 96 per cent on average over five years (Reich & Ruipérez-Valiente, 2019) in on-line courses.

This could be explained by the need of support for the instructors to create and integrate on-line content, the lack of institutions offering on-line education (Brahimi & Sarirete, 2015), or the failure of simulators in engineering education in motivating the students (Kiili, 2005), amongst other factors. A reason behind unsuccessful integration of digital technology had been the loss of normal interaction that occurs in a real classroom or laboratory as the students are isolated from their peers and instructors (Balamuralithara & Woods, 2009). Therefore, students miss a collaborative learning experience, i.e. they miss the social and environmental elements in their traditional learning.

In this work, we intend to develop a collaborative e-learning for bioprocess systems engineering, which is integrated inside a computer-aided tool. Bioprocess development reaches from discovery to distribution of bio-products. Therefore, it is a necessity for engineering students to gain the ability to connect and use the knowledge and competences that those students acquire during their education. This is a challenge that can be tackled through a knowledge transfer computer-aided tool, in the form of a chatbot.

2. Collaborative e-learning

Collaborative e-learning (Figure 1) is a type of learning process. Here, a computer-aided media (acting as a teacher) provides the content, task and the assessment to the students. On the other side, a peer (the chatbot) communicates with the learner, who compares, argues and reflects with itself and the chatbot about ideas or practices. Although it is part of a natural learning process (Laurillard, 2009), it must be actively considered during the design of the learning experience.

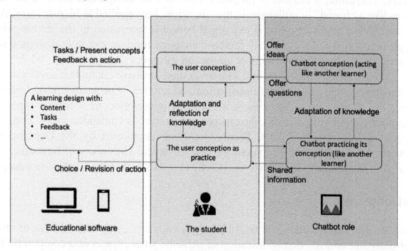

Figure 1. Collaborative e-learning scheme that provides a frame for the interactions between learners and their concepts and practice.

Collaborative e-learning has been investigated through the use of chats (Monahan, et al., 2008) and in fewer cases, chatbots (Kane, 2016). A chatbot is a computer program that works as a conversational agent and has huge potential as helper in education. A previous study had investigated the use of a chatbot for a negotiated learner model (Kerly, 2009), finding an improving accuracy in students' self-assessment. In another case, the co-development of a chatbot with students was tested, by incorporating their own questions, which increased their motivation and interest for the subject (Crown, et al., 2011). However, in those cases the chatbot is an independent tool, not supported by an educational software that provides them with tasks, content…, and it lacks some of the characteristics of a peer, like the possibility of being wrong.

Mistakes are rather usual to make and critical thinking is an important tool in the education of process engineers. Therefore, collaborative e-learning provides a frame not only for the students to reflect upon and share ideas, but also to be critical, using their own knowledge while an external agent attempts to influence them.

3. Chatbot Architecture

The chatbot is acting as a peer inside the collaborative e-learning (Figure 1). The software architecture can be seen in Figure 2.

This chatbot is developed considering its objective as an educational tool for process engineering applied to bioprocesses. Based on its educational frame, the chatbot includes:

- *Engage the user.* It needs to be contextual and focused on the individual and on the objectives of the process (operational, economic and sustainability). For example, some enjoyable facts about the process and industrial information can be used to refer back to the main topic.
- *Learn.* Leverage machine learning to develop context and resolve issues in an automated fashion.
- *Communicate.* Create a comfortable and adapted mode of communication with the use of gifs, emojis or memes.
- *Promote curiosity.* By providing a possibility to connect one bioprocess concept to another.

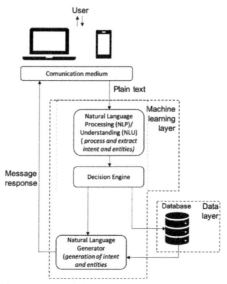

Figure 2. Chatbot architecture, in which is represented the transport of information and the different processes that form the chatbot.

The chatbot (Figure 2) is composed of a machine learning (data-driven) layer and a data layer. The machine learning layer contains the natural language processing (NLP), understanding (NLU) and generator (NLG) as well as the decision engine, and is programmed in Python and TensorFlow using predefined routines.

Meanwhile, the data layer is in charge of storing the information used in the training of the chatbot and therefore, it embeds the chatbots' specifications. Along other routine dialogs, the chatbot database involves specific example dialogs for training purposes, information related to bioprocesses and information related to the pedagogically oriented software in which it is implemented. The training example dialogs are a collection of questions of the Bioprocess Technology course, a course shared by the Bachelor of Science study plans of Human Life Science Engineering, Biotechnology and Chemical Engineering at the Technical University of Denmark, along with other sources of information. In this course, undergraduate students learn to do systematic mass and energy balances, to analyse and predict fluid behavior, and to design basic equipment used in bioprocess engineering (DTU, 2019).

An example question from a student used in the training dialog database has been:

Student: "In pumps, I am seeing two equations for the Net Positive Suction Head (NPSH); one with all the common terms and another one that it is missing the velocity term. Why is that?"

In this action, the Natural Language Processing (NLP) and Natural Language Understanding (NLU) modules, that use machine learning in Python, extract entities such as *equation, NSPH, missing, velocity,* and intents, like *containNSPH* (the verb and the noun of the sentence). Then, it performs a comparison through the information collected from the database and the Natural Language Generator (NLG) will provide a reply:

Chatbot: "It is due to the calculation of the NPSH in a specific point in order to calculate the net positive suction head, not needing the velocity. To get more information, I like this one: http://www.pumpschool.com/applications/NPSH.pdf (explained the different between the NPSH available and required and the different terms)"

As it has been briefly mentioned, a novel feature of this chatbot is confronting misleading ideas or wrong understandings during the training process. As the chatbot is acting as a peer learner inside the collaborative learning (Figure 1), it is possible that a peer learner will give a false advise. Thereby, we hope to engage the students in the necessary critical thinking. In order to implement this feature, another database is developed (an evil twin database) that includes slightly wrong answers. This database can be activated by the students as a special feature. An example can be seen in Figure 3.

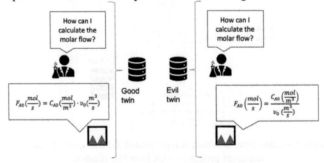

Figure 3. Example of the two databases

Furthermore, in the data layer, the two example dialog databases are connected together with a database developed for a pedagogically oriented software developed at the Department of Chemical and Biochemical Engineering of the Technical University of Denmark, called *FermProc*. The aim of *FermProc* is to be the educational software that presents the content and tasks to the students as well as feedback over the learning of bioprocesses and a revision of the content and activities after the action of the student (Figure 1) in the collaborative e-learning.

4. Software integration

FermProc is based on a previously developed systematic methodology (de las Heras et al., 2018). This computer-aided tool has its prime pedagogical objectives in training people in the area of bioprocess operation. The interactive prototype includes understandably described and implemented mechanistic models, the possibility to modify them, learning-hints, questionnaires, mini-games, and the possibility to learn by failure. However, *FermProc* was not yet integrating the use of collaborative e-learning inside the platform and in the next development stage, the chatbot is added inside the software architecture.

FermProc is a three-layer software architecture. In its current state, the chatbot is a parallel feature in the software architecture of *FermProc*, connected through a shared data layer as well as the graphic user interface (Figure 4). However, in the future development, the chatbot will pass to be inside of the "special features" of the application layer of *FermProc*, together with the multimedia resources, or bioprocess mini-games implemented.

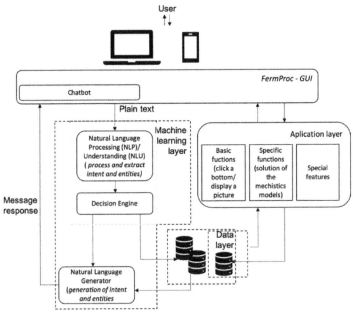

Figure 4. Integrated software architecture of the chatbot and *FermProc*. In this schema, the two combined architectures can be seen and the flux of information either from the chatbot or from *FermProc*.

5. Conclusions

Complexity is an intrinsic part of process systems and understanding such complexity requires the connection of different subjects and knowledge that undergraduate and graduate students acquire during their education. Although digital platforms could be excellent tools, they present some issues such as the lack of interaction between peers as well as the sharing and comparison of information. In this work, we proposed the use of a tailored chatbot. Through its data layer trained by actual questions from the students, we hope to simplify the work of instructors and reduce the fear of students to ask questions. Furthermore, as peers are not always right, a novel system of twin databases is developed. This twin database system aims at enhancing the critical thinking of the students as the chatbot will not always provide the correct answer but the mechanisms to evaluate if the answer is wrong. Although the chatbot is specifically trained for the learning of bioprocess system engineering, its design is generic and it can be expanded to other fields and areas. Finally, the chatbot of this work has been implemented inside an educational bioprocess prototype software (*FermProc*) to provide a complete environment for a collaborative e-learning process.

References

Balamuralithara, B., & Woods, P. C. (2009). Virtual laboratories in engineering education: the simulation lab and remote lab. *Computer Applications in Engineering Education*. https://doi.org/10.1002/cae.20186

Brahimi, T., & Sarirete, A. (2015). Learning outside the classroom through MOOCs. *Computers in Human Behavior*, *51*, 604–609. https://doi.org/10.1016/j.chb.2015.03.013

Conole, G. (2016). MOOCs as disruptive technologies: strategies for enhancing the learner experience and quality of MOOCs. *Revista de Educación a Distancia (RED)*, (50), 1–18. https://doi.org/10.6018/red/50/2

Crown, S., Fuentes, A., Jones, R., Nambiar, R., & Crown, D. (2011). Anne G. Neering: Interactive chatbot to engage and motivate engineering students. *Computers in Education Journal*, *21*(2), 24–34. https://doi.org/10.1016/j.futures.2006.01.008

de Las Heras, S. C., Gutschmann, B., Gernaey, K. V., Krühne, U., & Mansouri, S. S. (2019). Facilitating learning by failure through a pedagogical model-based tool for bioprocesses. In *29th European Symposium on Computer Aided Process Engineering* (Vol. 46). https://doi.org/10.1016/b978-0-12-818634-3.50305-2

de las Heras, S. C., Mansouri, S. S., Cignitti, S., Uellendahl, H., Weitze, C. L., Gernaey, K. V., … Krühne, U. (2018). A Methodology for Development of a Pedagogical Simulation Tool used in Fermentation Applications. *Computer Aided Chemical Engineering*, *44*, 1621–1626. https://doi.org/10.1016/B978-0-444-64241-7.50265-2

DTU, C. (2019). Bio-Process Technology course description. Retrieved November 20, 2019, from https://kurser.dtu.dk/course/28025

Dyrberg, N. R., Treusch, A. H., & Wiegand, C. (2017). Virtual laboratories in science education: students' motivation and experiences in two tertiary biology courses. *Journal of Biological Education*, *51*(4), 358–374. https://doi.org/10.1080/00219266.2016.1257498

Ebner, M., & Holzinger, A. (2007). Successful implementation of user-centered game based learning in higher education: An example from civil engineering. *Computers and Education*, *49*(3), 873–890. https://doi.org/10.1016/j.compedu.2005.11.026

Kane, D. (2016). The role of chatbots in teaching and learning. *E-Learning and the Academic Library: Essays on Innovative Initiatives*, 131–147. https://doi.org/10.7280/D1P075

Kerly, A. (2009). *Negotiated Learner Modelling with a Conversational Agent*. (June).

Kiili, K. (2005). Digital game-based learning: Towards an experiential gaming model. *Internet and Higher Education*, *8*(1), 13–24. https://doi.org/10.1016/j.iheduc.2004.12.001

Laurillard, D. (2009). The pedagogical challenges to collaborative technologies. *International Journal of Computer-Supported Collaborative Learning*, *4*(1), 5–20. https://doi.org/10.1007/s11412-008-9056-2

Monahan, T., McArdle, G., & Bertolotto, M. (2008). Virtual reality for collaborative e-learning. *Computers and Education*, *50*(4), 1339–1353. https://doi.org/10.1016/j.compedu.2006.12.008

Reich, J., & Ruipérez-Valiente, J. A. (2019). The MOOC pivot. *Science*, *363*(6423), 130–131. https://doi.org/10.1126/science.aav7958

Zendesk. (n.d.). Prodigy. Retrieved November 19, 2019, from https://www.prodigygame.com

Sauro Pierucci, Flavio Manenti, Giulia Bozzano, Davide Manca (Eds.)
Proceedings of the 30th European Symposium on Computer Aided Process Engineering
(ESCAPE30), May 24-27, 2020, Milano, Italy. © 2020 Elsevier B.V. All rights reserved.
http://dx.doi.org/10.1016/B978-0-12-823377-1.50339-6

Knowledge Transfer, Experiences and Prospects from the Collaboration between an Energy Company and the University

Emilia M. Kondili[a*], Ioannis K. Kaldellis[b], Evangelos Demenagas[c],
Athanasios Stefanakis[c]

[a] *Optimisation of Production Systems Laboratory, Dept. of Mechanical Engineering,*
[b]*Soft Energy Applications and Environmental Protection Laboratory,*
Dept. of Mechanical Engineering, University of West Attica, Campus 2, P. Ralli &
Thivon Street, 12244, Egaleo, Greece
[c]*Hellenic Petroleum Grou of Companies, 17th km of Athens – Patras National Road*

ekondili@uniwa.gr

Abstract

The international trend towards cleaner fuels and carbon footprint minimisation puts a severe pressure on the prospects of the oil and gas companies worldwide. Commitment in knowledge development and innovation are required in today's severe conditions and call for collaboration with Universities and Research Centres. The objective of the present work is to describe the main parameters, the design and implementation issues and the future prospects of a successful collaboration between an energy industrial group and a University in an innovative Postgraduate MSc Course in Oil and Gas Process Systems Engineering.

Keywords: PSE, Oil and Gas, Energy transformation, Industrial collaboration

1. Introduction and Background of the work

Oil industry is one of the biggest and most important industries in the world with a crucial role in energy market in the future. The international trend towards cleaner fuels and carbon footprint minimisation puts a severe pressure on the prospects of the oil and gas companies worldwide. However, the continuous development of new products with better environmental behaviour, the important projects of oil and gas transportation, the excellent competitiveness of the refining units make this field interesting and attractive with very good research, development and innovation prospects.

The Mechanical Engineering Department of the University of West Attica, in collaboration with Hellenic Petroleum Group of Companies and Aspropyrgos Municipality have recently developed a Postgraduate Program in "MSc Oil and Gas Process Systems Engineering". The objective of the new Postgraduate Course is to provide students with a scientific background and extensive integrated and applied knowledge in hydrocarbons engineering and enable them to develop a successful career in the oil and gas process and supply chain management companies. Furthermore, the well-educated and trained professionals will be able to advance the communication of the local and regional authorities with these sectoral companies for the benefit of the society.

The postgraduate course leads to a Master of Science (MSc) degree and intends to educate professionals in the fields of oil and gas processing, storage, supply chain management as well as in the new hydrocarbon fuel products and their applications in the light of the international pressure towards clean fuels and minimisation of the carbon footprint, the associated downstream processing technologies, operations and economics; process safety and operations integrity; and methods for the optimal design and operation of process systems. Furthermore, students will have learnt about the general economics of the energy sector, oil and gas production, transportation and logistics. In addition, advanced and practical knowledge related to the environmental behaviour of oil and gas processes, as well as special know-how on the novel transportation projects will also have been gained after the completion of the course.

2. The collaborating organisations

2.1. The University of West Attica

The University of West Attica - a newly developed University from the merging of two Technological Universities in the area of West Attica - has the vision to make collaborations with the organisations and industries in the area in order to support them with scientific knowledge and academic experience and, on the other hand, provide the University with the knowledge and experience of the real production world, interchange personnel and provide its students with a continuous contact with employment opportunities. The Department of Mechanical Engineering that participates in the Course development and implementation has a very successful track record in the design and operation of Postgraduate courses in the fields of energy and environmental technologies and business.

2.2. Hellenic Petroleum Group of Companies

Hellenic Petroleum is one of the leading energy groups in South East Europe with activities spanning across the energy value chain and presence in six countries. The Group's wide range of activities include: Supply, refining and trading of petroleum products both in Greece and abroad, Fuels marketing, Petrochemicals, chemicals production and trading, Oil and gas exploration and production, Power generation and natural gas, Renewable energy sources and Engineering services.

Hellenic Petroleum is one of the top 100 pioneer energy groups worldwide. The most significant vision of HELPE Group is the successful transition to a new competitive production model of sustainable development in the framework of Industry 4.0 and digitalisation critical changes. The main directions towards this new era are the 3Ds (HELPE, a): Decarbonisation, decentralization and digitalisation. Furthermore, HELPE adapts the model of the Knowledge Triangle (Figure 1, HELPE a) for the transition towards the Knowledge Society and – to that effect – encourages strategic alliances with Universities and Research Centers. The company is pioneer in the country in that respect also collaborating practically with most Universities and Research Centers.

2.3. Aspropyrgos Municipality

Aspropyrgos Municipality is very much interested in the development of this specific PG Course since Aspropyrgos is the area of Greece with the most significant hydrocarbons production plants and industries. Therefore, a number of employees are recruited from the area in these plants and there is a high interest for developing qualified scientists and engineers able to contribute to the optimal operation of these plants. Furthermore, the municipality communicates and cooperates in many respects with these companies; therefore, qualified human resources are required in various other relevant job positions that will be able to understand the complex issues for the mutual benefit of the companies and the local society.

3. Best Practices in Collaboration between Energy Companies and Universities

The need for continuous innovation and development of new knowledge and novel technologies in the oil and gas sector has been recognised from the largest companies worldwide. A great experience concerning the collaboration between Universities and oil and gas companies has been already recorded, leading to strategic alliances with world class quality measurable benefits for both sides.

As an example of the best practices worldwide, ExxonMobil cooperates with the best universities in USA in education and research. For example, in their cooperation with Princeton University they run five projects that focus on solar and battery technologies, plasma physics, Arctic sea-ice modeling, and the impact of carbon dioxide absorption on the world's oceans. ($5 million over five years to Princeton). They also announced a $15 million investment as a leading member of the University of Texas at Austin Energy Institute to pursue technologies to help meet growing energy demand while reducing environmental impacts and the risk of climate change. Research projects are expected to cover a range of emerging technologies and will take advantage of the university's capabilities in renewable energy, battery technologies and power grid modeling.

Scientists from ExxonMobil and the Georgia Institute of Technology have developed a potentially revolutionary new technology that could significantly reduce the amount of energy and emissions associated with manufacturing plastics. The University of Wisconsin-Madison and ExxonMobil continue to partner together to research the fundamental chemistry of converting biomass into transportation fuels. UW-Madison has long been known for its expertise in biomass conversion.

ExxonMobil is also a founding member of the Global Climate and Energy Project at Stanford University. In addition, the company is funding a broad portfolio of biofuels research programs including our ongoing efforts on algae as well as programs on converting alternative, non-food based biomass feedstocks, such as cellulosic biomass, to advanced biofuels.

4. Program Overview - Course Structure and Content

Expanding its collaboration with Greek Universities, Hellenic Petroleum has launched along with the Mechanical Engineering Department of the University of West Attica and Aspropyrgos Municipality a Postgraduate Program in "MSc Oil and Gas Process Systems Engineering". The objective of the new PG Course is to provide students with a scientific background and extensive integrated and applied knowledge in hydrocarbons engineering and enable them to develop a successful career in the oil and gas process and supply chain management companies. Furthermore, the well-educated and trained professionals will be able to advance the communication of the local and regional authorities with these sectoral companies for the benefit of the society.

In West Attica region, where the University of West Attica is located, the largest hydrocarbons processing production units are sited (Aspropyrgos and Elefsina Refineries of HELPE, Pachi - Megara installations, Aspropyrgos and Elefsina Docks, DEPA installations, Revythousa LNG Plant, EPA of Attica, DESFA etc.). In the context of the above discussion, the need of a new course is dictated by at least three reasons:

1. The geographical region of Attica as mentioned above.
2. The innovative characteristics of the program content that combines technologies, operations, economical and business issues.

3. The fact that participation of a local communities and societies and the most important sectoral companies in the design and organisation of the course.

The students of the PG Course will need to attend successfully eight taught Modules (Table 1) and carry out a research project (Dissertation) as well as a two months Practical Industrial Placement that will be organised for the students.

Table 1: Structure and Contents of Oil and Gas PSE Postgraduate Course

Structure and Contents of Oil and Gas PSE Postgraduate Course
1st Semester
Conventional and Renewable Energy Technologies
Basics of Refinery Processes
Process Safety in Hydrocarbons Processes-Risk Assessment
2nd Semester
Economics of Petroleum & Natural Gas/ Hydrocarbons Business – Evaluation of Investments
Advanced Process Control in Oil Refineries – Digital Transformation
Design and Operations of Refinery Processes
Attendance of two advanced seminars or Specialized Lectures or Conferences
3rd Semester
Supply Chain Management in Oil and Gas Industries
Selection of two between the following Modules
Environmental Technologies – Sustainable Development Applications
Optimisation and Decision Making in Oil and Gas Process Engineering
Strategic Management and Business Planning for the Oil Industries
Process Modelling and Simulation
Natural Gas Processing, Transportation and Distribution
4th Semester
Industrial Placement and Research Dissertation

Hellenic Petroleum as the partner in the course organisation has contributed substantially not only in the design and the development and the curriculum of the Course but also with the experienced high level employees has undertaken a very large percentage of the Modules implementation (Figure 2, CSR of HELPE, HELPE b).

5. The emerging technological and business needs and the PSE relevance of the PG Course

The oil and gas sector faces very serious and emerging issues, such as the digital transformation with special focus in the supply chain. Digital transformation can be used to refer to any element of technical progression within a company that utilises digital technology (Mahdi Asghari et al, 2013). There has been an active push for oil and gas companies to embrace the digital revolution, and as a result, the previously slow-to-adapt industry is now at the forefront of many types of emergent technology – including artificial intelligence, augmented reality, and the Industrial Internet of things.

As an asset-heavy industry, the oil and gas sector has been in immense need for digital operations for decades – but the cost and difficulty of properly implementing a strategy in such a hardware-intensive environment has slowed progress in the past. Digital transformation is no longer an option that some companies are choosing to pursue – it is rapidly becoming impossible to function without strategies in place.

Furthermore, there is an important issue that needs to be considered more carefully and this is the digital integration of the entire supply chain. Reviews for the optimisation of a digitalised successful supply chain may be found in Büyüközkan et al, 2018.

The course under consideration icludes Modules completely focused in the PSE implementation in oil and gas industry. More specifically, the following courses are completely relevant to PSE.

- Advanced Process Control in Oil Refineries – Digital Transformation
- Design and Operations of Refinery Processes
- Supply Chain Management in Oil and Gas Industries
- Optimisation and Decision Making in Oil and Gas Process Engineering
- Process Modelling and Simulation
- Natural Gas Processing, Transportation and Distribution

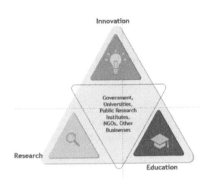

MSc in Oil & Gas Process Systems Engineering

New Postgraduate Program in collaboration with the University of West Attica

We supported the development of a new innovative postgraduate refining studies program, namely the **"MSc in Oil and Gas Process Systems Engineering"** offered by the newly founded University of West Attica and specifically the Department of Mechanical Engineering.

As part of the Corporate Social Responsibility "360° Actions" Program, the Group has adopted a twofold approach to subsidizing the University, firstly by awarding for 3 academic years 10 scholarships a year to outstanding performance-wise postgraduate students, and secondly by providing support to strengthening the University's research and educational goals.

The program **which begun in April 2019** aims to meet the refining market's needs through **the up-to-date, comprehensive curriculum** designed by **the University's academic staff** which has also had input from the **Group's experienced IT, Technical Support, R & D and Refinery executives**. The curriculum includes courses in design and optimum refinery operations, supply chain organizational issues, the application of modern IT technologies, economics and business, thereby creating the opportunity for **new and existing executives for advanced training and further education.**

This collaboration serves one of our key objectives to widen the scope of cooperation with the academic community in order to facilitate the interconnection between research and production process.

Figure 1: The Knowledge Triangle (HELPE, 2019, a)

Figure 2: CSR of HELPE referring to the PG Course (HELPE, 2019, b)

PSE methods and tools as well as the use of relevant software are included in the courses. In addition, specific and specialized themes of high added value will be included in the Module, either in the form of seminars, invited presentations or taught courses. Indicatively, the organisation of an advanced seminar concerning Oil Industry Digitalisation and one focused in the Supply Chain Optimisation in the digitalisation era are planned for spring 2020.

6. Future Steps – Strengthening of the Collaboration

The energy sector in Greece has very significant challenges to face in the future years. The ability to continuously innovate and be able to provide optimal technical, commercial and business solutions to the energy oil and gas industry is nowadays a necessity.

The Energy Plan of the country for the future years include 44 billion euros investments for the next decade, mainly in RES and power and Natural Gas transmission networks. To respond to the needs for continuous innovation in a very rapidly changing (in technological and business respect) environment, energy companies need to make strategic collaborations with universities.

There is not only the Postgraduate Course is only one of the collaboration fields that directs us towards the future. Within a global knowledge economy, there is more than ever a pressing need for strategic industry – academia partnerships that go much beyond the traditional funding of discrete programs. In that respect, the collaborating engineers of HELPE and UNIWA identify areas with the most scientific potential, particularly ones that build on the university's existing strengths and interests in emerging energy technologies (conventional and RES) in order to develop an Energy Consortium to link energy companies with UNIWA in schemes like forums and partnerships.

The benefits of the companies joining an industry – university Consortium include:

- Continuous access to academics from many disciplinary areas and to well-trained energy/hydrocarbons focused MSc, PhD Students and Post-Doctoral Researchers.
- Opportunity to exploit research and development opportunities and guide research and development towards their own business needs.
- Collaboration offers possibilities for partnerships in research projects.
- Links to other UNIWA Departments and specialised accredited Laboratories.
- Opportunity to networking with other companies.
- Privileged access to excellent quality postgraduate courses and intensive innovative long life education programs focused in energy technologies and energy systems.

The key elements of a successful collaboration (Liew MS et al, 2015, adjusted) are shown in Table 2.

Table 2: Benefits of an Energy – University Consortium

Benefits to Academia	Benefits to Energy Companies
Access to the latest technologies and best practices	Access to excellent quality of seminars and postgraduate courses
Knowledge and experience transfer	Networking with other similar companies
Larger pool of professionals for attending of seminars and postgraduate courses	Access to new research ideas and R&D programs
Access to real projects and test beds for new research ideas	Access to specialised and very well educated personnel
Access to real technical/ business problems	Access to other Departments academics

7. Conclusions

A new successful collaboration in the development of a postgraduate course with very good prospects between the largest oil company of Greece and the University of West Attica has been described in the work. The Process Systems Engineering focus of the PG program with the continuous cooperation with a highly experienced and specialised PSE academic team in the University has provided the opportunity for further advancement of the already existing HELPE activities in the supply chain optimization, in the implementation of novel process modelling and simulation software as well as in the support of the company on their digitalization

References

www.helpe.gr Corporate Social Responsibility Panorama 2019, Issue 1. Hellenic Petroleum)

HELPE Group Edition,'Future Prospects of HELPE Group of Companies: The Knowledge Triangle', Athens 2019, in Greek, HELPE edition

Collaborating with leading universities to meet global energy demand, Sept18, 2018, https://corporate.exxonmobil.com (site accessed Nov30, 2019)

Mahdi Asghari, Mohammad Ali Rakhshanikia, Technology transfer in oil industry, significance and challenges, PROCEDIA Procedia - Social and Behavioral Sciences 75 (2013) 264 – 271

Gülçin Büyüközkan, Fethullah Göçer, Digital Supply Chain: Literature review and a proposed framework for future research, Computers in Industry 97 (2018), 155-157

Liew MS, Eik LH, Zawawi NAWA Towards a sustainable collaboration between the oil and gas industry and university, http://dx.doi.org/10.5339/qproc.2015.elc2014.52

Sauro Pierucci, Flavio Manenti, Giulia Bozzano, Davide Manca (Eds.)
Proceedings of the 30th European Symposium on Computer Aided Process Engineering
(ESCAPE30), May 24-27, 2020, Milano, Italy. © 2020 Elsevier B.V. All rights reserved.
http://dx.doi.org/10.1016/B978-0-12-823377-1.50340-2

Industrial Software for Computer Aided Process Engineering (CAPE) Modeling and Programming Skills Development

Jeffrey D. Kelly,[a,*] Brenno C. Menezes,[b]

[a]*Industrial Algorithms Ltd., 15 St. Andrews Road, Toronto M1P 4C3, Canada*

[b]*Division of Engineering Management and Decision Sciences, College of Science and Engineering, Hamad Bin Khalifa University, Qatar Foundation, Doha, Qatar*

jdkelly@industrialgorithms.ca

Abstract

The Industrial Modeling and Programming Language (IMPL) software designed for the process system engineering (PSE) and operations research (OR) communities is architected to be a structural unit-operation-port-state superstructure (UOPSS) and a semantic quantity-logic-quality phenomena (QLQP) modeling language embedded into a computer programming language with the capability to model and solve industrial optimization, estimation or simulation problems (or sub-problems). In such computer aided process engineering (CAPE) systems, to evolve towards the requirements of advanced modeling and programming skills in a staged fashion, there is a mixture, blend or combination of IML (Industrial Modeling Language), IPL (Industrial Programming Language) and IMPC (Industrial Modeling and Programming Code) for convenience, expressiveness and expedience. IML is how the user may configure the problem using a flat file to fill specific fields or frames by configuring (without coding) the embedded sets (from the UOPSS and QLQP), parameters, variables, and constraints. IPL is how a user may code problems by using computer programming languages to manipulate IMPL using any of its receiving and retrieving routines and with and without using the IML facilities for configuration when required. IMPC is implemented into a machine-coded language (Intel Fortran) to allow IMPL's modeling facilities to be combined with a powerful general-purpose programming language to formulate any new type of set, parameter, variable and/or constraint. To summarize, IMPL may be considered as a confluence with the scientific disciplines of applied engineering, information and computing technologies, statistics, data analytics and decision sciences, that deliveries easy-to-handle and integrative capabilities for modeling and programming in a progressive-learning evolution and high-performance shareable work amongst PSE and OR teams.

Keywords: Modeling languages, Programming skills, Industrial Modeling and Programming Language, Computer programming languages, Exploitation of CAPE tools.

1. Introduction

To progress from a mere user of commercial software solutions supplied by vendors to the development of home-grown tools highly demanded in the process system engineering (PSE) and operations research (OR) communities in both academia and industry, there is a need for handy, integrative-method, progressive-learning and shared-work modeling and programming capabilities that are not difficult and costly to develop, deploy and sustain. For this, a new generation of industrial modeling and programming language has been researched and developed, which is the *raison d'etre* of IMPL, and covers the computer aided process engineering (CAPE) needs among PSE and OR peers with the underlying concepts, constructs and configurations of its unit-operation-port-state superstructure (UOPSS) and its quantity-logic-quality phenomena (QLQP). IMPL models a super-problem, found in the batch- and continuous-process industries to solve design, planning, scheduling, coordination, real-time optimization, control, parameter estimation, data reconciliation and simulation problems and ultimately to capture significant economic, efficiency and environmental benefits. Toward advanced modeling and programming skills in a progressive pace, in IMPL there is a combination of configuration and codification modeling as well as mathematical and computer languages. They are: IML (Industrial Modeling Language), IPL (Industrial Programming Language) and IMPC (Industrial Modeling and Programming Code), as showed in Figure 1.

```
IML
&sUnit,&sOperation,@rSetup_Lower,@rSetup_Upper,@rBegin_Time,@rEnd_Time
BLACKBOX,,1,1,BEGIN,END
&sUnit,&sOperation,@rSetup_Lower,@rSetup_Upper,@rBegin_Time,@rEnd_Time
IPL
for ivv_NLP in range (0,iv):
    #for ispecs_NLP in range (0,specs):
    spec1 = str(ivSpecs[ivv_NLP][1])

    if spec1 == 'UOPScomponent':

        uname = c_char_p(str(ivSpecs[ivv_NLP][2]).encode("utf-8"))
        oname = c_char_p(str(ivSpecs[ivv_NLP][3]).encode("utf-8"))
        pname = c_char_p(str(ivSpecs[ivv_NLP][4]).encode("utf-8"))
        sname = c_char_p(str(ivSpecs[ivv_NLP][5]).encode("utf-8"))
        sname = c_char_p(b" ")
        cname = c_char_p(str(ivSpecs[ivv_NLP][6]).encode("utf-8"))
        value = c_double(value_lhs_x[nn_NLP+3][ivv_NLP+1])
        rtnstat = interacter.IMPLreceiveUOPScomponent(uname,oname,pname,sname,cname,value,value,c_double( ),IMPLkeep)

IMPC
            if (structure$ == SPARSIC$) then

c       25 - x1*x2*x3*x4 <= 0
            rtnstat = sdcreceive(rc1_f(1),25d+0 - sdvretrieve(rv1_x(1))*sdvretrieve(rv1_x(2))*
        &                             sdvretrieve(rv1_x(3))*sdvretrieve(rv1_x(4)))
            if (succession$ == FIRSTSUCCESSION$) then
                rtnstat = sddratio(rc1_f(1),
        &                      4,[rv1_x(1),rv1_x(2),rv1_x(3),rv1_x(4)])
                rtnstat = sdcretype(rc1_f(1),type=NONLINEAR_LE)
            end if

c       40 - x1^2 - x2^2 - x3^2 - x4^2 = 0
            rtnstat = sdcreceive(rc1_f(2),40d+0 - sdvretrieve(rv1_x(1))**2d+0 - sdvretrieve(rv1_x(2))**2d+0 -
```

Figure 1. IML configuration and IPL and IMPC codifications found in IMPL.

In IML the problem is configured in a flat file by filling specific fields into frames with keywords that call the embedded sets (from the UOPSS and QLQP), parameters, variables, and constraints. Currently, with the IML configuration, the user can invoke 621 set and parameter types, 196 variable types, and 309 constraint types. IPL is how a user may code problems by using computer programming languages as such as C, C++, C#, Fortran, Julia, Python, Visual Basic, Java, Matlab, R, etc., to manipulate IMPL using any of its receiving and retrieving routines by coding in the aforementioned computer programming languages, combined or not with the IML facilities for configuration. For a standalone and prototyping problem, IML is preferred since there is usually no need to retrieve its solution results to be used in further solving steps. However, IPL is necessary to program iterative problems such as decomposition heuristics and on-line solutions, whereby an algorithm to manage the retrieving of a solution to be fed (received) in another problem run must be codified to manipulate IMPL configurations and solutions externally in a computer programming language.

IMPC is the internal coding infrastructure of the problem's model and data in IMPL's specialized mathematical programming form by the IMPL Modeler library and is accessible via a developer user's, modeler's or analyst's Intel Fortran code. The fundamental essence of IMPC is to allow the developer user the capability to code and create any kind of discrete, nonlinear and dynamic (DND) formula, relation or constraint using sparse memory-resident arrays within Intel Fortran from one to eight dimensions (i.e., sparse vectors, matrices and tensors) with an omni-present ninth (9th) dimension typically populated with time-period, time-series or trial-sampling data. This makes IMPL by using IMPC very suitable for the developer user to design, develop, deploy and distribute their own compiled and proprietary dynamic link libraries (DLL's) or shared objects (SO's) for third-party commercial use without having to share or expose their proprietary source code. Modeling and programming facilities found in the IML configuration and IPL codification integrated into the specialized mathematical programming form of the IMPC allows an effective and high-performance exploitation of CAPE tools among teams in manufacturing sites, R&D centers, headquarters and service teams (within the same company) integrated or not to third-part companies.

2. IMPL's facilities for IML configuration and IPL codification

The network in Figure 2 is constructed in the UOPSS network (Kelly, 2005) embedded in the open-source flowsheet software Gnome DIA. The main UOPSS palette for structures, shapes or objects are defined as: a) unit-operations for sources and sinks ($\Diamond$), tanks or inventories ($\triangle$), batch-processes ($\square$) and continuous-processes ($\boxtimes$) and b) the connectivity involving arrows ($\rightarrow$), inlet-ports i ($\bigcirc$) and outlet-ports j ($\otimes$). Unit-operations and arrows have binary and continuous variables and the ports hold the states as process flows, yields and qualities.

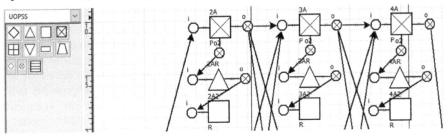

Figure 2. IMPL's drag and drop facilities for the UOPSS flowsheet network set.

IMPL modeling facilities in the UOPSS and QLPQ structures and relationships can be broken-down into several data categories or classes where these data categories are quantity (flows, holdups, yields), logic (discrete decisions such as setups, startups, shutdowns, etc.) and quality (densities, components, properties such as sulfur content, density, etc.). These are solved in linear (LP) or quantity, nonlinear (NLP) or quality and mixed-integer linear (MILP) or quantity-logic (or logistics) problems. Besides, these are categorized in static (non-time-varying) and dynamic (time-varying) cases suitable for optimization and estimation problems such as design, planning, scheduling, coordinating, control and data reconciliation and regression in either off- or on-line environments.

As a superset of the state-task network (STN) (Kondili et al., 1993; Shah et. al., 1993) and the resource-task network (RTN) (Pantelides, 1994) superstructures, the unit-operation-port-state superstructure (UOPSS) built into IMPL provides the arbitrary, ad hoc or anywhere-to-anywhere connectivity generally referred to as a flowsheet, topology, mapping, routing or block-diagram in terms of its various shapes, objects or structures necessary to construct and configure it (Kelly and Menezes, 2019). UOPSS is more than a single network given that it is comprised of two networks we call the physical network (unit-port) and the procedural network (operation-state). The physical network involves the units and ports (equipment, structural) and the procedural network involves the operations (tasks) and states (activities, functional). Brunaud et al. (2020) showed the CPU or computer processing time reduction of large discrete optimization from hours to minutes and seconds by better modeling formulation of the quantity and logic flow networks in the UOPSS when compared to STN and RTN.

Moreover, in IMPL, multiple scenarios may be modeled and solved simultaneously into one problem where certain variables are linked or tied together to find essentially one solution to multiple sub-problems simultaneously, i.e., one solution to a family, group or collection of problems is known as scenario optimization or decision regression. This can be used in IML by configuring flags to access the results from one solution to be read in another solution, only for a single iteration. For several steps of iteration, this should be coded in a computer language to access IMPL's results using IPL and/or IMPC.

3. Industrial modeling and programming code (IMPC)

Also known as the internal mathematical programming code, IMPC is built upon Industrial Algorithms Limited's *Industrial Fortran Infrastructure* (I4I) that enables the developer user, modeler or analyst the capability to enhance, extend and encapsulate the standard or super-problem UOPSS-QLQP (structure-driven and semantic-driven) modeling in IMPL. This involves its own resource-entity roster-enumerators of sets, catalogs, lists, parameters, variables, constraints, derivatives, expressions and formulas (global / common data memory structures) which is machine-code protected via Intel Fortran. Essentially, the purpose of IMPC is to give the developer user complete accessibility and autonomy to the solvers through IMPC's imperative and declarative modeling framework where a model is defined as any collection of the resource-entities that models and solves a problem or sub-problem. This means that the developer user may both integrate and isolate to any degree the standard or super-problem IMPL modeling using IMPC where all of the data contained in IMPL are completely interoperable with IML, IPL and IMPC as these are all based on IMPL's global or common sparse memory data structures.

Programming with IMPC is useful when the developer user is required to model or sub-model with IMPL's *blackblank* unit-operation subtypes and/or when some amount of non-standard and non-supported (non-UOPSS and non-QLQP) custom modeling is necessary which can be combined and coordinated with any of the standard and super-problem UOPSS-QLQP modeling constructs involving multiple unit-operation constraints, etc. IMPC does not embed any third-party algebraic modeling language (AML) such as GAMS, AIMMS, AMPL, MPL, OPL (CPLEX), MOSEL (XPRESS), ZIMPL (SCIP), CMPL (COIN-OR), GMPL (GLPK), SolverStudio, etc., and is similar to other computer programming based AML add-ons, plug-ins or toolboxes such as Matlab's YALMIP and CVX, Python's OptLang, PuLP, Pyomo and PyOpt, Java's OptimJ (no longer supported), Julia's JuMP, APMonitor's GEKKO in Python and R's ROI though IMPC is function-based and not object-oriented. The major difference between IMPC and the others mentioned is that IMPC is implemented into a machine-coded language (Intel Fortran), not an interpreted byte-coded language (e.g., C#, Java, Javascript, Matlab, Python, Julia and R) and is what we call an *arrayic* language due to its whole-array vector processing approach to modeling. Of notable mention is the open-source (COIN-OR) FLOPC++ / FLOPCPP ("Formulation of Linear Optimization Problems in C++") which compiles into C++ machine-code, although it is not suitable for nonlinear problems. However, FLOPC++'s principal strength, like IMPC, lies in the fact that its modeling facilities are combined with a powerful general-purpose programming language.

Programming with IMPC empowers the developer user to not only model problems of industrial scale, size and scope, but also to solve these problems using any of the commercial solvers in addition to allowing access to IMPL's proprietary SLPQPE (Successive Linear Programming and Quadratic Programming Engine) solver which is a very competitive alternative to other nonlinear solvers. One of the primary reasons IMPL's SLPQPE algorithm has a competitive advantage in terms of performance and reliability, is due to the fact that it embeds all commercial LP and QP algorithms such as GUROBI, CPLEX, XPRESS, OPTONOMY and LINDO. Other useful IMPL solvers, accessible via IMPC, are the Successive Equality-Constrained Quadratic Programming Engine (SECQPE) and the Supplemental Observability, Redundancy and Variability Estimator (SORVE) for nonlinear and dynamic data reconciliation and parameter estimation with diagnostics (observability, redundancy and variance). And finally, as IMPC is empowered and embedded in the machine-coded language Intel Fortran, the speed of generating any model of any industrial-scale problem will be faster than any byte-coded language especially suited to on-line real-time applications. Furthermore, the memory management of IMPL and IMPC is such that it can be tuned and tailored to any problem or sub-problem in order to minimize the memory requirements so as to enable multi-problem parallelism.

4. Modeling and programming skills for shared working process

Figure 4 shows a structure of a teamwork involving the manufacturing site's employees as the core modeler to validate the formulation and results of a development of a solution determined by its headquarters.

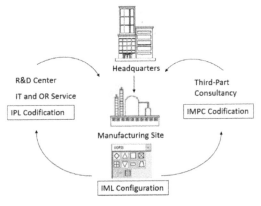

Figure 3. IMPL's modeling and programming steps within a company or organization.

This shared process-of-work considering the final user as the main actor can be achieved by using the IML configuration considering the vast number of parameters, variables and constraints and the UOPSS-QLQP elements found in IMPL. More complex requirements for system integrations with database and application program interface (API) and specific libraries may be achieved in non-manufacturing centers using IPL and IMPL codifications. Therefore, the end-users will evolve from mere spectator of off-the-shelf software packages to high-skilled modelers capable to be involved in the development of solutions to be validated, operated and propagated by their own.

5. Conclusions

We present the concept for modeling and programming skills suitable for exploiting CAPE tools within a company among all segments to be involved in the development of a final solution. IMPL's feature to use IML configuration as well as IPL and IMPC codification allows the end-user to be involved as the main actor in the development of a system for its own future deployment. How the development and deployment (operational) teams work together and the perceptiveness of their accomplishments is a key factor for the involvement of the individuals and the success of the integrated groups with different skills and duties. IMPL is a highly comprehensive structure- and semantic-based language and has been successfully implemented in a broad range of industrial sectors such as oil and gas, petrochemicals, mining, pulp and paper, agriculture, among others. Its combination of configuration and codification modeling as well as mathematical and computer languages become the industrial modeling and programming language of IMPL the integrative system for development of industrial solutions to be demonstrated, deployed and disseminated in an organizational structure.

References

B. Brunaud, S. Amaran, S. Bury, J. Wassick, I.E. Grossmann, 2020, Batch Scheduling with Quality-Based Changeovers, Computer and Chemical Engineering, Computers and Chemical Engineering, 132, 106617.

J.D. Kelly, 2005, The Unit-Operation-Stock Superstructure (UOSS) and the Quantity-Logic-Quality Paradigm (QLQP) for Production Scheduling in The Process Industries, In Multidisciplinary International Scheduling Conference Proceedings: New York, United States, 327-333.

J.D. Kelly, B.C. Menezes, 2019, Industrial Modeling and Programming Language (IMPL) for Off- and On-Line Optimization and Estimation Applications. In: Fathi M., Khakifirooz M., Pardalos P. (eds) Optimization in Large Scale Problems. Springer Optimization and Its Applications, 152, 75-96.

E. Kondili, C.C. Pantelides, R.W.H. Sargent, 1993, A General Algorithm for Short-Term Scheduling Of Batch Operations – I MILP Formulation, Computers and Chemical Engineering, 17, 211-227.

B.C. Menezes, J.D Kelly, A.G. Leal, G.C. Le Roux, 2019, Predictive, Prescriptive and Detective Analytics for Smart Manufacturing in the Information Age, IFAC-PapersOnline, 52, 1, 568-573.

N. Shah, C.C. Pantelides, R.W.H. Sargent, 1993, A General Algorithm for Short-Term Scheduling of Batch Operations – II. Computational Issues. Computers and Chemical Engineering, 17, 229-244.

C.C. Pantelides. Unified Frameworks for the Optimal Process Planning and Scheduling. Proceedings on the Second Conference on Foundations of Computer Aided Operations. 1994, 253-274.

Sauro Pierucci, Flavio Manenti, Giulia Bozzano, Davide Manca (Eds.)
Proceedings of the 30th European Symposium on Computer Aided Process Engineering
(ESCAPE30), May 24-27, 2020, Milano, Italy. © 2020 Elsevier B.V. All rights reserved.
http://dx.doi.org/10.1016/B978-0-12-823377-1.50341-4

Studying Computational Fluid Dynamics in a New Dimension with Virtual Reality

Gregor D. Wehinger[a,b,*], Steffen Flaischlen[a,b]

*a*Institute of Chemical and Electrochemical Process Engineering, Clausthal University
of Technology, Leibnizstr. 17, 38678 Clausthal-Zellerfeld, Germany
*b*Research Center Energy Storage Technologies (EST), Clausthal University of
Technology, Am Stollen 19A, 38640 Goslar, Germany
wehinger@icvt.tu-clausthal

Abstract

Communication strategies for complex problems in the field of chemical and process engineering is becoming more and more important. Especially computational fluid dynamics (CFD) results require well-established spatial reasoning skills. In this contribution, we show how we implemented virtual reality (VR) into the Master course "CFD for process engineering" at Clausthal University of Technology. We discuss advantages and disadvantages of applying VR during the course. In addition, we show how VR can enable students to get a thorough understanding of the interplay between reactor design and performance.

Keywords: Virtual reality (VR), Computational fluid dynamics (CFD), higher education, chemical and process engineering

1. Introduction

A clear communication of scientific results is essential, especially nowadays where we are flooded by information. Similarly in education, communication is one key to success. In chemical engineering, transport phenomena play a paramount role and interact with local kinetics. Computational fluid dynamics (CFD) simulations in three dimensions, which are complex in terms of the underlying geometry and involve multi-phase and multi-physics phenomena, can help to identify potentials to improve existing designs or operating conditions. However, the presentation of these CFD results in two dimensions require high spatial reasoning skills. These skills are directly connected to good finale degrees in engineering programs (Sorby 2009). However, the same author highlights that 3D spatial skills are not given by birth but can be improved by training. The application of virtual reality (VR) can improve different learning concepts across many different fields, like material science, chemistry, medicine, and aerospace engineering (Caro et al. 2018, Merchant et al. 2012, Nicholson et al. 2006, Okutsu et al. 2013). A recent review states that especially head-mounted devices (HMD) in education are useful to improve cognitive skills related to remembering and understanding spatial and visual information and knowledge, as well as psychomotor skills related to head movement, such as visual scanning or observational skills (Jensen and Konradsen 2018). In light of these findings, VR could assist the students in deeper understanding of the complex interactions between reactor design and physics/chemistry in the field of chemical and process engineering. Exemplarily, Figure 1 shows a flow through a fixed-bed reactor in a 2D animated vector scene (A) and in a virtual environment (B). The dimensions of the occurring eddy is much easier to realize in three dimensions.

(A)   **(B)**

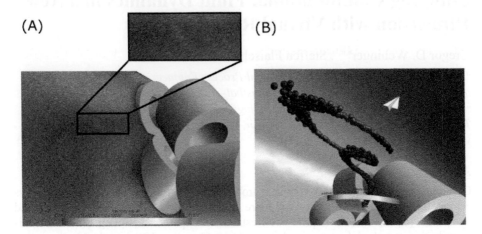

Figure 1: Flow through a fixed-bed reactor. (A) 2D vector scene. (B) 3D virtual environment.

In the Master's course "CFD for process engineering" at Clausthal University of Technology, small groups of students work on real-world problems from different areas of the chemical and process industry. First, the group learns the basics of CFD including governing equations, meshing and solving algorithms, as well as modeling techniques for multi-phase flows, etc. Second, the student groups work with customized input from the professor and CFD tutors on their specific problem. One fundamental part of the problem-solving process is the investigation of design variables in order to improve the process. Therefore, the group applies VR to explore their design proposition and its effect towards for example heat and mass transfer or conversion in the chemical reactor. Exemplarily, Figure 2 visualizes a "fly" through a fixed-bed reactor. Finally, VR supports the communication within the group and the understanding of the interplay between design and reactor performance.

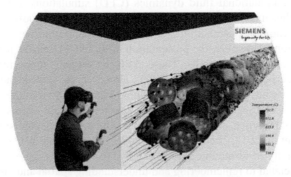

Figure 2: Virtual reality application of flow and heat transfer inside a fixed-bed reactor.

In this contribution, we show how we implemented VR into this Master's course at Clausthal University of Technology. We further discuss advantages and disadvantages of applying VR during the course. In addition, we show how VR can enable students to get a thorough understanding of the interplay between reactor design and performance.

2. Methods

2.1. Computational fluid dynamics and VR software

In computational fluid dynamics, the continuity, energy, and momentum conservation equations are solved numerically, in many cases with the Finite Volume Method. The CFD workflow consists of (i) pre-processing, (ii) solving, and (iii) post-processing. Hence, the typical CFD engineer needs a solid background in mathematics, fluid dynamics, heat transfer and computer programming. One type of CFD courses at universities focuses on the numerical methods part with only a few CFD applications. The other type of courses introduces a CFD software and let the students apply it to given problems. The inclusion of commercial CFD packages, such as ANSYS Fluent or STAR-CCM+ from Siemens PLM, guarantees a steep learning curve without having a strong theoretical background (Hu et al. 2008).

In this course, the commercial Computational Aided Engineering (CAE) solution package Simcenter STAR-CCM+ from Siemens PLM is used in order to teach the students the entire CFD workflow in one single integrated software environment. The software combines import and creation of geometries, mesh generation, solution of the governing equations, analysis of the results, and the connection to other CAE software. Figure 3 (A) shows the user interface with the appearing elements of the STAR-CCM+ software.

Over the last few years, the usage of VR for CFD post-processing has increased steadily in order to interpret the simulation results and communicate them to non-experts (Wu et al. 2010). Several software is capable to visualize the CFD results in three dimensions, e.g. ParaView, Unity3D, Ceetron 3D Viewer, and others. In this course, STAR-CCM+ VR is used which allows the students to explore CFD simulation results in a virtual environment. The running or already converged CFD solution can be loaded into STAR-CCM+ VR and the viewer can enter the virtual environment that the headset then displays. The viewer literally stands inside the CFD solution and examine the flow, temperature, and or concentration fields interacting with the digital prototype, see Figure 3 (B). In STAR-CCM+ VR, a floor below the model and a ceiling above appear. The floor in the scene corresponds to the real floor and the ceiling is set at a predefined position.

2.2. Hardware

STAR-CCM+ VR is designed to run with the head-mounted display "HTC Vive". This device applies a room-scale technology with two sensors to capture the movement in the room. Two wireless controllers mimicking hands allow haptic feedback in the virtual reality. In addition, the controllers provide several options for controlling view, movement, and other aspects of the scene. In order to guarantee a fluent meshing and solving with STAR-CCM+ and flying through the STAR-CCM+ VR scene, Siemens PLM suggests the following minimum requirements (Siemens PLM, 2019):

- Surface remesher: ~0.5 GB RAM per million faces
- Volume meshing: ~1 GB RAM per million cells for polyhedral cells
- Solving a single phase RANS model with the Segregated Solver: ~1 GB RAM per million polyhedral cells
- Using STAR-CCM+ VR: Windows 10 64-bit and NVIDIA Quadro P4000 or better and SteamVR software, which is installed as part of the HTC Vive setup

HTC recommends the following space for a fluent VR experience:

- Standing or sitting position: no minimum space requirements
- Room filling VR: minimum are of 2 m x 1.5 m required, maximum room size of 3.5 m x 3.5 m

From our experience, it is possible to use the VR environment in the standing or sitting position for testing and quick development of VR CFD scenes. Nevertheless, the room filling VR provides the full experience and leads to better understanding of e.g. geometric dimensions by a "real" walk through the scene. For this purpose, we have developed a VR lab, where the students have the chance to use 3 VR stations located on a full space of 120 m^2.

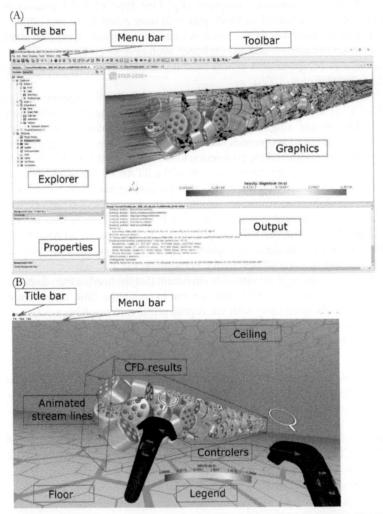

Figure 3: Graphical user interface of (A) Simcenter STAR-CCM+ and (B) STAR-CCM+ VR environment.

2.3. Online learning system

Moodle is used as an online learning management platform. It includes the weekly schedule, problems, documents, a chat forum, and the URL for all video tutorials. In addition, the students can participate in online tests and can hand in electronic documents, like posters and final reports. There are two types of video tutorials: CFD simulations and VR scenes. The video tutorials are basically records of the computer screen, on which the tutors guide the viewer through different CFD simulation workflows or through the VR scenes and explains the steps to take.

3. Seminar contents

The seminar covers four ECTS credits and consists of four different phases: (i) a seminar for introducing CFD, (ii) hands-on training, (iii) students' projects, and (iv) the assessment. In five seminar sessions, the theoretical background of CFD is presented and discussed with the students. In this part of the course, an overview about recent CFD applications in industry is given, the concept of conservation equations is repeated, solving strategies are presented, different types of meshes and local mesh refinement approaches are discussed, and finally, special phenomena, like turbulence, multi-phase flows, and chemically reacting flows, are examined.

The four hands-on training sessions give the students the possibility to get in touch with the commercial software STAR-CCM+ and solve small problems individually at the computer. The students are personally assisted during the training by CFD tutors, which are Master students from higher semesters and PhD students. The problems to be solved are supported by short video tutorials, which are available on the Moodle webpage of this course. They give a short overview about geometry generation, meshing, solving, and post-processing in 2D and 3D Scenes in STAR-CCM+.

After the four hands-on training sessions, an individual test assesses the theoretical knowledge of CFD and the practical problem solving strategies within STAR-CCM+. With a positive result in the test, the students qualify for the group project phase. If students fail the test, they have the opportunity to repeat it one week later.

In the group project phase, groups of three students team up and work on a given CFD problem for at least 8 weeks. The problems typically consists of a validation case based on literature data. In a consecutive step, the students change certain geometrical features in the problem in order to obtain an improved process. During this phase, the students actively apply VR to explore their problem in three dimensions. This helps the students to identify quickly how the geometry/reactor/device interacts with the local flow field, temperature and/or concentration distribution. Consequently, the students are early enabled to judge on their geometrical feature modification. In addition, VR helps to communicate within the team, since more than one viewer can enter the VR scene.

After half of the project phase, the students communicate their preliminary results with posters and within the VR environment. The setting is similar to a classic poster session at a scientific conference, whereas PhD students and professors from the department act as conference participants. The basic principles of creating a well designed poster are taught earlier with each group individually. After the poster conference, the students received feedback from many experts such that they can proceed with the group project. At the end of the semester, each group hands in a final report written as a scientific communication. In Moodle, evaluation criteria for the final report are given in order to keep the evaluation process as transparent as possible.

4. Discussion

Jensen and Konradsen (2018) give a comprehensive review about using VR HMDs in education and training. The authors recognized a number of situations where HMDs are useful for skills acquisition. Especially important for this CFD course are cognitive skills related to remembering and understanding spatial and visual information and knowledge as well as visual scanning or observational skills. We were able to observe this skills acquisition. Nevertheless, we have also witnessed cybersickness, especially where the visual animation was not presented fluently. This was manly attributed to the technical limitation of the peripheral device. In order to not overcharge the students with new software and theoretical input, we decided to introduce the usage of VR in a stepwise approach. In the first third of the semester, the students use VR in prepared scenes. This guarantees a quick start into VR. At this time, the students should be familiar with the CFD workflow and developed a rough CFD problem solving strategy. After the first third of the semester, the students apply VR independently to investigate their CFD simulations.

5. Conclusion

In this contribution, we report on the integration of VR into a Master course for CFD simulations in the field of chemical and process engineering at Clausthal University of Technology. STAR-CCM+ is used as a user-friendly CFD software in order to guarantee learning success for students with a heterogeneous background in numerical mathematics, transport phenomena, and fluid mechanics. The CFD results obtained with STAR-CCM+ can be visualized with relatively small effort with the head-mounted display system HTC Vive and the STAR-CCM+ VR software. The total costs for an appropriate computer and the HMD is roughly 3,000 € plus enough space to walk inside the VR environment. During our CFD course, we have already observed a very positive attitude of the students towards using VR for immersing in the CFD results. The students projects guarantee a thorough examination with CFD and VR. In general, the entry threshold into VR is low, since many of the students are familiar with 3D gaming or even already use VR in their spare time. Still, we need the feedback of a larger number of students to make significant statements about the efficiency of including VR to this course.

References

V. Caro, B. Carter, S. Dagli, M. Schissler, J. Millunchick, 2018, Can Virtual Reality Enhance Learning: A Case Study in Materials Science, In 2018 IEEE Frontiers in Education Conference (FIE), 1-4

J. Hu, L. Zhang, X. Xiong, 2008, Teaching Computational Fluid Dynamics (CFD) to Design Engineers, ASEE

L. Jensen, F. Konradsen, 2018, A review of the use of virtual reality head-mounted displays in education and training, Education and Information Technologies, 23(4), 1515-1529

Z. Merchant, E.T. Goetz, W. Keeney-Kennicutt, O.M. Kwok, L. Cifuentes, T.J. Davis, 2012, The learner characteristics, features of desktop 3D virtual reality environments, and college chemistry instruction: A structural equation modeling analysis, Computers & Education, 59(2), 551-568

D.T. Nicholson, C. Chalk, W.R.J. Funnell, S.J. Daniel, 2006, Can virtual reality improve anatomy education? A randomised controlled study of a computer- generated three- dimensional anatomical ear model. Medical education, 40(11), 1081-1087

M. Okutsu, D. DeLaurentis, S. Brophy, J. Lambert, 2013, Teaching an aerospace engineering design course via virtual worlds: A comparative assessment of learning outcomes, Computers & Education, 60(1), 288-298

Siemens PLM, 2019, What are approximate RAM requirements for meshing and solving? The Steve Portal, https://thesteveportal.plm.automation.siemens.com

S.A. Sorby, 2009, Educational research in developing 3- D spatial skills for engineering students, International Journal of Science Education, 31(3), 459-480

B. Wu, G, Chen, J. Moreland, D. Huang, D. Zheng, C.Q. Zhou, 2010, Industrial application of CFD simulation and VR visualization. In ASME 2010 World Conference on Innovative Virtual Reality, 51-59, American Society of Mechanical Engineers.

Sauro Pierucci, Flavio Manenti, Giulia Bozzano, Davide Manca (Eds.)
Proceedings of the 30th European Symposium on Computer Aided Process Engineering
(ESCAPE30), May 24-27, 2020, Milano, Italy. © 2020 Elsevier B.V. All rights reserved.
http://dx.doi.org/10.1016/B978-0-12-823377-1.50342-6

Academic Education Involvement in Refinery Advanced Process Control

Cristian Pătrășcioiu*, Marian Popescu, Nicolae Paraschiv, Cristina R. Popa,
Nicoleta Nicolae

*Automatic Control, Computers and Electronics Department, Petroleum-Gas University
of Ploiesti, Bd. Bucuresti, 39, Ploiesti 100680, Romania*
cpatrascioiu@upg-ploiesti.ro

Abstract

The paper presents the achievements of Automatic Control, Computers and Electronics
Department of Petroleum-Gas University of Ploiesti in the direction of developing the
skills for the engineers' activity in the field of Refinery Advanced Process Control. In
order to reach this objective, the teachers of the department have developed the
specializations of Bachelor, Master and Doctorate in the field of Systems Engineering, a
research area recognized in Romania. The paper is structured in four parts, each part
presenting the organization of the education process and the obtained results.
Keywords: education, advanced process control, modelling, simulation, identification.

1. Curriculum of Advanced Control System Education

To increase the performance of chemical process control systems is necessary to
develops components of Advanced Control Systems. Achieving this objective involves
the following stages of study:

- Modelling and simulation of processes from refineries
- Dynamic identification of processes
- Design of advanced control algorithms

The final objective of the applied research is the design and testing of advanced
automatic systems for refineries processes. From the point of view of the educational
process carried out in Petroleum - Gas University of Ploiesti, Romania, the previously
defined objective is achieved by going through the disciplines of the Master's degree
specializations, presented in Table 1.

Table 1. Disciplines associated with Advanced Process Control Curriculum

Discipline	Study program
Advanced automation of chemical processes	Computer Aided Chemical Engineering in Refineries and Petrochemistry
Dynamic simulation of chemical processes	Computer Aided Chemical Engineering in Refineries and Petrochemistry
Advanced control systems for chemical processes	Advanced Technologies in Oil Processing
Advanced control algorithms	Advanced Automation
Distributed supervisory and control systems	Advanced Automation
Automatic control of chemical processes	Advanced Automation

All these disciplines contribute to the training of the specialists of chemical engineering and control engineering. The training of specialists in the field of Advanced Control Systems is continued in the doctoral studies. There is an average periodicity of 3 years in the completion of theses in the field of Advanced Process Control, a fact that attests the scientific and research concerns of the University but also the involvement of the industrial environment. Some examples of PhD theses in this field are: Research on the model-based control of fractionation processes, Contributions regarding the hierarchical control of the catalytic cracking process, Contributions regarding the development of a hierarchized distributed control system for fractionation processes, Contributions regarding the advanced control of the refining gas purification process.

All the elements listed above support the training of engineers from Petroleum - Gas University of Ploiesti in the field of Advanced Process Control.

2. Process modelling and simulation

From the automatic control point of view, the processes in the refineries can be approached are the following: tubular furnaces, distillation columns, absorption columns, catalytic cracking reactor. The modelling have been developed using analytical or simulation software way. The used software simulators have been HYSYS, Unisim Design and PRO II. Results of modelling and simulation refer to steady state model, process sensibility analysis, and process channels gains.

For tubular furnaces from refineries (e.g. furnaces in atmospheric distillation units), mathematical models for fuel combustion and heat transfer have been developed, in order to be used for optimal combustion control (Pătrășcioiu and Marinoiu, 1997, 1998). Other research focused on modelling the tubular furnaces using Unisim FPH simulator, the aim being the validation of the developed analytical model (Pătrășcioiu, 2016).

For the distillation columns, the research started from the distillation columns of binary mixtures (propylene-propane). The researches progressively followed several stages:

- Steady-state process modelling (Pătrășcioiu et al., 2008, Pătrășcioiu and Petre, 2017, Pătrășcioiu and Cao, 2017);
- Dynamic process modelling and control systems modelling (Pătrășcioiu et al., 2014, Popa and Pătrășcioiu, 2010, Popa, 2013, Popa et al., 2015);
- Study of quality control systems (Mihaescu et al., 2013, Popescu, 2018, Pătrășcioiu et al., 2015, Pătrășcioiu and Florea, 2018).

Another research direction is the modelling of distillation columns equipped with heat pumps. The results highlighted the complexity of the process compared to the classic one and implicitly the difficulties of modelling the installation (Pătrășcioiu and Cao, 2017). However, some progress has been made, with the prospect of designing, modelling and simulating a quality control system (Pătrășcioiu and Cao, 2016).

Of the reactors existing in refineries, a special interest is represented by the reactor - regenerator block from the catalytic cracking plant, due to its special economic effect. An analytical mathematical model of the reactor and reaction block and subsequently a dynamic model (Popa, 2013) were developed.

3. Dynamic identification technique

Dynamic identification can be defined as a simple construction of the dynamic mathematical model, model determined on the basis of experimental data or on the basis of results obtained by simulation, test or normal operation.

The researchers used two software tools for systems identification. The first instrument was developed within the university and disseminated through publications (Pătrășcioiu and Mihaescu, 2011). The second instrument is the System Identification Toolbox – MATLAB (Pătrăşcioiu and Popa, 2014). This computer tool has some using particularities. Thus, the input and output data of the discrete function subjected to numerical processing are organized in the form $(\Delta u_i, \Delta y_i)$, $i=1,...,n$. The time associated with the dynamics of the system is built internally, specifying the initial moment and the associated incremental value. Consequently, all sampling time intervals will be equal.

In the following are presented some of the transfer functions associated with the catalytic cracking process from a refinery, functions obtained using the System Identification Toolbox software tool.

The catalytic cracking process is a multivariable system, its dynamic characterization being extremely difficult. The decomposition of the multivariable system into monovariable subsystems is shown in Figure 1 (Popa, 2013).

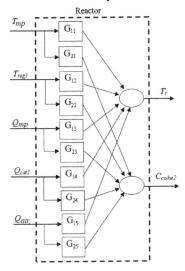

Figure 1. FCC reactor

Using the technique described above, the transfer functions of the sub-processes that characterize the catalytic cracking reactor were determined, Table 2.

Table 2. Identification of sub-processes from FCC

Input	Output	
	Riser output temperature	The amount of coke deposited on the catalyst from the cracking reaction
Temperature of raw material	$G_{11}(s) = \dfrac{0.17}{0.048s+1}$	$G_{21}(s) = \dfrac{2.2 \cdot 10^{-4}}{0.047s+1}$
Temperature of the regenerated catalyst	$G_{12}(s) = \dfrac{0.76}{0.048s+1}$	$G_{22}(s) = \dfrac{0.0013}{0.06s+1}$
Flowrate of raw material	$G_{13}(s) = \dfrac{-7.72 \cdot 10^{-4}}{0.052s+1}$	$G_{23}(s) = \dfrac{-9.5 \cdot 10^{-7}}{0.048s+1}$
Flowrate of the regenerated catalyst	$G_{14}(s) = \dfrac{1.751 \cdot 10^{-4}}{0.062s+1}$	$G_{25}(s) = \dfrac{2.6 \cdot 10^{-8}}{0.047s+1}$

4. Advanced control algorithms

The advanced control systems developed at Petroleum-Gas University of Ploiesti are based on the following advanced control algorithms:

- Feedforward control
- Model-based control
- Optimal control

In the following will be presented some results of the research regarding model-based control.

The two model based algorithms presented in the following are IMC (internal model control) and MPC (model predictive control). Both algorithms were used for the quality control of a butylene-butane distillation column.

The internal model control technique uses a representation of the process in the algorithm, based on the process parameters obtained using identification methods. Thus, such a model (Cîrtoaje and Băieşu, 2018) is

$$G_M(s) = \frac{K_M e^{-T_m s}}{(T_M s + 1)^2} \qquad (1)$$

where K_M is the model gain (which usually is considered equal to process gain), T_M - model time constant (which depends on the process transient time), T_m – process dead time.

After tuning the two IMC controllers associated to the quality control of the separated products from the butylene-butane distillation column, the best system responses were obtained to set-point changes (Pătrăşcioiu and Popescu, 2018), Figure 2.

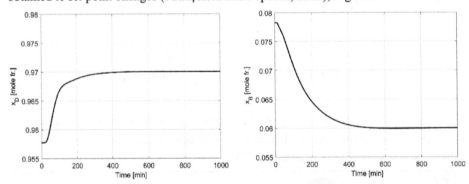

Figure 2. Concentrations evolutions to set-point changes when using IMC

Another model-based control algorithm used in the advanced control research is MPC. A control structure for the butylene-butane distillation column which involves MPC is presented in Figure 3. The multivariable MPC controller has a structure which uses the process transfer functions identified for the control agents – outputs channels and disturbances – outputs channels.

The MPC controller is tuned (by modifying sample time, prediction horizon and control horizon) so that the control system response to set-point changes (Figure 4) does not have overshoot or oscillations and the transient time is comparable to or smaller than the process transient time (Nicolae et al., 2019). Also, the system response to disturbances modifications is adequate, with the control system managing to bring back the controlled variable to the set-point value.

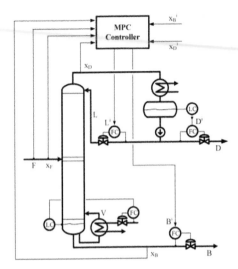

Figure 3. Control structure based on MPC controller

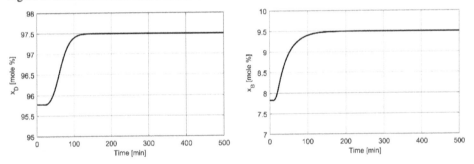

Figure 4. Concentrations evolutions to set-point changes when using MPC

5. Conclusions

At the Petroleum - Gas University of Ploiesti, the didactic structures aim to develop the skills for the engineers' activity in the field of Refinery Advanced Process Control. The didactic activity for engineers is carried out within the Master's specializations and in the doctoral courses. The activity was materialized by the elaboration of doctoral theses in the field of Refinery Advanced Process Control.

The components of scientific research developed within the doctoral theses refer to process modelling and simulation, dynamic identification techniques, advanced control algorithms. Each research direction is exemplified by results published in the academic literature.

All the elements presented in the article demonstrate the efficiency and performance of higher education within the University of Petroleum - Gases in Ploiesti.

References

V. Cîrtoaje, A. Băieşu, 2018, On a Model Based Practical Control Algorithm, Studies in Informatics and Control, vol. 27, No. 1, 83-96.

D. Mihaescu, N. Paraschiv, C. Pătrăşcioiu, A. Băieşu, 2013, Advanced Control System for a Refinery Hydrogen Sulphide Absorption Plant, REV. CHIM. (Bucharest), vol. 64, no. 9, 1028-1036.

N. Nicolae, M. Popescu, C. Pătrăşcioiu, 2019, Implementation of Advanced Process Control in Refineries, Proc. of the 23rd International Conference on System Theory, Control and Computing (ICSTCC), Sinaia, Romania, 95-100.

C. Popa, C. Pătrăşcioiu, 2010, New Approach in Modelling, Simulation and Hierarchical Control of the Fluid Catalytic Cracking Process I - Process modelling, REV. CHIM. (Bucharest), vol. 61, no. 4, 419-426.

C. Popa, 2013, Hierarchical control of the catalytic cracking process (in Romanian: Reglarea ierarhica a procesului de cracare catalitica), MatrixRom, Bucharest.

C. Popa, C. Pătrăşcioiu, O. Cangea, 2015, Performance Analysis of the Four Lump Kinetic Model of the Riser Catalytic Cracking, REV. CHIM. (Bucharest), vol. 66, no. 6, 883-885.

M. Popescu, 2018, Distillation column hierarchical control, REV. CHIM. (Bucharest), vol. 69, No. 9, 2585-2590.

C. Pătrăşcioiu, V. Marinoiu, 1997, Automatic control system for tubular furnaces from the atmospheric and vacuum distillation installation of crude oil I. Mathematical modelling of combustion and thermal transfer (In Romanian: Sistem automat evoluat pentru cuptoarele tubulare din instalatia de distilare atmosferica si in vid a titeiului I. Modelarea matematica a combustiei si transferului termic), REV. CHIM. (Bucharest), vol. 48, no. 4, 357-369.

C. Pătrăşcioiu, V. Marinoiu, 1998, Modelling and Optimal Control of an Industrial Furnace, Proceedings from the 5th IFAC Symposium, Corfu, Greece, 8 -10 June 1998, 477-482.

C. Pătrăşcioiu, M. Petre, I. Rabahi, 2008, Modeling, simulation and optimal control of the natural gas Jibissa plant, Proc. of the 8th conference on Simulation, modelling and optimization (SMO'08), 133-137.

C. Pătrăşcioiu D. Mihaescu, 2011, The Numerical Algorithms Used to the Identification of the First Order Dynamic Models. Case Study, Proceedings of the IASTED International Conference Modelling, Identification, and Control (MIC 2011), 167-173.

C. Pătrăşcioiu, C. Popa, 2014, System identification. System Identification Toolbox or properly algorithms?, Advances in Automatic Control - Proceedings of the 16th International Conference on Automatic Control, Modelling & Simulation (ACMOS '14), Brasov, Romania, 2014, 305-310.

C. Pătrăşcioiu, M. Popescu, N. Paraschiv, 2014, Specific Problems of Using Unisim Design in the Dynamic Simulation of the Propylene-Propane Distillation Column, REV. CHIM. (Bucharest), vol. 65, No. 9, 1086-1091.

C. Pătrăşcioiu, N. Paraschiv, M.A. Cao, M. Popescu, 2015, Robust Control of Industrial Propylene-Propane Fractionation Process, Computer Aided Chemical Engineering, Elsevier, Vol. 37, 1745-1750.

C. Pătrăşcioiu, 2016, The Modeling and Simulation of the Convection Section of the Atmospheric Distillation Plant Heaters, REV. CHIM. (Bucharest), vol. 67, no. 8, 1599-1606.

C. Pătrăşcioiu, M.A. Cao, 2016, Characterization and control of the distillation column with heat pump, Proc. of the 8th International Conference on Electronics, Computers and Artificial Intelligence (ECAI), Ploiesti, Romania, 1-8.

C. Pătrăşcioiu, M.V. Petre, 2017, Tubular furnaces performances study using UniSim FPH simulator, REV. CHIM. (Bucharest), vol. 68, no. 8, 1790-1795.

C. Pătrăşcioiu, M.A. Cao, 2017, A Comparative Study of the Modeling and Quality Control of the Propylene-Propane Classical Distillation and Distillation Column with Heat Pump, World Academy of Science, Engineering and Technology International Journal of Chemical and Molecular Engineering, Vol. 11, No. 5, 394-399.

C. Pătrăşcioiu, A. Florea, 2018, Simulation of benzene column distillation for quality control system design, Proc. of the 22nd International Conference on System Theory, Control and Computing (ICSTCC), Sinaia, Romania, 39-45.

C. Pătrăşcioiu, M. Popescu, 2018, Study of the control systems of a distillation process equipped with heat pump, REV. CHIM. (Bucharest), vol. 69, no. 9, 2535-2540.

Sauro Pierucci, Flavio Manenti, Giulia Bozzano, Davide Manca (Eds.)
Proceedings of the 30th European Symposium on Computer Aided Process Engineering
(ESCAPE30), May 24-27, 2020, Milano, Italy. © 2020 Elsevier B.V. All rights reserved.
http://dx.doi.org/10.1016/B978-0-12-823377-1.50343-8

Aspen Hysys – Unity Interconnection. An Approach for Rigorous Computer- Based Chemical Engineering Training

Pedro Santos*, Tom Van Gerven

KU Leuven - CIT, Celestijnenlaan 300F, Leuven, Belgium
pedro.santosb@kuleuven.be

Abstract

Virtual educational simulations, ranging from realistic plant simulators for operators over internal visualizations of process units to virtual labs for students, are a focus of interest for chemical engineers in both industry and universities, as they can provide advantages of real life training without the costly requirements of real training setups. However, the application of these technologies is restricted by the fact that the design is complex, time demanding, and a task that most chemical engineers are not familiar with. One challenging aspect is the need to provide a simulation that behaves realistically, especially for complex systems: solutions such as hand-coding the behaviour of each element or directly coding a custom model of the system can often be exceedingly demanding, and are generally hard to reuse for new projects due to being highly targeted. Instead, a more favourable option is to use an available industry-standard flowsheet simulator (e.g. Aspen Plus, Aspen HYSYS, UniSim, CHEMCAD, DWSim), software with which most chemical engineers are familiar, and that can both guarantee rigorous behaviour and minimize design time. The main challenge with this option (beyond access to a license of the software) is connecting the model to the educational simulation, typically designed in a different software. In this work we study the interconnection between Aspen HYSYS and Unity (a game engine used to design interactive environments) using ActiveX, as opposed to some other popular methods such as OPC, and elaborate on both the technical aspects and the advantages and disadvantages of this methodology.

Keywords: Virtual educational simulations, Aspen HYSYS, Unity

1. Introduction

Virtual educational simulations (VESs) are popular educational tools, with research been done on the usefulness of this tools both in general (Aldrich, 2005) and for the process industry in particular, focusing generally on either virtual laboratories (see the bibliometric analysis by Heradio et al. (2016)) or operator training simulators (OTSs) (such as those developed by Manca et al. (2013), Ahmad et al. (2016), or Ouyang et al. (2017), among others). However, there is not much information on how to develop such tools from a technical point of view: while one can expect a multinational company to subcontract a targeted 3D VR environment for their operator training, it is probably overly ambitious to expect researchers, teachers, and even small companies, to have access to such resources. In these latter cases, any new VESs are often developed in-house, and complexity of design will be the main factor as to whether any solution is attempted or abandoned.

One of the challenges of designing a VES is providing a realistic behaviour to the underlying model. It is obvious that a simulation that behaves incorrectly will encourage the learning of wrong knowledge, as the user believes the behaviour to be correct. A first approach to provide rigorous behaviour is to directly code all interactions possible in the simulation and their effects. For this approach the complexity grows exponentially with the addition of new elements (that must implement the interactions with all previous elements), and so it is best practice to keep possible interactions limited: Nazir and Manca (2015), provide an example of an OTS where the user must select correctly which valves to open or close to prevent an accident, while Ouyang et al. (2017), implement a multiplayer simulation of a whole coking plant, but limit the possible interactions by users to a small set.

However, many scenarios cannot be properly reflected with such a limited set of options, and, for these, implementing a mathematical model of the simulated process can be a better choice. A first alternative is to implement the model directly, by coding it into whichever tool chosen to create the environment, but here the complexity of the dynamics of the system will play a large role in workload, making it often preferable to represent ideal behaviour with limited elements: for example, Mendes et al. (2010), implement a VES for ideal multicomponent distillation in this way, and Pavol et al. (2017) develop a laboratory for basic control in Matlab.

Modeling software is widely used in process engineering, and most engineers are at least familiar with the more widely known tools, such as Aspen Plus, Aspen HYSYS, UniSim, CHEMCAD, DWSim. Some of these tools provide their own VES software, but this is often expensive, rarely available in universities, and, more importantly in the eyes of the authors, in all cases oriented towards operator training, so that the functionalities and tools are heavily limited for any other purpose. Ahmad et al. (2016) provide an example of use for this technology for training of operators in biodiesel synthesis using Aspen OTS Framework.

When not using these specialized tools for VES design, one can instead benefit from some of the available general design tools, such as game engines, which are widely used for the design of a variety of virtual environments. Then the challenge of communicating between the simulation and the environment appears, that is, how to transfer information (such as the position of a valve or a temperature value) from the software where the chemical engineering models are being calculated, to the software which renders the environment that the user interacts with. The authors believe this challenge to constitute one of the major impediments for this approach, and in this work propose a methodology for implementing such a data exchange between Aspen HYSYS as simulator and Unity as virtual environment.

2. Choice of tools

2.1. Virtual environment designer

Unity 2019.2.19f1 has been chosen as the virtual environment design tool. Unity is a game engine, capable of creating both 3d and 2d environments, and designed in C++. It allows for the designer to include programmed behaviours in C#, implemented in Mono, an open-source platform-neutral implementation of the .NET standard, which eases the task of using ActiveX (see lower section).

Beyond lending itself naturally to the implementation of an ActiveX connection, Unity has been favoured as a choice because it is widely used, relatively easy to learn, and it can develop environments to be implemented in all major formats (pc, phone, virtual reality glasses, etc). Previous works have already used the Unity engine for development of VESs in the process industry, such as the previously mentioned coking plant by Ouyang et al. (2017).

2.2. Process simulator

Aspen HYSYS V10 (AspenTech, 2011) has been chosen as the process simulator. HYSYS is one of the first process simulators developed, and has been widely used in research, industry and education, particularly for petrochemical processes. It was developed in C++, and the decision was made in an early stage to leave all program objects and functions open (AspenTech, 2011), which eases interconnection significantly, an attractive quality for the work proposed. It provides a variety of available thermodynamic and unit operation models, as well as vast thermodynamic libraries (generally the same included in Aspen Plus since V7).

The uses of this software in the process industry would be too many to elaborate, but particular interest is placed in the work of Santos et al. (2016), who used this same tool as a base process simulator for a VES of a petrochemical platform, developed as well in Unity.

2.3. Interconnection

ActiveX is used to communicate between Unity and Aspen HYSYS. Previous literature often uses OPC (OLE for process control) to enable a connection between environment and process simulator (e.g. Santos et al., 2016). This technology was developed for inter-software communication in the process industry, and has several advantages, such as parallel communication (two servers accessing the same client simultaneously), implementation in a network through tunnelling, and robustness. It is, however, lacking flexibility, as the variables that can be communicated must be determined during the setup of the server (so changes to the simulation like adding a new flow stream are not possible), and, while current process simulators often include tools to set up an OPC, the process is still complex, especially for engineers unfamiliar with OPC. An exception to this general OPC use are Manca et al. (2013), where an OTS is developed which mentions data exchange through OLE (former name of ActiveX) to both UniSim and an in-house accident simulator.

ActiveX has been used in previous work on interconnection, such as by Vaquerizo and Cocero (2018) where it is used as a part of data extraction from Aspen Plus to ANSYS Fluent, and it allows for a higher degree of control over the program, as well as more flexibility, since the variables and methods available are any that are enabled by the provider.

3. Technical implementation

The basics for interconnection with Aspen Hysys through ActiveX can be found in the automation manual provided by the supplier (AspenTech, 2011), which expands on basic functionalities, giving examples for Visual Basic for Applications (VBA). As indicated there, a necessary element of the process is the file Hysys.tlb, a type library that allows for the use of the interfaces and methods of Aspen HYSYS and that can be found in the installation directory of Aspen HYSYS.

Unity does not accept the type library extension. One possible approach to solve this problem is to convert the file to a dynamic library (dll) with the use of the Type Library Importer tool of Visual Studio. Once this is done, the dll file can be included into any

Unity project that requires this communication, where Unity will automatically recognize it and add it into the C# project. The explanations of the Aspen HYSYS automation manual (AspenTech, 2011) can be followed generally, with the peculiarity that the programming language is C# and the specific structure of the Unity Engine environment. C# scripting in the Unity engine works by adding new scripts into game objects, which by default include the class "MonoBehaviour": this class implements several default methods that execute during different events, such as Awake, that executes at the start of the environment, and Update, that executes each frame. Generally we propose to include an object for each simulation to be interconnected, so that each simulation can be started at the Awake method of its object, and can be stored as a public interface of the hysys.Simulation type within the object, accessible to other objects.

3.1. Technical challenges

The major limitation found in the study is a consistent error when interacting with vectors retrieved from HYSYS (concentrations, temperature profiles in a column, etc). Any of this variables cannot be returned to Unity, as an error will be displayed when trying to retrieve any value.

However, the problem can be fully solved by preparing the simulation so that all relevant values can be recovered as a scalar: e.g. in order to measure the concentrations in a stream, separating a stream into pure components and measuring the ratios by means of molar flows; in order to measure the temperature at a plate of the column, extracting a 0 flow outlet in the relevant column plate and measuring the temperature of that flow. Also, as the ActiveX connection allows for full flexibility and manipulation, it is possible to do these fixes dynamically when the value is needed, instead of previously for all possible wanted variables.

A second problem found is that executables built will not work: particularly, they will stop execution when trying to access the HYSYS simulation: this means that the VES can only be used within the Unity editor in play mode. However, since this software is free and any computer that can execute HYSYS can also execute the Unity editor, the authors did not find much problem with this. This issue would become significant when commercial releases are intended, or in hardware with very limited memory storage.

In any case, it should be noted that these technical issues are unexpected errors and not inherent to the technology. It is possible that some technical reworking or future releases will fix them entirely.

3.2. Resulting interconnection

Once the communication is achieved, and taking into account the limitation described in the previous subsection, all values from the simulation can be accessed from the training simulation. The experienced average time for both writing and reading values is 1.5 ms, with a maximum recorded delay of 2s (more than a thousand times the average). Measurements done in a DELL laptop XPS 15 9570 with Windows 10 Enterprise. The authors recommend using the multithreading capabilities of Unity to prevent the virtual environment from freezing due to spikes in communication delay by instead relegating this task to a background thread.

As many simulations as required can be connected, although the authors recommend restricting to a single simulation per scene to restrict complexity and troubleshooting. In some cases, however, use of many simultaneous simulations might be advisable: for example, virtual educational simulations designed to show learners the different behaviours of same systems under different inputs or thermodynamic packages simultaneously.

The hysys type library is comprehensive, and as far as the authors have been able to observe, any interaction that a user can perform though the user interface can be performed as well through the framework: creating new operations, flow streams, changing any connection, setting the properties package, etc., are all feasible. However, the authors discourage giving too much freedom to the user, since flowsheet simulators are well known to crash under badly calculated changes: designers should keep limitations in mind.

4. Demonstration example

For demonstration, a dynamic simulation of the esterification of acetic anhydride with methanol, using sulphuric acid as homogeneous catalyst in a CSTR is implemented in Aspen HYSYS (see Figure 1), using the data provided by Chiara et al. (2018). The reaction has the potential to produce a runaway in the reactor when incorrectly handled.

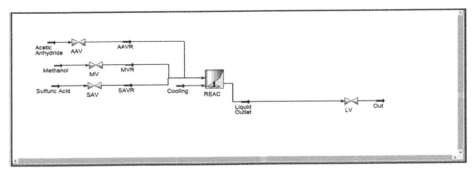

Figure 1: HYSYS Simulation of an esterification CSTR.

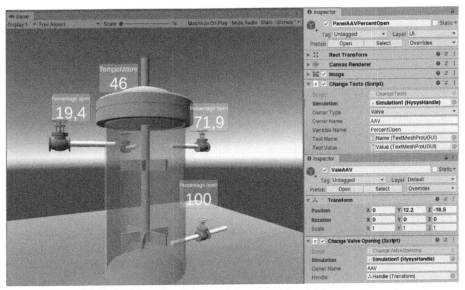

Figure 2: left: visual interface of Figure 1 in Unity. Right: objects interacting with HYSYS.

A VES is set up in Unity (see Figure 2 left, valve and reactor models thanks to GrabCAD (2019)), with a single "Simulation1" object that starts the simulation and stores it, and other objects that interact with the simulation: valves whose handle-rotation value will set the value of the valves in HYSYS, and texts that display the name and value of desired variables (Figure 2 right). It can be seen that once the connection is established, adding new linked objects in Unity requires no additional coding, as any variable from any object can be introduced just as text in the properties of the object, and all variables and elements are dynamically accessed. In the same way, adding new elements to the Aspen HYSYS simulation requires only saving the file.

5. Conclusion

A methodology was proposed for implementing the data exchange between Aspen HYSYS as simulator and Unity as virtual environment, through the use of ActiveX. The major limitation found was that vectors retrieved from HYSYS cannot be returned to Unity, which can be fully solved by preparing the simulation so that all relevant values can be recovered as a scalar. To demonstrate the methodology, a dynamic simulation was implemented of the esterification of acetic anhydride with methanol, using sulphuric acid as homogeneous catalyst in a CSTR.

Acknowledgements

This work has received funding from the European Union's EU Framework Programme for Research and Innovation Horizon 2020 under Grant Agreement 812716 as part of the CHARMING project (https://charming-etn.eu). This publication reflects only the author's view exempting the Community from any liability.

References

Ouyang, S. G., Wang, G., Yao, J. Y., Zhu, G. H. W., Liu, Z. Y., and Feng, C., 2018, A Unity3D-based interactive three-dimensional virtual practice platform for chemical engineering. Computer Applications in Engineering Education.

Ahmad, Z., Patle, D. S., and Rangaiah, G. P., 2016, Operator training simulator for biodiesel synthesis from waste cooking oil. Process Safety and Environmental Protection.

Heradio, R., De La Torre, L., Galan, D., Cabrerizo, F. J., Herrera-Viedma, E., and Dormido, S., 2016, Virtual and remote labs in education: A bibliometric analysis. Computers and Education.

Nazir, S., and Manca, D., 2015, How a plant simulator can improve industrial safety. Process Safety Progress.

Manca, D., Brambilla, S., and Colombo, S., 2013, Bridging between Virtual Reality and accident simulation for training of process-industry operators. Advances in Engineering Software.

Vaquerizo, L., and Cocero, M. J., 2018, CFD–Aspen Plus interconnection method. Improving thermodynamic modeling in computational fluid dynamic simulations. Computers and Chemical Engineering.

Mendes, D., Marangoni, C., Meneguelo, A. P., MacHado, R. A. F., and Bolzan, A., 2010, Educational simulator for multicomponent distillation research and teaching in chemical engineering, Computer Applications in Engineering Education.

Aldrich, C., 2005, Learning by Doing : A Comprehensive Guide to Simulations, Computer Games, and Pedagogy in e-Learning and Other Educational Experiences.

AspenTech, 2011, Aspen HYSYS: Customization Guide, Chapter 2: Automation.

GrabCAD, 2019, http://grabcad.com, Model authors: reactor: Edson M. J., valves: Yateesh P. A.

AUTHOR INDEX

Printed and bound by CPI Group (UK) Ltd, Croydon, CR0 4YY

03/10/2024

01040326-0011